Second Edition

Contemporary Business Mathematics

with Canadian Applications

Second Edition

Contemporary Business Mathematics

with Canadian Applications

S.A. HUMMELBRUNNER

PRENTICE-HALL CANADA INC.
SCARBOROUGH, ONTARIO

Canadian Cataloguing in Publication Data

Hummelbrunner, S.A. (Siegfried August).
  Contemporary business mathematics with Canadian
  applications

Includes index.

ISBN 0-13-169780-3

1. Business mathematics.   I. Title.

QA107.H85 1985   513′.93   C85-099757-7

Prentice-Hall Inc., Englewood Cliffs, New Jersey
Prentice-Hall International, Inc., London
Prentice-Hall of Australia, Pty., Sydney
Prentice-Hall of India Pvt., Ltd., New Delhi
Prentice-Hall of Japan, Inc., Tokyo
Prentice-Hall of Southeast Asia (Pte.) Ltd., Singapore
Editora Prentice-Hall do Brasil Ltda., Rio de Janeiro
Prentice-Hall Hispanoamericana, S.A., Mexico

ISBN 0-13-169780-3

1 2 3 4 5 JD 90 89 88 87 86

Cover calculator courtesy of Texas Instruments
Text design: Robert Garbutt Productions
Cover design: Janet Eidt
Production editor: Monica Schwalbe
Manufacturing buyer: Sheldon Fischer
Printed and bound in Canada by John Deyell

Contents

PART THREE *Mathematics of Finance and Investments*

13 *Compound Interest—Amount and Present Value*   **426**

14 *Compound Interest—Further Topics*   **467**

Preface

Contemporary Business Mathematics is intended for use in introductory mathematics of finance courses in business administration programs. In more general application it also provides a comprehensive basis for those who wish to review and extend their understanding of business mathematics.

The primary objective of the text is to increase the student's knowledge and skill in the solution of practical financial and mathematical problems encountered in the business community. It also provides a supportive base for mathematical topics in finance, accounting and marketing.

Contemporary Business Mathematics is essentially a teaching text using the objectives approach. The systematic and sequential development of the material is supported by carefully selected and worked examples. These detailed step-by-step solutions presented in a clear and uncluttered layout are particularly helpful in allowing students, in either independent studies or in the traditional classroom setting, to carefully monitor their own progress.

Each topic in each chapter is followed by an exercise containing numerous drill questions and application problems. The review exercise and self-test at the end of each chapter are designed to assist in the integration of the material studied.

The first six chapters are intended for students with little or no background in algebra and provide an opportunity to review arithmetic and algebraic processes.

The text is based on Canadian practice, and reflects current trends utilizing available technology—specifically the availability of reasonably priced electronic pocket calculators.

Students using this book should have access to calculating equipment having a power function and a natural logarithm function. The use of such calculators eliminates the arithmetic constraints often associated with financial problems and frees the student from reliance on financial tables.

The power function and the natural logarithm function are often needed to determine values which will be used for further computation. Such values should not be rounded and all available digits should be retained. The student is encouraged to use the memory to retain such values.

When using the memory the student needs to be aware that the number of digits retained in the registers of the calculator is greater than the number of digits displayed.

Depending on whether the memory or the displayed digits are used, slight differences may occur. Such differences will undoubtedly be encountered when working the examples presented in the text. However, they are insignificant and should not be of concern. In most cases the final answers will agree, whichever method is used.

Students are encouraged to use preprogrammed financial calculators though this is not essential. The use of preprogrammed calculators facilitates the solving of most financial problems and is demonstrated extensively in Chapters 13 to 17.

The second edition of the text has taken into account the suggestions, comments and criticisms received from reviewers, publisher's representatives and users of the first edition including students. Major changes include the elimination of the topic on quadratic equations in Chapter 6; a change in the approach to solving Case 2 in Chapter 7, Section 7.1; an update of the payroll topics covered in Chapter 8; the elimination of the approximate method when compounding with fractional values of n; the replacement of all self-test questions with new problems; the expansion of most review exercises; and the inclusion of an appendix containing computer programs which provide samples of those text problems most suited to solution by computer. Retained in the revision are the basic aims, structure and contents of the original edition. I hope the text continues to prove useful.

SIEG HUMMELBRUNNER

Mississauga
November 1985

PART ONE

Mathematics fundamentals

1 *Review of arithmetic*

Introduction

Electronic calculators are now in general use in business to perform arithmetic computations. The fundamental operations of addition, subtraction, multiplication and division with whole numbers and decimal fractions can be readily done with any model on the market. However, the ability to perform the fundamental operations of arithmetic with reasonable facility without the help of a calculator continues to be a valuable skill, and an understanding of the underlying principles enhances the use of a calculator as a tool in solving problems.

Objectives

Upon completion of this chapter you will be able to

1. perform the fundamental operations of addition, subtraction, multiplication and division with whole numbers and decimals;
2. perform the fundamental operations with common fractions;
3. convert mixed numbers to common fractions and perform the fundamental operations with mixed numbers;
4. convert fractions to decimals and decimals to fractions, and compute with fractional equivalents for commonly used decimals;
5. simplify arithmetic expressions involving the basic order of operations;
6. solve basic problems, including arithmetic averages, involving the fundamental operations.

1.1 *Fundamental operations with whole numbers and decimal fractions*

A. *Addition*

Addition is the process of combining two or more numbers into a single number called the **sum**. Each individual number is referred to as an **addend**.

A crucial feature in the process of addition is the retention of the place values through a proper alignment of the digits. For whole numbers the proper alignment is accomplished by placing the last digit of each addend (the units digit) into the same column. When adding decimal fractions the alignment is accomplished by placing the decimal point into the same column.

To assure that the answer is correct, addition, like any manual computation, should be checked. For addition this is commonly done *by adding the numbers in reverse order.*

Of the two methods used when adding numbers—addition with carrying or addition without carrying—only the later procedure is illustrated in the following examples.

Example 1.1a   Add 328, 6437, 74, 985 and check your answer.

> **Solution**

Add:	328		Check:	328	
	6437			6437	
	74			74	
	985			985	

24	← 8 + 7 + 4 + 5		24	← 5 + 4 + 7 + 8	
20	← 2 + 3 + 7 + 8		20	← 8 + 7 + 3 + 2	
16	← 3 + 4 + 9		16	← 9 + 4 + 3	
6	← + 6		6	← + 6	
7824			7824		

Example 1.1b   Add $13.63, $172, $0.84, $30.09 and check your answer.

> **Solution**

Add:	$ 13.63		Check:	$ 13.63	
	172.00			172.00	
	0.84			0.84	
	30.09			30.09	

.16	← 3 + 0 + 4 + 9		.16	← 9 + 4 + 0 + 3	
1.4	← 6 + 0 + 8 + 0		1.4	← 0 + 8 + 0 + 6	
5.	← 3 + 2 + 0 + 0		5.	← 0 + 0 + 2 + 3	
11 .	← 1 + 7 + 3		11 .	← 3 + 7 + 1	
1 .	← + 1		1 .	← + 1	
$216.56			$216.56		

Addition is subject to two basic mathematical properties.

1. The **commutative property of addition** simply means that *two numbers may be added in any order.*

$$6 + 3 = 9 \text{ and } 3 + 6 = 9$$

that is

$$6 + 3 = 3 + 6$$

2. The **associative property of addition** means that three numbers may be grouped in any order for addition, and thus the *three numbers may be added in any order.*

$$4 + 5 + 6 = (4 + 5) + 6 = 9 + 6. \ = 15, \text{ and}$$
$$4 + 5 + 6 = 4 + (5 + 6) = 4 + 11 = 15$$

that is

$$(4 + 5) + 6 = 4 + (5 + 6)$$

The importance of these two properties lies in their effect on the order in which numbers should be added.

> NUMBERS MAY BE ADDED IN ANY ORDER

B. Subtraction

Subtraction is the process of finding the **difference** (or **remainder**) between two numbers. The number to be subtracted is called the **subtrahend**, and the number from which the subtrahend is deducted is called the **minuend**. Since subtraction is the *inverse operation* to addition, the answer may be checked by adding the difference (or remainder) to the subtrahend.

Example 1.1c From 1372 subtract 498 and check.

Solution

Minuend	1372	Check:	Remainder	874
Less subtrahend	− 498		Add subtrahend	+ 498
Difference (Remainder)	874			1372

Example 1.1d Subtract $20.78 from $415.60.

Solution

$415.60	Check:	$394.82
− 20.78		+ 20.78
$394.82		$415.60

C. Multiplication

Multiplication as an arithmetic operation is a shortcut to repetitive addition. The result of multiplication is referred to as the **product** while the two numbers involved are referred to as the **multiplicand** and the **multiplier** (or they are both referred to as **factors**).

Multiplication is subject to three important mathematical properties.

1. The **commutative property of multiplication** simply means that *two numbers* can be *multiplied in any order*.

$$4 \times 7 = 28 \text{ and } 7 \times 4 = 28$$

that is

$$4 \times 7 = 7 \times 4$$

2. The **associative property of multiplication** means that *three numbers* may be grouped in any order for multiplication and thus can be *multiplied in any order*.

$$3 \times 4 \times 5 = (3 \times 4) \times 5 = 12 \times 5 = 60, \text{ and}$$
$$3 \times 4 \times 5 = 3 \times (4 \times 5) = 3 \times 20 = 60$$

that is

$$(3 \times 4) \times 5 = 3 \times (4 \times 5)$$

3. The **distributive property of multiplication over addition** means that the product of the sum of two numbers is equal to the *sum of the individual products*.

$$3(4 + 5) = 3 \times 9 = 27, \text{ and}$$
$$3(4 + 5) = 3 \times 4 + 3 \times 5 = 12 + 15 = 27$$

that is

$$3(4 + 5) = 3 \times 4 + 3 \times 5$$

As in the case of addition, the effect of the commutative property and the associative property is to permit *multiplication of numbers in any order*. This permits checking of the answer by exchanging the multiplicand and multiplier and reworking the problem.

***Example* 1.1e** Find the product of 286 and 67 and check the answer.

Solution

Multiplicand	286		Check: Multiplicand	67	
Multiplier	× 67		Multiplier	× 286	
	2002	⟵ 286 × 7		402	⟵ 67 × 6
	1716	⟵ 286 × 6		536	⟵ 67 × 8
				134	⟵ 67 × 2
Product	19162		Product	19162	

Note

1. Each digit in the multiplier gives rise to a partial product. These partial products are aligned according to the position of the digits in the multiplier to allow for their place value. The first partial product ($286 \times 7 = 2002$) is

aligned with the units column; the second partial product (286 × 6 = 1716) is shifted one column to the left.

2. When multiplying decimals, perform the multiplication as if dealing with whole numbers and obtain the product. Determine the combined number of decimal places in the multiplicand and multiplier and insert the decimal point in the product by counting the combined number of decimal places beginning with the last digit in the product.

Example **1.1f**   Multiply   (i) 0.36 by 0.17;   (ii) 625.45 by 1.125.

Solution

(i)   0.36 ⟵ 2 decimal places   (ii)   625.45 ⟵ 2 decimal places
        × 0.17 ⟵ 2 decimal places   ×   1.125 ⟵ 3 decimal places
        ─────   ──────

        2 52   3 127 25
        3 6   12 509 0
        ─────   62 545
        0.06 12 ⟵ 4 decimal places   625 45
                                         ─────────
                                         703.631 25 ⟵ 5 decimal places

Special cases

1. *Multiplication by 10, 100, 1000, etc.*

   When multiplying by 10, 100, 1000, etc., the product can be written immediately by moving the decimal point *to the right* by as many places as there are zeroes in the multiplier (or by adding as many zeros to the multiplicand as there are zeros in the multiplier).

Example **1.1g**

(i) 254 × 10 = 2540   ⟵ move the decimal point in the
(ii) 13.67 × 10 = 136.7   multiplicand 1 place to the right

(iii) 67 × 100 = 6700   ⟵ move the decimal point in the
(iv) 251.25 × 100 = 25125   multiplicand 2 places to the right

(v) 1.176 25 × 1000 = 1176.25 ⟵ move the decimal point 3 places
                               to the right

(vi)   10000 × 1.215 506 25
     = 1.21550625 × 10000 = 12155.0625 ⟵ move the decimal point
                                         4 places to the right

2. *Multiplication by 0.1, 0.01, 0.001, etc*

   When multiplying by 0.1, 0.01, 0.001, etc., the product can be written immediately by moving the decimal point *to the left* by the number of places which the digit '1' is located to the right of the decimal point in the multiplier.

Example 1.1h

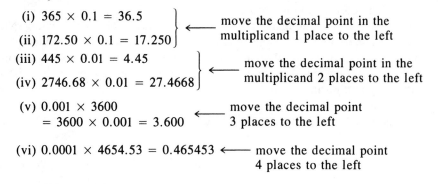

(i) $365 \times 0.1 = 36.5$

(ii) $172.50 \times 0.1 = 17.250$

move the decimal point in the multiplicand 1 place to the left

(iii) $445 \times 0.01 = 4.45$

(iv) $2746.68 \times 0.01 = 27.4668$

move the decimal point in the multiplicand 2 places to the left

(v) 0.001×3600
$= 3600 \times 0.001 = 3.600$

move the decimal point 3 places to the left

(vi) $0.0001 \times 4654.53 = 0.465453$ ← move the decimal point 4 places to the left

D. Division

Division is the inverse operation to multiplication. The result of a division is called the **quotient**; the number to be divided is called the **dividend** and the number by which the dividend is divided is called the **divisor**:

$$54 \div 9 = 6$$

Dividend ÷ Divisor = Quotient

$$6 \leftarrow \text{Quotient}$$
Divisor $\rightarrow 9\overline{)54} \leftarrow$ Dividend

If the divisor does not divide evenly into the dividend, the part left over is referred to as the **remainder**:

$$57 \div 9 = 6, \text{ Remainder 3}.$$

When checking division, the usual procedure is to multiply the quotient by the divisor and add any remainder to obtain the dividend. This procedure is based on the *division relationship*.

QUOTIENT × DIVISOR + REMAINDER = DIVIDEND

Example 1.1i Divide 235 by 17, and check your answer.

Solution

```
                      13  ←——— Quotient        Check:      13  ←——— Quotient
   Divisor ——→ 17 )235  ←——— Dividend                    × 17  ←——— Divisor
                      17                                     91
                      ——                                     13
                      65                                    221
                      51                                  + 14  ←——— Remainder
                      ——                                    235  ←——— Dividend
                      14  ←——— Remainder
```

When, as in Example 1.1i, the divisor does not divide evenly into the dividend, the remainder may be shown as part of the quotient either as a common fraction or as a decimal fraction.

If the remainder is to be shown as part of the quotient in form of a common fraction, the remainder is the numerator of the common fraction and the divisor is its denominator such as in Example 1.1h where $235 \div 17 = 13$, remainder 4, may be shown as having a quotient $13\frac{4}{17}$.

If the remainder is to be shown as part of the quotient in form of a decimal fraction, the division can be carried through until there is no remainder (that is, until the decimal terminates) or to a desired number of decimal places.

Example 1.1j   Divide each of the following showing the remainder as part of the quotient.

       (a) as a common fraction;
       (b) as a decimal fraction.
   (i) 165 by 12   (ii) 250 by 3   (iii) 38 by 7

Solution

(i)
```
        13.75
   12 165.00
      12
      ----
      45
      36
      ----
       9 0
       8 4
       ----
         60
         60
         ---
          0
```

(a) The whole number part of the quotient is 13 with a remainder of 9. Thus the quotient is $13\frac{9}{12}$ or $13\frac{3}{4}$.

(b) The decimal part of the quotient terminates; the quotient is 13.75.

(ii)
```
        83.3333...
   3 250.0000...
     24
     ---
     10
      9
      --
      1 0
        9
        --
        10
         9
         --
         10
          9
          --
          10
           9
           --
           1
```

(a) The whole number part of the quotient is 83 with a remainder 1. Thus the quotient is $83\frac{1}{3}$.

(b) The decimal part of the quotient does not terminate. The answer correct to two decimals is 83.33.

(iii)

$$
\begin{array}{r}
5.428\ldots \\
7\overline{)38.0000\ldots} \\
\underline{35} \\
3\ 0 \\
\underline{2\ 8} \\
20 \\
\underline{14} \\
60 \\
\underline{56} \\
4
\end{array}
$$

(a) the whole number part of the quotient is 5 with a remainder of 3. Thus the quotient is $5\frac{3}{7}$.

(b) The decimal part of the quotient does not terminate. The answer correct to two decimals is 5.43.

Note When the decimal portion of the quotient does not terminate the complete quotient may be written by adding the remainder after any selected decimal place in fractional form.

$$250 \div 3 = 83\frac{1}{3} = 83.3\frac{1}{3} = 83.33\frac{1}{3} = 83.333\frac{1}{3} \text{ and so on}$$

$$38 \div 7 = 5\frac{3}{7} = 5.4\frac{2}{7} = 5.42\frac{6}{7} = 5.428\frac{4}{7} \text{ and so on}$$

Great care must be taken in placing the decimal point in the quotient. If the divisor is a whole number the decimal point in the quotient is located directly over the decimal point in the dividend (see Example 1.1j). However, if the divisor has decimals, the usual procedure is to change the divisor to a whole number by moving the decimal point to the right and placing it after the last digit in the divisor. If this is done, the decimal point in the dividend must also be moved the same number of places to the right as required to convert the divisor into a whole number. The decimal point in the quotient is then located directly above the new position of the decimal point in the dividend.

Example 1.1k Divide 12.248 by 0.08.

Solution

$0.08\overline{)12.248}$ ⟵—— To set up the division move the decimal point in both divisor and dividend 2 places to the right.

$8\overline{)1224.8}$ ⟵—— Insert the decimal point in the quotient directly above the new position of the decimal point in the dividend.

$$
\begin{array}{r}
153.1 \\
8\overline{)1224.8}
\end{array}
$$
⟵—— Carry out the division making sure that the digits are properly placed.

***Example* 1.1l** Divide (i) 412 by 1.03; (ii) 693.75 by 0.925.

   Solution

   (i) $1.03\overline{)412}$

$$
\begin{array}{r}
400. \\
103\overline{)41200.} \\
412 \\
\hline
0
\end{array}
$$

   (ii) $0.925\overline{)693.75}$

$$
\begin{array}{r}
750. \\
925\overline{)693750.} \\
6475 \\
\hline
4625 \\
4625 \\
\hline
0
\end{array}
$$

Division by 10, 100, 1000, etc.
When dividing by 10, 100, 1000, etc., the quotient can be obtained immediately by *moving the decimal point in the dividend to the left* by as many places as there are zeros in the divisor.

***Example* 1.1m**

   (i) $365 \div 10 = 36.5$

   (ii) $147.5 \div 10 = 14.75$ ⟵ move the decimal point in the dividend 1 place to the left

   (iii) $17 \div 100 = 0.17$

   (iv) $644.89 \div 100 = 6.4489$ ⟵ 2 places to the left

   (v) $25 \div 1000 = 0.025$ ⟵ 3 places to the left

   (vi) $3.75 \div 10000 = 0.000375$ ⟵ 4 places to the left

Note Division by 10, 100, 1000, etc. is equivalent to multiplication by 0.1, 0.01, 0.001, etc.

Division by 0.1, 0.01, 0.001, etc.
When dividing by 0.1, 0.01, 0.001, etc., the quotient can be obtained immediately by moving the decimal point in the dividend to the *right* by the number of places which the digit '1' is located to the right of the decimal point in the divisor.

***Example* 1.1n**

   (i) $14 \div 0.1 = 140$

   (ii) $3.25 \div 0.1 = 32.5$ ⟵ move the decimal point in the dividend 1 place to the right

   (iii) $5 \div 0.01 = 500$

   (iv) $0.0825 \div 0.01 = 8.25$ ⟵ 2 places to the right

(v) $7.25 \div 0.001 = 7250$ ⟵ 3 places to the right

(vi) $0.04 \div 0.0001 = 400$ ⟵ 4 places to the right

Note   Division by 0.1, 0.01, 0.001, etc., is equivalent to multiplication by 10, 100, 1000, etc.

E. Rounding

Answers to problems, particularly when obtained with the help of a calculator, often need to be rounded to a desired number of decimal places. In most business problems involving money values the rounding needs to be done to the nearest cent, that is two decimal positions.

While there are different methods of rounding in use for most business purposes the following procedure is suitable.

1. If the first digit in the group of decimal digits which is to be dropped is the digit 5 or 6 or 7 or 8 or 9, the last digit retained is *increased* by 1.

2. If the first digit in the group of decimal digits which is to be dropped is the digit 0 or 1 or 2 or 3 or 4, the last digit retained is left *unchanged*.

Example 1.10

   (i) 7.384   ⟶ 7.38 ⟵ drop the digit '4'

  (ii) 7.385   ⟶ 7.39 ⟵ round the digit '8' up to '9'

 (iii) 12.9448 ⟶ 12.94 ⟵ discard '48'

 (iv) 9.32838 ⟶ 9.33 ⟵ round the digit '2' up to '3'

  (v) 24.8975 ⟶ 24.90 ⟵ round the digit '9' up to '0'
                                                  this requires round '89' to '90'

 (vi) 1.996   ⟶ 2.00 ⟵ round the second digit '9' up to '0'
                                                  this requires rounding '1.99' to '2.00'

(vii) 3199.99833 ⟶ 3200.00

Exercise 1.1

A.   Add or subtract as indicated. Check your answers.

   1. Find the sum of each of the following.

       (a) 465, 94, 8, 1445

       (b) 10732, 948, 73, 4892, 2600

       (c) 314.72, 2.98, 13.57, 0.93

       (d) $15, $123.85, $600, $1.60, $0.87

2. Find the difference as indicated.

    (a) From 954 subtract 767.

    (b) Subtract 1491 from 12804.

    (c) Subtract $74.73 from $103.65.

    (d) From $1115.72 subtract $87.33.

B. Multiply or divide as indicated. Check your answers.

1. Find the product of each of the following.

    (a) 73, 57   **(b)** 247, 83

    (c) 3.45, 17   **(d)** 58, 5.07

    (e) 40.85, 1.15   **(f)** 1.025, 145.64

    (g) 0.76, 0.43   **(h)** 11.05, 0.0135

2. Find the quotient and the remainder, if any, in each of the following.

    (a) $945 \div 27$ **(b)** $8136 \div 72$

    (c) $544 \div 63$ **(d)** $4901 \div 84$

    (e) $672 \div 1.05$ **(f)** $529.20 \div 0.98$

    (g) $44 \div 0.5$ **(h)** $0.625 \div 0.025$

3. Divide each of the following showing the remainder as part of the quotient.

    (i) as a common fraction, such as $5\frac{1}{3}$;

    (ii) as a decimal fraction rounded to two decimals, such as 5.33;

    (iii) as a mixed decimal fraction with two decimal places, such as $5.33\frac{1}{3}$.

    (a) $19 \div 6$ **(b)** $32 \div 3$

    (c) $65 \div 12$ **(d)** $106 \div 15$

    (e) $5 \div 6$ **(f)** $7 \div 9$

C. Write the product or quotient as required.

1. Write the product of each of the following.

    (a) 374×10 **(b)** 10×1232

    (c) 11.54×10 **(d)** 10×100.035

    (e) 100×75 **(f)** 31.65×100

    (g) 3.0156×100 **(h)** 100×0.0585

    (i) $100 \times 0.33\frac{1}{3}$ **(j)** $1.16\frac{2}{3} \times 100$

    (k) 34.16536×1000 **(l)** 1000×1.0404

    (m) 10000×2.31567 **(n)** 0.0083156×100000

2. Write the quotient of each of the following.

    (a) $72 \div 10$ **(b)** $13.6 \div 10$

    (c) $48 \div 100$ **(d)** $760 \div 100$

(e) 37.5 ÷ 100   (f) 0.025 ÷ 100
(g) 0.5 ÷ 100   (h) 7.5 ÷ 100
(i) 625 ÷ 1000   (j) 25 ÷ 1000
(k) 87.5 ÷ 10000   (l) 0.775 ÷ 10000

3. Write the product of each of the following.

(a) 200 × 0.1   (b) 0.1 × 56.70
(c) 0.01 × 450   (d) 22.8 × 0.01
(e) 3.5 × 0.01   (f) 0.4 × 0.01
(g) 0.001 × 625   (h) 50 × 0.001
(i) 75 × 0.0001   (j) 2.25 × 0.0001

4. Write the quotient of each of the following.

(a) 45 ÷ 0.1   (b) 6.5 ÷ 0.1
(c) 12 ÷ 0.01   (d) 3.75 ÷ 0.01
(e) 0.8 ÷ 0.01   (f) 0.04 ÷ 0.01
(g) 3 ÷ 0.001   (h) 0.075 ÷ 0.001
(i) 0.5 ÷ 0.0001   (j) 0.0925 ÷ 0.0001

D. Round each of the following to two decimal places.

1. 5.633   **2.** 17.449   **3.** 18.0046   **4.** 253.4856

5. 57.69875   **6.** 3.09475   **7.** 12.995   **8.** 39.999

1.2 *Fundamental operations with common fractions*

A. *Basic nature and types*

Common fractions are created by writing a division involving two whole numbers in an alternate way in which the division sign is replaced by a fraction line. Thus, a fraction line indicates division and a division written in the form of a fraction is called **indicated division**. When writing a division in fractional form, the dividend, referred to as the **numerator** of the fraction, is written *above* the fraction line, and the divisor, referred to as the **denominator** of the fraction, is written *below* the fraction line.

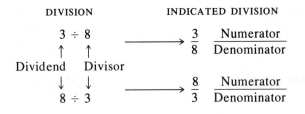

A **proper fraction** is a fraction in which the numerator is *smaller than* the denominator, such as $\frac{3}{8}$. An **improper fraction** is a .fraction in which the numerator is *greater than or equal to* the denominator, such as $\frac{8}{3}$.

B. Equivalent fractions

Equivalent fractions may be obtained by changing the **terms of the fraction** (the *numerator* and the *denominator*) without changing the value of the fraction.

Equivalent fractions in higher terms may be obtained by multiplying both the numerator and the denominator of a fraction by the *same* number. For any fraction an unlimited number of equivalent fractions in higher terms may be obtained.

Example 1.2a Convert $\frac{3}{4}$ into higher terms by multiplying successively by 2, 2, 3, 5, 5 and 7.

Solution

$$\frac{3}{4} = \frac{3 \times 2}{4 \times 2} = \frac{6}{8} = \frac{6 \times 2}{8 \times 2} = \frac{12}{16} = \frac{12 \times 3}{16 \times 3} = \frac{36}{48} = \frac{36 \times 5}{48 \times 5} = \frac{180}{240}$$

$$= \frac{180 \times 5}{240 \times 5} = \frac{900}{1200} = \frac{900 \times 7}{1200 \times 7} = \frac{6300}{8400}$$

Thus $\dfrac{3}{4} = \dfrac{6}{8} = \dfrac{12}{16} = \dfrac{36}{48} = \dfrac{180}{240} = \dfrac{900}{1200} = \dfrac{6300}{8400}$.

Equivalent fractions in lowest terms may be obtained if both the numerator and the denominator of a fraction are divisible by the same number or numbers. The process of obtaining such equivalent fractions is referred to as **reducing to lower terms**.

Example 1.2b Reduce $\frac{210}{252}$ to lower terms.

Solution $\dfrac{210}{252} = \dfrac{210 \div 2}{252 \div 2} = \dfrac{105}{126} = \dfrac{105 \div 3}{126 \div 3} = \dfrac{35}{42} = \dfrac{35 \div 7}{42 \div 7} = \dfrac{5}{6}$

Note

1. The numbers 2, 3, and 7 are common divisors of 210 and 252, so are 6, 14, 21, and 42.

2. The numbers 2, 3, and 7 are prime factors (factors which are evenly divisible by themselves only). The factors 6, 14, 21 and 42 are products of the prime factors.

3. To obtain all the possible lower term equivalents of $\frac{210}{252}$ divide the numerator 210 and the denominator 252 in turn by 2, 3, 6, 7, 14, 21 and 42.

$$\frac{210}{252} = \frac{105}{126} = \frac{70}{84} = \frac{35}{42} = \frac{30}{36} = \frac{15}{18} = \frac{10}{12} = \frac{5}{6}$$

4. The fraction $\frac{5}{6}$ cannot be reduced any further and represents the simplest form of $\frac{210}{252}$ or the lowest terms of $\frac{210}{252}$

5. The lowest terms of $\frac{210}{252}$ can be obtained directly by dividing both terms of the fraction by 42.

$$\frac{210}{252} = \frac{210 \div 42}{252 \div 42} = \frac{5}{6}$$

6. The common divisor 42 is the greatest common divisor or **highest common factor** of the terms of the fraction.

C. *Reducing fractions to lowest terms*

The most efficient way of reducing a fraction to lowest terms is to divide the terms of the fraction by the *highest common factor* (H.C.F.) of the terms.

Example 1.2c Reduce each of the following fractions to lowest terms.

(i) $\dfrac{16}{36}$ (ii) $\dfrac{96}{144}$ (iii) $\dfrac{135}{360}$ (iv) $\dfrac{360}{216}$ (v) $\dfrac{770}{462}$

Solution

(i) $\dfrac{16}{36} = \dfrac{16 \div 4}{36 \div 4} = \dfrac{4}{9}$ ⟵ by inspection the H.C.F. of 16 and 36 is 4

(ii) If the H.C.F. of the terms of a fraction are not easily discernible, the fraction may be reduced in stages.

$$\frac{96}{144} = \frac{96 \div 4}{144 \div 4} = \frac{24}{36} = \frac{24 \div 12}{36 \div 12} = \frac{2}{3}$$

Alternately, the H.C.F. may be determined by finding the *prime factors* common to the terms.

```
              96   144    ⟵  list the numbers to be reduced
       ÷ 2 | 48    72  ⎫
       ÷ 2 | 24    36  ⎪
       ÷ 2 | 12    18  ⎬  ⟵  divide by the common prime factors until
       ÷ 2 |  6     9  ⎪      the numbers have no factors in common
       ÷ 3 |  2     3  ⎭
```

The H.C.F. is the *product* of the prime factors.

H.C.F. $= 2 \times 2 \times 2 \times 2 \times 3 = 48$ ⟶ $\dfrac{96}{144} = \dfrac{96 \div 48}{144 \div 48} = \dfrac{2}{3}$

(iii) *Reducing in stages*

$$\frac{135}{360} = \frac{135 \div 5}{360 \div 5} = \frac{27}{72} = \frac{27 \div 9}{72 \div 9} = \frac{3}{8}$$

Reducing by first finding the H.C.F.

$$\begin{array}{r|cc} & 135 & 360 \\ \hline \div\ 3 & 45 & 120 \\ \div\ 3 & 15 & 40 \\ \div\ 5 & 3 & 8 \end{array}$$

H.C.F. $= 3 \times 3 \times 5 = 45$

$$\frac{135}{360} = \frac{135 \div 45}{360 \div 45} = \frac{3}{8}$$

(iv)

$$\begin{array}{r|cc} & 360 & 216 \\ \hline \div\ 2 & 180 & 108 \\ \div\ 2 & 90 & 54 \\ \div\ 2 & 45 & 27 \\ \div\ 3 & 15 & 9 \\ \div\ 3 & 5 & 3 \end{array}$$

$\longrightarrow \quad \dfrac{360}{216} = \dfrac{5}{3}$

(v)

$$\begin{array}{r|cc} & 770 & 462 \\ \hline \div\ 2 & 385 & 231 \\ \div\ 7 & 55 & 33 \\ \div\ 11 & 5 & 3 \end{array}$$

$\longrightarrow \quad \dfrac{770}{462} = \dfrac{5}{3}$

D. Multiplication of common fractions

Basic Rule To find the product of two or more fractions
1. *multiply the numerators to obtain the numerator of the product;*
2. *multiply the denominators to obtain the denominator of the product.*

$$\boxed{\frac{\text{NUMERATOR} \times \text{NUMERATOR} \times \text{NUMERATOR} \ldots}{\text{DENOMINATOR} \times \text{DENOMINATOR} \times \text{DENOMINATOR} \times \ldots}}$$

Example 1.2d

(i) $\dfrac{2}{3} \times \dfrac{5}{7} = \dfrac{2 \times 5}{3 \times 7} = \dfrac{10}{21}$

(ii) $\dfrac{3}{2} \times \dfrac{5}{4} \times \dfrac{1}{7} = \dfrac{3 \times 5 \times 1}{2 \times 4 \times 7} = \dfrac{15}{56}$

(iii) $\dfrac{5}{8} \times \dfrac{4}{3} = \dfrac{5 \times 4}{8 \times 3} = \dfrac{20}{24} = \dfrac{20 \div 4}{24 \div 4} = \dfrac{5}{6}$

Note The reducing process should be undertaken *before* multiplying out in order to keep the numbers as low as possible.

$$\frac{5}{\overset{}{\underset{2}{8}}} \times \frac{\overset{1}{4}}{3} = \frac{5 \times 1}{2 \times 3} = \frac{5}{6}$$

$$\text{(iv)} \ \frac{\overset{5}{\cancel{15}}}{\underset{4}{\cancel{12}}} \times \frac{\overset{3}{\cancel{21}}}{\underset{2}{\cancel{14}}} \times \frac{\overset{4}{\cancel{8}}}{\underset{3}{\cancel{6}}} = \frac{5 \times \overset{1}{\cancel{3}} \times \overset{1}{\cancel{4}}}{\cancel{4} \times 2 \times \cancel{3}} = \frac{5 \times 1 \times 1}{1 \times 2 \times 1} = \frac{5}{2}$$

E. Division with common fractions

To divide one common fraction by another common fraction, multiply the dividend by the **reciprocal** of the divisor.

$$\frac{5}{3} \div \frac{7}{2} \quad = \quad \frac{5}{3} \times \frac{2}{7} \quad = \frac{10}{21}$$

| DIVIDEND ÷ DIVISOR = DIVIDEND × RECIPROCAL OF DIVISOR = QUOTIENT |

Note   The reciprocal of a fraction is its *inverted* value.

Example 1.2e

$$\text{(i)} \ \frac{15}{12} \div \frac{9}{8} = \frac{\overset{5}{\cancel{15}}}{\underset{4}{\cancel{12}}} \times \frac{8}{9} = \frac{5 \times \overset{2}{\cancel{8}}}{\cancel{4} \times 9} = \frac{5 \times 2}{1 \times 9} = \frac{10}{9}$$

$$\text{(ii)} \ \frac{5}{7} \div \frac{15}{28} \times \frac{9}{10} = \frac{\overset{1}{\cancel{5}}}{\cancel{7}} \times \frac{\overset{4}{\cancel{28}}}{\underset{3}{\cancel{15}}} \times \frac{9}{10} = \frac{1 \times \overset{2}{\cancel{4}} \times \overset{3}{\cancel{9}}}{1 \times \underset{1}{\cancel{3}} \times \underset{5}{\cancel{10}}} = \frac{1 \times 2 \times 3}{1 \times 1 \times 5} = \frac{6}{5}$$

F. Addition and subtraction of common fractions

Only common fractions having the *same denominator* can be added or subtracted. This is done by adding the numerators of the various fractions and *retaining* the common denominator.

Example 1.2f

$$\text{(i)} \ \frac{4}{15} + \frac{3}{15} + \frac{6}{15} = \frac{4 + 3 + 6}{15} = \frac{13}{15} \quad \longleftarrow \text{ combine the numerators}$$
$$\longleftarrow \text{ retain the common denominator}$$

$$\text{(ii)} \ \frac{7}{12} - \frac{2}{12} = \frac{7 - 2}{12} = \frac{5}{12}$$

(iii) $\dfrac{8}{3} - \dfrac{2}{3} - \dfrac{5}{3} + \dfrac{1}{3} = \dfrac{8 - 2 - 5 + 1}{3} = \dfrac{2}{3}$

To add or subtract fractions that do not have the same denominator, you must change the fractions to *equivalent fractions* with a *common denominator*. While an unlimited number of common denominators is possible, it is best to obtain the **least common denominator** when adding or subtracting. The least common denominator (L.C.D.) is the *lowest* number into which each of the denominators divides evenly. It is the **lowest common multiple** (L.C.M.) of the denominators.

Example 1.2g

(i) $\dfrac{2}{3} + \dfrac{5}{7}$ ⟵ the lowest common multiple of the denominators
3 and 7 is 21 ⟶ L.C.D. = 21

$= \dfrac{2 \times 7}{3 \times 7} + \dfrac{5 \times 3}{7 \times 3}$ ⟵ change to equivalent fractions in higher terms

$= \dfrac{14}{21} + \dfrac{15}{21}$ ⟵ having the same denominator which is the L.C.D.

$= \dfrac{14 + 15}{21}$ ⟵ add the numerators
⟵ retain the common denominator

$= \dfrac{29}{21}$

(ii) $\dfrac{5}{4} + \dfrac{4}{3} - \dfrac{3}{2}$ ⟵ L.C.D. = 12

$= \dfrac{5 \times 3}{4 \times 3} + \dfrac{4 \times 4}{3 \times 4} - \dfrac{3 \times 6}{2 \times 6}$ ⟵ change to equivalent fractions

$= \dfrac{15}{12} + \dfrac{16}{12} - \dfrac{18}{12}$ ⟵ with lowest common denominator 12

$= \dfrac{15 + 16 - 18}{12}$

$= \dfrac{13}{12}$

(iii) $\dfrac{5}{12} - \dfrac{7}{5} + \dfrac{11}{20} + \dfrac{9}{4}$

If the lowest common multiple (L.C.M.) of a group of numbers is not immediately apparent it can be determined using the following systematic approach.

$$12 \quad 5 \quad 20 \quad 4 \longleftarrow \text{ list the numbers (denominators)}$$

$$
\begin{array}{r|cccc}
\div\ 2 & 6 & 5 & 10 & 2 \\
\div\ 2 & 3 & 5 & 5 & 1 \\
\div\ 3 & 1 & 5 & 5 & 1 \\
\div\ 5 & 1 & 1 & 1 & 1 \\
\end{array}
$$

$\longleftarrow$ divide by any *prime* factor, if necessary repeatedly, which is a factor of any of the denominators listed until all denominators are reduced to '1'

The L.C.M., which is also the L.C.D., is the *product* of all the prime factors used including repetitions.

$$\text{L.C.D.} = 2 \times 2 \times 3 \times 5 = 60$$

$$\frac{5}{12} - \frac{7}{5} + \frac{11}{20} + \frac{9}{4}$$

$$= \frac{5 \times 5}{12 \times 5} - \frac{7 \times 12}{5 \times 12} + \frac{11 \times 3}{20 \times 3} + \frac{9 \times 15}{4 \times 15}$$

$$= \frac{25}{60} - \frac{84}{60} + \frac{33}{60} + \frac{135}{60}$$

$$= \frac{25 - 84 + 33 + 135}{60}$$

$$= \frac{109}{60}$$

(iv) $\quad \dfrac{5}{6} + \dfrac{7}{9} - \dfrac{5}{14} - \dfrac{11}{21} \longleftarrow$ *Finding the L.C.D.*

$$
\begin{array}{r|cccc}
 & 6 & 9 & 14 & 21 \\
\div\ 2 & 3 & 9 & 7 & 21 \\
\div\ 3 & 1 & 3 & 7 & 7 \\
\div\ 3 & 1 & 1 & 7 & 7 \\
\div\ 7 & 1 & 1 & 1 & 1 \\
\end{array}
$$

$$= \frac{5 \times 21}{6 \times 21} + \frac{7 \times 14}{9 \times 14} - \frac{5 \times 9}{14 \times 9} - \frac{11 \times 6}{21 \times 6}$$

$$= \frac{105 + 98 - 45 - 66}{126}$$

$$= \frac{92}{126}$$

$$= \frac{46}{63}$$

$$\text{L.C.D.} = 2 \times 3 \times 3 \times 7 = 126$$

Exercise 1.2

A. Reduce each of the following fractions to lowest terms.

1. $\dfrac{24}{12}$ 2. $\dfrac{28}{56}$ 3. $\dfrac{210}{360}$ 4. $\dfrac{330}{360}$

5. $\dfrac{225}{360}$ 6. $\dfrac{315}{360}$ 7. $\dfrac{144}{360}$ 8. $\dfrac{288}{360}$

9. $\dfrac{25}{365}$ **10.** $\dfrac{115}{365}$ **11.** $\dfrac{73}{365}$ **12.** $\dfrac{219}{365}$

B. Simplify each of the following.

1. $\dfrac{6}{5} \times \dfrac{8}{9}$

2. $\dfrac{15}{16} \times \dfrac{10}{9}$

3. $\dfrac{8}{100} \times \dfrac{270}{360}$

4. $\dfrac{15}{100} \times \dfrac{292}{365}$

5. $\dfrac{2}{5} \div \dfrac{3}{4}$

6. $\dfrac{14}{15} \div \dfrac{21}{25}$

7. $\dfrac{8}{15} \times \dfrac{9}{10} \times \dfrac{20}{36}$

8. $\dfrac{3}{8} \times \dfrac{16}{21} \times \dfrac{35}{44}$

9. $\dfrac{6}{5} \div \dfrac{9}{15} \times \dfrac{5}{8}$

10. $\dfrac{8}{3} \times \dfrac{7}{12} \div \dfrac{28}{15}$

C. Simplify each of the following.

1. $\dfrac{3}{8} + \dfrac{17}{8} + \dfrac{9}{8}$

2. $\dfrac{7}{6} - \dfrac{5}{6}$

3. $\dfrac{4}{3} + \dfrac{5}{8}$

4. $\dfrac{13}{8} + \dfrac{7}{12}$

5. $\dfrac{7}{6} - \dfrac{2}{5}$

6. $\dfrac{5}{9} - \dfrac{5}{12}$

7. $\dfrac{3}{4} + \dfrac{5}{8} + \dfrac{7}{12}$

8. $\dfrac{7}{15} + \dfrac{5}{6} + \dfrac{11}{12} + \dfrac{9}{8}$

9. $\dfrac{6}{7} - \dfrac{2}{3} + \dfrac{7}{6} - \dfrac{5}{12}$

10. $\dfrac{13}{15} - \dfrac{16}{21} - \dfrac{5}{12} + \dfrac{17}{20}$

1.3 *Working with mixed numbers*

A. *Conversion of mixed numbers to common fractions*

Mixed numbers are numbers consisting of a whole number and a fraction, such as $5\frac{3}{4}$. Such numbers represent the *sum* of a whole number and a common fraction and can be converted into an improper fraction by treating the whole number as a fraction with denominator '1' and adding this fraction to the fractional part of the mixed number.

Example 1.3a

(i) $5\frac{3}{4} = 5 + \frac{3}{4}$ ⟵ write the mixed number as a sum

$\quad\quad = \frac{5}{1} + \frac{3}{4}$ ⟵ write the whole number as an improper fraction with denominator '1'

$\quad\quad = \frac{5 \times 4}{1 \times 4} + \frac{3}{4}$ ⟵ L.C.D. = 4

$\quad\quad = \frac{20}{4} + \frac{3}{4}$

$\quad\quad = \frac{23}{4}$

(ii) $6\frac{2}{3} = 6 + \frac{2}{3} = \frac{6}{1} + \frac{2}{3} = \frac{6 \times 3}{1 \times 3} + \frac{2}{3} = \frac{18}{3} + \frac{2}{3} = \frac{20}{3}$

B.   Multiplication and division with mixed numbers

When multiplying or dividing with mixed numbers it is best to first convert the mixed numbers into improper fractions.

Example 1.3b

(i) $3\frac{1}{3} \times 2\frac{1}{4} = \frac{10}{3} \times \frac{9}{4}$ ⟵ convert the mixed numbers into improper fractions

$\quad\quad = \frac{5}{1} \times \frac{3}{2}$ ⟵ reduce

$\quad\quad = \frac{15}{2}$

(ii) $4\frac{1}{2} \div 5\frac{1}{3} = \frac{9}{2} \div \frac{16}{3}$ ⟵ convert the mixed numbers into improper fractions

$\quad\quad = \frac{9}{2} \times \frac{3}{16}$ ⟵ convert the division to a multiplication

$\quad\quad = \frac{27}{32}$

(iii) $7 \div 5\frac{1}{4} = \frac{7}{1} \div \frac{21}{4} = \frac{7}{1} \times \frac{4}{21} = \frac{1}{1} \times \frac{4}{3} = \frac{4}{3} = 1\frac{1}{3}$

(iv) $2\dfrac{1}{5} \div 4 \times 3\dfrac{1}{2} = \dfrac{11}{5} \div \dfrac{4}{1} \times \dfrac{7}{2} = \dfrac{11}{5} \times \dfrac{1}{4} \times \dfrac{7}{2} = \dfrac{77}{40} = 1\dfrac{37}{40}$

C. Addition and subtraction with mixed numbers

Mixed numbers may be added or subtracted by converting them first into improper fractions. However, addition and subtraction are facilitated by first *separating* the whole number part from the fractional part of the mixed numbers and then combining the whole numbers and the common fractions *separately*.

Example 1.3c

(i) $5\dfrac{2}{3} + 4\dfrac{1}{4} = 5 + \dfrac{2}{3} + 4 + \dfrac{1}{4}$ ⟵ separate the common fraction
   from the whole number

$= (5 + 4) + \left(\dfrac{2}{3} + \dfrac{1}{4}\right)$ ⟵ combine the whole numbers
   and the fractions separately

$= 9 + \dfrac{8}{12} + \dfrac{3}{12}$

$= 9 + \dfrac{11}{12}$

$= 9\dfrac{11}{12}$

(ii) $13\dfrac{1}{5} + 17\dfrac{3}{4} - 14\dfrac{7}{8} = 13 + \dfrac{1}{5} + 17 + \dfrac{3}{4} - 14 - \dfrac{7}{8}$

$= (13 + 17 - 14) + \left(\dfrac{1}{5} + \dfrac{3}{4} - \dfrac{7}{8}\right)$

$= 16 + \dfrac{8 + 30 - 35}{40}$

$= 16 + \dfrac{3}{40}$

$= 16\dfrac{3}{40}$

Exercise 1.3

A. Convert each of the following mixed numbers to a common fraction.

1. $3\dfrac{3}{8}$ 2. $3\dfrac{2}{5}$ 3. $8\dfrac{1}{3}$ 4. $16\dfrac{2}{3}$

5. $33\dfrac{1}{3}$ 6. $83\dfrac{1}{3}$ 7. $7\dfrac{7}{9}$ 8. $7\dfrac{1}{12}$

B. Simplify each of the following. Show your answer as a mixed number.

1. $3\frac{3}{4} \times 4\frac{2}{5}$

2. $2\frac{5}{8} \times 4\frac{2}{7}$

3. $6\frac{2}{3} \div 1\frac{7}{9}$

4. $4\frac{1}{5} \div 2\frac{11}{12}$

5. $1\frac{3}{4} \times 2\frac{2}{7} \div 2\frac{2}{5}$

6. $3 \div \frac{6}{5} \times \frac{7}{10}$

C. Simplify each of the following. Show your answer as a mixed number.

1. $3\frac{2}{3} + 4\frac{1}{5}$

2. $4\frac{3}{4} - 3\frac{3}{8}$

3. $2\frac{1}{4} + 3\frac{1}{3} + 5\frac{1}{2}$

4. $5\frac{5}{6} - 3\frac{2}{3} + 4\frac{3}{4}$

5. $25\frac{3}{8} + 17\frac{5}{7} + 15\frac{3}{14}$

6. $20\frac{7}{12} - 15\frac{3}{5} + 40\frac{8}{15}$

1.4 Common fractions and decimal fractions

A. Converting common fractions into decimal fractions

The conversion of common fractions into decimal fractions is accomplished by performing the indicated division to the desired number of decimal places or until the decimal terminates.

Example 1.4a

(i) $\frac{9}{8} = 9 \div 8 = 1.125$

(ii) $\frac{1}{3} = 1 \div 3 = 0.33333\ldots = 0.\dot{3}$ or $0.33\frac{1}{3}$

(iii) $\frac{7}{6} = 7 \div 6 = 1.16666\ldots = 1.1\dot{6}$ or $1.16\frac{2}{3}$

B. Converting decimals to common fractions

Computations involving multiplication and division with decimals are often facilitated by using equivalent common fractions. The required conversion of the decimals to fractions is accomplished by writing the decimals in fraction form with denominator 10, 100, 1000, etc. as needed.

Example 1.4b

(i) $0.5 = 5 \text{ tenths} = \dfrac{5}{10} = \dfrac{1}{2}$

(ii) $0.75 = 75 \text{ hundredths} = \dfrac{75}{100} = \dfrac{3}{4}$

(iii) $0.05 = 5 \text{ hundredths} = \dfrac{5}{100} = \dfrac{1}{20}$

(iv) $0.625 = 625 \text{ thousandths} = \dfrac{625}{1000} = \dfrac{5}{8}$

(v) $0.025 = 25 \text{ thousandths} = \dfrac{25}{1000} = \dfrac{1}{40}$

(vi) $0.0005 = 5 \text{ ten-thousandths} = \dfrac{5}{10000} = \dfrac{1}{2000}$

(vii) $0.25 = \dfrac{25}{100} = \dfrac{1}{4}$

Note   The denominator may be written immediately by writing a '1' followed by as many zeros as there are decimal places.

(viii) $0.0075 = \dfrac{75}{10000} = \dfrac{3}{400}$ ⟵ the denominator is '1' followed by four zeros (4 decimal places)

(ix) $0.00012 = \dfrac{12}{100000} = \dfrac{3}{25000}$ ⟵ denominator is '1' followed by five zeros

Mixed decimals, such as $0.33\frac{1}{3}$ may be converted to common fractions in a similar manner with additional steps as shown in Example 1.4c.

Example 1.4c

(i) $0.33\dfrac{1}{3} = \dfrac{33\frac{1}{3}}{100}$ ⟵ write the decimal without the decimal point in the numerator, and write as denominator a '1' followed by as many zeros as there are digits between the decimal point and the fraction

$= \dfrac{\frac{100}{3}}{\frac{100}{1}}$ ⟵ change the numerator from a mixed number to a common fraction ⟵ write the denominator as a common fraction

$= \dfrac{100}{3} \div \dfrac{100}{1}$ ⟵ write the indicated division as a division

$= \dfrac{100}{3} \times \dfrac{1}{100}$ ⟵ change the division to multiplication

$= \dfrac{1}{3}$ ⟵ reduce to lowest terms

(ii) $0.81\dfrac{1}{4} = \dfrac{81\frac{1}{4}}{100} = \dfrac{\frac{325}{4}}{\frac{100}{1}} = \dfrac{325}{4} \div \dfrac{100}{1} = \dfrac{325}{4} \times \dfrac{1}{100} = \dfrac{13}{4} \times \dfrac{1}{4} = \dfrac{13}{16}$

(iii) $1.83\dfrac{1}{3} = 1 + 0.83\dfrac{1}{3}$ ⟵ separate the whole number from the decimal fraction and convert the decimal to a fraction

$$0.83\dfrac{1}{3} = \dfrac{83\frac{1}{3}}{100} = \dfrac{\frac{250}{3}}{\frac{100}{1}} = \dfrac{250}{3} \times \dfrac{1}{100} = \dfrac{5}{3} \times \dfrac{1}{2} = \dfrac{5}{6}$$

$$1.83\dfrac{1}{3} = 1 + 0.83\dfrac{1}{3} = 1 + \dfrac{5}{6} = \dfrac{11}{6}$$

C. Computation with commonly used decimals

While any terminating or repeating decimal can be converted into a common fraction, the effort of converting may negate the benefits of using a fraction in a computation. However, certain decimals are frequently encountered and should be memorized. The most important such decimals and their fractional equivalent are listed in Table 1.1.

TABLE 1.1 *Commonly used decimals and their fractional equivalents*

(i)	(ii)	(iii)	(iv)	(v)
$0.25 = \dfrac{1}{4}$	$0.16\dfrac{2}{3} = \dfrac{1}{6}$	$0.125 = \dfrac{1}{8}$	$0.2 = \dfrac{1}{5}$	$0.08\dfrac{1}{3} = \dfrac{1}{12}$
$0.50 = \dfrac{1}{2}$	$0.33\dfrac{1}{3} = \dfrac{1}{3}$	$0.375 = \dfrac{3}{8}$	$0.4 = \dfrac{2}{5}$	$0.06\dfrac{2}{3} = \dfrac{1}{15}$
$0.75 = \dfrac{3}{4}$	$0.66\dfrac{2}{3} = \dfrac{2}{3}$	$0.625 = \dfrac{5}{8}$	$0.6 = \dfrac{3}{5}$	$0.06\dfrac{1}{4} = \dfrac{1}{16}$
	$0.83\dfrac{1}{3} = \dfrac{5}{6}$	$0.875 = \dfrac{7}{8}$	$0.8 = \dfrac{4}{5}$	

Example 1.4d

(i) $64 \times 0.25 = 64 \times \dfrac{1}{4} = 16$

(ii) $90 \times 0.33\dfrac{1}{3} = 90 \times \dfrac{1}{3} = 30$

(iii) $72 \times 0.625 = 72 \times \dfrac{5}{8} = 9 \times 5 = 45$

(iv) $42 \times 0.83\dfrac{1}{3} = 42 \times \dfrac{5}{6} = 7 \times 5 = 35$

(v) $240 \times 1.33\frac{1}{3} = 240\left(1 + \frac{1}{3}\right) = 240 \times \frac{4}{3} = 80 \times 4 = 320$

(vi) $88 \times 3.125 = 88\left(3 + \frac{1}{8}\right) = 88 \times \frac{25}{8} = 11 \times 25 = 275$

Example 1.4e

(i) $12 \div 0.75 = 12 \div \frac{3}{4} = 12 \times \frac{4}{3} = 4 \times 4 = 16$

(ii) $48 \div 0.66\frac{2}{3} = 48 \div \frac{2}{3} = 48 \times \frac{3}{2} = 24 \times 3 = 72$

(iii) $35 \div 1.16\frac{2}{3} = 35 \div \left(1 + \frac{1}{6}\right) = 35 \div \frac{7}{6} = 35 \times \frac{6}{7} = 5 \times 6 = 30$

(iv) $99 \div 1.83\frac{1}{3} = 99 \div \left(1 + \frac{5}{6}\right) = 99 \div \frac{11}{6} = 99 \times \frac{6}{11} = 9 \times 6 = 54$

Exercise 1.4

A. Convert each of the following fractions into a decimal fraction. If the result is a repeating decimal, write your answer as a mixed decimal, such as $0.33\frac{1}{3}$.

1. $\frac{11}{8}$ **2.** $\frac{7}{4}$ **3.** $\frac{5}{3}$ **4.** $\frac{5}{6}$

5. $\frac{11}{6}$ **6.** $\frac{7}{9}$ **7.** $\frac{13}{12}$ **8.** $\frac{19}{15}$

B. Convert each of the following decimals to a common fraction.

1. 0.375   **2.** 0.075   **3.** 0.005   **4.** 0.0025

5. $0.66\frac{2}{3}$ **6.** $0.16\frac{2}{3}$ **7.** $0.08\frac{1}{3}$ **8.** $0.03\frac{1}{3}$

9. $1.33\frac{1}{3}$ **10.** $2.83\frac{1}{3}$ **11.** $0.55\frac{5}{9}$ **12.** $2.22\frac{2}{9}$

C. Use fractional equivalents to perform each of the following computations.

1. 16×0.125 **2.** 36×0.25 **3.** 96×0.75 **4.** 56×0.625

5. $42 \times 0.33\frac{1}{3}$ **6.** $54 \times 0.83\frac{1}{3}$ **7.** $66 \times 1.16\frac{2}{3}$ **8.** 120×1.25

9. $63 \times 2.33\frac{1}{3}$ **10.** 144×1.875 **11.** $45 \times 0.55\frac{5}{9}$ **12.** $108 \times 1.11\frac{1}{9}$

1.5 Order of operations

A. The basic order of operations

To ensure that operations are performed in a consistent manner we must adhere to the *order of operations*.

If an arithmetic expression contains brackets as well as any or all of powers, multiplicaton, division, addition and subtraction, the following procedure should be used:

1. perform all operations *inside* a bracket subject to doing the operations inside the bracket in proper order;
2. perform powers;
3. perform multiplications and divisions in order;
   > *Note* It is permissible and often desirable to do division before multiplication.
4. perform addition and subtraction.

Example 1.5a

(i) $9 - 4 \times 2 = 9 - 8 = 1$ ⟵ do multiplication before subtraction

(ii) $(9 - 4) \times 2 = 5 \times 2 = 10$ ⟵ work inside the bracket first

(iii) $(13 + 5) \div 6 - 3 = 18 \div 6 - 3$ ⟵ work inside the bracket
$$= 3 - 3$$
$$= 0$$
first, then do division before subtraction

(iv) $18 \div 6 + 3 \times 2 = 3 + 6 = 9$ ⟵ do multiplication and division before adding

(v) $18 \div (6 + 3) \times 2 = 18 \div 9 \times 2$ ⟵ work inside the bracket
$$= 2 \times 2$$
$$= 4$$
first, then do division and multiplication in order

(vi) $18 \div (3 \times 2) + 3 = 18 \div 6 + 3$ ⟵ work inside bracket first,
$$= 3 + 3$$
$$= 6$$
then divide before adding

(vii) $8(9 - 4) - 4(12 - 5) = 8(5) - 4(7)$ ⟵ work inside brackets first
$$= 40 - 28$$
$$= 12$$
then multiply before subtracting

(viii) $\dfrac{12 - 4}{6 - 2} = (12 - 4) \div (6 - 2)$ ⟵ the fraction line indicates
$$= 8 \div 4$$
$$= 2$$
brackets as well as division

(ix) $5 \times 2^3 = 5 \times 8 = 40$ ←——————————— do the power $2^3 = 2 \times 2$
$\times\ 2$ before multiplying
by 5

(x) $(5 \times 2)^3 = 10^3 = 10 \times 10 \times 10 = 1000$ ←——— work inside bracket first

B. Complex fractions

Complex fractions are mathematical expressions containing one or more fractions in the numerator or denominator or both. Certain formulae used in simple interest and simple discount calculations result in complex fractions. When such fractions are encountered, care must be taken in using the order of operations properly whether computing manually or with the help of a calculator.

Example 1.5b

(i) $\dfrac{\frac{3}{7}}{\frac{6}{5}} = \dfrac{3}{7} \div \dfrac{6}{5} = \dfrac{3}{7} \times \dfrac{5}{6} = \dfrac{1 \times 5}{7 \times 2} = \dfrac{5}{14}$

(ii) $\dfrac{\frac{4}{3} - \frac{5}{8}}{\frac{1}{2} + \frac{2}{5}} = \dfrac{\frac{32 - 15}{24}}{\frac{5 + 4}{10}} = \dfrac{\frac{17}{24}}{\frac{9}{10}} = \dfrac{17}{24} \div \dfrac{9}{10} = \dfrac{17}{24} \times \dfrac{10}{9} = \dfrac{17}{12} \times \dfrac{5}{9} = \dfrac{85}{108}$

(iii) $\dfrac{420}{1600 \times \frac{315}{360}} = \dfrac{420}{1600 \times \frac{7}{8}} = \dfrac{420}{200 \times 7} = \dfrac{60}{200} = \dfrac{3}{10}$

(iv) $\dfrac{450}{3600 \times 0.16\frac{2}{3}} = \dfrac{450}{3600 \times \frac{1}{6}} = \dfrac{450}{600} = \dfrac{3}{4}$

(v) $\quad 500\left(1 + 0.16 \times \dfrac{225}{360}\right)$

$= 500\left(1 + 0.16 \times \dfrac{5}{8}\right)$ ←——— reduce $\frac{225}{360}$ to lowest terms

$= 500(1 + 0.02 \times 5)$ ←——— divide 8 into 0.16

$= 500(1 + 0.10)$ ←——————— multiply 0.02 by 5

$= 500(1.10)$ ←——————— add inside bracket

$= 550$

(vi) $1000\left(1 - 0.18 \times \dfrac{288}{360}\right) = 1000\left(1 - 0.18 \times \dfrac{4}{5}\right)$

$= 1000(1 - 0.036 \times 4)$

$= 1000(1 - 0.144)$

$= 1000(0.856)$

$= 856$

(vii) $\dfrac{824}{1 + 0.15 \times \frac{73}{365}} = \dfrac{824}{1 + 0.15 \times \frac{1}{5}} = \dfrac{824}{1 + 0.03 \times 1} = \dfrac{824}{1.03} = 800$

(viii) $\dfrac{1755}{1 - 0.21 \times \frac{210}{360}} = \dfrac{1755}{1 - 0.21 \times \frac{7}{12}} = \dfrac{1755}{1 - 0.07 \times \frac{7}{4}}$

$$= \dfrac{1755}{1 - 0.0175 \times 7} = \dfrac{1755}{1 - 0.1255} = \dfrac{1755}{0.8775} = 2000$$

Mathematics fundamentals

Exercise 1.5

A. Simplify each of the following.

1. $12 + 6 \div 3$ **2.** $(12 + 6) \div 3$

3. $(7 + 4) \times 5 - 2$ **4.** $7 + 4 \times 5 - 2$

5. $5 \times 3 + 2 \times 4$ **6.** $5(3 + 2) - 12 \div 3$

7. $6(7 - 2) - 3(5 - 3)$ **8.** $8(9 - 6) + 4(6 + 5)$

9. $\dfrac{16 - 8}{8 - 2}$ **10.** $\dfrac{20 - 16}{15 + 9}$

11. 4×3^2 **12.** $(4 \times 3)^2$

B. Simplify each of the following.

1. $\dfrac{\frac{9}{10}}{\frac{8}{15}}$ **2.** $\dfrac{3\frac{3}{4}}{2\frac{11}{12}}$

3. $\dfrac{\frac{5}{6} - \frac{3}{4}}{\frac{1}{4} + \frac{2}{5}}$ **4.** $\dfrac{\frac{7}{8} + \frac{2}{5}}{\frac{11}{6} - \frac{10}{7}}$

5. $\dfrac{54}{0.12 \times \frac{225}{360}}$ **6.** $\dfrac{264}{4400 \times \frac{146}{365}}$

7. $620\left(1 + 0.14 \times \dfrac{45}{360}\right)$ **8.** $375\left(1 + 0.16 \times \dfrac{292}{365}\right)$

9. $2100\left(1 - 0.135 \times \dfrac{240}{360}\right)$ **10.** $8500\left(1 - 0.17 \times \dfrac{216}{360}\right)$

11. $\dfrac{250250}{1 + 0.15 \times \frac{330}{360}}$ **12.** $\dfrac{2358}{1 + 0.12 \times \frac{146}{365}}$

13. $\dfrac{3460}{1 - 0.18 \times \frac{270}{360}}$ **14.** $\dfrac{2901}{1 - 0.165 \times \frac{73}{365}}$

1.6 Applications

A. Basic problems

Example 1.6a The local cooperative received $36\frac{3}{4}$ tonnes of feed at \$240 per tonne. Sales for the following five days were

$$3\tfrac{5}{8}\text{ tonnes, }4\tfrac{3}{4}\text{ tonnes, }7\tfrac{2}{3}\text{ tonnes, }5\tfrac{1}{2}\text{ tonnes and }6\tfrac{3}{8}\text{ tonnes.}$$

What was the value of inventory at the end of Day 5?

Solution

$$
\begin{aligned}
\text{Total sales (in tonnes)} &= 3\frac{5}{8} + 4\frac{3}{4} + 7\frac{2}{3} + 5\frac{1}{2} + 6\frac{3}{8} \\[2mm]
&= 3 + 4 + 7 + 5 + 6 + \frac{5}{8} + \frac{3}{4} + \frac{2}{3} + \frac{1}{2} + \frac{3}{8} \\[2mm]
&= 25 + \frac{15 + 18 + 16 + 12 + 9}{24} \\[2mm]
&= 25 + \frac{70}{24} \\[2mm]
&= 25 + 2 + \frac{22}{24} \\[2mm]
&= 27\frac{11}{12}
\end{aligned}
$$

$$
\begin{aligned}
\text{Inventory (in tonnes)} &= 36\frac{3}{4} - 27\frac{11}{12} = 36 - 27 + \frac{3}{4} - \frac{11}{12} \\[2mm]
&= 9 + \frac{9}{12} - \frac{11}{12} = 8 + \frac{12}{12} + \frac{9}{12} - \frac{11}{12} \\[2mm]
&= 8 + \frac{10}{12} = 8\frac{5}{6}
\end{aligned}
$$

$$
\text{Value of Inventory} = 8\frac{5}{6} \times 240 = \frac{53}{6} \times 240 = 53 \times 40 = \$2120
$$

Example 1.6b Complete the following excerpt from an invoice.

Quantity	Unit price	Amount
72	\$0.875	\$ _____
45	$0.66\frac{2}{3}$	_____
54	$0.83\frac{1}{3}$	_____
42	$1.33\frac{1}{3}$	_____
32	1.375	_____
	TOTAL	\$ _____

Solution

If invoicing is done manually and unit prices are readily convertible into common fractions, the process of extending is simplified by using common fractions rather than decimals.

$$72 \times 0.875 = 72 \times \frac{7}{8} = 9 \times 7 = \$63.00$$

$$45 \times 0.66\frac{2}{3} = 45 \times \frac{2}{3} = 15 \times 2 = 30.00$$

$$54 \times 0.83\frac{1}{3} = 54 \times \frac{5}{6} = 9 \times 5 = 45.00$$

$$42 \times 1.33\frac{1}{3} = 42 \times \frac{4}{3} = 14 \times 4 = 56.00$$

$$32 \times 1.375 = 32 \times \frac{11}{8} = 4 \times 11 = \underline{44.00}$$

$$\$238.00$$

B. Problems involving simple arithmetic average

The *arithmetic mean* of a set of values is a widely used average found by adding the values and dividing by the number of values in the set.

Example 1.6c   The marks obtained by Jim Pearson for the seven tests comprising Section 1 of his Mathematics of Finance course were 82, 68, 88, 72, 78, 96 and 83.
(i) If all tests count equally, what was his average mark for Section 1?
(ii) If his marks for Section 2 and Section 3 of the course were 72.4 and 68.9 respectively and all Section marks have equal value, what was his course average?

Solution

$$\text{(i) Section Average} = \frac{\text{Sum of the Test Marks for the Section}}{\text{Number of Tests}}$$

$$= \frac{82 + 68 + 88 + 72 + 78 + 96 + 83}{7}$$

$$= \frac{567}{7}$$

$$= 81.0$$

(ii) Course Average $= \dfrac{\text{Sum of the Section Marks}}{\text{Number of Sections}}$

$= \dfrac{81.0 + 72.4 + 68.9}{3}$

$= \dfrac{222.3}{3}$

$= 74.1$

Example 1.6d   Monthly sales of Sheridan Service for last year were

January	$13 200	July	$13 700
February	11 400	August	12 800
March	14 600	September	13 800
April	13 100	October	15 300
May	13 600	November	14 400
June	14 300	December	13 900

What were Sheridan's average monthly sales for the year?

Solution

Total sales $= 164\ 100$

Average monthly sales $= \dfrac{\text{Total sales}}{\text{Number of Months}} = \dfrac{164\ 100}{12} = \$13\ 675$

C.   Weighted average

If the items to be included in computing an arithmetic mean are arranged in groups or if the items are not equally important, a *weighted arithmetic average* can be obtained by multiplying each item by the numbers involved or by a weighting factor representing its importance.

Example 1.6e   During last season Fairfield Farms sold strawberries as follows: 800 boxes at $1.25 per box in the early part of the season; 1600 boxes at $0.90 per box and 2000 boxes at $0.75 per box at the height of the season; and 600 boxes at $1.10 per box during the late season.
(i) What was the average price charged?
(ii) What was the average price per box?

Solution
(i) The average price charged is a simple average of the four different prices charged during the season.

Average Price $= \dfrac{1.25 + 0.90 + 0.75 +, 1.10}{4} = \dfrac{4.00}{4} = \$1.00$

(ii) To obtain the average price realized per box, allowance must be made for the number of boxes sold at each price; that is, a weighted average must be computed.

$$
\begin{array}{lll}
800 \text{ boxes @ } \$1.25 \text{ per box} \longrightarrow & \$1000.00 \\
1600 \text{ boxes @ } \$0.90 \text{ per box} \longrightarrow & 1440.00 \\
2000 \text{ boxes @ } \$0.75 \text{ per box} \longrightarrow & 1500.00 \\
600 \text{ boxes @ } \$1.10 \text{ per box} \longrightarrow & 660.00 \\
\hline
5000 \text{ boxes} \longleftarrow \quad \text{TOTALS} \longrightarrow & \$4600.00
\end{array}
$$

$$
\text{Average Price per box} = \frac{\text{Total Value}}{\text{Number of Boxes}} = \frac{4600.00}{5000} = \$0.92
$$

Example 1.6f The Dutch Cheese Shop creates its house brand by mixing 13 kg of coffee priced at $7.50 per kg, 16 kg of coffee priced at $6.25 per kg, and 11 kg of coffee priced at $5.50 per kg. At what price should the house blend be sold to realize the same revenue that could be made by selling the three types of coffee separately?

Solution

$$
\begin{array}{lll}
13 \text{ kg @ } \$7.50 \text{ per kg} \longrightarrow & \$ \ 97.50 \\
16 \text{ kg @ } \$6.25 \text{ per kg} \longrightarrow & 100.00 \\
11 \text{ kg @ } \$5.50 \text{ per kg} \longrightarrow & 60.50 \\
\hline
40 \text{ kg} \longleftarrow \quad \text{TOTALS} \longrightarrow & \$258.00
\end{array}
$$

$$
\text{Average value} = \frac{\text{Total Value}}{\text{Number of Units}} = \frac{258.00}{40} = \$6.45
$$

The house blend should be sold for $6.45 per kg.

Example 1.6g The course credit hours and grades for Dana's first term subjects are listed here.

Subject	Credit hours	Grade
Accounting	5	A
Economics	3	B
English	4	C
Law	2	D
Marketing	4	A
Mathematics	3	A
Elective	2	D

According to the grading system A's, B's, C's and D's are worth 4, 3, 2 and 1 quality points respectively. Based on this information determine
(i) Dana's average course grade;
(ii) Dana's grade-point average (average per credit hour).

Solution

(i) The average course grade is the average quality points obtained.

$$\frac{4 + 3 + 2 + 1 + 4 + 4 + 1}{7} = \frac{19}{7} = 2.71$$

(ii) The average obtained in (i) is misleading since the courses are not equal from the credit point of view. The grade-point average is considered a more appropriate average and is a weighted average allowing for the number of credit hours per course.

Subject	Credit hours	×	Quality points	=	Weighted points
Accounting	5	×	4	=	20
Economics	3	×	3	=	9
English	4	×	2	=	8
Law	2	×	1	=	2
Marketing	4	×	4	=	16
Mathematics	3	×	4	=	12
Elective	2	×	1	=	2
	23	← Totals →			69

$$\text{Grade-Point Average} = \frac{\text{Total Weighted Point}}{\text{Total Credit Hours}} = \frac{69}{23} = 3.00$$

Example 1.6h A partnership agreement provides for the distribution of the yearly profit or loss on the basis of the partners' average monthly investment. The investment account of one of the partners showed the following entries.

Balance, January 1	$25 750
April 1, withdrawal	3 250
June 1, investment	4 000
November 1, investment	2 000

Determine the partner's average monthly investment.

Solution

To determine the average monthly investment, determine the balance in the investment account after each change and weigh this balance by the number of months invested.

Date	Change	Balance	×	Number of months invested	=	Weighed value
January 1		25750	×	3	=	77250
April 1	−$3250	22500	×	2	=	45000
June 1	+ 4000	26500	×	5	=	132500
November 1	+ 2000	28500	×	2	=	57000
		Totals		12		311750

$$\text{Average monthly investment} = \frac{\text{Weighted Value}}{\text{Number of Months}} = \frac{311750}{12} = \$25979.17$$

Example 1.6i Several shoe stores in the city carry the same make of shoes. The number of pairs of shoes sold and the price charged by each store are shown below.

Store	Number of Pairs Sold	Price per Pair
A	60	$43.10
B	84	38.00
C	108	32.00
D	72	40.50

(i) What was the average number of pairs of shoes sold per store?
(ii) What was the average price per store?
(iii) What was the average sales revenue per store?
(iv) What was the average price per pair of shoes?

Solution

(i) The average number of pairs of shoes sold per store

$$= \frac{60 + 84 + 108 + 72}{4} = \frac{324}{4} = 81$$

(ii) The average price per store

$$= \frac{43.10 + 38.00 + 32.00 + 40.50}{4} = \frac{153.60}{4} = \$38.40$$

(iii) The average sales revenue per store

$$
\begin{array}{rl}
60 \times 43.10 = & \$\ 2586.00 \\
84 \times 38.00 = & 3192.00 \\
108 \times 32.00 = & 3456.00 \\
72 \times 40.50 = & \underline{2916.00} \\
& \$12150.00
\end{array}
$$

$$\text{Average} = \frac{12150.00}{4} = \$3037.50$$

(iv) The average price per pair of shoes

$$= \frac{12150.00}{324} = \$37.50$$

Exercise 1.6

A. Answer each of the following questions.

1. Heart Lake Developments sold four lakefront lots for $27 500 per hectare. If the size of the lots in hectares was $3\frac{3}{4}$, $2\frac{2}{3}$, $3\frac{5}{8}$ and $4\frac{5}{6}$ respectively, what was the total sales value of the four lots?

2. A construction job was completed by five carpenters working $15\frac{1}{2}$, $13\frac{3}{4}$, $18\frac{1}{2}$, $21\frac{1}{4}$ and $22\frac{3}{4}$ hours respectively. What was the total cost of labour if the carpenters were paid $12.75 each per hour?

3. A piece of property valued at $56 100 is assessed for property tax purposes at $\frac{6}{11}$ of its value. If the property tax rate is $3.75 on each $100 of assessed value, what is the amount of tax levied on the property?

4. A retailer returned 2700 defective items to the manufacturer and received a credit for the retail price of $0.83\frac{1}{3}$ per item less a discount of $\frac{3}{8}$ of the retail price. What was the amount of the credit received by the retailer?

5. Use equivalent common fractions to extend the following invoice.

Quantity	Description	Unit Price	$
64	A	$0.75	____
54	B	$0.83\frac{1}{3}$	____
72	C	0.375	____
42	D	$1.33\frac{1}{3}$	____
		TOTAL	____

6. Use equivalent common fractions to complete the following inventory sheet.

Item	Quantity	Cost per Unit	Total
1	96	$0.875	____
2	330	$0.16\frac{2}{3}$	____
3	144	1.75	____
4	240	$1.66\frac{2}{3}$	____
	TOTAL		____

B. Solve each of the following problems involving an arithmetic average.

1. Records of fuel oil consumption for the Sheridan Service for the last six-month period show that Sheridan has paid 38.5 cents per litre for the first 1100 litres, 41.5 cents per litre for the next 1600 litres and 42.5 cents per litre for the last delivery of 1400 litres. Determine the average cost of fuel oil per litre for the six-month period.

2. On a trip a motorist purchased gasoline as follows: 56 litres at 39.0 cents per litre; 64 litres at 40.5 cents per litre; 70 litres at 41.5 cents per litre; and 54 litres at 39.5 cents per litre.

   (i) What was the average number of litres per purchase?

   (ii) What was the average cost per litre?

   (iii) If the motorist averaged 8.75 km per litre, what was his average cost of gasoline per km?

3. The course credit hours and grades for Bill's fall semester are given below. At the college an A is worth six quality points, a B four points, a C two points and a D one point

Credit hours:	3	5	2	4	4	2
Grade :	B	C	A	C	D	A

   What is Bill's grade-point average?

4. Kim Blair invested $7500 in a business on January 1. She withdrew $900 on March 1, reinvested $1500 on August 1 and withdrew $300 on September 1. What is Kim's average monthly investment for the year?

Review exercise

1. Perform the operations as indicated.

   (a) 22.75 + 113.05 + 0.35 + 17.00

   (b) 163.89 − 84.97

   (c) 4800.00 × 1.015

   (d) 0.75 × 0.125

   (e) 861 ÷ 1.025

   (f) 342 ÷ 0.95

2. Write each of the following as a mixed decimal fraction with two decimal places.

   (a) 14 ÷ 3   (b) 1 ÷ 6   (c) 7 ÷ 12   (d) 4 ÷ 9

3. Write the product or quotient of each of the following as required.

   (a) 0.063 × 100   (b) 10000 × 1.017625

(c) $62.5 \div 100$ **(d)** $7.5 \div 1000$

(e) 1645×0.001 **(f)** 0.55×0.02

(g) $48.75 \div 0.01$ **(h)** $0.0875 \div 0.001$

4. Simplify each of the following showing your answer in lowest terms.

(a) $\dfrac{96}{72}$ **(b)** $\dfrac{42}{98}$

(c) $\dfrac{7}{8} \times \dfrac{12}{21}$ **(d)** $\dfrac{24}{35} \div \dfrac{18}{21}$

(e) $0.08 \times \dfrac{315}{360}$ **(f)** $0.15 \times \dfrac{146}{365}$

(g) $\dfrac{15}{8} \times \dfrac{12}{21} \times \dfrac{14}{25}$ **(h)** $\dfrac{35}{42} \div \dfrac{22}{21} \times \dfrac{11}{15}$

5. Simplify each of the following.

(a) $\dfrac{5}{6} + \dfrac{3}{4} + \dfrac{7}{8}$ **(b)** $\dfrac{11}{15} + \dfrac{9}{20} - \dfrac{7}{12} + \dfrac{3}{5}$

6. Simplify each of the following. Show your answer as a mixed number.

(a) $6\dfrac{2}{3} \times 7\dfrac{7}{8}$ **(b)** $4\dfrac{4}{9} \div 2\dfrac{1}{12}$

(c) $3\dfrac{2}{5} + 2\dfrac{3}{4} + 5\dfrac{1}{3} + 4\dfrac{5}{6}$ **(d)** $21\dfrac{2}{7} + 13\dfrac{3}{4} - 12\dfrac{9}{14} + 18\dfrac{1}{6}$

7. Convert each of the following decimals to a common fraction.

(a) 0.875 **(b)** 0.0075 **(c)** $0.83\dfrac{1}{3}$

(d) $0.06\dfrac{2}{3}$ **(e)** $1.66\dfrac{2}{3}$ **(f)** $1.16\dfrac{2}{3}$

8. Use fractional equivalents to perform each of the following computations.

(a) 64×0.375 **(b)** $45 \times 0.66\dfrac{2}{3}$

(c) $33 \times 1.33\dfrac{1}{3}$ **(d)** $72 \times 0.88\dfrac{8}{9}$

9. Simplify each of the following.

(a) $32 - 24 \div 8$ **(b)** $(48 - 18) \div 15 - 10$

(c) $(8 \times 6 - 4) \div (16 - 4 \times 3)$ **(d)** $9(6 - 2) - 4(3 + 4)$

(e) $\dfrac{18 - 12}{9 - 6}$ **(f)** 3×5^2

(g) $\dfrac{\frac{14}{9}}{\frac{28}{15}}$ **(h)** $\dfrac{\frac{5}{6} - \frac{3}{4}}{\frac{5}{8} + \frac{1}{3}}$

$$\textbf{(i)} \quad \frac{108}{0.18 \times \frac{216}{360}}$$

$$\textbf{(j)} \quad \frac{288}{2400 \times \frac{292}{365}}$$

$$\textbf{(k)} \quad 320\left(1 + 0.10 \times \frac{225}{360}\right)$$

$$\textbf{(l)} \quad 1000\left(1 - 0.12 \times \frac{150}{360}\right)$$

$$\textbf{(m)} \quad \frac{660}{1 + 0.14 \times \frac{144}{360}}$$

$$\textbf{(n)} \quad \frac{1120.00}{1 - 0.13 \times \frac{292}{365}}$$

10. Sales of a particular make and size of nails during a day were $4\frac{1}{3}$ kg, $3\frac{3}{4}$ kg, $5\frac{1}{2}$ kg and $6\frac{5}{8}$ kg.

(a) How many kilograms of nails were sold?
(b) What is the total sales value at $1.20 per kilogram?
(c) What was the average weight per sale?
(d) What was the average sales value per sale?

11. Extend and total the following invoice. Show your computations using equivalent common fractions.

Quantity	Description	Unit Price	Total
56	Item A	$0.625	_____
180	Item B	$0.83\frac{1}{3}$	_____
126	Item C	$1.16\frac{2}{3}$	_____
144	Item D	1.75	_____
		TOTAL	_____

12. The basic pay categories, hourly rate of pay and the number of employees in each category for the machining department of a company are as shown below.

Category	Hourly Pay	Number of Employees
Supervisors	$15.45	2
Machinists	12.20	6
Assistants	9.60	9
Helpers	7.50	13

(a) What is the average rate of pay per category?
(b) What is the average rate of pay per employee?

13. Bruce invested $15 000 on January 1 in a partnership. He withdrew $2000 on June 1, withdrew a further $1500 on August 1 and reinvested $4000 on November 1. What was his average monthly investment for the year?

14. Brent DeCosta invested $12 000 in a business on January 1 and an additional $2400 on April 1. He withdrew $1440 on June 1 and invested $2880 on October 1. What was Brent's average monthly investment for the year?

Self-test

1. Evaluate each of the following.

(a) $4320 \left(1 + 0.18 \times \dfrac{45}{360} \right)$

(b) $2160 \left(0.15 \times \dfrac{105}{360} \right)$

(c) $2880 \left(1 - 0.12 \times \dfrac{285}{360} \right)$

(d) $\dfrac{410.40}{0.24 \times \dfrac{135}{360}}$

(e) $\dfrac{5124}{1 + 0.09 \times \dfrac{270}{360}}$

2. The following information is shown in your investment account for last year: balance on January 1 was $7200; a withdrawal of $480 on March 1; deposits of $600 on August 1 and $120 on October 1. What was the average monthly balance for the year in your account?

3. Extend each of the following and determine the total.

Quantity	Unit Price
72	1.25
84	$0.16\frac{2}{3}$
40	0.875
48	$1.33\frac{1}{3}$

4. Purchases of an inventory item during the last accounting period were as follows:

No. of Items	Unit Price
5	9
6	7
3	8
6	6

What was the average price per item?

5. Ace Realty sold lots for $15 120 per hectare. What is the total sales value if the size of the lots, in hectares, was $5\frac{1}{4}$, $6\frac{1}{3}$, $4\frac{3}{8}$ and $3\frac{5}{6}$?

6. Property valued at $130 000 is assessed at $\frac{2}{13}$ of its value. What is the amount of tax due for this year, if the tax rate is $3.25 per $100 of assessed value?

Glossary of terms used

Addends   the individual numbers in an addition

Associative property of addition   the property which indicates that numbers may be grouped in any order when adding

Associative property of multiplication   the property which indicates that numbers may be grouped in any order when multiplying

Commutative property of addition   the property which indicates that two numbers may be added in any order

Commutative property of multiplication   the property which indicates that two numbers may be multiplied in any order

Complex fractions   mathematical expressions containing one or more fractions in either the numerator or the denominator or both

Denominator   the divisor in an indicated division

Difference   the result of a subtraction

Distributive property of multiplication over addition   the property which indicates that the product of the sum of two numbers equals the sum of the individual products

Dividend   the number which is to be divided

Divisor   the number by which another number, called the dividend, is to be divided

Equivalent fractions   fractions obtained by changing the two terms of a given fraction by multiplying or by dividing by the same factor

Equivalent fractions in higher terms   fractions obtained by multiplying both terms of a given fraction by the same number

Equivalent fractions in lower terms   fractions obtained by dividing both terms of a given fraction by the same number

Highest common factor (H.C.F.)   the greatest number which divides without remainder into two (or more) given numbers

Improper fractions   fractions in which the numerator is greater than the denominator

Indicated division   a division written in fractional form

Least common denominator (L.C.D.)   the smallest number into which a given set of denominators divides evenly

Minuend   the number from which a second number, called the subtrahend, is to be subtracted

Mixed decimals   decimals consisting of a decimal and a fraction, such as $0.33\frac{1}{3}$

Mixed numbers   numbers consisting of a whole number and a fraction

Multiplicand   the number to be multiplied

Multiplier   the number by which another number, called the multiplicand, is to be multiplied

Numerator   the dividend of an indicated division

Product   the result of a multiplication

Proper fraction   a fraction in which the numerator is smaller than the denominator

Quotient   the result of a division

Reciprocal   the inverted value of a fraction

Reducing fractions to lowest terms   the process of obtaining equivalent fractions in which the terms have no common factor

Remainder   see _difference_

Subtrahend   the number to be subtracted

Sum   the result of an addition

Terms of a fraction   the numerator and the denominator

2 *Review of basic algebra*

Introduction

The use of letter symbols assists in the establishment of relationships between variables and permits generalizations which prove helpful in solving mathematical problems.

Many problems in business and finance can be solved by means of predetermined formulae generally applicable to similar problems.

When formulae are used, the student needs to have manipulative skills, such as being able to deal with algebraic substitution and simplification. For other problems, no predetermined formulae may be available. However, often such problems can be solved by setting up and solving an algebraic equation.

Objectives

Upon completion of this chapter you will be able to

1. identify basic terms and apply the basic laws of algebra;
2. perform the fundamental operations with signed numbers;
3. simplify algebraic expressions using the fundamental operations and evaluate algebraic expressions by substitution;
4. perform common factoring;
5. simplify and evaluate powers with positive exponents, negative exponents and exponent zero.

2.1 Basic laws, rules and definitions

A. The fundamental operations

The fundamental operations of algebra are *addition, subtraction, multiplication* and *division*. The symbols used to indicate these operations are the same as used in arithmetic.

For any two numbers 'a' and 'b' the fundamental operations are indicated as follows.

1. *Addition* is denoted by '$a + b$' and referred to as the sum of 'a' and 'b'.
> If $a = 7$ and $b = 4$,
> then $a + b = 7 + 4 = 11$.

2. *Subtraction* is denoted by '$a - b$' and referred to as the difference between 'a' and 'b'.
> If $a = 7$ and $b = 4$,
> then $a - b = 7 - 4 = 3$.

3. *Multiplication* is denoted by '$a \times b$' or '$(a)(b)$' or 'ab'. 'a' and 'b' are called **factors** and 'ab' is referred to as the product of 'a' and 'b'.
> If $a = 7$ and $b = 4$,
> then $ab = (7)(4) = 28$.

4. *Division* is denoted by '$a : b$' or '$\frac{a}{b}$' or 'a/b'. 'a' is the dividend, 'b' is the divisor and '$\frac{a}{b}$' is referred to as the quotient.
> If $a = 7$ and $b = 4$,
> then $\frac{a}{b} = \frac{7}{4}$.

B. Basic laws

The basic laws governing algebraic operations are the same as those used for arithmetic operations.

1. *The Commutative Laws for Addition and Multiplication*

(a) When adding two numbers, the two numbers (addends) may be interchanged.

$$\boxed{a + b = b + a} \quad \longleftarrow \quad \textbf{\textit{Formula 2.1}}$$

> If $a = 7$ and $b = 4$,
> then $7 + 4 = 4 + 7 = 11$.

(*b*) When multiplying two numbers, the two factors may be interchanged.

$$\boxed{ab = ba} \quad \longleftarrow \quad \textbf{\textit{Formula 2.2}}$$

> If $a = 7$ and $b = 4$,
> then $(7)(4) = (4)(7) = 28$.

2. *The Associative Laws for Addition and Multiplication*

(a) When adding three or more numbers, the numbers (addends) may be combined in any order.

$$a + b + c = (a + b) + c = a + (b + c) = b + (a + c) \quad \leftarrow \textit{Formula } \mathbf{2.3}$$

If $a = 7$, $b = 4$, $c = 2$,
then $7 + 4 + 2 = (7 + 4) + 2 = 7 + (4 + 2) = 4 + (7 + 2) = 13$.

(*b*) When multiplying three or more numbers, the numbers (factors) may be combined in any order.

$$abc = (ab)c = a(bc) = b(ac) \quad \longleftarrow \textbf{Formula 2.4}$$

If $a = 7$, $b = 4$, $c = 2$,
then $7 \times 4 \times 2 = (7 \times 4) \times 2 = 7 \times (4 \times 2) = 4 \times (7 \times 2) = 56$.

3. *The Distributive Law of Multiplication over Addition*

The product of 'a' times the sum of 'b' and 'c' is equal to the sum of the products 'ab' and 'ac'.

$$a(b + c) = ab + ac \quad \longleftarrow \textbf{Formula 2.5}$$

If $a = 7$, $b = 4$ and $c = 2$,
then $7(4 + 2) = 7 \times 4 + 7 \times 2 = 42$.

4. *Special Properties of 1*

(a)
$$a \times 1 = 1 \times a = a$$
When any number 'a' is multiplied by '1', the product is the number 'a'.

If $a = 5$, then $5 \times 1 = 1 \times 5 = 5$.

(b)
$$\frac{a}{1} = a$$
When any number 'a' is divided by '1', the quotient is the number 'a'.

If $a = 5$, then $\frac{5}{1} = 5$.

(c)
$$\frac{a}{a} = 1$$
When any number 'a' is divided by itself, the quotient is '1'.

If $a = 5$, then $\frac{5}{5} = 1$.

5. *Special Properties of '0'*

(a) *Addition with '0'*

$$a + 0 = 0 + a = a$$

⟵ When '0' is added to any number 'a', the sum is the number 'a'.

If $a = 5$, then $5 + 0 = 0 + 5 = 5$.

(b) *Subtraction with '0'*

(i) $$a - 0 = a$$

⟵ When '0' is subtracted from any number 'a', the difference is the number 'a'.

If $a = 5$, then $5 - 0 = 5$.

(ii) $$0 - a = -a$$

⟵ When any number 'a' is subtracted from '0', the diffference is the inverse value of 'a', that is 'a' with the sign changed.

If $a = 5$, then $0 - 5 = -5$.

(c) *Multiplication with '0'*

$$a \times 0 = 0 \times a = 0$$

⟵ When '0' is multiplied by any number 'a', the product is '0'.

If $a = 5$, then $5 \times 0 = 0 \times 5 = 0$.

(d) *Division with '0'*

(i) $$\frac{0}{a} = 0$$

⟵ When '0' is divided by any number 'a' other than '0', the quotient is '0'.

If $a = 5$, then $\frac{0}{5} = 0$.

(ii) $$\frac{a}{0} = \text{undefined}$$

⟵ Division by '0' has no meaning.

If $a = 5$, then $\frac{5}{0} = \text{undefined}$.

C. Definitions

1. An **algebraic expression** is a combination of numbers, variables representing numbers, and symbols indicating an algebraic operation.

$$7ab, \quad 3a - 5b, \quad x^2 - 3x + 4, \quad \frac{3}{4}x - \frac{1}{5}y$$

2. A **term** is a part of an algebraic expression separated from other parts by a positive $(+)$ sign or by a negative $(-)$ sign. The preceding $(+)$ sign or $(-)$ sign is part of the term.

The terms for the algebraic expressions listed in (1) are

$$7ab;\ 3a\ and\ -5b;\ x^2,\ -3x,\ and\ +4;\ \frac{3}{4}x\ and\ -\frac{1}{5}y$$

3. A **monomial** is an algebraic expression consisting of *one* term, such as $7ab$.

A **binomial** is an algebraic expression consisting of *two* terms, such as $3a - 5b$ or $\frac{3}{4}x - \frac{1}{5}y$.

A **trinomial** is an algebraic expression consisting of *three* terms, such as $x^2 - 3x + 4$.

A **polynomial** is an algebraic expression consisting of *more than one* term.

4. A **factor** is one of the numbers which when multiplied by another number or numbers yields a given product.

The factors of the term $7ab$ are 7, a, and b.

5. A *factor of a term* is called the *coefficient* of the rest of the term.

In the term $7ab$, 7 is the coefficient of ab,

$7a$ is the coefficient of b,

$7b$ is the coefficient of a.

6. The **numerical coefficient** is the part of a term formed by *numerals*.

In the term $7ab$, the numerical coefficient is 7;

in the term x^2, the numerical coefficient is *understood* to be 1 (and is usually not written);

in the term $-\frac{1}{5}y$ the numerical coefficient is $-\frac{1}{5}$ (the sign is considered to be part of the numerical coefficient).

7. The **literal coefficient** of a term is the part of the term formed with *letter* symbols.

In the term $7ab$, ab is the literal coefficient;

in the term $3x^2$, x^2 is the literal coefficient.

8. **Like terms** are terms having the *same* literal coefficients.

$$7a,\ -\ 3a,\ a,\ -\frac{1}{3}a\ \text{are like terms};$$

$$x^2,\ -2x^2,\ -\frac{1}{2}x,\ 5x^2\ \text{are like terms}.$$

9. **Combining like terms** or **collecting like terms** means *adding* like terms. Only like terms can be added.

10. **Signed numbers** are numbers preceded by a positive $(+)$ or by a negative $(-)$ sign. Numbers preceded by a positive $(+)$ sign are referred to as **positive numbers**, while numbers preceded by a negative $(-)$ sign are called **negative numbers**.

11. **Like signed numbers** are numbers having the *same* sign while numbers having *different* signs are called **unlike signed numbers**.

$$+7 \text{ and } +8 \text{ are like signed numbers;}$$
$$-7 \text{ and } -8 \text{ are like signed numbers;}$$
$$+7 \text{ and } -8 \text{ are unlike signed numbers;}$$
$$-7 \text{ and } 8 \text{ are unlike signed numbers.}$$

Note If no sign is written in front of a number, a plus (+) sign is understood to precede the number.

'6' means '+6'.

12. The **absolute value** of a signed number is the value of the number *without* the sign and is denoted by the symbol $|\ |$.

$$\text{The absolute value of } +5 = |+5| = 5;$$
$$\text{the absolute value of } -5 = |-5| = 5.$$

Exercise 2.1

A. Answer each of the following questions.

1. List the terms contained in each of the following expressions.

(a) $-3xy$

(b) $4a - 5c - 2d$

(c) $x^2 - \frac{1}{2}x - 2$

(d) $1.2x - 0.5xy + 0.9y - 0.3$

2. Name the numerical coefficient of each of the following terms.

(a) $-3b$ (b) $7c$ (c) $-a$ (d) x

(e) $12a^2b$ (f) $-3ax$ (g) $-\frac{1}{2}x^2$ (h) $\frac{x}{5}$

3. Name the literal coefficient of each of the following.

(a) $3x$ (b) ab (c) $-4y$ (d) $-xy$

(e) $-15x^2y^2$ (f) $3.5abx$ (g) $\frac{4}{3}x^3$ (h) $\frac{by}{6}$

2.2 Fundamental operations with signed numbers

A. Addition with signed numbers

1. *Addition of Like Signed Numbers*

To add like signed numbers
(i) add their absolute values, and
(ii) prefix the common sign.

Example 2.2a Add each of the following.

(i) -6 and -8

Solution

The absolute values are 6 and 8;
the sum of 6 and 8 is 14;
the common sign is $(-)$.
$$(-6) + (-8) = -6 - 8 = -14$$

(ii) $+6$, $+5$ and $+12$

Solution

The absolute values are 6, 5 and 12;
the sum of 6, 5 and 12 is 23;
the common sign is $(+)$.
$$(+6) + (+5) + (+12) = +6 + 5 + 12 = +23 \text{ or } 23$$

(iii) -9, -3, -1 and -15

Solution

The absolute values are 9, 3, 1, 15;
the sum of the four numbers is 28;
the common sign is $(-)$.
$$(-9) + (-3) + (-1) + (-15) = -9 - 3 - 1 - 15 = -28$$

2. *Addition of Unlike Signed Numbers*

To add unlike signed numbers
(i) subtract the smaller absolute value from the larger absolute value, and
(ii) prefix the sign of the *larger* absolute value.

Example 2.2b Add each of the following.

(i) 8 and -5

Solution

The absolute values are 8 and 5;
the difference between the absolute values is 3;
the sign of the larger absolute value is $(+)$.
$$(+8) + (-5) = +8 - 5 = +3 \text{ or } 3$$

(ii) 4 and −9

Solution

The absolute values are 4 and 9;
the difference between the absolute values is 5;
the sign of the larger absolute value is (−).
$$(+4) + (-9) = 4 - 9 = -5$$

(iii) −6, +8, +3, −4 and −5

Solution

When more than two numbers are involved and unlike signs appear,
two approaches are available.

METHOD 1   Add the first two numbers and then add the sum to the
next number, and so on.
$$(-6) + (+8) + (+3) + (-4) + (-5)$$
$$= -6 + 8 + 3 - 4 - 5$$
$$= +2 + 3 - 4 - 5 \longleftarrow \text{ add } -6 \text{ and } +8 \text{ which equals } +2$$
$$= +5 - 4 - 5 \longleftarrow \text{ add } +2 \text{ and } +3 \text{ which equals } +5$$
$$= +1 - 5 \longleftarrow \text{ add } +5 \text{ and } -4 \text{ which equals } +1$$
$$= -4 \longleftarrow \text{ add } +1 \text{ and } -5 \text{ which equals } -4$$

METHOD 2   First add the numbers having like signs, then add the
two resulting unlike signed numbers.
$$(-6) + (+8) + (+3) + (-4) + (-5)$$
$$= -6 + 8 + 3 - 4 - 5$$
$$= (-6 - 4 - 5) + (+8 + 3)$$
$$= (-15) + (+11)$$
$$= -15 + 11$$
$$= -4$$

B.   Subtraction with signed numbers

The subtraction of signed numbers is changed to addition by using the inverse of
the subtrahend. Thus, to subtract with signed numbers, change the sign of the
subtrahend and add.

Example 2.2c   Perform each of the following subtractions.

(i) (+6) from (4)

Solution

$$(+4) - (+6)$$
$$= (+4) + (-6) \longleftarrow \text{ change the subtrahend } (+6) \text{ to } (-6) \text{ and change the}$$
$$\text{subtraction to an addition}$$
$$= +4 - 6 \longleftarrow \text{ use the rules of addition to add } +4 \text{ and } -6$$
$$= -2$$

(ii) (-12) from $(+7)$

Solution

$(+7) - (-12)$
$= (+7) + (+12)$ ⟵ change the subtrahend (-12) to $(+12)$
$= +7 + 12$ ⟵ and add
$= 19$

(iii) $(+9)$ from (-6)

Solution

$(-6) - (+9)$
$= (-6) + (-9)$
$= -6 - 9$
$= -15$

C. Multiplication with signed numbers

The product of two signed numbers is positive or negative according to the following.

(a) If the signs of the two numbers are *like*, the product is *positive*.
$$(+)(+) = (+)$$
$$(-)(-) = (+)$$

(b) If the signs of the two numbers are *unlike*, the product is *negative*.
$$(+)(-) = (-)$$
$$(-)(+) = (-)$$

Example 2.2d

(i) $(+7)(+4) = 28$ ⟵ both signs are like (both positive); the product is positive

(ii) $(-9)(-3) = 27$ ⟵ the two signs are like (both negative); the product is positive

(iii) $(-8)(3) = -24$ ⟵ The signs are unlike; the product is negative

(iv) $(7)(-1) = -7$ ⟵ the signs are unlike; the product is negative

(v) $(-8)(0) = 0$ ⟵ the product of any number and 0 is 0

(vi) $(-7)(3)(-4) = (-21)(-4)$ ⟵ (-7) times (3) is (-21)
$= 84$

(vii) $(-2)(-1)(-4)(3) = (2)(-4)(3) = (-8)(3) = -24$

Note Brackets around one or both numbers may be used to indicate multiplication.

D. Division with signed numbers

The quotient of two signed numbers is positive or negative according to the following.

(a) If the signs are *like*, the quotient is *positive*.
$$(+) \div (+) = (+)$$
$$(-) \div (-) = (+)$$

(b) If the signs are *unlike*, the quotient is *negative*.
$$(+) \div (-) = (-)$$
$$(-) \div (+) = (-)$$

Example 2.2e

(i) $15 \div (+5)$ $= 3$ ⟵—————— the two signs are like; the quotient is positive

(ii) $(-24) \div (-4) = 6$ ⟵—————— the two signs are like; the quotient is positive

(iii) $(-18) \div 2$ $= -9$ ⟵—————— the two signs are unlike; the quotient is negative

(iv) $(12) \div (-1)$ $= -12$ ⟵—————— the two signs are unlike; the quotient is negative

(v) $0 \div (-10)$ $= 0$ ⟵—————— 0 divided by any number is 0

(vi) $(-16) \div 0$ $=$ undefined ⟵——— division by 0 has no meaning

E. Absolute value of signed numbers

The absolute value of signed numbers, denoted by $| \ |$, is the value of the numbers without the signs.

Example 2.2f

(i) $|-7| = 7$

(ii) $|-3 + 8| = |+5| = 5$

(iii) $|4 - 9| = |-5| = 5$

(iv) $|-9 - 4| = |-13| = 13$

(v) $|4(-7)| = |-28| = 28$

(vi) $|(-9)(-3)| = |27| = 27$

(vii) $|(-12) \div (4)| = |-3| = 3$

(viii) $|(-30) \div (-5)| = |+6| = 6$

Exercise 2.2

A. Simplify.

1. $(+3) + (+7)$ 2. $(+12) + (+6)$ 3. $(-5) + (-9)$
4. $(-15) + (-12)$ 5. $4 + (+5)$ 6. $(+6) + 8$
7. $-8 + (-7)$ 8. $(-18) - 7$ 9. $+3 + 14$
10. $+12 + 1$ 11. $-6 - 9$ 12. $-14 - 3$
13. $-8 + 3$ 14. $-12 + 16$ 15. $8 - 12$
16. $0 - 9$ 17. $1 - 0.6$ 18. $1 - 0.02$
19. $(-4) + (6) + (-3) + (+2)$ 20. $12 + (-15) + (+8) + (-10)$
21. $-3 - 7 + 9 + 6 - 5$ 22. $10 - 8 - 12 + 3 - 7$

B. Simplify.

1. $(+9) - (+8)$ 2. $(+11) - (+14)$ 3. $(+6) - (-6)$
4. $(+11) - (-12)$ 5. $(-8) - (-7)$ 6. $(-9) - (-13)$
7. $(-4) - (+6)$ 8. $(-15) - (+3)$ 9. $0 - (-9)$
10. $1 - (-0.4)$ 11. $1 - (-0.03)$ 12. $0 - (+15)$
13. $6 - (-5) + (-8) - (+3) + (-2)$
14. $-12 - (-6) - (+9) + (-4) - 7$

C. Simplify.

1. $(+5)(+4)$ 2. $11(+3)$ 3. $(-4)(-6)$ 4. $-7(-3)$
5. $(+7)(-1)$ 6. $10(-5)$ 7. $-3(12)$ 8. $-9(1)$
9. $0(-6)$ 10. $-12(0)$ 11. $6(-4)(-3)(2)$ 12. $-3(5)(-2)(-1)$

D. Simplify.

1. $(+18) \div (+3)$ 2. $(32) \div (+4)$ 3. $(+45) \div (-9)$ 4. $(63) \div (-3)$
5. $(-28) \div (+7)$ 6. $(-36) \div (+12)$ 7. $(-16) \div (-1)$ 8. $(-48) \div (-8)$
9. $0 \div (-5)$ 10. $0 \div 10$ 11. $(+4) \div 0$ 12. $(-12) \div 0$

E. Simplify.

1. $|-9|$ 2. $|+4|$ 3. $|6 - 10|$ 4. $|-5 + 12|$
5. $|-7 - 8|$ 6. $|0 - 3|$ 7. $|(-3) \times 3|$ 8. $|4 \times (-5)|$
9. $|20 \div (-5)|$ 10. $|(-35) \div (7)|$

2.3   Simplification of algebraic expressions

A.   Addition and subtraction

1. *Simplification Involving Addition and Subtraction*
In algebra only like terms may be added or subtracted. This is done by *adding*

or *subtracting* the *numerical* coefficients of the like terms according to the rules used for adding and subtracting signed numbers, and *retaining* the common *literal* coefficient. The process of adding and subtracting like terms is referred to as combining like terms or collecting like terms.

Example 2.3a

(i) $6x + 3x + 7x$ ⟵────── all three terms are like terms
$= (6 + 3 + 7)x$ ⟵────── add the numerical coefficients
$= 16x$ ⟵────── retain the common literal coefficient

(ii) $9a - 5a - 7a + 4a$
$= (9 - 5 - 7 + 4)a$
$= a$

(iii) $-5m - (-3m) - (+6m)$
$= -5m + (+3m) + (-6m)$ ⟵── change the subtraction to addition
$= -5m + 3m - 6m$
$= (-5 + 3 - 6)m$
$= -8m$

(iv) $7x - 4y - 3x - 6y$ ⟵── the two sets of like terms are $7x$, $-3x$ and
$= (7 - 3)x + (-4 - 6)y$ $-4y$, $-6y$, and are collected separately
$= 4x - 10y$

(v) $5x^2 - 3x - 4 + 2x - 5 + x^2$
$= (5 + 1)x^2 + (-3 + 2)x + (-4 - 5)$
$= 6x^2 - x - 9$

2. Simplification Involving Brackets

When simplifying algebraic expressions involving brackets, remove the brackets according to the following rules and collect like terms.

(a) If the brackets are preceded by a $(+)$ sign or no sign, drop the brackets and retain the terms inside the brackets with their signs unchanged.
    $(-7a + 5b - c)$ becomes $-7a + 5b - c$.

(b) If the brackets are preceded by a $(-)$ sign, drop the brackets and change the sign of every term inside the brackets.
    $-(-7a + 5b - c)$ becomes $7a - 5b + c$.

Example 2.3b

(i) $(7a - 3b) - (4a + 3b)$
$= 7a - 3b - 4a - 3b$ ⟵── $(7a - 3b)$ becomes $7a - 3b$
                            $-(4a + 3b)$ becomes $-4a - 3b$
$= 3a - 6b$

(ii) $-(3x^2 - 8x - 5) + (2x^2 - 5x + 4)$
$= -3x^2 + 8x + 5 + 2x^2 - 5x + 4$
$= -x^2 + 3x + 9$

(iii) $4b - (3a - 4b - c) - (5c + 2b)$
  $= 4b - 3a + 4b + c - 5c - 2b$
  $= -3a + 6b - 4c$

B. Multiplication

1. Multiplication of Monomials

The product of two or more monomials is the product of their numerical coefficients multiplied by the product of their literal coefficients.

Example 2.3c

(i) $5(3a)$
  $= (5 \times 3)a$ ⟵———— obtain the product of the numerical
  $= 15a$ coefficients

(ii) $(-7a)(4b)$
  $= (-7 \times 4)(a \times b)$ ⟵——— obtain the product of the numerical
  $= -28ab$ coefficients -7 and 4, and the product of the
                                     literal coefficients a and b

(iii) $(-3)(4x)(-5x)$
  $= [(-3)(4)(-5)][(x)(x)]$
  $= 60x^2$

(iv) $7a(-2ab)(5bc)$
  $= [(7)(-2)(5)][(a)(ab)(bc)]$
  $= -70a^2b^2c$

2. Multiplication of Monomials with Polynomials

The product of a polynomial and a monomial is obtained by multiplying each term of the polynomial by the monomial.

Example 2.3d

(i) $5(a - 3)$
  $= 5(a) + 5(-3)$ ⟵——— multiply 5 by a and 5 by (-3)
  $= 5a - 15$

(ii) $-4(3x^2 - 2x - 1)$
  $= -4(3x^2) + (-4)(-2x) + (-4)(-1)$ ⟵——— multiply each term of the
  $= (-12x^2) + (+8x) + (+4)$ trinomial by (-4)
  $= -12x^2 + 8x + 4$

(iii) $3a(4a - 5b - 2c)$
  $= (3a)(4a) + (3a)(-5b) + (3a)(-2c)$
  $= (12a^2) + (-15ab) + (-6ac)$
  $= 12a^2 - 15ab - 6ac$

3. *Simplification Involving Brackets and Multiplication*

Example 2.3e

(i)　$3(x - 5) - 2(x - 7)$
　　$= 3x - 15 - 2x + 14 \longleftarrow$ carry out the multiplication
　　$= x - 1 \longleftarrow$ collect like terms

(ii)　$a(3a - 1) - 4(2a + 3)$
　　$= 3a^2 - a - 8a - 12$
　　$= 3a^2 - 9a - 12$

(iii)　$5(m - 7) - 8(3m - 2) - 3(7 - 3m)$
　　$= 5m - 35 - 24m + 16 - 21 + 9m$
　　$= -10m - 40$

(iv)　$-4(5a - 3b - 2c) + 5(-2a - 4b + c)$
　　$= -20a + 12b + 8c - 10a - 20b + 5c$
　　$= -30a - 8b + 13c$

4. *Multiplication of a Polynomial by a Polynomial*

The product of two polynomials is obtained by multiplying each term of one polynomial by each term of the other polynomial and collecting like terms.

Example 2.3f

(i)　$(3a + 2b)(4c - 3d)$　　　　　each term of the first polynomial
　　$= 3a(4c - 3d) + 2b(4c - 3d) \longleftarrow$ is to be multiplied by the second
　　　　　　　　　　　　　　　polynomial
　　$= 12ac - 9ad + 8bc - 6bd \longleftarrow$ carry out the multiplication

(ii)　$(5x - 2)(3x + 4)$
　　$= 5x(3x + 4) - 2(3x + 4)$
　　$= 15x^2 + 20x - 6x - 8$
　　$= 15x^2 + 14x - 8$

(iii)　$(a - b)(a^2 + ab + b^2)$
　　$= a(a^2 + ab + b^2) - b(a^2 + ab + b^2)$
　　$= a^3 + a^2b + ab^2 - a^2b - ab^2 - b^3$
　　$= a^3 - b^3$

C.　Division

1. *Division of Monomials*

The quotient of two monomials is the quotient of their numerical coefficients multiplied by the quotient of their literal coefficients.

Example 2.3g

(i) $32ab \div 8b = \dfrac{32ab}{8b} = \left(\dfrac{32}{8}\right)\left(\dfrac{ab}{b}\right) = 4a$

(ii) $24x^2 \div (-6x) = \left(\dfrac{24}{-6}\right)\left(\dfrac{x^2}{x}\right) = -4x$

2. *Division of a Polynomial by a Monomial*

To determine the quotient of a polynomial divided by a monomial, divide each term of the polynomial by the monomial.

Example 2.3h

(i) $(12a + 8) \div 4 = \dfrac{12a + 8}{4} = \dfrac{12a}{4} + \dfrac{8}{4} = 3a + 2$

(ii) $(18x - 12) \div 6 = \dfrac{18x - 12}{6} = \dfrac{18x}{6} - \dfrac{12}{6} = 3x - 2$

(iii) $(12a^3 - 15a^2 - 9a) \div (-3a)$

$= \dfrac{12a^3 - 15a^2 - 9a}{-3a}$

$= \dfrac{12a^3}{-3a} + \dfrac{-15a^2}{-3a} + \dfrac{-9a}{-3a}$

$= -4a^2 + 5a + 3$

D. Substitution

The evaluation of algebraic expressions for given values of the variables requires the replacement of the variables by the given values. The replacement or substitution of the variables by the given values takes place each time the variables appear in the expression.

Example 2.3i

(i) Evaluate $7x - 3y - 5$ for $x = -2, y = 3$

Solution

$7x - 3y - 5$
$= 7(-2) - 3(3) - 5 \longleftarrow$ replace x by (-2) and y by 3
$= -14 - 9 - 5$
$= -28$

(ii) Evaluate $6a^2b - 10ac + bc$ for $a = \frac{1}{3}, b = \frac{-5}{6}, c = \frac{2}{5}$.

Solution

$$6a^2b - 10ac + bc$$

$$= 6\left(\frac{1}{3}\right)^2\left(\frac{-5}{6}\right) - 10\left(\frac{1}{3}\right)\left(\frac{2}{5}\right) + \left(\frac{-5}{6}\right)\left(\frac{2}{5}\right)$$

$$= \frac{6(1)(-5)}{(9)(6)} - \frac{10(1)(2)}{(3)(5)} + \frac{(-5)(2)}{(6)(5)}$$

$$= \frac{-5}{9} - \frac{4}{3} - \frac{1}{3}$$

$$= \frac{-5}{9} - \frac{12}{9} - \frac{3}{9}$$

$$= \frac{-20}{9}$$

(iii) Evaluate $\dfrac{2NC}{P(n+1)}$ for N = 12, C = 220, P = 1500, n = 15.

Solution

$$\frac{2NC}{P(n+1)} = \frac{2(12)(220)}{1500(15+1)} = \frac{\overset{1}{\cancel{2}}\overset{4}{\cancel{(12)}}\overset{110}{\cancel{(220)}}}{\underset{500}{\cancel{1500}}\underset{1}{\cancel{(16)}}\,\overset{}{\underset{1}{\cancel{2}}}} = \frac{11}{50} \text{ (or 0.22)}$$

(iv) Evaluate $\frac{I}{RT}$ for I = 126, R = 0.125, T = $\frac{324}{360}$.

Solution

$$\frac{I}{RT} = \frac{126}{0.125 \times \frac{324}{360}} = \frac{126}{\frac{1}{8} \times \frac{9}{10}} = \frac{126}{\frac{9}{80}} = \frac{\overset{14}{\cancel{126}}}{1} \times \frac{80}{\underset{1}{\cancel{9}}} = 1120$$

(v) Evaluate P(1 + RT) for P = 900, R = 0.15, T = $\frac{240}{360}$.

Solution

$$P(1 + RT) = 900\left(1 + 0.15 \times \frac{240}{360}\right)$$

$$= 900\left(1 + 0.15 \times \frac{2}{3}\right)$$

$$= 900(1 + 0.05 \times 2)$$

$$= 900(1 + 0.10)$$

$$= 900(1.10)$$

$$= 990$$

(vi) Evaluate $A(1 - dt)$ for $A = 800$, $d = 0.135$, $t = \frac{288}{360}$.

Solution

$$A(1 - dt) = 800\left(1 - 0.135 \times \frac{288}{360}\right)$$

$$= 800\left(1 - 0.135 \times \frac{4}{5}\right)$$

$$= 800(1 - 0.027 \times 4)$$

$$= 800(1 - 0.108)$$

$$= 800(0.892)$$

$$= 713.60$$

(vii) Evaluate $\frac{A}{1 + RT}$ for $A = 1644$, $R = 0.16$, $T = \frac{219}{365}$.

Solution

$$\frac{A}{1 + RT} = \frac{1644}{1 + 0.16 \times \frac{219}{365}} = \frac{1644}{1 + 0.16 \times \frac{3}{5}} = \frac{1644}{1 + 0.032 \times 3}$$

$$= \frac{1644}{1 + 0.096} = \frac{1644}{1.096} = 1500$$

(viii) Evaluate $\frac{P}{1 - dt}$ for $P = 1002$, $d = 0.18$, $t = \frac{330}{360}$.

Solution

$$\frac{P}{1 - dt} = \frac{1002}{1 - 0.18 \times \frac{330}{360}} = \frac{1002}{1 - 0.18 \times \frac{11}{12}} = \frac{1002}{1 - 0.015 \times 11}$$

$$= \frac{1002}{1 - 0.165} = \frac{1002}{0.835} = 1200$$

Exercise 2.3

A. Simplify.

1. $9a + 3a + 7a$
2. $6m - 2m - m$
3. $-4a - 8 + 3a - 2$
4. $2x - 3y - 4y - y$
5. $x - 0.2x$
6. $x + 0.06x$
7. $x + 0.4x$
8. $x - 0.02x$
9. $x^2 - 2x - 5 + x - 3 - 2x^2$
10. $3ax - 2x + 1 - 3 + 3x - 4ax$
11. $(2x - 3y) - (x + 4y)$
12. $-(4 - 5a) - (-2 + 3a)$

13. $(a^2 - ab + b^2) - (3a^2 + 5ab - 4b^2)$

14. $-(3m^2 - 4m - 5) - (4 - 2m - 2m^2)$

15. $6 - (4x - 3y + 1) - (5x + 2y - 9)$

16. $(7a - 5b) - (-3a + 4b) - 5b$

B. Simplify.

1. $3(-4x)$ **2.** $-7(8a)$

3. $-5x(2a)$ **4.** $-9a(-3b)$

5. $-x(2x)$ **6.** $-6m(-4m)$

7. $-4(5x)(-3y)$ **8.** $2a(-3b)(-4c)(-1)$

9. $-2(x - 2y)$ **10.** $5(2x - 4)$

11. $a(2x^2 - 3x - 1)$ **12.** $-6x(4 - 2b - b^2)$

13. $4(5x - 6) - 3(2 - 5x)$ **14.** $-3(8a - b) - 2(-7a + 9b)$

15. $-3a(5x - 1) + a(5 - 2x) - 3a(x + 1)$

16. $8(3y - 4) - 2(2y - 1) - (1 - y)$

17. $(3x - 1)(x + 2)$

18. $(5m - 2n)(m - 3n)$

19. $(x + y)(x^2 - xy + y^2)$

20. $(a - 1)(a^2 - 2a + 1)$

21. $(5x - 4)(2x - 1) - (x - 7)(3x + 5)$

22. $2(a - 1)(2a - 3) - 3(3a - 2)(a + 1)$

C. Simplify.

1. $20ab \div 5$ **2.** $30xy \div (-6x)$

3. $(-12x^2) \div (-3x)$ **4.** $(-42ab) \div (7ab)$

5. $(20m - 8) \div 2$ **6.** $(14x - 21) \div (-7)$

7. $(10x^2 - 15x - 30) \div (-5)$ **8.** $(-a^3 - 4a^2 - 3a) \div (-a)$

D. Evaluate each of the following for the values given.

1. $3x - 2y - 3$ for $x = -4$, $y = -5$

2. $7ab - 4ac + 3bc$ for $a = \dfrac{1}{2}$, $b = -\dfrac{1}{4}$, $c = \dfrac{1}{3}$

3. $-3(m - 3n) + 4(2n - 5m)$ for $m = \dfrac{2}{3}$, $n = -\dfrac{5}{6}$

4. $\dfrac{1}{2}(3x^2 - x - 1) - \dfrac{1}{4}(5 - 2x - x^2)$ for $x = -3$

5. $\dfrac{RP(n + 1)}{2N}$ for R = 0.21, P = 1200, n = 77, N = 26

6. $\dfrac{I}{PT}$ for I = 63, P = 840, T = $\dfrac{216}{360}$

7. $\dfrac{I}{RT}$ for I = 198, R = 0.165, T = $\dfrac{146}{365}$

8. $\dfrac{2NC}{P(n + 1)}$ for N = 52, C = 60, P = 1800, n = 25

9. P(1 + RT) for P = 880, R = 0.12, T = $\dfrac{75}{360}$

10. A(1 − RT) for A = 1200, R = 0.175, T = $\dfrac{252}{360}$

11. $\dfrac{P}{1 - dt}$ for P = 1253, d = 0.135, t = $\dfrac{280}{360}$

12. $\dfrac{A}{1 + RT}$ for A = 1752, R = 0.152, T = $\dfrac{225}{360}$

2.4   *Common Factoring*

A.   *Basic Concept*

In arithmetic certain computations, such as multiplication and division involving common fractions, are facilitated by factoring. In a similar manner, algebraic manipulation can be made easier by the process of finding the factors which make up an algebraic expression.

Factoring an algebraic expression means writing the expression as a product in component form. Depending on the type of factors which are contained in the expression, the process of factoring takes a variety of forms. Of the various types of factoring, only the simplest type has application to the subject matter dealt with in this text. Accordingly only this type, called **common factoring**, is explained in this section.

A common factor is one which is divisible without remainder into each term of an algebraic expression. The factor which is common to each term is usually found by inspection, and the remaining factor is then obtained by dividing the expression by the common factor.

B.   *Examples*

Example 2.4a   Factor $14a + 21b$.

Solution

By inspection recognize that the two terms $14a$ and $21b$ are both divisible by 7.

The common factor is 7.

The second factor is now found by dividing the expression by 7.

$$\frac{14a + 21b}{7} = \frac{14a}{7} + \frac{21b}{7} = 2a + 3b$$

Thus the factors of $14a + 21b$ are 7 and $2a + 3b$
$$14a + 21b = 7(2a + 3b)$$

Example 2.4b   Factor $18a - 45$.

Solution

By inspection, the highest common factor is 9;

the second factor is $\dfrac{18a - 45}{9} = 2a - 5$.

$$18a - 45 = 9(2a - 5)$$

Note   If 3 is used as common factor, the second factor is $6a - 15$ which contains a common factor 3 and can be factored into $3(2a - 5)$.

Thus $18a - 45 = 3\big[6a - 15\big]$
$$= 3\big[3(2a - 5)\big]$$
$$= 9(2a - 5)$$

When factoring, the accepted procedure is to always take out the *highest* common factor.

Example 2.4c   Factor $mx - my$.

Solution

The common factor is m.

The second factor is $\dfrac{mx - my}{m} = x - y$.

$$mx - my = m(x - y)$$

Example 2.4d   Factor $15x^3 - 25x^2 - 20x$.

Solution

The common factor is $5x$.

The second factor is $\dfrac{15x^3 - 25x^2 - 20x}{5x} = 3x^2 - 5x - 4$.

$$15x^3 - 25x^2 - 20x = 5x(3x^2 - 5x - 4)$$

Example 2.4e   Factor $P + Prt$.

Solution

The common factor is P.

The second factor is $\dfrac{P + Prt}{P} = \dfrac{P}{P} + \dfrac{Prt}{P} = 1 + rt$.

$$P + Prt = P(1 + rt)$$

Example 2.4f Factor $a(x + y) - b(x + y)$.

Solution

The common factor is $(x + y)$.

The second factor is $\dfrac{a(x + y) - b(x + y)}{x + y} = \dfrac{a(x + y)}{x + y} - \dfrac{b(x + y)}{x + y} = a - b$

$$a(x + y) - b(x + y) = (x + y)(a - b)$$

Example 2.4g Factor $(1 + i) + (1 + i)^2 + (1 + i)^3$.

Solution

The common factor is $(1 + i)$.

The second factor is $\dfrac{(1 + i) + (1 + i)^2 + (1 + i)^3}{(1 + i)}$

$$= \dfrac{(1 + i)}{(1 + i)} + \dfrac{(1 + i)^2}{(1 + i)} + \dfrac{(1 + i)^3}{(1 + i)}$$

$$= 1 + (1 + i) + (1 + i)^2$$

$$(1 + i) + (1 + i)^2 + (1 + i)^3 = (1 + i)\left[1 + (1 + i) + (1 + i)^2\right]$$

Exercise 2.4

A. Factor each of the following.

1. $8x - 12$ 2. $27 - 36a$

3. $4n^2 - 8n$ 4. $9x^2 - 21x$

5. $5ax - 10ay - 20a$ 6. $4ma - 12mb + 24mab$

B. Factor each of the following.

1. $mx + my$ 2. $xa - xb$

3. $m(a - b) + n(a - b)$ 4. $k(x - 1) - 3(x - 1)$

5. $P + Pi$ 6. $A - Adt$

7. $r - r^2 - r^3$ 8. $(1 + i)^4 + (1 + i)^3 + (1 + i)^2$

2.5 *Integral Exponents*

A. *Basic Concept and Definition*

If a number is to be used as a factor several times the mathematical expression can be written in a more efficient form by using exponents.

$$5 \times 5 \times 5 \times 5 \text{ may be written as } 5^4.$$

Note In the expression 5^4 ⟶ 5 is called the **base**

⟶ 4 is called the **exponent**

⟶ 5^4 is called the **power.**

Example 2.5a

(i) $7 \times 7 \times 7 \times 7 \times 7 = 7^5$

(ii) $(-4)(-4)(-4) = (-4)^3$

(iii) $(1.01)(1.01)(1.01)(1.01) = (1.01)^4$

(iv) $(a)(a)(a)(a)(a)(a)(a) = a^7$

(v) $(1 + i)(1 + i)(1 + i)(1 + i)(1 + i)(1 + i) = (1 + i)^6$

Definition When 'n' is a positive integer, 'a^n' represents the product of 'n' equal factors whose value is 'a'.

$$\boxed{a^n = (a)(a)(a)(a) \dots (a) \text{ to } n \text{ factors}}$$

a is called the **base**

n is called the **exponent**

a^n is called the **power**

$$\boxed{\text{POWER} = \text{BASE}^{\text{to the EXPONENT}}}$$

Note If a number is raised to the exponent '1', the power equals the base.

$$5^1 = 5 \quad \text{and} \quad a^1 = a;$$
$$\text{conversely} \quad 6 = 6^1 \quad \text{and} \quad x = x^1.$$

B. *Numerical Evaluation of Powers with Positive Integral Exponents*

1. *Evaluation when the Base is a Positive Integer*

To evaluate a power we may rewrite the power in factored form and obtain the product by multiplication.

Example 2.5b

(i) 2^5 $\longleftarrow$ means that 2 is a factor 5 times
   $= (2)(2)(2)(2)(2)$ $\longleftarrow$ power rewritten in factored form
   $= 32$ $\longleftarrow$ product

(ii) $(5)^3$ $\longleftarrow$ 5 is a factor 3 times
   $= (5)(5)(5)$
   $= 125$

(iii) 1^7 $\longleftarrow$ 1 is a factor 7 times
   $= (1)(1)(1)(1)(1)(1)(1)$
   $= 1$

(iv) a^n if $a = 4$, $n = 6$
   $a^n = 4^6$
   $= (4)(4)(4)(4)(4)(4)$
   $= 4096$

2. *Evaluation when the Base is a Negative Integer*

If a power has a negative base the number of equal factors indicated by the exponent determines the sign of the product.
(a) If the exponent is an even positive integer the product is positive.
(b) If the exponent is an odd positive integer the product is negative.

Example 2.5c

(i) $(-4)^3$ $\longleftarrow$ (-4) is a factor 3 times
   $= (-4)(-4)(-4)$
   $= -64$ $\longleftarrow$ the answer is negative (n is odd)

(ii) $(-2)^8$ $\longleftarrow$ (-2) is a factor 8 times
   $= (-2)(-2)(-2)(-2)(-2)(-2)(-2)(-2)$
   $= 256$ $\longleftarrow$ the answer is positive (n is even)

   Note -2^8 means $-(2)^8 = -(2)(2)(2)(2)(2)(2)(2)(2) = -256$

(iii) $(-1)^{55}$
   $= (-1)(-1)(-1)(-1) \ldots.$ to 55 factors
   $= -1$

(iv) $3a^n$ for $a = -5$, $n = 4$
   $3a^n = 3(-5)^4$
   $= 3(-5)(-5)(-5)(-5)$
   $= 3(625)$
   $= 1875$

3. Evaluation when the Base is a Common Fraction or Decimal

Example 2.5d

(i) $\left(\dfrac{3}{2}\right)^5$ ←————————— $\dfrac{3}{2}$ is a factor 5 times

$= \left(\dfrac{3}{2}\right)\left(\dfrac{3}{2}\right)\left(\dfrac{3}{2}\right)\left(\dfrac{3}{2}\right)\left(\dfrac{3}{2}\right)$

$= \dfrac{(3)(3)(3)(3)(3)}{(2)(2)(2)(2)(2)}$

$= \dfrac{243}{32}$

(ii) $(0.1)^4$ ←————————— 0.1 is a factor 4 times

$= (0.1)(0.1)(0.1)(0.1)$

$= 0.0001$

(iii) $\left(-\dfrac{1}{3}\right)^3$ ←———— $\left(-\dfrac{1}{3}\right)$ is a factor 3 times

$= \left(-\dfrac{1}{3}\right)\left(-\dfrac{1}{3}\right)\left(-\dfrac{1}{3}\right)$

$= \dfrac{(-1)(-1)(-1)}{(3)(3)(3)}$

$= \dfrac{-1}{27}$

(iv) $(1.02)^2$

$= (1.02)(1.02)$

$= 1.0404$

(v) $(1 + i)^n$ for $i = 0.03$, $n = 4$:

$(1 + i)^n = (1 + 0.03)^4$

$= (1.03)(1.03)(1.03)(1.03)$

$= 1.12550881$

C. Operations with Powers

1. Multiplication of Powers.

To multiply powers which have the same base retain the common base and add the exponents.

$$\boxed{a^m \times a^n = a^{m+n}} \longleftarrow \text{Formula 2.6}$$

$$\boxed{a^m \times a^n \times a^p = a^{m+n+p}} \longleftarrow \text{Formula 2.6A}$$

Example 2.5e

(i) $3^5 \times 3^2$ retain the common base 3
    $= 3^{5+2} \longleftarrow$ and add the exponents
    $= 3^7$ 5 and 2

(ii) $(-4)^3(-4)^7(-4)^5$ retain the common base
    $= (-4)^{3+7+5} \longleftarrow$ (-4) and add the exponents
    $= (-4)^{15}$ 3, 7 and 5

(iii) $\left(\dfrac{1}{8}\right)^5\left(\dfrac{1}{8}\right) = \left(\dfrac{1}{8}\right)^{5+1} = \left(\dfrac{1}{8}\right)^6$

(iv) $(x^3)(x^5)(x) = x^{3+5+1} = x^9$

(v) $(1.06)^{16}(1.06)^{14} = (1.06)^{16+14} = 1.06^{30}$

(vi) $(1+i)(1+i)^5(1+i)^{20} = (1+i)^{1+5+20} = (1+i)^{26}$

2. Division of Powers.

To divide powers having the same base retain the common base and subtract the exponent of the divisor from the exponent of the dividend.

$$\boxed{a^m \div a^n = a^{m-n}} \longleftarrow \text{Formula 2.7}$$

Example 2.5f

(i) $2^8 \div 2^5$ retain the common base 2 and
    $= 2^{8-5} \longleftarrow$ subtract the exponent of the
    $= 2^3$ divisor, 5, from the exponent
                      of the dividend, 8.

(ii) $(-10)^8 \div (-10)^7$
    $= (-10)^{8-7} \longleftarrow$ retain the common base (-10) and
    $= (-10)^1$ or -10 subtract the exponents

(iii) $\left(-\dfrac{2}{5}\right)^6 \div \left(-\dfrac{2}{5}\right)^2 = \left(-\dfrac{2}{5}\right)^{6-2} = \left(-\dfrac{2}{5}\right)^4$

(iv) $a^{15} \div a^{10} = a^{15-10} = a^5$

(v) $(1.10)^{24} \div 1.10 = (1.10)^{24-1} = 1.10^{23}$

(vi) $(1+i)^{80} \div (1+i)^{60} = (1+i)^{80-60} = (1+i)^{20}$

3. *Raising a Power to a Power.*

To raise a power to a power retain the base and multiply the exponents.

$$\boxed{(a^m)^n = a^{mn}} \quad \longleftarrow \text{ Formula 2.8}$$

Example 2.5g

(i) $(3^2)^5$

    $= 3^{2 \times 5} \quad\longleftarrow$ retain the base 3 and multiply the

    $= 3^{10}$ exponents 2 and 5

(ii) $\left[(-4)^5\right]^3$

    $= (-4)^{5 \times 3} \quad\longleftarrow$ retain the base and multiply the

    $= (-4)^{15}$ exponents

(iii) $= \left[\left(\dfrac{4}{3}\right)^6\right]^{10} = \left(\dfrac{4}{3}\right)^{6 \times 10} = \left(\dfrac{4}{3}\right)^{60}$

(iv) $(a^7)^3 = a^{7 \times 3} = a^{21}$

(v) $\left[(1.005)^{50}\right]^4 = (1.005)^{50 \times 4} = 1.005^{200}$

(vi) $\left[(1+i)^{75}\right]^2 = (1+i)^{75 \times 2} = (1+i)^{150}$

4. *Power of a Product and Power of a Quotient.*

The power of a product, written in factored form, is the product of individual factors raised to the given exponent.

$$\boxed{(ab)^m = a^m b^m} \quad \longleftarrow \text{ Formula 2.9}$$

Note ab^2 is not the same as $(ab)^2$ since ab^2 means $(a)(b)(b)$ *while*
$(ab)^2 = (ab)(ab) = (a)(a)(b)(b) = a^2 b^2$.

The power of a quotient is the quotient of the dividend and the divisor raised to the given exponent.

$$\boxed{\left(\frac{a}{b}\right)^m = \frac{a^m}{b^m}} \quad \longleftarrow \text{ Formula 2.10}$$

Example 2.5h

(i) $(2 \times 3)^5 = 2^5 \times 3^5$

(ii) $(6 \times 2^7)^4 = 6^4 \times (2^7)^4 = 6^4 \times 2^{28}$

(iii) $\left(-\dfrac{5}{7}\right)^3 = \dfrac{(-5)^3}{7^3}$

(iv) $(a^3 b)^4 = (a^3)^4 \times b^4 = a^{12} b^4$

(v) $\left|\dfrac{(1+i)}{i}\right|^3 = \dfrac{(1+i)^3}{i^3}$

D.   Zero exponent

A zero exponent results when using the law of division of powers when the exponents are equal.

$$3^5 \div 3^5$$
$$= 3^{5-5}$$
$$= 3^0$$

The result may be interpreted as follows.

$$3^5 \div 3^5 = \frac{3^5}{3^5} = \frac{3 \times 3 \times 3 \times 3 \times 3}{3 \times 3 \times 3 \times 3 \times 3} = 1$$

$$\boxed{3^0 = 1}$$

Similarly $a^6 \div a^6 = a^{6-6} = a^0$

and since $a^6 \div a^6 = \dfrac{a^6}{a^6} = \dfrac{(a)(a)(a)(a)(a)(a)}{(a)(a)(a)(a)(a)(a)} = 1$

$$\boxed{a^0 = 1}$$

In general, *any number raised to the exponent zero is 1*, except zero itself. The expression 0^0 has no meaning and is said to be *undefined*.

E.   Negative exponents

A negative exponent results when using the law of division of powers when the exponent of the divisor is greater than the exponent of the dividend.

$$4^3 \div 4^5$$
$$= 4^{3-5}$$
$$= 4^{-2}$$

The result may be interpreted as follows.

$$4^3 \div 4^5 = \frac{4^3}{4^5} = \frac{4 \times 4 \times 4}{4 \times 4 \times 4 \times 4 \times 4} = \frac{1}{4 \times 4} = \frac{1}{4^2}$$

$$\boxed{4^{-2} = \frac{1}{4^2}}$$

Similarly, $\quad a^5 \div a^8 = a^{5-8} = a^{-3}$

and since $\quad a^5 \div a^8 = \dfrac{a^5}{a^8} = \dfrac{(a)(a)(a)(a)(a)}{(a)(a)(a)(a)(a)(a)(a)(a)}$

$$= \frac{1}{(a)(a)(a)} = \frac{1}{a^3}$$

$$\boxed{a^{-3} = \frac{1}{a^3}}$$

$$\boxed{a^{-m} = \frac{1}{a^m}}$$

In general a base raised to a negative exponent is equivalent to 1 divided by the same base raised to the corresponding positive exponent.

Example 2.5i

(i) $2^{-3} = \dfrac{1}{2^3} = \dfrac{1}{8}$

(ii) $(-3)^{-2} = \dfrac{1}{(-3)^2} = \dfrac{1}{9}$

(iii) $\left(\dfrac{1}{4}\right)^{-4} = \dfrac{1}{(\frac{1}{4})^4} = \dfrac{1}{\frac{1}{256}} = \dfrac{1}{1} \times \dfrac{256}{1} = 256$

(iv) $\left(-\dfrac{3}{5}\right)^{-3} = \dfrac{1}{(-\frac{3}{5})^3} = \dfrac{1}{\frac{-27}{125}} = \dfrac{-125}{27}$

Note Since $\dfrac{-125}{27} = \dfrac{(-5)^3}{3^3} = \left(-\dfrac{5}{3}\right)^3 \longrightarrow \left(-\dfrac{3}{5}\right)^{-3} = \left(-\dfrac{5}{3}\right)^3$

$$\boxed{\left(\frac{y}{x}\right)^{-m} = \left(\frac{x}{y}\right)^m}$$

(v) $(-4)^0 = 1$

(vi) $(1.05)^{-2} = \dfrac{1}{1.05^2} = \dfrac{1}{1.1025} = 0.9070295$

(vii) $(1 + i)^{-10} = \dfrac{1}{(1 + i)^{10}}$

(viii) $(1 + i)^{-1} = \dfrac{1}{1 + i}$

(ix) $(1 + i)^0 = 1$

Exercise 2.5

A. Evaluate each of the following.

1. 3^4 **2.** 1^5 **3.** $(-2)^4$ **4.** $(-1)^{12}$

5. $\left(\dfrac{2}{3}\right)^4$ **6.** $\left(-\dfrac{1}{4}\right)^3$ **7.** $(0.5)^2$ **8.** $(-0.1)^3$

9. $(-4)^0$ **10.** m^0 **11.** 3^{-2} **12.** $(-5)^{-3}$

13. $\left(\dfrac{1}{5}\right)^{-3}$ **14.** $\left(\dfrac{2}{3}\right)^{-4}$ **15.** 1.01^{-1} **16.** $(1.05)^0$

B. Simplify.

1. $2^5 \times 2^3$ **2.** $(-4)^3 \times (-4)$

3. $4^7 \div 4^4$ **4.** $(-3)^9 \div (-3)^7$

5. $(2^3)^5$ **6.** $\left[(-4)^3\right]^6$

7. $a^4 \times a^{10}$ **8.** $m^{12} \div m^7$

9. $3^4 \times 3^6 \times 3$ **10.** $(-1)^3(-1)^7(-1)^5$

11. $\dfrac{6^7 \times 6^3}{6^9}$ **12.** $\dfrac{(x^4)(x^5)}{x^7}$

13. $\left(\dfrac{3}{5}\right)^4\left(\dfrac{3}{5}\right)^7$ **14.** $\left(\dfrac{1}{6}\right)^5 \div \left(\dfrac{1}{6}\right)^3$

15. $\left(-\dfrac{3}{2}\right)\left(-\dfrac{3}{2}\right)^6\left(-\dfrac{3}{2}\right)^4$ **16.** $\left(-\dfrac{3}{4}\right)^8 \div \left(-\dfrac{3}{4}\right)^7$

17. $(1.025^{80})(1.025^{70})$ **18.** $1.005^{240} \div 1.005^{150}$

19. $\left[1.04^{20}\right]^4$ **20.** $\left[\left(-\dfrac{3}{7}\right)^5\right]^3$

21. $(1 + i)^{100}(1 + i)^{100}$ **22.** $(1 - r)^2(1 - r)^2(1 - r)^2$

23. $\left[(1 + i)^{80}\right]^2$ **24.** $\left[(1 - r)^{40}\right]^3$

25. $(ab)^5$

26. $(2xy)^4$

27. $(m^3n)^8$

28. $\left(\dfrac{a^3b^2}{x}\right)^4$

29. $2^3 \times 2^5 \times 2^{-4}$

30. $5^2 \div 5^{-3}$

31. $\left(\dfrac{a}{b}\right)^{-8}$

32. $\left(\dfrac{1+i}{i}\right)^{-n}$

Review exercise

1. Simplify.

(a) $(+6) + (-9)$

(b) $(-4) + (-6)$

(c) $-5 + 8$

(d) $-2 - 7$

(e) $(3) - (-4)$

(f) $0 - (+10)$

(g) $-3 - (-6)$

(h) $1 - (-1)$

(i) $-7 + (-3) - 4 - (-9)$

(j) $-3 - 8 + 4 - 10 + 3$

2. Simplify.

(a) $-10(4)$

(b) $(-3)(-12)$

(c) $6(-1)$

(d) $(-8)(0)$

(e) $20 \div (-5)$

(f) $(-18) \div (-6)$

(g) $0 \div (-3)$

(h) $(-1) \div 0$

(i) $-3(-4)(-5)(-1)$

(j) $4(-12)(7)(0)$

3. Simplify.

(a) $\left|-4\right|$

(b) $\left|0 - 6\right|$

(c) $\left|(-4) \times 3\right|$

(d) $\left|(+28) \div (-4)\right|$

4. Simplify.

(a) $3x - 4y - 3y - 5x$

(b) $2x - 0.03x$

(c) $(5a - 4) - (3 - a)$

(d) $-(2x - 3y) - (-4x + y) + (y - x)$

(e) $(5a^2 - 2b - c) - (3c + 2b - 4a^2)$

(f) $-(2x - 3) - (x^2 - 5x + 2)$

5. Simplify.

(a) $3(-5a)$

(b) $-7m(-4x)$

(c) $14m \div (-2m)$

(d) $(-15a^2b) \div (5a)$

(e) $-6(-3x)(2y)$

(f) $4(-3a)(b)(-2c)$

(g) $-4(3x - 5y - 1)$

(h) $x(1 - 2x - x^2)$

(i) $(24x - 16) \div (-4)$

(j) $(21a^2 - 12a) \div 3a$

(k) $4(2a - 5) - 3(3 - 6a)$

(l) $2a(x - a) - a(3x + 2) - 3a(-5x - 4)$

(m) $(m - 1)(2m - 5)$

(n) $(3a - 2)(a^2 - 2a - 3)$

(o) $3(2x - 4)(x - 1) - 4(x - 3)(5x + 2)$

(p) $-2a(3m - 1)(m - 4) - 5a(2m + 3)(2m - 3)$

6. Evaluate each of the following for the values given.

(a) $3xy - 4x - 5y$ for $x = -2$, $y = 5$

(b) $-5(2a - 3b) - 2(a + 5b)$ for $a = -\dfrac{1}{4}$, $b = \dfrac{2}{3}$

(c) $\dfrac{2NC}{P(n + 1)}$ for N $= 12$, C $= 432$, P $= 1800$, $n = 35$

(d) $\dfrac{365I}{RP}$ for I $= 600$, R $= 0.15$, P $= 7300$

(e) $A(1 - dt)$ for A $= 720$, $d = 0.135$, $t = \dfrac{280}{360}$

(f) $\dfrac{S}{1 + RT}$ for S $= 2755$, R $= 0.17$, T $= \dfrac{219}{365}$

7. Simplify.

(a) $(-3)^5$

(b) $\left(\dfrac{2}{3}\right)^4$

(c) $(-5)^0$

(d) $(-3)^{-1}$

(e) $\left(\dfrac{2}{5}\right)^{-4}$

(f) $(1.01)^0$

(g) $(-3)^5(-3)^4$

(h) $4^7 \div 4^2$

(i) $\left[(-3)^2\right]^5$

(j) $(m^3)^4$

(k) $\left(\dfrac{2}{3}\right)^3\left(\dfrac{2}{3}\right)^7\left(\dfrac{2}{3}\right)^{-6}$

(l) $\left(-\dfrac{5}{4}\right)^5 \div \left(-\dfrac{5}{4}\right)^3$

(m) $(1.03^{50})(1.03^{100})$

(n) $(1 + i)^{180} \div (1 + i)^{100}$

(o) $\left[(1.05)^{30}\right]^5$

(p) $(-2xy)^4$

(q) $\left(\dfrac{a^2b}{3}\right)^{-4}$

(r) $(1 + i)^{-n}$

8. Factor each of the following.

(a) $27x - 18$

(b) $18a^2 - 21a$

(c) $P + Prt$

(d) $(1 + i)^2 - (1 + i)$

Self-test

1. Simplify each of the following.

   (a) $8 + (-6) - (-3)$ (b) $4(-1)(-2)(-5)$

   (c) $(-48) \div (-12)$ (d) $0 \div (-5)$

2. Simplify.

   (a) $4 - 3x - 6 - 5x$ (b) $(5x - 4) - (7x + 5)$

   (c) $-2(3a - 4) - 5(2a + 3)$ (d) $-6(x-2)(x+1)$

3. Simplify.

   (a) $(-2)^3$ (d) $(3)^2(3)^5$

   (b) $\left(\dfrac{-2}{3}\right)^2$ (e) $\left(\dfrac{4}{3}\right)^{-2}$

   (c) $(4)^0$ (f) $(-x^3)^5$

4. Evaluate each of the following for the values given.

   (a) $2x^2 - 5xy - 4y^2$ for $x = -3$, $y = +5$

   (b) $3(7a - 4b) - 4(5a + 3b)$ for $a = \dfrac{2}{3}$, $b = -\dfrac{3}{4}$

   (c) $\dfrac{2\,NC}{P(n+1)}$ for $N = 12$, $C = 400$, $P = 2000$, $n = 24$

   (d) $\dfrac{I}{Pr}$ for $I = 324$, $P = 5400$, $r = 0.15$

   (e) $S(1 - dt)$ for $S = 1606$, $d = 0.125$, $t = \dfrac{240}{365}$

   (f) $\dfrac{S}{1 + rt}$ for $S = 1566$, $r = 0.10$, $t = \dfrac{292}{365}$

Summary of formulae (laws) used

Formula 2.1	$a + b = b + a$	the commutative law for addition which permits the addition of two numbers in any order
Formula 2.2	$ab = ba$	the commutative law for multiplication which permits the multiplication of two numbers in any order
Formula 2.3	$a + b + c = (a + b) + c$ $= a + (b + c)$ $= b + (a + c)$	the associative law for addition which permits the addition of three or more numbers in any order

Formula 2.4	$abc = (ab)c$	the associative law for multiplication
	$= a(bc)$	which permits the multiplication of
	$= b(ac)$	three or more numbers in any order

Formula 2.5	$a(b + c) = ab + ac$	the distributive law of multiplication over addition which provides the basis for the multiplication of algebraic expressions

Formula 2.6	$a^m \times a^n = a^{m+n}$	the rule for multiplying two powers having the same base

Formula 2.6a	$a^m \times a^n \times a^p = a^{m+n+p}$	the rule for multiplying three or more powers having the same base

Formula 2.7	$a^m \div a^n = a^{m-n}$	the rule for dividing two powers having the same base

Formula 2.8	$(a^m)^n = a^{mn}$	the rule for raising a power to a power

Formula 2.9	$(ab)^m = a^m b^m$	the rule for taking the power of a product

Formula 2.10	$\left(\dfrac{a}{b}\right)^m = \dfrac{a^m}{b^m}$	the rule for taking the power of a quotient

Glossary of terms used

Absolute value   the value of a number without its sign

Algebraic expression   a combination of numbers, variables representing numbers, and symbols indicating an algebraic operation

Base   one of the equal factors in a power

Binomial   an algebraic expression consisting of two terms

Collecting like terms   adding like terms

Combining like terms   see *Collecting like terms*

Common factor   a factor which is divisible without remainder into each term of an algebraic expression

Exponent   the number of equal factors in a power

Factor   one of the numbers which when multiplied with the other number or numbers yields a given product

Like signed numbers   numbers having the same sign

Like terms   terms having the same literal coefficient

Literal coefficient   part of a term formed with letter symbols

Monomial   an algebraic expression consisting of one term

Negative number   a signed number preceded by a minus ($-$) sign

Numerical coefficient   the part of a term formed with numerals

Polynomial   an algebraic expression consisting of more than one term

Positive number   a signed number preceded by a plus (+) sign

Power   a mathematical operation indicating the multiplication of a number of equal factors

Signed number   a number preceded by a plus (+) or by a minus (−) sign

Term   a part of an algebraic expression separated from other parts by a plus (+) sign or by a minus (−) sign

Trinomial   an algebraic expression consisting of three terms

Unlike signed numbers   numbers having different signs

Mathematics
fundamentals

3 Linear equations in one variable

Introduction

An equation is a statement of equality between two algebraic expressions. If an equation contains only one letter symbol (variable) and if that variable occurs with power '1' only, the equation is said to be a linear or first degree equation in one unknown.

Equations of this type may be set up for many types of business problems and the solution to a particular problem is obtained when solving the equation.

Objectives

Upon completion of this chapter you will be able to

1. solve basic equations using addition, subtraction, multiplication and division;
2. solve equations involving algebraic simplification;
3. solve word problems by means of equations.

3.1 Solving basic equations

A. Basic terms and concepts

1. An **equation** is a statement of equality between two algebraic expressions.

$$7x = 35$$
$$3a - 4 = 11 - 2a$$
$$5(2k - 4) = -3(k + 2)$$

2. If an equation contains only one variable and the variable occurs with power 1 only, then the equation is said to be a **linear** or **first degree equation** in one unknown. The three equations listed above are linear equations in one unknown.

3. The two expressions which are equated are called the sides or **members of the equation**. Every equation has a left side (left member) and a right side (right member).

In the equation $3a - 4 = 11 - 2a$

$3a - 4$ is the left side (left member) and

$11 - 2a$ is the right side (right member).

4. The process of finding a replacement value (number) for the variable which when substituted into the equation makes the two members of the equation equal, is called *solving the equation*. The replacement value that makes the two members equal is called a *solution* or **root of the equation**. A linear or first degree equation has only one root and the root, when substituted into the equation, is said to *satisfy* the equation.

The root (solution) of the equation

$3a - 4 = 11 - 2a$ is 3 because when

3 is substituted for a

the left side $3a - 4 = 3(3) - 4 = 9 - 4 = 5$ and

the right side $11 - 2a = 11 - 2(3) = 11 - 6 = 5$.

Thus for $a = 3$, Left Side $=$ Right Side and

hence 3 satisfies the equation.

5. Equations which have the same root are called **equivalent equations**.

$$6x + 5 = 4x + 17$$
$$6x = 4x + 12$$
$$2x = 12$$
$$x = 6$$

are equivalent equations because the root of all four equations is 6; that is, when 6 is substituted for x each of the equations will be satisfied.

Equivalent equations are useful in solving equations, and may be obtained

(a) by multiplying or dividing both sides of the equation by a non-zero number; and

(b) by adding or subtracting the same number on both sides of the equation.

6. When solving an equation, the basic aim in selecting the operations which will generate useful equivalent equations is to

(a) isolate the terms containing the variable on one side of the equation (this is achieved by addition or subtraction);

(b) make the numerical coefficient of the single term containing the variable equal to $+1$ (this is achieved by multiplication or division).

B. Solving equations using division

If each side of an equation is divided by the same non-zero number, the resulting equation is equivalent to the original equation.

$$15x = 45 \quad \longleftarrow \text{original equation}$$

divide by 3 $\longrightarrow$ $5x = 15$
or divide by 5 $\longrightarrow$ $3x = 9$ $\Bigg\} \longleftarrow$ equivalent equations
or divide by 15 $\longrightarrow$ $x = 3$

Division is used in solving equations when the numerical coefficient of the single term containing the variable is an integer or a decimal fraction.

Example 3.1a

(i) $12x = 36 \quad \longleftarrow \text{original equation}$

$\dfrac{12x}{12} = \dfrac{36}{12} \quad \longleftarrow$ divide each side by the
numerical coefficient 12

$x = 3 \quad \longleftarrow$ solution

(ii) $-7x = 42$

$\dfrac{-7x}{-7} = \dfrac{42}{-7} \longleftarrow$ divide each side by the
numerical coefficient -7

$x = -6$

(iii) $0.2x = 3$

$\dfrac{0.2x}{0.2} = \dfrac{3}{0.2}$

$x = 15$

(iv) $x - 0.3x = 14$

$0.7x = 14$

$\dfrac{0.7x}{0.7} = \dfrac{14}{0.7}$

$x = 20$

C. Solving equations using multiplication

If each side of an equation is multiplied by the same non-zero number, the resulting equation is equivalent to the original equation.

$$-3x = 6 \quad \longleftarrow \text{original equation}$$

multiply by 2 $\longrightarrow$ $-6x = 12$
or multiply by -1 $\longrightarrow$ $3x = -6$ $\Big] \longleftarrow$ equivalent equations

Multiplication is used in solving equations containing common fractions in order to eliminate the denominator or denominators.

Example 3.1b

(i)
$$\frac{1}{2}x = 3 \longleftarrow \text{original equation}$$

$$2\left(\frac{1}{2}x\right) = 2(3) \longleftarrow \text{multiply each side by 2 to eliminate the denominator}$$

$$x = 6 \longleftarrow \text{solution}$$

(ii)
$$-\frac{1}{4}x = 2 \longleftarrow \text{original equation}$$

$$4\left(-\frac{1}{4}x\right) = = 4(2) \longleftarrow \text{multiply each side by 4 to eliminate the denominator}$$

$$-1x = 8$$

$$(-1)(-x) = (-1)(8) \longleftarrow \text{multiply by } (-1) \text{ to make the coefficient of the term in } x \text{ positive}$$

$$x = -8$$

(iii)
$$-\frac{1}{7}x = -2$$

$$(-7)\left(-\frac{1}{7}x\right) = (-7)(-2) \longleftarrow \text{multiply by } (-7) \text{ to eliminate the denominator and make the coefficient of } x \text{ equal to } +1$$

$$x = 14$$

D.   Solving equations using addition

If the same number is added to each side of an equation, the resulting equation is equivalent to the original equation.

$$x - 5 = 4 \longleftarrow \text{original equation}$$

$$\text{add 3} \longrightarrow x - 5 + 3 = 4 + 3$$
$$\text{or add 5} \longrightarrow x - 5 + 5 = 4 + 5 \left.\right\} \longleftarrow \text{equivalent equations}$$

Addition is used to isolate the term or terms containing the variable when terms which have a negative numerical coefficient appear in the equation.

Example 3.1c

(i) $x - 6 = 4$

$$x - 6 + 6 = 4 + 6 \longleftarrow \text{add 6 to each side of the equation to eliminate the term } -6 \text{ on the left side of the equation}$$

$$x = 10$$

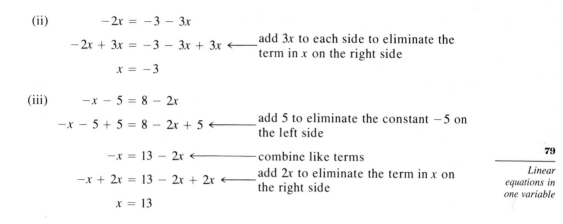

(ii)
$$-2x = -3 - 3x$$
$$-2x + 3x = -3 - 3x + 3x \longleftarrow \text{add } 3x \text{ to each side to eliminate the term in } x \text{ on the right side}$$
$$x = -3$$

(iii)
$$-x - 5 = 8 - 2x$$
$$-x - 5 + 5 = 8 - 2x + 5 \longleftarrow \text{add 5 to eliminate the constant } -5 \text{ on the left side}$$
$$-x = 13 - 2x \longleftarrow \text{combine like terms}$$
$$-x + 2x = 13 - 2x + 2x \longleftarrow \text{add } 2x \text{ to eliminate the term in } x \text{ on the right side}$$
$$x = 13$$

E.   Solving equations using subtraction

If the same number is *subtracted from each side* of an equation, the resulting equation is equivalent to the original equation.

$$x + 8 = 9 \longleftarrow \text{original equation}$$
$$\text{subtract 4} \longrightarrow x + 8 - 4 = 9 - 4$$
$$\text{or subtract 8} \longrightarrow x + 8 - 8 = 9 - 8 \left.\right\} \longleftarrow \text{equivalent equations}$$

Subtraction is used to isolate the term or terms containing the variable when terms having a positive numerical coefficient appear in the equation.

Example 3.1d

(i)
$$x + 10 = 6$$
$$x + 10 - 10 = 6 - 10 \longleftarrow \text{subtract 10 from each side of the equation}$$
$$x = -4$$

(ii)
$$7x = 9 + 6x$$
$$7x - 6x = 9 + 6x - 6x \longleftarrow \text{subtract } 6x \text{ from each side to eliminate the term } 6x \text{ on the right side}$$
$$x = 9$$

(iii)
$$6x + 4 = 5x - 3$$
$$6x + 4 - 4 = 5x - 3 - 4 \longleftarrow \text{subtract 4 from each side to eliminate the term 4 on the left side}$$
$$6x = 5x - 7 \longleftarrow \text{combine like terms}$$
$$6x - 5x = 5x - 7 - 5x \longleftarrow \text{subtract } 5x \text{ from each side of the equation to eliminate the term } 5x \text{ on the right side}$$
$$x = -7$$

F. Using two or more operations to solve equations

When more than one operation is needed to solve an equation, the operations are usually applied as follows.

(a) First, use addition and subtraction to isolate the terms containing the variable on one side of the equation (usually the left side).

(b) Secondly, after combining like terms, use multiplication and division to make the coefficient of the term containing the variable equal to $+1$.

Example 3.1e

(i) $\left(-\dfrac{3}{5}\right)x = 12$

$5\left(-\dfrac{3}{5}\right)x = 5(12)$ ⟵———————— multiply by 5 to eliminate the denominator

$-3x = 60$

$\dfrac{-3x}{-3} = \dfrac{60}{-3}$ ⟵——————— divide by -3

$x = -20$

(ii) $7x - 5 = 15 + 3x$

$7x - 5 + 5 = 15 + 3x + 5$ ⟵——— add 5

$7x = 20 + 3x$ ⟵——————— combine like terms

$7x - 3x = 20 + 3x - 3x$ ⟵——— subtract $3x$

$4x = 20$

$x = 5$ ⟵——————————— divide by 4

(iii) $3x + 9 - 7x = 24 - x - 3$

$9 - 4x = 21 - x$ ⟵——————— combine like terms

$9 - 4x - 9 = 21 - x - 9$

$-4x = 12 - x$

$-4x + x = 12 - x + x$

$-3x = 12$

$x = -4$

G. Checking equations

To check the solution to an equation, substitute the solution into each side of the equation and determine the value of each side.

Example 3.1f

(i) For $-\dfrac{3}{5}x = 12$, the solution shown is $x = -20$.

Check

Left Side $= -\dfrac{3}{5}x = \left(-\dfrac{3}{5}\right)(-20) = -3(-4) = 12$

Right Side $= 12$
Since the Left Side $=$ Right Side, -20 is the solution to the equation.

(ii) For $7x - 5 = 15 + 3x$, the solution shown is $x = 5$.

Check
LS $= 7x - 5 = 7(5) - 5 = 35 - 5 = 30$
RS $= 15 + 3x = 15 + 3(5) = 15 + 15 = 30$
   Since the LS $=$ RS, 5 is the solution.

(iii) For $3x + 9 - 7x = 24 - x - 3$, the solution shown is $x = -4$.

Check
LS $= 3(-4) + 9 - 7(-4) = -12 + 9 + 28 = 25$
RS $= 24 - (-4) - 3 = 24 + 4 - 3 = 25$
   Since LS $=$ RS, -4 is the solution.

Exercise 3.1

A. Solve each of the following equations.

1. $15x = 45$ 2. $-7x = 35$ 3. $0.9x = 72$

4. $0.02x = 13$ 5. $\dfrac{1}{6}x = 3$ 6. $\quad -\dfrac{1}{8}x = 7$

7. $\dfrac{3}{5}x = -21$ 8. $-\dfrac{4}{3}x = -32$

9. $x - 3 = -7$ 10. $-2x = 7 - 3x$

11. $x + 6 = -2$ 12. $3x = 9 + 2x$

13. $4 - x = 9 - 2x$ 14. $2x + 7 = x - 5$

15. $x + 0.6x = 32$ 16. $x - 0.3x = 210$

17. $x - 0.04x = 192$ 18. $x + 0.07x = 64.20$

B. Solve each of the following equations and check.

1. $3x + 5 = 7x - 11$ 2. $5 - 4x = -4 - x$
3. $2 - 3x - 9 = 2x - 7 + 3x$ 4. $4x - 8 - 9x = 10 + 2x - 4$

3.2 Equation solving involving algebraic simplification

A. Solving linear equations involving the product of integral constants and binomials

To solve this type of equation, multiply first then simplify.

Example 3.2a

(i) $3(2x - 5) = -5(7 - 2x)$
$6x - 15 = -35 + 10x$ ⟵ expand
$6x - 10x = -35 + 15$ ⟵ isolate the terms in x
$-4x = -20$
$x = 5$

Check

LS $= 3[2(5) - 5] = 3(10 - 5) = 3(5) = 15$
RS $= -5[7 - 2(5)] = -5(7 - 10) = -5(-3) = 15$
Since LS = RS, 5 is the solution.

(ii) $x - 4(3x - 7) = 3(9 - 5x) - (x - 11)$
$x - 12x + 28 = 27 - 15x - x + 11$ ⟵ expand
$-11x + 28 = 38 - 16x$ ⟵ combine like terms
$-11x + 16x = 38 - 28$ ⟵ isolate the terms in x
$5x = 10$
$x = 2$

Check

LS $= 2 - 4[3(2) - 7]$ RS $= 3[9 - 5(2)] - (2 - 11)$
$= 2 - 4(6 - 7)$ $= 3(9 - 10) - (-9)$
$= 2 - 4(-1)$ $= 3(-1) + 9$
$= 2 + 4$ $= -3 + 9$
$= 6$ $= 6$
Since LS = RS, 2 is the solution.

B. Solving linear equations containing common fractions

The approach recommended when solving equations containing common fractions is to first obtain an equivalent equation without common fractions by multiplying each term of the equation by the lowest common denominator of the fractions.

Example 3.2b

(i) $\dfrac{4}{5}x - \dfrac{3}{4} = \dfrac{7}{12} + \dfrac{11}{15}x$ ⟵ L.C.D. = 60

$60\left(\dfrac{4}{5}x\right) - 60\left(\dfrac{3}{4}\right) = 60\left(\dfrac{7}{12}\right) + 60\left(\dfrac{11}{15}x\right)$ ⟵ multiply each term by 60

$$12(4x) - 15(3) = 5(7) + 4(11x) \longleftarrow \text{reduce to eliminate the fractions}$$
$$48x - 45 = 35 + 44x$$
$$48x - 44x = 35 + 45$$
$$4x = 80$$
$$x = 20$$

Check

$$\text{LS} = \frac{4}{5}(20) - \frac{3}{4} = 4(4) - \frac{3}{4} = 16 - \frac{3}{4} = 15\frac{1}{4}$$

$$\text{RS} = \frac{7}{12} + \frac{11}{\cancel{15}_{\,3}}\overset{4}{(\cancel{20})} = \frac{7}{12} + \frac{44}{3} = \frac{7}{12} + \frac{176}{12} = \frac{183}{12} = 15\frac{1}{4}$$

Since LS = RS, 20 is the solution.

(ii)
$$\frac{5}{8}x - 3 = \frac{3}{4} + \frac{5x}{6} \longleftarrow \text{L.C.D.} = 24$$

$$24\left(\frac{5x}{8}\right) - 24(3) = 24\left(\frac{3}{4}\right) + 24\left(\frac{5x}{6}\right)$$

$$3(5x) - 72 = 6(3) + 4(5x)$$
$$15x - 72 = 18 + 20x$$
$$-5x = 90$$
$$x = -18$$

Check

$$\text{LS} = \frac{5}{8}(-18) - 3 = \frac{5}{4}(-9) - 3 = \frac{-45}{4} - \frac{12}{4} = \frac{-57}{4}$$

$$\text{RS} = \frac{3}{4} + \frac{5}{6}(-18) = \frac{3}{4} + 5(-3) = \frac{3}{4} - 15 = \frac{3}{4} - \frac{60}{4} = \frac{-57}{4}$$

Since LS = RS, the solution is -18.

C. Solving linear equations involving fractional constants and multiplication

When solving this type of equation, the recommended approach is first to eliminate the fractions and then to expand.

Example 3.2c

(i)
$$\frac{3}{2}(x - 2) - \frac{2}{3}(2x - 1) = 5 \longleftarrow \text{L.C.D.} = 6$$

$$6\left(\frac{3}{2}\right)(x - 2) - 6\left(\frac{2}{3}\right)(2x - 1) = 6(5) \longleftarrow \text{multiply each side by 6}$$

$$3(3)(x - 2) - 2(2)(2x - 1) = 30 \quad \longleftarrow \quad \text{reduce to eliminate fractions}$$

$$9(x - 2) - 4(2x - 1) = 30$$

$$9x - 18 - 8x + 4 = 30$$

$$x - 14 = 30$$

$$x = 44$$

Check

$$\text{LS} = \frac{3}{2}(44 - 2) - \frac{2}{3}(2 \times 44 - 1) = \frac{3}{2}(42) - \frac{2}{3}(87) = 63 - 58 = 5$$

$$\text{RS} = 5$$

Since LS = RS, 44 is the solution.

(ii) $$-\frac{3}{5}(4x - 1) + \frac{5}{8}(4x - 3) \quad = \frac{-11}{10} \quad \longleftarrow \quad \text{LCD} = 40$$

$$40\left(\frac{-3}{5}\right)(4x - 1) + 40\left(\frac{5}{8}\right)(4x - 3) = 40\left(\frac{-11}{10}\right)$$

$$8(-3)(4x - 1) + 5(5)(4x - 3) = 4(-11)$$

$$-24(4x - 1) + 25(4x - 3) = -44$$

$$-96x + 24 + 100x - 75 = -44$$

$$4x - 51 = -44$$

$$4x = 7$$

$$x = \frac{7}{4}$$

Exercise 3.2

A. Solve each of the following equations and check.

1. $12x - 4(9x - 20) = 320$
2. $5(x - 4) - 3(2 - 3x) = -54$
3. $3(2x - 5) - 2(2x - 3) = -15$
4. $17 - 3(2x - 7) = 7x - 3(2x - 1)$

B. Solve each of the following equations.

1. $x - \frac{1}{4}x = 15$ 2. $x + \frac{5}{8}x = 26$

3. $\dfrac{2}{3}x - \dfrac{1}{4} = -\dfrac{7}{4} - \dfrac{5}{6}x$

4. $\dfrac{5}{3} - \dfrac{2}{5}x = \dfrac{1}{6}x - \dfrac{1}{30}$

5. $\dfrac{3}{4}x + 4 = \dfrac{113}{24} - \dfrac{2}{3}x$

6. $2 - \dfrac{3}{2}x = \dfrac{2}{3}x + \dfrac{31}{9}$

C. Solve each of the following equations.

1. $\dfrac{3}{4}(2x - 1) - \dfrac{1}{3}(5 - 2x) = -\dfrac{55}{12}$

2. $\dfrac{4}{5}(4 - 3x) + \dfrac{53}{40} = \dfrac{3}{10}x - \dfrac{7}{8}(2x - 3)$

3. $\dfrac{2}{3}(2x - 1) - \dfrac{3}{4}(3 - 2x) = 2x - \dfrac{20}{9}$

4. $\dfrac{4}{3}(3x - 2) - \dfrac{3}{5}(4x - 3) = \dfrac{11}{60} + 3x$

3.3 Solving Problems

Many business problems may be solved by means of a linear equation in one unknown. To solve problems by means of an algebraic equation, follow the systematic procedure outlined below.

STEP 1   *Introduce the variable* to be used by means of a complete sentence to assure a clear understanding and a record of what the variable is intended to represent.

STEP 2   *Translate* the information in the problem statement in terms of the variable.

STEP 3   *Set up* an algebraic equation. This usually means matching the algebraic expressions developed in Step 2 to a specific number.

STEP 4   *Solve* the equation, state a conclusion and check the conclusion against the problem statement.

Example 3.3a A TV set was sold during a sale for $575. Determine the regular selling price of the set if the price of the set had been reduced by $\frac{1}{6}$ of the regular price.

Solution

STEP 1   *Introduce the variable.* Let the regular selling price be represented by $x.

STEP 2   *Translate.* The reduction in price is $\frac{1}{6}x$, and the reduced price is $(x - \frac{1}{6}x)$.

Set up an equation. Since the reduced price is given to be $575,

$$x - \frac{1}{6}x = 575$$

STEP 4   *Solve* the equation, state a conclusion and check.

$$\frac{5}{6}x = 575$$

$$x = \frac{6(575)}{5}$$

$$x = 690$$

The regular selling price is $690.

Check Regular selling price $690
           Reduction: $\frac{1}{6}$ of 690   115
                                              ‾‾‾‾‾
           Reduced price $575

Example 3.3b   The material cost of a product is $4 less than twice the cost of the direct labour, and the overhead is $\frac{5}{6}$ of the direct labour cost. If the total cost of the product is $157, determine the amount of each of the three elements of cost.

Solution
Three values are needed and any of the three values could be represented by the variable. However, in problems of this type, representing the proper item by the variable leads to a much easier solution than selecting any of the other items. The *proper* item is the one to which the other item or items are *directly related*. In this problem that item is direct labour.

   Let the cost of direct labour be represented by $x,
   then the cost of direct material is $(2x − 4)$ and
   the cost of overhead is $\frac{5}{6}x$.

The total cost is $(x + 2x − 4 + \frac{5}{6}x)$

Since the total cost is given to be $157

$$x + 2x - 4 + \frac{5}{6}x = 157$$

$$3x + \frac{5}{6}x = 161$$

$$18x + 5x = 966$$

$$23x = 966$$

$$x = 42$$

Material cost is $80, direct labour cost $42 and overhead is $35.

Check Material cost: $2x - 4 = 2(42) - 4 = $ $80
Direct labour cost: x $= $ $42
Overhead cost: $\frac{5}{6}x = \frac{5}{6}(42)$ $= $ $35

Total cost $157

Example 3.3c Sheridan Service paid $240 for heat and power during January. If heat was $40 less than three times the cost of power, how much was the cost of heat for January?

Solution

Although the cost of heat is required, it is more convenient to represent the cost of power by the variable since heat cost is expressed in terms of power cost.

Let the cost of power be represented by x, then the cost of heat is $(3x - 40)$ and the total cost is $(x + 3x - 40)$. Since the total cost is given to be $240

$$x + 3x - 40 = 240$$
$$4x = 280$$
$$x = 70$$

The cost of heat is $170

Check Power: $70
Heat: $3x - 40 = 3(70) - 40 = $170

Total cost $240

Example 3.3d The Clarkson Soccer League has set a budget of $3840 for soccer balls. High quality game balls cost $36 each while lower quality practice balls cost $20 each. If 160 balls are to be purchased, how many balls of each type can be bought to exactly use up the budgeted amount?

Solution

When, as in this case, the items referred to in the problem are not directly related, either one or the other may be represented by the variable.

Let the number of game balls be represented by x, then the number of practice balls is $(160 - x)$.

Since the unit values differ, the total value of each type of balls must now be represented in terms of x.

The value of x game balls is $36x$;

the value of $(160 - x)$ practice balls is $20(160 - x)$;

the total value is $\left[36x + 20(160 - x) \right]$.

Since the total budgeted value is given to be $3840

$$36x + 20(160 - x) = 3840$$
$$36x + 3200 - 20x = 3840$$
$$16x = 640$$
$$x = 40$$

The number of game balls is 40 and
the number of practice balls is 120.

Check Number $40 + 120 = 160$
  Value game balls: $36(40)$ = $1440
  practice balls: $20(120)$ = $2400

  Total value $3840

Example 3.3e During last year a repair shop used 1200 small bushings. The shop paid $33\frac{1}{3}$ cents per bushing for the first shipment and $37\frac{1}{2}$ cents per bushing for the second shipment. If the total cost was $430, how many bushings were there in the second shipment?

Solution
Let the number of bushings in the second shipment be x, then the number of bushings in the first shipment was $1200 - x$. The cost of the second shipment was $0.37\frac{1}{2}x$ or $\frac{3}{8}x$ and the cost of the first shipment was $0.33\frac{1}{3}(1200 - x)$ or $\frac{1}{3}(1200 - x)$.
Total cost is $[\frac{3}{8}x + \frac{1}{3}(1200 - x)]$, and since total cost is $430,

$$\frac{3}{8}x + \frac{1}{3}(1200 - x) = 430$$

$$24\left(\frac{3}{8}x\right) + 24\left(\frac{1}{3}\right)(1200 - x) = 24(430)$$

$$3(3x) + 8(1200 - x) = 10320$$

$$9x + 9600 - 8x = 10320$$

$$x = 720$$

The second shipment consisted of 720 bushings.

Check Total number of bushings: $720 + 480 = 1200$

$$\text{Total value} \quad 720\left(\frac{3}{8}\right) + 480\left(\frac{1}{3}\right)$$

$$= 90(3) + 160(1)$$
$$= 270 + 160$$
$$= \$430$$

Exercise 3.3

A. For each of the following problems set up an equation in one unknown and solve.

1. A sweater was sold by a department store for $49.49. The selling price included a mark-up of $\frac{3}{4}$ of the cost to the department store. What was the cost?

2. A stereo set was sold during a sale for $576. Determine the regular selling price of the set if the price of the set had been reduced by $\frac{1}{3}$ of the original regular selling price.

3. After an increase of $\frac{1}{8}$ of his current hourly wage a mechanic will receive a new hourly wage of $10.35. How much is the mechanic's hourly wage before the increase?

4. This month's commodity index decreased by $\frac{1}{12}$ of last month's index to 176. What was last month's index?

5. Nancy's sales last week were $140 less than three times Vera's sales. What were Nancy's sales if together their sales amounted to $940?

6. A metal pipe 90 cm long is cut into two pieces so that the longer piece is 15 cm longer than twice the length of the shorter piece. What is the length of the longer piece?

7. Ken and Fred agreed to form a partnership. The partnership agreement requires that Fred invest $2500 more than two-thirds of what Ken is to invest. If the partnership's capital is to be $55 000, how much should Fred invest?

8. A furniture company has been producing 2320 chairs a day working two shifts. The second shift has produced 60 chairs fewer than four-thirds of the number of chairs produced by the first shift. Determine the number of chairs produced by the second shift.

9. An inventory of two types of floodlights showed a total of sixty lights valued at $2580. If Type A cost $40 each while Type B cost $50 each, how many Type B floodlights were in inventory?

10. A machine requires four hours to make a unit of Product A and three hours to make a unit of Product B. Last month the machine operated for 200 hours producing a total of 60 units. How many units of Product A were produced?

11. Bruce has saved $8.80 in nickels, dimes and quarters. If he has four nickels fewer than three times the number of dimes and one quarter more than $\frac{3}{4}$ the number of dimes, how many coins of each type does Bruce have?

12. The local amateur football club spent $1475 on tickets to a professional football game. If the club bought ten more eight-dollar tickets than three times the number of twelve-dollar tickets and three fewer fifteen-dollar tickets than $\frac{4}{5}$ the number of twelve-dollar tickets, how many of each type of tickets did the club buy?

Review exercise

1. Solve each of the following equations.

(a) $9x = -63$

(b) $0.05x = 44$

(c) $-\frac{1}{7}x = 3$

(d) $\frac{5}{6}x = -15$

(e) $x - 8 = -5$

(f) $x + 9 = -2$

(g) $x + 0.02x = 255$

(h) $x - 0.1x = 36$

(i) $4x - 3 = 9x + 22$

(j) $9x - 6 - 3x = 15 + 4x - 7$

(k) $x - \frac{1}{3}x = 26$

(l) $x + \frac{3}{8}x = 77$

2. Solve each of the following equations and check.

(a) $-9(3x - 8) - 8(9 - 7x) = 5 + 4(9x + 11)$

(b) $21x - 4 - 7(5x - 6) = 8x - 4(5x - 7)$

(c) $\frac{5}{7}x + \frac{1}{2} = \frac{5}{14} + \frac{2}{3}x$

(d) $\frac{4x}{3} + 2 = \frac{9}{8} - \frac{x}{6}$

(e) $\frac{7}{5}(6x - 7) - \frac{3}{8}(7x + 15) = 25$

(f) $\frac{5}{9}(7 - 6x) - \frac{3}{4}(3 - 15x) = \frac{1}{12}(3x - 5) - \frac{1}{2}$

(g) $\frac{5}{6}(4x - 3) - \frac{2}{5}(3x + 4) = 5x - \frac{16}{15}(1 - 3x)$

3. For each of the following problems set up an equation and solve.

(a) A company laid off one-sixth of the work force because of falling sales. If the number of employees after the layoff is 690, how many employees were laid off?

(b) The current average property value is two-sevenths more than last year's average value. What was last year's average property value if the current average is $81 450?

(c) The total amount paid for a banquet, including sales tax of one-twentieth of the price quoted for the banquet, was $2457.00. How much of the amount paid was sales tax?

(d) A piece of property with a commercial building is acquired by H & A Investments for $184 000. If the land is valued at $2000 less than one-third the value of the building, how much of the amount paid should be assigned to land?

(e) The total average monthly cost of heat, power and water for Sheridan Service for last year was $2010. If this year's average is expected to increase by one-tenth over last year's average, and heat is $22 more than three-quarters the cost of power while water is $11 less than one-third the cost of power, how much should be budgeted on the average for each month for each item?

(f) A company has a promotional budget of $87 500. The budget is to be allocated to direct selling, TV advertising and newspaper advertising according to a formula which requires that the amount spent on TV advertising be $1000 more than three times the amount spent on newspaper advertising, and that the amount spent on direct selling be three-fourths of the total spent on TV advertising and newspaper advertising combined. How much of the budget should be allocated to direct selling?

(g) A product requires processing on three machines. Processing time on Machine A is three minutes less than four-fifths of the number of minutes on Machine B and processing time on Machine C is five-sixths of the time needed on Machines A and B together. How many minutes processing time is required on Machine C if the total processing time on all three machines is 77 minutes?

(h) A sporting goods store sold 72 pairs of ski poles. Superlight poles sell at $30 per pair while ordinary poles sell at $16 per pair. If total sales value was $1530, how many pairs of each type were sold?

(i) A cash box contains $74.00 made up of quarters, half-dollars and one-dollar bills. How many quarters are in the box if the number of half-dollar coins is one more than three-fifths of the number of one-dollar bills, and the number of quarters is four times the number of one-dollar bills and half-dollar coins together?

(j) Direct distribution costs are to be allocated to three product lines on the basis of sales value for an accounting period. Product A sells for $20 per unit, Product B for $15 per unit and Product C for $10 per unit. For last month the number of units of Product A was five-eighths the number of units of Product B and the number of units of Product C was 16 less than three times the number of units of Product B. How much of the total direct distribution cost of $6280 is to be allocated to each product line?

Self-test

1. Solve each of the following equations.

(a) $-\frac{2}{3}x = 24$

(b) $x - 0.06x = 8.46$

(c) $0.2x - 4 = 6 - 0.3x$

(d) $(3 - 5x) - (8x - 1) = 43$

(e) $4(8x - 2) - 5(3x + 5) = 18$

(f) $x + \frac{3}{10}x + \frac{1}{2} + x + \frac{3}{5}x + 1 = 103$

(g) $x + \frac{4}{5}x - 3 + \frac{5}{6}\left(x + \frac{4}{5}x - 3\right) = 77$

(h) $\frac{2}{3}\left(3x - 1\right) - \frac{3}{4}\left(5x - 3\right) = \frac{9}{8}x - \frac{5}{6}\left(7x - 9\right)$

2. For each of the following problems set up an equation and solve.

(a) After a reduction of $\frac{1}{5}$ of the regular selling price, a TV set was sold for $192. Determine the regular selling price.

(b) The weaving department of a factory occupies 400 square metres more than 2 times the floor space occupied by the shipping department. The total floor space is 6700 square metres. Determine the floor space occupied by the weaving department.

(c) A machine requires 3 hours to make a unit of Product A and 5 hours to make a unit of Product B. The machine operated for 395 hours producing a total of 95 units. How many units of Product B were produced?

(d) You invested a sum of money in a bank certificate yielding an annual return of $\frac{1}{12}$ of the sum invested. A second sum of money invested in a Credit Union certificate yields an annual return of $\frac{1}{9}$ of the sum invested. The Credit Union investment is $500 more than $\frac{2}{3}$ of the bank investment and the total annual return is $1000. What is the sum of money invested in the Credit Union certificate?

Glossary of terms used

Equation   a statement of equality between two algebraic expressions

Equivalent equations   equations which have the same root

First degree equation   an equation in which the variable (or variables) appear with power '1' only

Linear equation   see *First degree equation*

Members of an equation   the two sides of an equation; the left member is the left side; the right member is the right side

Root of an equation   the solution (replacement value) which when substituted for the variable makes the two sides equal

4 Ratio, proportion, and percent

Introduction

Business information is often based on a comparison of related quantities stated in the form of a ratio. When two or more ratios are equivalent a **proportion** equating the ratios can be set up. Allocation problems generally involve ratios, and many of the physical, economic and financial relationships affecting business activities may be stated in the form of ratios or proportions.

The fractional form of a ratio is frequently replaced by the percent form since relative magnitudes are more readily perceived in this way. Skill in the manipulation of percents, finding percentages, computing rates percent, and dealing with problems of increase and decrease is fundamental to solving a multitude of business problems.

Objectives

Upon completion of this chapter you will be able to

1. set up ratios, manipulate ratios and use ratios to solve allocation problems;
2. set up proportions, solve proportions and use proportions to solve problems involving the equivalence of two ratios;
3. change percents to common fractions and to decimals and conversely, change fractions and decimals to percents;
4. find percentages, compute rates percent, find the base for a rate percent and apply these skills to solve business problems;
5. solve problems of increase and decrease including the finding of the rate of increase or decrease and the original quantity on which the increase or decrease is based;
6. solve a variety of business problems involving percents.

4.1 Ratios

A. Setting up ratios

1. A **ratio** is a comparison of the *relative* values of numbers or quantities by division and may be written in three alternate ways:
   (a) by using the word to, such as in '5 to 3';
   (b) by using a colon, such as in '5:3';
   (c) as a common fraction, such as in '$\frac{5}{3}$'.

2. When comparing more than two numbers or quantities, the use of the *colon* is preferred.
   To compare the quantities 5 kg, 3 kg and 2 kg, the ratio comparing the quantities is written

   $$5 \text{ kg}:3 \text{ kg}:2 \text{ kg}$$

3. When using a ratio to compare quantities, the unit of measurement is usually dropped.
   If three items weigh 5 kg, 3 kg and 2 kg respectively, their weights are compared by the ratio

   $$5:3:2$$

4. The numbers appearing in a ratio are called the **terms of the ratio**. If the terms are in different units, the terms need to be expressed in the same unit of measurement before the units can be dropped.
   The ratio of 1 quarter to 1 dollar becomes 25 cents to 100 cents or 25:100; or the ratio of 3 hours to 40 minutes becomes 180 min:40 min or 180:40.

5. When, as is frequently done, rates are expressed in ratio form, such rates may be written as a ratio by simply dropping the units of measurement even though the terms of the ratio represent different things.
   100 km/h becomes 100:1;
   50 m in 5 seconds becomes 50:5;
   $1.49 for 2 items becomes 1.49:2.

6. Any statement containing a comparison of two or more numbers or quantities can be used to set up a ratio.

   Example 4.1a
   (i) In a company, the work of 40 employees is supervised by five foremen.
       The ratio of employees to foremen is 40:5.
   (ii) Variable cost is $4000 for a sales volume of $24 000.
        The ratio of variable cost to sales volume is 4000:24 000.
   (iii) The cost of a product is made up of $30 of material, $12 of direct labour and $27 of overhead.
         The elements of cost are in the ratio 30:12:27.

B. Reducing ratios to lowest terms

When ratios are used to express a comparison, they are usually reduced to *lowest* terms. Since ratios may be expressed in the form of fractions, ratios may be manipulated according to the rules used for working with fractions. Thus the procedure used to reduce ratios to lowest terms is the same as used when reducing fractions to lowest terms. However, when a ratio is expressed by an improper fraction which reduces to a whole number, the denominator '1' must be written to indicate that two quantities are compared.

Example 4.1b Reduce each of the following ratios to lowest terms.

  (i) $80:35$ (ii) $48:30:18$

(iii) $225:45$ (iv) $81:54:27$

Solution

  (i) Since each term of the ratio $80:35$ contains a common factor 5, each term can be reduced.

$$80:35 = (16 \times 5):(7 \times 5) = 16:7$$

$$\text{or } \frac{80}{35} = \frac{16 \times 5}{7 \times 5} = \frac{16}{7}$$

 (ii) The terms of the ratio $48:30:18$ contain a common factor 6.
$$48:30:18 = (8 \times 6):(5 \times 6):(3 \times 6) = 8:5:3$$

(iii) $225:45 = (45 \times 5):(45 \times 1) = 5:1$

$$\text{or } \frac{225}{45} = \frac{5}{1}$$

(iv) $81:54:27 = (3 \times 27):(2 \times 27):(1 \times 27) = 3:2:1$

C. Equivalent ratios in higher terms

Equivalent ratios in higher terms may be obtained by *multiplying* each term of a ratio by the same number, and are used to eliminate decimals from the terms of a ratio.

Example 4.1c State each of the following ratios in higher terms so as to eliminate the decimals from the terms of the ratios.

  (i) $2.5:3$ (ii) $1.25:3.75:7.5$

(iii) $\dfrac{1.8}{2.7}$ (iv) $\dfrac{19.25}{2.75}$

Solution

(i) $2.5:3 = 25:30$ ⟵————————— multiply each term by 10 to eliminate the decimal

  $= 5:6$ ⟵————————— reduce to lowest terms

(ii) $1.25:3.75:7.5$
  $= 125:375:750$ ⟵————————— multiply each term by 100 to eliminate the decimals
  $= (1 \times 125):(3 \times 125):(6 \times 125)$
  $= 1:3:6$

(iii) $\dfrac{1.8}{2.7} = \dfrac{18}{27} = \dfrac{2}{3}$

(iv) $\dfrac{19.25}{2.75} = \dfrac{1925}{275} = \dfrac{7 \times 275}{1 \times 275} = \dfrac{7}{1}$

D. Allocation according to a ratio

Allocation problems require the division of a whole into a number of parts according to a ratio. The number of parts into which the whole is to be divided is the sum of the terms of the ratio.

Example 4.1d Allocate $480 in the ratio $5:3$.

Solution

The division of $480 in the ratio $5:3$ may be achieved by dividing the amount of $480 into $(5 + 3)$ or 8 parts.
  The value of each part $= 480 \div 8 = 60$.
  The first term of the ratio consists of 5 of the 8 parts; that is, the first term $= 5 \times 60 = 300$ and the second term $= 3 \times 60 = 180$.
Hence $480 is to be divided into $300 and $180.
Alternatively, the division of $480 in the ratio $5:3$ may be effected by using fractions.

5 of 8 ⟶ $\dfrac{5}{8} \times 480 = 300$

3 of 8 ⟶ $\dfrac{3}{8} \times 480 = 180$

Example 4.1e If net income of $72 000 is to be divided among three business partners in the ratio $4:3:2$, how much should each partner receive?

Solution

Divide the net income into $4 + 3 + 2 = 9$ parts,
then each part has a value of $72\,000 \div 9 = \$8000$.

Partner 1 receives 4 of the 9 parts $\longrightarrow$ 4 × 8000 = $32 000
Partner 2 receives 3 of the 9 parts $\longrightarrow$ 3 × 8000 = $24 000
Partner 3 receives 2 of the 9 parts $\longrightarrow$ 2 × 8000 = $16 000

TOTAL $72 000

Alternatively

Partner 1 receives $\frac{4}{9}$ of 72 000 = $\frac{4}{9}$ × 72 000 = 4 × 8000 = $32 000

Partner 2 receives $\frac{3}{9}$ of 72 000 = $\frac{3}{9}$ × 72 000 = 3 × 8000 = $24 000

Partner 3 receives $\frac{2}{9}$ of 72 000 = $\frac{2}{9}$ × 72 000 = 2 × 8000 = $16 000

TOTAL $72 000

Example 4.1f   A business suffered a fire loss of $224 640. It was covered by an insurance policy according to which any claim was to be paid by three insurance companies in the ratio $\frac{1}{3} : \frac{3}{8} : \frac{5}{12}$. What is the amount to be paid by each of the three companies?

Solution

When an amount is to be allocated in a ratio whose terms are fractions, the terms need to be converted into equivalent fractions with the same denominators and the numerators of these fractions may then be used as the ratio by which the amount is to be allocated.

STEP 1   Convert the fractions into equivalent fractions with the same denominators.

$\frac{1}{3} : \frac{3}{8} : \frac{5}{12}$ $\longleftarrow$ L.C.D. = 24

$= \frac{8}{24} : \frac{9}{24} : \frac{10}{24}$ $\longleftarrow$ equivalent fraction with the same denominators

STEP 2   Allocate according to the ratio formed by the numerators.

The numerators form the ratio 8:9:10;
the number of parts is 8 + 9 + 10 = 27;
the value of each part is 224 640 ÷ 27 = 8320

First company's share of claim   = 8320 × 8 = $ 66 560
Second company's share of claim = 8320 × 9 = $ 74 880
Third company's share of claim   = 8320 × 10= $ 83 200

TOTAL $224 640

Exercise 4.1

A. Simplify each of the following ratios.

1. Reduce to lowest terms.

(a) 12 to 32

(b) 84 to 56

(c) 15 to 24 to 39

(d) 21 to 42 to 91

2. Set up a ratio for each of the following and reduce to lowest terms.

(a) 12 dimes to 5 quarters

(b) 15 hours to 3 days

(c) 6 seconds for 50 metres

(d) $72 per dozen

(e) $40 per day for 12 employees for 14 days

(f) 2 percent per month for 24 months for $5000

3. Use equivalent ratios in higher terms so as to eliminate decimals and fractions from the terms of the following ratios.

(a) 1.25 to 4

(b) 2.4 to 8.4

(c) 0.6 to 2.1 to 3.3

(d) 5.75 to 3.50 to 1.25

(e) $\frac{1}{2}$ to $\frac{2}{5}$

(f) $\frac{5}{3}$ to $\frac{7}{5}$

(g) $\frac{3}{8}$ to $\frac{2}{3}$ to $\frac{3}{4}$

(h) $\frac{2}{5}$ to $\frac{4}{7}$ to $\frac{5}{14}$

(i) $2\frac{1}{5}$ to $4\frac{1}{8}$

(j) $5\frac{1}{4}$ to $5\frac{5}{6}$

B. Set up a ratio for each of the following and reduce the ratio to lowest terms.

1. Gino's restaurant budgets food costs to account for 40 percent and beverage costs for 35 percent of total cost. What is the ratio of food costs to beverage costs?

2. Direct selling expense amounted to $2500 while sales volume was $87 500 for last month. What is the ratio of direct selling expense to sales volume?

3. A company employs 6 supervisors for 9 office employees and 36 production workers. What is the ratio of supervisors to office employees to production workers?

4. The cost of a unit is made up of $4.25 direct material cost, $2.75 direct labour cost and $3.25 overhead. What is the ratio that exists between the three elements of cost?

C. Solve each of the following allocation problems.

1. A dividend of $3060 is to be distributed among three shareholders in the ratio of shares held. If the three shareholders have nine shares, two shares and one share respectively, how much does each receive?

2. The cost of operating the Maintenance Department is to be allocated to four production departments on the basis of floor space occupied. Department A occupies 1000 m²; Department B, 600 m²; Department C, 800 m², and Department D, 400 m². If the July cost was $21 000, how much of the cost of operating the Maintenance Department should be absorbed by each production department?

3. Insurance cost is to be distributed among manufacturing, selling and administration in the ratio $\frac{5}{8}$ to $\frac{1}{3}$ to $\frac{1}{6}$. If the total insurance cost was $9450, how should the insurance cost be distributed?

4. Executive salaries are to charged to three operating divisions on the basis of capital investment in the three divisions. If the investment in the Northern Division is $10.8 million, $8.4 million in the Eastern Division and $14.4 million in the Western Division, how should executive salaries of $588 000 be allocated to the three divisions?

4.2 *Proportions*

A. *Solving proportions*

When two ratios are equal they form a proportion.

$$
\left.
\begin{array}{l}
2:3 = 4:6 \\[4pt]
x:5 = 7:35 \\[4pt]
\dfrac{2}{3} = \dfrac{8}{x} \\[10pt]
\dfrac{a}{b} = \dfrac{c}{d}
\end{array}
\right\} \longleftarrow \text{are proportions}
$$

Note that each proportion consists of *four terms* which form an equation whose sides are common fractions.

If one of the four terms is unknown, the proportions form a linear equation in one variable which may be solved by using the operations discussed in Chapter 3.

Example 4.2a   Solve the proportion $2:5 = 8:x$.

Solution

$2:5 = 8:x \longleftarrow$ original form of proportion

$\dfrac{2}{5} = \dfrac{8}{x} \longleftarrow$ change the proportion into fractional form

$5x\left(\dfrac{2}{5}\right) = 5x\left(\dfrac{8}{x}\right) \longleftarrow$ multiply by the L.C.D. = $5x$

$2x = 40$

$x = 20$

Check   LS $= \dfrac{2}{5}$, RS $= \dfrac{8}{20} = \dfrac{2}{5}$.

Note The two operations usually applied to solve proportions are multiplication and division. This permits the use of a simplified technique referred to as **cross-multiplication** which involves

(a) the multiplication of the numerator of the ratio on the left side with the denominator of the ratio on the right side of the proportion, and

(b) the multiplication of the numerator of the ratio on the right side with the denominator of the ratio on the left side.

When cross-multiplication is used to solve Example 4.2a the value of x is obtained as follows.

$$\frac{2}{5} = \frac{8}{x}$$

$$x(2) = 5(8) \longleftarrow \text{cross multiply}$$

$$2x = 40$$

$$x = 20$$

Example 4.2b Solve each of the following proportions.

(i) $\quad x:5 = 7:35 \longleftarrow$ original proportion

$$\frac{x}{5} = \frac{7}{35} \longleftarrow \text{in fractional form}$$

$$35(x) = 5(7) \longleftarrow \text{cross multiply}$$

$$35x = 35$$

$$x = 1$$

(ii) $\quad 2\frac{1}{2}:x = 5\frac{1}{2}:38\frac{1}{2}$

$$2.5:x = 5.5:38.5 \qquad \textbf{or} \qquad \frac{5}{2}:x = \frac{11}{2}:\frac{77}{2}$$

$$\frac{2.5}{x} = \frac{5.5}{38.5} \qquad\qquad\qquad \frac{\frac{5}{2}}{\frac{x}{1}} = \frac{\frac{11}{2}}{\frac{77}{2}}$$

$$38.5(2.5) = x(5.5) \qquad\qquad \left(\frac{5}{2}\right)\left(\frac{77}{2}\right) = \left(\frac{11}{2}\right)(x)$$

$$96.25 = 5.5x \qquad\qquad\qquad \frac{(5)(77)}{4} = \frac{11x}{2}$$

$$x = \frac{96.25}{5.5} \qquad\qquad\qquad x = \frac{(5)(\cancel{77})^{7}}{\cancel{4}_{2}} \times \frac{\cancel{2}^{1}}{\cancel{11}_{1}}$$

$$x = 17.5$$

$$x = 17\frac{1}{2} \qquad\qquad\qquad\qquad x = \frac{35}{2}$$

$$x = 17\frac{1}{2}$$

(iii) $\dfrac{5}{6} : \dfrac{14}{3} = x : \dfrac{21}{10}$

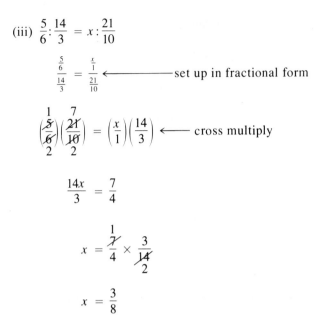

$\dfrac{\frac{5}{6}}{\frac{14}{3}} = \dfrac{\frac{x}{1}}{\frac{21}{10}}$ ←————————set up in fractional form

$\left(\dfrac{\cancel{5}}{\cancel{6}}\right)\left(\dfrac{\cancel{21}}{\cancel{10}}\right) = \left(\dfrac{x}{1}\right)\left(\dfrac{14}{3}\right)$ ←———— cross multiply

$\dfrac{14x}{3} = \dfrac{7}{4}$

$x = \dfrac{\cancel{7}}{4} \times \dfrac{3}{\cancel{14}}$

$x = \dfrac{3}{8}$

B.   *Problems involving proportions*

Many problems contain information which permits the setting up of two ratios which are in proportion, but in which one term of one ratio is unknown. In such cases a letter symbol for the unknown term may be used to complete the proportion statement.

To assure that the proportion is set up correctly, the following procedure is recommended.

STEP 1   *Introduce* the *letter* symbol which is used to represent the missing terms by means of a complete sentence.

STEP 2   Set up the *known ratio* on the *left* side of the proportion making sure to retain the units or a description of the quantities in the ratio.

STEP 3   Set up the ratio using the *letter symbol* on the *right* side of the proportion. Make certain that the unit or description of the numerator in the ratio on the right side corresponds to the unit or description of the numerator in the ratio on the left side.

Example 4.2c   Solve each of the following problems involving a proportion.

(i) If five kilograms of sugar cost $9.20, what is the cost of two kilograms of sugar?

Solution

STEP 1   Introduce the variable.
Let the cost of two kilograms of sugar be x.

STEP 2   Set up the known ratio retaining the units.
5 kg : $9.20

STEP 3   Set up the ratio involving the variable.
2 kg : $x

Hence $\dfrac{5 \text{ kg}}{\$9.20} = \dfrac{2 \text{ kg}}{\$x}$ ←——— make certain the units in the numerators correspond

$$\dfrac{5}{9.20} = \dfrac{2}{x}$$

$$x(5) = 9.20(2)$$

$$x = \dfrac{18.40}{5}$$

$$x = 3.68$$

Two kilograms of sugar cost $3.68.

(ii) If your car can travel 385 km on 35 L of gasoline, how far can it travel on 24 L?

Solution

Let the distance travelled on 24 L be n km;
then the known ratio is 385 km : 35 ℓ;
the second ratio is n km : 24 ℓ.

$$\dfrac{385 \text{ km}}{35 \, \ell} = \dfrac{n \text{ km}}{24 \, \ell}$$

$$\dfrac{385}{35} = \dfrac{n}{24}$$

$$n = \dfrac{\overset{11}{\cancel{385}} \times 24}{\underset{1}{\cancel{35}}}$$

$$n = 264$$

The car can travel 264 km on 24 L.

(iii) Past experience indicates that a process requires $17.50 worth of material for every $12.00 spent on labour. How much should be budgeted for material if the budget for labour is $17 760?

Solution

Let the material budget be k.

The known ratio is $\dfrac{\$17.50 \text{ material}}{\$12.00 \text{ labour}}$;

the second ratio is $\dfrac{\$k \text{ material}}{\$17\,760 \text{ labour}}$.

$$\frac{\$17.50 \text{ material}}{\$12.00 \text{ labour}} = \frac{\$k \text{ material}}{\$17\,760 \text{ labour}} .$$

$$\frac{17.50}{12.00} = \frac{k}{17760}$$

$$k = \frac{17.50 \times 17760}{12.00}$$

$$k = 25900$$

The material budget should be $25\,900.

Example 4.2d   Two contractors agreed to share revenue from a job in the ratio 2:3. Contractor A, receiving the smaller amount, made a profit of $480 on the job. If contractor A's profit compared to his revenue is in the ratio 3:8, determine
(i) the revenue of Contractor A;
(ii) the total revenue on the job.

Solution

(i)   Let contractor A's revenue be represented by $x.

Then $\dfrac{\text{A's Profit}}{\text{A's Revenue}} = \dfrac{3}{8}$ ⟵ known ratio

and $\dfrac{\text{A's Profit}}{\text{A's Revenue}} = \dfrac{\$480}{\$x}$ ⟵ second ratio

Hence $\dfrac{3}{8} = \dfrac{480}{x}$

$$3x = 480 \times 8$$

$$x = \frac{480 \times 8}{3}$$

$$x = 160 \times 8$$

$$x = 1280$$

Contractor A's revenue on the job is $1280.

(ii) Let Contractor B's revenue be represented by $y.

Then $\dfrac{\text{A's Revenue}}{\text{B's Revenue}} = \dfrac{2}{3}$ ⟵ known ratio

and $\dfrac{\text{A's Revenue}}{\text{B's Revenue}} = \dfrac{\$1280}{\$y}$ ⟵ second ratio

$$\frac{2}{3} = \frac{1280}{y}$$

$$2y = 1280 \times 3$$

$$y = \frac{1280 \times 3}{2}$$

$$y = 1920$$

$$x + y = 1280 + 1920 = 3200$$

Total revenue on the job is $3200.

Alternatively Let total revenue be $z.

Then $\dfrac{\text{A's Revenue}}{\text{Total Revenue}} = \dfrac{2}{5} = \dfrac{\$1280}{\$z}$

$$\frac{2}{5} = \frac{1280}{z}$$

$$2z = 1280 \times 5$$

$$z = 3200$$

Exercise 4.2

A. Find the unknown term in the following proportions.

1. $3:n = 15:20$ 　　　　　　　**2.** $n:7 = 24:42$

3. $3:8 = 21:x$ 　　　　　　　**4.** $7:5 = x:45$

5. $1.32:1.11 = 8.8:k$ 　　　　　**6.** $2.17:1.61 = k:4.6$

7. $m:3.4 = 2.04:2.89$ 　　　　**8.** $3.15:m = 1.4:1.8$

9. $t:\dfrac{3}{4} = \dfrac{7}{8}:\dfrac{15}{16}$ 　　　　　**10.** $\dfrac{3}{4}:t = \dfrac{5}{8}:\dfrac{4}{9}$

11. $\dfrac{9}{8}:\dfrac{3}{5} = t:\dfrac{8}{15}$ 　　　　　**12.** $\dfrac{16}{7}:\dfrac{4}{9} = \dfrac{15}{14}:t$

B. Use proportions to solve each of the following problems.

1. A company pays a dividend of $1.25 per share every three months. How many months would it take to earn dividends amounting to $8.75 per share?

2. A community sets a property tax rate of $28 per $1000 assessed valuation. What is the assessment if a tax of $854 is paid on a property?

3. A car requires nine litres of gasoline for 72 km. At the same rate of gasoline consumption, how far can the car travel if the gas tank holds 75 litres?

4. A manufacturing process requires $85 supervision cost for every 64 labour hours. At the same rate, how much supervision cost should be budgeted for 16 000 labour hours?

5. Mr. C has a two-fifths interest in a partnership. He sold five-sixths of his interest for $3000.

  (a) What was the total amount of his interest prior to selling?

  (b) What is the value of the partnership?

6. Five-eights of Black's inventory was destroyed by fire. He sold the remaining part which was slightly damaged for one-third of its value and received $1300.

  (a) What was the value of the destroyed part of the inventory?

  (b) What was the value of the inventory before the fire?

7. Last year net profits of Herd Inc. were two-sevenths of revenue. If the company declared a dividend of $12 800 and five-ninths of the net profit were retained in the company, what was last year's revenue?

8. Material cost of an article is five-eighths of total cost and labour cost is one-third of material cost. If labour cost is $15, what is the total cost of the article?

4.3 *Percent*

A. *The meaning of percent*

The easiest method of comparing quantities is to use ratios in which the *second* term is the number 100; that is, to use fractions with denominator 100. The preferred form of writing such ratios is the *percent* form.

| PERCENT means HUNDREDTHS | $\longrightarrow$ | % means $\overline{100}$ |

When dealing with percents *four* different forms may be used interchangeably.

  (i) the *percent* form

 (ii) a *ratio* with second term 100

(iii) a *common fraction* with denominator 100

(iv) a *decimal* fraction

For example, 'seven percent' may be written

  (i) in percent form   7%

 (ii) in ratio form   7 : 100

(iii) as a common fraction $\frac{7}{100}$

(iv) as a decimal 0.07

Conversely any fraction involving 'hundredths' may be written in the same four forms.

(i) as a decimal 0.13

(ii) as a common fraction $\frac{13}{100}$

(iii) in ratio form $13:100$

(iv) in percent form 13%

Mathematics
fundamentals

B. *Changing percents to common fractions*

When computing with percents, use the corresponding common fraction or decimal fraction. To convert a percent into a common fraction replace the symbol % by the symbol $\frac{}{100}$. The resulting fraction should then be reduced to lowest terms.

Example 4.3a

(i) $24\% \quad = \frac{24}{100} \longleftarrow$ replace % by $\frac{}{100}$

$= \frac{6}{25} \longleftarrow$ reduce to lowest terms

(ii) $175\% \quad = \frac{175}{100} = \frac{7 \times 25}{4 \times 25} = \frac{7}{4}$

(iii) $6.25\% \quad = \frac{6.25}{100}$

$= \frac{625}{10000} \longleftarrow$ multiply by 100 to change the numerator to a whole number

$= \frac{125}{2000} = \frac{25}{400} = \frac{5}{80} \longleftarrow$ reduce gradually or in one step

$= \frac{1}{16}$

(iv) $0.8\% \quad = \frac{0.8}{100} = \frac{8}{1000} = \frac{1}{125}$

(v) $0.025\% = \frac{0.025}{100} = \frac{25}{100000} = \frac{1}{4000}$

(vi) $\dfrac{1}{4}\% = \dfrac{\frac{1}{4}}{\frac{100}{1}}$ ←————— replace by $\dfrac{100}{1}$

$= \dfrac{1}{4} \times \dfrac{1}{100}$ ←———— invert and multiply

$= \dfrac{1}{400}$

(vii) $\dfrac{3}{8}\% = \dfrac{\frac{3}{8}}{\frac{100}{1}} = \dfrac{3}{8} \times \dfrac{1}{100} = \dfrac{3}{800}$

(viii) $33\dfrac{1}{3}\% = \dfrac{33\frac{1}{3}}{100}$ ←————— replace % by $\dfrac{1}{100}$

$= \dfrac{\frac{100}{3}}{\frac{100}{1}}$ ←————— convert the mixed number $33\frac{1}{3}$ into a common fraction

$= \dfrac{100}{3} \times \dfrac{1}{100}$

$= \dfrac{1}{3}$

(ix) $216\dfrac{2}{3}\% = \dfrac{216\frac{2}{3}}{100} = \dfrac{\frac{650}{3}}{\frac{100}{1}} = \dfrac{\overset{13}{\cancel{650}}}{3} \times \dfrac{1}{\underset{2}{\cancel{100}}} = \dfrac{13}{6}$

Alternatively

$216\dfrac{2}{3}\% = 200\% + 16\dfrac{2}{3}\%$ ←—— separate the multiple of 100% (the whole number part) from the fractional part

$= 2 + \dfrac{\frac{50}{3}}{\frac{100}{1}}$

$= 2 + \dfrac{50}{3} \times \dfrac{1}{100}$

$= 2 + \dfrac{1}{6}$

$= \dfrac{13}{6}$

C. Changing Percents into Decimals

Replacement of the symbol % by $\frac{1}{100}$ indicates a division by 100. Since division by 100 is readily performed by moving the decimal point *two places to the left*, changing a percent to a decimal is quickly done by dropping the symbol % and by moving the decimal point two places to the left.

Example 4.3b

(i) $52\% = 0.52$ ⟵ drop the percent symbol and move the decimal point two places to the left

(ii) $175\% = 1.75$

(iii) $6\% = 0.06$

(iv) $0.75\% = 0.007\,5$

(v) $\frac{1}{4}\% = 0.25\%$ ⟵ first change the fraction to a decimal

$= 0.002\,5$ ⟵ then drop the % symbol and move the decimal point two places to the left

(vi) $\frac{3}{8}\% = 0.375\%$

$= 0.003\,75$

(vii) $\frac{2}{3}\% = 0.66\frac{2}{3}\%$ ⟵ change the fraction to a mixed decimal with at least two decimal positions

$= 0.006\,6\frac{2}{3}$ ⟵ drop the percent symbol and move the decimal two places to the left

(viii) $\frac{5}{8}\% = 0.625\%$

$= 0.006\,25$

D. Changing decimals into percents

Changing decimals into percents is the inverse operation to changing percents into decimals and is accomplished by multiplying by 100%. Since multiplication by 100 is readily performed by moving the decimal point *two places to the right* a decimal is easily changed to a percent by moving the decimal point two places to the right and adding the % symbol.

Example 4.3c

(i) $0.36 \quad = 0.36(100\%)$

$= 36\%$ ⟵ move the decimal point two places to the right and add the % symbol

(ii) $1.65 \quad = 165\%$

(iii) $0.075 = 7.5\%$

(iv) $0.4 = 40\%$

(v) $0.001 = 0.1\%$

(vi) $2 = 200\%$

(vii) $0.0005 = 0.05\%$

(viii) $0.33\frac{1}{3} = 33\frac{1}{3}\%$

(ix) $1.16\frac{2}{3} = 116\frac{2}{3}\%$

(x) $1\frac{5}{6} = 1.83\frac{1}{3} = 183\frac{1}{3}\%$

E. Changing fractions to percents

When changing a fraction to a percent it is best to convert the fraction to a decimal and then to change the decimal into a percent.

Example 4.3d

(i) $\frac{1}{4} = 0.25$ ⟵ convert the fraction to a decimal

$= 25\%$ ⟵ convert the decimal into a percent

(ii) $\frac{7}{8} = 0.875 = 87.5\%$

(iii) $\frac{9}{5} = 1.8 = 180\%$

(iv) $\frac{5}{6} = 0.83\frac{1}{3} = 83\frac{1}{3}\%$

(v) $\frac{5}{9} = 0.55\frac{5}{9} = 55\frac{5}{9}\%$

(vi) $1\frac{2}{3} = 1.66\frac{2}{3} = 166\frac{2}{3}\%$

Exercise 4.3

A. Change each of the following percents into a decimal.

1. 64%   2. 300%   3. 2.5%   4. 0.1%

5. 0.5%   6. 85%   7. 250%   8. 4.8%

9. 450% 10. 7.5% 11. 0.9% 12. 95%

13. 6.25% 14. 0.4% 15. 99% 16. 225%

17. 0.05% 18. $8\frac{1}{4}\%$ 19. $\frac{1}{2}\%$ 20. $112\frac{1}{2}\%$

21. $9\frac{3}{8}\%$ 22. 0.75% 23. $162\frac{1}{2}\%$ 24. $\frac{2}{5}\%$

25. $\frac{1}{4}\%$ 26. $187\frac{1}{2}\%$ 27. $1\frac{3}{4}\%$ 28. 0.025%

29. $137\frac{1}{2}\%$ 30. $\frac{5}{8}\%$ 31. 0.875% 32. $2\frac{1}{4}\%$

33. $33\frac{1}{3}\%$ 34. $166\frac{2}{3}\%$ 35. $16\frac{2}{3}\%$ 36. $116\frac{2}{3}\%$

37. $183\frac{1}{3}\%$ 38. $83\frac{1}{3}\%$ 39. $133\frac{1}{3}\%$ 40. $66\frac{2}{3}\%$

B. Change each of the following percents into a common fraction in lowest terms.

1. 25% 2. $62\frac{1}{2}\%$ 3. 175% 4. 5%

5. $37\frac{1}{2}\%$ 6. 75% 7. 4% 8. 225%

9. 8% 10. 125% 11. 40% 12. $87\frac{1}{2}\%$

13. 250% 14. 2% 15. $12\frac{1}{2}\%$ 16. 60%

17. 2.25% 18. 0.5% 19. $\frac{1}{8}\%$ 20. $33\frac{1}{3}\%$

21. $\frac{3}{4}\%$ 22. $66\frac{2}{3}\%$ 23. 6.25% 24. 0.25%

25. $16\frac{2}{3}\%$ 26. 7.5% 27. 0.75% 28. $\frac{7}{8}\%$

29. 0.1% 30. $\frac{3}{5}\%$ 31. $83\frac{1}{3}\%$ 32. 2.5%

33. $133\frac{1}{3}\%$ 34. $183\frac{1}{3}\%$ 35. $166\frac{2}{3}\%$ 36. $116\frac{2}{3}\%$

C. Express each of the following as a percent.

1. 3.5 2. 0.075 3. 0.005 4. 0.375

5. 0.025 6. 2 7. 0.125 8. 0.001

9. 0.225 10. 0.008 11. 1.45 12. 0.0225

13. 0.0025 14. 0.995 15. 0.09 16. 3

17. $\frac{3}{4}$ 18. $\frac{3}{25}$ 19. $\frac{5}{3}$ 20. $\frac{7}{200}$

21. $\dfrac{9}{200}$ **22.** $\dfrac{5}{8}$ **23.** $\dfrac{3}{400}$ **24.** $\dfrac{5}{6}$

25. $\dfrac{9}{800}$ **26.** $\dfrac{7}{6}$ **27.** $\dfrac{3}{8}$ **28.** $\dfrac{11}{40}$

29. $\dfrac{4}{3}$ **30.** $\dfrac{9}{400}$ **31.** $\dfrac{13}{20}$ **32.** $\dfrac{4}{5}$

4.4   The basic percentage problem

A. Computing percentages

Percentages are found by multiplying a number by a percent.

$$50\% \text{ of } 60 = 0.50 \times 60 = 30$$

Note: 50% is called the *rate*;
60   is called the *base* or *original number*;
30   is called the *percentage* or *new number*.

$$\boxed{\text{PERCENTAGE} = \text{RATE} \times \text{BASE}} \longleftarrow \textbf{\textit{Formula}} \ \textbf{4.1}$$

$$\boxed{\text{NEW NUMBER} = \text{RATE} \times \text{ORIGINAL NUMBER}}$$

To determine a percent of a given number change the percent to a decimal fraction or a common fraction and then multiply by the given number.

Example 4.4a

(i) $80\% \text{ of } 400 = 0.80 \times 400 \longleftarrow$ convert the percent
$= 320$ into a decimal and multiply

(ii) $5\% \text{ of } 1200 = 0.05 \times 1200 = 60$

(iii) $240\% \text{ of } 15 = 2.40 \times 15 = 36$

(iv) $1.8\% \text{ of } \$600 = 0.018 \times 600 = \$10.80$

(v) $33\frac{1}{3}\% \text{ of } \$45.60 = \frac{1}{3} \times 45.60 = \$15.20$

(vi) $0.25\% \text{ of } \$8000 = 0.0025 \times 8000 = \$20$

(vii) $\frac{3}{8}\% \text{ of } \$1800 = 0.375\% \text{ of } \$1800 = 0.00375 \times 1800 = \$6.75$

B. Computation with commonly used percents

Many of the more commonly used percents can be converted into fractions which may be used to advantage when computing manually. The most important such percents and their fractional equivalents are listed in Table 4.1. *Note* Table 4.1 corresponds to Table 1.1.

TABLE 4.1 *Commonly used percents and their fractional equivalents*

(i)	(ii)	(iii)	(iv)	(v)
$25\% = \frac{1}{4}$	$16\frac{2}{3}\% = \frac{1}{6}$	$12\frac{1}{2}\% = \frac{1}{8}$	$20\% = \frac{1}{5}$	$8\frac{1}{3}\% = \frac{1}{12}$
$50\% = \frac{1}{2}$	$33\frac{1}{3}\% = \frac{1}{3}$	$37\frac{1}{2}\% = \frac{3}{8}$	$40\% = \frac{2}{5}$	$6\frac{2}{3}\% = \frac{1}{15}$
$75\% = \frac{3}{4}$	$66\frac{2}{3}\% = \frac{2}{3}$	$62\frac{1}{2}\% = \frac{5}{8}$	$60\% = \frac{3}{5}$	$6\frac{1}{4}\% = \frac{1}{16}$
	$83\frac{1}{3}\% = \frac{5}{6}$	$87\frac{1}{2}\% = \frac{7}{8}$	$80\% = \frac{4}{5}$	

Example 4.4b

(i) 25% of $32 = \dfrac{1}{4} \times 32 = 8$

(ii) $33\dfrac{1}{3}\%$ of $150 = \dfrac{1}{3} \times 150 = 50$

(iii) $87\dfrac{1}{2}\%$ of $96 = \dfrac{7}{8} \times 96 = 7 \times 12 = 84$

(iv) $83\dfrac{1}{3}\%$ of $48 = \dfrac{5}{6} \times 48 = 5 \times 8 = 40$

(v) $116\dfrac{2}{3}\%$ of $240 = \left(100\% + 16\dfrac{2}{3}\%\right)$ of 240

$$= \left(1 + \frac{1}{6}\right)(240)$$

$$= \frac{7}{6} \times 240$$

$$= 7 \times 40$$

$$= 280$$

(vi) 275% of $64 = \left(2 + \dfrac{3}{4}\right)(64)$

$$= \dfrac{11}{4} \times 64$$

$$= 11 \times 16$$

$$= 176$$

C. Using the 1% method

Percentages may be computed by determining 1% of the given number and then computing the value of the given percent. While this method can be used to compute any percentage, it is recommended when dealing with *small* percents.

Example 4.4c Use the 1% method to determine each of the following percentages.

(i) 3% of $1800

> **Solution** 1% of $1800 = $18
>
> 3% of $1800 = 3 \times $18 = $54

(ii) $\frac{1}{2}\%$ of $960

> **Solution** 1% of $960 = $9.60
>
> $\dfrac{1}{2}\%$ of $960 = \dfrac{1}{2} \times 9.60 = $4.80

(iii) $\frac{5}{8}\%$ of $4440

> **Solution** 1% of $4440 = $44.40
>
> $\dfrac{1}{8}\%$ of $4440 = \dfrac{1}{8} \times 44.40 = $5.55
>
> $\dfrac{5}{8}\%$ of $4440 = 5 \times 5.55 = $27.75

(iv) $2\frac{1}{4}\%$ of $36\,500

> **Solution** 1% of $36500 = $365.00
>
> 2% of $36500 = 2 \times 365.00 = $730.00
>
> $\dfrac{1}{4}\%$ of $36500 = \dfrac{1}{4} \times 365.00 = \underline{91.25}$
>
> $2\frac{1}{4}\%$ of $36500 \longrightarrow$ $821.25

D. Finding a rate percent

Finding a rate involves a *comparison* of two numbers. This comparison involves a **ratio** which is usually written in the form of a common fraction. When the common fraction is converted into a percent, a rate percent results.

When setting up the ratio, the base (or original number) is always the denominator of the fraction, and the percentage (or new number) is always the numerator.

$$\text{RATE} = \frac{\text{PERCENTAGE}}{\text{BASE}} \text{ or } \frac{\text{NEW NUMBER}}{\text{ORIGINAL NUMBER}} \longleftarrow \textit{Formula } \textbf{4.2}$$

The problem statement indicating that a rate percent is to be found is usually of the form

> "What percent of x is y?", or
> "y is what percent of x?"

This means that y is to be compared to x and requires the setting up of the ratio $y:x$ or the fraction $\frac{y}{x}$. x is the base (or original number) while y is the percentage (or new number).

Example 4.4d Answer each of the following questions.

(i) What percent of 15 is 6?

Solution

$$\text{Rate} = \frac{6 \longleftarrow \text{percentage (or new number)}}{15 \longleftarrow \text{base (or original number)}}$$

$$= 0.40$$

$$= 40\%$$

(ii) 90 is what percent of 72?

Solution

$$\text{Rate} = \frac{90}{72} \longleftarrow \text{original number}$$

$$= \frac{5}{4}$$

$$= 125\%$$

(iii) \$9.90 is what percent of \$550?

Solution

$$\text{Rate} = \frac{9.90}{550} = \frac{99}{5500} = \frac{9}{500} = 0.018 = 1.8\%$$

(iv) What percent of $112.50 is $292.50?

    Solution

$$\text{Rate} = \frac{292.50}{112.50} = 2.60 = 260\%$$

E.   *Finding the base*

A great number of business problems involve the relationship

PERCENTAGE = BASE × RATE
(or NEW NUMBER = RATE × ORIGINAL NUMBER).

Since three variables are involved, three different problems may be solved using this relationship.

(a) finding the percentage (see Sections A, B, C)
(b) finding the rate per cent (see Section D)
(c) finding the base

Of the three, the problem of finding the rate is easily recognizable. However, confusion often arises in deciding whether the percentage or the base is to be found. In such cases it is useful to represent the unknown value by a variable and set up an equation.

Example 4.4e Solve each of the following problems by setting up an equation.

(i) What number is 25% of 84?

    Solution

    Introduce a variable for the unknown value and write the statement in equation form.

What number is 25% of 84
$$\Downarrow \qquad \Downarrow \ \Downarrow \qquad \Downarrow$$
$$x \qquad = 25\% \text{ of } 84$$

$$x \qquad = \frac{1}{4} \times 84 \quad \longleftarrow \quad \text{change the percent to a fraction or a decimal}$$

$$x \qquad = 21$$

The number is 21.

(ii) 60% of what number is 42?

Solution

$$60\% \text{ of what number is } 42$$
$$\Downarrow \qquad\qquad\qquad \Downarrow \quad \Downarrow\Downarrow$$
$$60\% \text{ of} \qquad\qquad x \quad = 42$$

$$0.6x \quad = 42$$

$$x \quad = \frac{42}{0.6}$$

$$x \quad = 70$$

The number is 70.

(iii) How much is $16\frac{2}{3}\%$ of \$144?

Solution

$$x = 16\frac{2}{3}\% \text{ of } 144$$

$$x = \frac{1}{6} \times 144$$

$$x = 24$$

The amount is \$24.

(iv) \$160 is 250% of what amount?

Solution

$$160 = 250\% \text{ of } x$$

$$160 = 2.5x$$

$$x = \frac{160}{2.5}$$

$$x = 64$$

The amount is \$64.

F. Applications

Example 4.4f   Solve each of the following problems.

(i) Variable cost on monthly sales of \$48 600 amounted to \$30 375. What is the variable cost based on sales volume?

Solution

$$\text{Rate} = \frac{\text{Variable Cost}}{\text{Sales Volume}} \longleftarrow \text{base for the comparison}$$

$$= \frac{30375}{48600}$$

$$= 0.625$$

$$= 62.5\%$$

The variable cost is 62.5% of sales volume.

(ii) What is the annual dividend on a preferred share paying 11.5% on a par value of $20?

Solution

Let the annual dividend be $x.
Since the annual dividend is 11.5% of $20

$$x = 11.5\% \text{ of } 20$$

$$x = 0.115 \times 20$$

$$x = 2.30$$

The annual dividend is $2.30.

(iii) What was the amount of October sales if November sales of $14 352 were 115% of October sales?

Solution

Let October sales be represented by $x.
Since November sales equal 115% of October sales

$$14352 = 115\% \text{ of } x$$

$$14352 = 1.15x$$

$$x = \frac{14352}{1.15}$$

$$x = 12480$$

October sales amounted to $12 480.

(iv) The 7% sales tax charged on the regular selling price of a typewriter amounted to $93.80. What was the total cost of the typewriter?

Solution

Let the regular selling price be $x.
Since the sales tax is 7% of the regular selling price

$$93.80 = 7\% \text{ of } x$$

$$93.80 = 0.07x$$

$$x = \frac{93.80}{0.07}$$

$$x = 1340$$

The regular selling price is $1340.00

Add 7% of $1340   93.80

TOTAL COST $1433.80

Exercise 4.4

A. Compute each of the following.

1. 40% of 90

2. 0.1% of 950

3. 250% of 120

4. 7% of 800

5. 3% of 600

6. 15% of 240

7. 0.5% of 1200

8. 300% of 80

9. 0.02% of 2500

10. $\frac{1}{2}$% of 500

11. $\frac{1}{4}$% of 800

12. 0.05% of 9000

13. 0.075% of 10000

14. $\frac{7}{8}$% of 3600

15. 2.5% of 700

16. 0.025% of 40000

B. Use fractional equivalents to compute each of the following.

1. $33\frac{1}{3}$% of $48

2. $137\frac{1}{2}$% of $400

3. $162\frac{1}{2}$% of $1200

4. $66\frac{2}{3}$% of $72

5. $37\frac{1}{2}$% of $24

6. 175% of $1600

7. 125% of $160

8. $12\frac{1}{2}$% of $168

9. $83\frac{1}{3}$% of $720

10. $166\frac{2}{3}$% of $90

11. $116\frac{2}{3}$% of $42

12. $16\frac{2}{3}$% of $54

13. 75% of $180

14. $183\frac{1}{3}$% of $24

15. $133\frac{1}{3}$% of $45

16. 25% of $440

C. Use the 1% method to compute each of the following.

1. $\frac{1}{2}$% of $3120

2. $\frac{3}{4}$% of $2140

3. $\frac{3}{8}$% of $432

4. $\frac{4}{5}$% of $1120

5. $1\frac{1}{3}$% of $3630

6. $1\frac{1}{2}$% of $782

7. $2\frac{3}{8}$% of $944

8. $2\frac{3}{4}$% of $1632

D. Solve each of the following equations.

1. $x + 40\%$ of $x = 28$

2. $x - 20\%$ of $x = 240$

3. $x - 5\%$ of $x = 418$

4. $x + 7\%$ of $x = 214$

5. $x + 16\frac{2}{3}\%$ of $x = 42$

6. $x - 33\frac{1}{3}\%$ of $x = 54$

7. $x + 150\%$ of $x = 75$

8. $x + 200\%$ of $x = 36$

E. Find the rate percent for each of the following.

1. Original amount 60; new amount 36

2. Original amount 72; new amount 54

3. Base $800; percentage $920

4. Base $140; percentage $490

5. New amount $6; original amount, $120

6. New amount $11; original amount, $440

7. Percentage $132; base, $22

8. Percentage $30; base, $45

9. New amount $150; base, $90

10. Percentage $39; original amount, $18

F. Answer each of the following questions.

1. $60 is 30% of what amount?

2. $36 is what percent of 15?

3. What is 0.1% of $3600?

4. 150% of what amount is $270?

5. $\frac{1}{2}$% of $612 is what amount?

6. 250% of what amount is $300?

7. 80 is 40% of what amount?

8. $120 is what percent of $60?

9. What is $\frac{1}{8}$% of $880?

10. $180 is what percent of $450?

11. $600 is 250% of what amount?

12. 25% of what amount is $28?

13. What percent of $70 is $350?

14. $90 is 30% of what amount?

15. 350% of what amount is $1050?

16. What is $\frac{1}{5}$% of $1200?

G. Answer each of the following questions.

1. The price of a product was reduced by 40%. If the original price was $70, what was the amount by which the price was reduced?

2. Labour content in an article is $37\frac{1}{2}$% of total cost. How much is the labour cost if the total cost is $72?

3. If waste is normally 6% of the material used in a production process, how much of $25 000 worth of material will be wasted?

4. If total deductions on a yearly salary of $18 600 amounted to $16\frac{2}{3}$%, how much was deducted?

5. If the actual sales of $40 500 for last month were 90% of the budgeted sales, how much was the sales budget for the month?

6. The Canada Pension Plan premium deducted from an employee's wages was $4.86. If the premium rate is 1.8% of gross wages, how much were the employee's gross wages?

7. A town's current population is 54 000. If this is 120% of the population five years ago, what was the town's population then?

8. A property was sold for 300% of what the vendor originally paid. If the vendor sold the property for $180 000, how much did he originally pay for the property?

4.5 Problems involving increase or decrease

A. Percent change

Problems involving a *change* (increase or decrease) are identifiable by such phrases as

"is 20% *more than*", "is 40% *less than*",
"is *increased by* 150%", "is *decreased by* 30%".

The amount of change is to be added in the case of an increase or subtracted in the case of a decrease from the *original number* (*base*) and is usually stated as a percent of the original number.

The existing relationship may be stated as

ORIGINAL NUMBER $\begin{array}{c} + \text{ INCREASE} \\ - \text{ DECREASE} \end{array}$ = NEW NUMBER ⟵ *Formula* **4.3**

where the change (increase or decrease) is understood to be a *percent of the original number*.

***Example* 4.5a**   Answer each of the following questions.

(i) 36 increased by 25% is what number?

   Solution

   The original number is 36; ⟵
   the change (increase) is 25% of 36. ⟵ $\left\{ \begin{array}{l} \text{in such problems the} \\ \text{change is a percent} \\ \text{of the original number} \end{array} \right.$
   Since the original number is known,
   let the new number be represented by x.

$$36 + 25\% \text{ of } 36 = x$$

$$36 + \frac{1}{4} \times (36) = x$$

$$36 + 9 = x$$

$$x = 45$$

   The number is 45.

(ii) What number is 40% less than 75?

   Solution

   The change (decrease) is 40% of 75.
   The original number is 75.
   Let the new number be represented by x.

$$75 - 40\% \text{ of } 75 = x$$

$$75 - 0.40 \times 75 = x$$

$$75 - 30 = x$$

$$x = 45$$

   The number is 45.

(iii) How much is $160 increased by 250%?

Solution

The increase is 250% of $160 and
the original number is $160.
Let the new amount be x.

$$160 + 250\% \text{ of } 160 = x$$
$$160 + 2.50 \times 160 = x$$
$$160 + 400 = x$$
$$x = 560$$

The amount is $560.

B. Finding the rate of increase or decrease

This type of problem is indicated by such phrases as
(a) ''20 is what percent *more than* 15?'', or
(b) ''What percent *less than* 96 is 72?''
In (a) the increase, which is the difference between 15, the original number, and 20, the number after the increase, is to be compared to the original number 15.

$$\text{The rate of increase} = \tfrac{5}{15} = \tfrac{1}{3} = 33\tfrac{1}{3}\%.$$

In (b) the decrease, which is the difference between 96, the number before the decrease (the original number), and 72, the number after the decrease, is to be expressed as a percent of the original number.

$$\text{The rate of decrease} = \tfrac{24}{96} = \tfrac{1}{4} = 25\%.$$

In more generalized form, the problem statement is:

$$\text{''}y \text{ is what percent } \begin{Bmatrix} \text{more} \\ \text{less} \end{Bmatrix} \text{ than } x?\text{''}$$

This means the difference between x, the number before the change (original number), and y, the number after the change, is to be expressed as a percent of the original number.

$$\boxed{\text{RATE OF CHANGE} = \frac{\text{AMOUNT OF CHANGE}}{\text{ORIGINAL NUMBER}}} \longleftarrow \textbf{\textit{Formula 4.4}}$$

Example 4.5b Answer each of the following questions.

(i) $425 is what percent more than $125?

Solution

The amount before the change (original number) is $125.
The change (increase) = 425 − 125 = $300.

$$\text{Rate of Increase} = \frac{\text{Amount of Increase}}{\text{Original Amount}}$$

$$= \frac{300}{125} = 2.40 = 240\%$$

(ii) What percent less than $210 is $175?

Solution

The amount before the decrease is $210.
The decrease is 210 − 175 = $35.

$$\text{Rate of Decrease} = \frac{35}{210} = \frac{1}{6} = 0.16\frac{2}{3} = 16\frac{2}{3}\%$$

C. Finding the original amount

If the quantity *after* the change has taken place is known, the quantity *before* the change (the original quantity) may be found by using the relationship stated in Formula 4.3.

Example 4.5c Answer each of the following questions.

(i) 88 is 60% more than what number?

Solution

88 is the number after the increase;
the number before the increase in unknown.
Let the original number be x;
then the increase is 60% of x.

$$x + 60\% \text{ of } x = 88 \longleftarrow \text{using Formula 4.3}$$

$$x + 0.6x = 88$$

$$1.6x = 88$$

$$x = \frac{88}{1.6}$$

$$x = 55$$

The original number is 55.

(ii) 75 is 40% less than what number?

Solution

75 is the number after the decrease.
Let the original number be x;
then the decrease is 40% of x.

$$x - 40\% \text{ of } x = 75$$
$$x - 0.4x = 75$$
$$0.6x = 75$$
$$x = \frac{75}{0.6}$$
$$x = 125$$

The original number is 125.

(iii) What sum of money increased by 175% amounts to \$143?

Solution

\$143 is the amount after the increase.
Let the original sum of money be \$$x$;
then the increase is 175% of x.

$$x + 175\% \text{ of } x = 143$$
$$x + 1.75x = 143$$
$$2.75x = 143$$
$$x = \frac{143}{2.75}$$
$$x = 52$$

The original amount is \$52.

(iv) What sum of money when diminished by $33\frac{1}{3}\%$ is \$48?

Solution

\$48 is the amount after the decrease.
Let the original sum of money be \$$x$;
then the decrease is $33\frac{1}{3}\%$ of x.

$$x - 33\frac{1}{3}\% \text{ of } x = 48$$
$$x - \frac{1}{3}x = 48$$
$$\frac{2}{3}x = 48$$

$$x = \frac{48 \times 3}{2}$$

$$x = 72$$

The original sum of money is $72.

Exercise 4.5

A. Answer each of the following questions.

   1. What is 120 increased by 40%?

   2. What is 900 decreased by 20%?

   3. How much is $1200 decreased by 5%?

   4. How much is $24 increased by 200%?

   5. What number is $83\frac{1}{3}\%$ more than 48?

   6. What amount is $16\frac{2}{3}\%$ less than $66?

B. Find the rate of change for each of the following.

   1. What percent more than 30 is 45?

   2. What percent less than $90 is $72?

   3. $240 is what percent more than $80?

   4. $110 is what percent less than $165?

   5. What percent less than $300 is $294?

   6. $2025 is what percent more than $2000?

C. Answer each of the following questions.

   1. 24 is 25% less than what number?

   2. 605 is $37\frac{1}{2}\%$ more than what number?

   3. What amount increased by 150% will equal $325?

   4. What sum of money decreased by $16\frac{2}{3}\%$ will equal $800?

   5. After deducting 5% from a sum of money the remainder is $4.18. What was the original sum of money?

   6. After an increase of 7% the new amount was $749. What was the original amount?

4.6 Applications

A. Summary of useful relationships

Problems involving percents abound in the field of business. The terminology used varies depending on the nature of the situation. However, most problems can be solved by means of the two basic relationships.

$$\boxed{\text{RATE} \times \text{ORIGINAL AMOUNT} = \text{NEW AMOUNT}} \longleftarrow \text{\textit{Formula} \textbf{4.1}}$$

and

$$\boxed{\text{ORIGINAL AMOUNT} \begin{array}{l} +\left[\text{INCREASE}\right. \\ -\left[\text{DECREASE}\right. \end{array} = \text{NEW AMOUNT}} \longleftarrow \text{\textit{Formula} \textbf{4.3}}$$

or, in case of finding a rate percent, by means of the formulae

$$\boxed{\text{RATE} = \frac{\text{NEW AMOUNT}}{\text{ORIGINAL AMOUNT}}} \longleftarrow \text{\textit{Formula} \textbf{4.2}}$$

and

$$\boxed{\text{RATE OF CHANGE} = \frac{\text{AMOUNT OF CHANGE}}{\text{ORIGINAL AMOUNT}}} \longleftarrow \text{\textit{Formula} \textbf{4.4}}$$

B. Problems involving the computation of a rate percent

Example 4.6a Solve each of the following problems.

(i) Material content in a lighting fixture is $40. If the total cost of the fixture is $48, what percent of cost is the material cost?

Solution

$$\frac{\text{MATERIAL COST}}{\text{TOTAL COST}} = \frac{40}{48} = \frac{5}{6} = 83\frac{1}{3}\%$$

(ii) A cash discount of $3.60 was allowed on an invoice of $120.00. What was the rate of discount?

Solution

$$\text{Rate of Discount} = \frac{\text{AMOUNT OF DISCOUNT}}{\text{INVOICE AMOUNT}}$$

$$= \frac{3.60}{120.00} = \frac{360}{12000} = \frac{3}{100} = 3\%$$

(iii) What percent increase did an employee receive if the monthly salary rose from $800 to $920?

Solution

Salary before the increase (original salary) is $800;
the raise is 920 − 800 = $120.

$$\text{Rate of Increase} = \frac{\text{AMOUNT OF INCREASE}}{\text{ORIGINAL SALARY}}$$

$$= \frac{120}{800} = 0.15 = 15\%$$

(iv) Expenditures for a government program were reduced from $75 000 to $60 000. What percent change does this represent?

Solution

Expenditure before the change is $75 000;
the change (decrease) = 75000 − 60000 = $15000.

$$\text{Rate of change} = \frac{\text{AMOUNT OF CHANGE}}{\text{ORIGINAL AMOUNT}}$$

$$= \frac{15000}{75000} = 0.20 = 20\%$$

Expenditures were reduced by 20%.

C. Problems involving the basic percentage relationship

Example **4.6b** Solve each of the following problems.

(i) Sales for this year are budgeted at $112\frac{1}{2}\%$ of last year's sales of $360 000. What is the sales budget for this year?

Solution

This year's sales = $112\frac{1}{2}\%$ of 360 000

$$= \frac{9}{8} \times 360000$$

$$= 9 \times 45000$$

$$= 405000$$

Budgeted sales for the year are $405 000.

(ii) A commission of $300 was paid to a broker's agent for the sale of a bond. If the commission was $\frac{3}{4}\%$ of the sale value of the bond, for how much was the bond sold?

Solution

$$\text{Commission Paid} = \frac{3}{4}\% \text{ of the bond sale}$$

$$300 = \frac{3}{4}\% \text{ of } x$$

$$300 = \frac{3}{400}x$$

$$x = \frac{300 \times 400}{3}$$

$$x = 40000$$

The bond was sold for $40 000.

(iii) Based on past experience a credit union estimates uncollectible loans at $1\frac{1}{4}\%$ of the total loan balances outstanding. If at the end of March the loan account shows a balance of $3 248 000, how much should the credit union have in the provision for uncollectible loans at the end of March?

Solution

$$\text{Provision for Uncollectible Loans} = 1\frac{1}{4}\% \text{ of } 3248000$$

$$1\% \text{ of } 3248000 \longrightarrow \$32480$$

$$\frac{1}{4} \text{ of } 1\% \text{ of } 3248000 \longrightarrow \underline{\quad 8120}$$

$$1\frac{1}{4}\% \text{ of } 3248000 \longrightarrow \$40600$$

The credit union should have a provision of $40 600 for uncollectible loans by the end of March.

(iv) The consumer price index in July of this year was 225 or 180% of the index ten years ago. What was the index ten years ago?

Solution

$$\text{This year's index} = 180\% \text{ of the index ten years ago}$$

$$225 = 180\% \text{ of } x$$

$$225 = 1.80x$$

$$x = \frac{225}{1.8}$$

$$x = 125$$

The index ten years ago was 125.

D. Problems of increase or decrease

Example 4.6c Solve each of the following problems.

(i) Daily car loadings for August were 5% more than for July. If August car loadings were 76 020 what were the July car loadings?

Solution

The chronologically earlier July car loadings are the original number and are not known. Let them be represented by x.

$$x + 5\% \text{ of } x = 76020$$
$$x + 0.05x = 76020$$
$$1.05x = 76020$$
$$x = \frac{76020}{1.05}$$
$$x = 72400$$

Car loadings in July numbered 72 400.

(ii) The trading price of a mining stock dropped 40% to $7.20. Determine the trading price before the drop.

Solution

The trading price before the drop is the original value and is not known. Let it be represented by $x.

$$x - 40\% \text{ of } x = 7.20$$
$$x - 0.4x = 7.20$$
$$0.6x = 7.20$$
$$x = \frac{7.20}{0.6}$$
$$x = 12.00$$

The trading price before the drop was $12.00.

(iii) Dorian Guy sold his house for $149 500. If he sold the house for $187\frac{1}{2}\%$ more than what he paid for it, how much did he gain?

Solution

The base for the percent gain is the original amount paid for the house. Since this amount is not known let it be represented by $x.

ORIGINAL AMOUNT PAID + GAIN = SELLING PRICE

$$x + 187\tfrac{1}{2}\% \text{ of } x = 149500$$

$$x + 1.875x = 149500$$

$$2.875x = 149500$$

$$x = \frac{149500}{2.875}$$

$$x = 52000$$

The amount originally paid was $52 000.
Gain = 149 500 − 52 000 = $97 500.

(iv) The amount paid for an article, including 7% sales tax, was $100.58. How much was the marked price of the article?

Solution

The unknown marked price, represented by $x, is the base for the sales tax.

MARKED PRICE + SALES TAX = AMOUNT PAID

$$x + 7\% \text{ of } x = 100.58$$

$$x + 0.07x = 100.58$$

$$1.07x = 100.58$$

$$x = \frac{100.58}{1.07}$$

$$x = 94.00$$

The marked price of the article is $94.00.

(v) After taking off a discount of 5%, a retailer settled an invoice by paying $532.00. How much was the amount of the discount?

Solution

The unknown amount of the invoice, represented by $x, is the base for the discount.

AMOUNT OF INVOICE − DISCOUNT = AMOUNT PAID

$$x − 5\% \text{ of } x = 532$$

$$x − 0.05x = 532$$

$$0.95x = 532$$

$$x = 560$$

Discount = 5% of 560 = 0.05 × 560 = $28.00.

Exercise 4.6

A. Solve each of the following problems.

1. Of a company's 1200 employees $2\frac{1}{4}\%$ did not report to work last Friday. How many employees were absent?

2. A storekeeper bought merchandise for $1575. If she sells the merchandise at $33\frac{1}{3}\%$ above cost, how much gross profit does she make?

3. A clerk whose salary was $280 per week was given a raise of $35 per week. What percent increase did the clerk receive?

4. Your hydro bill for March is $174.40. If you pay after the due date a late payment penalty of $8.72 is added. What is the percent penalty?

5. A salesman receives a commission of $16\frac{2}{3}\%$ on all sales. How much must his weekly sales be so that he will make a commission of $720 per week?

6. A financial collection agency retains a collection fee of 25% of any amounts collected. How much did the agency collect on a bad debt if the agency forwarded $2490 to a client?

7. A commercial building is insured under a fire policy whose face value is 80% of the building's appraised value. The annual insurance premium is $\frac{3}{8}\%$ and the premium for one year amounts to $675.

(a) What is the face value of the policy?

(b) What is the appraised value of the building?

8. A residential property is assessed for tax purposes at 40% of its market value. The residential property tax rate is $3\frac{1}{3}\%$ of the assessed value and the tax is $1200.

(a) What is the assessed value of the property?

(b) What is the market value of the property?

B. Solve each of the following problems.

1. A merchant bought an article for $7.92. For how much did the article sell if he sold the article at an increase of $83\frac{1}{3}\%$?

2. A retailer is offered a discount of $2\frac{1}{2}\%$ for payment in cash of an invoice of $840. If the retailer accepted the offer, how much was the cash payment?

3. From March 1971 to March 1981 the price of gasoline increased 220%. If the price in 1971 was 10.5 cents per litre, what was the price per litre in 1981?

4. A ski shop reduced its selling price on a pair of skis by $33\frac{1}{3}\%$. If the regular selling price was $225 what was the reduced price?

5. The 7% sales tax on a pair of shoes amounted to $5.18. What was the total amount paid by the buyer?

6. Miss Daisy pays $37\frac{1}{2}\%$ of her monthly gross salary as rent on a townhouse. If the monthly rent is $660, what is her monthly salary?

7. The annual interest on a bond is $12\frac{1}{2}\%$ of its face value and amounts to $625. What is the face of the bond?

8. A broker charges a fee of $2\frac{1}{4}\%$. If his fee on a stock purchase was $432, what was the amount of the purchase?

9. A wage earner's hourly rate of pay was increased from $9.60 to $10.32. What was the percent raise?

10. Profit last quarter decreased from $6540 in the previous quarter to $1090. What was the percent decrease in profit?

11. A property purchased for $42 000 is now appraised at $178 500. What is the percent gain in the value of the property?

12. A financial institution reduced its annual lending rate from 20% to 19.75%. What is the percent reduction in the lending rate?

13. After a reduction of $33\frac{1}{3}\%$ of the marked price an article was sold for $64.46. What was the marked price?

14. A special purpose index has increased 125% during the last ten years. If the index now is 279, what was the index ten years ago?

15. After a cash discount of 5% an invoice was settled by a payment of $646. What was the invoice amount?

16. Sales in May increased $16\frac{2}{3}\%$ over April sales. If May sales amounted to $24 535, what were the April sales?

17. The working capital at the end of the third quarter was 75% higher than at the end of the second quarter. What was the amount of working capital at the end of the second quarter if the working capital at the end of the third quarter was $78 400?

18. Employee compensation expense for August including 4% vacation pay was $23 400. How much was the amount of vacation pay expense?

19. After real estate fees of 8% had been deducted from the proceeds of the sale of a property, the vendor of the property received $88 090. What was the amount of the fee retained by the realtor?

20. A car was sold for $8862 including 5% sales tax. How much was the sales tax on the car?

Review exercise

1. Set up ratios to compare each of the following sets of quantities and reduce each ratio to its lowest terms.

(a) 25 dimes and three dollars

(b) five hours to 50 min.

(c) $6.75 for thirty litres of gasoline

(d) $21 for three and a half hours

(e) 1440 words for 120 lines for 6 pages

(f) 90 kg for 24 hectares for 18 weeks

2. Solve each of the following proportions.

(a) $5:n = 35:21$

(b) $10:6 = 30:x$

(c) $1.15:0.85 = k:1.19$

(d) $3.60:m = 10.8:8.10$

(e) $\dfrac{5}{7}:\dfrac{15}{14} = \dfrac{6}{5}:t$

(f) $y:\dfrac{9}{8} = \dfrac{5}{4}:\dfrac{45}{64}$

3. Change each of the following percents into a decimal.

(a) 185%

(b) 7.5%

(c) 0.4%

(d) 0.025%

(e) $1\dfrac{1}{4}\%$

(f) $\dfrac{3}{4}\%$

(g) $162\dfrac{1}{2}\%$

(h) $11\dfrac{3}{4}\%$

(i) $8\dfrac{1}{3}\%$

(j) $83\dfrac{1}{3}\%$

(k) $266\dfrac{2}{3}\%$

(l) $10\dfrac{3}{8}\%$

4. Change each of the following percents into a common fraction in lowest terms.

(a) 50%

(b) $37\dfrac{1}{2}\%$

(c) $16\dfrac{2}{3}\%$

(d) $166\dfrac{2}{3}\%$

(e) $\dfrac{1}{2}\%$

(f) 7.5%

(g) 0.75%

(h) $\dfrac{5}{8}\%$

5. Express each of the following as a percent.

(a) 2.25

(b) 0.02

(c) 0.009

(d) 0.1275

(e) $\dfrac{5}{4}$

(f) $\dfrac{11}{8}$

(g) $\dfrac{5}{200}$

(h) $\dfrac{7}{25}$

6. Compute each of the following

(a) 150% of 140

(b) 3% of 240

(c) $9\dfrac{3}{4}\%$ of 2000

(d) 0.9% of 400

7. Use fractional equivalents to compute each of the following.

(a) $66\dfrac{2}{3}\%$ of \$168

(b) $37\dfrac{1}{2}\%$ of \$2480

(c) 125% of \$924

(d) $183\dfrac{1}{3}\%$ of \$720

8. Use the 1% method to determine each of the following.

(a) $\dfrac{1}{4}\%$ of \$2664

(b) $\dfrac{5}{8}\%$ of \$1328

(c) $1\dfrac{2}{3}\%$ of \$5400

(d) $2\dfrac{1}{5}\%$ of \$1260

9. Answer each of the following questions.

   (a) What is the rate percent if the base is 88 and the percentage is 55?

   (b) 63 is what percent of 36?

   (c) What is $\frac{3}{4}$% of $64.00?

   (d) 450% of $5.00 is what amount?

   (e) $245 is $87\frac{1}{2}$% of what amount?

   (f) $2\frac{1}{4}$% of what amount is $9.90?

   (g) What percent of $62.50 is $1.25?

   (h) $30 is what percent of $6?

   (i) $166\frac{2}{3}$% of what amount is $220?

   (j) $1.35 is $\frac{1}{3}$% of what amount?

10. Answer each of the following questions.

   (a) How much is $8 increased by 125%?

   (b) What amount is $2\frac{1}{4}$% less than $2000?

   (c) What percent less than $120 is $100?

   (d) $975 is what percent more than $150?

   (e) $98 is 75% more than what amount?

   (f) After a reduction of 15% the amount paid was $289. What was the price before the reduction?

   (g) What sum of money increased by 250% will amount to $490?

11. D, E and F owned a business jointly and shared profits and losses in proportion of their investments. How much of a profit of $4500 will each receive if their investment were $4000, $6000 and $5000 respectively?

12. Departments A, B and C occupy floor space of $80m^2$, $140m^2$ and $160m^2$ respectively. If the total rental cost for the floor space is $11 400 per month, how much of the rental cost should be borne by each department?

13. Four beneficiaries are to divide an estate of $189 000 in the ratio $\frac{1}{3}:\frac{1}{4}:\frac{3}{8}:\frac{1}{24}$. How much should each receive?

14. Three insurance companies have insured a building in the ratio $\frac{1}{2}$ to $\frac{1}{3}$ to $\frac{2}{5}$. How much of a fire loss of $185 000 should each company pay?

15. A hot water tank with a capacity of 220 L can be heated in twenty minutes. At the same rate, how many minutes will it take to heat a tank containing 176 L?

16. If the variable cost amounts to $130 000 when sales are $250 000, what should variable cost amount to when sales are $350 000?

17. Gross profit for April was two-fifths of net sales, and net income was two-sevenths of gross profit. Net income was $4200.

(a) What was the gross profit for April?

(b) What were net sales for April?

18. In a college $\frac{4}{9}$ of all employees are faculty and the ratio of faculty to support staff is 5:4. How many people does the college employ if the support staff numbers 192?

19. At the last municipal election $62\frac{1}{2}\%$ of the population of 94 800 were eligible to vote, and of those eligible $33\frac{1}{3}\%$ voted.

(a) What was the number of eligible voters?

(b) How many voted?

20. An investment portfolio of $150 000 consists of the following: $37\frac{1}{2}\%$ in bonds, $56\frac{1}{4}\%$ in common stock and the remainder in preferred shares. How much money is invested in each type of investment security?

21. A salesman's orders for May were $16\frac{2}{3}\%$ less than his April orders which amounted to $51 120.

(a) How much were the salesman's orders in May?

(b) By what amount did his orders decrease?

22. The value of a property has increased $233\frac{1}{3}\%$ since it was purchased by the present owner. The cost of the property was $120 000.

(a) How much is the appraised value?

(b) How much would the owner gain by selling at the appraised value?

23. The direct material cost of manufacturing a product was $103.95, direct labour cost was $46.20 and overhead was $57.75.

(a) What is the percent content of each element of cost in the product?

(b) What is the overhead percent rate based on direct labour?

24. Inspection of a production run of 2400 items showed that 180 items did not meet specifications. Of the 180 items that did not pass inspection 150 could be reworked. The remainder had to be scrapped.

(a) What percent of the production run did not pass inspection?

(b) What percent of the items that did not meet specifications had to be scrapped?

25. The price of a stock a week ago was $56.25 per share. Today the price per share is $51.75.

(a) What is the percent change in price?

(b) What is the new price as a percent of the old price?

26. A wage earner's hourly rate of pay increased from $6.30 to $16.80 during the last decade.

(a) What has been the percent change in the hourly rate of pay?

(b) What is the current rate of pay as a percent of the rate a decade ago?

27. A firm's bad debts of \$7875 were $2\frac{1}{4}\%$ of sales. What were the firm's sales?

28. A ski shop lists ski boots at 240% of cost. If the DX2 Model is marked by the ski shop at \$396.00, what was the cost of the ski boot to the dealer?

29. A property owner listed his property for 160% more than he paid for it. The owner eventually accepted an offer $12\frac{1}{2}\%$ below his asking price and sold the property for \$191 100. For how much did the owner buy the property?

30. A marina listed a yacht at $33\frac{1}{3}\%$ above cost. At the end of the season the list price was reduced by 22.5% and the yacht was sold for \$15 500. What was the cost of the yacht to the marina?

31. A & E Holdings' profit and loss statement showed a net income of $9\frac{3}{4}\%$ or \$29 250. 20% of net income was paid in corporation tax and 75% of the net income after tax was paid out as dividend to A and E who hold shares in the ratio 5 to 3.

 (a) What was the revenue of A & E Holdings?

 (b) How much was the after tax income?

 (c) How much was paid out in dividend?

 (d) What percent of net income did A receive as dividend?

32. A farm was offered for sale at 350% above cost. The farm was finally sold at $8\frac{1}{3}\%$ below the asking price for \$330 000.

 (a) What was the original cost of the farm to the owner?

 (b) How much gain did the owner realize?

 (c) What percent gain does this represent?

Self-test

1. Compute each of the following.

 (a) 125% of \$280

 (b) $\frac{3}{8}\%$ of \$20280

 (c) $83\frac{1}{3}\%$ of \$174

 (d) $1\frac{1}{4}\%$ of \$1056

2. Solve each of the following proportions.

 (a) $65 : 39 = x : 12$

 (b) $\frac{7}{6} : \frac{35}{12} = \frac{6}{5} : x$

3. Change each of the following percents into a decimal.

(a) 175%

(b) $\frac{3}{8}\%$

4. Change each of the following percents into a common fraction in lowest terms.

(a) $2\frac{1}{2}\%$

(b) $116\frac{2}{3}\%$

5. Express each of the following as a percent.

(a) 1.125

(b) $\frac{9}{400}$

6. The results of a market survey indicated that 24 respondents preferred Brand X, 36 preferred Brand Y and 20 had no preference. What percent of the sample preferred Brand Y?

7. Departments A, B and C occupy floor space of 40, 80 and 300 square metres respectively. If the total rental for the space is $25 200 per month, how much rent should be paid by Department B?

8. Past experience indicates that the clientele of a restaurant spends $9.60 on beverages for every $12.00 spent on food. If it is expected that food sales will amount to $12 500 for a month, how much should be budgeted for beverage sales?

9. After a reduction of $16\frac{2}{3}\%$ of the marked price, an article sold for $60.00. What was the marked price?

10. A bonus is to be divided among four employees in the ratio $\frac{1}{2} : \frac{1}{3} : \frac{1}{5} : \frac{1}{6}$. What is each employee's share of a bonus of $40 500?

11. A wage earner's hourly rate of pay was increased from $11.00 to $12.54. What was the percent raise?

12. An article was sold for $265.00. The selling price included a sales tax of 6%. Find the amount of sales tax on the article.

13. An article originally advertised at $220.00 is reduced to $209.00 during a sale. By what percent was the price reduced?

14. A special consumer index has increased 100% during the last 10 years. If the index is now 360, what was it 10 years ago?

15. Mr. Braid owned $\frac{3}{8}$ of a store. He sold $\frac{2}{3}$ of his interest in the store for $18 000. What was the value of the store?

Summary of formulae used

Formula 4.1.

$$\text{PERCENTAGE} = \text{RATE} \times \text{BASE}$$

Or

$$\text{NEW NUMBER} = \text{RATE} \times \text{ORIGINAL NUMBER}$$

the basic percentage relationship

Formula 4.2

$$\text{RATE} = \frac{\text{PERCENTAGE}}{\text{BASE}} \quad \text{or} \quad \frac{\text{NEW NUMBER}}{\text{ORIGINAL NUMBER}}$$

formula for finding the rate percent when comparing a number (the percentage) to another number (the base or original number)

Formula 4.3

$$\text{ORIGINAL NUMBER} \pm \left\{ \begin{array}{c} \text{INCREASE} \\ \text{DECREASE} \end{array} \right\} = \begin{array}{c} \text{NEW} \\ \text{NUMBER} \end{array}$$

the relationship which is useful in dealing with problems of increase or decrease (problems of change)

Formula 4.4

$$\text{RATE OF CHANGE} = \frac{\text{AMOUNT OF CHANGE}}{\text{ORIGINAL NUMBER}}$$

formula for finding the rate of change (rate of increase or decrease)

Glossary of terms used

Cross-multiplication a short-cut method for solving proportions

Equivalent ratios in higher terms ratios obtained by multiplying each term of a ratio by the same number

Percent a special form of writing a ratio whose second term is 100; a common fraction whose denominator is 100

Proportion a statement of equality between two ratios

Ratio a comparison of the relative values of numbers or quantities by division

Terms of a ratio the numbers appearing in a ratio

5 *Linear systems*

Introduction

In many types of problems the relationship between two or more variables may be represented by setting up linear equations or linear inequalities. Graphical as well as algebraic techniques are available to solve such problems.

Objectives

Upon completion of this chapter you will be able to

1. graph linear equations in two variables in a set of rectangular coordinates;
2. graph linear inequalities in two variables in a set of rectangular coordinates;
3. graph linear systems consisting of two or three linear relations in two variables;
4. solve linear systems consisting of two simultaneous equations in two variables using the method of elimination by addition or subtraction;
5. solve linear systems consisting of three simultaneous equations in three variables using the method of elimination by addition or subtraction;
6. solve problems by setting up systems of linear equations in two or three variables.

5.1   *Graphing linear equations*

A.   *Graphing in a system of rectangular coordinates*

A system of rectangular coordinates, as shown in Figure 5.1 below, consists of two straight lines which intersect at right angles in a plane. The *horizontal* line is called the **X axis** while the *vertical* line is called the **Y axis**. The point of intersection of the two axes is called the **origin**.

FIGURE 5.1 *Rectangular coordinates*

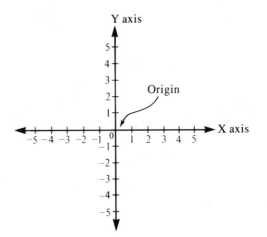

The two axes are used as number lines. By agreement, on the X axis the numbers are positive to the right of the origin and negative to the left. On the Y axis the numbers are positive above the origin and negative below the origin.

The position of any point relative to the pair of axes is defined by an *ordered pair* of numbers (x,y) such that the first number (the x value or **X coordinate**) always represents the directed distance of the point from the Y axis. The second number (the y value or **Y coordinate**) always represents the directed distance of the point from the X axis.

The origin is identified by the ordered pair $(0,0)$; that is, the coordinates of the origin are $(0,0)$ since the distance of the point from either axis is zero.

As shown in Figure 5.2 below, the point marked A is identified by the

FIGURE 5.2 *Locating a point*

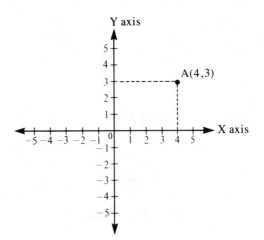

Mathematics fundamentals

coordinates (4,3) since the directed distance of the point is four units to the right of the Y axis, (its x value (x coordinate) is +4) and the directed distance of the point is three units above the X axis (its y coordinate is +3). Note that the point may be located by counting four units to the right along the X axis and then moving three units up parallel to the Y axis.

Example 5.1a Determine the coordinates of the points A, B, C, D, E, F, G and H as marked in the following diagram.

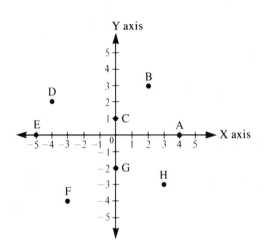

Solution

POINT	COORDINATES	
A	(4, 0)	← 4 units to the right of the origin (x = 4) on the X axis (y = 0)
B	(2, 3)	← 2 units to the right (x = 2) and 3 units up (y = 3)
C	(0, 1)	← on the Y axis (x = 0) 1 unit up (y = 1)
D	(−4, 2)	← 4 units to the left (x = −4) and 2 units up (y = 2)
E	(−5, 0)	← 5 units to the left (x = −5) on the X axis (y = 0)
F	(−3, −4)	← 3 units to the left (x = −3) and 4 units down (y = −4)
G	(0, −2)	← on the Y axis (x = 0) 2 units down (y = −2)
H	(3, −3)	← 3 units to the right (x = 3) and 3 units down (y = −3)

In order to draw the graphs of linear relations, two or more points must be plotted in a set of rectangular axes. To *plot* a Point (x, y) count the number of units represented by x along the X axis (to the right if x is positive or to the left if x is negative) and then count the number of units represented by y up or down (up if y is positive, down if y is negative).

Example 5.1b   Plot the following points in a set of rectangular axes.

(i) $A(-3, 4)$ (ii) $B(2, -4)$

(iii) $C(-4, -4)$ (iv) $D(3, 3)$

(v) $E(-3, 0)$ (vi) $F(0, -2)$

Solution

(i) To plot Point A count 3 units to the left (x is negative) and 4 units up (y is positive).

(ii) To plot Point B count 2 units to the right (x is positive) and 4 units down (y is negative).

(iii) To plot Point C count 4 units to the left and 4 units down.

(iv) To plot Point D count 3 units to the right and 3 units up.

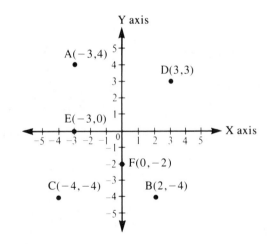

(v) To plot Point E count 3 units to the left and mark the point on the X axis since $y = 0$.

(vi) To plot Point F count 2 units down and mark the point on the Y axis since $x = 0$.

B. Constructing a table of values

Linear equations may be graphed by plotting a set of points whose coordinates *satisfy* the equation and then joining the points.

A suitable set of points may be obtained by constructing a table of values. This is done by substituting arbitrarily chosen values of x or y in the equation and computing the value of the second variable. The value chosen and the corresponding computed value form an ordered pair (x, y). A listing of such ordered pairs forms a table of values.

Example 5.1c   Construct a table of values for

(i) $x = 2y$ for integral values of y from $y = +3$ to $y = -3$;

(ii) $y = 2x - 3$ for integral values of x from $x = -2$ to $x = +4$.

Solution

(i) To obtain the desired ordered pairs substitute assumed values of y into the equation $x = 2y$.

$$y = +3 \longrightarrow x = 2(3) = 6$$
$$y = +2 \longrightarrow x = 2(2) = 4$$
$$y = +1 \longrightarrow x = 2(1) = 2$$
$$y = 0 \longrightarrow x = 2(0) = 0$$
$$y = -1 \longrightarrow x = 2(-1) = -2$$
$$y = -2 \longrightarrow x = 2(-2) = -4$$
$$y = -3 \longrightarrow x = 2(-3) = -6$$

A listing of the values obtained in the form of ordered pairs gives the following table of values.

x	6	4	2	0	-2	-4	-6	$\longleftarrow$ corresponding computed x values
y	3	2	1	0	-1	-2	-3	$\longleftarrow$ chosen y values

(ii) To obtain the desired ordered pairs substitute assumed values of x into the equation $y = 2x - 3$.

$$x = -2 \longrightarrow y = 2(-2) - 3 = -4 - 3 = -7$$
$$x = -1 \longrightarrow y = 2(-1) - 3 = -2 - 3 = -5$$
$$x = 0 \longrightarrow y = 2(0) - 3 = 0 - 3 = -3$$
$$x = 1 \longrightarrow y = 2(1) - 3 = 2 - 3 = -1$$
$$x = 2 \longrightarrow y = 2(2) - 3 = 4 - 3 = +1$$
$$x = 3 \longrightarrow y = 2(3) - 3 = 6 - 3 = +3$$
$$x = 4 \longrightarrow y = 2(4) - 3 = 8 - 3 = +5$$

Table of values

x	-2	-1	0	1	2	3	4
y	-7	-5	-3	-1	1	3	5

←——— chosen x values

←——— corresponding computed y values

Guidelines for constructing a table of values

1. Values may be chosen arbitrarily for either x or y.
2. The values chosen are usually integers.
3. Preferred are those integers that yield an integer for the computed value.

Example 5.1d Construct a table of values for the equation $3x - 2y = -3$ consisting of five ordered pairs (x,y) such that x and y are integers.

Solution

(i) $y = 0$
$$3x - 2(0) = -3$$
$$3x = -3$$
$$x = -1$$

(ii) $x = 1$
$$3(1) - 2y = -3$$
$$-2y = -6$$
$$y = 3$$

(iii) $y = -3$
$$3x - 2(-3) = -3$$
$$3x = -9$$
$$x = -3$$

(iv) $x = 3$
$$3(3) - 2y = -3$$
$$-2y = -12$$
$$y = 6$$

(v) $x = -5$
$$-15 - 2y = -3$$
$$-2y = 12$$
$$y = -6$$

Table of Values

x	-5	-3	-1	1	3
y	-6	-3	0	3	6

C. Graphing linear equations

To graph a linear equation a minimum of two points is required, a third point is useful for checking purposes. To graph linear equations

(1) *construct* a table of values consisting of at least two (preferably three) ordered pairs (x,y);
(2) *plot* the points in a system of rectangular axes;
(3) *join* the points by a straight line.

Example 5.1e Graph each of the following equations.

(i) $x + y = 4$ (ii) $x - y = 5$

(iii) $4x + 3y = 12$ (iv) $2x - 3y = -6$

(v) $x = y$ (vi) $y = -2x$

Solution

(i) Equation: $x + y = 4$

Table of Values

x	0	4	2
y	4	0	2

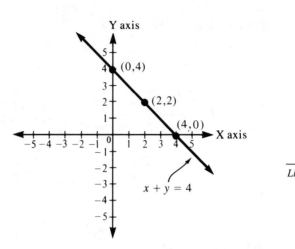

(ii) Equation: $x - y = 5$

Table of Values

x	0	5	3
y	-5	0	-2

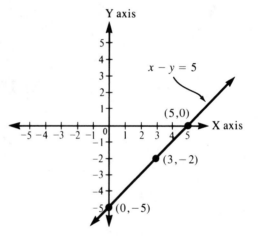

(iii) Equation: $4x + 3y = 12$

Table of Values

x	0	3	6
y	4	0	-4

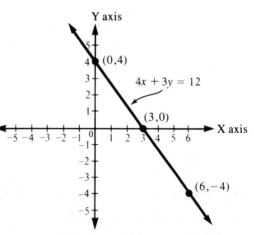

(iv) Equation: $2x - 3y = -6$

Table of Values

x	0	-3	3
y	2	0	4

Mathematics fundamentals

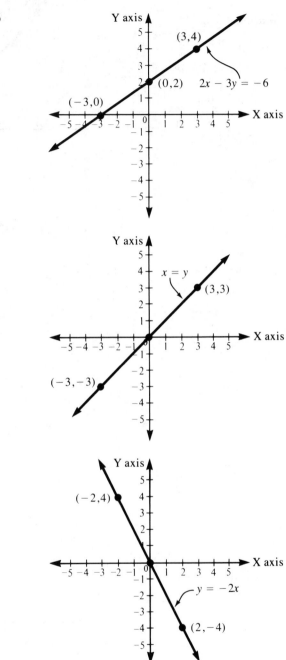

(v) Equation: $x = y$

Table of Values

x	0	3	-3
y	0	3	-3

(vi) Equation: $y = -2x$

Table of Values

x	0	2	-2
y	0	-4	4

D. Special cases—lines parallel to the axes

(a) *Lines Parallel to the X axis*

Lines parallel to the X axis are formed by sets of points all of which have the *same y* coordinates. Such lines are defined by the equation $y = k$ where k may be any real number.

Example 5.1f Graph the lines represented by

(i) $y = 3$;   (ii) $y = -3$.

Solution

(i) The line represented by $y = 3$ is a line parallel to the X axis and three units above it.

(ii) The line represented by $y = -3$ is a line parallel to the X axis and three units below it.

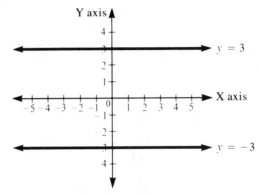

(b) *Lines Parallel to the Y axis*

Lines parallel to the Y axis are formed by sets of points all of which have the *same x* coordinates. Such lines are defined by equation $x = k$ where k may be any real number.

Example 5.1g Graph the lines represented by

(i) $x = 3$ (ii) $x = -3$.

Solution

(i) The line represented by $x = 3$ is a line parallel to the Y axis and three units to the right of it.

(ii) The line represented by $x = -3$ is a line parallel to the Y axis and three units to the left of it.

(c) *The Axes*

    X *axis* The y coordinates of the set of points forming the **X** axis are zero.
    Thus the equation $y = 0$ represents the **X** axis.
    Y *axis* The x coordinates of the set of points forming the **Y** axis are zero.
    Thus the equation $x = 0$ represents the **Y** axis.

Exercise 5.1

A. Do each of the following.

    1. Write the coordinates of the points A, B, C, D, E, F, G and H marked in the diagram below.

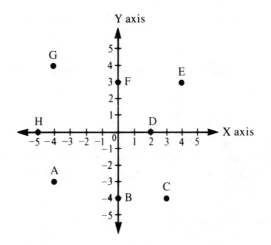

    2. Plot the given sets of points in a system of rectangular axes.

        (a) A$(-4, -5)$, B$(3, -2)$, C$(-3,5)$, D$(0, -4)$, E$(4,1)$, F$(-2,0)$
        (b) K$(4, -2)$, L$(-3,2)$, M$(0,4)$, N$(-2, -4)$, P$(0, -5)$, Q$(-3,0)$

    3. Construct a table of values for each of the following as indicated.

        (a) $x = y - 2$ for integral values of y from -3 to $+5$
        (b) $y = 2x - 1$ for integral values of x from $+3$ to -2
        (c) $y = 2x$ for integral values of x from $+3$ to -3
        (d) $x = -y$ for integral values of y from $+5$ to -5

B. Graph each of the following equations.

    1. $x - y = 3$ **2.** $x + 2y = 4$
    3. $y = -x$ **4.** $x = 2y$
    5. $3x - 4y = 12$ **6.** $2x + 3y = 6$
    7. $y = -4$ **8.** $x = 5$

5.2 Graphing inequalities

A. Basic concepts and method

A straight line drawn in a plane divides the plane into two regions:

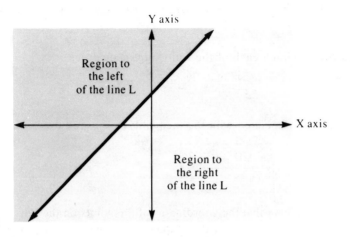

(a) the region to the left of the line drawn in the plane;
(b) the region to the right of the line drawn in the plane.

When a system of axes is introduced into the plane each region consists of a set of points which may be represented by ordered pairs (x,y). Relative to the dividing line, the two sets of ordered pairs (x,y) representing the points in the regions are defined by the two **inequalities** that are associated with the equation of the dividing line.

For the equation $x = 5$ the associated inequalities are $x < 5$ (x is less than 5) and $x > 5$ (x is greater than 5). For the equation $y = -3$ the associated inequalities are $y < -3$ and $y > -3$. For the equation $2x + 3y = 6$ the associated inequalities are $2x + 3y < 6$ and $2x + 3y > 6$.

Graphing an inequality means identifying the region consisting of the set of points whose coordinates satisfy the given inequality. To do this, the following method may be used.

1. *Draw* the graph of the equation associated with the inequality.

2. *Test* an arbitrarily selected point which is not a point on the line by substituting its coordinates in the inequality. The preferred point for testing is (0,0), and if (0,0) is not available because the line passes through the origin, then the points (0,1) or (1,0) are recommended.

3. (a) If substituting the coordinates of the selected point in the inequality yields a mathematical statement that is true, the selected point is a point in the region defined by the inequality. Thus the region is identified as the area containing the selected point.

(b) If substituting the coordinates of the selected point in the inequality yields a mathematical statement that is false, the selected point is not a point in the region defined by the inequality. Thus the region defined by the inequality is the area which does not contain the point tested.

B. Graphing inequalities of the form $ax + by > c$ and $ax + by < c$

Example 5.2a   Graph each of the following inequalities.

(i) $x - y > -3$ (ii) $3x + 2y < -8$

Solution

(i) The equation associated with the inequality $x - y > -3$ is $x - y = -3$.

Table of values	x	0	-3	2
	y	3	0	5

Note   To indicate that the coordinates of the points on the line $x - y = -3$ do not satisfy the inequality, the graph of the equation is drawn as a broken line.

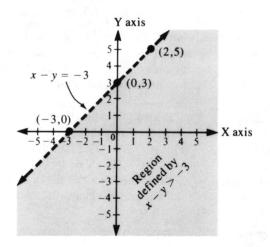

Since the line does not pass through the origin the point $(0,0)$ may be used for testing.

Substituting $x = 0$ and $y = 0$ in the inequality $x - y > -3$ yields the statement

$$0 - 0 > -3$$

$$0 > -3$$

Since the statement $0 > -3$ is true, the point $(0,0)$ is a point in the region.

Hence the region defined by the inequality $x - y > -3$ is the area to the right of the line as shown in the diagram above.

(ii) The equation associated with the inequality $3x + 2y < -8$ is $3x + 2y = -8$.

Table of values

x	0	−2	−4
y	−4	−1	2

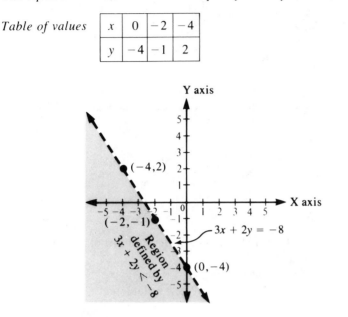

Testing the point $(0,0)$

$$3(0) + 2(0) < -8$$
$$0 \quad + 0 < -8$$
$$0 < -8$$

Since the statement $0 < -8$ is false, the point $(0,0)$ is not a point in the region defined by $3x + 2y < -8$. The region defined by the inequality is the area to the left of the line as shown.

C. Graphing inequalities of the form $ax > by$ or $ax < by$

Example 5.2b   Graph each of the following inequalities.
(i) $y \leqslant -x$ (ii) $3x < 2y$

Solution

(i) The equation associated with the inequality $y \leqslant -x$ is $y = -x$.

Table of values

x	0	3	−3
y	0	−3	3

Note Since the inequality includes $y = -x$, the graph of the equation is drawn as a full line since the points on the line meet the condition stated.

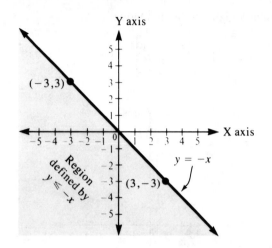

Mathematics fundamentals

Since the line passes through the origin, the point $(0,0)$ cannot be used for testing and we test $(1,0)$.

Substituting $x = 1$, $y = 0$ in the inequality $y < -x$ yields the statement

$$0 < -1$$

Since the statement $0 < -1$ is false, the point $(1,0)$ is not a point in the region defined by $y \leqslant -x$. The region defined by the inequality is the area to the left of the line *including* the line.

(ii) The equation associated with the inequality $3x < 2y$ is $3x = 2y$.

Table of values

x	0	2	−2
y	0	3	−3

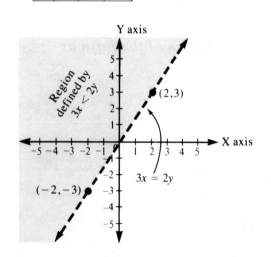

Since (0,0) is not available, test (0,1).
Substituting $x = 0$, $y = 1$ in the
inequality $3x < 2y$ yields the statement

$$0 < 2$$

Since the statement $0 < 2$ is true, the point (0,1) is a point in the region
defined by $3x < 2y$. The region defined by the inequality is the area to the left
of the line as shown.

D. Graphing inequalities involving lines parallel to the axes

Example 5.2c Graph each of the following inequalities.
(i) $x < 3$ (ii) $y \geqslant -3$

Solution

(i) The equation associated with the inequality $x < 3$ is $x = 3$. The graph of $x = 3$
is a line parallel to the Y axis three units to the right.

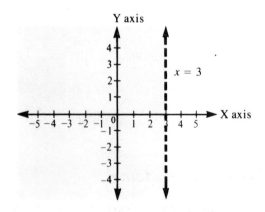

Test (0,0)
Substituting $x = 0$ in the
inequality $x < 3$ yields the statement

$$0 < 3$$

Since the statement $0 < 3$ is true, (0,0) is a point in the region defined by the
inequality $x < 3$. The region defined by the inequality is the region to the left
of the line as shown.

(ii) The equation associated with the inequality $y \geqslant -3$ is $y = -3$. The graph of
$y = -3$ is a line parallel to the X axis three units below it.

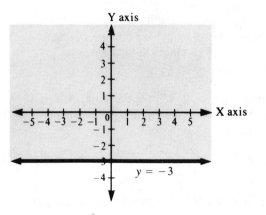

Y axis

X axis

$y = -3$

Test (0,0). Substituting $y = 0$ in the inequality $y > -3$ yields the statement
$$0 > -3$$

Since the statement $0 > -3$ is true, (0,0) is a point in the region defined by $y \geq -3$. The region defined by the inequality is the area above the line as shown.

Exercise 5.2

A. Graph each of the following inequalities.

1. $x + y > 4$
2. $x - y < -2$
3. $x - 2y \leq 4$
4. $3x - 2y \geq -10$
5. $2x < -3y$
6. $4y \geq 3x$
7. $x \geq -2$
8. $y < 5$

5.3   Graphing linear systems

A.   Graphing systems of equations in two unknowns

Systems consisting of two linear equations in two variables may be solved by drawing the graph of each equation. The graph of the system (or solution) is the point of intersection of the two lines representing the equations.

Example 5.3a   Graph the linear system $x + y = 5$ and $x - y = 3$.

Solution

Table of values
for $x + y = 5$

x	0	5	2
y	5	0	3

Table of values
for $x - y = 3$

x	0	3	2
y	-3	0	-1

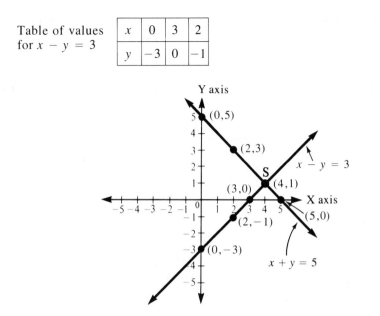

The graph of the system is S, the point of intersection of the two lines, whose coordinates apparently are (4,1). The coordinates (4,1) satisfy the equation of either line and are referred to as the *solution* of the system.

Example 5.3b   Graph the system $x = -2y$ and $y = 3$.

Solution

Table of values
for $x = -2y$

x	0	-4	4
y	0	2	-2

The graph of $y = 3$ is a line parallel to the X axis three units above it.

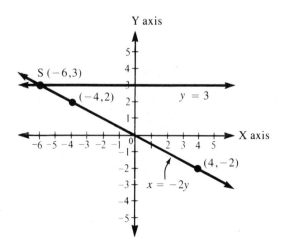

The graph of the system is S, the point of intersection of the two lines. The coordinates of S are apparently $(-6,3)$, and represent the solution of the system.

Example 5.3c Graph the triangle formed by $3x + 4y = 12$, $3x + 2y = 0$ and $x = 2$.

Solution

Table of values for $3x + 4y = 12$

x	0	4	-4
y	3	0	6

Table of values for $3x - 2y = 0$

x	0	2	-2
y	0	-3	3

As shown in the diagram the triangle ABC is formed by the intersection of pairs of lines representing the three equations.

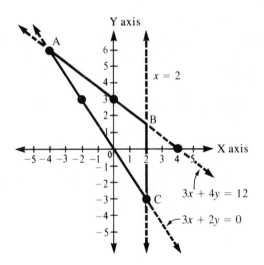

B. Graphing systems of linear inequalities

Systems consisting of two or more linear inequalities in two variables may be drawn by graphing each of the inequalities in the system. The graph of the system is the region *common* to all inequalities.

Example 5.3d Graph the region defined by $x > -2$ and $y > x - 3$.

Solution

The equation associated with the inequality $x > -2$ is $x = -2$. The graph of $x = -2$ is a line parallel to the y axis and two units to the left of it. The substitution of 0 for x yields the true statement $0 > -2$. The point $(0,0)$ is a point in the region defined by $x > -2$. Hence the region defined by the inequality is the area to the right of the line.

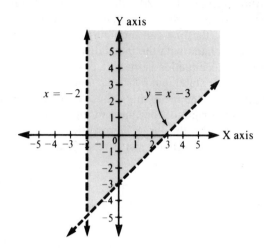

The equation associated with the inequality $y > x - 3$ is $y = x - 3$. The graph of $y = x - 3$ is a line passing through the points $(3,0)$ and $(0,-3)$. The substitution of $x = 0$ and $y = 0$ yields the statement $0 > 0 - 3$, that is $0 > -3$. Since this is a true statement, the point $(0,0)$ is a point in the region defined by the inequality $y > x - 3$. The region defined by the inequality is the area to the left of the line $y = x - 3$.

The region defined by the two inequalities is the area formed by the intersection of the two regions, that is the common region as shown in the diagram.

Example 5.3e Graph the region defined by $y \geqslant 0$, $4x + 5y \leqslant 20$ and $4x - 3y \geqslant -12$.

Solution

The equation associated with the inequality $y \geqslant 0$ is $y = 0$. The graph of $y = 0$ is the X axis. The region defined by the inequality $y \geqslant 0$ is the area above the X axis including the points forming the x axis.

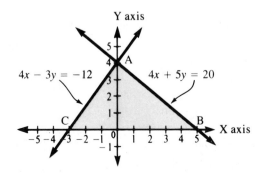

The equation associated with the inequality $4x + 5y \leqslant 20$ is $4x + 5y = 20$. The graph of the equation is the line passing through the points A(0,4) and B(5,0). The true statement $0 < 20$ indicates that the origin is a point in the region defined by the inequality. Thus the region defined by $4x + 5y \leqslant 20$ is the area to the left of the line and including the line itself.

The equation associated with the inequality $4x - 3y \geqslant -12$ is $4x - 3y = -12$. The graph of this equation is the line passing through the points A(0,4) and C(-3,0). The true statement $0 > -12$ indicates that the origin is a point in the region defined by the inequality. Thus the region defined by $4x - 3y \geqslant -12$ is the area to the right of the line and including the line itself.

The region defined by the three inequalities is the area formed by the intersection of the three regions; that is, the Triangle ABC as shown in the diagram.

Exercise 5.3

A. Solve graphically each of the following linear systems.

1. $x + y = 4$ and $x - y = -4$
2. $x - y = 3$ and $x + y = 5$
3. $x = 2y - 1$ and $y = 4 - 3x$
4. $2x + 3y = 10$ and $3x - 4y = -2$
5. $3x - 4y = 18$ and $2y = -3x$
6. $4x = -5y$ and $2x + y = 6$
7. $5x - 2y = 20$ and $y = 5$
8. $3y = -5x$ and $x = -3$

B. Graph the triangle formed by the following.

1. $x = y$, $x = 4$ and $y = 0$
2. $y = -2x$, $y = 4$ and $x = 2$
3. $3x + 4y = 12$, $x = 0$ and $y = 0$
4. $x + y = -5$, $x - y = -5$ and $x = -2$

C. Graph the region defined by each of the following linear systems.

1. $y < 3$ and $x + y > 2$
2. $x - 2y < 4$ and $x > -3$
3. $3x - y \leqslant 6$ and $x + 2y > 8$
4. $5x > -3y$ and $2x - 5y \geqslant 10$
5. $2y - 3x \leqslant 9$, $x \leqslant 3$ and $y \geqslant 0$
6. $2x + y \leqslant 6$, $x \geqslant 0$ and $y \geqslant 0$
7. $y \geqslant -3x$, $y \leqslant 3$ and $2x - y \leqslant 6$
8. $2x \leqslant y$, $x \geqslant -3y$ and $x - 2y \geqslant -6$

5.4 Algebraic solution of systems of linear equations in two variables

A. Basic concept

Although any linear system consisting of two equations in two variables can be solved graphically as illustrated in Section 5.3, more efficient techniques are available. One of these techniques is based on the elimination of one of the two variables from the system by addition or subtraction. Only this method is explained and illustrated in this text.

Solving a system of two equations requires finding a pair of values for the two variables which satisfies each of the two equations. The value of one of the two variables can be determined by first reducing the system of equations to one equation in one variable and solving this equation. The value of the variable obtained is then substituted in one of the original equations to find the value of the second variable.

B. Solving a system of two linear equations by addition or subtraction

If the coefficients of one variable are the *same* in both equations the system can be reduced to one equation by addition or subtraction as follows.

(a) If the coefficients are numerically equal but opposite in sign then addition will eliminate the variable.

(b) If the coefficients are numerically equal and have the same sign, subtraction may be used to eliminate the variable. Alternatively, one equation may be multiplied by -1 and addition may then be used.

Example 5.4a   Solve each of the following system of equations.

(i) $x + y = 1$
$\quad x - y = 7$

(ii) $5x + 4y = 7$
$\quad 3x - 4y = 17$

(iii) $2x + 3y = -2$
$\quad\ 2x - 5y = -34$

(iv) $x - 3y = 2$
$\quad 4x - 3y = -10$

Solution

(i) $x + y = 1$ $\longleftarrow$ equation ①
$\;\; x - y = 7$ $\longleftarrow$ equation ②
$\overline{}$
$\;\; 2x \quad\ = 8$ $\longleftarrow$ add ① and ② to eliminate y

  Note   The coefficient of y in ① is 1;
  the coefficient of y in ② is -1.

  Since the coefficients are the same but opposite in sign, addition of the two equations will eliminate the term in y.

$\quad\;\; x = 4$

$4 + y = 1$ $\longleftarrow$ substitute the value of x in ①
$\quad\;\; y = -3$

$\boxed{x = 4,\ y = -3}$ $\longleftarrow$ solution

Check

in ①   LS $= 4 + (-3) = 4 - 3 = 1$
         RS $= 1$

in ②   LS $= 4 - (-3) = 4 + 3 = 7$
         RS $= 7$

(ii) $5x + 4y = 7$ ⟵ equation ①
     $3x - 4y = 17$ ⟵ equation ②

     $8x = 24$ ⟵ add ① and ② to eliminate y
         $x = 3$
     $5(3) + 4y = 7$ ⟵ substitute 3 for x in ①
       $15 + 4y = 7$
           $4y = -8$
            $y = -2$

$$\boxed{x = 3, y = -2}$$

Check

in ① LS $= 5(3) + 4(-2) = 15 - 8 = 7$
      RS $= 7$

in ② LS $= 3(3) - 4(-2) = 9 + 8 = 17$
      RS $= 17$

(iii) $2x + 3y = {-2}$ ⟵ equation ①
      $2x - 5y = -34$ ⟵ equation ②

             $8y = 32$ ⟵ subtract ② from ① to eliminate x
              $y = 4$
     $2x + 3(4) = -2$ ⟵ substitute 4 for y *in* ①
       $2x + 12 = -2$
          $2x = -14$
           $x = -7$

$$\boxed{x = -7, y = 4}$$

Check

in ① LS $= 2(-7) + 3(4) = -14 + 12 = -2$
      RS $= -2$

in ② LS $= 2(-7) - 5(4) = -14 - 20 = -34$
      RS $= -34$

(iv) $x - 3y = \quad 2 \longleftarrow$ ①
        $4x - 3y = -10 \longleftarrow$ ②

        $-4x + 3y = \quad 10 \longleftarrow$ ② multiplied by -1 to set up addition
        $\underline{\quad x - 3y = \quad 2 \longleftarrow ①}$

        $-3x \qquad = \quad 12 \longleftarrow$ add
        $\qquad x = -4$
        $-4 - 3y = \quad 2 \longleftarrow$ substitute -4 for x in ①
        $\qquad -3y = \quad 6$
        $\qquad y = -2$

$$\boxed{x = -4, \; y = -2}$$

Check

in ① LS $= -4 - 3(-2) = -4 + 6 = 2 =$ RS
in ② LS $= 4(-4) - 3(-2) = -16 + 6 = -10 =$ RS

C. Solving a system of two linear equations when the coefficients are not numerically equal

Sometimes numerical equality of one pair of coefficients must be *created* before addition or subtraction can be used to eliminate a variable. This is usually achieved by multiplying one or both equations by a number or numbers which will make the coefficients of the variable to be eliminated numerically equal.

***Example* 5.4b**   Solve each of the following system of equations.

(i) $x - 3y = -12$
    $3x + \; y = -6$

(ii) $x + 4y = 18$
    $2x + 5y = 24$

(iii) $3x - 4y = 8$
    $4x + 5y = 21$

(iv) $6x - 5y + 70 = 0$
    $4x = 3y - 44$

Solution

(i) $x - 3y = -12 \longleftarrow$ ①
    $3x + \; y = - \; 6 \longleftarrow$ ②

    To eliminate the term in y multiply equation ② by 3.
    $9x + 3y = -18 \longleftarrow$ ② multiplied by 3
    $\underline{\; x - 3y = -12 \longleftarrow ①}$

    $10x \qquad = -30 \longleftarrow$ Add
    $\qquad x = -3$

$$-3 - 3y = -12 \longleftarrow \text{ substitute } -3 \text{ for } x \text{ in } ①$$
$$-3y = -9$$
$$y = 3$$

$$\boxed{x = -3, \ y = 3}$$

(ii) $x + 4y = 18 \longleftarrow ①$
$\quad 2x + 5y = 24 \longleftarrow ②$

To eliminate the term in x multiply ① by 2.
$$2x + 8y = \quad 36 \longleftarrow ① \text{ multiplied by 2}$$
$$-2x - 5y = -24 \longleftarrow ② \text{ multiplied by } -1 \text{ to set up addition}$$

$$3y = \quad 12 \longleftarrow \text{ add}$$
$$y = \quad 4$$
$$x + 4(4) = 18 \quad \longleftarrow \text{ substitute 4 for } y \text{ in } ①$$
$$x + 16 = 18$$
$$x = 2$$

$$\boxed{x = 2, \ y = 4}$$

(iii) $3x - 4y = \quad 8 \longleftarrow ①$
$\quad\ 4x + 5y = 21 \longleftarrow ②$

To eliminate the term in y multiplying ① by 5 and ② by 4.
$$15x - 20y = 40 \longleftarrow \text{ multiplied by 5}$$
$$16x + 20y = 84 \longleftarrow \text{ multiplied by 4}$$

$$31x \quad\quad = 124 \longleftarrow \text{ add}$$
$$x = 4$$
$$4(4) + 5y = 21 \longleftarrow \text{ substitute 4 for } x \text{ in } ②$$
$$16 + 5y = 21$$
$$5y = 5$$
$$y = 1$$

$$\boxed{x = 4, \ y = 1}$$

(iv) $6x - 5y + 70 = 0 \longleftarrow ①$
$\quad\ 4x = 3y - 44 \quad\quad \longleftarrow ②$

Rearrange the two equations in suitable (the same) order.
$$6x - 5y = -70 \longleftarrow ①$$
$$4x - 3y = -44 \longleftarrow ②$$

To eliminate the term in y multiply ① by 3 and ② by -5.

$18x - 15y = -210$ ⟵ ① multiplied by 3
$-20x + 15y = 220$ ⟵ ② multiplied by -5

$-2x = 10$ ⟵ add
$ x = -5$
$6(-5) - 5y = -70$ ⟵ substitute -5 for x in ①
$-30 - 5y = -70$
$ -5y = -40$
$ y = 8$

$$\boxed{x = -5, \ y = 8}$$

D. Solving linear systems in two variables involving fractions

When one or both equations contain decimal fractions or common fractions it is best to eliminate the fractions by multiplying; then solve as shown in the previous examples.

Example 5.4c Solve each of the following systems of equations.

(i) $\ 1.5x + 0.8y = 1.2$
$ 0.7x + 1.2y = -4.4$

(ii) $\ \dfrac{5x}{6} + \dfrac{3y}{8} = -1$

$ \dfrac{2x}{3} - \dfrac{3y}{4} = -5$

Solution

(i) $\ 1.5x + 0.8y = 1.2$ ⟵ ①
$ 0.7x + 1.2y = -4.4$ ⟵ ②

To eliminate the decimals multiply each equation by 10.

$15x + 8y = 12$ ⟵ ③
$7x + 12y = -44$ ⟵ ④

To eliminate the term in y multiply ③ by 3 and ④ by 2.

$45x + 24y = 36$ ⟵ ③ multiplied by 3
$14x + 24y = -88$ ⟵ ④ multiplied by 2

$31x = 124$ ⟵ subtract
$ x = 4$
$15(4) + 8y = 12$ ⟵ substitute 4 for x in ③
$60 + 8y = 12$
$ 8y = -48$
$ y = -6$

$$\boxed{x = 4, \ y = -6}$$

(ii) $\dfrac{5x}{6} + \dfrac{3y}{8} = -1 \longleftarrow$ ①

$\dfrac{2x}{3} - \dfrac{3y}{4} = -5 \longleftarrow$ ②

To eliminate the fractions multiply ① by 24 and ② by 12.

$\dfrac{24(5x)}{6} + \dfrac{24(3y)}{8} = 24(-1) \longleftarrow$ ① multiplied by 24

$4(5x) + 3(3y) = -24$

$20x + 9y = -24 \longleftarrow$ ③

$\dfrac{12(2x)}{3} - \dfrac{12(3y)}{4} = 12(-5) \longleftarrow$ ② multiplied by 12

$4(2x) - 3(3y) = -60$

$8x - 9y = -60 \longleftarrow$ ④

To eliminate the term in y add ③ and ④ .

$20x + 9y = -24 \longleftarrow$ ③

$\underline{8x - 9y = -60 \longleftarrow\ ④}$

$28x \qquad = -84$

$x = -3$

$20(-3) + 9y = -24 \longleftarrow$ substitute -3 for x in ③

$-60 + 9y = -24$

$9y = 36$

$y = 4$

$$\boxed{x = -3,\ y = 4}$$

Exercise 5.4

A. Solve each of the following systems of equations and check.

1. $x + y = -9$
$\quad x - y = -7$

2. $x + 5y = 0$
$\quad x + 2y = 6$

3. $5x + 2y = 74$
$\quad 7x - 2y = 46$

4. $2x + 9y = -13$
$\quad 2x - 3y = 23$

5. $y = 3x + 12$
$\quad x = -y$

6. $3x = 10 - 2y$
$\quad 5y = 3x - 38$

B. Solve each of the following systems of equations and check.

1. $4x + y = -13$
$x - 5y = -19$

2. $6x + 3y = 24$
$2x + 9y = -8$

3. $7x - 5y = -22$
$4x + 3y = 5$

4. $8x + 9y = 129$
$6x + 7y = 99$

5. $12y = 5x + 16$
$6x + 10y - 54 = 0$

6. $3x - 8y + 44 = 0$
$7x = 12y - 56$

C. Solve each of the following systems of equations.

1. $0.4x + 1.5y = 16.8$
$1.1x - 0.9y = 6.0$

2. $6.5x + 3.5y = 128$
$2.5x + 4.5y = 106$

3. $2.4x + 1.6y = 7.60$
$3.8x + 0.6y = 7.20$

4. $2.25x + 0.75y = 2.25$
$1.25x + 1.75y = 2.05$

5. $\dfrac{3x}{4} - \dfrac{2y}{3} = \dfrac{-13}{6}$
$\dfrac{4x}{5} + \dfrac{3y}{4} = \dfrac{123}{10}$

6. $\dfrac{9x}{5} + \dfrac{5y}{4} = \dfrac{47}{10}$
$\dfrac{2x}{9} + \dfrac{3y}{8} = \dfrac{5}{36}$

7. $\dfrac{x}{3} + \dfrac{2y}{5} = \dfrac{7}{15}$
$\dfrac{3x}{2} - \dfrac{7y}{3} = -1$

8. $\dfrac{x}{4} + \dfrac{3y}{7} = \dfrac{-2}{21}$
$\dfrac{2x}{3} + \dfrac{3y}{2} = \dfrac{-7}{36}$

5.5   *Systems of linear equations in three variables*

A.   *Solving by the method of elimination*

Systems consisting of three linear equations in three variables may be solved by a process of elimination similar to the one used in Section 5.4.

The first step in the process involves the reduction of the system of three equations in three variables to a system of two equations in two variables. Since two equations are needed, the same variable must be eliminated from two sets of equations. While any of the three variables may be eliminated, the decision to eliminate a particular variable should be based on ease of elimination.

The second step involves the solving of the new system by the method used in Section 5.4.

Once the value of one variable has been obtained the values of the second and third variables may be obtained by successive substitution.

B.   *Worked examples*

Example 5.5a   Solve the system $x + y + z = 0$, $2x + 3y - z = -6$, $5x - 3y + 2z = 21$.

Solution

$$x + y + z = 0 \quad \longleftarrow \quad ①$$
$$2x + 3y - z = -6 \quad \longleftarrow \quad ②$$
$$5x - 3y + 2z = 21 \quad \longleftarrow \quad ③$$

Step 1 Eliminate z from the system and set up two equations in x and y.

(i) Eliminate z from ① and ② by adding.

$$x + y + z = 0$$
$$2x + 3y - z = -6$$

$$3x + 4y = -6 \quad \longleftarrow \quad ④$$

(ii) Eliminate z from ② and ③.

$$2x + 3y - z = -6$$
$$5x - 3y + 2z = 21$$

To eliminate z multiply ② by 2 and add.

$$4x + 6y - 2z = -12 \quad \longleftarrow \quad ② \text{ multiplied by } 2$$
$$5x - 3y + 2z = 21$$

$$9x + 3y = 9 \quad \longleftarrow \quad ⑤$$

Step 2 Now solve the new system consisting of ④ and ⑤.

$$3x + 4y = -6$$
$$9x + 3y = 9$$

To eliminate the term in x multiply ④ by 3.

$$9x + 12y = -18 \quad \longleftarrow \quad ④ \text{ multiplied by } 3$$
$$9x + 3y = 9$$

$$9y = -27 \quad \longleftarrow \quad \text{subtract}$$
$$y = -3$$

Step 3 Substitute -3 for y in an equation having two variables.

$$3x + 4(-3) = -6 \quad \longleftarrow \quad \text{Substitute in } ④$$
$$3x - 12 = -6$$
$$3x = 6$$
$$x = 2$$

Step 4 Substitute 2 for x and -3 for y in an equation having three variables.

$$2 + (-3) + z = 0 \quad \longleftarrow \quad \text{Substitute in } ①$$
$$-1 + z = 0$$
$$z = 1$$

$$\boxed{x = 2, \, y = -3, \, z = 1}$$

Check

in ① LS $= 2 - 3 + 1 = 0$ RS $= 0$

in ② LS $= 2(2) + 3(-3) - 1$
$= 4 - 9 - 1$
$= -6$ RS $= -6$

in ③ LS $= 5(2) - 3(-3) + 2(1)$
$= 10 + 9 + 2$
$= 21$ RS $= 21$

Example 5.5b Solve the system $3a + 4b - 2c = -28$, $5a - 3c = -19$, $2a - 3b + c = 11$.

Solution

$$3a + 4b - 2c = -28 \longleftarrow ①$$
$$5a \qquad - 3c = -19 \longleftarrow ②$$
$$\underline{2a - 3b + c = \quad 11 \longleftarrow ③}$$

Since ② has the two variables 'a' and 'c', the variable 'b' should be eliminated from the system to set up a second equation in 'a' and 'c'. This can be done by multiplying ① by 3 and ③ by 4.

$$9a + 12b - 6c = -84 \longleftarrow ① \text{ multiplied by 3}$$
$$\underline{8a - 12b + 4c = \quad 44 \longleftarrow ③ \text{ multiplied by 4}}$$

$$17a \qquad -2c = -40 \longrightarrow ④$$

Now solve the system in two variables consisting of ② and ④.

$$5a - 3c = -19 \longleftarrow ②$$
$$\underline{17a - 2c = -40 \longleftarrow ④}$$

To eliminate the term in c multiply ② by 2 and ④ by -3.

$$10a - 6c = -38 \longleftarrow ② \text{ multiplied by 2}$$
$$\underline{-51a + 6c = \quad 120 \longleftarrow ④ \text{ multiplied by } -3}$$

$$-41a \qquad = 82$$
$$a = -2$$

Now substitute $-2 = a$ in ② (one of the two equations in two variables).

$$5(-2) - 3c = -19$$
$$-10 - 3c = -19$$
$$-3c = -9$$
$$c = 3$$

Now substitute $-2 = a$, $3 = c$ in ③ (one of the equations in three variables).

$$2(-2) - 3b + 3 = 11$$
$$-4 - 3b + 3 = 11$$
$$-3b = 12$$
$$b = -4$$

$$\boxed{a = -2, b = -4, c = 3}$$

Check

in ① LS $= 3(-2) + 4(-4) - 2(3)$
$= -6 - 16 - 6$
$= -28$
RS $= -28$

in ② LS $= 5(-2) - 3(3)$
$= -10 - 9$
$= -19$
RS $= -19$

in ③ LS $= 2(-2) - 3(-4) + 3$
$= -4 + 12 + 3$
$= 11$
RS $= 11$

Example 5.5c Solve the system $3m + 2n = 4$, $5m - 4k = 0$, $3n + 5k = 13$.

Solution

$$3m + 2n \qquad = 4 \longleftarrow ①$$
$$5m \qquad - 4k = 0 \longleftarrow ②$$
$$3n + 5k = 13 \longleftarrow ③$$

To set up a system of two equations in m and n use ① and eliminate the term in k from ② and ③.

$$25m \qquad - 20k = 0 \longleftarrow ② \text{ multiplied by } 5$$
$$+ 12n + 20k = 52 \longleftarrow ③ \text{ multiplied by } 4$$

$$25m + 12n \qquad = 52 \longrightarrow ④$$

Now solve the system consisting of ① and ④.

$$3m + 2n = 4 \longleftarrow ①$$
$$25m + 12n = 52 \longleftarrow ④$$

To eliminate the term in n multiply ① by -6.

$$-18m - 12n = -24 \longleftarrow ① \text{ multiplied by } -6$$
$$25m + 12n = 52$$

$$7m \qquad = 28$$
$$m = 4$$

Substitute $4 = m$ in ①.

$$3(4) + 2n = 4$$
$$12 + 2n = 4$$
$$2n = -8$$
$$n = -4$$

Substitute $4 = m$ in ②.

$$5(4) - 4k = 0$$
$$-4k = -20$$
$$k = 5$$

$$\boxed{m = 4, \, n = -4, \, k = 5}$$

Check

in ① LS $= 3(4) + 2(-4) = 12 - 8 = 4 \qquad$ RS $= 4$

in ② LS $= 5(4) - 4(5) = 20 - 20 = 0 \qquad$ RS $= 0$

in ③ LS $= 3(-4) + 5(5) = -12 + 25 = 13$ RS $= 13$

Exercise 5.5

A. Solve each of the following systems of equations and check.

1. $x + 2y - z = 0$
$3x - 2y + 2z = -17$
$5x + 3y - 4z = -25$

2. $4x - 3y + 2z = 43$
$3x + 2y - 5z = -13$
$6x - 5y + 3z = 66$

3. $7a + 3b + 5c = 181$
$4a + 5b = 100$
$8a + 2b + 3c = 149$

4. $5a + 9b + 8c = 389$
$12a + 7b = 220$
$6b + 9c = 321$

5. $9m + 8n = 12$
$12n + 9k = 18$
$7m + 12k = 20$

6. $5p + 9q = 6$
$9p + 6r = 9$
$5q + 10r = 5$

5.6 Problem solving

A. Problems leading to one equation in two variables

In many problems the relationships between two or more variables may be represented by setting up linear equations. To solve such problems uniquely, there must be as many equations as there are variables.

In the case of problems involving two variables, two equations are needed to obtain a solution. If only one equation can be set up, the relationship between the two variables can be represented graphically.

Example 5.6a A manufacturer processes two types of products through the Finishing Department. Each unit of Product A requires 20 time units in Finishing while each unit of Product B requires 30 time units. 1200 time units are available per day. Set up an equation which describes the relationship between the number of units of each product that can be processed daily in Finishing, and graph the relationship.

Solution

Let the number of units of Product A that can be processed daily be represented by x, and let number of units of Product B be represented by y. Then the number of time units required per day for Product A is $20x$ and the number of units for Product B is $30y$. The total number of time units per day required by both products is $20x + 30y$ and since 1200 time units are available

$$20x + 30y = 1200$$

Graphical representation

*Table of
values*

x	60	0	30
y	0	40	20

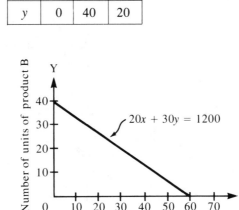

Example 5.6b The Olympic Swim Club rents pool facilities from the city at $2000 per month. Coaching fees and other expenses amount to $40 per swimmer per month. Set up an equation which describes the relationship between the number of swimmers and the total monthly cost of operating the swim club and graph the relationship.

Solution

Let the number of swimmers be represented by x; let the total monthly cost be represented by y; then the monthly coaching fees and expenses are $40x$ and total monthly costs amount to $(2000 + 40x)$.

$$y = 2000 + 40x$$

Graphical representation

Table of values

x	0	50	100
y	2000	4000	6000

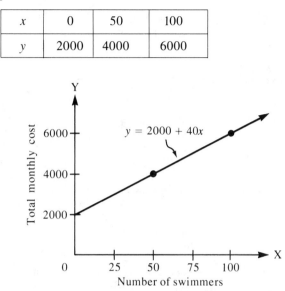

B. Problems leading to systems of equations

The problems in Chapter 3 were solved by using one variable, expressing all the information in terms of that variable and setting up one equation. For many problems the solution is facilitated by using more than one variable and setting up a system of equations.

Example 5.6c The sum of two numbers is 64 and their difference is 10. Find the two numbers.

Solution

Let the greater number be x and the smaller number be y. Their sum is $x + y$ and their difference is $x - y$.

$$x + y = 64 \longleftarrow ①$$
$$x - y = 10 \longleftarrow ②$$
$$\overline{}$$
$$2x = 74$$
$$x = 37$$
$$37 + y = 64$$
$$y = 27$$

The larger number is 37 and the smaller number is 27.

Check Sum $37 + 27 = 64$
Difference $37 - 27 = 10$

Example 5.6d   Sheridan Service paid $240 for heat and power during January. If heat was $40 less than three times the cost of power, how much was the cost of heat for January? (See Chapter 3, Example 3.3c).

Solution

Let the cost of heat be represented by x; and let the cost of power be represented by y and the cost of heat and power together is $(x + y)$.

$$x + y = 240 \longleftarrow ①$$

Heat is represented by $(3y - 40)$.

$$x = 3y - 40 \longleftarrow ②$$
$$x - 3y = -40 \longleftarrow ②$$
$$x + y = 240 \longleftarrow ①$$
$$\overline{}$$
$$-4y = -280 \longleftarrow \text{subtract}$$
$$y = 70$$
$$x + 70 = 240 \longleftarrow \text{substitute in } ①$$
$$x = 170$$

The cost of heat for January was $170.

Example 5.6e   The Clarkson Soccer League has set a budget of $3840 for soccer balls. High quality game balls cost $36 each while lower quality practice balls cost $20 each. If 160 balls are to be purchased, how many balls of each type can be bought to exactly use up the budgeted amount? (See Chapter 3, Example 3.3d)

Solution

Let the number of game balls be x;
let the number of practice balls be y;
then the total number of balls is $x + y$.

$$x + y = 160 \longleftarrow ①$$

The value of the x game balls is $36x$;
the value of the y practice balls is $20y$;
the total value of the balls is $(36x + 20y)$.

$$36x + 20y = 3840 \longleftarrow ②$$
$$-20x - 20y = -3200 \longleftarrow ① \text{ times } -20$$
$$36x + 20y = 3840 \longleftarrow ②$$
$$\overline{}$$
$$16x = 640 \longleftarrow \text{add}$$
$$x = 40$$
$$40 + y = 160 \longleftarrow \text{substitute in } ①$$
$$y = 120$$

40 game balls and 120 practice balls can be bought.

Example 5.6f The Dutch Nook sells two brands of coffee—one for $7.90 per kg, the other for $9.40 per kg. If the store owner mixes 20 kg and intends to sell the mixture for $8.50 per kg, how many kilograms of each brand should she use to realize the same revenue as if sold unmixed?

Solution

Let the number of kilograms of coffee sold for $7.90 be x;
let the number of kilograms of coffee sold for $9.40 be y;
then the number of kilograms of coffee in the mixture is $x + y$;

$$x + y = 20 \longleftarrow ① \text{ weight relationship}$$

The value of coffee in the mixture selling for $7.90 is $7.90x$;
the value of coffee in the mixture selling for $9.40 is $9.40y$;
the total value of the mixture is $(7.90x + 9.40y)$. Since each kilogram of mixture is to be sold at $8.50, the value is $8.50(20)$ that is $170.

$$7.90x + 9.40y = 170.00 \longleftarrow ② \text{ value relationship}$$
$$79x + 94y = 1700 \longleftarrow ② \text{ times 10}$$
$$79x + 79y = 1580 \longleftarrow ① \text{ times 79}$$

$$\begin{aligned} 15y &= 120 \longleftarrow \text{subtract} \\ y &= 8 \\ x + 8 &= 20 \longleftarrow \text{substitute in } ① \\ x &= 12 \end{aligned}$$

The store owner should mix 12 kg of coffee selling for $7.90 per kilogram with 8 kg of coffee selling for $9.40 per kilogram.

Check   Weight $12 + 8 = 20$ kg
Value $12 \times 7.90 + 8 \times 9.40 = 94.80 + 75.20 = \$170.00$

Example 5.6g Material cost of a product is $4 less than twice the cost of direct labour and overhead is $\frac{5}{6}$ of direct labour cost. If the total cost of the product is $157, determine the amount of each of the three elements of cost. (See Chapter 3, Example 3.3b).

Solution

Let the cost of material be represented by x;
let the cost of direct labour be represented by y;
let the cost of overhead be represented by z;
then the total cost is $x + y + z$.

$$x + y + z = 157 \longleftarrow ①$$

also, $4 less than twice the cost of direct labour is $2y - 4$.

$$x = 2y - 4 \longleftarrow ②$$

$\frac{5}{6}$ of direct labour cost is $(\frac{5}{6})x$.

$$z = \frac{5y}{6} \longleftarrow ③$$

The system of equations may now be solved by the process of elimination shown in Section 5.5, or in this case more directly by replacing x and z in ①.

$$(2y - 4) + y + \left(\frac{5y}{6}\right) = 157$$
$$12y - 24 + 6y + 5y = 942$$
$$23y = 966$$
$$y = 42$$

$$x = 2(42) - 4 \longleftarrow \text{substituting in ②}$$
$$x = 80$$
$$z = \frac{5(42)}{6} \longleftarrow \text{substituting in ③}$$
$$z = 35$$

Material cost is $80, labour cost is $42 and overhead is $35.

Example 5.6h A sum of money amounting to $12 consists of nickels, dimes and quarters. If there are 95 coins in total and if the ratio of the number of nickels to the number of dimes is 8 to 5, how many are there of each type of coin?

Solution

Let the number of nickels be x;
let the number of dimes be y;
let the number of quarters be z;
then the total number of coins is $x + y + z$.

$$x + y + z = 95 \longleftarrow ①$$

The value of the x nickels is $\$\frac{1}{20}x$;

the value of the y dimes is $\$\frac{1}{10}y$;

the value of the z quarters is $\$\frac{1}{4}z$;

the total value of the coins is $\$(\frac{1}{20}x + \frac{1}{10}y + \frac{1}{4}z)$.

$$\frac{1}{20}x + \frac{1}{10}y + \frac{1}{4}z = 12 \longleftarrow ②$$

The ratio of nickels to dimes is $x:y$ *or* $\frac{x}{y}$.

$$x:y = 8:5 \text{ or } \frac{x}{y} = \frac{8}{5} \longleftarrow ③$$

To eliminate the fraction from ② multiply by 20.

$$x + 2y + 5z = 240 \longleftarrow ④$$

For suitable order, cross multiply in ③ and rearrange terms.

$$5x = 8y \longleftarrow \text{cross multiplying in ③}$$
$$5x - 8y = 0 \longleftarrow ⑤$$

Now solve the system of equations numbered ①, ④ and ⑤.

$$x + y + z = 95 \longleftarrow ①$$
$$x + 2y + 5z = 240 \longleftarrow ④$$
$$5x - 8y \qquad = 0 \longleftarrow ⑤$$

To eliminate the term in z from the system, multiply ① by 5 and subtract ④.

$$5x + 5y + 5z = 475$$
$$x + 2y + 5z = 240$$

$$4x + 3y \qquad = 235 \longleftarrow ⑥$$

Now solve the system in two variables.

$$5x - 8y = 0 \longleftarrow ⑤$$
$$4x + 3y = 235 \longleftarrow ⑥$$

To eliminate the term in y from the system multiply ⑤ by 3 and ⑥ by 8.

$$15x - 24y = 0$$
$$32x + 24y = 1880$$

$$47x \qquad = 1880$$
$$x = 40$$

Substitute $40 = x$ in ⑤.

$$5(40) - 8y = 0$$
$$-8y = -200$$
$$y = 25$$

Substitute $40 = x, 25 = y$ *in* ①.

$$40 + 25 + z = 95$$
$$z = 30$$

The sum of money consists of 40 nickels, 25 dimes and 30 quarters.

Check Number of coins $40 + 25 + 30 = 95$

Value $40 \times 0.05 + 25 \times 0.10 + 30 \times 0.25 = \$12.00$

Ratio of nickels to dimes $40 : 25 = 8 : 5$

Exercise 5.6

A. Set up an equation which describes the relationship between the two variables and graph the relationship in each of the following.

1. A manufacturer makes two types of products. Profit on Product A is $30 per unit while profit on Product B is $40 per unit. Budgeted monthly profit is $6000.

2. Smith Company manufactures two products. Product 1 requires three hours machine time per unit while Product 2 requires four hours of machine time per unit. There are 120 hours of machine time available per week.

3. A tax consulting service rents space at $200 per week and pays the accounting personnel $4 per completed tax return.

4. George Bell is offered a position as a salesman. The job pays a salary of $500 per month plus a commission of 10% on all sales.

B. Set up a system of simultaneous equations to solve each of the following problems.

1. The sum of two numbers is 24. If twice the larger number is three more than three times the smaller number, what are the two numbers?

2. The difference between seven times the first number and four times the second number is 12. The sum of three-fourths of the first number and two-thirds of the second number is 21. Find the two numbers.

3. A store sold two brands of sauerkraut. Brand X sells for $2.25 per jar while the No-Name brand sells for $1.75 per jar. If 140 jars were sold for a total of $290, how many jars of each brand were sold?

4. Nancy's sales last week were $140 less than three times Vera's sales. Together they sold $940. Determine how much each girl sold last week.

5. Ken and Fred agreed to form a partnership. The partnership agreement requires that Fred invest $2500 more than two-thirds of what Ken is to invest. If the total investment in the partnership is to be $55 000, how much should each partner invest?

6. A furniture company has been producing 2320 chairs a day working two shifts. The second shift has produced 60 chairs fewer than four-thirds of the number of chairs produced by the first shift. Determine the number of chairs produced by each shift.

7. An inventory of two types of floodlights showed a total of sixty lights valued at $2580. If Type A cost $40 each while Type B cost $50 each, how many of each type of floodlights were in inventory?

8. A machine requires four hours to make a unit of Product A and three hours to make a unit of Product B. Last month the machine operated for 200 hours producing a total of 60 units. How many units of each type of product were produced?

9. Bruce has saved $8.80 in nickels, dimes and quarters. If he has four nickels fewer than three times the number of dimes and one quarter more than three-fourths the number of dimes, how many coins of each type does Bruce have?

10. The local amateur football club spent $1475 on tickets to a professional football game. If the club bought ten more eight-dollar tickets than three times the number of twelve-dollar tickets, and three fewer fifteen-dollar tickets than four-fifths the number of twelve-dollar tickets, how many tickets of each type did the club buy?

Review exercise

1. Graph each of the following.

   (a) $2x - y = 6$

   (b) $3x + 4y = 0$

   (c) $5x + 2y = 10$

   (d) $y = -3$

   (e) $3x + 5y < 15$

   (f) $5x - 4y > 0$

   (g) $x > -2$

   (h) $4x + 3y < -12$

2. Graphically solve each of the following.

   (a) $3x + y = 6$ and $x - y = 2$

   (b) $x + 4y = -8$ and $3x + 4y = 0$

   (c) $5x = 3y$ *and* $y = -5$

   (d) $2x + 6y = 8$ and $x = -2$

3. Graph the regions defined by each of the following.

   (a) $y < 3x - 2$ and $y < 3$

   (b) $y > -2x$ and $x < 4$

   (c) $x \geqslant -2$, $y \geqslant 0$ and $3x + 4y \leqslant 12$

   (d) $x \geqslant 0$, $y \geqslant -2$ and $5x + 3y \leqslant 15$

4. Solve each of the following system of equations.

   (a) $3x + 2y = -1$
   $5x + 3y = -2$

   (b) $4x - 5y = 25$
   $3x + 2y = 13$

   (c) $y = -10x$
   $3y = 29 - x$

   (d) $2y = 3x + 17$
   $3x = 11 - 5y$

   (e) $2x - 3y = 13$
   $3x - 2y = 12$

   (f) $2x = 3y - 11$
   $y = 13 + 3x$

   (g) $2a - 3b - 4c = 6$
   $2a - b - c = 8$
   $a + b - c = 0$

   (h) $a + b + c = -4$
   $3a - 5b = 0$
   $8a + 4c = 0$

   (i) $4a - 3b - 2c = 9$
   $2a + 3b - 3c = -13$
   $a - 2b + 4c = 15$

   (j) $3a - 2b + 4c = 4$
   $a + 3b - 3c = -8$
   $2a + b - c = -6$

   (k) $5m + 3n + 2k = 74$

   $3m + 7n = 74$

   $4m + 5k = 74$

   (l) $\dfrac{3}{4}m + \dfrac{5}{8}n = \dfrac{3}{4}$

   $\dfrac{6}{5}m + \dfrac{1}{3}k = \dfrac{21}{20}$

   $\dfrac{5}{6}n + \dfrac{2}{3}k = \dfrac{5}{6}$

5. Write an equation describing the relationship between the two variables in each of the following problem statements and graph the relationship.

   (a) A firm pays for radio advertising at the fixed rate of $1000 per week plus $75 per announcement during the week.

(b) The Bi-Products Company markets two products. Each unit of Product A requires five units of labour while each unit of Product B requires two units of labour. There are 200 units of labour available per time period.

6. Set up a system of simultaneous equations to solve each of the following problems.

(a) Find two numbers such that the sum of six times the first number and five times the second number is 93 and the difference between three-quarters of the first number and two-thirds of the second number is zero.

(b) The college theatre collected $1300 from the sale of 450 tickets. If the tickets were sold for $2.50 and $3.50 each respectively, how many tickets were sold at each price?

(c) A jacket and two pairs of pants together cost $175. The jacket is valued at three times the price of one pair of pants. What is the value of the jacket?

(d) Three cases of White Bordeaux and five cases of Red Bordeaux cost together $438. Each case of Red Bordeaux costs $6 less than twice the cost of a case of White Bordeaux. Determine the cost of a case of each type.

(e) A product requires processing on three machines. Processing time on Machine A is three minutes less than four-fifths of the number of minutes on Machine B and processing time on Machine C is five-sixths of the time needed on Machines A and B together. How many minutes processing time is required on each machine if the total processing time on all three machines is 77 minutes?

(f) The total average monthly cost of heat, power and water for Sheridan service for last year was $2010. If this year's average is expected to increase by one-tenth over last year's average, and heat is expected to be $22 more than three-fourths the cost of power while water is expected to be $11 less than one-third the cost of power, how much should be budgeted on the average for each month for each item?

(g) A company has a promotional budget of $87 500. The budget is to be allocated to direct selling, TV advertising and newspaper advertising according to a formula which requires that the amount spent on TV advertising be $1000 more than three times the amount spent on newspaper advertising and that the amount spent on direct selling be three-fourths of the total spent on TV advertising and newspaper advertising combined. How should the budget be allocated?

(h) A cash box contains $74 made up of quarters, half-dollars and one-dollar bills. How many coins of each type and how many one-dollar bills does the box contain if the number of half-dollar coins is one more than three-fifths of the number of one-dollar bills and the number of quarters is four times the number of one-dollar bills and half-dollar coins together?

Self-test

1. Graphically solve each of the following systems of equations.

(a) $x + y = -2$ and $x - y = 4$

(b) $3x = -2y$ and $x = 2$

2. Graph the region defined by each of the following.

    (a) $y < 3 - x$ and $y < 3$

    (b) $x \geqslant 0$, $y \geqslant -2$ and $3x + 2y \leqslant 12$

3. Solve each of the following systems of equations.

    (a) $6x + 5y = 9$
           $4x - 3y = 25$

    (b) $12 - 7x = 4y$
           $6 - 2y = 3x$

    (c) $5a - b + 4c = 5$
           $2a + 3b + 5c = 2$
           $7a - 2b + 6c = 5$

    (d) $6a + b - 2c = 0$
           $4b - c = -13$
           $5a + 3c = 25$

4. An investment of $12 000 is made so that part earns interest at 8% per annum and part at 12% per annum. If the total annual interest on the investment is $1020, how much is invested at each rate?

5. Jack and Jill divide a profit of $12 700. If Jack is to receive $2200 more than two-fifths of Jill's share, how much will Jill receive?

6. Direct distribution costs are to be allocated to three product lines on the basis of sales value for an accounting period. Product A sells for $20 per unit, Product B for $15 per unit and Product C for $10 per unit. For last month the number of units of Product A was five-eighths the number of units of Product B and the number of units of Product C was 16 less than three times the number of units of Product B. How much of the total direct distribution cost of $6280 is to be allocated to each product line?

Glossary of terms used

Inequality   a mathematical statement involving relationships between variables described as 'greater than' or 'less than'

Origin   the point of intersection of the two axes in a system of rectangular coordinates

X axis   the horizontal reference line in a system of rectangular coordinates

X coordinate   the first number in the ordered pair of numbers describing the position of a point relative to the axes or the directed distance of a point from the vertical axis (Y axis)

Y axis   the vertical reference line in a system of rectangular coordinates

Y coordinate   the second number in the ordered pair of numbers describing the position of a point relative to the axes or the directed distance of a point from the horizontal axis (X axis)

6 Additional topics in algebra

Introduction

The topics covered in this chapter include fractional exponents, basic aspects of arithmetic progressions, geometric progressions and logarithms. These topics provide a useful background for certain of the topics in the following chapters and should be reviewed when encountered.

Objectives

Upon completion of this chapter you will be able to

1. use an electronic calculator equipped with a power function to compute the numerical value of arithmetic expressions involving fractional exponents;
2. compute the value of any term in an arithmetic progression, compute the sum to n terms and insert a desired number of terms between two numbers;
3. compute the value of any term in a geometric progression, compute the sum to n terms and insert a desired number of geometric means between two numbers;
4. write exponential equations in logarithmic form and use an electronic calculator equipped with a natural logarithm function to determine the value of natural logarithms.

6.1 Fractional exponents

A. Radicals

When the product of two or more equal factors is expressed in exponential form, one of the equal factors is referred to as the **root of the product** and the exponent indicates the number of equal factors; that is, the **power of the root**.

For example

$25 = 5^2 \longrightarrow$ 5 is the second power root (square root) of 25

$8 = 2^3 \longrightarrow$ 2 is the third power root (cube root) of 8

$81 = 3^4 \longrightarrow$ 3 is the fourth (power) root of 81

$a^5 \longrightarrow a$ is the fifth root of a^5

$7^n \longrightarrow$ 7 is the nth root of 7^n

$x^n \longrightarrow x$ is the nth root of x^n

The operational symbol for finding the root of an expression is $\sqrt{}$. This symbol is understood to represent the *positive* root only. If the negative root is desired a minus sign is placed in front of the symbol; that is, the negative root is represented by $-\sqrt{}$.

The power of a root is written at the upper left of the symbol as in $\sqrt[3]{}$ or $\sqrt[n]{}$.

The indicated root is called a **radical**, the power indicated is called the **index** and the number under the symbol is called the **radicand**.

$$\text{In } \sqrt[5]{32} \text{ the index is 5,}$$
$$\text{the radicand is 32 and}$$
$$\text{the radical is } \sqrt[5]{32}.$$

When the square root is to be found it is customary to omit the index 2. Thus the symbol $\sqrt{}$ is understood to mean the positive square root of the radicand.

$$\sqrt{49} \text{ means } \sqrt[2]{49} \text{ or } 7.$$

In special cases, when the radicand is an integral power of the root, the root can readily be found by expressing the radicand in exponential form such that the index of the root and the exponent are the same.

Example 6.1a

(i) $\sqrt{64} = \sqrt{8^2} \longleftarrow$ the radicand 64 is expressed in exponential form as a square

$= 8 \longleftarrow$ one of the two equal factors 8 is the root

(ii) $\sqrt[5]{32} = \sqrt[5]{2^5} \longleftarrow$ express the radicand 32 as the 5th power of 2

$= 2 \longleftarrow$ one of the five equal factors 2 is the root

(iii) $\sqrt[3]{0.125} = \sqrt[3]{0.5^3} = 0.5$

In most cases however, the radicand can not be easily rewritten in exponential form. In such cases the arithmetic determination of the numerical value of the root is a laborious process. But computation of the root is easily accomplished using electronic calculators equipped with a power function. The problems in

Example 6.1b are intended to assure that students are able to use the power function and should be done using an electronic calculator.

Example 6.1b

(i) $\sqrt{1425} = 37.7492$ *Check* $37.7492^2 = 1425$

(ii) $\sqrt[5]{12960} = 6.6454$ *Check* $6.6454^5 = 12960$

(iii) $\sqrt[15]{40000} = 2.0268$ *Check* $2.0268^{15} = 40009$ (due to rounding)

(iv) $\sqrt[20]{1048576} = 2$ *Check* $2^{20} = 1048576$

(v) $\sqrt{0.005184} = 0.072$ *Check* $0.072^2 = 0.005184$

(vi) $\sqrt[7]{0.038468} = 0.6279$ *Check* $0.6279^7 = 0.03848$ (due to rounding)

(vii) $\sqrt[45]{1.954213} = 1.015$ *Check* $1.015^{45} = 1.954213$

(viii) $\sqrt[36]{0.0225284} = 0.9$ *Check* $0.9^{36} = 0.0225284$

(ix) $\sqrt{2^6} = \sqrt{64} = 8$

(x) $\sqrt[3]{5^6} = \sqrt[3]{15625} = 25$

B. Fractional exponents

Radicals may be written in exponential form and fractional exponents may be represented in radical form according to the following definitions stated as formulae.

(a) The exponent is a positive fraction with numerator 1.

$$\boxed{a^{\frac{1}{n}} = \sqrt[n]{a}} \quad \longleftarrow \textbf{\textit{Formula 6.1}}$$

$4^{\frac{1}{2}} = \sqrt{4} = 2$

$27^{\frac{1}{3}} = \sqrt[3]{27} = \sqrt[3]{3^3} = 3$

$625^{\frac{1}{4}} = \sqrt[4]{625} = \sqrt[4]{5^4} = 5$

(b) The exponent is a negative fraction with numerator 1

$$\boxed{a^{-\frac{1}{n}} = \frac{1}{a^{\frac{1}{n}}} = \frac{1}{\sqrt[n]{a}}} \quad \longleftarrow \textbf{\textit{Formula 6.2}}$$

$8^{-\frac{1}{3}} = \dfrac{1}{8^{\frac{1}{3}}} = \dfrac{1}{\sqrt[3]{8}} = \dfrac{1}{\sqrt[3]{2^3}} = \dfrac{1}{2}$

$243^{-\frac{1}{5}} = \dfrac{1}{243^{\frac{1}{5}}} = \dfrac{1}{\sqrt[5]{243}} = \dfrac{1}{\sqrt[5]{3^5}} = \dfrac{1}{3}$

(c) The exponent is a positive or negative fraction with numerator other than 1.

$$\boxed{a^{\frac{m}{n}} = \sqrt[n]{a^m} = (\sqrt[n]{a})^m}$$ ⟵ *Formula* **6.3**

$$\boxed{a^{-\frac{m}{n}} = \frac{1}{\sqrt[n]{a^m}} = \frac{1}{(\sqrt[n]{a})^m}}$$ ⟵ *Formula* **6.4**

$$16^{\frac{3}{4}} = \sqrt[4]{16^3} = (\sqrt[4]{16})^3 = (\sqrt[4]{2^4})^3 = (2)^3 = 8$$
$$27^{\frac{4}{3}} = \sqrt[3]{27^4} = (\sqrt[3]{27})^4 = (\sqrt[3]{3^3})^4 = (3)^4 = 81$$

$$36^{-\frac{3}{2}} = \frac{1}{(\sqrt[2]{36})^3} = \frac{1}{(\sqrt{6^2})^3} = \frac{1}{6^3} = \frac{1}{216}$$

For calculator use fractional exponents should be converted into decimals and the computation accomplished by means of the power function.

Example 6.1c

(i) $36^{\frac{3}{2}} = 36^{1.5} = 216$

(ii) $3^{\frac{5}{4}} = 3^{1.25} = 3.948222$

(iii) $\sqrt[5]{12} = 12^{\frac{1}{5}} = 12^{0.2} = 1.6437518$

(iv) $\sqrt[8]{325^5} = 325^{\frac{5}{8}} = 325^{0.625} = 37.147287$

(v) $\sqrt[6]{1.075} = 1.075^{\frac{1}{6}} = 1.075^{0.1666667} = 1.0121264$

Exercise 6.1

A. Use an electronic calculator equipped with a power function to compute each of the following correct to four decimals.

1. $\sqrt{5184}$ 2. $\sqrt{205.9225}$

3. $\sqrt[7]{2187}$ 4. $\sqrt[10]{1.1046221}$

5. $\sqrt[20]{4.3184}$ 6. $\sqrt[16]{0.00001526}$

7. $\sqrt[6]{1.0825}$ 8. $\sqrt[12]{1.15}$

B. Compute each of the following.

1. $3025^{\frac{1}{2}}$ 2. $2401^{\frac{1}{4}}$

3. $525.21875^{\frac{2}{5}}$ 4. $21.6^{\frac{4}{3}}$

5. $\sqrt[12]{1.125^7}$ 6. $\sqrt[6]{1.095}$

7. $4^{-\frac{1}{3}}$ 8. $1.06^{-\frac{1}{12}}$

9. $\dfrac{1.03^{60} - 1}{0.03}$ 10. $\dfrac{1 - 1.05^{-36}}{0.05}$

6.2 Arithmetic progressions

A. Basic concepts

A **sequence** of numbers is a set of numbers arranged in a definite pattern according to a definite rule. The numbers in the sequence are called **terms**, and these terms are designated according to their position in the sequence, such as "first term", "second term", "nth term".

The major types of sequences considered in this chapter are called **arithmetic progressions** and **geometric progressions**.

An **arithmetic progression** is a sequence of numbers in which the successive terms, after the first term, are formed by adding a constant to the preceding term. This constant is referred to as the **common difference** and may be positive or negative (that is the terms in the progression may increase or decrease).

Example 6.2a

	ARITHMETIC PROGRESSION	MISSING TERMS	COMMON DIFFERENCE
(i)	1, 4, 7, __ , __ , __	10, 13, 16	$4 - 1 = 3$
(ii)	$-10, -5, 0,$ __ , __	5, 10	$-5 - (-10) = -5 + 10 = 5$
(iii)	100, 75, __ , __	50, 25	$75 - 100 = -25$
(iv)	$0, -2, -4,$ __ , __	$-6, -8$	$-2 - 0 = -2$

Note The common difference is found by subtracting the first term from the second term (or by subtracting from a selected term the preceding term).

To deal with arithmetic progressions in a general way the following symbols will be used:

a — the value of the first term
d — the common difference
n — the number of terms
L — the value of the last term (nth term)
S_n — the sum of the first n terms.

B. The general term of an arithmetic progression

A formula for finding the value of any term in an arithmetic progression may be developed as follows by generalizing the pattern by which arithmetic progressions are created.

Let us use the letter 't' subscripted by 1, 2, 3, ... , n to represent the *position* numbers of the terms in the arithmetic progression. Then

$$t_1 = \text{first term}$$
$$t_2 = \text{second term}$$

$$t_3 = \text{third term}$$

$$\cdot \qquad \cdot$$
$$\cdot \qquad \cdot$$

$$t_n = n\text{th term (or last term)}$$

Also, let the value of the first term be represented by a and let the common difference be represented by d. Then

$$t_1 = = a$$
$$t_2 = t_1 + d = a + d$$
$$t_3 = t_2 + d = (a + d) + d = a + 2d$$
$$t_4 = t_3 + d = (a + 2d) + d = a + 3d$$
$$t_5 = t_4 + d = (a + 3d) + d = a + 4d$$

$\left.\begin{array}{}\\ \\ \\ \\ \\\end{array}\right\}$ ⟵ note that the coefficient of d
is always 1 less
than the position
number of the
term

$$\cdot \qquad \cdot \qquad\qquad \cdot$$
$$\cdot \qquad \cdot \qquad\qquad \cdot$$

position number
$$t_{10} = t_9 + d = (a + 8d) + d = a + 9d \quad ⟵ \text{of term is 10, co-}$$
efficient of d is 9

$$\cdot \qquad \cdot \qquad\qquad \cdot$$
$$\cdot \qquad \cdot \qquad\qquad \cdot$$

$$t_n = t_{n-1} + d = = a + (n - 1)d$$

The expression obtained for the nth term may be used to determine the value of any term.

$$\boxed{t_n = L = a + (n - 1)d} \quad ⟵ \textbf{\textit{Formula 6.5}}$$

***Example* 6.2b** Use the given information about each of the following arithmetic progressions to compute the value of the terms as indicated.

(i) $a = 6$, $d = 5$; find t_4, t_{20} and t_n.

Solution

Using Formula 6.5 $\quad t_n = a + (n - 1)d$
$$t_4 = a + (4 - 1)d ⟵ \text{the position number } n = 4$$
$$= 6 + 3(5) ⟵ \text{substitute } a = 6, d = 5$$
$$= 6 + 15$$
$$= 21$$

Check The arithmetic progression is 6, 11, 16, 21, 26, ... and the fourth term is 21.

$$t_{20} = a + (20 - 1)d$$
$$= 6 + 19(5)$$
$$= 6 + 95$$
$$= 101$$

$$t_n = a + (n - 1)d$$
$$= 6 + (n - 1)(5)$$
$$= 6 + 5n - 5$$
$$= 1 + 5n$$

(ii) $a = 24$, $d = -7$; find t_4 and t_{30}.

Solution

$$t_4 = a + 3d \longleftarrow n - 1 = 4 - 1 = 3$$
$$= 24 + 3(-7)$$
$$= 24 - 21$$
$$= 3$$

$$t_{30} = a + 29d$$
$$= 24 + 29(-7)$$
$$= 24 - 203$$
$$= -179$$

(iii) Find t_9 for the arithmetic progression 27, 33, 39, ...

Solution

First term $a = 27$;

Common difference $d = 33 - 27 = 6$

$$t_9 = a + 8d = 27 + 8(6) = 27 + 48 = 75$$

(iv) Find the twentieth term of the arithmetic progression 96, 87, 78...

Solution

$n = 20$, $a = 96$, $d = 87 - 96 = -9$

$$t_{20} = a + 19d = 96 + 19(-9) = 96 - 171 = -75$$

Example 6.2c Find the first term, the common difference and the 16th term of the arithmetic progression in which the 8th term is 95 and the 20th term is 275.

Solution

$$t_8 = a + 7d \longrightarrow a + 7d = 95 \longleftarrow ①$$
$$t_{20} = a + 19d \longrightarrow a + 19d = 275 \longleftarrow ②$$

$$\text{Subtract} \longrightarrow -12d = -180$$
$$d = 15$$

Substitute $d = 15$ in ①.
$$a + 7(15) = 95$$
$$a + 105 = 95$$
$$a = -10$$
$$t_{16} = a + 15d = -10 + 15(15) = -10 + 225 = 215$$

The first term is -10, the common difference is 15 and the value of the 16th term is 215.

C. Arithmetic progression means

The terms between two given terms of an arithmetic progression are referred to as the **arithmetic means** between the two terms. To insert a given number of arithmetic means between two given terms, the two given terms are considered to be the first term and the last term of the progression and the number of terms in the progression is 2 plus the number of terms to be inserted.

Example 6.2d Insert three arithmetic means between 12 and 64.

Solution

$$n = 2 + 3 = 5$$
$$t_1 = 12 \longrightarrow a = 12 \longleftarrow ①$$
$$t_5 = 64 \longrightarrow a + 4d = 64 \longleftarrow ②$$

$$\text{subtract} \longrightarrow -4d = -52$$
$$d = 13$$

The arithmetic means are $t_2 = t_1 + 13 = 12 + 13 = 25, t_3 = t_2 + 13 = 25 + 13 = 38$ and $t_4 = 38 + 13 = 51$.

D. The sum of an arithmetic progression

The sum of a given number of terms of an arithmetic progression may be found by using the following technique which yields a quick answer and is useful in developing a general formula.

1. Write the sum of the terms as an indicated addition.
2. Write the sum of the terms in reversed order.
3. Add the corresponding terms of the two sequences.
4. Multiply the sum of two corresponding terms by the number of terms in the sequences and divide by 2.

For example, to find the sum of the progression 3, 6, 9, 12, 15, 18

Step 1 $3 + 6 + 9 + 12 + 15 + 18 \longleftarrow$ write the sum

Step 2 $18 + 15 + 12 + 9 + 6 + 3 \longleftarrow$ write in reversed order

Step 3 $21 + 21 + 21 + 21 + 21 + 21 \longleftarrow$ add the corresponding terms

Step 4 $\text{Sum} = \dfrac{(21 \times 6)}{2} = 63 \longleftarrow$ multiply the sum 21 by the number of terms 6 and divide by 2

This method indicates that the sum of an arithmetic progression for a given number of terms can be found by adding the first term and the last term, multiplying the sum by the number of terms and dividing by 2. This approach is also reflected in the formula for finding the sum of the first n terms of an arithmetic progression

$$S_n = \frac{n}{2}(a + L) \quad \longleftarrow \textit{Formula 6.6}$$

where a is the first term

L is the last term

n is the number of terms

S_n is the sum of the terms.

Development of formula

$$S_n = t_1 + t_2 + t_3 + t_4 + \ldots\ldots + t_n$$
$$= a + (a + d) + (a + 2d) + (a + 3d) + \ldots + (a + (n - 1)d)$$

List the terms in reverse order.

$$S_n = t_n + \ldots\ldots + t_4 + t_3 + t_2 + t_1$$

If $t_n = L$ then the terms are, in reversed order,

L, L $-$ d, L $-$ 2d, L $-$ 3d, etc. until the first term

L $-$ $(n - 1)d$ is reached. Thus:

$$S_n = L + (L - d) + (L - 2d) + (L - 3d) + \ldots + (L - (n - 1)d)$$

Set up the original progression and its reversed order for the addition of the corresponding terms.

$$S_n = a + (a + d) + (a + 2d) + (a + 3d) + \ldots\ldots + (a + (n - 1)d)$$
$$S_n = L + (L - d) + (L - 2d) + (L - 3d) + \ldots\ldots + (L - (n - 1)d)$$

$$2S_n = (a + L) + (a + L) + (a + L) + (a + L) + \ldots,. + (a + L)$$

There are n terms in the sum.

$$2S_n = n(a + L)$$

$$S_n = \frac{n}{2}(a + L) \quad \longleftarrow \textit{Formula 6.6}$$

Further, since L $= a + (n - 1)d$, Formula 6.7 may be written

$$S_n = \frac{n}{2}[2a + (n - 1)d] \quad \longleftarrow \textit{Formula 6.6A}$$

Example 6.2e   Find the sum of the first twenty terms of the arithmetic progression 2, 6, 10, ...

Solution

First term $a = 2$

Common difference $d = 6 - 2 = 4$

Number of terms $n = 20$

Last term $t_{20} = a + 19d = 2 + 19(4) = 2 + 76 = 78$

Sum of the first 20 terms $S_{20} = \left(\dfrac{20}{2}\right)(2 + 78)$

$$= 10(80)$$
$$= 800$$

Alternatively $S_{20} = \left(\dfrac{20}{2}\right)[2(2) + 19(4)] \longleftarrow$ using Formula 6.6A

$$= 10(4 + 76)$$
$$= 800$$

Example 6.2f   For the arithmetic progression 50, 45, 40, ... find

(i) the tenth term and the sum of the first ten terms;
(ii) the twentieth term and the sum of the first twenty terms;
(iii) the sum of the first thirty terms.

Solution

$$a = 50; d = 45 - 50 = -5$$

(i) $n = 10; t_{10} = a + 9d \longleftarrow$ using Formula 6.5
$$= 50 + 9(-5)$$
$$= 50 - 45$$
$$= 5$$

$$S_{10} = \left(\dfrac{10}{2}\right)(50 + 5) \longleftarrow \text{using Formula 6.6}$$

$$= 5(55)$$
$$= 275$$

(ii) $n = 20; t_{20} = a + 19d$
$$= 50 + 19(-5)$$
$$= 50 - 95$$
$$= -45$$

$$S_{20} = \left(\dfrac{20}{2}\right)(50 - 45)$$

$$= 10(5)$$
$$= 50$$

(iii) $n = 30; S_{30} = \dfrac{30}{2}(2a + 29d) \longleftarrow \text{using Formula 6.6A}$

$$= 15[2(50) + 29(-5)]$$
$$= 15(100 - 145)$$
$$= 15(-45)$$
$$= -675$$

Exercise 6.2

A. For each of the following arithmetic progressions find the value of the term as indicated.

1. t_7 for 8, 12, 16, ...
2. t_{25} for -25, -15, -5, ...
3. t_{12} for 144, 132, 120, ...
4. t_{20} for 0, -3, -6, ...
5. t_8 for 2.50, 3.25, 4.00, ...
6. t_{17} for $2\frac{2}{3}$, $2\frac{1}{2}$, $2\frac{1}{3}$, ...

B. Insert arithmetic means between the two given values as indicated.

1. Insert five arithmetic means between 3 and 39.
2. Insert four arithmetic means between $+40$ and -40.
3. Insert seven arithmetic means between 1 and 3.
4. Insert five arithmetic means between $+1$ and -1.

C. For each of the following arithmetic progressions determine the sum to the number of terms indicated.

1. Find the sum of the first fifteen terms of 1, 2, 3, ...
2. Find the sum of the first twenty terms of 0, 2, 4, ...
3. Find the sum of the first twelve terms of 15, 12, 9, ...
4. Find the sum of the first ten terms of 0, -5, -10, ...
5. Find the sum of the first n terms of 1, 3, 5, ...
6. Find the sum of the first n terms of 1, 2, 3, ...

D. Use the information given about each of the following arithmetic progressions to determine the value indicated.

1. The 12th term is -53 and the common difference is -6. Find the value of the first term.
2. The 25th term is $4\frac{1}{3}$; the common difference is $\frac{1}{6}$. Find the sum of the first ten terms.
3. The sum of the first twenty terms is -290; $d = 9$. Find the value of the 12th term.
4. $S_{17} = 0$; $d = -2.25$. Find S_{20}.
5. The sum of the first nine terms is -36; $a = -5$. Find t_6.
6. The sum of the first fifty terms is -1275; the first term is -1. Find the sum of the first 100 terms.
7. The 16th term is -26; the sum of the first five terms is zero. Find the value of the first term.
8. $t_7 = 3$; $S_7 = 38.5$. Find S_3.
9. $t_8 = 50$; $t_{33} = 250$. Find t_{40}.

10. The 13th term is 20; the 25th term is -64. Find S_{16}.

11. The sum of the first six terms is 30; the sum of the first twelve terms is 132. Find t_1.

12. The sum of the first nine terms is 4.5 and the sum of the first 25 terms is -12.5. Find the value of the fifth term.

6.3 Geometric progressions

A. Basic concepts

A **geometric progression** is a sequence of numbers in which the successive terms, after the first term, are formed by multiplying the preceding term by a constant. This constant is referred to as the **common ratio** and may be positive or negative.

Example 6.3a

GEOMETRIC PROGRESSION	NEXT TWO TERMS	COMMON RATIO
(i) 2, 4, 8, ...	16, 32	$4 \div 2 = 2$
(ii) 3, 9, 27, ...	81, 243	$9 \div 3 = 3$
(iii) 2, 10, 50, ...	250, 1250	$10 \div 2 = 5$
(iv) 3, -6, 12, ...	-24, 48	$(-6) \div 3 = -2$
(v) $\dfrac{-1}{2}, \dfrac{-1}{4}, \dfrac{-1}{8}, \cdots$	$\dfrac{-1}{16}, \dfrac{-1}{32}$	$\left(\dfrac{-1}{4}\right) \div \left(\dfrac{-1}{2}\right) = \dfrac{1}{2}$
(vi) -0.3, 1.2, -4.8, ..	19.2, -76.8	$(1.2) \div (-0.3) = -4$

Note The common ratio is found by dividing the second term by the first term (or may be found by dividing a selected term by the preceding term).

To deal with geometric progressions in a general way the following symbols will be used:

a — the value of the first term
r — the common ratio
n — the number of terms
L — the value of the last term (nth term)
S_n — the sum of the first n terms.

B. The general term of a geometric progression

A formula for finding the value of any term in a geometric progression may be developed as follows by generalizing the pattern by which geometric progressions are created.

$$
\left.\begin{array}{lllll}
t_1 = & & & = a \\
t_2 = & (t_1)(r) & = (a)(r) & = ar \\
t_3 = & (t_2)(r) & = (ar)(r) & = ar^2 \\
t_4 = & (t_3)(r) & = (ar^2)(r) & = ar^3 \\
t_5 = & (t_4)(r) & = (ar^3)(r) & = ar^4
\end{array}\right\}\longleftarrow
\begin{array}{l}
\text{note that the} \\
\text{exponent of } r \text{ is} \\
\text{always one less than} \\
\text{the position number} \\
\text{of the term}
\end{array}
$$

$$
t_{10} = (t_9)(r) = (ar^8)(r) = ar^9 \longleftarrow
\begin{array}{l}
\text{the position number is 10} \\
\text{the exponent of } r \text{ is 9}
\end{array}
$$

$$
t_n = (t_{n-1})(r) = \qquad = ar^{n-1}
$$

$$
\boxed{t_n = L = ar^{n-1}} \longleftarrow \qquad \textbf{\textit{Formula 6.7}}
$$

Example 6.3b Use the information given about each of the following geometric progressions to compute the value of the terms as indicated.

(i) $a = 5$, $r = 2$; find t_4, t_{10} and t_n.

Solution

Using Formula 6.7 $t_n = ar^{n-1}$

$t_4 = ar^{4-1}$ $\longleftarrow$ the position number $n = 4$

$\quad = 5(2)^3$

$\quad = 5(8)$

$\quad = 40$

Check The geometric progression is 5, 10, 20, 40, 80, ... ; the fourth term is 40.

$t_{10} = ar^{10-1}$

$\quad = 5(2)^9$

$\quad = 5(512)$

$\quad = 2560$

$t_n = ar^{n-1}$

$\quad = 5(2)^{n-1}$

$\quad = 5(2^n)(2^{-1}) \longleftarrow$ see Formula 2.5 or 2.6

$\quad = 5(2^n)\left(\dfrac{1}{2}\right) \longleftarrow$ see Chapter 2, negative exponents

$\quad = \dfrac{5 \times 2^n}{2}$

(ii) $a = -4$, $r = -2$; find t_8 and t_{15}.

Solution

$$t_8 = ar^{8-1} = (-4)(-2)^7 = (-4)(-128) = 512$$
$$t_{15} = ar^{15-1} = (-4)(-2)^{14} = (-4)(16384) = -65536$$

(iii) Find t_6 for the geometric progression $72, -24, 8, \ldots$

Solution

First term $a = 72$

Common ratio $r = \dfrac{-24}{72} = \dfrac{-1}{3}$

$$t_6 = ar^{6-1} = 72\left(\dfrac{-1}{3}\right)^5 = 72\left(\dfrac{-1}{243}\right) = 8\left(\dfrac{-1}{27}\right) = \dfrac{-8}{27}$$

(iv) Find the eighth term of the geometric progression $\frac{4}{9}, \frac{2}{3}, 1, \ldots$

Solution

First term $a = \dfrac{4}{9}$

Common ratio $r = \dfrac{2}{3} \div \dfrac{4}{9} = \dfrac{2}{3} \times \dfrac{9}{4} = \dfrac{3}{2}$

$$t_8 = ar^7 = \dfrac{4}{9}\left(\dfrac{3}{2}\right)^7 = \dfrac{4}{9} \times \dfrac{2187}{128} = \dfrac{243}{32}$$

Example 6.3c Find the first term, the common ratio and the tenth term of a geometric progression in which the fourth term is 324 and the seventh term is -8748.

Solution

$t_4 = ar^3 \longrightarrow ar^3 = 324 \longleftarrow ①$
$t_7 = ar^6 \longrightarrow ar^6 = -8748 \longleftarrow ②$

divide ② by ① $\longrightarrow \dfrac{ar^6}{ar^3} = \dfrac{-8748}{324}$

$$r^3 = -27$$
$$r = \sqrt[3]{-27}$$
$$r = -3$$

substitute in ① $\longrightarrow a(-3)^3 = 324$
$$-27a = 324$$
$$a = -12$$

$t_{10} = ar^9 = (-12)(-3)^9 = (-12)(-19683) = 236196$

Example 6.3d State the first four terms of a geometric progression if the fourth term is $-\frac{16}{9}$ and the ninth term is $\frac{-512}{2187}$.

Solution

$$t_4 = ar^3 \longrightarrow ar^3 = \frac{-16}{9} \quad \longleftarrow \; ①$$

$$t_9 = ar^8 \longrightarrow ar^8 = \frac{-512}{2187} \quad \longleftarrow \; ②$$

divide ② by ① $\longrightarrow \dfrac{ar^8}{ar^3} = \dfrac{\frac{-512}{2187}}{\frac{-16}{9}}$

$$r^5 = \frac{-512}{2187} \times \frac{9}{-16}$$

$$r^5 = \frac{32}{243}$$

$$r = \sqrt[5]{\frac{32}{243}}$$

$$r = \frac{2}{3}$$

substitute in ① $\longrightarrow a\left(\dfrac{2}{3}\right)^3 = \dfrac{-16}{9}$

$$\frac{8}{27}a = \frac{-16}{9}$$

$$a = \frac{-16}{9} \times \frac{27}{8}$$

$$a = -6$$

$t_1 = -6;$

$t_2 = (-6)\left(\dfrac{2}{3}\right) = -4$

$t_3 = (-4)\left(\dfrac{2}{3}\right) = \dfrac{-8}{3}$

$t_4 = \left(\dfrac{-8}{3}\right)\left(\dfrac{2}{3}\right) = \dfrac{-16}{9}$

The first four terms of the geometric progression are -6, -4, $\frac{-8}{3}$, $\frac{-16}{9}$.

C. Geometric means

The terms between two given terms of a geometric progression are referred to as the **geometric means** between the two terms. When inserting a specific number of geometric means between two given numbers, the two given numbers are considered to be the first term and the last term of the progression and the number of terms in the progression is 2 plus the number of geometric means to be inserted.

Example 6.3e Insert four geometric means between -1 and $\frac{1}{32}$.

Solution

$$n = 2 + 4 = 6$$

$$t_1 = -1 \longrightarrow a = -1 \longleftarrow \text{①}$$

$$t_6 = \frac{1}{32} \longrightarrow ar^5 = \frac{1}{32} \longleftarrow \text{②}$$

divide ② by ① $\longrightarrow r^5 = \dfrac{-1}{32}$

$$r = \sqrt[5]{\frac{-1}{32}}$$

$$r = \frac{-1}{2}$$

$$t_2 = (t_1)(r) = (-1)\left(\frac{-1}{2}\right) = \frac{1}{2}$$

$$t_3 = (t_2)(r) = \left(\frac{1}{2}\right)\left(\frac{-1}{2}\right) = \frac{-1}{4}$$

$$t_4 = (t_3)(r) = \left(\frac{-1}{4}\right)\left(\frac{-1}{2}\right) = \frac{1}{8}$$

$$t_5 = (t_4)(r) = \left(\frac{1}{8}\right)\left(\frac{-1}{2}\right) = \frac{-1}{16}$$

D. The sum of a geometric progression

The sum of a given number of terms of a geometric progression may be found by using the following technique which yields a quick answer and is useful in developing a general formula.

1. Write the sum of the terms as an indicated addition.

2. Multiply the indicated sum in (1) by the common ratio and list the resulting progression shifting each term one position to the right.

3. Subtract the progression in (2) from the progression in (1). This leaves as remainder the first term of the progression in (1) less the last term of the progression in (2).

4. Divide by the coefficient of S_n which is always $(1 - r)$.

For example, to find the sum of the geometric progression 2, 6, 18, 54, 162, 486 (where $r = 3$)

Step 1 $S_6 = 2 + 6 + 18 + 54 + 162 + 486$ ←——— write as an indicated addition

Step 2 $3S_6 = \quad\; 6 + 18 + 54 + 162 + 486 + 1458$ ←——— multiply each term by 3 and shift one position

Step 3 $S_6 - 3S_6 = 2 + 0 + 0 + 0 + 0 + 0 - 1458$ ←——— subtract

$\quad\quad -2S_6 = -1456$

Step 4 $S_6 = \dfrac{-1456}{-2}$ ←——— divide by the coefficient of S_6

$\quad\quad S_6 = 728$

This method of solution indicates that the sum of a geometric progression for a given number of terms can be found by multiplying the last term by the common ratio, subtracting the result from the first term, and dividing by the difference between 1 and the common ratio. This approach is reflected in the formula for finding the sum of the first n terms of a geometric progression

$$S_n = \frac{a - ar^n}{1 - r} = \frac{a(1 - r^n)}{1 - r}$$ ←——— *Formula 6.8*

where $a =$ the first term
$r =$ the common ratio
$n =$ the number of terms
$S_n =$ the sum to n terms.

Development of formula

$S_n = a + ar + ar^2 + ar^3 + \ldots + ar^{n-1}$ ←——————list terms

$rS_n = \quad\quad ar + ar^2 + ar^3 + \ldots + ar^{n-1} + ar^n$ ←——— multiply by r and shift

$S_n - rS_n = a + 0 + 0 + 0 + \ldots + 0 \quad - ar^n$ ←——— subtract

$S_n - rS_n = a - ar^n$ or $rS_n - S_n = ar^n - a$

$S_n(1 - r) = a(1 - r^n)$ or $S_n(r - 1) = a(r^n - 1)$

$$S_n = \frac{a(1 - r^n)}{1 - r}$$ or $$S_n = \frac{a(r^n - 1)}{r - 1}$$ ←——— *Formula 6.8*

⇑ used when $r < 1$ ⇑ used when $r > 1$

Example 6.3f Find the sum of the geometric progression 4, 12, 36, 108, 324, 972, 2916.

Solution

$$a = 4; r = \frac{12}{4} = 3; n = 7$$

Since $r > 1$, use $S_n = \frac{a(r^n - 1)}{r - 1}$.

$$S_7 = \frac{4(3^7 - 1)}{3 - 1}$$

$$= \frac{4(2187 - 1)}{2}$$

$$= 2(2186)$$

$$= 4372$$

Example 6.3g Find the sum of each of the following geometric progressions to the number of terms indicated.

(i) 3, −6, 12, ... to ten terms

  Solution

$$a = 3; r = \frac{(-6)}{3} = -2; n = 10$$

Since $r < 1$, use $S_n = \frac{a(1 - r^n)}{1 - r}$.

$$S_{10} = \frac{3\left[1 - (-2)^{10}\right]}{1 - (-2)}$$

$$= \frac{3(1 - 1024)}{1 + 2}$$

$$= -1023$$

(ii) 24, −12, 6, −3, ... to twelve terms

  Solution

$$a = 24; r = \frac{(-12)}{24} = \frac{-1}{2}; n = 12$$

$$S_{12} = \frac{24\left[1 - \left(-\frac{1}{2}\right)^{12}\right]}{1 - \left(-\frac{1}{2}\right)} \quad \longleftarrow r < 1$$

$$= \frac{24\left[1 - \frac{1}{4096}\right]}{1 + \frac{1}{2}}$$

$$= \frac{24\left[\frac{4096 - 1}{4096}\right]}{\frac{3}{2}}$$

$$= 24\left(\frac{4095}{4096}\right)\left(\frac{2}{3}\right)$$

$$= \frac{4095}{256}\left(\text{or } 15\frac{255}{256}\right)$$

(iii) $\dfrac{-4}{9}, \dfrac{-2}{3}, -1, \ldots$ to eight terms

Solution

$$a = \frac{-4}{9}; r = \left(\frac{-2}{3}\right) \div \left(\frac{-4}{9}\right) = \left(\frac{-2}{3}\right)\left(\frac{9}{-4}\right) = \frac{3}{2}; n = 8$$

$$t_8 = \frac{\left(\frac{-4}{9}\right)\left[\left(\frac{3}{2}\right)^8 - 1\right]}{\frac{3}{2} - 1} \quad \longleftarrow r > 1$$

$$= \frac{\left(\frac{-4}{9}\right)\left[\frac{6561}{256} - 1\right]}{\frac{1}{2}}$$

$$= \left(\frac{-4}{9}\right)\left(\frac{2}{1}\right)\left(\frac{6561 - 256}{256}\right)$$

$$= \left(\frac{-8}{9}\right)\left(\frac{6305}{256}\right)$$

$$= \frac{-6305}{(9)(32)}$$

$$= \frac{-6305}{288}\left(\text{or } -21\frac{257}{288}\right)$$

(iv) $1, 1.02, 1.02^2, 1.02^3, \ldots$ to sixteen terms

Solution

$$a = 1; r = \frac{1.02}{1} = 1.02; n = 16$$

$$S_{16} = \frac{1(1.02^{16} - 1)}{1.02 - 1} \quad \longleftarrow r > 1$$

$$= \frac{1.02^{16} - 1}{0.02}$$

$$= \frac{1.3727857 - 1}{0.02}$$

$$= \frac{0.3727857}{0.02}$$

$$= 18.639285$$

(v) $1, (1 + i), (1 + i)^2, (1 + i)^3, \ldots$ to 60 terms $(i > 0)$

Solution

$a = 1; r = (1 + i); n = 60$

$$S_{60} = \frac{1\left[(1 + i)^{60} - 1\right]}{(1 + i) - 1}$$

$$= \frac{(1 + i)^{60} - 1}{i}$$

Exercise 6.3

A. For each of the following geometric progressions find the value of the term as indicated.

   1. t_{10} for 6, 12, 24, ...

   2. t_6 for $-5, 15, -45, \ldots$

   3. t_7 for 12, 6, 3, ...

   4. t_5 for $-36, -24, -16, \ldots$

B. Insert geometric means between the two given values as indicated.

   1. Insert one geometric mean between 3 and 48.

   2. Insert two geometric means between 24 and -3.

C. For each of the following geometric progressions determine the sum to the number of terms indicated.

   1. Find the sum of the first twelve terms of 1, 2, 4, ...

   2. Find the sum of the first seven terms of 2, -6, 18, ...

   3. Find the sum of the first six terms of 128, 32, 8, ...

   4. Find the sum of the first four terms of $\frac{9}{4}, \frac{-3}{2}, 1, \ldots$

   5. Use a calculator to determine the sum of $1, 1.05, 1.05^2, \ldots$ to 15 terms.

   6. Use a calculator to determine the sum of $1, \frac{1}{1.02}, \frac{1}{1.02^2}, \ldots$ to ten terms.

D. Use the information given about each of the following geometric progressions to determine the value indicated (optional).

   1. The first term is 1; the fourth term is -125. Find r.

   2. $a = 8; t_7 = \frac{1}{8}$; find t_4.

   3. $a = -6; r = 3; t_n = -486$; find n.

   4. The first term is -16; the common ratio is $-\frac{1}{4}; t_n = \frac{1}{64}$. Find S_n.

   5. $a = -2; r = 3; S_n = -728$. Find t_4.

   6. $t_1 = \frac{1}{16}; r = -2; S_n = \frac{-85}{16}$. Find t_n.

7. $a = -1; t_n = 125; S_n = 104$. Find n.

8. $a = \frac{1}{8}; t_n = 128; S_n = \frac{1365}{8}$. Find n.

9. $r = -3; t_n = -729; S_n = -547$. Find t_5.

10. $r = \frac{2}{3}; t_n = \frac{4}{9}; S_n = \frac{211}{36}$. Find t_1.

6.4 Logarithms—basic aspects

A. The concept of logarithm

In Chapter 2 Section 2.5, and Chapter 6 Section 6.1, the exponential form of writing numbers was considered.

$64 = 2^6 \longrightarrow$ the number 64 is represented as a power of 2

$243 = 3^5 \longrightarrow$ the number 243 is represented as a power of 3

$10000 = 10^4 \longrightarrow$ the number 10 000 is represented as a power of 10

$5 = 125^{\frac{1}{3}} \longrightarrow$ the number 5 is represented as a power of 125

$0.001 = 10^{-3} \longrightarrow$ the number 0.001 is represented as a power of 10

In general, when a number is represented as a base raised to an exponent, the exponent is called a logarithm. A **logarithm** is defined as the *exponent* to which a base must be raised in order to produce a given number.

Accordingly, and referring back to the previous examples,

in $64 = 2^6$,   6 is the logarithm of 64 to the base 2 which is written $6 = \log_2 64$;

in $243 = 3^5$,   5 is the logarithm of 243 to the base 3 which is written
$5 = \log_3 243$;

in $10000 = 10^4$, 4 is the logarithm of 10 000 to the base 10 which is written
$4 = \log_{10} 10000$;

in $5 = 125^{\frac{1}{3}}, \frac{1}{3}$ is the logarithm of 5 to the base 125 which is written $\frac{1}{3} = \log_{125} 5$

in $0.001 = 10^{-3}$, -3 is the logarithm of 0.001 to the base 10 which is written
$-3 = \log_{10} 0.001$.

In general   if $N = b^y$ $\longleftarrow$ *exponential* form

then $y = \log_b N \longleftarrow$ *logarithmic* form

Example 6.4a Write each of the following numbers in exponential form and in logarithmic form using the base as indicated.

(i) 32 base 2

(ii) 81 base 3

(iii) 256 base 4

(iv) 100000 base 10

(v) 6 base 36

(vi) 3 base 27

(vii) 0.0001 base 10

(viii) $\frac{1}{8}$ base 2

Solution

Exponential Form	Logarithmic Form

(i) Since $32 = 2 \times 2 \times 2 \times 2 \times 2$

$\qquad 32 = 2^5$ $\qquad\qquad\qquad\qquad 5 = \log_2 32$

(ii) Since $81 = 3 \times 3 \times 3 \times 3$

$\qquad 81 = 3^4$ $\qquad\qquad\qquad\qquad 4 = \log_3 81$

(iii) Since $256 = 4 \times 4 \times 4 \times 4$

$\qquad 256 = 4^4$ $\qquad\qquad\qquad\qquad 4 = \log_4 256$

(iv) Since $100000 = 10 \times 10 \times 10 \times 10 \times 10$

$\qquad 100000 = 10^5$ $\qquad\qquad\qquad\qquad 5 = \log_{10} 100000$

(v) Since $6 = \sqrt{36}$

$\qquad\qquad 6 = 36^{\frac{1}{2}}$ $\qquad\qquad\qquad\qquad \frac{1}{2} = \log_{36} 6$

(vi) Since $3 = \sqrt[3]{27}$

$\qquad\qquad 3 = 27^{\frac{1}{3}}$ $\qquad\qquad\qquad\qquad \frac{1}{3} = \log_{27} 3$

(vii) Since $0.0001 = \dfrac{1}{10000} = \dfrac{1}{10^4}$

$\qquad\qquad 0.0001 = 10^{-4}$ $\qquad\qquad\qquad\qquad -4 = \log_{10} 0.0001$

(viii) Since $\dfrac{1}{8} = \dfrac{1}{2^3}$

$\qquad\qquad \dfrac{1}{8} = 2^{-3}$ $\qquad\qquad\qquad\qquad -3 = \log_2 \dfrac{1}{8}$

B.   Common logarithms

While the base b may be any positive number other than 1, only the numbers 10 and e are used in practice.

Logarithms with base 10 are referred to as **common logarithms**. Obtained from the exponential function $x = 10^y$, the notation used to represent common logarithms is $y = \log x$. (The base 10 is understood and thus not written).

By definition then, the common logarithm of a number is the exponent to which the base 10 must be raised to give that number.

$\log 1000 = 3$ since $1000 = 10^3$

$\log 1000000 = 6$ since $1000000 = 10^6$

$\log 0.01 = -2$ since $0.01 = 10^{-2}$

$\log 0.0001 = -4$ since $0.0001 = 10^{-4}$

$\log 1 = 0$ since $1 = 10^0$

Historically common logarithms were used for numerical calculations such as required in problems involving compound interest. However with the availability of electronic calculators equipped with a power function, the need for common logarithms as a computational tool has largely disappeared. Accordingly no further consideration is given to common logarithms in this text.

C. Natural logarithms

The most common exponential function is $y = e^x$
where $e = \lim_{n \to \infty} (1 + \frac{1}{n})^n = 2.718\ 281\ 828\ 5$ approximately.

The logarithmic form of this function is $x = \log_e y$ but is always written as $x = \ln y$ and is referred to as **natural logarithm**.

Electronic calculators equipped with the universal power function are also generally equipped with the e^x function and the $\ln x$ function (natural logarithm function).

This latter function eliminates any need for common logarithms and should be used to solve certain problems involving compound interest.

D. Useful relationships

The following relationships are helpful when using natural logarithms.

1. The logarithm of a product of two or more positive numbers is the sum of the logarithms of the factors.

$$\ln (ab) = \ln a + \ln b \quad \longleftarrow \textit{Formula \textbf{6.9}}$$

$$\ln (abc) = \ln a + \ln b + \ln c$$

2. The logarithm of the quotient of two positive numbers is equal to the logarithm of the dividend (numerator) minus the logarithm of the divisor (denominator).

$$\ln \left(\frac{a}{b}\right) = \ln a - \ln b \quad \longleftarrow \textit{Formula \textbf{6.10}}$$

3. The logarithm of a power of a positive number is the exponent of the power multiplied by the logarithm of the number.

$$\ln (a^k) = k(\ln a) \quad \longleftarrow \textit{Formula \textbf{6.11}}$$

4. (i) $\ln e = 1$ since $e = e^1$
   (ii) $\ln 1 = 0$ since $1 = e^0$

Example 6.4b Use an electronic calculator equipped with a natural logarithm function to find n in each of the following.

(i) $2000 = 1500(1.05^n)$

(ii) $10000(1.0125^{-n}) = 8057.32$

(iii) $2.00 = 1.00e^{0.1n}$

Solution

(i)　　$2000 = 1500(1.05^n)$

$\ln 2000 = \ln 1500(1.05^n)$ ←——— take the natural logarithm of each side

$\ln 2000 = \ln 1500 + \ln 1.05^n$ ←——— using Formula 6.9

$\ln 2000 = \ln 1500 + n \ln 1.05$ ←——— using Formula 6.11

$7.6009025 = 7.3132204 + n(0.04879016)$ ←——— using the $\ln x$ function

$0.2876821 = 0.04879016n$

$$n = \frac{0.2876821}{0.04879016}$$

$n = 5.896$ (approximately)

Alternatively (and more efficiently)

$2000 = 1500(1.05^n)$

$1.05^n = \dfrac{2000}{1500}$ ←——— divide by 1500 to isolate the term containing n

$1.05^n = 1.3333333$ ←——— simplify

$n \ln 1.05 = \ln 1.3333333$ ←——— using Formula 6.11

$n(0.04879016) = 0.2876821$

$$n = \frac{0.2876821}{0.04879016}$$

$n = 5.896$

(ii)　　$10000(1.0125^{-n}) = 8057.32$

$1.0125^{-n} = 0.805732$

$(-n)(\ln 1.0125) = \ln 0.805732$

$(-n)(0.0124225) = -0.2160041$

$$n = \frac{0.2160041}{0.0124225}$$

$n = 17.388$ (approximately)

(iii) $\qquad 2.00 = 1.00 e^{0.1n}$

$\qquad e^{0.1n} = 2.00$

$\qquad (0.1n)(\ln e) = \ln 2.00$

$\qquad (0.1n)(1) = \ln 2.00 \longleftarrow \ln e = 1$

$\qquad 0.1n = 0.6931472$

$\qquad n = 6.93$

Exercise 6.4

A. Express each of the following in logarithmic form.

  1. $2^9 = 512$ **2.** $3^7 = 2187$

  3. $5^{-3} = \frac{1}{125}$ **4.** $10^{-5} = 0.00001$

  5. $e^{2j} = 18$ **6.** $e^{-3x} = 12$

B. Write each of the following in exponential form.

  1. $\log_2 32 = 5$ **2.** $\log_3 \frac{1}{81} = -4$

  3. $\log_{10} 10 = 1$ **4.** $\ln e^2 = 2$

C. Use an electronic calculator equipped with a natural logarithm function to evaluate each of the following.

  1. $\ln 2$ **2.** $\ln 200$

  3. $\ln 0.105$ **4.** $\ln 0.01$

  5. $6500.00 = 575.00(1.01)\left[\dfrac{(1.01^n - 1)}{0.01}\right]$

  6. $5400.00 = 600.00\left[\dfrac{1 - 1.035^{-n}}{0.035}\right]$

Review exercise

1. Use an electronic calculator to compute each of the following.

  (a) $\sqrt{0.9216}$

  (b) $\sqrt[6]{1.075}$

  (c) $14.974458^{\frac{1}{40}}$

  (d) $1.08^{-\frac{5}{12}}$

  (e) $\ln 3$

  (f) $\ln 0.05$

(g) $140000.00 = 5500.00(1.1146213)\left(\dfrac{1.1146213^n - 1}{0.1146213}\right)$

(h) $21500.00 = 375.00(1.0099016^{-9})\left(\dfrac{1 - 1.0099016^{-n}}{0.0099016}\right)$

2. Using the information given about each of the following arithmetic progressions, compute the values indicated.

(a) Find t_{12} for 32, 25, 18, ...

(b) Find t_9 for $t_1 = -2$, $d = \frac{2}{5}$.

(c) Insert three arithmetic means between $+8$ and -12.

(d) Find the sum of the first eleven terms of -11, -7, -3, ...

(e) Find S_{16} when $t_1 = 3$ and $d = 4$.

(f) Find S_{20} if $S_6 = 60$ and $S_{13} = 494$.

3. Using the information given about each of the following geometric progressions, compute the values indicated.

(a) Find t_7 for 2, -6, 18, ...

(b) Find t_6 for $t_1 = 48$, $r = \frac{1}{4}$.

(c) Insert two geometric means between 16 and 2.

(d) Find the sum of the first nine terms of -1, 2, -4, ...

(e) Find the sum of 1, 1.01, 1.01^2, ... to 24 terms.

(f) Find the sum of 1.03^{-1}, 1.03^{-2}, 1.03^{-3} ... to 20 terms.

(g) Find n if $a = 24$, $r = \frac{1}{2}$, $t_n = \frac{3}{2}$.

(h) Find r and n if $a = 5$, $t_n = 40$, $S_n = 75$.

Self-test

1. Use an electronic calculator to compute each of the following.

(a) $\sqrt[10]{1.35}$

(b) $\dfrac{1 - 1.03^{-40}}{0.03}$

(c) $\ln 1.025$

(d) $\ln 0.05$

2. Solve each of the following equations.

(a) $\dfrac{1}{81} = \left(\dfrac{1}{3}\right)^{n-2}$

(b) $\dfrac{5}{2} = 40\left(\dfrac{1}{2}\right)^{n-1}$

3. Find the sum of the first forty terms of the arithmetic progression -15, -13, -11, ...

4. Find the first term and the common difference in an arithmetic progression in which $S_{18} = 873$ and $S_{30} = -165$.

5. Determine the value of the sixth term in a geometric progression with first term 24 and common ratio $-\frac{1}{3}$.

6. Find the sum of the first five terms of the sequence $-\frac{1}{25}, \frac{1}{5}, -1, \ldots$

7. Find n in $15480.20 = 1600.00(1.0418198)\left(\dfrac{1 - 1.0418198^{-n}}{0.0418198}\right)$.

8. Find the common ratio if the first term of a geometric progression is $-\frac{1}{9}$ and $t_5 = -9$.

Summary of formulae used

Formula 6.1	$a^{\frac{1}{n}} = \sqrt[n]{a}$	the definition of a fractional exponent with numerator 1
Formula 6.2	$a^{-\frac{1}{n}} = \dfrac{1}{\sqrt[n]{a}}$	the definition of a fractional exponent with numerator -1
Formula 6.3	$a^{\frac{m}{n}} = \sqrt[n]{a^m}$	the definition of a positive fractional exponent
Formula 6.4	$a^{-\frac{m}{n}} = \dfrac{1}{\sqrt[n]{a^m}}$	the definition of a negative fractional exponent
Formula 6.5	$t_n = L = a + (n - 1)d$	the expression used to represent the nth term of an arithmetic progression
Formula 6.6	$S_n = \dfrac{n}{2}(a + L)$ or $S_n = \dfrac{n}{2}\left[2a + (n - 1)d\right]$	the formula used to determine the sum of the first n terms of an arithmetic progression
Formula 6.7	$t_n = L = ar^{n-1}$	the expression used to represent the nth term of a geometric progression
Formula 6.8	$S_n = \dfrac{a(1 - r^n)}{1 - r}$	formula used for finding the sum to n terms of a geometric progression
Formula 6.9	$\ln(ab) = \ln a + \ln b$	relationship used to find the logarithm of a product

Formula 6.10 $\ln\left(\dfrac{a}{b}\right) = \ln a - \ln b$ relationship used to find the logarithm of a quotient

Formula 6.11 $\ln(a^k) = k(\ln a)$ relationship used to find the logarithm of a power

Glossary of terms used

Index   the power of the root indicated with the radical symbol

Power of a root   the exponent indicating the number of equal factors

Radical   the indicated root when using the radical symbol for finding a root

Radicand   the number under the radical symbol

Root of a product   one of the equal factors in the product

Arithmetic means   the terms between two terms of an arithmetic progression

Arithmetic progression   a sequence of numbers in which the successive terms after the first term are formed by adding a constant to the preceding term

Common difference   the constant used to generate the terms of an arithmetic progression

Common ratio   the constant used to generate the terms of a geometric progression

Geometric means   the terms between two given terms of a geometric progression

Geometric progression   a sequence of numbers in which the successive terms after the first term are formed by multiplying the preceding term by a constant

Sequence   a set of numbers arranged in a definite pattern according to a definite rule

Terms   the numbers in a sequence

Common logarithms   logarithms with base 10 represented by the notation $\log x$

Logarithm   the exponent to which a base must be raised to produce a given number

Natural logarithms   logarithms with base e represented by the notation $\ln x$

PART TWO

Mathematics of business and management

7 *Linear application*

Introduction

The main concern for owners and management in operating a business is profitability. To achieve or maintain a desired level of profitability, decisions must be made which affect product mix, total revenue and total cost.

A valuable tool in evaluating the potential effects of decisions on profitability is known as cost-volume-profit analysis. Linear programming is a useful mathematical technique in making decisions regarding product mix.

Objectives

Upon completion of this chapter you will be able to

1. perform linear cost-volume-profit analysis including the development of a detailed break-even chart and algebraic computations of break-even point, net income for various levels of output and output required to generate a desired net income;

2. graphically solve two-product linear programming problems involving the maximization of profit.

7.1 *Cost-volume-profit analysis*

A. *Cost-volume-profit relationships*

A primary function of accounting is the collection of cost and revenue data which may then be used to examine the existing relationships between cost behaviour and revenue behaviour.

Any analysis, whether graphical or algebraic, makes certain assumptions about the behaviour of costs and revenue. In its simplest form, cost-volume-profit analysis makes the following assumptions.

1. Revenue per unit of output is constant. Thus total revenue varies directly with volume.

2. Costs can be classified to be either fixed or variable.

3. **Fixed costs** are those costs which remain constant over the time period considered for all levels of output. Examples of costs in this category are depreciation, rent, property taxes, supervision and management salaries.
   Since fixed costs are constant in total, they vary per unit of output. They decrease per unit of output as volume increases and increase per unit of output as volume decreases.

4. **Variable costs** are costs that are constant per unit of output regardless of volume and thus fluctuate in total amount as volume fluctuates. Examples of costs in this category are direct material costs, direct labour costs and sales commissions.

The above assumptions present a simplified view of the real world. Fixed costs are not constant across all levels of output but tend to change in a step-like manner. Per unit variable costs are not always constant but are influenced by economies of scale. There is no black and white classification of costs into fixed costs and variable costs; rather many costs are semi-variable, that is they contain a fixed component as well as a variable component. However, for purposes of an uncomplicated introductory analysis, the assumptions made serve a useful purpose.

Using these simplifying assumptions, the behaviour of revenue and the behaviour of costs may be represented graphically by straight-line diagrams as shown in Figures 7.1 and 7.2.

FIGURE 7.1 *Revenue behaviour*

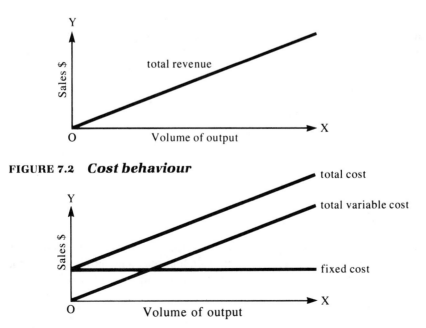

FIGURE 7.2 *Cost behaviour*

The following components are basic to cost-volume-profit relationships and mathematical notation will be used for these components as indicated.

$$X = \text{Volume of output}$$
$$P = \text{Selling price (revenue) per unit of output}$$
$$TR = \text{Total revenue}$$
$$TC = \text{Total cost}$$
$$FC = \text{Fixed cost}$$
$$TVC = \text{Total variable cost}$$
$$VC = \text{Variable cost per unit of output}$$
$$NI = \text{Net income (profit).}$$

The accounting relationship (income statement equation)

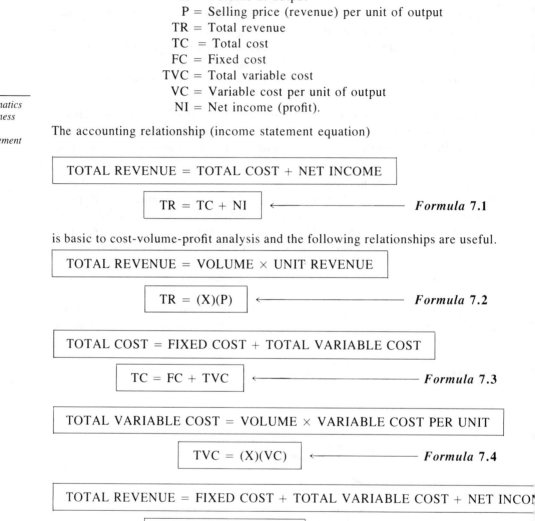

TOTAL REVENUE = TOTAL COST + NET INCOME

$$TR = TC + NI \qquad \longleftarrow \qquad \textit{Formula 7.1}$$

is basic to cost-volume-profit analysis and the following relationships are useful.

TOTAL REVENUE = VOLUME × UNIT REVENUE

$$TR = (X)(P) \qquad \longleftarrow \qquad \textit{Formula 7.2}$$

TOTAL COST = FIXED COST + TOTAL VARIABLE COST

$$TC = FC + TVC \qquad \longleftarrow \qquad \textit{Formula 7.3}$$

TOTAL VARIABLE COST = VOLUME × VARIABLE COST PER UNIT

$$TVC = (X)(VC) \qquad \longleftarrow \qquad \textit{Formula 7.4}$$

TOTAL REVENUE = FIXED COST + TOTAL VARIABLE COST + NET INCOME

$$TR = FC + TVC + NI \qquad \longleftarrow \qquad \textit{Formula 7.5}$$

B. Break-even analysis

The most popular approach to cost-volume-profit analysis is referred to as **break-even analysis**. The break-even approach focuses on the profitability of the business and is specifically concerned with identifying the level of output at which the business neither makes a profit nor sustains a loss, that is the level of output at which

$$\text{NET INCOME} = 0$$

The level of output at which NI = 0 is referred to as the **break-even point** and is obtainable from Formula 7.1 (or Formula 7.5). Since NI = 0, the break-even point is the level of output at which

$$\text{TOTAL REVENUE} = \text{TOTAL COST}$$

The relationship between revenue and costs at different levels of output may be portrayed graphically by showing revenue behaviour (Figurue 7.1) and cost behaviour (Figure 7.2) on the same graph. The resulting graph shows the break-even point and is known as a break-even chart (see Figure 7.3).

FIGURE 7.3 *Break-even chart*

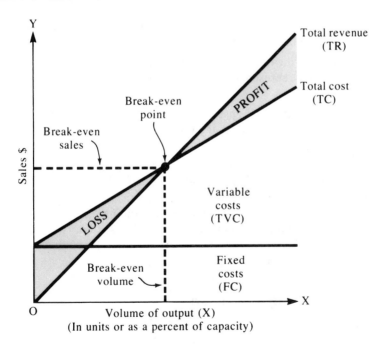

Notes to the charts

1. The horizontal axis is used to represent volume of output either as a number of units or as a percent of capacity. The vertical axis represents dollar values (sales revenue). The origin is at zero—representing zero volume and zero dollars.

2. The total revenue line is drawn by plotting two or more total revenue points (one of which is always the origin) and joining them.

3. The fixed cost line is drawn parallel to the horizontal axis from a point on the vertical axis which represents total fixed cost dollars.

4. The total cost line is drawn by plotting two or more total cost points (one of which is always the point were the fixed cost line starts on the vertical axis) and joining them.

5. The point where the total revenue line and the total cost line intersect is the break-even point.

6. The point of intersection on the horizontal axis of the perpendicular drawn from the break-even point to the horizontal axis indicates the break-even volume in units or as a percent of capacity.

7. The point of intersection on the vertical axis of the perpendicular drawn from the break-even point to the vertical axis indicates the break-even volume in dollars ($Sales).

8. The area between the horizontal axis and the fixed cost line represents the fixed cost in dollars.

9. The area between the fixed cost line and the total cost line represents the total variable cost in dollars for the various levels of operations.

10. The area between the total revenue line and the total cost line to the left of the break-even point represents the loss area where total revenue is less than total cost.

11. The area between the total cost line and the total revenue line to the right of the break-even point represents the profit area where total revenue is greater than total cost.

The graphical approach resulting in a break-even chart is complemented by an algebraic approach which utilizes Formulae 7.1 and 7.5.

Both approaches are illustrated in the examples that follow involving the two distinct situations which may be encountered depending on the accounting data that is available. For the first situation, illustrated in section C, the accounting information is in terms of units. For the second situation, illustrated in section D, the accounting information is in terms of total dollars.

C. Break-even analysis—Case 1

The available accounting data is in terms of units.

Example 7.1a   Market research for a new product indicates that the product can be sold at $50.00 per unit. Cost analysis provides the following information.

Fixed cost per period = $8640.00
Variable cost per unit = $30.00
Production capacity per period = 900 units

Perform a break-even analysis providing

(i) an algebraic statement of
    (a) the **revenue function,**
    (b) the **cost function,**

(ii) a detailed break-even chart,

(iii) computation of the break-even point
    (a) in units,
    (b) as a percent of capacity,
    (c) in dollars.

Solution

(i) Let the volume in units be X.

(a) TR = (X)(P) ⟵——— using Formula 7.2
        = (X)(50.00)
        = 50.00X

The revenue function is TR = 50X.

(b) TVC = (X)(VC) ⟵——— using Formula 7.4
         = (X)(30.00)
         = 30.00X

TC = FC + TVC ⟵——— using Formula 7.3
   = 8640.00 + 30.00X

The cost function is TC = 8640 + 30X.

(ii) *Break-Even Chart*

The break-even chart can be drawn by graphing the revenue function, TR = 50X, and the cost function, TC = 8640 + 30X.
    Since capacity is 900 units, the horizontal scale needs to allow for X values up to 900. The vertical scale must allow for maximum sales dollars of (900)(50) = 45 000.

Graphing the revenue function, TR = 50X

To graph the revenue function, assume at least two values of X and compute the corresponding value of TR.

   For X = 0, TR = (50)(0) = 0 ⟶ Graph point (0,0)

   For X = 900, TR = (50)(900) = 45000 ⟶ Graph point (900, 45 000)

   While any value of X may be used, the two values selected are the preferred values as they represent the two extreme values (minimum and maximum volume) for the situation.

Graphing the cost function, TC = 8640 + 30 X

Assume two values of X and compute the corresponding value of TC.

For X = 0,   TC = 8640 + 30(0)   = 8640 $\longrightarrow$ Graph point (0,8640)

For X = 900, TC = 8640 + 30(900)

= 8640 + 27000   = 35640 $\longrightarrow$ Graph (900,35 640)

FIGURE 7.4   *Break-even chart for example 7.1a*

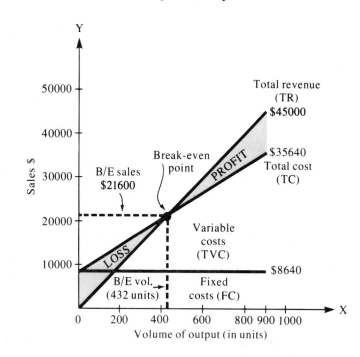

(iii) To determine the break-even point, the basic relationship between revenue and total cost is useful.

$$TR = FC + TVC + NI \longleftarrow \textit{Formula 7.5}$$

To break-even, NI = 0.

TR   = FC + TVC

50X = 8640 + 30X

20X = 8640

X = 432

(a) The break-even volume in units is 432.

(b) As a percent of capacity, the break-even volume is $\dfrac{432}{900}$ = 0.48 = 48%.

(c) The break-even volume in dollars = (432)(50) = $21 600.

D. Break-even analysis—Case 2

The available accounting data is in terms of total dollars.

Example 7.1b The following information is available about the operations of the King Corp. for the current year.

Sales		$40000
Fixed costs	$12600	
Variable costs	16000	
Total cost		28600
Net income		$11400

Capacity is a sales volume of $60 000.
Perform a break-even analysis providing

(i) an algebraic statement of
  (a) the revenue function,
  (b) the cost function;

(ii) a detailed break-even chart;

(iii) computation of the break-even point
  (a) in sales dollars,
  (b) as a percent of capacity.

Solution
(i) When the data is in terms of dollars rather than units, the functions should be expressed in terms of sales volume.

Let X represent the sales volume in dollars.

(a) The revenue function is TR = X.

(b) Since variable costs are directly related to sales volume, they may be expressed as a percent of sales volume.
In this example, total variable costs are $16 000 for a sales volume of $40 000.

$$\frac{TVC}{TR} = \frac{16000}{40000} = 0.40 = 40\%$$

$$TVC = 0.40 \text{ TR} = 40\% \text{ of TR}$$

The cost function is TC = 12600 + 0.40 TR
or TC = 12600 + 0.40 X

(ii) When the accounting data is in terms of total dollars, the horizontal axis is used to represent output in terms of percent of sales capacity. The horizontal scale should be subdivided to allow percent sales levels up to 100%. The vertical scale must allow for the maximum sales level of $60 000.

Graphing the Revenue Function, TR = X

To graph the revenue function assume at least two sales volume levels expressed as a percent of capacity.
For X = 0,   TR = 0 ——→ Graph point (0,0)
For X = 60000, TR = 60000 ——→ Graph point (60000, 60000)

The revenue function is represented by the line joining the two points.

Graphing the Cost Function, TC = 12600 + 0.40X

Assume two sales volume levels and compute TC.

For X = 0,   TC = 12600 + 0.40(0)
                  = 12600 ——→ Graph Point (0,12600)
For X = 60000, TC = 12600 + 0.40 (60000)
                  = 12600 + 24000
                  = 36600 ——→ Graph Point (60000, 36600)

FIGURE 7.5   ***Break-even chart for example 7.1b***

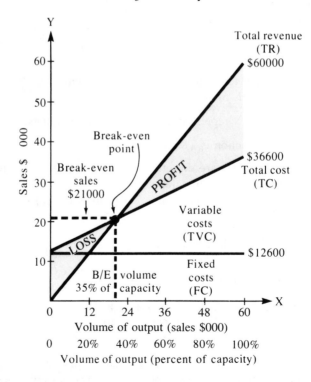

(iii) Using the basic relationship

$$TR = FC + TVC + NI \longleftarrow \textit{Formula 7.5}$$

and letting NI = 0

the break-even point is given by

$$X = 12600 + 0.40 \, X$$
$$0.60 \, X = 12600$$
$$X = 21000$$

(a) The break-even volume in dollars is $21 000.

(b) The break-even point is $\dfrac{21000}{60000} = 35\%$ of sales capacity.

E. Algebraic analysis

Break-even analysis focuses on one particular level of operations. However the accounting relationship

$$TR = FC + TVC + NI \longleftarrow \textit{Formula 7.5}$$

can be used to extend cost-volume-profit analysis to any desired level of operations. It is thus possible to determine the net income at any level of operations and to analyze what effect changes in selling price, fixed cost or variable costs have on profitability at any level of operations.

Example 7.1c Use the information in Example 7.1a to answer each of the following questions.

(i) What is the net income at a volume of

(a) 385 units?   (b) 780 units?

Solution

$$TR = 50X$$
$$TC = 8640 + 30X$$

The basic accounting relationship (using Formula 7.5) is
$$50X = 8640 + 30X + NI.$$

(a)   For X = 385
$$50(385) = 8640 + 30(385) + NI$$
$$19250 = 8640 + 11550 + NI$$
$$NI = -940 \text{ (a loss)}$$

The net income (loss) at a volume of 385 units is ($940).

(b)   For X = 780
$$50(780) = 8640 + 30(780) + NI$$
$$39000 = 8640 + 23400 + NI$$
$$NI = 6960$$

The net income at a volume of 780 units is $6960.

(ii) What is the net income at a sales volume of
    (a) $17 500?   (b) $40 000?

Solution

(a) At a sales volume of $17 500

$$50X = 17500$$
$$X = 350 \text{ (units)}$$
$$50(350) = 8640 + 30(350) + NI$$
$$17500 = 8640 + 10500 + NI$$
$$NI = -1640$$

The net income (loss) at a volume of $17 500 is ($1640).

(b) At a sales volume of $40 000,

$$50X = 40000$$
$$X = 800 \text{ (units)}$$
$$50(800) = 8640 + 30(800) + NI$$
$$40000 = 8640 + 24000 + NI$$

$$NI = 7360$$

The net income at a sales volume of $40 000 is $7360.

(iii) What is the net income at a sales volume of
    (a) 36% of capacity?   (b) 95% of capacity?

Solution

(a) Sales volume is 36% of 900 = 324 units.

$$50(324) = 8640 + 30(324) + NI$$
$$16200 = 8640 + 9720 + NI$$
$$NI = -2160$$

The net income at 36% of capacity is ($2160).

(b) Sales volume is 95% of 900 = 855 units.

$$50(855) = 8640 + 30(855) + NI$$
$$42750 = 8640 + 25650 + NI$$
$$NI = 8460$$

The net income at 95% capacity is $8460.

(iv) What is the number of units that must be sold to generate a net income of
    (a) ($1000)?   (b) $3000?

Solution

(a) $50X = 8640 + 30X - 1000$
      $20X = 7640$
         $X = 382$

To generate a net income of ($1000) the sales volume must be 382 units.

(b) $50X = 8640 + 30X + 3000$

   $\ 20X = 11640$

   $X = 582$

To generate a net income of $3000 the sales volume must be 582 units.

(v) What is the sales volume in dollars that generates a net income of
   (a) ($1600)?   (b) $7200?

   Solution

   (a) $50X = 8640 + 30X - 1600$

   $\ 20X = 7040$

   $X = 352$ (units)

   The sales volume is $(352)(50) = \$17600$.

   (b) $50X = 8640 + 30X + 7200$

   $\ 20X = 15840$

   $X = 792$ (units)

   The sales volume is $(792)(50) = \$39600$.

(vi) What is the output required, as a percent of capacity, to generate a net income of

   (a) $360?   (b) $5760?

   Solution

   (a) $50X = 8640 + 30X + 360$

   $\ 20X = 9000$

   $X = 450$ (units)

   The required output is $\frac{450}{900} = 0.50 = 50\%$ of capacity.

   (b) $50X = 8640 + 30X + 5760$

   $\ 20X = 14400$

   $X = 720$ (units)

   The required output is $\frac{720}{900} = 0.80 = 80\%$ of capacity.

(vii) What is the break-even point if fixed costs are increased to $10 400
   (a) in units?   (b) in dollars?   (c) as a percent of capacity?

   Solution

   If fixed costs are increased to $10 400, the basic relationship (Formula 7.5) becomes

   $$50X = 10400 + 30X + NI$$

   To break-even, $NI = 0$.

   $\ 50X = 10400 + 30X$

   $\ 20X = 10400$

   $X = 520$ (units)

(a) The break-even point in units is 520.

(b) The break-even point in dollars is 520(50) = $26 000.

(c) The break-even point as a percent of capacity is
$\frac{520}{900}$ = 0.57777778 = 57.8%

(viii) What is the break-even point in dollars if fixed costs are reduced by $990 and variable cost per unit is increased by $2?

Solution

The new fixed cost is 8640 − 990 = $7650 and the new variable cost per unit is 30 + 2 = $32. The basic relationship (Formula 7.5) becomes

$50X = 7650 + 32X + NI$

To break-even, $NI = 0$.
$$50X = 7650 + 32X$$
$$18X = 7650$$
$$X = 425 \text{ (units)}$$

The break-even point is (425)(50) = $21 250.

(ix) What is the break-even point as a percent of capacity if the selling price is reduced by 10%?

Solution

The new selling price = 90% of $50 = $45.
The basic relationship becomes

$45X = 8640 + 30X + NI$

To break-even, $NI = 0$.
$$45X = 8640 + 30X$$
$$15X = 8640$$
$$X = 576 \text{ (units)}$$

The break-even point is $\frac{576}{900}$ = 0.64 = 64% of capacity.

(x) To generate a profit of $4860, what dollar sales must be attained if selling price per unit is

(a) reduced to $48?   (b) increased to $55?

Solution

(a) $48X = 8640 + 30X + 4860$
$$18X = 13500$$
$$X = 750 \text{ (units)}$$

Sales volume must be (750)(48) = $36 000.

(b) $55X = 8640 + 30X + 4860$
$$25X = 13500$$
$$X = 540 \text{ (units)}$$

Sales volume must be (540)(55) = $29 700.

(xi) What is the output as a percent of capacity that must be achieved to generate a profit of $7830 if the production setup is modified so that fixed costs increase by 25% while variable costs are reduced by 10%?

Solution

The new fixed costs $= 1.25(8640) = \$10800$; the new variable cost per unit $= (0.90)(30) = \$27$.

$$50X = 10800 + 27X + 7830$$
$$23X = 18630$$
$$X = 810 \text{ (units)}$$

The required output is $\frac{810}{900} = 0.90 = 90\%$ of capacity.

Example 7.1d Use the information in Example 7.1b to answer each of the following questions.

(i) What is the net income at a sales volume of $34 500?

Solution

At a sales volume of 34500
$$X = 34500$$

At a sales volume of $34500 the basic relationship is
$$X = 12600 + 0.40\,X + NI$$
$$34500 = 12600 + 0.40 \times 34500 + NI$$
$$34500 = 12600 + 13800 + NI$$
$$NI = 8100$$

The net income at a volume of $34 500 is $8100.

(ii) What is the net income at a volume of 95% of capacity?

Solution

Let X represent the sales volume.
$$TR = X$$
$$TC = 12600 + 40\% \text{ of } TR = 12600 + 0.40\,X$$

The basic relationship (Formula 7.5) is
$$X = 12600 + 0.40\,X + NI$$

At 95% of capacity, $X = 0.95\,(60000) = 57000$.
$$57000 = 12600 + 0.40\,(57000) + NI$$
$$57000 = 12600 + 22800 + NI$$
$$NI = 21\,600$$

The net income at 95% of capacity is $21600.

(iii) What volume of output as a percent of capacity is required to produce a net income of $13 320?

Solution
$$X = 12600 + 0.40\,X + 13320$$
$$0.60\,X = 25920$$
$$X = 43200$$

The volume of output required is $\dfrac{43200}{60000} = 72\%$ of capacity.

(iv) What sales volume is required to generate a net income of $3240?

Solution

$$X = 12600 + 0.40X + 3240$$
$$0.60X = 15840$$
$$X = 26400$$

The sales volume required is $26 400.

(v) If fixed costs are increased by 25%, what is the break-even point
(a) in sales dollars?   (b) as a percent of capacity?

Solution

New fixed cost is $12600(1.25) = $15 750.
$$X = 15750 + 0.40X + NI$$
To break-even, NI $= 0$.
$$X = 15750 + 0.40X$$
$$0.60X = 15750$$
$$X = 26250$$

(a) The break-even point is $26 250.

(b) The break-even point is $\dfrac{26250}{60000} = 43.75\%$ of capacity.

(vi) What is the break-even point in sales dollars if fixed costs are increased to $14 880 while variable costs are decreased to 38% of sales?

Solution

The basic relationship becomes
$$X = 14880 + 38\% \text{ of } X + NI$$
$$X = 14880 + 0.38X + NI$$
To break-even, NI $= 0$.
$$X = 14880 + 0.38X$$
$$0.62X = 14880$$
$$X = 24000$$

The break-even point is $24 000.

(vii) To generate a profit of $5250, what output, as a percent of capacity, must be attained if fixed costs are increased by 5% and variable costs by 10%?

Solution

$$FC = 12600(1.05) = \$13230$$
$$TVC = 1.10(40\% \text{ of } TR)$$
$$= 1.10(0.40X)$$
$$= 0.44X$$

The basic relationship becomes

$$X = 13230 + 0.44X + 5250$$
$$0.56X = 18480$$
$$X = 33000$$

The required volume is $\dfrac{33000}{60000} = 55\%$ of capacity.

F. Computer application 1—Break-even analysis

Many of the problems dealt with in this text are suited to solution by computers. A sampling of such problems may be solved by the programs included in the Appendix. The programs are written in BASIC for use on the IBM PC or IBM compatibles.

Program 1—Break-even analysis—provides a numerical computer solution for Case 1 illustrated in this text (see Appendix p. 845).

Exercise 7.1

A. For each of the following perform a break-even analysis showing

(a) an algebraic statement of

(i) the revenue function,

(ii) the cost function;

(b) a detailed break-even chart;

(c) computation of the break-even point

(i) in units (if applicable),

(ii) as a percent of capacity,

(iii) in sales dollars.

1. Engineering estimates indicate the variable cost of manufacturing a new product will be $35 per unit. Based on market research, the selling price of the product is to be $120 per unit and variable selling expense is expected to be $15 per unit. The fixed costs applicable to the new product are estimated to be $2800 per period and capacity per period is 100 units.

2. A firm manufactures a product which sells for $12.00 per unit. Variable cost per unit is $8.00 and fixed cost per period is $1200. Capacity per period is 1000 units.

3. The following data pertains to the operating budget of Matt Mfg.

Sales		$720000
Fixed Cost	$220000	
Total Variable Cost	324000	544000
Net Income		$176000

Capacity is a sales volume of $800 000 per period.

4. A company has compiled the following estimates regarding operations.

Sales		$120000
Fixed Cost	$43200	
Variable Costs	48000	91200
Net Income		$ 28800

Capacity is a sales volume of $150 000.

B. Answer each of the following questions.

1. For question 1 in Part A of this exercise determine

(a) the net income at a volume of 70 units;

(b) the net income at a volume of 30% of capacity;

(c) the net income at a sales volume of $10 200;

(d) the level of operations as a percent of capacity, to generate a net income of $2240;

(e) the number of units that must be sold to make a net income of $1050;

(f) the sales volume in dollars, to suffer a loss of no more than $350;

(g) the break-even point in units, if fixed costs are increased to $3150;

(h) the break-even point as a percent of capacity, if fixed costs are reduced by $160 and the variable cost of manufacturing is increased to $39 per unit;

(i) the break-even point in dollars, if selling price is reduced to $100 per unit.

2. For question 3 in Part A of this exercise determine

(a) the net income at 85% of capacity;

(b) the net income at 30% of capacity;

(c) the level of operations as a percent of capacity, to realize a net income of $66 000;

(d) the level of operations in dollars, to sustain a loss of no more than $6600;

(e) the break-even point in dollars, if fixed costs are increased by 15%;

(f) the break-even point as a percent of capacity, if fixed costs are decreased by $18 400 and variable costs are increased to 52% of sales.

3. The Peel Credit Union is organizing a charter flight to Bermuda for the March break. A package offered by a carrier requires a fixed payment of $9900 plus $325 per person. The Credit Union intends to price the one-week package at $550 per person to cover the cost of flight, accommodation, meals and tips. With a charge of $550 per person the Credit Union estimates that the smallest number of participants would be 30 and the greatest number would be 70. If the price of the package is reduced to $475 per person, the minimum number of participants is expected to be 50 and the maximum number 120.

(a) How many participants are needed to break even

(i) at $550 per person? (ii) at $475 per person?

(b) What is the variation between the maximum and the minimum expected profit

(i) at \$550 per person?   (ii) at \$475 per person?

4. The student senate of the college is planning the annual convocation dinner dance. Rental of facilities is \$2000 and the local rock group can be engaged for \$660 plus 10% of gate receipts. Meal costs are \$26 per couple. The senate expects to set a price of \$40 per couple. At that price estimated minimum ticket sales are 180 and maximum ticket sales are 400. The treasurer argues that the price should be set at \$50 per couple at which price minimum sales are estimated at 100 tickets and maximum sales at 300.

(a) What is the number of couples that must buy tickets to break even at

(i) \$40 per couple?   (ii) \$50 per couple?

(b) What is the variation between the maximum and the minimum expected profit

(i) at \$40 per couple?   (ii) at \$50 per couple?

7.2   Linear programming—the two-product case

A.   Basic concepts

Linear programming is a mathematical technique which aids the manager in making the best use of a firm's economic resources which are in limited supply, such as money, material, labour, machinery, space, etc. These limited resources have to be allocated among competing uses so as to maximize profits or minimize costs.

A typical problem of this type is found in the case of a manufacturer who produces four different products each of which requires a specified amount of time in each of five processes. In each of the five processes, only a limited number of hours are available per time period. Furthermore the profit per unit of output is different for each of the five products.

The problem that must be solved requires the optimization of output with the available resources. The optimal output in this context is the number of units of each product that should be produced to maximize the total profit.

Linear programming problems are of differing complexity. Simple linear programming problems involving two products only can be solved using two-dimensional graphs; multi-product problems require the use of more advanced algebraic techniques.

In this text we are only concerned with an introduction to the concept of linear programming and the solution of the simplest cases. To deal with the two-product case graphically the following approach should be taken.

1. State the problem in algebraic terms.

   (a) Represent the number of units of each product by X_1 and X_2 respectively and organize the data in the form of a chart.

(b) State the **objective function** in equation form. The objective function is a mathematical presentation of the goal to be achieved—either a profit which is to be maximized or a cost which is to be minimized.

(c) List the **operational constraints** imposed on the objective function. The operational constraints indicate that the total amount of each type of economic resource used has to be consistent with the available amount of each resource.

(d) List the **non-negative constraints**. These constraints indicate that X_1 and X_2 cannot be *less* than zero; that is, the number of units produced cannot be negative.

2. Graphically represent the algebraic relationships.

(a) Represent the constraints graphically in a two-dimensional system of rectangular axes to obtain the **area of feasibility**. This is the area that contains all points (X_1, X_2) which represent the *possible* combinations of X_1 and X_2 which can be produced consistent with the availabilty of the resources.

(b) Introduce graphs of the objective function to identify the **optimal point**. The optimal point is the point (X_1, X_2) for which the profit will be maximized or the cost will be minimized. If a single solution exists, the optimal point is *always* a corner point on the boundary of the area of feasibility.

3. Algebraically determine the coordinates of the optimal point to find the optimal solution and the value of the objective function at that point.

B. Graphical solution

Example 7.2a A manufacturer markets two products. Each unit of Product A requires three hours in the molding department, four hours in the paint shop and one hour in finishing. Each unit of Product B requires three hours in molding, two hours in painting and two hours in finishing. Each week there are 210 hours available in molding, 200 hours in painting and 120 hours in finishing. Shipping can handle no more than 40 units of Product A per week. Each unit of Product A contributes $20 to profit while each unit of product B contributes $30.
Determine how many units of each product should be manufactured per week to maximize profit.

Solution

Step 1 **Algebraic statement of problem**

(a) Let the number of units of Product A be represented by X_1; let the number of units of Product B be represented by X_2.

	Data Summary		
	Resource quantity required per unit for		Available resource quantity
Constraints	Product A	Product B	
1. Molding	3	3	210
2. Painting	4	2	200
3. Finishing	1	2	120
4. Shipping	1	N/A	40
Profit	$20	$30	Maximize

(b) *The objective function*

The goal is to maximize profit. The value of the total profit may be represented by P. The amount of profit contributed by Product A is $20 per unit or $20X_1 and the profit contributed by Product B is $30 per unit or $30X_2. The total profit is $20X_1 + 30X_2$. The objective function then is $P = 20X_1 + 30X_2$ with X_1 and X_2 to be chosen so that P becomes as large as possible.

(c) *The operational constraints*

Production in the given situation depends on limited resources: the availability of time in the molding department, in the paint shop, and in finishing as well as the ability of shipping to handle Product A.

Each of the constraints on the operations of the business can be expressed algebraically by relating the resource requirements per unit of product to the total resource available.

For the molding department each unit of Product A requires 3 hours as does each unit of Product B. The total time used in the molding department to manufacture the two products must be less than, or at most equal to, 210 hours per week.

$$3X_1 + 3X_2 \leq 210$$

Similarly with respect to the paint shop

$$4X_1 + 2X_2 \leq 200$$

and with respect to finishing

$$X_1 + 2X_2 \leq 120$$

As far as shipping is concerned, the total number of units of Product A must be less than or equal to 40.

$$X_1 \leq 40$$

(d) *The non-negative constraints*

The minimum number of units of each product that can be produced is zero.

This fact is represented by the inequalities $X_1 \geq 0$ and $X_2 \geq 0$, referred to as the non-negative constraints.

(e) *General form of a linear programming problem*

The problem is now stated in the general form of a linear programming problem which consists of three parts.

(i) The objective function $\qquad P = 20X_1 + 30X_2$

(ii) The operational constraints
1. Molding $\qquad\qquad 3X_1 + 3X_2 \leq 210$
2. Painting $\qquad\qquad 4X_1 + 2X_2 \leq 200$
3. Finishing $\qquad\qquad X_1 + 2X_2 \leq 120$
4. Shipping $\qquad\qquad\qquad X_1 \leq 40$

(iii) The non-negative constraints $\qquad\qquad X_1 \geq 0$
$\qquad\qquad\qquad\qquad\qquad\qquad\qquad X_2 \geq 0$

Step 2 **Graphical representation of the algebraic relationships.**

(a) *Preliminary considerations*

(i) The non-negative constraints

Use a set of rectangular axes with the horizontal axis representing values of X_1 and the vertical axis representing values of X_2. The constraint $X_1 \geq 0$ describes the region to the right of the vertical axis while the constraint $X_2 \geq 0$ describes the region above the horizontal axis.

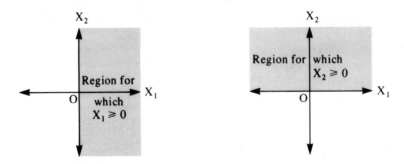

The region for which both conditions hold ($X_1 \geq 0$ and $X_2 \geq 0$) is the first quadrant. This is true for all linear programming problems.

(ii) Graphical representation of the objective function

The objective function may be represented graphically for various profit levels by assuming specific values for P.

Let $P_1 = 1500$.
Then the specific objective function becomes
$20X_1 + 30X_2 = 1500$
For $X_1 = 0 \longrightarrow X_2 = 50 \longrightarrow$ Graph point A(0,50)
For $X_2 = 0 \longrightarrow X_1 = 75 \longrightarrow$ Graph point B(75,0)

The line AB (see Figure 7.6) joining the two points represents all combinations for which the profit is $1500.

(0,50) $\longrightarrow$ 0 units of Product A and 50 units of Product B
(75,0) $\longrightarrow$ 75 units of Product A and 0 units of Product B
(45,20) $\longrightarrow$ 45 units of Product A and 20 units of Product B
(15,40) $\longrightarrow$ 15 units of Product A and 40 units of Product B

Let $P_2 = 3000$

Then the specific objective function becomes

$$20X_1 + 30X_2 = 3000$$
For $X_1 = 0 \longrightarrow X_2 = 100 \longrightarrow$ Graph point C(0,100)
For $X_2 = 0 \longrightarrow X_1 = 150 \longrightarrow$ Graph point D(150,0)

The line CD joining the two points represents all combinations (X_1,X_2) for which the profit is $3000.

In a similar manner additional lines may be drawn for any convenient profit figure such as $P_3 = 4500$ (see line EF in Figure 7.6) and $P_4 = 6000$ (see line GH).

FIGURE 7.6 *Graphical representation of the objective function*

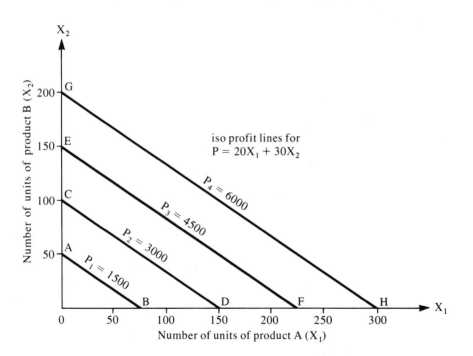

Note

1. Each profit level results in a specific profit line. Since X_1 and X_2 cannot be negative the lines are not extended across the two axes.
2. The various combinations of X_1 and X_2 that satisfy the equation of a particular

profit line will be points on the line and produce the same amount of profit. For this reason such lines are referred to as **iso-profit lines**.

3. The various iso-profit lines have the same slope and run parallel to each other. Thus, all the possible iso-profit lines for a particular objective function represent a family of parallel lines.

4. The total profit represented by each of the iso-profit lines increases with increasing distance of the line from the origin.

5. The parallel nature of the iso-profit lines and the increase in profit with the increase in distance from the origin is of crucial importance in locating the optimal point graphically.

(iii) Graphing the operational constraints

Each constraint involves an inequality which, when graphed, represents a region referred to as the area of feasibility for the resource represented by the inequality. Each inequality can be graphed by first graphing the associated equality and testing for the region.

For the molding department, the inequality $3X_1 + 3X_2 \leq 210$ is associated with the equation $3X_1 + 3X_2 = 210$.

For $X_1 = 0$, $X_2 = 70 \longrightarrow$ Graph the point F(0,70)
For $X_2 = 0$, $X_1 = 70 \longrightarrow$ Graph the point G(70,0)

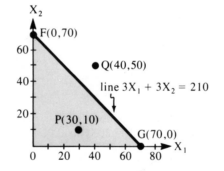

Test the point (0,0)
$3X_1 + 3X_2 = 3(0) + 3(0) = 0 \leq 210$
Since the coordinates (0,0) satisfy the inequality, the point (0,0) is a point in the region described by the inequality. Hence the region described by $3X_1 + 3X_2 \leq 210$ is the area to the left of the line $3X_1 + 3X_2 = 210$. However, since X_1 and X_2 cannot be negative, the combinations (X_1,X_2) that are feasible are represented by the points inside the triangle OFG as shown in the diagram.

The point P(30,10) lies inside the triangle OFG. This indicates that the combination (30,10) is possible. The coordinates (30,10) indicate a combination of 30 units of Product A and 10 units of Product B.

To produce 30 units of Product A requires $3(30) = 90$ hours in molding; to produce 10 units of Product B requires $3(10) = 30$ hours in molding. Thus the combination requires a total of 120 hours in molding which is less than the 210 hours available. The combination 30 units of Product A and 10 units of Product B is feasible.

The point Q(40,50) representing a production of 40 units of Product A and 50 units of Product B, lies outside the area of feasibility indicating that this combination is not possible.

To produce 40 units of Product A requires $3(40) = 120$ hours in molding; to produce 50 units of Product B requires $3(50) = 150$ hours in molding. Thus the combination requires a total of 270 hours in molding and since only 210 hours are available, the combination 40 units of Product A and 50 units of Product B is not feasible.

For the paint shop, the inequality $4X_1 + 2X_2 \leq 200$ is associated with the equation $4X_1 + 2X_2 = 200$.

For $X_1 = 0$, $X_2 = 100 \longrightarrow$ Graph point H(0,100)
For $X_2 = 0$, $X_1 = 50 \longrightarrow$ Graph point J(50,0)

The area of feasibility for the paint shop is the triangle OHJ as shown in the diagram below.

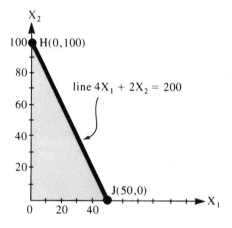

The area of feasibility for finishing, defined by the inequality $X_1 + 2X_2 \leq 120$ and the non-negative constraints, is the triangle OAK as shown in the diagram below.

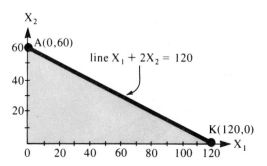

Finally, the area of feasibility for shipping, defined by the inequality $X_1 \leq 40$ and the non-negative constraints, is the area between the X_2 axis and the line represented by $X_1 = 40$ as shown below.

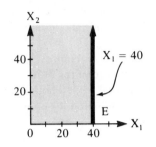

*Mathematics
of business
and
management*

(b) *Graphing the area of feasibility*

The area of feasibility for the combined resources is the area containing the points which satisfy all operational constraints. This area is found by graphing the individual constraints on the same set of axes (see Figure 7.7).

For molding and painting combined the area of feasibility is the intersection of the two triangles OFG and OHJ that is, the area OFCJ as shown below.

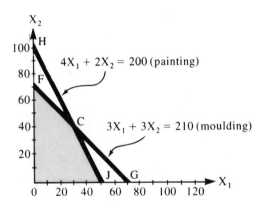

For molding, painting and finishing combined the area of feasibility is the area OABCJ as shown below.

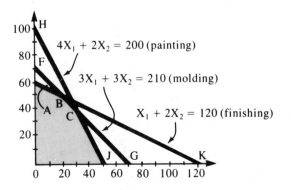

When shipping is also considered the area of feasibility is reduced to the area OABCDE as shown in Figure 7.7.

FIGURE 7.7 *Area of feasibility*

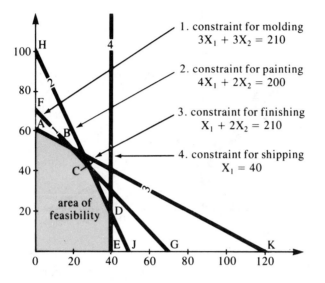

(c) *Locating the optimal point*

Once the area of feasiblity has been determined by graphing the operational constraints, the optimal point—the point whose coordinates are the combination (X_1,X_2) which generates the maximum profit—needs to be located. This is done by introducing graphs of the objective function $P = 20X_1 + 30X_2$ by the method previously explained.

In this case, a convenient value of $P = \$1500$.

For $X_1 = 0 \longrightarrow X_2 = 50 \longrightarrow$ Graph point S(0,50).
For $X_2 = 0 \longrightarrow X_1 = 75 \longrightarrow$ Graph point T(75.0).

Draw the profit line ST (see Figure 7.8).

Part of the iso-profit line ST passes through the area of feasibility. Any combination (X_1,X_2) which represents the coordinates of a point on this line provides a profit of $1500.

The line ST is one of the family of parallel lines defined by the equation $P = 20X_1 + 30X_2$. Some of the lines represent a profit lower than $1500, others a profit greater than $1500, depending on whether such lines are closer to the origin or farther away from the origin.

For example, a line parallel to ST through the point A(0, 60)—see Figure 7.8—yields a profit of
$$P = 20(0) + 30(60) = 0 + 1800 = \$1800.$$
This particular iso-profit line passes through the area of feasibility and any combination of (X_1,X_2) falling on this line generates a profit of $1800.

FIGURE 7.8 *Locating the optimal point*

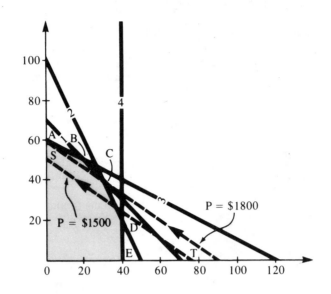

As long as a profit line passes through the area of feasibility OABCDE and is farther away from the origin, it will generate a profit higher than obtainable from a profit line closer to the origin. However, for profit lines which do not pass through the area of feasibility, any combination (X_1,X_2) which represents a point on such a line does not satisfy all the constraint and is thus not attainable.

Hence, the profit line which will generate the greatest possible profit is the line which is located farthest away from the origin such that at least one point on the line is still within the area of feasibility OABCDE.

When considering possible lines parallel to the two profit lines drawn in Figure 7.8 it becomes apparent that the profit line farthest from the origin which still passes through the area OABCDE is a line drawn through the point B.

Hence the point B is the optimal point representing the combination (X_1,X_2) for which the profit is the maximum amount attainable with the given combination of resources.

Note The optimal point is a point in the boundary of the area of feasibility. This is generally true for any linear programming problem.

Step 3 Finding the optimal combination (X_1,X_2) and the maximum amount of profit

The coordinates of point B represent the number of units of Product A and Product B which should be produced to maximize the profit. This combination (X_1,X_2) provides for optimal utilization of the available resources and may be found algebraically by solving the system of equations representing the two lines which form the point B.

From Figure 7.7 it is apparent that point B is formed by the intersection of Line AK represented by $X_1 + 2X_2 = 120$ and Line FG represented by $3X_1 + 3X_2 = 210$.

Equation ① $\longrightarrow$ $X_1 + 2X_2 = 120$
Equation ② $\longrightarrow$ $3X_1 + 3X_2 = 210$

To eliminate X_1
multiply ① by 3 $\longrightarrow$ $3X_1 + 6X_2 = 360$
subtract ② $\longrightarrow$ $3X_1 + 3X_2 = 210$

$$3X_2 = 150$$
$$X_2 = 50$$

To find X_1, substitute $50 = X_2$ in ①
$$X_1 + 2(50) = 120$$
$$X_1 + 100 = 120$$
$$X_1 = 20$$

The solution to the system is $(X_1, X_2) = (20, 50)$.

For $(X_1, X_2) = (20, 50)$
$P = 20X_1 + 30X_2 = 20(20) + 30(50) = 400 + 1500 = 1900$

The optimal production is 20 units of Product A and 50 units of Product B for a maximum profit of $1900.

Note   The available resources are used as follows.

Molding $3x_1 + 3X_2 = 3(20) + 3(50) = 60 + 150 = 210$
Since the maximum available time in molding is 210 hours, molding capacity is totally used.

Painting $4X_1 + 2X_2 = 4(20) + 2(50) = 80 + 100 = 180$
Since the maximum available time is 200 hours, 20 hours are unused.

Finishing $X_1 + 2x_2 = 20 + 2(50) = 20 + 100 = 120$
Since the maximum available time is 120 hours, finishing capacity is totally used.

Shipping $X_1 = 20$. Since capacity is 40 units, 50% of shipping's capability to handle Product A is used.

Example 7.2b   A company makes two kinds of ladies boots. X_1 is top quality; X_2 is ordinary quality. Production of top quality boots takes twice as long as ordinary quality. If only ordinary quality boots are made, 3000 pairs of boots can be made per week. Enough material is available to make 2400 pairs of boots. The top quality boots require a special zipper and enough zippers are available for 1100 pairs per week. Ordinary zippers are available to make 2200 ordinary pairs per week. Top quality boots give a profit of $32 and ordinary quality boots give a profit of $24 per pair. Use the graphical method of linear programming to find the optimal production mix, the total contribution to profit of this mix and the use of the resources available.

Solution

Constraints	Resource quantity required per pair of boots		Available resource quantity
	Top quality	Ord. quality	
1. Time units	2	1	3000
2. Material	1	1	2400
3. Spec. zipper	1	N/A	1100
4. Ord. zipper	N/A	1	2200
PROFIT	$32	$24	MAXIMIZE

Step 1 Statement of problem in algebraic form

(a) Objective function $\qquad P = 32X_1 + 24X_2$

(b) Operational constraints
$$1.\ 2X_1 + X_2 \leqq 3000$$
$$2.\ \ X_1 + X_2 \leqq 2400$$
$$3.\qquad\quad X_1 \leqq 1100$$
$$4.\qquad\quad X_2 \leqq 2200$$

(c) Non-negative constraints $\qquad X_1 \geqq 0\ ;\ X_2 \geqq 0$

Step 2 Graphical solution

Area OABCDE is the area of feasibility. The optimal point is C.

FIGURE 7.9 *Graphical solution*

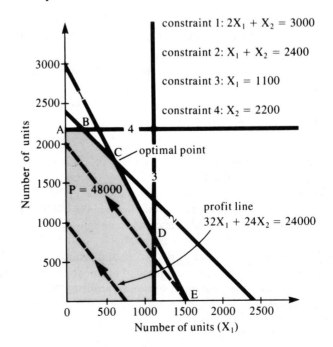

Mathematics of business and management

Step 3   Conclusion

The optimal point C is formed by the intersection of

    Constraint ① $\longrightarrow$ $2X_1 + X_2 = 3000$ and

    Constraint ② $\longrightarrow$ $X_1 + X_2 = 2400$

        subtract $\longrightarrow$ $X_1 = 600$

                       $X_2 = 1800$

The coordinates of the optimal point are (600, 1800).
The optimal solution requires production of 600 pairs of top quality boots and 1800 pairs of ordinary quality boots.
The maximum profit that can be generated is

$$P = 32(600) + 24(1800) = 19200 + 43200 = \$62\,400$$

Resource use for the optimal production is as follows.

1. Time used $2(600) + 1800 = 3000$; since 3000 time units are available, time capacity is totally used.

2. Material $600 + 1800 = 2400$; since material for 2400 pairs is available, the supply of material is 100% utilized.

3. Special zippers   600 pairs used; 1100 pairs available
500 pairs unused.

4. Ordinary zippers   1800 pairs used; 2200 pairs available;
400 pairs unused.

Exercise 7.2

A. Solve each of the following linear programming problems showing in your answer

    (a) an algebraic statement of the problem;

    (b) a graph of the area of feasibility showing the optimal point;

    (c) an algebraic computation of the optimal solution including the amount of profit and utilization of the resources.

1. A manufacturer produces two products. Product A contributes $7 per unit to profit and Product B contributes $5 per unit. The manufacturing process requires time on each of three machines. Product A requires 8 hours on Machine I, two hours on Machine II and four hours on Machine III. Product B requires five hours on each of Machines I and II, and six hours on Machine III. Machine I is available for 4200 hours; Machine II for 2000 hours and Machine III for 2800 hours.

2. Swim Quip has production facilities for assembling and distributing residential pool heaters and pool filters. The facilities consist of departments for sub-assembly, final assembly, finishing and testing. Each filter requires twelve hours in sub-assembly, two hours in final assembly and one hour in finishing. Each heater requires thirty-six hours in sub-assembly, 3.2 hours in final assembly, four hours in finishing and two hours in testing. Capacity is 3600 hours in sub-assembly, 480 hours in final assembly, 324 hours in finishing and 100 hours in testing. Each filter contributes $60 to profit whereas each heater contributes $180 to profit.

Review exercise

1. The lighting division of Universal Electric Company intends to introduce a new street light based on the following accounting information.

   Fixed costs per period are $3136; variable cost per unit is $157; selling price per unit is $185; and capacity per period is 320 units.

   (a) Draw a detailed break-even chart.

   (b) Compute the break-even point

       (i) in units;   (ii) as a percent of capacity;

       (iii) in dollars.

   (c) Determine the net income at a sales volume of

       (i) 25% of capacity;   (ii) $24 975.

   (d) Determine the level of operation as a percent of capacity to generate a net income of

       (i) $2240;   (ii) $6720.

   (e) Determine the break-even point as a percent of capacity

       (i) if fixed costs are reduced to $2688;

       (ii) if fixed costs increase to $4588 and variable costs are reduced to 80% of the selling price;

       (iii) if selling price is reduced to $171.

2. The following information is available from the accounting records of Eva Corporation.

   Fixed costs per period are $4800; sales volume for the last period was $19 360 and variable costs were $13 552.

   Capacity per period is a sales volume of $32 000.

   (a) Draw a detailed break-even chart.

   (b) Compute the break-even point

       (i) in dollars;   (ii) as a percent of capacity.

   (c) Determine the net income at a sales volume of

       (i) $24 000;   (ii) 30% of capacity.

   (d) Determine the level of operations as a percent of capacity to generate a net income of $3264.

   (e) Determine the break-even point

       (i) if fixed costs are decreased by $600;

       (ii) if fixed costs are increased to $5670 and variable costs are changed to 55% of sales.

3. The operating budget of the Bea Company contains the following information.

Sales at 80% of capacity		$400000
Fixed costs	$105000	
Variable costs	260000	365000
Net Income		$ 35000

(a) Draw a detailed break-even chart.

(b) Compute the break-even point

   (i) as a percent of capacity;   (ii) in dollars.

(c) Determine the net income at 40% of capacity.

(d) Determine the sales volume as a percent of capacity to generate a net income of $61 250.

(e) Determine the break-even point in dollars if fixed costs are reduced by $11 200 while variable costs are changed to 72% of sales.

4. A manufacturer of major appliances provides the following information about the operations of the refrigerator division.

     Fixed costs per period are $26 880; variable costs per unit are $360;
                  selling price per unit is $640; and capacity is 150 units.

(a) Compute the break-even point

   (i) in units;   (ii) as a percent of capacity;   (iii) in dollars.

(b) Determine the net income at a sales volume of

   (i) $78 080;   (ii) 48% of capacity.

(c) Determine the volume of output as a percent of capacity to generate a net income of $4200.

(d) Determine the break-even point in dollars if fixed costs are increased to $32 200.

(e) Determine the break-even point as a percent of capacity if fixed costs are reduced to $23 808 while variable costs are increased to 60% of sales.

5. A manufacturer makes two types of brackets. Brackets of either type are formed in Department A from a piece of steel of which 750 are available for the time period. Each ordinary bracket requires four time units in Department A while each fancy bracket requires ten time units. The total number of time units available in Department A for the time period is 4800. The ordinary bracket is finished in Department B and requires four time units while the fancy bracket is finished in Department C and requires six time units. 2400 time units are available in each of the two finishing departments. The ordinary bracket contributes $4 to profit and the fancy bracket contributes $6.

(a) State the problem in the algebraic form.

(b) Graphically solve the problem.

(c) Find the optimal solution algebraically and give the maximum profit and the utilization of the manufacturing facilities.

6. The Debris Company intends to market two types of containers. Each square container costs the company $20 and each round container costs $30. Each square container occupies 20 square units of floor space while each round container occupies 10 square units. $12 000 is available per period to purchase containers of either type and 8000 units of floor space is available to store them. Each container weighs 100 kg and the floor of the storage room will not support more than 45 000 kg. Each square container contributes $30 to profit while each round container contributes $20. Demand is such that no more than 350 round containers can be sold. Using the graphical method of linear programming, find the optimum product mix, the total contribution to profit of this mix and the utilization of resources.

Self-test

1. The Superior Records Company sells albums for $5 each. Manufacturing cost is $1.30 per album; marketing costs are $1.20 per album; and royalty payments are 20% of selling price. The fixed cost of preparing the albums is $9000. Capacity is 15 000 albums.

(a) Draw a detailed break-even chart.

(b) Compute the break-even point
    (i) in units;   (ii) in dollars;   (iii) as a percent of capacity.

(c) Determine the net income at a sales volume of 55% of capacity.

(d) Determine the sales volume in dollars to generate a net income of $6900.

(e) Determine the break-even point in units if fixed costs are increased by $800 while manufacturing cost is reduced $0.25 per album.

(f) Determine the break-even point in units if the selling price is increased by 10% while fixed costs are increased by $1450.

2. The management of Lambda Corporation has received the following forecast for the next year.

Sales Revenue		$600000
Fixed costs	$275000	
Variable costs	270000	545000
Net Income		$ 55000

Capacity is a sales volume of $80 000.

(a) Compute the break-even point
    (i) in dollars;   (ii) as a percent of capacity.

(b) Determine the net income at 50% of capacity.

(c) Determine the sales volume in dollars to generate a net income of $82 500.

(d) Determine the break-even volume in dollars if fixed costs are increased by $40 000 while variable costs are held to 40% of sales.

3. A manufacturer produces two types of product. Product A requires 3 units of material, 1 unit of time in fabricating and 1 unit of time in finishing. Product B requires 1 unit of material, 3 units of time in fabricating and 1 unit of time in finishing. Maximum daily resources are 24 units of material, 30 units of time in fabricating and 12 units of time in finishing. Product A contributes $30 per unit to profit while Product B contributes $40 per unit.

(a) State the problem in algebraic form.

(b) Graphically solve the problem.

(c) Find the optimal solution algebraically and determine the maximum profit.

(d) Determine the utilization of resources for the optimal solution.

Summary of formulae used

Formula 7.1	$TR = TC + NI$	$\dfrac{\text{TOTAL}}{\text{REVENUE}} = \dfrac{\text{TOTAL}}{\text{COST}} + \dfrac{\text{NET}}{\text{INCOME}}$
Formula 7.2	$TR = (X)(P)$	$\dfrac{\text{TOTAL}}{\text{REVENUE}} = \dfrac{\text{VOLUME}}{\text{IN UNITS}} \times \dfrac{\text{UNIT}}{\text{REVENUE}}$
Formula 7.3	$TC = FC + TVC$	$\dfrac{\text{TOTAL}}{\text{COST}} = \dfrac{\text{FIXED}}{\text{COST}} + \dfrac{\text{TOTAL}}{\text{VARIABLE}}_{\text{COST}}$
Formula 7.4	$TVC = (X)(VC)$	$\dfrac{\text{TOTAL}}{\text{VARIABLE}}_{\text{COST}} = \dfrac{\text{VOLUME}}{\text{IN UNITS}} \times \dfrac{\text{VARIABLE}}{\text{COST}}_{\text{PER UNIT}}$
Formula 7.5	$TR = FC + TVC + NI$	$\dfrac{\text{TOTAL}}{\text{REVENUE}} = \dfrac{\text{FIXED}}{\text{COST}} + \dfrac{\text{TOTAL}}{\text{VARIABLE}}_{\text{COST}} + \dfrac{\text{NET}}{\text{INCOME}}$

Glossary of terms used

Break-even analysis a method of determining the level of output at which a business neither makes a profit nor sustains a loss

Break-even chart a graphical representation of cost-volume-profit relationships used to identify the break-even point

Break-even point the level of output at which net income is zero

Cost function an algebraic expression stating the relationship between cost and volume

Fixed costs costs which remain constant for the time period for all levels of output considered

Revenue function an algebraic expression representing the behaviour of revenue

Variable costs costs that are constant per unit of output regardless of volume and thus fluctuate in total amount as volume fluctuates

Linear programming a mathematical technique used to determine the optimal allocation of limited resources

Area of feasibility in a linear programming graph, the area containing all the points (X_1, X_2) which represent the possible combinations in the product mix

Iso-profit line the line representing the various possible combinations in the product mix which yield the same amount of profit

Non-negative constraints algebraic expressions stating that the variables used are limited to positive values

Objective function an algebraic representation of the goal to be achieved in a linear programming problem

Operational constraints an algebraic representation of the limitations imposed on operations because of the limited availability of various resources

Optimal point the point whose coordinates represent the product mix at which the profit is maximized or the cost minimized

8 Payroll

Introduction

Employees can be remunerated for their services in a variety of ways. The main methods of remuneration include salaries, hourly wage rates and commission. While the computations involved in preparing a payroll are fairly simple, utmost care is needed to assure that all calculations are accurate.

The calculations required concern the computation of gross earnings, deductions and net pay. The determination of the deductions is the main complicating factor in preparing a payroll. Some of the deductions are required by federal or provincial regulations, others are authorized by the employee himself.

Various records must be kept, reports must be submitted and payments must be made by the business to satisfy the requirements of legislation affecting employee remuneration.

Objectives

Upon completion of this chapter you will be able to

1. determine gross earnings for employees remunerated by the payment of salaries, hourly wages or commissions;
2. determine statutory federal payroll deductions, compute net pay, determine the employer's payroll tax expenses and the monthly remittances which must be made by the employer to the Receiver General of Canada;
3. prepare basic payroll records.

8.1 Computing gross earnings

A. Salaries

Compensation of employees by means of **salaries** is usually on a monthly or a yearly basis. Monthly salaried personnel get paid either monthly or semi-monthly. Personnel on a yearly salary basis may get paid monthly, semi-monthly, every two weeks or weekly, or according to a special schedule such as used by some Boards of Education to pay their teachers. If salary is paid weekly or every two weeks, the year is assumed to consist of exactly 52 weeks.

Calculation of **gross earnings** per pay period is fairly simple. A computational problem arises in the computation of overtime for salaried personnel since overtime is usually paid on the basis of an hourly rate.

Example 8.1a An employee on an annual salary of $23 296.00 is paid every two weeks. The regular work week is 40 hours.

(i) What is the gross pay per pay period?

(ii) What is the hourly rate of pay?

(iii) What are the gross earnings for a pay period in which the employee worked six hours of overtime and is paid one-and-a-half times the regular hourly rate of pay?

Solution

(i) An employee paid every two weeks receives the annual salary over 26 pay periods.

$$\text{Gross pay per two-week period} = \frac{23296.00}{26} = \$896.00$$

(ii) Given a 40-hour week, the employees's compensation for two weeks covers 80 hours.

$$\text{Hourly rate of pay} = \frac{896.00}{80} = \$11.20$$

(iii) Regular gross earnings for two-week period $896.00
Overtime pay
   6 hours @ $11.20 times 1.5 = 6 × 11.20 × 1.5   100.80

Total gross earnings $996.80

Example 8.1b Mike Paciuc receives a monthly salary of $2080.00 paid semi-monthly. Mike's regular work week is 37.5 hours. Any hours worked in excess of 37.5 hours during a week are overtime paid at time-and-a-half regular pay. During the first half of October Mike worked 7.5 hours overtime.

(i) What is Mike's hourly rate of pay?

(ii) What are his gross earnings for the pay period ending October 15?

Solution

(i) When computing the hourly rate of pay for personnel employed on a monthly salary basis, the correct approach requires that the yearly salary be determined first. The hourly rate of pay may then be computed on the basis of 52 weeks per year.

$$\text{Yearly gross earnings} = 2080.00 \times 12 = \$24960.00$$

$$\text{Weekly gross earnings} = \frac{24960.00}{52} = \$480.00$$

$$\text{Hourly rate of pay} = \frac{480.00}{37.5} = \$12.80$$

(ii) Regular semi-monthly gross earnings $= \dfrac{2080.00}{2} = \$1040.00$

Overtime pay $= 7.5 \times 12.80 \times 1.5$ $\qquad = \quad 144.00$

Total gross earnings for pay period $\qquad \underline{\$1184.00}$

***Example* 8.1c** The Mississagi Board of Education pays its teachers who are under contract for 200 teaching days per year according to the following schedule:

8% of annual salary on the first day of school;
4% of annual salary for each of 20 two-week pay periods;
12% of annual salary at the end of the last pay period in June.

Fern Brooks, a teacher employed by the Board, is paid an annual salary of $21 350.00.

(i) What is Fern's daily rate of pay?

(ii) What is Fern's gross pay
 (a) for the first pay period?
 (b) for the last pay period?
 (c) for all other pay periods?

(iii) If Fern takes an unpaid leave of absence for three days during a pay period ending in April, what is her gross pay for that pay period?

Solution

(i) Daily rate of pay $= \dfrac{21350.00}{200} = \$106.75$

(ii) (a) First gross pay $= 0.08 \times 21350.00 = \$1708.00$
 (b) Last gross pay $= 0.12 \times 21350.00 = \$2562.00$
 (c) All other gross pay $= 0.04 \times 21350.00 = \$854.00$

(iii) Gross pay for pay period ending in April $= \$854.00$

 Less 3 days of pay $= \frac{3}{200}$ of $21 350.00

$$= 3 \times 106.75 \qquad = \quad 320.25$$

    Gross pay $\qquad \underline{\$533.75}$

B. Commission

A person engaged in the buying and selling functions of a business is often compensated in the form of a **commission**. Of the variations designed to meet the specific circumstances of a particular business, the most commonly encountered are straight commission, graduated (or sliding-scale) commission and base salary plus commission.

Straight commission is usually calculated as a percent of net sales for a given time period. Net sales are the difference between the gross sales for the time period and any sales returns and allowances.

Graduated commission usually involves the payment of an increasing percent for increasing sales levels during a given time period.

Salary plus commission is a method which guarantees a minimum income per pay period to the salesperson. However, the rate of commission in such cases is either at a lower rate or is not paid until a minimum sales level (referred to as **quota**) for the time period has been reached.

Sales personnel on commission often have a drawing account with their employer. Funds may be withdrawn by the salesperson from such an account in advance to meet business and personal expenses. However, any money advanced is deducted from the commission earned when the salesperson is paid.

Example 8.1d   Robin Thomas receives a commission of 11.5% on her net sales and is entitled to drawings of up to $1000.00 per month. During August, Robin's gross sales amounted to $15540.00 and sales returns and allowances were $360.00.

(i) What are Robin's net sales for August?

(ii) How much is her commission for August?

(iii) If Robin drew $875.00 in August, what is the amount due to her?

Solution

(i) Gross sales $15540.00
    Less sales returns and allowances   360.00
        Net sales $15180.00

(ii) Commission $= 11.5\%$ of net sales
           $= 0.115 \times 15180.00$
           $= \$1745.70$

(iii) Gross commission earned $1745.70
     Less drawings   875.00
       Amount due $ 870.70

Example 8.1e   Valerie works as a salesperson for the local Minutemen Press. She receives a commission of 7.5% on monthly sales up to $8000.00, 9.25% on the next $7000.00 and 11% on any additional sales during the month. If Valerie's September sales amounted to $18 750.00, what is her gross commission for the month?

Solution

Commission on the first $8000.00 = 0.075 × 8000.00   = $600.00
Commission on the next $7000.00 = 0.0925 × 7000.00 =   647.50
Commission on sales over $15000.00 = 0.11 × 3750.00 =   412.50

Total commission for September $1660.00

Example 8.1f   Rita is employed as a salesclerk in a fabric store. She receives a weekly salary of $175.00 plus a commission of $6\frac{1}{4}$% on all weekly sales subject to a weekly sales quota of $2000.00. Derek works in the shoe store located next door. He receives a minimum of $200.00 per week or a commission of 8% on all sales for the week, whichever is the greater. If both Rita and Derek had sales of $2960.00 last week, how much compensation does each receive for the week?

Solution

Rita's compensation

Base salary $175.00
Plus commission = $6\frac{1}{4}$% on sales over $2000.00
              = 0.0625 × 960.00   60.00

Total compensation $235.00

Derek's compensation
Minimum weekly pay $200.00
Commission = 8% of $2960.00 = 0.08 × 2960.00 = $236.80

Since the commission is greater than the guaranteed minimum pay of $200.00, Derek's compensation is $236.80.

C.   Wages

The term **wages** usually applies to compensation paid to *hourly* rated employees whose gross earnings are found by multiplying the number of hours worked by the hourly rate of pay plus any overtime pay. Overtime is most often paid at time and one-half the regular hourly rate for any hours exceeding an established number of regular hours per week or per day. The number of regular hours is often established by agreement between the employer and the employees. The most common regular workweek is 40 hours. If no agreement exists, federal or provincial employment standard legislation provides for a maximum number of hours per week, such as 44 hours for most employers in Ontario. Any hours in excess of the set maximum must be paid at least at time and one-half the regular hourly rate.

When overtime is involved, gross earnings can be calculated by either one of two methods.

Method A

The most common method and the method best understood by the wage earner determines total gross earnings by adding overtime pay to the gross pay for a regular work week.

Method B

In the second method, the overtime excess (or **overtime premium**) is computed separately and added to gross earnings for all hours at the regular rate of pay. Computation of the excess labour cost due to overtime emphasizes the additional expense due to overtime and provides management with information that is useful from the point of view of cost control.

Example 8.1g Mario is employed as a machinist by Scott Tool and Die and is paid $7.20 per hour. The regular work week is 40 hours and overtime is paid at time and one-half the regular hourly rate. If Mario worked $46\frac{1}{2}$ hours last week, what were his gross earnings?

Solution

    Method A

      Gross earnings for a regular work week = 40 × 7.20   = $288.00
      Overtime pay = 6.5 × 7.20 × 1.5   =   70.20

                         Gross pay   = $358.20

    Method B

      Earnings at the regular hourly rate = 46.5 × 7.20   = $334.80
      Overtime premium = 6.5 × ($\frac{1}{2}$ of 7.20) = 6.5 × 3.60   =   23.40

                         Gross pay   = $358.20

Example 8.1h Gloria works for $8.44 an hour under a union contract which provides for overtime on a daily basis for all hours worked over eight hours. Overtime includes hours worked on Saturdays and is paid at time and one-half the regular rate of pay. Hours worked on Sundays or holidays are to be paid at double the regular rate of pay. Use both methods to determine Gloria's gross earnings for a week in which she worked the following hours:

	Monday	9 hours	Tuesday	$10\frac{1}{2}$ hours

Monday   9 hours   Tuesday $10\frac{1}{2}$ hours
Wednesday   7 hours   Thursday $9\frac{1}{2}$ hours
Friday   8 hours   Saturday   6 hours
Sunday   6 hours

Solution

Day	Mo	Tu	We	Thu	Fr	Sat	Su	Total
Regular hours	8	8	7	8	8			39
Overtime at time and one-half	1	2.5		1.5		6		11
Overtime at double time							6	6
Total hours worked	9	10.5	7	9.5	8	6	6	56

Method A

Gross earnings for regular hours = 39 × 8.44 = $329.16
Overtime pay
    at time and one-half   = 11 × 8.44 × 1.5 = $139.26
    at double time   = 6 × 8.44 × 2   =   101.28   240.54
                         Total gross pay $569.70

Method B

Earnings at regular hourly rate = 56 × 8.44 = $472.64
Overtime premium
    at time and one-half   = 11($\frac{1}{2}$ of $8.44)
                          = 11 × 4.22   = $ 46.42
    at double time   = 6 × 8.44   =   50.64   97.06
                         Total gross pay $569.70

Exercise 8.1

A. Answer each of the following questions.

1. R. Burton is employed at an annual salary of $16 585.92 paid semi-monthly. The regular work week is 36 hours.

   (a) What is the regular salary per pay period?

   (b) What is the hourly rate of pay?

   (c) What is the gross pay for a pay period in which the employee worked 11 hours overtime at time and one-half regular pay?

2. C. Hall receives a yearly salary of $23 868.00. She is paid bi-weekly and her regular work week is 37.5 hours.

   (a) What is the gross pay per pay period?

(b) What is the hourly rate of pay?

(c) What is the gross pay for a pay period in which she works $7\frac{1}{2}$ hours overtime at time and one-half regular pay?

3. Carole is paid a monthly salary of $1101.10. Her regular work week is 35 hours.

   (a) What is Carole's hourly rate of pay?

   (b) What is Carole's gross pay for May if she worked $7\frac{3}{4}$ hours overtime during the month at time and one-half regular pay?

4. Herb receives a semi-monthly salary of $863.20 and works a regular work week of 40 hours.

   (a) What is Herb's hourly rate of pay?

   (b) If Herb's gross earning in one pay period were $990.19, for how many hours of overtime was he paid at time and one-half regular pay?

5. An employee of a Board of Education is paid an annual salary in twenty-two bi-weekly payments of $1123.00 each. If the employee is under contract for 200 work-days of $7\frac{1}{2}$ hours each

   (a) what is the hourly rate of pay?

   (b) what is the gross pay for a pay period in which the employee was away for two days at no pay?

6. Geraldine Moog is paid a commission of $9\frac{3}{4}\%$ on her net sales and is authorized to draw up to $800.00 a month. What is the amount due to Geraldine at the end of a month in which she drew $720.00, had sales of $12 660.00 and sales returns were $131.20?

7. What is a salesperson's commission on net sales of $16 244.00 if the commission is paid on a sliding scale of $8\frac{1}{4}\%$ on the first $6000.00, $9\frac{3}{4}\%$ on the next $6000.00 and 11.5% on any additional sales?

8. A salesman selling auto parts receives a commission of 4.5% on net sales up to $10 000.00, 6% on the next $5000.00 and 8% on any further sales. If his sales for a month were $24 250.00 and sales returns were $855.00, what was his commission for the month?

9. A sales clerk at a local boutique receives a weekly base salary of $225.00 on a quota of $4500.00 per week plus a commission of $6\frac{1}{2}\%$ on sales exceeding the quota.

   (a) What are the gross earnings for a week if sales are $4125.00?

   (b) What are the gross earnings for a week if sales amount to $6150.00?

10. A clothing store salesman is paid a weekly salary of $250.00 or a commission of 12.5% of his sales whichever is the greater. What is his salary for a week in which his sales were

    (a) $1780.00?   (b) $2780.00?

11. For October, Monique Lemay earned a commission of $1884.04 on gross sales of $21 440.00. If returns and allowances were 5% of gross sales, what is her rate of commission based on net sales?

12. Jim Scott had gross earnings of $354.30 for last week. Jim earns a base salary of $270.00 on a weekly quota of $4000.00. If his sales for the week were $5124.00, what is his commission rate?

13. Doug Wilson earned a commission of $2036.88 for March. If his rate of commission is 11.25% of net sales, and returns and allowances were 8% of gross sales, what were Doug's gross sales for the month?

14. Corrie Daley had gross earnings of $337.50 for the week. If she receives a base salary of $264.00 on a quota of $4800.00 and a commission of 8.75% on sales exceeding the quota, what were Corrie's sales for the week?

15. Tiffany Shastri is employed at an hourly rate of $8.42. Regular work week is 40 hours and overtime is paid at time and one-half regular pay. Using the two methods illustrated earlier, compute Tiffany's gross earnings for a week in which she worked 47 hours.

16. Kim Ferrill earns $10.60 per hour. Overtime from Monday through Friday is paid at time and one-half regular pay for any hours over $7\frac{1}{2}$ per day. Overtime on weekends is paid at double the regular rate of pay. Last week Kim worked regular hours on Monday, Wednesday and Friday, 9 hours on Tuesday, $10\frac{1}{2}$ hours on Thursday and 6 hours on Saturday. Determine Kim's gross wages by each of the two methods in use.

17. An employee of a repair shop receives a gross pay of $261.80 for a regular work week of 44 hours. What is the hourly rate of pay?

18. A wage statement shows gross earnings of $361.00 for 45 hours of work. What is the hourly rate of pay if the regular work week is 40 hours and overtime is paid at time and one-half the regular rate of pay?

8.2 *Deductions and net pay*

A. *Statutory federal deductions*

Every employer is required by law to deduct income tax, **Canada Pension Plan** contributions and **Unemployment Insurance** premiums from the remuneration paid to employees.

The amounts withheld as Canada Pension Plan contribution and as Unemployment Insurance premium are based on the *pensionable* and *insurable* wages, salaries, or other remuneration and are limited to the maxima established annually by the federal government.

The maximum amount deducted as Canada Pension Plan contribution is based on an annual maximum. For 1985 the year's maximum pensionable earnings were $23 400 and the year's basic exemption was $2300. At the set contribution rate of 1.8% the maximum employee contribution for 1985 was 1.8% of $21 100, that is $379.80.

Once the maximum annual amount has been contributed by an employee, no further CPP contributions will be deducted for the remainder of the year provided that the contributor stays with the same employer. In case of a change in employer, CPP contributions are accumulated again from zero until the maximum has been reached. However, any excess contributions will be refunded when filing the income tax return the following year.

The amount of gross earnings subject to Unemployment Insurance are referred to as insurable earnings. For 1985 the year's maximum insurable earnings were $23 920. At the premium rate of 2.35% the maximum premium for 1985 was $562.12. However, the maximum amount deducted from gross earnings as unemployment insurance contribution is based on the maximum insurable earnings per pay period and does not exceed that amount if gross earnings are higher than the maximum established. For example, for 1985 maximum weekly insurable earnings were $460.00 and the maximum weekly premium was $10.81.

Income tax must be deducted from any type of remuneration paid to employees. The amount withheld as income tax depends on the tax rates in effect and is affected by the amount of personal exemption claimed by the employee. To establish the amount claimed as personal exemption each employee must file Form TD1—Employee's Tax Deduction Return—with the employer. The employer will withhold income tax on the basis of the **Net Claim Code** shown on Form TD1.

While the three statutory federal deductions may be computed using arithmetic techniques, most employers will determine the amounts to be deducted by referring to a Table of Income Tax Deductions at Source and a Canada Pension Plan Contribution and Unemployment Insurance Table provided by Revenue Canada at least once a year for various pay periods (daily, weekly, bi-weekly, semi-monthly, monthly).

Table 8.1 in the Appendix to this chapter is an excerpt from the 1985 Canada Pension Plan Contribution Table covering the deductions for a weekly pay period.

An employee's Canada Pension Plan contribution is based on the gross earnings for the pay period and is found by locating in the Remuneration column the bracket that contains the amount of the employee's gross earnings and reading the corresponding amount in the C.P.P. column.

Table 8.2 in the Appendix to this chapter is an excerpt from the 1985 Unemployment Insurance Premium Table.

An employee's Unemployment Insurance premium is based on the gross earnings for the pay period and is found by locating in the Remuneration column the bracket that contains the amount of the employee's gross earnings and reading the corresponding amount in the U.I. Premium column.

Since the tables are used for all periods (weekly, bi-weekly, monthly, etc.) attention must be paid to the maximum premium deduction for a particular pay period. For example, for a weekly pay period the maximum deduction is $10.81. It should be noted that it may be more efficient to compute the premium (2.35% of gross earnings) than to use tables.

Table 8.3 in the Appendix to this chapter, is an excerpt from the 1985 Table of Income Tax Deductions at Source for the Province of Ontario for a weekly pay period.

To determine the amount of income tax to be withheld from an employee's remuneration for the week, locate in the Weekly Pay column the bracket that contains the employee's *taxable* earnings for the week and follow this line across to the column headed by the Net Claim Code as certified by the employee on Form TD1. The amount shown at this point is the amount to be withheld.

Under the regulations of the Income Tax Acts it is unlikely that an employee's gross remuneration is also his taxable income. While there are various factors which may have to be considered in determining an employee's taxable income, for the majority of wage earners the gross earnings should be reduced by their Canada Pension Plan contribution, their Unemployment Insurance premium as well as contributions by the employees to a registered pension fund in an amount not exceeding $3500.00 in the year.

$$\begin{array}{c} \text{TAXABLE} \\ \text{EARNINGS} \end{array} = \begin{array}{c} \text{GROSS} \\ \text{EARNINGS} \end{array} - \left(\begin{array}{c} \text{C.P.P.} \\ \text{CONTRIBUTION} \end{array} + \begin{array}{c} \text{U.I.} \\ \text{PREMIUM} \end{array} + \begin{array}{c} \text{REGISTERED} \\ \text{PENSION FUND} \\ \text{CONTRIBUTION} \end{array} \right) \qquad \textit{Formula}\ \textbf{8.1}$$

Example 8.2a Doris Leroy earned gross wages of $394.00 during the current week. Her net claim code is 6 and she contributes 6% of her gross earnings to her company's pension fund.

   (i) What is the amount of her pension fund contribution?

   (ii) What is the amount withheld as C.P.P. contribution and as U.I. premium?

   (iii) What is the amount withheld as income tax?

Solution

   (i) Pension fund contribution = 0.06 x 394.00 = $23.64

   (ii) The Canada Pension Plan contribution for gross earnings of $394.00 is found in Table 8.1 in the Remuneration bracket $393.96—394.50.
        C.P.P. contribution = $6.30

   (iii) The Unemployment Insurance premium for gross earnings of $394.00 is found in Table 8.2 in the Remuneration bracket $393.83—$394.25.
        U.I. premium = $9.26

   (iv) For income tax purposes, Doris's 'Weekly Pay' is determined as follows.

Gross earnings for week		$394.00
Less C.P.P. contribution	$6.30	
U.I. premium	9.26	
Pension fund contribution	23.64	39.20
Taxable Weekly Pay		$354.80

The income tax deduction for a Weekly Pay of $354.80 is found in Table 8.3 on the line for the Weekly Pay bracket $352.00—356.99.

    Follow the line across to the column headed by the Net Claim Code 6.
        Income tax withheld = $47.55

B. Other deductions and net pay

In addition to the **statutory federal deductions**, an employee's gross earnings may be subject to other deductions either compulsory or voluntary, such as the aforementioned registered pension fund contribution, provincial hospitalization premiums, group insurance premiums, union dues, credit union savings, etc.

While some of these deductions may reduce an employee's taxable earnings, none of these, with the exception of registered pension fund contributions, is considered in determining the amount of income tax that is to be withheld. However, all deductions are considered in computing an employee's **net pay**.

NET PAY = GROSS EARNINGS − TOTAL DEDUCTIONS	⟵ *Formula* **8.2**

***Example* 8.2b**   In example 8.2a: determine Doris Leroy's net pay.

Solution

Gross earnings		$394.00
Less deductions		
C.P.P. contribution	$ 6.30	
U.I. premium	9.26	
Income tax	47.55	
Pension fund contribution	23.64	86.75
Net pay		$307.25

***Example* 8.2c**   Jack Power worked 51 hours last week. His regular rate of pay is $6.84 for a 44-hour work week. Overtime is paid at time and one-half. Jack's net claim code is 2 and deductions other than statutory federal deductions amounted to $17.80. What was his net pay?

Solution

Gross earnings			
Regular earnings = 44 × 6.84	=	$300.96	
Overtime pay = 7 × 6.84 × 1.5	=	71.82	
Total gross pay		$372.78	

Less deductions		
C.P.P. contributions	$ 5.91	
U.I. premium	8.76	
Income tax on a Weekly Pay of		
= 372.78 − (5.91 + 8.76) = 358.11	63.55	
Other deductions	17.80	96.02
Net pay		$276.76

C. Employer's payroll taxes and remittance to receiver general

Every employer must contribute to the Canada Pension Plan and pay Unemployment Insurance premiums. The employer's share, referred to as *payroll taxes*, is determined by the amounts contributed by the employees.

At present these payroll taxes are computed as follows.

(a) The Canada Pension Plan contribution by the employer is *equal* to the amounts withheld from the employees; that is, the employer pays $1.00 for every $1.00 contributed by the employees.

(b) Unless the employer qualifies for a premium reduction, the employer's premium is 1.4 times the premium paid by the employees; that is, the employer pays $1.40 for every $1.00 contributed by the employees.

Every employer must remit to the Receiver General for Canada by the 15th day of the month following the month in which the remuneration was paid to the employees, all amounts withheld as statutory federal deductions (Canada Pension Plan contributions, Unemployment Insurance premiums, income tax) plus the employer's matching Canada Pension Plan contribution and Unemployment Insurance premium.

Example 8.2d   In Example 8.2c

(i) what is the employer's C.P.P. contribution?

(ii) what is the employer's U.I. premium?

(iii) how much of the total remittance due to the Receiver General by the 15th of the next month relates to Jack Power's remuneration for the week?

Solution

(i) The employer's C.P.P. contribution must equal Jack Power's contribution, that is, $5.91.

(ii) The employer's U.I. premium is equal to 1.4 times Jack Power's premium, that is $1.4 \times 8.76 = \$12.26$.

(iii)
Jack Power's income tax payment	$63.55
Jack Power's C.P.P. contribution	5.91
Jack Power's U.I. premium	8.76
Employer's C.P.P. contribution	5.91
Employer's U.I. premium	12.26
Total amount included in the payment to the Receiver General which relates to Jack Power	$96.39

Example 8.2e The following information is available in the accounting records of Peel Credit Union for October.

Income tax withheld from employees, $345.60;
employees' C.P.P. contributions, $73.46;
employees' U.I. premiums, $65.45.

What amount is to be remitted by the Credit Union by November 15 to the Receiver General for Canada?

Solution

Income tax withheld	$345.60
Employees' C.P.P. contributions	73.46
Employees' U.I. premiums	65.45
Credit Union's C.P.P. contribution	73.46
Credit Union's U.I. premium—1.4 × 65.45	91.63
Total remittance to Receiver General	$649.60

Exercise 8.2

A. For each of the following determine

(a) the C.P.P. contribution   (b) the U.I. premium

(c) the amount of income tax   (d) the net pay

Problem number	Weekly gross earnings	Net claim code	Registered pension fund contribution	Other deductions
1.	$254.55	8	—	—
2.	$364.00	1	—	—
3.	$285.00	3	6% of gross	—
4.	$484.50	11	7% of gross	—
5.	$392.00	6	—	$16.00
6.	$258.00	13	5% of gross	$12.00

B. Answer each of the following questions.

1. Mercedes Milieux earned a base salary of $240.00 on a quota of $4000.00 and a commission of 6.5% on total weekly sales of $5324.00. Determine her net pay if her net claim code is 1.

2. Karl is paid an hourly wage of $8.24 for a 44 hour week. Compute Karl's usual net pay if his claim code is 10.

3. Pierre Gervais is employed at an hourly rate of $11.60 for a 40-hour week. Overtime is paid at time and one-half regular pay. Pierre contributes 6% of his gross wages to a registered pension fund and pays $6.00 in union dues every week. What is Pierre's net pay for a week in which he worked $46\frac{1}{2}$ hours?

4. Joyce Ryan is employed in sales on a weekly commission basis. She is paid a base salary of $180.00 for a quota of $3600.00 per week. She also receives a commission of 7% on the next $1800.00 of sales and 9.5% on any additional sales. Her net claim code is 2 and miscellaneous weekly deductions amount to $44.00. What is her net pay for a week in which her sales were $6500.00?

5. With regard to Joyce Ryan's remuneration for the given week in (4)
   (a) what is her employer's C.P.P. contribution?
   (b) what is her employer's U.I. premium?
   (c) how much of the total remittance due to the Receiver General of Canada by the 15th day of the next month relates to Joyce's remuneration for the week?

6. The payroll summary record for Sheridan Service for the month of October shows the following:

   Wages, $2454.50;
   Employer's Canada Pension Plan contributions, $84.54;
   Employer's Unemployment Insurance premium, $91.63;
   Income tax withheld from employees, $344.65.

   (a) What is the employees' C.P.P. contribution?
   (b) What is the U.I. premium paid by the employees?
   (c) What amount must be remitted to the Receiver General of Canada by November 15?

8.3   Payroll records

A.   Individual records

The maintenance of payroll data occupies an important place in the information system of a business. Various methods are used for the accumulation of payroll information but all systems need to keep track of a minimum amount of information with regard to individual employees and to summary records for all employees.

Personal information about an employee together with a record of hours worked, gross earnings, deductions and net pay is maintained on the employee's **individual earnings record**. This information, required under the provisions of employment legislation, indicates when an employee's Canada Pension Plan contribution and Unemployment Insurance premium have reached the maximum (for 1985, $379.80 for C.P.P. and $562.12 for U.I.), and provides the data for the employee's annual income tax return (T-4 Form).

Figure 8.1 illustrates an individual earnings record which provides the essential information to satisfy legislative requirements.

FIGURE 8.1 Employee earnings record

NAME: Mariel Dawn Logan   S.I.N.: 441-365-822   DATE EMPLOYED: 1980-05-10

ADDRESS: 2100 Main Street Oaktown   D.o.B.: 1958-08-25   TERMINATED:

JOB DESCRIPTION: Lab Technician   METHOD OF PAYMENT: Hourly   REGULAR HOURS: 40 per week

| PAY PERIOD ENDING | | | HOURS | HOURLY RATE | GROSS EARNINGS | | | NET CLAIM CODE | DEDUCTIONS | | | | | | TOTAL DEDUCTIONS | NET PAY | UNINSURED EARNINGS |
MONTH	WEEK	DAY			REGULAR	OVERTIME	TOTAL		INCOME TAX	C.P.P.	U.I.P.	PENSION FUND	UNION DUES	INSUR.			
JANUARY	1	7	40	10 60	424 00	- -	424 00	2	69 50	6 84	9 96	25 44	5 00	12 50	129 24	294 76	
	2	14	40	10 60	424 00	- -	424 00	2	69 50	6 84	9 96	25 44	5 00		116 74	307 26	
	3	21	36	10 60	381 60	- -	381 60	2	59 15	6 07	8 97	22 90	5 00		102 09	279 51	
	4	28	42	10 60	424 00	31 80	455 80	2	78 35	7 44	10 71	27 35	5 00		128 85	326 95	
	5																
	MO. TOTAL		158		1653 60	31 80	1685 40		276 50	27 19	39 60	101 13	20 00	12 50	476 92	1208 48	NIL
YEAR-TO-DATE TOTAL			1676		16140 00	890 00	17030 00		2670 30	272 00	400 20	1021 80	205 00	125 00	4694 30	12335 70	NIL
NOVEMBER	1	4	44	11 20	448 00	67 20	515 20	2	95 40	8 52	10 81	30 91	5 00	12 50	163 14	352 06	55 20
	2	11	42	11 20	448 00	33 60	481 60	2	85 75	7 89	10 81	28 90	5 00		138 35	343 25	21 60
	3	18	40	11 20	448 00	- -	448 00	2	76 90	7 27	10 53	26 88	5 00		126 58	321 42	
	4	25	40	11 20	448 00	- -	448 00	2	76 90	7 27	10 53	26 88	5 00		126 58	321 42	
	5																
	MO. TOTAL		166		1792 00	100 80	1892 80		334 95	30 95	42 68	113 57	20 00	12 50	554 65	1338 15	76 80
YEAR-TO-DATE TOTAL			1842		17932 00	990 80	18922 80		3005 25	302 95	442 88	1135 37	225 00	137 50	5248 95	13673 85	76 80
DECEMBER	1	2	46	11 20	448 00	100 80	548 80	2	105 60	9 06	10 81	32 93	5 00	12 50	175 90	372 90	88 80
	2	9	46	11 50	460 00	103 50	563 50	2	111 60	9 33	10 81	33 81	5 00		170 55	392 95	103 50
	3	16	40	11 50	460 00	- -	460 00	2	79 85	7 44	10 81	27 60	5 00		130 70	329 30	
	4	23	40	11 50	460 00	- -	460 00	2	79 85	7 44	10 81	27 60	5 00		130 70	329 30	
	5	30	40	11 50	460 00	- -	460 00	2	79 85	7 44	10 81	27 60	5 00		130 70	329 30	
	MO. TOTAL		212		2288 00	204 30	2492 30		456 75	40 71	54 05	149 54	25 00	12 50	738 55	1753 75	192 30
TOTAL FOR YEAR			2054		20220 00	1195 10	21415 10		3462 00	343 66	496 93	1284 91	250 00	150 00	5987 50	15427 60	269 10

Note Figure 8.1 ties in with employee 'D' in Figure 8.2 (see December, week 4)

Notes for Figure 8.1

1. Note the use of the Social Insurance Number (referred to as **S.I.N.**) which every person in Canada must have to be legally employable.

2. The details of hours, earnings, deductions and net pay are obtained from the weekly payroll register and summarized monthly.

3. *Uninsured* earnings represents the excess of gross earnings over the maximum earnings insurable for Unemployment Insurance purposes. (For 1985 the maximum insurable earnings per week were $460.00).

4. Computation of Year-to-Date Totals assists in reconciling individual earnings records with aggregate earnings records of all employees.

B.   Payroll register

Summary information about the remuneration of all employees is usually maintained in a **Payroll Register**. An illustration of a weekly payroll register is shown in Figure 8.2.

Notes for Figure 8.2

1. The work week begins on Thursday and ends on Wednesday and consists of 40 regular hours. Overtime is paid at time and one-half regular pay.

2. In this case the earnings for all hours at the regular rate of pay are determined and the overtime premium recorded separately. (See Section 8.1, section C, method B).

3. Gross pay for the week is obtained by adding the overtime premium to earnings at regular rate of pay.

4. C.P.P. contributions and U.I. premiums are looked up in Table 8.1 and Table 8.2. The Pension Fund contributions are computed at 6% of gross pay.

5. The Taxable Weekly Pay is obtained by Formula 8.1

6. The amount of income tax is looked up in Table 8.3 using the Net Claim Code given for each employee.

7. The total deductions are determined next and the net pay computed.

8. If total gross earnings for an employee exceed the maximum insurable earnings (for 1985 $460.00 per week), the excess is recorded as Uninsured Earnings.

9. The totals provide essential accounting information and serve as a check on the accuracy of the additions and subtractions.
   (a) Daily total hours must check out with the grand total of all hours worked for the week.
   (b) Total Regular Pay plus Total Overtime Premium = Total Gross Pay.
   (c) Total Income Tax + Total C.P.P. + Total U.I. + Total Pension Fund + Total Union Dues + Total Insurance = Total Deductions.
   (d) Total Gross Pay less the Grand total of all Deductions = Total Net Pay.

FIGURE 8.2 *Payroll register*

PAYROLL FOR WEEK ENDING DEC. 23, 1981

NAME	DAILY HOURS						TOTAL HOURS	O.T. HOURS	RATE PER HOUR	GROSS EARNINGS					
	TH	FR	SA	MO	TU	WE				REGULAR PAY		O.T. PREMIUM		TOTAL	
A	8	9	4	9	9	8	47	7	12.00	564	00	42	00	606	00
B	10	8	–	10	8	8	44	4	9.20	404	80	18	40	423	20
C	8	8	4	8	8	8	44	4	7.60	334	40	15	20	349	60
D	8	8	–	8	8	8	40	–	11.50	460	00	–	–	460	00
E	9	8	8	7	7	6	45	5	10.60	477	00	26	50	503	50
Total	43	41	16	42	40	38	220	20	–	2240	20	102	10	2342	30

(PAYROLL REGISTER CONTINUED)

	NET CL'M CODE	TAXABLE WEEKLY PAY		DEDUCTIONS										TOTAL DED'N		NET PAY		UNIN-SURED EARNINGS	
				INCOME TAX		C.P.P.		U.I.		PENSION 6%		DUES	INS.						
A	8	548	69	101	65	10	14	10	81	36	36	5.00		163	96	442	04	88	69
B	3	381	04	65	55	6	82	9	95	25	39	5.00		112	71	210	49	–	–
C	11	314	90	18	65	5	50	8	22	20	98	5.00		58	35	291	25	–	–
D	2	414	15	79	85	7	44	10	81	27	60	5.00		130	70	329	30	–	–
E	4	454	23	83	95	8	25	10	81	30	21	5.00		138	22	365	28	43	50
Total		—		349	65	38	15	50	60	140	54	25.00		603	94	1738	36	132	19

Exercise 8.3

A. Complete each of the following payrolls to the computation of gross earnings.

1. Complete the following commission payroll.

| | | NET SALES | | | | | | | | GROSS |
| WEEK ENDING JUNE 12, 19___ | | | | | | | | | | |
NAME	MON	TUE	WED	THU	FRI	SAT	TOTAL	RATE	COMMISSION
Abels, Brian	730	685	—	710	805	780		7%	
Bujak, Tracy	690	590	635	—	680	530		8%	
Chow, Gail	—	710	570	590	620	680		8%	
Gaunt, Joel	585	—	510	640	425	720		7.5%	
Spoto, Jeff	—	680	515	580	560	575		8.5%	
Totals								—	

2. Complete the following payroll. Regular hours are 8 hours per day. Overtime pay is time and one-half regular pay for all hours over eight per day and double time for all weekend hours.

WEEK ENDING SEPTEMBER 24, 19___

NAME	DAILY HOURS WORKED							TOTAL HOURS	REG. TIME	TIME AND ONE HALF	DOUBLE TIME	REGULAR HOURLY RATE	EARNINGS			EARNINGS TOTAL
	MO	TU	WE	TH	FR	SA	SU						REGULAR	TIME AND ONE-HALF	DOUBLE TIME	
Cook, Dan	9	7	8	8	7	6	4					$9.40				
Dunn, Paul	8	8	10	8	7	—	—					9.20				
Gray, Owen	8	8	10	8	8	6	—					8.80				
Korr, Alan	7	8	9	8	8	—	4					8.60				
Page, Greg	10	8	9	8	6	—	—					8.60				
Sims, David	7	8	10	9	8	6	—					8.40				
Total												—				

B. Complete each of the following payrolls, using Tables 8.1 to 8.3 to determine the federal pay deductions.

1. Complete the following payroll. Regular work week is 40 hours. Overtime pay is time and one-half regular pay. Registered pension fund contribution is 6% of gross earnings.

WEEK ENDING DECEMBER 12, 19____

	NAME	HOURS WORKED						TOTAL HOURS	RATE PER HOUR	GROSS EARNINGS		
		TH	FR	SA	MO	TU	WE			REGULAR PAY	OVERTIME PREMIUM	TOTAL
1	Daly, Jim	8	7	4	9	10	8		$8.80			
2	Frey, Ray	8	8	–	8	8	8		10.62			
3	Hull, Cy	10	10	8	–	8	8		9.84			
4	Muir, Pat	9	9	–	9	9	9		10.32			
5	Watt, Ann	7	10	–	10	7	8		9.44			
	Total							——				

(PAYROLL CONTINUED)

	NET CLAIM CODE	TAXABLE WEEKLY PAY	DEDUCTIONS					TOTAL DED'N	NET PAY	UNIN-SURED WAGES
			INCOME TAX	C.P.P.	U.I.	PENSION FUND	UNION DUES			
1	3						8 00			
2	1						8 00			
3	8						8 00			
4	4						8 00			
5	1						8 00			
	Totals									

2. Complete the following commission payroll.

WEEK ENDING OCTOBER 25, 19___										
	SALES									
NAME	GROSS	RET & ALLOW	NET	QUOTA	COMM. SALES	RATE	GROSS COMM.	BASE SALARY		GROSS EARNINGS
1 Cino, Lina	$4780	$130		$4000		8%		$300	00	
2 Emo, Gavin	5305	80		3500		7%		475	00	
3 Gold, Eric	5160	245		5000		6%		500	00	
4 Macri, Seve	6225	–		4000		8%		200	00	
5 Rabba, Cal	4930	440		–		11%		–		
6 Sims, Joe	3220	–		–		12%		–		
Totals				–		–				

(PAYROLL CONTINUED)											
	NET CLAIM CODE	TAXABLE WEEKLY PAY	DEDUCTIONS				TOTAL DEDUCTIONS	NET PAY		UNINS'D EARNINGS	
			INCOME TAX	C.P.P.	U.I.	OTHER DED'N					
1	9					35 00					
2	2					32 00					
3	1					24 00					
4	7					40 00					
5	10					29 00					
6	2					34 00					
Totals											

Review exercise

1. Maria is paid a semi-monthly salary of $800.80. Her regular work week is 40 hours. Overtime is paid at time and one-half regular pay.

   (a) What is Maria's hourly rate of pay?

   (b) What is Maria's gross pay if she worked $8\frac{1}{2}$ hours overtime in one pay period?

2. Casey receives an annual salary of $17 472.00, is paid monthly and works 35 regular hours per week.

   (a) What is Casey's gross remuneration per pay period?

   (b) What is his hourly rate of pay?

   (c) How many hours overtime did Casey work during a month for which his gross pay was $1693.60?

3. Tim is employed at an annual salary of $20 292.48. His regular work week is 36 hours and he is paid semi-monthly.

   (a) What is Tim's gross pay per pay period?

   (b) What is his hourly rate of pay?

   (c) What is his gross pay for a pay period in which he worked $12\frac{1}{2}$ hours overtime at time and one-half regular pay?

4. A salesman is paid a weekly commission of 4% on net sales of $3000.00, 8% on the next $1500.00 and 12.5% on all further sales. His sales for a week were $5580.00 and sales returns and allowances were $60.00.

   (a) What were his gross earnings for the week?

   (b) What was his average hourly rate of pay for the week if he worked 43 hours?

   (c) If his net claim code is 6 and miscellaneous deductions were $21.50, what was his net pay for the week?

5. Last week June worked 44 hours. She is paid $8.20 per hour for a regular work week of 37.5 hours and overtime at time and one-half regular pay. Her net claim code is 3 and she pays 7% of her gross pay into her company's registered pension fund. Other deductions per week amount to $34.00.

   (a) What were June's gross wages for last week?

   (b) What is the amount of the overtime premium?

   (c) What was her net pay?

   (d) How much of her employer's remittance to the Receiver General of Canada relates to June's earnings for the week?

6. A salesman is paid a monthly commission on a graduated basis of $7\frac{1}{2}$% on net sales of $7000.00, 9% on the next $8000.00 and 11% on any additional sales. If sales for April were $21 500.00 and sales returns were $325.00, what were the salesman's gross earnings for the month?

7. Margit is paid on a weekly commission basis. She is paid a base salary of $240.00 on a weekly quota of $8000.00 and a commission of 4.75% on any sales in excess of the quota. Margit's net claim code is 1.

   (a) If Margit's sales for last week were $11 340.00, what were her gross earnings?

   (b) What are Margit's average hourly earnings, if she worked 35 hours?

   (c) What is her net pay for the week?

8. Last week Lisa had gross earnings of $321.30. Lisa receives a base salary of $255.00 and a commission on sales exceeding her quota of $5000.00. What is her rate of commission if her sales were $6560.00?

9. John earned a gross commission of $2101.05 during July. What were his sales if his rate of commission is 10.5% of net sales and sales returns and allowances for the month were 8% of his sales?

10. Edith worked 47 hours during a week for which her gross remuneration was $426.22. Based on a regular work week of 40 hours and overtime payment at time and one-half regular pay, what is Edith's hourly rate of pay?

11. Norm is paid a semi-monthly salary of $682.50. Regular hours are $37\frac{1}{2}$ per week and overtime is paid at time and one-half regular pay.

    (a) What is Norm's hourly rate of pay?

    (b) How many hours overtime did Norm work in a pay period for which his gross pay was $846.30?

12. Silvio's gross earnings for last week were $328.54. His remuneration consists of a base salary of $280.00 plus a commission of 6% on net sales exceeding his weekly quota of $5000.00. What were Silvio's sales for the week if sales returns and allowances were $136.00?

13. Kevin is paid an hourly rate of $9.60. His regular work week is 36 hours and overtime is paid at time and one-half regular pay. Kevin's net claim code is 2. He pays 5% of his gross wages into the company's registered pension fund and has other deductions amounting to $24.50 per week. Last week Kevin worked $43\frac{1}{2}$ hours.

    (a) What are Kevin's gross earnings for the week?

    (b) How much is his net pay?

    (c) What is the amount of the overtime premium for the week?

    (d) What is his employer's C.P.P. expense on his pay?

    (e) What is his employer's Unemployment Insurance expense on his pay?

14. Sean's gross wages for a week were $541.20. His regular work week is 40 hours and overtime is paid at time and one-half regular pay. What is Sean's regular hourly wage if he worked $47\frac{1}{2}$ hours?

15. An employee's pay stub shows gross earnings of $304.30 for a week. His regular rate of pay is $6.80 per hour for a 35-hour week and overtime is paid at time and one-half regular pay. How many hours did the employee work?

16. The payroll summary record of Sheridan Service for November shows the following:

Salaries, $2145.00;

C.P.P. expense, $43.52;

U.I. expense, $46.83;

Income tax withheld, $325.00.

(a) What is the employees' C.P.P. contribution?

(b) What is the employees' U.I. premium?

(c) What amount is to be remitted to the Receiver General of Canada by December 15?

Self-test

1. A salesperson earned a commission of $806.59 for last week on gross sales of $5880. If returns and allowances were 11.5% of gross sales, what is his rate of commission based on net sales?

2. A.Y. receives an annual salary of $26 478.40. She is paid monthly on a 38-hour work week. What is the gross pay for a pay period in which she works 8.75 hours overtime at time and one-half regular pay?

3. J.B. earns $16.60 an hour, with time and one-half for hours worked over 8 a day. His clock hours for a week are 8.25, 8.25, 9.5, 11.5, 11.25. Determine his gross earnings for a week.

4. A wage earner receives a gross pay of $513.98 for 52.5 hours of work. What is the hourly rate of pay if a regular work week is 42 hours and overtime is paid at time and one-half the regular rate of pay.

5. A salesperson receives a weekly base salary of $200.00 on a quota of $2500. On the next $2000 she receives a commission of 11%. On any additional sales, the commission rate is 15%. Find her gross earnings for a week during which her sales amount to $6280.

6. C.D. is paid a semi-monthly salary of $780.00. If her regular work week is 40 hours, what is her hourly rate of pay?

7. Mrs. T. had gross earnings of $450.00 last week. She contributes 6% of her gross earnings to a registered pension plan and weekly miscellaneous deductions amount to $42.00. Her net claim code is 5. Determine her net pay for the week.

8. Complete the following payroll. Overtime is paid for all hours over eight hours per day at time and one-half regular pay. Registered pension plan contribution by all employees is 4% of gross pay.

WEEK ENDING FEBRUARY 25, 19													
NAME	DAILY HOURS					HOURS FOR WEEK			RATE PER HOUR	GROSS EARNINGS			
	MO	TU	WE	TH	FR	REG.	O.T.	TOTAL		REGULAR PAY	OVERTIME PREMIUM		TOTAL
A	8	8	8	8	8				$12 15				
B	8	7	9	6	8				10 20				
C	10	9	8	9	8				10 20				
D	11	7	8	8	6				9 20				
E	7	8	6	10	10				9 20				
Total									——				

(PAYROLL CONTINUED)											
	NET CLAIM CODE	TAXABLE WEEKLY PAY	DEDUCTIONS						TOTAL DED'N	NET PAY	UNIN- SURED WAGES
			INCOME TAX	C.P.P.	U.I.	PENSION FUND	OTHER				
A	4						—				
B	1						20 00				
C	10						16 00				
D	4						16 00				
E	7						—				
Total											

Summary of formulae used

Formula 8.1 $$\text{TAXABLE EARNINGS} = \text{GROSS EARNINGS} - \left(\text{C.P.P CONTRIBUTION} + \text{U.I. PREMIUM} + \text{REGISTERED PENSION FUND} \right)$$

Formula 8.2 NET PAY = GROSS EARNINGS − TOTAL DEDUCTIONS

Glossary of terms used

Canada pension plan (C.P.P.) Canada's national contributory retirement pension system

Commission the term applied to remuneration of sales personnel on the basis of their sales performance

Graduated commission remuneration paid as an increasing percent for increasing sales levels for a fixed period of time

Gross earnings the amount of an employee's remuneration before deductions

Individual earnings record a record showing details of essential personal information about an employee plus hours worked, gross pay, deductions and net pay

Insurable earnings the amount of gross earnings which are subject to Unemployment Insurance (1985 maximum $460.00 per week)

Net claim code A number which identifies a range of exemptions from tax deductions which is used to determine the amount of income tax to be deducted

Net pay gross pay less deductions

Overtime premium excess labour cost due to overtime

Payroll register a summary record of the remuneration of all the employees of a business

Quota a sales level required before the commission percent is paid usually associated with remuneration by base salary and commission.

Salary the term usually applied to remuneration of personnel on a monthly or annual basis

Salary plus commission a method of remunerating sales personnel which guarantees a minimum income per period

S.I.N. abbreviation for 'Social Insurance Number' which every person must have to be legally employable in Canada

Statutory federal deductions deductions from an employee's remuneration which must be withheld by an employer (C.P.P. contribution, U.I. premium, income tax)

Straight commission remuneration as a percent of net sales

Unemployment insurance Canada's employee-employer-financed unemployment insurance system

Wages the term usually applied to the remuneration of hourly rated employees

Appendix

TABLE 1 Canada pension plan contributions (weekly pay period—$0.00—$203.95)

Remuneration Rémunération From-de	To-à	C.P.P. R.P.C.	Remuneration Rémunération From-de	To-à	C.P.P. R.P.C.	Remuneration Rémunération From-de	To-à	C.P.P. R.P.C.	Remuneration Rémunération From-de	To-à	C.P.P. R.P.C.
.00 -	44.23	.00	83.96 -	84.50	.72	123.96 -	124.50	1.44	163.96 -	164.50	2.16
44.24 -	45.06	.01	84.51 -	85.06	.73	124.51 -	125.06	1.45	164.51 -	165.06	2.17
45.07 -	45.61	.02	85.07 -	85.61	.74	125.07 -	125.61	1.46	165.07 -	165.61	2.18
45.62 -	46.17	.03	85.62 -	86.17	.75	125.62 -	126.17	1.47	165.62 -	166.17	2.19
46.18 -	46.72	.04	86.18 -	86.72	.76	126.18 -	126.72	1.48	166.18 -	166.72	2.20
46.73 -	47.28	.05	86.73 -	87.28	.77	126.73 -	127.28	1.49	166.73 -	167.28	2.21
47.29 -	47.84	.06	87.29 -	87.84	.78	127.29 -	127.84	1.50	167.29 -	167.84	2.22
47.85 -	48.39	.07	87.85 -	88.39	.79	127.85 -	128.39	1.51	167.85 -	168.39	2.23
48.40 -	48.95	.08	88.40 -	88.95	.80	128.40 -	128.95	1.52	168.40 -	168.95	2.24
48.96 -	49.50	.09	88.96 -	89.50	.81	128.96 -	129.50	1.53	168.96 -	169.50	2.25
49.51 -	50.06	.10	89.51 -	90.06	.82	129.51 -	130.06	1.54	169.51 -	170.06	2.26
50.07 -	50.61	.11	90.07 -	90.61	.83	130.07 -	130.61	1.55	170.07 -	170.61	2.27
50.62 -	51.17	.12	90.62 -	91.17	.84	130.62 -	131.17	1.56	170.62 -	171.17	2.28
51.18 -	51.72	.13	91.18 -	91.72	.85	131.18 -	131.72	1.57	171.18 -	171.72	2.29
51.73 -	52.28	.14	91.73 -	92.28	.86	131.73 -	132.28	1.58	171.73 -	172.28	2.30
52.29 -	52.84	.15	92.29 -	92.84	.87	132.29 -	132.84	1.59	172.29 -	172.84	2.31
52.85 -	53.39	.16	92.85 -	93.39	.88	132.85 -	133.39	1.60	172.85 -	173.39	2.32
53.40 -	53.95	.17	93.40 -	93.95	.89	133.40 -	133.95	1.61	173.40 -	173.95	2.33
53.96 -	54.50	.18	93.96 -	94.50	.90	133.96 -	134.50	1.62	173.96 -	174.50	2.34
54.51 -	55.06	.19	94.51 -	95.06	.91	134.51 -	135.06	1.63	174.51 -	175.06	2.35
55.07 -	55.61	.20	95.07 -	95.61	.92	135.07 -	135.61	1.64	175.07 -	175.61	2.36
55.62 -	56.17	.21	95.62 -	96.17	.93	135.62 -	136.17	1.65	175.62 -	176.17	2.37
56.18 -	56.72	.22	96.18 -	96.72	.94	136.18 -	136.72	1.66	176.18 -	176.72	2.38
56.73 -	57.28	.23	96.73 -	97.28	.95	136.73 -	137.28	1.67	176.73 -	177.28	2.39
57.29 -	57.84	.24	97.29 -	97.84	.96	137.29 -	137.84	1.68	177.29 -	177.84	2.40
57.85 -	58.39	.25	97.85 -	98.39	.97	137.85 -	138.39	1.69	177.85 -	178.39	2.41
58.40 -	58.95	.26	98.40 -	98.95	.98	138.40 -	138.95	1.70	178.40 -	178.95	2.42
58.96 -	59.50	.27	98.96 -	99.50	.99	138.96 -	139.50	1.71	178.96 -	179.50	2.43
59.51 -	60.06	.28	99.51 -	100.06	1.00	139.51 -	140.06	1.72	179.51 -	180.06	2.44
60.07 -	60.51	.29	100.07 -	100.61	1.01	140.07 -	140.61	1.73	180.07 -	180.61	2.45
60.62 -	61.17	.30	100.62 -	101.17	1.02	140.62 -	141.17	1.74	180.62 -	181.17	2.46
61.18 -	61.72	.31	101.18 -	101.72	1.03	141.18 -	141.72	1.75	181.18 -	181.72	2.47
61.73 -	62.28	.32	101.73 -	102.28	1.04	141.73 -	142.28	1.76	181.73 -	182.28	2.48
62.29 -	62.84	.33	102.29 -	102.84	1.05	142.29 -	142.84	1.77	182.29 -	182.84	2.49
62.85 -	63.39	.34	102.85 -	103.39	1.06	142.85 -	143.39	1.78	182.85 -	183.39	2.50
63.40 -	63.95	.35	103.40 -	103.95	1.07	143.40 -	143.95	1.79	183.40 -	183.95	2.51
63.96 -	64.50	.36	103.96 -	104.50	1.08	143.96 -	144.50	1.80	183.96 -	184.50	2.52
64.51 -	65.06	.37	104.51 -	105.06	1.09	144.51 -	145.06	1.81	184.51 -	185.06	2.53
65.07 -	65.61	.38	105.07 -	105.61	1.10	145.07 -	145.61	1.82	185.07 -	185.61	2.54
65.62 -	66.17	.39	105.62 -	106.17	1.11	145.62 -	146.17	1.83	185.62 -	186.17	2.55
66.18 -	66.72	.40	106.18 -	106.72	1.12	146.18 -	146.72	1.84	186.18 -	186.72	2.56
66.73 -	67.28	.41	106.73 -	107.28	1.13	146.73 -	147.28	1.85	186.73 -	187.28	2.57
67.29 -	67.84	.42	107.29 -	107.84	1.14	147.29 -	147.84	1.86	187.29 -	187.84	2.58
67.85 -	68.39	.43	107.85 -	108.39	1.15	147.85 -	148.39	1.87	187.85 -	188.39	2.59
68.40 -	68.95	.44	108.40 -	108.95	1.16	148.40 -	148.95	1.88	188.40 -	188.95	2.60
68.96 -	69.50	.45	108.96 -	109.50	1.17	148.96 -	149.50	1.89	188.96 -	189.50	2.61
69.51 -	70.06	.46	109.51 -	110.06	1.18	149.51 -	150.06	1.90	189.51 -	190.06	2.62
70.07 -	70.61	.47	110.07 -	110.61	1.19	150.07 -	150.61	1.91	190.07 -	190.61	2.63
70.62 -	71.17	.48	110.62 -	111.17	1.20	150.62 -	151.17	1.92	190.62 -	191.17	2.64
71.18 -	71.72	.49	111.18 -	111.72	1.21	151.18 -	151.72	1.93	191.18 -	191.72	2.65
71.73 -	72.28	.50	111.73 -	112.28	1.22	151.73 -	152.28	1.94	191.73 -	192.28	2.66
72.29 -	72.84	.51	112.29 -	112.84	1.23	152.29 -	152.84	1.95	192.29 -	192.84	2.67
72.85 -	73.39	.52	112.85 -	113.39	1.24	152.85 -	153.39	1.96	192.85 -	193.39	2.68
73.40 -	73.95	.53	113.40 -	113.95	1.25	153.40 -	153.95	1.97	193.40 -	193.95	2.69
73.96 -	74.50	.54	113.96 -	114.50	1.26	153.96 -	154.50	1.98	193.96 -	194.50	2.70
74.51 -	75.06	.55	114.51 -	115.06	1.27	154.51 -	155.06	1.99	194.51 -	195.06	2.71
75.07 -	75.61	.56	115.07 -	115.61	1.28	155.07 -	155.61	2.00	195.07 -	195.61	2.72
75.62 -	76.17	.57	115.62 -	116.17	1.29	155.62 -	156.17	2.01	195.62 -	196.17	2.73
76.18 -	76.72	.58	116.18 -	116.72	1.30	156.18 -	156.72	2.02	196.18 -	196.72	2.74
76.73 -	77.28	.59	116.73 -	117.28	1.31	156.73 -	157.28	2.03	196.73 -	197.28	2.75
77.29 -	77.84	.60	117.29 -	117.84	1.32	157.29 -	157.84	2.04	197.29 -	197.84	2.76
77.85 -	78.39	.61	117.85 -	118.39	1.33	157.85 -	158.39	2.05	197.85 -	198.39	2.77
78.40 -	78.95	.62	118.40 -	118.95	1.34	158.40 -	158.95	2.06	198.40 -	198.95	2.78
78.96 -	79.50	.63	118.96 -	119.50	1.35	158.96 -	159.50	2.07	198.96 -	199.50	2.79
79.51 -	80.06	.64	119.51 -	120.06	1.36	159.51 -	160.06	2.08	199.51 -	200.06	2.80
80.07 -	80.61	.65	120.07 -	120.61	1.37	160.07 -	160.61	2.09	200.07 -	200.61	2.81
80.62 -	81.17	.66	120.62 -	121.17	1.38	160.62 -	161.17	2.10	200.62 -	201.17	2.82
81.18 -	81.72	.67	121.18 -	121.72	1.39	161.18 -	161.72	2.11	201.18 -	201.72	2.83
81.73 -	82.28	.68	121.73 -	122.28	1.40	161.73 -	162.28	2.12	201.73 -	202.28	2.84
82.29 -	82.84	.69	122.29 -	122.84	1.41	162.29 -	162.84	2.13	202.29 -	202.84	2.85
82.85 -	83.39	.70	122.85 -	123.39	1.42	162.85 -	163.39	2.14	202.85 -	203.39	2.86
83.40 -	83.95	.71	123.40 -	123.95	1.43	163.40 -	163.95	2.15	203.40 -	203.95	2.87

TABLE 1 Canada pension plan contributions (weekly pay period— $203.96—$363.95)

Remuneration / Rémunération From-de — To-à	C.P.P. R.P.C.	Remuneration / Rémunération From-de — To-à	C.P.P. R.P.C.	Remuneration / Rémunération From-de — To-à	C.P.P. R.P.C.	Remuneration / Rémunération From-de — To-à	C.P.P. R.P.C.
203.96 – 204.50	2.88	243.96 – 244.50	3.60	283.96 – 284.50	4.32	323.96 – 324.50	5.04
204.51 – 205.06	2.89	244.51 – 245.06	3.61	284.51 – 285.06	4.33	324.51 – 325.06	5.05
205.07 – 205.61	2.90	245.07 – 245.61	3.62	285.07 – 285.61	4.34	325.07 – 325.61	5.05
205.62 – 206.17	2.91	245.62 – 246.17	3.63	285.62 – 286.17	4.35	325.62 – 326.17	5.07
206.18 – 206.72	2.92	246.18 – 246.72	3.64	286.18 – 286.72	4.36	326.18 – 326.72	5.08
206.73 – 207.28	2.93	246.73 – 247.28	3.65	286.73 – 287.28	4.37	326.73 – 327.28	5.09
207.29 – 207.84	2.94	247.29 – 247.84	3.66	287.29 – 287.84	4.38	327.29 – 327.84	5.10
207.85 – 208.39	2.95	247.85 – 248.39	3.67	287.85 – 288.39	4.39	327.85 – 328.39	5.11
208.40 – 208.95	2.96	248.40 – 248.95	3.68	288.40 – 288.95	4.40	328.40 – 328.95	5.12
208.96 – 209.50	2.97	248.96 – 249.50	3.69	288.96 – 289.50	4.41	328.96 – 329.50	5.13
209.51 – 210.06	2.98	249.51 – 250.06	3.70	289.51 – 290.06	4.42	329.51 – 330.06	5.14
210.07 – 210.61	2.99	250.07 – 250.61	3.71	290.07 – 290.61	4.43	330.07 – 330.61	5.15
210.62 – 211.17	3.00	250.62 – 251.17	3.72	290.62 – 291.17	4.44	330.62 – 331.17	5.15
211.18 – 211.72	3.01	251.18 – 251.72	3.73	291.18 – 291.72	4.45	331.18 – 331.72	5.17
211.73 – 212.29	3.02	251.73 – 252.28	3.74	291.73 – 292.28	4.46	331.73 – 332.28	5.18
212.29 – 212.84	3.03	252.29 – 252.84	3.75	292.29 – 292.84	4.47	332.29 – 332.84	5.19
212.85 – 213.39	3.04	252.85 – 253.39	3.76	292.85 – 293.39	4.48	332.85 – 333.39	5.20
213.40 – 213.95	3.05	253.40 – 253.95	3.77	293.40 – 293.95	4.49	333.40 – 333.95	5.21
213.96 – 214.50	3.06	253.96 – 254.50	3.78	293.96 – 294.50	4.50	333.96 – 334.50	5.22
214.51 – 215.05	3.07	254.51 – 255.06	3.79	294.51 – 295.06	4.51	334.51 – 335.06	5.23
215.07 – 215.61	3.08	255.07 – 255.61	3.80	295.07 – 295.61	4.52	335.07 – 335.61	5.24
215.62 – 216.17	3.09	255.62 – 256.17	3.81	295.62 – 296.17	4.53	335.62 – 336.17	5.25
216.18 – 216.72	3.10	256.18 – 256.72	3.82	296.18 – 296.72	4.54	336.18 – 336.72	5.25
216.73 – 217.29	3.11	256.73 – 257.28	3.83	296.73 – 297.28	4.55	336.73 – 337.28	5.27
217.29 – 217.84	3.12	257.29 – 257.84	3.84	297.29 – 297.84	4.56	337.29 – 337.84	5.28
217.85 – 218.39	3.13	257.85 – 258.39	3.85	297.85 – 298.39	4.57	337.85 – 338.39	5.29
218.40 – 218.95	3.14	258.40 – 258.95	3.86	298.40 – 298.95	4.58	338.40 – 338.95	5.30
218.96 – 219.50	3.15	258.96 – 259.50	3.87	298.96 – 299.50	4.59	338.96 – 339.50	5.31
219.51 – 220.06	3.16	259.51 – 260.06	3.88	299.51 – 300.06	4.60	339.51 – 340.06	5.32
220.07 – 220.61	3.17	260.07 – 260.61	3.89	300.07 – 300.61	4.61	340.07 – 340.61	5.33
220.62 – 221.17	3.18	260.62 – 261.17	3.90	300.62 – 301.17	4.62	340.62 – 341.17	5.34
221.18 – 221.72	3.19	261.18 – 261.72	3.91	301.18 – 301.72	4.63	341.18 – 341.72	5.35
221.73 – 222.28	3.20	261.73 – 262.28	3.92	301.73 – 302.28	4.64	341.73 – 342.28	5.36
222.29 – 222.84	3.21	262.29 – 262.84	3.93	302.29 – 302.84	4.65	342.29 – 342.84	5.37
222.85 – 223.39	3.22	262.85 – 263.39	3.94	302.85 – 303.39	4.66	342.85 – 343.39	5.38
223.40 – 223.95	3.23	263.40 – 263.95	3.95	303.40 – 303.95	4.67	343.40 – 343.95	5.39
223.96 – 224.50	3.24	263.96 – 264.50	3.96	303.96 – 304.50	4.68	343.96 – 344.50	5.40
224.51 – 225.06	3.25	264.51 – 265.06	3.97	304.51 – 305.06	4.69	344.51 – 345.06	5.41
225.07 – 225.61	3.26	265.07 – 265.61	3.98	305.07 – 305.61	4.70	345.07 – 345.61	5.42
225.62 – 226.17	3.27	265.62 – 266.17	3.99	305.62 – 306.17	4.71	345.62 – 346.17	5.43
226.18 – 226.72	3.28	266.18 – 266.72	4.00	306.18 – 306.72	4.72	346.18 – 346.72	5.44
226.73 – 227.28	3.29	266.73 – 267.28	4.01	306.73 – 307.28	4.73	346.73 – 347.28	5.45
227.29 – 227.84	3.30	267.29 – 267.84	4.02	307.29 – 307.84	4.74	347.29 – 347.84	5.46
227.85 – 228.39	3.31	267.85 – 268.39	4.03	307.85 – 308.39	4.75	347.85 – 348.39	5.47
228.40 – 228.95	3.32	268.40 – 268.95	4.04	308.40 – 308.95	4.76	348.40 – 348.95	5.48
228.96 – 229.50	3.33	268.96 – 269.50	4.05	308.96 – 309.50	4.77	348.96 – 349.50	5.49
229.51 – 230.06	3.34	269.51 – 270.06	4.06	309.51 – 310.06	4.78	349.51 – 350.06	5.50
230.07 – 230.61	3.35	270.07 – 270.61	4.07	310.07 – 310.61	4.79	350.07 – 350.61	5.51
230.62 – 231.17	3.36	270.62 – 271.17	4.08	310.62 – 311.17	4.80	350.62 – 351.17	5.52
231.18 – 231.72	3.37	271.18 – 271.72	4.09	311.18 – 311.72	4.81	351.18 – 351.72	5.53
231.73 – 232.29	3.38	271.73 – 272.28	4.10	311.73 – 312.28	4.82	351.73 – 352.28	5.54
232.29 – 232.84	3.39	272.29 – 272.84	4.11	312.29 – 312.84	4.83	352.29 – 352.84	5.55
232.85 – 233.39	3.40	272.85 – 273.39	4.12	312.85 – 313.39	4.84	352.85 – 353.39	5.56
233.40 – 233.95	3.41	273.40 – 273.95	4.13	313.40 – 313.95	4.85	353.40 – 353.95	5.57
233.96 – 234.50	3.42	273.96 – 274.50	4.14	313.96 – 314.50	4.86	353.96 – 354.50	5.58
234.51 – 235.06	3.43	274.51 – 275.06	4.15	314.51 – 315.06	4.87	354.51 – 355.06	5.59
235.07 – 235.61	3.44	275.07 – 275.61	4.16	315.07 – 315.61	4.88	355.07 – 355.61	5.60
235.62 – 236.17	3.45	275.62 – 276.17	4.17	315.62 – 316.17	4.89	355.62 – 356.17	5.61
236.18 – 236.72	3.46	276.18 – 276.72	4.18	316.18 – 316.72	4.90	356.18 – 356.72	5.62
236.73 – 237.28	3.47	276.73 – 277.28	4.19	316.73 – 317.28	4.91	356.73 – 357.28	5.63
237.29 – 237.84	3.48	277.29 – 277.84	4.20	317.29 – 317.84	4.92	357.29 – 357.84	5.64
237.85 – 238.39	3.49	277.85 – 278.39	4.21	317.85 – 318.39	4.93	357.85 – 358.39	5.65
238.40 – 238.95	3.50	278.40 – 278.95	4.22	318.40 – 318.95	4.94	358.40 – 358.95	5.66
238.96 – 239.50	3.51	278.96 – 279.50	4.23	318.96 – 319.50	4.95	358.96 – 359.50	5.67
239.51 – 240.06	3.52	279.51 – 280.06	4.24	319.51 – 320.06	4.96	359.51 – 360.06	5.68
240.07 – 240.61	3.53	280.07 – 280.61	4.25	320.07 – 320.61	4.97	360.07 – 360.61	5.69
240.62 – 241.17	3.54	280.62 – 281.17	4.26	320.62 – 321.17	4.98	360.62 – 361.17	5.70
241.18 – 241.72	3.55	281.18 – 281.72	4.27	321.18 – 321.72	4.99	361.18 – 361.72	5.71
241.73 – 242.28	3.56	281.73 – 282.28	4.28	321.73 – 322.28	5.00	361.73 – 362.28	5.72
242.29 – 242.84	3.57	282.29 – 282.84	4.29	322.29 – 322.84	5.01	362.29 – 362.84	5.73
242.85 – 243.39	3.58	282.85 – 283.39	4.30	322.85 – 323.39	5.02	362.85 – 363.39	5.74
243.40 – 243.95	3.59	283.40 – 283.95	4.31	323.40 – 323.95	5.03	363.40 – 363.95	5.75

TABLE 1 *Canada pension plan contributions (weekly pay period— $363.96—$1115.06*

Remuneration Rémunération From-de	To-à	C.P.P. R.P.C.	Remuneration Rémunération From-de	To-à	C.P.P. R.P.C.	Remuneration Rémunération From-de	To-à	C.P.P. R.P.C.	Remuneration Rémunération From-de	To-à	C.P.P. R.P.C.
363.96	364.50	5.75	403.96	404.50	6.48	443.96	444.50	7.20	755.07	760.06	12.84
364.51	365.05	5.77	404.51	405.06	6.49	444.51	445.06	7.21	760.07	765.06	12.93
365.07	365.61	5.78	405.07	405.61	6.50	445.07	445.61	7.22	765.07	770.05	13.02
365.62	366.17	5.79	405.62	406.17	6.51	445.62	446.17	7.23	770.07	775.06	13.11
366.18	366.72	5.80	406.18	406.72	6.52	446.18	446.72	7.24	775.07	780.06	13.20
366.73	367.28	5.81	406.73	407.28	6.53	446.73	447.28	7.25	780.07	785.06	13.29
367.29	367.84	5.82	407.29	407.84	6.54	447.29	447.84	7.26	785.07	790.06	13.38
367.85	368.39	5.83	407.85	408.39	6.55	447.85	448.39	7.27	790.07	795.06	13.47
368.40	368.95	5.84	408.40	408.95	6.56	448.40	448.95	7.28	795.07	800.06	13.56
368.96	369.50	5.85	408.96	409.50	6.57	448.96	449.50	7.29	800.07	805.05	13.65
369.51	370.05	5.86	409.51	410.06	6.58	449.51	450.05	7.30	805.07	810.06	13.74
370.07	370.61	5.87	410.07	410.61	6.59	450.07	455.06	7.35	810.07	815.06	13.83
370.62	371.17	5.88	410.62	411.17	6.60	455.07	460.06	7.44	815.07	820.06	13.92
371.18	371.72	5.89	411.18	411.72	6.61	460.07	465.06	7.53	820.07	825.05	14.01
371.73	372.29	5.90	411.73	412.28	6.62	465.07	470.06	7.62	825.07	830.06	14.10
372.29	372.84	5.91	412.29	412.84	6.63	470.07	475.06	7.71	830.07	835.06	14.19
372.85	373.39	5.92	412.85	413.39	6.64	475.07	480.06	7.80	835.07	840.05	14.28
373.40	373.95	5.93	413.40	413.95	6.65	480.07	485.06	7.89	840.07	845.06	14.37
373.96	374.50	5.94	413.96	414.50	6.66	485.07	490.06	7.98	845.07	850.06	14.46
374.51	375.05	5.95	414.51	415.06	6.67	490.07	495.06	8.07	850.07	855.05	14.55
375.07	375.61	5.96	415.07	415.61	6.68	495.07	500.06	8.16	855.07	860.05	14.64
375.62	376.17	5.97	415.62	416.17	6.69	500.07	505.06	8.25	860.07	865.05	14.73
376.18	376.72	5.98	416.18	416.72	6.70	505.07	510.06	8.34	865.07	870.06	14.82
376.73	377.28	5.99	416.73	417.28	6.71	510.07	515.06	8.43	870.07	875.06	14.91
377.29	377.94	6.00	417.29	417.84	6.72	515.07	520.06	8.52	875.07	880.06	15.00
377.85	378.39	6.01	417.85	418.39	6.73	520.07	525.06	8.61	880.07	885.06	15.09
378.40	378.95	6.02	418.40	418.95	6.74	525.07	530.06	8.70	885.07	890.05	15.18
378.96	379.50	6.03	418.96	419.50	6.75	530.07	535.06	8.79	890.07	895.06	15.27
379.51	380.05	6.04	419.51	420.06	6.76	535.07	540.06	8.88	895.07	900.05	15.36
380.07	380.61	6.05	420.07	420.61	6.77	540.07	545.06	8.97	900.07	905.06	15.45
380.62	381.17	6.06	420.62	421.17	6.78	545.07	550.06	9.06	905.07	910.06	15.54
381.18	381.72	6.07	421.18	421.72	6.79	550.07	555.06	9.15	910.07	915.06	15.63
381.73	382.28	6.08	421.73	422.28	6.80	555.07	560.06	9.24	915.07	920.06	15.72
382.29	382.84	6.09	422.29	422.84	6.81	560.07	565.06	9.33	920.07	925.06	15.81
382.85	383.39	6.10	422.85	423.39	6.82	565.07	570.06	9.42	925.07	930.06	15.90
383.40	383.95	6.11	423.40	423.95	6.83	570.07	575.06	9.51	930.07	935.06	15.99
383.96	384.50	6.12	423.96	424.50	6.84	575.07	580.06	9.60	935.07	940.06	16.08
384.51	385.05	6.13	424.51	425.06	6.85	580.07	585.06	9.69	940.07	945.06	16.17
385.07	385.61	6.14	425.07	425.61	6.86	585.07	590.06	9.78	945.07	950.06	16.26
385.62	386.17	6.15	425.62	426.17	6.87	590.07	595.06	9.87	950.07	955.05	16.35
386.18	386.72	6.16	426.18	426.72	6.88	595.07	600.06	9.96	955.07	960.06	16.44
386.73	387.28	6.17	426.73	427.28	6.89	600.07	605.06	10.05	960.07	965.06	16.53
387.29	387.84	6.18	427.29	427.84	6.90	605.07	610.06	10.14	965.07	970.06	16.62
387.85	388.39	6.19	427.85	428.39	6.91	610.07	615.06	10.23	970.07	975.06	16.71
388.40	388.95	6.20	428.40	428.95	6.92	615.07	620.06	10.32	975.07	980.06	16.80
388.96	389.50	6.21	428.96	429.50	6.93	620.07	625.06	10.41	980.07	985.06	16.89
389.51	390.05	6.22	429.51	430.06	6.94	625.07	630.06	10.50	985.07	990.06	16.98
390.07	390.61	6.23	430.07	430.61	6.95	630.07	635.06	10.59	990.07	995.06	17.07
390.62	391.17	6.24	430.62	431.17	6.96	635.07	640.06	10.68	995.07	1000.06	17.16
391.18	391.72	6.25	431.18	431.72	6.97	640.07	645.06	10.77	1000.07	1005.06	17.25
391.73	392.28	6.26	431.73	432.28	6.98	645.07	650.06	10.86	1005.07	1010.06	17.34
392.29	392.84	6.27	432.29	432.84	6.99	650.07	655.06	10.95	1010.07	1015.06	17.43
392.85	393.39	6.28	432.85	433.39	7.00	655.07	660.06	11.04	1015.07	1020.06	17.52
393.40	393.95	6.29	433.40	433.95	7.01	660.07	665.06	11.13	1020.07	1025.05	17.61
393.96	394.50	6.30	433.96	434.50	7.02	665.07	670.06	11.22	1025.07	1030.06	17.70
394.51	395.05	6.31	434.51	435.06	7.03	670.07	675.06	11.31	1030.07	1035.06	17.79
395.07	395.61	6.32	435.07	435.61	7.04	675.07	680.06	11.40	1035.07	1040.06	17.88
395.62	396.17	6.33	435.62	436.17	7.05	680.07	685.06	11.49	1040.07	1045.06	17.97
396.18	396.72	6.34	436.18	436.72	7.06	685.07	690.06	11.58	1045.07	1050.06	18.06
396.73	397.28	6.35	436.73	437.28	7.07	690.07	695.06	11.67	1050.07	1055.06	18.15
397.29	397.84	6.36	437.29	437.84	7.08	695.07	700.06	11.76	1055.07	1060.05	18.24
397.85	398.39	6.37	437.85	438.39	7.09	700.07	705.06	11.85	1060.07	1065.06	18.33
398.40	398.95	6.38	438.40	438.95	7.10	705.07	710.06	11.94	1065.07	1070.06	18.42
398.96	399.50	6.39	438.96	439.50	7.11	710.07	715.06	12.03	1070.07	1075.06	18.51
399.51	400.05	6.40	439.51	440.06	7.12	715.07	720.06	12.12	1075.07	1080.06	18.60
400.07	400.61	6.41	440.07	440.61	7.13	720.07	725.06	12.21	1080.07	1085.06	18.69
400.62	401.17	6.42	440.62	441.17	7.14	725.07	730.06	12.30	1085.07	1090.06	18.78
401.18	401.72	6.43	441.18	441.72	7.15	730.07	735.06	12.39	1090.07	1095.06	18.87
401.73	402.28	6.44	441.73	442.28	7.16	735.07	740.06	12.48	1095.07	1100.06	18.96
402.29	402.84	6.45	442.29	442.84	7.17	740.07	745.06	12.57	1100.07	1105.06	19.05
402.85	403.39	6.46	442.85	443.39	7.18	745.07	750.06	12.66	1105.07	1110.06	19.14
403.40	403.95	6.47	443.40	443.95	7.19	750.07	755.06	12.75	1110.07	1115.06	19.23

TABLE 2 Unemployment insurance premiums ($0.00—$122.76)

Remuneration Rémunération From-de	To-à	U.I. Premium Prime d'a.-c.	Remuneration Rémunération From-de	To-à	U.I. Premium Prime d'a.-c.	Remuneration Rémunération From-de	To-à	U.I. Premium Prime d'a.-c.	Remuneration Rémunération From-de	To-à	U.I. Premium Prime d'a.-c.
.00	.63	.01	30.86	31.27	.73	61.49	61.91	1.45	92.13	92.55	2.17
.64	1.06	.02	31.28	31.70	.74	61.92	62.34	1.46	92.56	92.97	2.18
1.07	1.48	.03	31.71	32.12	.75	62.35	62.76	1.47	92.98	93.40	2.19
1.49	1.91	.04	32.13	32.55	.76	62.77	63.19	1.48	93.41	93.82	2.20
1.92	2.34	.05	32.56	32.97	.77	63.20	63.61	1.49	93.83	94.25	2.21
2.35	2.76	.06	32.98	33.40	.78	63.62	64.04	1.50	94.26	94.68	2.22
2.77	3.19	.07	33.41	33.82	.79	64.05	64.46	1.51	94.69	95.10	2.23
3.20	3.61	.08	33.83	34.25	.80	64.47	64.89	1.52	95.11	95.53	2.24
3.62	4.04	.09	34.26	34.68	.81	64.90	65.31	1.53	95.54	95.95	2.25
4.05	4.46	.10	34.69	35.10	.82	65.32	65.74	1.54	95.96	96.38	2.26
4.47	4.89	.11	35.11	35.53	.83	65.75	66.17	1.55	96.39	96.80	2.27
4.90	5.31	.12	35.54	35.95	.84	66.18	66.59	1.56	96.81	97.23	2.28
5.32	5.74	.13	35.96	36.38	.85	66.60	67.02	1.57	97.24	97.65	2.29
5.75	6.17	.14	36.39	36.80	.86	67.03	67.44	1.58	97.66	98.08	2.30
6.18	6.59	.15	36.81	37.23	.87	67.45	67.87	1.59	98.09	98.51	2.31
6.60	7.02	.16	37.24	37.65	.88	67.88	68.29	1.60	98.52	98.93	2.32
7.03	7.44	.17	37.66	38.06	.89	68.30	68.72	1.61	98.94	99.36	2.33
7.45	7.87	.18	38.09	38.51	.90	68.73	69.14	1.62	99.37	99.78	2.34
7.88	8.29	.19	38.52	38.93	.91	69.15	69.57	1.63	99.79	100.21	2.35
8.30	8.72	.20	38.94	39.36	.92	69.58	69.99	1.64	100.22	100.63	2.36
8.73	9.14	.21	39.37	39.78	.93	70.00	70.42	1.65	100.64	101.06	2.37
9.15	9.57	.22	39.79	40.21	.94	70.43	70.85	1.66	101.07	101.48	2.38
9.58	9.99	.23	40.22	40.63	.95	70.86	71.27	1.67	101.49	101.91	2.39
10.00	10.42	.24	40.64	41.06	.96	71.28	71.70	1.68	101.92	102.34	2.40
10.43	10.85	.25	41.07	41.48	.97	71.71	72.12	1.69	102.35	102.76	2.41
10.86	11.27	.26	41.49	41.91	.98	72.13	72.55	1.70	102.77	103.19	2.42
11.28	11.70	.27	41.92	42.34	.99	72.56	72.97	1.71	103.20	103.61	2.43
11.71	12.12	.28	42.35	42.76	1.00	72.98	73.40	1.72	103.62	104.04	2.44
12.13	12.55	.29	42.77	43.19	1.01	73.41	73.82	1.73	104.05	104.46	2.45
12.56	12.97	.30	43.20	43.61	1.02	73.83	74.25	1.74	104.47	104.89	2.46
12.98	13.40	.31	43.62	44.04	1.03	74.26	74.68	1.75	104.90	105.31	2.47
13.41	13.82	.32	44.05	44.46	1.04	74.69	75.10	1.76	105.32	105.74	2.48
13.83	14.25	.33	44.47	44.89	1.05	75.11	75.53	1.77	105.75	106.17	2.49
14.26	14.68	.34	44.90	45.31	1.06	75.54	75.95	1.78	106.18	106.59	2.50
14.69	15.10	.35	45.32	45.74	1.07	75.96	76.38	1.79	106.60	107.02	2.51
15.11	15.53	.36	45.75	46.17	1.08	76.39	76.80	1.80	107.03	107.44	2.52
15.54	15.95	.37	46.18	46.59	1.09	76.81	77.23	1.81	107.45	107.87	2.53
15.96	16.38	.38	46.60	47.02	1.10	77.24	77.65	1.82	107.88	108.29	2.54
16.39	16.80	.39	47.03	47.44	1.11	77.66	78.08	1.83	108.30	108.72	2.55
16.81	17.23	.40	47.45	47.87	1.12	78.09	78.51	1.84	108.73	109.14	2.56
17.24	17.65	.41	47.88	48.29	1.13	78.52	78.93	1.85	109.15	109.57	2.57
17.66	18.08	.42	48.30	48.72	1.14	78.94	79.36	1.86	109.58	109.99	2.58
18.09	18.51	.43	48.73	49.14	1.15	79.37	79.78	1.87	110.00	110.42	2.59
18.52	18.93	.44	49.15	49.57	1.16	79.79	80.21	1.88	110.43	110.85	2.60
18.94	19.36	.45	49.58	49.99	1.17	80.22	80.63	1.89	110.86	111.27	2.61
19.37	19.78	.46	50.00	50.42	1.18	80.64	81.06	1.90	111.28	111.70	2.62
19.79	20.21	.47	50.43	50.85	1.19	81.07	81.48	1.91	111.71	112.12	2.63
20.22	20.63	.48	50.86	51.27	1.20	81.49	81.91	1.92	112.13	112.55	2.64
20.64	21.06	.49	51.28	51.70	1.21	81.92	82.34	1.93	112.56	112.97	2.65
21.07	21.48	.50	51.71	52.12	1.22	82.35	82.76	1.94	112.98	113.40	2.66
21.49	21.91	.51	52.13	52.55	1.23	82.77	83.19	1.95	113.41	113.82	2.67
21.92	22.34	.52	52.56	52.97	1.24	83.20	83.61	1.96	113.83	114.25	2.68
22.35	22.76	.53	52.98	53.40	1.25	83.62	84.04	1.97	114.26	114.68	2.69
22.77	23.19	.54	53.41	53.82	1.26	84.05	84.46	1.98	114.69	115.10	2.70
23.20	23.61	.55	53.83	54.25	1.27	84.47	84.89	1.99	115.11	115.53	2.71
23.62	24.04	.56	54.26	54.68	1.28	84.90	85.31	2.00	115.54	115.95	2.72
24.05	24.46	.57	54.69	55.10	1.29	85.32	85.74	2.01	115.96	116.38	2.73
24.47	24.89	.58	55.11	55.53	1.30	85.75	86.17	2.02	116.39	116.80	2.74
24.90	25.31	.59	55.54	55.95	1.31	86.18	86.59	2.03	116.81	117.23	2.75
25.32	25.74	.60	55.96	56.38	1.32	86.60	87.02	2.04	117.24	117.65	2.76
25.75	26.17	.61	56.39	56.80	1.33	87.03	87.44	2.05	117.66	118.06	2.77
26.18	26.59	.62	56.81	57.23	1.34	87.45	87.87	2.06	118.09	118.51	2.78
26.60	27.02	.63	57.24	57.65	1.35	87.88	88.29	2.07	118.52	118.93	2.79
27.03	27.44	.64	57.66	58.08	1.36	88.30	88.72	2.08	118.94	119.36	2.80
27.45	27.87	.65	58.09	58.51	1.37	88.73	89.14	2.09	119.37	119.78	2.81
27.88	28.29	.66	58.52	58.93	1.38	89.15	89.57	2.10	119.79	120.21	2.82
28.30	28.72	.67	58.94	59.36	1.39	89.58	89.99	2.11	120.22	120.63	2.83
28.73	29.14	.68	59.37	59.78	1.40	90.00	90.42	2.12	120.64	121.06	2.84
29.15	29.57	.69	59.79	60.21	1.41	90.43	90.85	2.13	121.07	121.48	2.85
29.58	29.99	.70	60.22	60.63	1.42	90.86	91.27	2.14	121.49	121.91	2.86
30.00	30.42	.71	60.64	61.06	1.43	91.28	91.70	2.15	121.92	122.34	2.87
30.43	30.85	.72	61.07	61.48	1.44	91.71	92.12	2.16	122.35	122.76	2.88

Maximum Premium Deduction for a Pay Period of the stated frequency.
Déduction maximale de prime pour une période de paie d'une durée donnée.

Weekly – Hebdomadaire	10.81
Bi-Weekly – Deux semaines	21.62
Semi-Monthly – Bi-mensuel	23.42
Monthly – Mensuellement	46.84

10 pp per year - 10 pp par année	56.21
13 pp per year - 13 pp par année	43.24
22 pp per year - 22 pp par année	25.55

TABLE 2 *Unemployment insurance premiums ($122.77—$245.31)*

Remuneration / Rémunération From-de	To-à	U.I. Premium Prime d'a.-c.	Remuneration / Rémunération From-de	To-à	U.I. Premium Prime d'a.-c.	Remuneration / Rémunération From-de	To-à	U.I. Premium Prime d'a.-c.	Remuneration / Rémunération From-de	To-à	U.I. Premium Prime d'a.-c.
122.77	123.19	2.89	153.41	153.82	3.61	184.05	184.46	4.33	214.69	215.10	5.05
123.20	123.61	2.90	153.83	154.25	3.62	184.47	184.89	4.34	215.11	215.53	5.06
123.62	124.04	2.91	154.26	154.68	3.63	184.90	185.31	4.35	215.54	215.95	5.07
124.05	124.46	2.92	154.69	155.10	3.64	185.32	185.74	4.36	215.96	216.38	5.08
124.47	124.89	2.93	155.11	155.53	3.65	185.75	186.17	4.37	216.39	216.80	5.09
124.90	125.31	2.94	155.54	155.95	3.66	186.18	186.59	4.38	216.81	217.23	5.10
125.32	125.74	2.95	155.96	156.38	3.67	186.60	187.02	4.39	217.24	217.65	5.11
125.75	126.17	2.96	156.39	156.80	3.68	187.03	187.44	4.40	217.66	218.08	5.12
126.18	126.59	2.97	156.81	157.23	3.69	187.45	187.87	4.41	218.09	218.51	5.13
126.60	127.02	2.98	157.24	157.65	3.70	187.88	188.29	4.42	218.52	218.93	5.14
127.03	127.44	2.99	157.66	158.08	3.71	188.30	188.72	4.43	218.94	219.36	5.15
127.45	127.87	3.00	158.09	158.51	3.72	188.73	189.14	4.44	219.37	219.78	5.16
127.88	128.29	3.01	158.52	158.93	3.73	189.15	189.57	4.45	219.79	220.21	5.17
128.30	128.72	3.02	158.94	159.36	3.74	189.58	189.99	4.46	220.22	220.63	5.18
128.73	129.14	3.03	159.37	159.78	3.75	190.00	190.42	4.47	220.64	221.06	5.19
129.15	129.57	3.04	159.79	160.21	3.76	190.43	190.85	4.48	221.07	221.48	5.20
129.58	129.99	3.05	160.22	160.63	3.77	190.86	191.27	4.49	221.49	221.91	5.21
130.00	130.42	3.06	160.64	161.06	3.78	191.28	191.70	4.50	221.92	222.34	5.22
130.43	130.85	3.07	161.07	161.48	3.79	191.71	192.12	4.51	222.35	222.76	5.23
130.86	131.27	3.08	161.49	161.91	3.80	192.13	192.55	4.52	222.77	223.19	5.24
131.28	131.70	3.09	161.92	162.34	3.81	192.56	192.97	4.53	223.20	223.61	5.25
131.71	132.12	3.10	162.35	162.76	3.82	192.98	193.40	4.54	223.62	224.04	5.26
132.13	132.55	3.11	162.77	163.19	3.83	193.41	193.82	4.55	224.05	224.46	5.27
132.56	132.97	3.12	163.20	163.61	3.84	193.83	194.25	4.56	224.47	224.89	5.28
132.98	133.40	3.13	163.62	164.04	3.85	194.26	194.68	4.57	224.90	225.31	5.29
133.41	133.82	3.14	164.05	164.46	3.86	194.69	195.10	4.58	225.32	225.74	5.30
133.83	134.25	3.15	164.47	164.89	3.87	195.11	195.53	4.59	225.75	226.17	5.31
134.26	134.68	3.16	164.90	165.31	3.88	195.54	195.95	4.60	226.18	226.59	5.32
134.69	135.10	3.17	165.32	165.74	3.89	195.96	196.38	4.61	226.60	227.02	5.33
135.11	135.53	3.18	165.75	166.17	3.90	196.39	196.80	4.62	227.03	227.44	5.34
135.54	135.95	3.19	166.18	166.59	3.91	196.81	197.23	4.63	227.45	227.87	5.35
135.96	136.38	3.20	166.60	167.02	3.92	197.24	197.65	4.64	227.88	228.29	5.36
136.39	136.80	3.21	167.03	167.44	3.93	197.66	198.08	4.65	228.30	228.72	5.37
136.81	137.23	3.22	167.45	167.87	3.94	198.09	198.51	4.66	228.73	229.14	5.38
137.24	137.65	3.23	167.88	168.29	3.95	198.52	198.93	4.67	229.15	229.57	5.39
137.66	138.08	3.24	168.30	168.72	3.96	198.94	199.36	4.68	229.58	229.99	5.40
138.09	138.51	3.25	168.73	169.14	3.97	199.37	199.78	4.69	230.00	230.42	5.41
138.52	138.93	3.26	169.15	169.57	3.98	199.79	200.21	4.70	230.43	230.85	5.42
138.94	139.36	3.27	169.58	169.99	3.99	200.22	200.63	4.71	230.86	231.27	5.43
139.37	139.78	3.28	170.00	170.42	4.00	200.64	201.06	4.72	231.28	231.70	5.44
139.79	140.21	3.29	170.43	170.85	4.01	201.07	201.48	4.73	231.71	232.12	5.45
140.22	140.63	3.30	170.86	171.27	4.02	201.49	201.91	4.74	232.13	232.55	5.46
140.64	141.06	3.31	171.28	171.70	4.03	201.92	202.34	4.75	232.56	232.97	5.47
141.07	141.48	3.32	171.71	172.12	4.04	202.35	202.76	4.76	232.98	233.40	5.48
141.49	141.91	3.33	172.13	172.55	4.05	202.77	203.19	4.77	233.41	233.82	5.49
141.92	142.34	3.34	172.56	172.97	4.06	203.20	203.61	4.78	233.83	234.25	5.50
142.35	142.76	3.35	172.98	173.40	4.07	203.62	204.04	4.79	234.26	234.68	5.51
142.77	143.19	3.36	173.41	173.82	4.08	204.05	204.46	4.80	234.69	235.10	5.52
143.20	143.61	3.37	173.83	174.25	4.09	204.47	204.89	4.81	235.11	235.53	5.53
143.62	144.04	3.38	174.26	174.68	4.10	204.90	205.31	4.82	235.54	235.95	5.54
144.05	144.46	3.39	174.69	175.10	4.11	205.32	205.74	4.83	235.96	236.38	5.55
144.47	144.89	3.40	175.11	175.53	4.12	205.75	206.17	4.84	236.39	236.80	5.56
144.90	145.31	3.41	175.54	175.95	4.13	206.18	206.59	4.85	236.81	237.23	5.57
145.32	145.74	3.42	175.96	176.38	4.14	206.60	207.02	4.86	237.24	237.65	5.58
145.75	146.17	3.43	176.39	176.80	4.15	207.03	207.44	4.87	237.66	238.08	5.59
146.18	146.59	3.44	176.81	177.23	4.16	207.45	207.87	4.88	238.09	238.51	5.60
146.60	147.02	3.45	177.24	177.65	4.17	207.88	208.29	4.89	238.52	238.93	5.61
147.03	147.44	3.46	177.66	178.08	4.18	208.30	208.72	4.90	238.94	239.36	5.62
147.45	147.87	3.47	178.09	178.51	4.19	208.73	209.14	4.91	239.37	239.78	5.63
147.88	148.29	3.48	178.52	178.93	4.20	209.15	209.57	4.92	239.79	240.21	5.64
148.30	148.72	3.49	178.94	179.36	4.21	209.58	209.99	4.93	240.22	240.63	5.65
148.73	149.14	3.50	179.37	179.78	4.22	210.00	210.42	4.94	240.64	241.06	5.66
149.15	149.57	3.51	179.79	180.21	4.23	210.43	210.85	4.95	241.07	241.48	5.67
149.58	149.99	3.52	180.22	180.63	4.24	210.86	211.27	4.96	241.49	241.91	5.68
150.00	150.42	3.53	180.64	181.06	4.25	211.28	211.70	4.97	241.92	242.34	5.69
150.43	150.85	3.54	181.07	181.48	4.26	211.71	212.12	4.98	242.35	242.76	5.70
150.86	151.27	3.55	181.49	181.91	4.27	212.13	212.55	4.99	242.77	243.19	5.71
151.28	151.70	3.56	181.92	182.34	4.28	212.56	212.97	5.00	243.20	243.61	5.72
151.71	152.12	3.57	182.35	182.76	4.29	212.98	213.40	5.01	243.62	244.04	5.73
152.13	152.55	3.58	182.77	183.19	4.30	213.41	213.82	5.02	244.05	244.46	5.74
152.56	152.97	3.59	183.20	183.61	4.31	213.83	214.25	5.03	244.47	244.89	5.75
152.98	153.40	3.60	183.62	184.04	4.32	214.26	214.68	5.04	244.90	245.31	5.76

Maximum Premium Deduction for a Pay Period of the stated frequency. Déduction maximale de prime pour une période de paie d'une durée donnée.		
Weekly – Hebdomadaire	10.81	10 pp per year – 10 pp par année 56.21
Bi-Weekly – Deux semaines	21.62	13 pp per year – 13 pp par année 43.24
Semi-Monthly – Bi-mensuel	23.42	22 pp per year – 22 pp par année 25.55
Monthly – Mensuellement	46.84	

TABLE 2 Unemployment insurance premiums ($245.32—$367.87)

Remuneration / Rémunération From-de	To-à	U.I. Premium Prime d'a.-c.	Remuneration / Rémunération From-de	To-à	U.I. Premium Prime d'a.-c.	Remuneration / Rémunération From-de	To-à	U.I. Premium Prime d'a.-c.	Remuneration / Rémunération From-de	To-à	U.I. Premium Prime d'a.-c.
245.32	245.74	5.77	275.96	276.38	6.49	306.60	307.02	7.21	337.24	337.65	7.93
245.75	246.17	5.78	276.39	276.80	6.50	307.03	307.44	7.22	337.66	338.08	7.94
246.18	246.59	5.79	276.81	277.23	6.51	307.45	307.87	7.23	338.09	338.51	7.95
246.60	247.02	5.80	277.24	277.65	6.52	307.88	308.29	7.24	338.52	338.93	7.96
247.03	247.44	5.81	277.66	278.08	6.53	308.30	308.72	7.25	338.94	339.36	7.97
247.45	247.87	5.82	278.09	278.51	6.54	308.73	309.14	7.26	339.37	339.78	7.98
247.88	248.29	5.83	278.52	278.93	6.55	309.15	309.57	7.27	339.79	340.21	7.99
248.30	248.72	5.84	278.94	279.36	6.56	309.58	309.99	7.28	340.22	340.63	8.00
248.73	249.14	5.85	279.37	279.78	6.57	310.00	310.42	7.29	340.64	341.06	8.01
249.15	249.57	5.86	279.79	280.21	6.58	310.43	310.85	7.30	341.07	341.48	8.02
249.58	249.99	5.87	280.22	280.63	6.59	310.86	311.27	7.31	341.49	341.91	8.03
250.00	250.42	5.88	280.64	281.06	6.60	311.28	311.70	7.32	341.92	342.34	8.04
250.43	250.85	5.89	281.07	281.48	6.61	311.71	312.12	7.33	342.35	342.76	8.05
250.86	251.27	5.90	281.49	281.91	6.62	312.13	312.55	7.34	342.77	343.19	8.06
251.28	251.70	5.91	281.92	282.34	6.63	312.56	312.97	7.35	343.20	343.61	8.07
251.71	252.12	5.92	282.35	282.76	6.64	312.98	313.40	7.36	343.62	344.04	8.08
252.13	252.55	5.93	282.77	283.19	6.65	313.41	313.82	7.37	344.05	344.46	8.09
252.56	252.97	5.94	283.20	283.61	6.66	313.83	314.25	7.38	344.47	344.89	8.10
252.98	253.40	5.95	283.62	284.04	6.67	314.26	314.68	7.39	344.90	345.31	8.11
253.41	253.82	5.96	284.05	284.46	6.68	314.69	315.10	7.40	345.32	345.74	8.12
253.83	254.25	5.97	284.47	284.89	6.69	315.11	315.53	7.41	345.75	346.17	8.13
254.26	254.68	5.98	284.90	285.31	6.70	315.54	315.95	7.42	346.18	346.59	8.14
254.69	255.10	5.99	285.32	285.74	6.71	315.96	316.38	7.43	346.60	347.02	8.15
255.11	255.53	6.00	285.75	286.17	6.72	316.39	316.80	7.44	347.03	347.44	8.16
255.54	255.95	6.01	286.18	286.59	6.73	316.81	317.23	7.45	347.45	347.87	8.17
255.96	256.38	6.02	286.60	287.02	6.74	317.24	317.65	7.46	347.88	348.29	8.18
256.39	256.80	6.03	287.03	287.44	6.75	317.66	318.08	7.47	348.30	348.72	8.19
256.81	257.23	6.04	287.45	287.87	6.76	318.09	318.51	7.48	348.73	349.14	8.20
257.24	257.65	6.05	287.88	288.29	6.77	318.52	318.93	7.49	349.15	349.57	8.21
257.66	258.08	6.06	288.30	288.72	6.78	318.94	319.36	7.50	349.58	349.99	8.22
258.09	258.51	6.07	288.73	289.14	6.79	319.37	319.78	7.51	350.00	350.42	8.23
258.52	258.93	6.08	289.15	289.57	6.80	319.79	320.21	7.52	350.43	350.85	8.24
258.94	259.36	6.09	289.58	289.99	6.81	320.22	320.63	7.53	350.86	351.27	8.25
259.37	259.78	6.10	290.00	290.42	6.82	320.64	321.06	7.54	351.28	351.70	8.26
259.79	260.21	6.11	290.43	290.85	6.83	321.07	321.48	7.55	351.71	352.12	8.27
260.22	260.63	6.12	290.86	291.27	6.84	321.49	321.91	7.56	352.13	352.55	8.28
260.64	261.06	6.13	291.28	291.70	6.85	321.92	322.34	7.57	352.56	352.97	8.29
261.07	261.48	6.14	291.71	292.12	6.86	322.35	322.76	7.58	352.98	353.40	8.30
261.49	261.91	6.15	292.13	292.55	6.87	322.77	323.19	7.59	353.41	353.82	8.31
261.92	262.34	6.16	292.56	292.97	6.88	323.20	323.61	7.60	353.83	354.25	8.32
262.35	262.76	6.17	292.98	293.40	6.89	323.62	324.04	7.61	354.26	354.68	8.33
262.77	263.19	6.18	293.41	293.82	6.90	324.05	324.46	7.62	354.69	355.10	8.34
263.20	263.61	6.19	293.83	294.25	6.91	324.47	324.89	7.63	355.11	355.53	8.35
263.62	264.04	6.20	294.26	294.68	6.92	324.90	325.31	7.64	355.54	355.95	8.36
264.05	264.46	6.21	294.69	295.10	6.93	325.32	325.74	7.65	355.96	356.38	8.37
264.47	264.89	6.22	295.11	295.53	6.94	325.75	326.17	7.66	356.39	356.80	8.38
264.90	265.31	6.23	295.54	295.95	6.95	326.18	326.59	7.67	356.81	357.23	8.39
265.32	265.74	6.24	295.96	296.38	6.96	326.60	327.02	7.68	357.24	357.65	8.40
265.75	266.17	6.25	296.39	296.80	6.97	327.03	327.44	7.69	357.66	358.08	8.41
266.18	266.59	6.26	296.81	297.23	6.98	327.45	327.87	7.70	358.09	358.51	8.42
266.60	267.02	6.27	297.24	297.65	6.99	327.88	328.29	7.71	358.52	358.93	8.43
267.03	267.44	6.28	297.66	298.08	7.00	328.30	328.72	7.72	358.94	359.36	8.44
267.45	267.87	6.29	298.09	298.51	7.01	328.73	329.14	7.73	359.37	359.78	8.45
267.88	268.29	6.30	298.52	298.93	7.02	329.15	329.57	7.74	359.79	360.21	8.46
268.30	268.72	6.31	298.94	299.36	7.03	329.58	329.99	7.75	360.22	360.63	8.47
268.73	269.14	6.32	299.37	299.78	7.04	330.00	330.42	7.76	360.64	361.06	8.48
269.15	269.57	6.33	299.79	300.21	7.05	330.43	330.85	7.77	361.07	361.48	8.49
269.58	269.99	6.34	300.22	300.63	7.06	330.86	331.27	7.78	361.49	361.91	8.50
270.00	270.42	6.35	300.64	301.06	7.07	331.28	331.70	7.79	361.92	362.34	8.51
270.43	270.85	6.36	301.07	301.48	7.08	331.71	332.12	7.80	362.35	362.76	8.52
270.86	271.27	6.37	301.49	301.91	7.09	332.13	332.55	7.81	362.77	363.19	8.53
271.28	271.70	6.38	301.92	302.34	7.10	332.56	332.97	7.82	363.20	363.61	8.54
271.71	272.12	6.39	302.35	302.76	7.11	332.98	333.40	7.83	363.62	364.04	8.55
272.13	272.55	6.40	302.77	303.19	7.12	333.41	333.82	7.84	364.05	364.46	8.56
272.56	272.97	6.41	303.20	303.61	7.13	333.83	334.25	7.85	364.47	364.89	8.57
272.98	273.40	6.42	303.62	304.04	7.14	334.26	334.68	7.86	364.90	365.31	8.58
273.41	273.82	6.43	304.05	304.46	7.15	334.69	335.10	7.87	365.32	365.74	8.59
273.83	274.25	6.44	304.47	304.89	7.16	335.11	335.53	7.88	365.75	366.17	8.60
274.26	274.68	6.45	304.90	305.31	7.17	335.54	335.95	7.89	366.18	366.59	8.61
274.69	275.10	6.46	305.32	305.74	7.18	335.96	336.38	7.90	366.60	367.02	8.62
275.11	275.53	6.47	305.75	306.17	7.19	336.39	336.80	7.91	367.03	367.44	8.63
275.54	275.95	6.48	306.18	306.59	7.20	336.81	337.23	7.92	367.45	367.87	8.64

Maximum Premium Deduction for a Pay Period of the stated frequency.
Déduction maximale de prime pour une période de paie d'une durée donnée.

Weekly - Hebdomadaire	10.81
Bi-Weekly - Deux semaines	21.62
Semi-Monthly - Bi-mensuel	23.42
Monthly - Mensuellement	46.84
10 pp per year - 10 pp par année	56.21
13 pp per year - 13 pp par année	43.24
22 pp per year - 22 pp par année	25.55

TABLE 2 *Unemployment insurance premiums ($367.88—$490.42)*

Remuneration From-de	To-à	U.I. Premium Prime d'a.-c.	Remuneration From-de	To-à	U.I. Premium Prime d'a.-c.	Remuneration From-de	To-à	U.I. Premium Prime d'a.-c.	Remuneration From-de	To-à	U.I. Premium Prime d'a.-c.
357.88	358.27	8.65	398.52	398.93	9.37	429.15	429.57	10.09	459.79	460.21	10.81
368.20	368.72	8.66	398.94	399.36	9.38	429.58	429.99	10.10	460.22	460.63	10.82
368.73	369.14	8.67	399.37	399.78	9.39	430.00	430.42	10.11	460.64	461.06	10.83
369.15	369.57	8.68	399.79	400.21	9.40	430.43	430.85	10.12	461.07	461.48	10.84
369.58	369.99	8.69	400.22	400.63	9.41	430.86	431.27	10.13	461.49	461.91	10.85
370.00	370.42	8.70	400.64	401.06	9.42	431.28	431.70	10.14	461.92	462.34	10.86
370.43	370.85	8.71	401.07	401.48	9.43	431.71	432.12	10.15	462.35	462.76	10.87
370.85	371.27	8.72	401.49	401.91	9.44	432.13	432.55	10.16	462.77	463.19	10.88
371.28	371.70	8.73	401.92	402.34	9.45	432.56	432.97	10.17	463.20	463.61	10.89
371.71	372.12	8.74	402.35	402.76	9.46	432.98	433.40	10.18	463.62	464.04	10.90
372.13	372.55	8.75	402.77	403.19	9.47	433.41	433.82	10.19	464.05	464.46	10.91
372.56	372.97	8.76	403.20	403.61	9.48	433.83	434.25	10.20	464.47	464.89	10.92
372.98	373.40	8.77	403.62	404.04	9.49	434.26	434.68	10.21	464.90	465.31	10.93
373.41	373.82	8.78	404.05	404.46	9.50	434.69	435.10	10.22	465.32	465.74	10.94
373.83	374.25	8.79	404.47	404.89	9.51	435.11	435.53	10.23	465.75	466.17	10.95
374.26	374.68	8.80	404.90	405.31	9.52	435.54	435.95	10.24	466.18	466.59	10.96
374.69	375.10	8.81	405.32	405.74	9.53	435.96	436.38	10.25	466.60	467.02	10.97
375.11	375.53	8.82	405.75	406.17	9.54	436.39	436.80	10.26	467.03	467.44	10.98
375.54	375.95	8.83	406.18	406.59	9.55	436.81	437.23	10.27	467.45	467.87	10.99
375.96	376.38	8.84	406.60	407.02	9.56	437.24	437.65	10.28	467.88	468.29	11.00
376.39	376.80	8.85	407.03	407.44	9.57	437.66	438.08	10.29	468.30	468.72	11.01
376.81	377.23	8.86	407.45	407.87	9.58	438.09	438.51	10.30	468.73	469.14	11.02
377.24	377.65	8.87	407.88	408.29	9.59	438.52	438.93	10.31	469.15	469.57	11.03
377.66	378.05	8.88	408.30	408.72	9.60	438.94	439.36	10.32	469.58	469.99	11.04
378.00	378.51	8.89	408.73	409.14	9.61	439.37	439.78	10.33	470.00	470.42	11.05
378.52	378.93	8.90	409.15	409.57	9.62	439.79	440.21	10.34	470.43	470.85	11.06
378.94	379.36	8.91	409.58	409.99	9.63	440.22	440.63	10.35	470.86	471.27	11.07
379.37	379.78	8.92	410.00	410.42	9.64	440.64	441.06	10.36	471.28	471.70	11.08
379.79	380.21	8.93	410.43	410.85	9.65	441.07	441.48	10.37	471.71	472.12	11.09
380.22	380.63	8.94	410.86	411.27	9.66	441.49	441.91	10.38	472.13	472.55	11.10
380.64	381.06	8.95	411.28	411.70	9.67	441.92	442.34	10.39	472.56	472.97	11.11
381.07	381.43	8.96	411.71	412.12	9.68	442.35	442.76	10.40	472.98	473.40	11.12
381.49	381.91	8.97	412.13	412.55	9.69	442.77	443.19	10.41	473.41	473.82	11.13
381.92	382.34	8.98	412.56	412.97	9.70	443.20	443.61	10.42	473.83	474.25	11.14
382.35	382.75	8.99	412.98	413.40	9.71	443.62	444.04	10.43	474.26	474.68	11.15
382.77	383.19	9.00	413.41	413.82	9.72	444.05	444.46	10.44	474.69	475.10	11.16
383.20	383.61	9.01	413.83	414.25	9.73	444.47	444.89	10.45	475.11	475.53	11.17
383.62	384.04	9.02	414.26	414.68	9.74	444.90	445.31	10.46	475.54	475.95	11.18
384.05	384.45	9.03	414.69	415.10	9.75	445.32	445.74	10.47	475.96	476.38	11.19
384.47	384.89	9.04	415.11	415.53	9.76	445.75	446.17	10.48	476.39	476.80	11.20
384.90	385.31	9.05	415.54	415.95	9.77	446.18	446.59	10.49	476.81	477.23	11.21
385.32	385.74	9.06	415.96	416.38	9.78	446.60	447.02	10.50	477.24	477.65	11.22
385.75	386.17	9.07	416.39	416.80	9.79	447.03	447.44	10.51	477.66	478.08	11.23
386.19	386.59	9.08	416.81	417.23	9.80	447.45	447.87	10.52	478.09	478.51	11.24
386.60	387.02	9.09	417.24	417.65	9.81	447.88	448.29	10.53	478.52	478.93	11.25
387.03	387.44	9.10	417.66	418.08	9.82	448.30	448.72	10.54	478.94	479.36	11.26
387.45	387.87	9.11	418.09	418.51	9.83	448.73	449.14	10.55	479.37	479.78	11.27
387.88	388.29	9.12	418.52	418.93	9.84	449.15	449.57	10.56	479.79	480.21	11.28
388.30	388.72	9.13	418.94	419.36	9.85	449.58	449.99	10.57	480.22	480.63	11.29
388.73	389.14	9.14	419.37	419.78	9.86	450.00	450.42	10.58	480.64	481.06	11.30
389.15	389.57	9.15	419.79	420.21	9.87	450.43	450.85	10.59	481.07	481.48	11.31
389.58	389.99	9.16	420.22	420.63	9.88	450.86	451.27	10.60	481.49	481.91	11.32
390.00	390.42	9.17	420.64	421.06	9.89	451.28	451.70	10.61	481.92	482.34	11.33
390.43	390.85	9.18	421.07	421.48	9.90	451.71	452.12	10.62	482.35	482.76	11.34
390.86	391.27	9.19	421.49	421.91	9.91	452.13	452.55	10.63	482.77	483.19	11.35
391.28	391.70	9.20	421.92	422.34	9.92	452.56	452.97	10.64	483.20	483.61	11.36
391.71	392.12	9.21	422.35	422.76	9.93	452.98	453.40	10.65	483.62	484.04	11.37
392.13	392.55	9.22	422.77	423.19	9.94	453.41	453.82	10.66	484.05	484.46	11.38
392.56	392.97	9.23	423.20	423.61	9.95	453.83	454.25	10.67	484.47	484.89	11.39
392.98	393.40	9.24	423.62	424.04	9.96	454.26	454.68	10.68	484.90	485.31	11.40
393.41	393.82	9.25	424.05	424.46	9.97	454.69	455.10	10.69	485.32	485.74	11.41
393.83	394.25	9.26	424.47	424.89	9.98	455.11	455.53	10.70	485.75	486.17	11.42
394.26	394.68	9.27	424.90	425.31	9.99	455.54	455.95	10.71	486.18	486.59	11.43
394.69	395.10	9.28	425.32	425.74	10.00	455.96	456.38	10.72	486.60	487.02	11.44
395.11	395.53	9.29	425.75	426.17	10.01	456.39	456.80	10.73	487.03	487.44	11.45
395.54	395.95	9.30	426.18	426.59	10.02	456.81	457.23	10.74	487.45	487.87	11.46
395.96	396.38	9.31	426.60	427.02	10.03	457.24	457.65	10.75	487.88	488.29	11.47
396.39	396.80	9.32	427.03	427.44	10.04	457.66	458.08	10.76	488.30	488.72	11.48
396.81	397.23	9.33	427.45	427.87	10.05	458.09	458.51	10.77	488.73	489.14	11.49
397.24	397.65	9.34	427.88	428.29	10.06	458.52	458.93	10.78	489.15	489.57	11.50
397.66	398.08	9.35	428.30	428.72	10.07	458.94	459.36	10.79	489.58	489.99	11.51
398.09	398.51	9.36	428.73	429.14	10.08	459.37	459.78	10.80	490.00	490.42	11.52

Maximum Premium Deduction for a Pay Period of the stated frequency.
Déduction maximale de prime pour une période de paie d'une durée donnée.

Weekly - Hebdomadaire	10.81	10 pp per year - 10 pp par année	56.21
Bi-Weekly - Deux semaines	21.62	13 pp per year - 13 pp par année	43.24
Semi-Monthly - Bi-mensuel	23.42	22 pp per year - 22 pp par année	25.55
Monthly - Mensuellement	46.84		

TABLE 3 Weekly tax deductions (weekly pay $0.00—$196.99)

WEEKLY PAY — Use appropriate bracket / PAIE PAR SEMAINE — Utilisez le palier approprié	IF THE EMPLOYEE'S "NET CLAIM CODE" ON FORM TD1 IS — SI LE "CODE DE DEMANDE NETTE" DE L'EMPLOYÉ SELON LA FORMULE TD1 EST DE													See note on page 26 / Voir remarque p. 26 / Column A / Colonne A
	1	2	3	4	5	6	7	8	9	10	11	12	13	
	DEDUCT FROM EACH PAY — RETENEZ SUR CHAQUE PAIE													
Under-Moins de $ 119.00	.00													
119.00 - 120.99	1.00													
121.00 - 122.99	1.70													
123.00 - 124.99	2.20													
125.00 - 126.99	2.65													
127.00 - 128.99	3.15	1.40												
129.00 - 130.99	3.60	1.85												
131.00 - 132.99	4.10	2.35												
133.00 - 134.99	4.55	2.80												
135.00 - 136.99	5.00	3.30												
137.00 - 138.99	5.50	3.75												
139.00 - 140.99	5.95	4.25	.55											
141.00 - 142.99	6.45	4.70	1.55											
143.00 - 144.99	6.95	5.20	2.05											
145.00 - 146.99	7.45	5.65	2.50											
147.00 - 148.99	7.95	6.15	3.00											
149.00 - 150.99	8.45	6.65	3.45											
151.00 - 152.99	8.95	7.15	3.95											
153.00 - 154.99	9.50	7.65	4.40	1.35										
155.00 - 156.99	10.00	8.15	4.90	1.85										
157.00 - 158.99	10.50	8.65	5.35	2.30										
159.00 - 160.99	11.00	9.15	5.85	2.80										
161.00 - 162.99	11.50	9.65	6.30	3.25										
163.00 - 164.99	12.00	10.15	6.80	3.75										
165.00 - 166.99	12.50	10.65	7.30	4.20	.10									
167.00 - 168.99	13.00	11.15	7.80	4.70	1.40									
169.00 - 170.99	13.50	11.65	8.35	5.15	1.90									
171.00 - 172.99	14.00	12.15	8.85	5.65	2.35									
173.00 - 174.99	14.50	12.65	9.35	6.10	2.85									
175.00 - 176.99	15.00	13.15	9.85	6.60	3.30									
177.00 - 178.99	15.50	13.70	10.35	7.10	3.80	.55								
179.00 - 180.99	16.00	14.20	10.85	7.60	4.25	1.60								
181.00 - 182.99	16.50	14.70	11.35	8.10	4.75	2.05								
183.00 - 184.99	17.05	15.20	11.85	8.60	5.20	2.50								
185.00 - 186.99	17.55	15.70	12.35	9.10	5.70	3.00	1.20							
187.00 - 188.99	18.05	16.20	12.85	9.60	6.15	3.45	1.80							
189.00 - 190.99	18.55	16.70	13.35	10.10	6.65	3.95	2.25							
191.00 - 192.99	19.05	17.20	13.85	10.60	7.15	4.40	2.75							
193.00 - 194.99	19.60	17.70	14.35	11.10	7.65	4.90	3.20							
195.00 - 196.99	20.10	18.20	14.85	11.65	8.15	5.35	3.70	.60						

TABLE 3 Weekly tax deductions (weekly pay $197.00—$321.99)

WEEKLY PAY / PAIE PAR SEMAINE — Use appropriate bracket / Utilisez le palier approprié	IF THE EMPLOYEE'S "NET CLAIM CODE" ON FORM TD1 IS — SI LE "CODE DE DEMANDE NETTE" DE L'EMPLOYÉ SELON LA FORMULE TD1 EST DE													See note on page 26 / Voir remarque p. 26
	1	2	3	4	5	6	7	8	9	10	11	12	13	Column A / Colonne A
	DEDUCT FROM EACH PAY — RETENEZ SUR CHAQUE PAIE													
$ 197.00 - 198.99	20.65	18.70	15.35	12.15	8.65	5.85	4.15	1.60						
199.00 - 200.99	21.20	19.25	15.85	12.65	9.15	6.30	4.65	2.05						
201.00 - 202.99	21.70	19.75	16.40	13.15	9.70	6.80	5.10	2.55						
203.00 - 204.99	22.25	20.30	16.90	13.65	10.20	7.30	5.60	3.00						
205.00 - 206.99	22.80	20.85	17.40	14.15	10.70	7.85	6.05	3.50						
207.00 - 208.99	23.30	21.35	17.90	14.65	11.20	8.35	6.55	3.95						
209.00 - 210.99	23.85	21.90	18.40	15.15	11.70	8.85	7.05	4.40						
211.00 - 212.99	24.40	22.45	18.90	15.65	12.20	9.35	7.55	4.90	1.30					
213.00 - 214.99	24.90	22.95	19.45	16.15	12.70	9.85	8.05	5.35	1.80					
215.00 - 216.99	25.45	23.50	19.95	16.65	13.20	10.35	8.55	5.85	2.30					
217.00 - 218.99	26.00	24.05	20.50	17.15	13.70	10.85	9.05	6.30	2.75					
219.00 - 220.99	26.50	24.55	21.05	17.65	14.20	11.35	9.55	6.85	3.25					
221.00 - 222.99	27.05	25.10	21.55	18.15	14.70	11.85	10.05	7.35	3.70					
223.00 - 224.99	27.60	25.65	22.10	18.65	15.20	12.35	10.55	7.85	4.20					
225.00 - 226.99	28.10	26.15	22.65	19.20	15.70	12.85	11.05	8.35	4.65					
227.00 - 228.99	28.65	26.70	23.15	19.75	16.20	13.35	11.55	8.85	5.15	1.25				
229.00 - 230.99	29.15	27.25	23.70	20.25	16.70	13.85	12.10	9.35	5.60	1.80				
231.00 - 232.99	29.70	27.75	24.25	20.80	17.20	14.35	12.60	9.85	6.10	2.30				
233.00 - 234.99	30.25	28.30	24.75	21.35	17.75	14.85	13.10	10.35	6.55	2.75				
235.00 - 236.99	30.75	28.85	25.30	21.85	18.25	15.40	13.60	10.85	7.10	3.25				
237.00 - 238.99	31.30	29.35	25.80	22.40	18.75	15.90	14.10	11.35	7.60	3.70				
239.00 - 240.99	31.85	29.90	26.35	22.90	19.25	16.40	14.60	11.85	8.10	4.15				
241.00 - 242.99	32.40	30.40	26.90	23.45	19.80	16.90	15.10	12.35	8.60	4.65				
243.00 - 244.99	32.95	30.95	27.40	24.00	20.35	17.40	15.60	12.85	9.10	5.10	.90			
245.00 - 246.99	33.50	31.50	27.95	24.50	20.85	17.90	16.10	13.35	9.60	5.60	1.70			
247.00 - 251.99	34.50	32.45	28.90	25.45	21.80	18.75	17.00	14.25	10.45	6.45	2.50			
252.00 - 256.99	35.90	33.85	30.20	26.80	23.10	20.10	18.25	15.50	11.75	7.70	3.70			
257.00 - 261.99	37.30	35.25	31.55	28.10	24.45	21.45	19.55	16.75	13.00	8.95	4.85	.45		
262.00 - 266.99	38.70	36.65	32.90	29.45	25.80	22.75	20.85	18.00	14.25	10.20	6.05	2.25		
267.00 - 271.99	40.10	38.05	34.35	30.80	27.10	24.10	22.20	19.30	15.50	11.45	7.30	3.45		
272.00 - 276.99	41.50	39.45	35.75	32.10	28.45	25.45	23.55	20.65	16.75	12.70	8.55	4.60	1.25	1.25
277.00 - 281.99	42.95	40.85	37.15	33.50	29.80	26.75	24.85	21.95	18.00	14.00	9.80	5.80	2.50	2.50
282.00 - 286.99	44.35	42.30	38.55	34.90	31.10	28.10	26.20	23.30	19.30	15.25	11.10	7.05	3.70	3.35
287.00 - 291.99	45.75	43.70	39.95	36.35	32.45	29.45	27.55	24.65	20.65	16.50	12.35	8.30	4.85	3.45
292.00 - 296.99	47.15	45.10	41.35	37.75	33.85	30.75	28.85	25.95	21.95	17.75	13.60	9.55	6.05	3.50
297.00 - 301.99	48.55	46.50	42.75	39.15	35.30	32.10	30.20	27.30	23.30	19.05	14.85	10.80	7.30	3.50
302.00 - 306.99	49.95	47.90	44.15	40.55	36.70	33.50	31.55	28.65	24.65	20.35	16.10	12.05	8.55	3.50
307.00 - 311.99	51.35	49.30	45.60	41.95	38.10	34.90	32.90	29.95	25.95	21.70	17.35	13.35	9.80	3.55
312.00 - 316.99	52.75	50.70	47.00	43.35	39.50	36.30	34.30	31.30	27.30	23.00	18.65	14.60	11.10	3.55
317.00 - 321.99	54.20	52.10	48.40	44.75	40.90	37.70	35.70	32.65	28.65	24.35	19.95	15.85	12.35	3.55

TABLE 3 Weekly tax deductions (weekly pay $322.00—$546.99)

IF THE EMPLOYEE'S "NET CLAIM CODE" ON FORM TD1 IS — SI LE -CODE DE DEMANDE NETTE. DE L'EMPLOYÉ SELON LA FORMULE TD1 EST DE

DEDUCT FROM EACH PAY — RETENEZ SUR CHAQUE PAIE

WEEKLY PAY / PAIE PAR SEMAINE	1	2	3	4	5	6	7	8	9	10	11	12	13	Column A / Colonne A (See note p.26 / Voir remarque p.26)
322.00 - 326.99	55.60	53.55	49.80	46.15	42.30	39.10	37.10	34.05	29.95	25.70	21.30	17.10	13.60	3.55
327.00 - 331.99	57.00	54.95	51.20	47.60	43.70	40.50	38.50	35.45	31.30	27.00	22.60	18.35	14.85	3.55
332.00 - 336.99	58.40	56.35	52.60	49.00	45.10	41.95	39.95	36.85	32.65	28.35	23.95	19.65	16.10	3.55
337.00 - 341.99	59.80	57.75	54.00	50.40	46.50	43.35	41.35	38.30	34.05	29.70	25.30	21.00	17.35	3.65
342.00 - 346.99	61.30	59.15	55.40	51.80	47.95	44.75	42.75	39.70	35.45	31.00	26.60	22.35	18.65	3.70
347.00 - 351.99	62.75	60.60	56.85	53.20	49.35	46.15	44.15	41.10	36.85	32.35	27.95	23.65	19.95	3.70
352.00 - 356.99	64.25	62.10	58.25	54.60	50.75	47.55	45.55	42.50	38.30	33.75	29.25	25.00	21.30	3.70
357.00 - 361.99	65.70	63.55	59.65	56.00	52.15	48.95	46.95	43.90	39.70	35.15	30.60	26.35	22.60	3.75
362.00 - 366.99	67.20	65.05	61.10	57.40	53.55	50.35	48.35	45.30	41.10	36.55	31.95	27.65	23.95	3.75
367.00 - 371.99	68.70	66.50	62.60	58.85	54.95	51.75	49.75	46.70	42.50	38.00	33.35	29.00	25.30	3.75
372.00 - 376.99	70.15	68.00	64.05	60.25	56.35	53.20	51.20	48.10	43.90	39.40	34.75	30.30	26.60	3.75
377.00 - 381.99	71.65	69.50	65.55	61.75	57.75	54.60	52.60	49.55	45.30	40.80	36.15	31.65	27.95	3.75
382.00 - 386.99	73.10	70.95	67.05	63.20	59.20	56.00	54.00	50.95	46.70	42.20	37.55	33.05	29.25	3.80
387.00 - 391.99	74.60	72.45	68.50	64.70	60.65	57.40	55.40	52.35	48.10	43.60	38.95	34.45	30.60	3.85
392.00 - 396.99	76.10	73.90	70.00	66.20	62.10	58.80	56.80	53.75	49.55	45.00	40.35	35.85	31.95	3.90
397.00 - 401.99	77.55	75.40	71.45	67.65	63.60	60.25	58.20	55.15	50.95	46.40	41.75	37.25	33.35	3.90
402.00 - 406.99	79.05	76.90	72.95	69.15	65.05	61.70	59.60	56.55	52.35	47.80	43.15	38.65	34.75	3.90
407.00 - 411.99	80.50	78.35	74.45	70.60	66.55	63.20	61.10	57.95	53.75	49.25	44.60	40.05	36.15	3.90
412.00 - 416.99	82.00	79.85	75.90	72.10	68.00	64.65	62.55	59.35	55.15	50.65	46.00	41.45	37.55	3.90
417.00 - 421.99	83.50	81.30	77.40	73.60	69.50	66.15	64.05	60.85	56.55	52.05	47.40	42.85	38.95	3.90
422.00 - 426.99	84.95	82.80	78.85	75.05	71.00	67.65	65.55	62.30	57.95	53.45	48.80	44.30	40.35	3.95
427.00 - 431.99	86.45	84.30	80.35	76.55	72.45	69.10	67.00	63.80	59.35	54.85	50.20	45.70	41.75	3.95
432.00 - 436.99	87.90	85.75	81.85	78.00	73.95	70.60	68.50	65.25	60.85	56.25	51.60	47.10	43.15	3.95
437.00 - 441.99	89.40	87.25	83.30	79.50	75.45	72.05	69.95	66.75	62.30	57.65	53.00	48.50	44.60	3.95
442.00 - 446.99	91.10	88.70	84.80	81.00	76.90	73.55	71.45	68.25	63.80	59.05	54.40	49.90	46.00	3.95
447.00 - 451.99	92.80	90.30	86.25	82.45	78.40	75.05	72.95	69.70	65.25	60.50	55.85	51.30	47.40	3.95
452.00 - 456.99	94.50	92.00	87.75	83.95	79.85	76.50	74.40	71.20	66.75	62.00	57.25	52.70	48.80	3.95
457.00 - 461.99	96.20	93.70	89.25	85.40	81.35	78.00	75.90	72.65	68.25	63.50	58.65	54.10	50.20	3.95
462.00 - 466.99	97.90	95.40	90.90	86.90	82.85	79.45	77.35	74.15	69.70	64.95	60.05	55.55	51.60	3.95
467.00 - 471.99	99.60	97.10	92.60	88.40	84.30	80.95	78.85	75.65	71.20	66.45	61.55	56.95	53.00	3.95
472.00 - 476.99	101.30	98.80	94.30	89.90	85.80	82.45	80.35	77.10	72.65	67.90	63.00	58.35	54.40	3.95
477.00 - 481.99	103.00	100.50	96.00	91.60	87.25	83.90	81.80	78.60	74.15	69.40	64.50	59.75	55.85	3.95
482.00 - 486.99	104.70	102.20	97.70	93.30	88.75	85.40	83.30	80.05	75.65	70.90	66.00	61.25	57.25	4.00
487.00 - 491.99	106.40	103.90	99.40	95.00	90.35	86.85	84.75	81.55	77.10	72.35	67.45	62.70	58.65	4.05
492.00 - 496.99	108.10	105.60	101.10	96.70	92.05	88.35	86.25	83.05	78.60	73.85	68.95	64.20	60.05	4.15
497.00 - 506.99	110.65	108.20	103.65	99.25	94.60	90.75	88.45	85.25	80.80	76.05	71.15	66.40	62.30	4.15
507.00 - 516.99	114.05	111.60	107.05	102.70	98.00	94.15	91.70	88.20	83.75	79.00	74.10	69.35	65.25	4.15
517.00 - 526.99	117.45	115.00	110.45	106.10	101.40	97.55	95.10	91.40	86.75	82.00	77.10	72.35	68.20	4.15
527.00 - 536.99	120.85	118.40	113.85	109.50	104.80	100.95	98.50	94.80	89.70	84.95	80.05	75.30	71.15	4.15
537.00 - 546.99	124.35	121.80	117.25	112.90	108.20	104.35	101.90	98.25	93.10	87.90	83.00	78.25	74.10	4.15

TABLE 3 Weekly tax deductions (weekly pay $547.00—$946.99)

IF THE EMPLOYEE'S "NET CLAIM CODE" ON FORM TD1 IS — SI LE -CODE DE DEMANDE NETTE- DE L'EMPLOYÉ SELON LA FORMULE TD1 EST DE

DEDUCT FROM EACH PAY — RETENEZ SUR CHAQUE PAIE

WEEKLY PAY Use appropriate bracket / PAIE PAR SEMAINE Utilisez le palier approprié	1	2	3	4	5	6	7	8	9	10	11	12	13	See note on page 26 / Voir remarque p. 26 / Column A / Colonne A
$ 547.00 - 556.99	128.05	125.35	120.70	116.30	111.60	107.75	105.35	101.65	96.50	91.05	85.95	81.20	77.10	4.15
557.00 - 566.99	131.75	129.05	124.10	119.70	115.00	111.15	108.75	105.05	99.95	94.45	88.90	84.15	80.05	4.15
567.00 - 576.99	135.45	132.75	127.80	123.10	118.40	114.55	112.15	108.45	103.35	97.85	92.25	87.15	83.00	4.15
577.00 - 586.99	139.15	136.45	131.50	126.75	121.80	117.95	115.55	111.85	106.75	101.25	95.65	90.15	85.95	4.20
587.00 - 596.99	142.85	140.15	135.20	130.45	125.35	121.35	118.95	115.25	110.15	104.65	99.05	93.60	88.90	4.70
597.00 - 606.99	146.55	143.85	138.90	134.15	129.05	124.85	122.35	118.65	113.55	108.10	102.45	97.00	92.25	4.75
607.00 - 616.99	150.25	147.55	142.60	137.85	132.75	128.55	125.95	122.05	116.95	111.50	105.85	100.40	95.65	4.75
617.00 - 626.99	153.95	151.25	145.30	141.55	136.45	132.25	129.65	125.60	120.35	114.90	109.25	103.80	99.05	4.75
627.00 - 636.99	157.65	154.95	150.00	145.25	140.15	135.95	133.35	129.30	123.75	118.30	112.65	107.20	102.45	4.75
637.00 - 646.99	161.35	158.65	153.70	148.95	143.85	139.65	137.05	133.00	127.45	121.70	116.05	110.60	105.85	4.75
647.00 - 656.99	165.05	162.35	157.40	152.65	147.55	143.35	140.75	136.70	131.15	125.20	119.45	114.00	109.25	4.75
657.00 - 666.99	168.75	166.05	161.10	156.35	151.25	147.05	144.45	140.40	134.85	128.90	122.85	117.40	112.65	4.75
667.00 - 676.99	172.65	169.80	164.80	160.05	154.95	150.75	148.15	144.10	138.55	132.60	126.50	120.80	116.05	4.75
677.00 - 686.99	176.65	173.75	168.50	163.75	158.65	154.45	151.85	147.80	142.25	136.30	130.20	124.25	119.45	4.80
687.00 - 696.99	180.55	177.70	172.45	167.45	162.35	158.15	155.55	151.50	145.95	140.00	133.90	127.95	122.85	5.10
697.00 - 706.99	184.50	181.65	176.40	171.30	166.05	161.85	159.25	155.20	149.65	143.70	137.60	131.65	126.50	5.15
707.00 - 716.99	188.45	185.60	180.35	175.25	169.85	165.55	162.95	158.90	153.35	147.40	141.30	135.35	130.20	5.15
717.00 - 726.99	192.40	189.55	184.30	179.20	173.80	169.30	166.65	162.60	157.05	151.10	145.00	139.05	133.90	5.15
727.00 - 736.99	196.35	193.50	188.25	183.15	177.75	173.25	170.45	166.30	160.75	154.80	148.70	142.75	137.60	5.15
737.00 - 746.99	200.25	197.45	192.20	187.10	181.70	177.20	174.40	170.10	164.45	158.50	152.40	146.45	141.30	5.15
747.00 - 756.99	203.95	201.25	196.15	191.05	185.65	181.15	178.35	174.05	168.15	162.20	156.10	150.15	145.00	5.15
757.00 - 766.99	207.65	204.95	200.05	195.00	189.60	185.10	182.30	178.00	172.05	165.90	159.80	153.85	148.70	5.15
767.00 - 776.99	211.35	208.65	203.75	198.95	193.55	189.05	186.20	181.95	176.00	169.65	163.50	157.55	152.40	5.15
777.00 - 786.99	215.05	212.35	207.45	202.65	197.50	193.00	190.20	185.90	179.95	173.60	167.20	161.25	156.10	5.15
787.00 - 796.99	219.05	216.05	211.15	206.35	201.30	196.95	194.15	189.85	183.90	177.55	171.05	164.95	159.80	5.15
797.00 - 806.99	223.50	220.25	214.85	210.05	205.00	200.80	198.10	193.80	187.85	181.50	175.05	168.65	163.50	5.15
807.00 - 816.99	227.95	224.70	218.80	213.75	208.70	204.50	201.85	197.75	191.80	185.45	178.95	172.60	167.20	5.40
817.00 - 826.99	232.35	229.10	223.25	217.50	212.40	208.20	205.55	201.55	195.75	189.40	182.90	176.55	171.05	5.50
827.00 - 836.99	236.80	233.55	227.65	221.75	216.10	211.90	209.25	205.25	199.70	193.30	186.85	180.55	175.00	5.50
837.00 - 846.99	241.25	238.00	232.10	226.40	220.30	215.60	212.95	208.95	203.40	197.30	190.80	184.45	178.95	5.50
847.00 - 856.99	245.70	242.45	236.55	230.85	224.70	219.70	216.65	212.65	207.10	201.15	194.75	188.40	182.90	5.50
857.00 - 866.99	250.15	246.90	241.00	235.25	229.15	224.15	220.95	216.35	210.80	204.85	198.70	192.35	186.85	5.50
867.00 - 876.99	254.55	251.30	245.45	239.70	233.60	228.55	225.40	220.60	214.50	208.55	202.45	196.30	190.80	5.50
877.00 - 886.99	259.00	255.75	249.85	244.15	238.05	233.00	229.85	225.00	218.35	212.25	206.15	200.20	194.75	5.50
887.00 - 896.99	263.45	260.20	254.30	248.60	242.50	237.45	234.30	229.45	222.80	215.95	209.85	203.90	198.70	5.50
897.00 - 906.99	267.90	264.65	258.75	253.05	246.90	241.90	238.75	233.90	227.25	220.10	213.55	207.60	202.45	5.50
907.00 - 916.99	272.35	269.10	263.20	257.45	251.35	246.35	243.15	238.35	231.70	224.55	217.25	211.30	206.15	5.50
917.00 - 926.99	276.75	273.50	267.65	261.90	255.75	250.75	247.60	242.80	236.10	229.00	221.65	215.00	209.85	5.50
927.00 - 936.99	281.20	277.95	272.05	266.35	260.25	255.20	252.05	247.20	240.55	233.45	226.10	218.95	213.55	5.50
937.00 - 946.99	285.65	282.40	276.50	270.80	264.70	259.65	256.50	251.65	245.00	237.85	230.55	223.40	217.25	6.15

9 Commercial discount, markup and markdown

Introduction

The merchandising chain is made up of retailers, wholesalers, distributors and manufacturers. Merchandise is usually bought and sold among the members of the chain on credit terms. The prices quoted to other members often involve trade discounts and payments may be subject to cash discounts.

In every situation the vendor must allow for markup which will permit the business to cover its purchase price and its overhead and provide a reasonable profit.

Competitive action or economic conditions may necessitate selling merchandise for less than the regular selling price.

This chapter deals with the various aspects of discount, markup and markdown.

Objectives

Upon completion of this chapter, you will be able to

1. solve problems involving trade discounts, including discount series and equivalent single rates of discount;
2. deal with the three most commonly used methods of cash discount;
3. solve problems involving markup based on either cost or selling price;
4. solve pricing problems involving markup, markdown and discounts.

9.1 Trade discount

A. Basic concepts and computations

A **trade discount** is a reduction of a catalogue or list price and is usually stated as a percent of the catalogue or list price.

Trade discounts are used by manufacturers, wholesalers and distributors as pricing tools for a number of reasons the most important of which are

(a) to facilitate the establishment of price differentials for different groups of customers;

(b) to facilitate the communication of changes in prices;

(c) to reduce the cost of making changes in prices.

When computing trade discounts it is important to keep in mind that the rate of discount is based on the list price.

| AMOUNT OF DISCOUNT = RATE OF DISCOUNT × LIST PRICE | ← *Formula* **9.1** |

The amount of discount is then subtracted from the list price. The resulting remainder is the net selling price (or simply the net price) for the vendor. For the buyer this remainder represents the net cost.

| NET PRICE OF NET COST = LIST PRICE − AMOUNT OF TRADE DISCOUNT | *Formula* **9** |

***Example* 9.1a** An item listed at $80.00 is subject to a trade discount of 25%.

Compute (i) the amount of discount;

(ii) the net price or net cost.

Solution

(i) Amount of Trade Discount = Rate of Discount × List Price
$$= (0.25)(80.00) = \$20.00$$

(ii) Net Price or Net Cost = List Price − Trade Discount
$$= 80.00 - 20.00 = \$60.00$$

B. The net factor approach to computing the net price or net cost

Instead of computing the amount of discount and then deducting this amount from the list price, the net price or net cost may be found by using the more efficient net factor approach developed in the following illustration.

Referring back to Example 9.1a, the solution may be restated as follows.

List Price	$80.00
Less Trade Discount 25% of 80.00	20.00
Net Price or Net Cost	$60.00

Since the discount is stated as a percent of the list price, the three dollar values may be stated as percents of list price.

List Price	$80.00	→	100% of List Price
Less Trade Discount	20.00	→	25% of List Price
Net Price or Net Cost	$60.00	→	75% of List Price

Note The "75%", referred to as the **Net Cost Factor** or Net Factor (in abbreviated form 'NCF') is obtained by deducting the 25% discount from 100%.

NET COST FACTOR (NCF) = 100% − % DISCOUNT

⟵ *Formula* **9.3**

The resulting relationship between net price or net cost and list price may be stated in a general way.

NET PRICE or NET COST = NET COST FACTOR (NCF) × LIST PRICE

⟵ *Formula* **9.4**

The two relationships represented by Formulae 9.3 and 9.4 may be restated in algebraic terms.

Convert the % discount into its decimal equivalent represented by d and express 100% by its decimal equivalent 1.

NET COST FACTOR = 1 − d

⟵ *Formula* **9.3A**

Let the List Price be represented by L and let the Net Price or Net Cost be represented by N.

$N = (1 − d)L$ or $N = L(1 − d)$

⟵ *Formula* **9.4A**

Example 9.1b Find the net price for

(i) List Price $36.00 less 15%;

(ii) List Price $125.64 less 37.5%;

(iii) List Price $86.85 less $33\frac{1}{3}$%;

(iv) List Price $49.98 less $16\frac{2}{3}$%.

Solution

(i) Net Price = Net Cost Factor × List Price ⟵ using Formula 9.4
   $= (100\% − 15\%)(36.00)$ ⟵ using Formula 9.3
   $= (85\%)(36.00)$ ⟵ Subtract
   $= (0.85)(36.00)$ ⟵ convert the percent into a decimal
   $= \$30.60$

(ii) Net Price $= (1 − d)L$ ⟵ using Formula 9.4A
   $= (1 − 0.375)(125.64)$ ⟵ 37.5% = 0.375
   $= (0.625)(125.64)$
   $= \$78.53$

(iii) Net Price $= (100\% − 33\frac{1}{3})(86.85)$ ⟵ using Formula 9.3
   $= (66\frac{2}{3}\%)(86.85)$
   $= (0.6666667)(86.85)$ ⟵ use a sufficient number of decimals
   $= \$57.90$

(iv) Net Price $= (1 - 0.16\frac{2}{3})(49.98)$ ←——————— using Formula 9.4A

$= (0.83\frac{1}{3})(49.98)$

$= (0.8333333)(49.98)$ ←——————— use a sufficient number
of decimals

$= \$41.65$

C. Discount series

If a list price is subject to two or more discounts, these discounts are referred to as a **discount series**. When computing the net price or net cost the discounts making up the discount series are applied to the list price successively. This means the net price resulting from the first discount becomes the list price for the second discount; the net price resulting from the second discount becomes the list price for the third discount; and so on. In fact, finding the net price when a list price is subject to a discount series consists of solving as many discount problems as there are discounts in the discount series.

Example 9.1c   An item listed at \$150.00 is subject to the discount series 20%, 10%, 5%. Determine the net price.

Solution

List Price	\$150.00	← Problem 1
Less 1st Discount 20% of 150.00	30.00	
Net Price After 1st Discount	\$120.00	← Problem 2
Less 2nd Discount 10% of 120.00	12.00	
Net Price After 2nd Discount	\$108.00	
Less 3rd Discount 5% of 108.00	5.40	← Problem 3
Net Price	\$102.60	

As the solution to Example 9.1c consists of three problems involving a simple discount, the net cost factor approach may be used to solve such a problem involving a series of discounts.

Problem 1 Net Price after the First Discount

$= $ NCF for 20% Discount $\times$ Original List Price

$= (1 - 0.20)(150.00)$

$= (0.80)(150.00)$

$= \$120.00$

Problem 2 Net Price after the Second Discount

$= $ NCF for 10% Discount $\times$ Net Price after the First Discount

$= (1 - 0.10)(120.00)$

$= (0.90)(120.00)$

$= \$108.00$

Problem 3 Net Price after the Third Discount

$$= \text{NCF for 5\% Discount} \times \text{Net Price after the Second Discount}$$
$$= (1 - 0.05)(108.00)$$
$$= (0.95)(108.00)$$
$$= \$102.60$$

The final net price of $102.60 is obtained from

$$(0.95)(0.90)(0.80)(150.00)$$
$$= (0.80)(0.90)(0.95)(150.00) \longleftarrow \text{the order of the factors may be rearranged}$$
$$= \text{NCF for 20\%} \times \text{NCF for 10\%} \times \text{NCF for 5\%} \times \text{Original List Price}$$
$$= \text{Product of the NCF's for the discounts in the discount series} \times \text{Original List Price}$$
$$= \text{Net Cost Factor for the Discount Series} \times \text{Original List Price}$$

This result may be generalized to find the net price or net cost for a list price subject to a discount series.

NCF FOR THE DISCOUNT SERIES = NCF FOR THE 1st DISCOUNT × NCF FOR THE 2nd DISCOUNT × .... × NCF FOR THE LAST DISCOUNT

$\longleftarrow$ *Formula 9.5*

NET PRICE or NET COST = NCF FOR THE DISCOUNT SERIES × LIST PRICE

$\longleftarrow$ *Formula 9.6*

The two relationships represented by Formulae 9.5 and 9.6 may be restated in algebraic terms.

Let the Net Price or Net Cost be represented by N,
 the original List Price by L,
 the first rate of discount by d_1,
 the second rate of discount by d_2,
 the third rate of discount by d_3,
 and the last rate of discount d_n.
Then Formula 9.5 may be shown as

NCF for a DISCOUNT SERIES $= (1 - d_1)(1 - d_2)(1 - d_3)\ldots\ldots\ldots(1 - d_n)$

$\longleftarrow$ *Formula 9.5A*

and Formula 9.6 may be shown as

NET PRICE or NET COST $= (1 - d_1)(1 - d_2)(1 - d_3)\ldots\ldots\ldots(1 - d_n)L$

$\longleftarrow$ *Formula 9.6A*

Example 9.1d   Determine the net cost for

(i) an office desk listed at $440.00 less 25%, 15%, 2%;

(ii) a power drill listed at $180.00 less 30%, 12.5%, 5%, 5%;

(iii) a home computer listed at $1260.00 less $33\frac{1}{3}$%, $16\frac{2}{3}$%, 2.5%;

(iv) an electronic chessboard at $1225.00 less $66\frac{2}{3}$%, $8\frac{1}{3}$%.

Solution

(i) Net Cost = NCF for the Discount Series × List Price $\longleftarrow$ using
$= (1 - 0.25)(1 - 0.15)(1 - 0.02)(440.00)$ Formula 9.6
$= (0.75)(0.85)(0.98)(440.00)$
$= \$274.89$

(ii) Net Cost = $L(1 - d_1)(1 - d_2)(1 - d_3)(1 - d_4)$ $\longleftarrow$ using Formula 9.6A
$= 180.00(1 - 0.30)(1 - 0.125)(1 - 0.05)(1 - 0.05)$
$= 180.00(0.70)(0.875)(0.95)(0.95)$
$= \$99.50$

(iii) Net Cost = $1260.00(1 - 0.33\frac{1}{3})(1 - 0.16\frac{2}{3})(1 - 0.025)$
$= 1260.00(0.66\frac{2}{3})(0.83\frac{1}{3})(0.975)$
$= 1260.00(0.6666667)(0.8333333)(0.975)$
$= \$682.50$

(iv) Net Cost = $(1 - 0.66\frac{2}{3})(1 - 0.08\frac{1}{3})(1225.00)$
$= (0.33\frac{1}{3})(0.91\frac{2}{3})(1225.00)$
$= (0.3333333)(0.9166667)(1225.00)$
$= \$374.31$

D. Computing rates of discount

Since the rate of trade discount is based on a list price, computing a rate of discount involves a comparison of the amount of discount to the list price.

$$\text{RATE OF TRADE DISCOUNT} = \frac{\text{AMOUNT OF DISCOUNT}}{\text{LIST PRICE}}$$ $\longleftarrow$ *Formula 9.7*

Example 9.1e   Find the rate of discount for
(i) skis listed at $280.00 less a discount of $67.20;
(ii) ski gloves listed at $36.80 whose net price is $23.92;
(iii) ski sweaters whose net cost is $55.68 after a discount of $40.32.

Solution

(i) Rate of Discount = $\dfrac{\text{Amount of Discount}}{\text{List Price}} = \dfrac{67.20}{280.00} = 0.24 = 24\%$

(ii) Amount of Discount = List Price − Net Price = $36.80 − 23.92 = \$12.88$

Rate of Discount = $\dfrac{\text{Amount of Discount}}{\text{List Price}} = \dfrac{12.88}{36.80} = 0.35 = 35\%$

(iii) Since Amount of Discount = List Price − Net Cost

List Price = Net Cost + Amount of Discount = 55.68 + 40.32 = $96.00

$$\text{Rate of Discount} = \frac{\text{Amount of Discount}}{\text{List Price}} = \frac{40.32}{96.00} = 0.42 = 42\%$$

Example 9.1f A manufacturer sells skidoos to dealers at a list price of $2100.00 less 40%, 10%, 5%. Determine

(i) the amount of discount;

(ii) the single rate of discount.

Solution

(i) Net Price = NCF × List Price
$$= (1 - 0.40)(1 - 0.10)(1 - 0.05)(2100.00)$$
$$= (0.60)(0.90)(0.95)(2100.00)$$
$$= \$1077.30$$

Amount of Discount = List Price − Net Price
$$= 2100.00 - 1077.30 = \$1022.70$$

$$\text{(ii) Rate of Discount} = \frac{\text{Amount of Discount}}{\text{List Price}} = \frac{1022.70}{2100.00} = 0.487 = 48.7\%$$

Note Taking off a single discount of 48.7% has the *same* effect as using the discount series 40%, 10%, 5%. Hence, the single discount of 48.7% is equivalent to the discount series 40%, 10%, 5%. Also note that the sum of the discounts in the series, 40% + 10% + 5% or 55%, is *not* equivalent to the single discount.

E. Single equivalent rates of discount

For every discount series a **single equivalent rate of discount** exists which may be found by choosing a suitable list price and computing first the amount of discount and then the rate of discount.

Example 9.1g Find the single equivalent rate of discount for the discount series 30%, 8%, 2%.

Solution

Assume a list price of $1000.00.
Net Price = NCF for the Series × List Price
$$= (0.70)(0.92)(0.98)(1000.00)$$
$$= (0.63112)(1000.00)$$
$$= \$631.12$$
Amount of Discount = 1000.00 − 631.12 = $368.88

$$\text{Single Equivalent Rate of Discount} = \frac{368.88}{1000.00} = 0.36888 = 36.888\%$$

Note   The Net Cost Factor for the Series $= (0.70)(0.92)(0.98) = 0.63112$, and $1 - 0.63112 = 0.36888$. Hence the single equivalent rate of discount may be found by subtracting the net cost factor for the series from 1.

SINGLE EQUIVALENT RATE OF DISCOUNT FOR A DISCOUNT SERIES
$= 1 - \text{NCF FOR THE DISCOUNT SERIES}$ ⟵ *Formula*
$= 1 - [(1 - d_1)(1 - d_2)(1 - d_3) \ldots\ldots\ldots (1 - d_n)]$

Example 9.1h   Determine the single equivalent rate of discount for each of the following discount series

(i) 25%, 20%, 10%   (ii) 30%, 12.5%, 2.5%   (iii) $33\frac{1}{3}\%$, 15%, 5%, 5%

Solution

(i) Single Equivalent Rate of Discount
$$= 1 - (1 - 0.25)(1 - 0.20)(1 - 0.10) \longleftarrow \text{Using Formula 9.8}$$
$$= 1 - (0.75)(0.80)(0.90)$$
$$= 1 - 0.540000$$
$$= 0.46$$
$$= 46\%$$

(ii) Single Equivalent Rate of Discount
$$= 1 - (1 - 0.30)(1 - 0.125)(1 - 0.025)$$
$$= 1 - (0.70)(0.875)(0.975)$$
$$= 1 - 0.5971875$$
$$= 0.4028125$$
$$= 40.28125\%$$

(iii) Single Equivalent Rate of Discount
$$= 1 - (1 - 0.33\tfrac{1}{3})(1 - 0.15)(1 - 0.05)(1 - 0.05)$$
$$= 1 - (0.66\tfrac{2}{3})(0.85)(0.95)(0.95)$$
$$= 1 - 0.5114167$$
$$= 0.4885833$$
$$= 48.85833\%$$

Note   When computing or using single equivalent rates of discount, a sufficient number of decimals should be used to assure an acceptable degree of accuracy (usually to the nearest cent).

Example 9.1i   Determine the amount of discount for each of the following list prices subject to the discount series 40%, 12.5%, $8\frac{1}{3}\%$, 2%.

(i) $625.00   (ii) $786.20   (iii) $1293.44

Solution

Single Equivalent Rate of Discount
$$= 1 - (1 - 0.40)(1 - 0.125)(1 - 0.08\tfrac{1}{3})(1 - 0.02)$$
$$= 1 - (0.60)(0.875)(0.91\tfrac{2}{3})(0.98)$$
$$= 1 - 0.471\ 6250$$
$$= 0.528375$$
$$= 52.8375\%$$

(i) Amount of Discount = Rate of Discount × List Price
$$= (0.528375)(625.00)$$
$$= \$330.23$$

(ii) Amount of Discount = $(0.528375)(786.20)$
$$= \$415.41$$

(iii) Amount of Discount = $(0.528375)(1293.44)$
$$= \$683.42$$

F. Additional problems

Example 9.1j The Local Home Hardware Store has listed a power saw for $136.00 less 30%. A catalogue store in a nearby shopping mall lists the same model for $126.00 less 20%, 15%. What additional discount must Home Hardware allow to meet the catalogue store price?

Solution

Home Hardware net price = 136.00(0.70) = $95.20
Catalogue store price = 126.00(0.80)(0.85)   85.68

Additional discount needed $ 9.52

$$\text{Additional rate of discount needed} = \frac{9.52}{95.20}$$
$$= 0.10$$
$$= 10\%$$

Example 9.1k A manufacturer can cover his cost and make a reasonable profit if he sells an article for $63.70. At what should the article be listed so that a discount of 30% can be allowed?

Solution

Let the list price be represented by $L.

The net cost factor (N.C.F.) is 0.70 and the net price is $63.70.
$$63.70 = 0.70\ L \longleftarrow \text{using Formula 9.4}$$

$$L = \frac{63.70}{0.70} = \$91.00$$

The article should be listed at $91.00.

Example 9.1l Redden Distributors bought a shipment of micro computers for $477.36 each. For what should the computers be listed if the list price is subject to discounts of 15%, 10%, 4%?

Solution

Let the list price be $L.

The net cost factor is $(0.85)(0.90)(0.96)$ ⟵ using Formula 9.6

The net price is $477.36.

$$477.36 = (0.85)(0.90)(0.96)L$$

$$L = \frac{477.36}{(0.85)(0.90)(0.96)} = \$650.00$$

The computers should be listed at $650.00.

Exercise 9.1

A. For each of the following questions find the missing value or values as indicated.

Problem number	Rate of discount	List price	Net price	Single equivalent rate of discount
1.	45%	$24.60	?	Not applicable
2.	$16\frac{2}{3}$%	$184.98	?	Not applicable
3.	37.5%	?	$84.35	Not applicable
4.	22%	?	$121.29	Not applicable
5.	?	$76.95	$51.30	Not applicable
6.	?	$724.80	$616.08	Not applicable
7.	25%, 10%	$44.80	?	?
8.	$33\frac{1}{3}$%, 5%	$126.90	?	?
9.	40%, 12.5%, 2%	$268.00	?	?
10.	20%, $16\frac{2}{3}$%, 3%	$72.78	?	?
11.	35%, $33\frac{1}{3}$%, 10%	?	$617.50	?
12.	20%, 20%, 10%	?	$53.28	?

B. Answer each of the following questions.

1. A patio chair is listed for $240.00 less 30%, 20%, 5%.
   (a) What is the net price?
   (b) How much is the amount of discount allowed?
   (c) What is the exact single rate of discount that was allowed?

2. A power saw is listed for $174.00 less $16\frac{2}{3}$%, 10%, 8%.
   (a) What is the net price?
   (b) How much is the amount of discount allowed?
   (c) What is the exact single rate of discount that was allowed?

3. A motorcycle listed for $975.00 is sold for $820.00. What is the rate of discount that was allowed?

4. A washer-dryer combination listed at $1136.00 has a net price of $760.00. What is the rate of discount?

5. Compute the equivalent single rate of discount for each of the following discount series.

(a) 30%, 12.5%   (b) $33\frac{1}{3}\%$, 20%, 3%

6. Determine the equivalent single rate of discount for each of the following series of discounts.

(a) $16\frac{2}{3}\%$, 7.5%   (b) 25%, $8\frac{1}{3}\%$, 2%

7. A $16\frac{2}{3}\%$ discount allowed on an article amounted to $14.82. What was the net price?

8. A store advertises a discount of $44.24 on ladies winterboots. If the discount is 35%, for how much were the boots sold?

9. A distributor lists an item for $85.00 less 20%. To improve lagging sales, the price of the item is to be reduced to $57.80. What additional rate of discount should be offered?

10. Crosstown Jewellers sell digital watches for $340.00 less 25%. Their competitors across the street offer the same type of watch for $360.00 less 30%, 15%. What additional rate of discount must Crosstown offer to meet the competitors' price?

11. The net purchase price of a freezer after a discount of $16\frac{2}{3}\%$ is $355.00. What is the list price?

12. The net price of an article is $63.31. What is the list price if a discount of 35% was allowed?

13. Arrow Manufacturing offers discounts of 25%, 12.5%, 4% on a line of products. For how much should an item be listed if it is to be sold for $113.40?

14. What is the suggested retail price of an article which is subject to discounts of $33\frac{1}{3}\%$, 10%, 2% if the net price is $564.48?

9.2 *Cash discount*

A. *Basic concepts*

Sales of goods among manufacturers, wholesalers, distributors and retailers are usually on credit rather than for cash. To encourage prompt payment, many businesses offer a reduction in the amount of the invoice. This reduction, referred to as a **cash discount**, is a sales discount for the seller and a purchase discount for the buyer.

Sales discounts are offered in a variety of ways. The three most commonly used methods are referred to as

1. **Ordinary Dating;**
2. **End-of-the-Month (or Proximo) Dating;**
3. **Receipt-of-Goods Dating.**

The method and size of cash discount are specified on the invoice by the terms of payment. Regardless of the method used, all **payment terms** have two things in common.

1. The cash discount is stated as *percent* of the net amount (face value) of the invoice.
2. The time period during which the cash discount may be taken is stipulated.

If payment is not made during the stipulated discount period, the net amount of the invoice is to be paid by the *due date* which is either stipulated by the terms of payment or implied by the prevailing business practice. If payment is not made by the due date the account is overdue and may be subject to late payment charges.

In dealing with cash discount, the major new problem is the ability to interpret the terms of payment. Otherwise the mathematical aspects of working with cash discounts are similar to those used in dealing with trade discounts.

B. Ordinary dating

The most frequently used method of offering a cash discount is ordinary dating and the most commonly used payment terms are *2/10, n/30* (read *two ten, net thirty*).

This payment term means that if payment is made *within* ten days of the date of the invoice, a discount of 2% may be taken, otherwise payment of the net amount of the invoice is due within thirty days.

FIGURE 9.1 *Interpretation of payment terms*

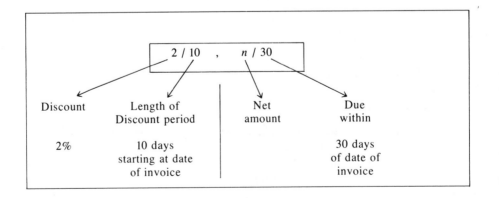

Example 9.2a Determine the payment needed to settle an invoice of $950.00 dated September 22, terms 2/10, n/30, if the invoice is paid

(i) on October 10;   (ii) on October 1.

Solution

The terms of the invoice indicate that a 2% discount may be taken off the invoice amount of $950.00 if the invoice is paid within ten days of the invoice date September 22.

Ten days after September 22 is October 2. The discount period ends October 2.

(i) Payment on October 10 is beyond the last day for taking the discount and therefore the discount may not be taken.

   The full amount of the invoice of $950.00 must be paid.

(ii) October 1 is within the discount period; the 2% discount may be taken.

$$\begin{aligned}
\text{Amount Paid} &= \text{Net Amount} - 2\% \text{ of the Net Amount} \\
&= 950.00 - 0.02(950.00) \\
&= 950.00 - 19.00 \\
&= \$931.00
\end{aligned}$$

Alternatively, using the net cost factor approach

$$\begin{aligned}
\text{Amount Paid} &= \text{N.C.F. for a 2\% discount} \times \text{Net Amount} \\
&= 0.98(950.00) \\
&= \$931.00
\end{aligned}$$

Example 9.2b An invoice of $2185.65 dated May 31, terms 3/15, n/60, is paid on June 15. What is the size of the payment?

Solution

The discount period ends June 15.
Since payment is made on June 15 (the last day for taking the discount), the 3% discount is allowed.

   Amount Paid $= 0.97(2185.65) = \$2120.08$

Example 9.2c An invoice for $752.84 dated March 25, terms 5/10, 2/30, n/60, is paid on April 20. What is the amount paid?

Solution

The payment terms indicate that

(i) a 5% discount may be taken within ten days of the invoice date if paid by April 4; or

(ii) a 2% discount may be taken within 30 days of the invoice date if paid after April 4 but no later than April 24; or

(iii) the net amount is due within 60 days of the invoice date if advantage is not taken of the cash discount offered.

The 5% cash discount is *not* allowed since payment on April 20 is after the end of the discount period for the 5% discount; however, the 2% discount *is* allowed since payment on April 20 is within the 30 day period for the 2% discount.

Amount Paid $= 0.98(752.84) = \$737.78$

Example 9.2d Three invoices with terms 5/10, 3/20, $n/60$ are paid on November 15. The invoices are for \$645.00 dated September 30, \$706.00 dated October 26 and \$586.00 dated November 7. What is the amount paid?

Solution

Invoice dated	End of discount period For 5%	For 3%	Discount allowed	Amount paid	
Sept. 30	Oct. 10	Oct. 20	None		$645.00
Oct. 26	Nov. 5	Nov. 15	3%	0.97(706.00)	684.82
Nov. 7	Nov. 17	Nov. 27	5%	0.95(586.00)	556.70
				Amount paid	$1886.52

C. End-of-the-month or proximo dating

End-of-the-month dating is indicated in the terms of payment by the abbreviation E.O.M. (end of month) such as in 2/10, E.O.M. The abbreviation E.O.M. means that the discount may be taken within the stipulated number of days following the end of the month shown in the invoice date. The abbreviation has the effect of shifting the invoice date to the last day of the month. The abbreviation 'prox.' (meaning 'in the following month') has a similar effect.

In either case the final date for paying the net amount of the invoice is usually not indicated but is commonly understood to be *twenty* days after the last day for taking the discount.

Example 9.2e An invoice for \$1233.95 dated July 16, terms 2/10 E.O.M, is paid on August 10. What is the amount paid?

Solution

The abbreviation E.O.M. indicates that the invoice is to be treated as if the invoice date were July 31 and the last day for taking the discount is August 10.

Amount Paid $= 0.98(1233.95) = \$1209.27$

D. Receipt-of-goods dating

When the abbreviation R.O.G. (*receipt of goods*) appears in the terms of payment, as in 2/10, n/30 R.O.G., the last day for taking the discount is the stipulated number of days after the date of receipt of the merchandise rather than the invoice date. This method of offering a cash discount is used when the transportation of the goods involves a longer period of time as in the case of long-distance overland shipments by rail or truck, or shipments by boat.

Example 9.2f Hansa Import Distributors have received an invoice of $8465.00 dated May 10, terms 3/10, n/30 R.O.G., for a shipment of cuckoo clocks which arrived on July 15. What is the last day for taking the cash discount and how much is to be paid if the discount is to be taken?

Solution

The last day for taking the discount is ten days after receipt of the shipment, that is, July 25.

$$\text{Amount Paid} = 0.97(8465.00) = \$8211.05$$

E. Partial payments and additional problems

The problem of a cash discount for a **partial payment** arises when a business pays *part* of an invoice within the discount period. In such cases the purchaser is entitled to the cash discount on the partial amount paid.

Example 9.2g Sheridan Service have received an invoice of $2780.00 dated August 18, terms 2/10 E.O.M. What payment must be made on September 10 to reduce the debt

(i) by $1000.00?   (ii) to $1000.00?

Solution

Since the terms of payment involve end-of-month dating, the last day for taking the cash discount is September 10. Hence the discount of 2% may be taken off the partial payment.

(i) To reduce the debt by $1000.00 requires a payment of $1000.00 less the discount.

$$\text{Amount Paid} = 1000.00(0.98) = \$980.00$$

(ii) To reduce the debt to $1000.00 requires a payment of ($2780.00 − $1000.00) that is $1780.00 less the discount.

$$\text{Amount Paid} = 1780.00(0.98) = \$1744.40$$

Example 9.2h A cheque for $1480.22 was received on June 24 in full payment of an invoice dated June 14, terms 3/10, n/30. What was the net amount of the invoice?

Solution

Since the payment was made by the last day of the discount period, the purchaser is entitled to the 3% cash discount. The payment of $1480.22 is the amount left *after* taking 3% off the net invoice amount.

Amount Paid = NCF × Net Amount of Invoice

1480.22 = 0.97 X

$$X = \frac{1480.22}{0.97} = \$1526.00$$

The net amount of the invoice was $1526.00

Example 9.2i A payment of $807.50 was received by Applewood Supplies from Sheridan Service on October 10 on an invoice of $2231.75 dated September 15, terms 5/10 PROX.

(i) How much credit should Applewood allow to Sheridan Service for the payment?

(ii) How much does Sheridan Service still owe on the invoice?

Solution

Since the payment terms involve proximo dating, the payment is within the discount period and Sheridan Service is entitled to the 5% discount on the partial payment.

The amount paid of $807.50 represents a partial payment reduced by 5%.

Amount Paid = NCF × CREDIT ALLOWED

807.50 = 0.95 X

$$X = \frac{807.50}{0.95} = \$850.00$$

(i) Applewood should credit the account of Sheridan Service with $850.00.

(ii) Sheridan Service still owes ($2231.75 − 850.00) = $1381.75.

Exercise 9.2

A. Determine the amount paid to settle each of the following invoices on the date indicated.

Problem number	Invoice amount	Payment terms	Date of invoice	Date goods received	Date paid
1.	$640.00	2/10, n/30	Aug 10	Aug 11	Sept 9
2.	$1520.00	3/15, n/60	Sept 24	Sept 27	Oct 8
3.	$783.95	3/10, 1/20, n/60	May 18	May 20	June 5
4.	$1486.25	5/10, 2/30, n/60	June 28	June 30	July 8
5.	$1160.00	2/10 E.O.M.	Mar 22	Mar 29	April 10
6.	$920.00	3/15 E.O.M.	Oct 20	Oct 30	Nov 12
7.	$4675.00	2/10 R.O.G.	April 15	May 28	June 5
8.	$2899.65	4/20 R.O.G.	July 17	Sept 21	Oct 10

B. Determine the missing values for each of the following. Assume that a partial payment was made on each of the invoices by the last day for taking the cash discount.

Problem number	Amount of invoice	Payment terms	Amount of credit for payment	Net payment received	Invoice balance due
1.	$1450.00	3/10, n/30	$600.00	?	?
2.	$3126.54	2/10 E.O.M.	$2000.00	?	?
3.	$964.50	5/20 R.O.G.	?	?	$400.00
4.	$1789.95	4/15, n /60	?	?	$789.95
5.	$1620.00	3/20 E.O.M.	?	$785.70	?
6.	$2338.36	2/10 R.O.G.	?	$1311.59	?

C. Answer each of the following questions.

1. Santucci Appliances received an invoice dated August 12 with terms 3/10 E.O.M. for the items listed below:

   5 G.E. Refrigerators at $980.00 each less 25%, 5%;
   4 Inglis Dishwashers at $696.00 each less $16\frac{2}{3}$%, 12.5%, 4%.

   (a) What is the last day for taking the cash discount?

   (b) What is the amount due if the invoice is paid on the last day for taking the discount?

   (c) What is the amount of the cash discount if a partial payment is made such that a balance of $2000.00 remains outstanding on the invoice?

2. Import Exclusives Ltd. received an invoice dated May 20 from Dansk Specialities of Copenhagen with terms 5/20 R.O.G. for

   100 teak trays at $34.30 each;
   25 teak icebuckets at $63.60 each;
   40 teak salad bowls at $54.50 each.

   All items are subject to trade discounts of $33\frac{1}{3}$%, $7\frac{1}{2}$%, 5%.

   (a) If the shipment was received on June 28, what is the last day of the discount period?

   (b) What is amount due if the invoice is paid in full on July 15?

   (c) If a partial payment only is made on the last day of the discount period, what is the amount due to reduce the outstanding balance to $2500.00?

3. What amount must be remitted if invoices dated July 25 for $929.00, August 10 for $763.00 and August 29 for $864.00, all with terms 3/15 E.O.M., are paid together on September 12?

4. The following invoices, all with terms 5/10, 2/30, n/60, were paid together on May 15. Invoice No. 234 dated March 30 is for $394.45; invoice No. 356 dated April 15 is for $595.50; and invoice No. 788 dated May 10 is for $865.20. What was the amount remitted?

5. An invoice for $5275.00 dated November 12, terms 4/10 E.O.M., was received on November 14. What payment must be made on December 10 to reduce the debt to $3000.00?

6. What amount will reduce the amount due on an invoice of $1940.00 by $740.00 if the terms of the invoice are 5/10, $n/30$ and the payment was made during the discount period?

7. Sheridan Service received an invoice dated September 25 from Wolfedale Automotive. The invoice amount was $2540.95 and the payment terms are 3/10, 1/20, $n/30$. Sheridan Service made a payment on October 5 to reduce the balance due by $1200.00, a second payment on October 15 to reduce the balance to $600.00 and paid the remaining balance on October 30.

   (a) How much did Sheridan Service pay on October 5?

   (b) How much was paid on October 15?

   (c) What was the amount of the final payment on October 30?

8. The Ski Shop received an invoice for $9600.00 dated August 11, terms 5/10, 2/30, $n/90$, for a shipment of skis. The Ski Shop made partial payments as indicated below.

   (a) How much was paid on August 20 to reduce the unpaid balance to $7000.00?

   (b) How much was paid on September 10 to reduce the outstanding balance by $3000.00?

   (c) What is the balance remaining unpaid on September 10?

9. Jelinek Sports received a cheque for $1867.25 in partial payment of an invoice owed by the Ski Shop. The invoice was for $5325.00 with terms 3/20 E.O.M. dated September 15 and the cheque was received on October 18.

   (a) With how much should Jelinek Sports credit the account of the Ski Shop?

   (b) How much does the Ski Shop still owe to Jelinek?

10. Darrigo Grape received an invoice for $13 780 dated September 28, terms 5/20 R.O.G., from Nappa Vineyards for a carload of grape juice received October 20. Darrigo made a partial payment of $5966.00 on November 8.

    (a) By how much did Darrigo reduce the amount due on the invoice?

    (b) How much does Darrigo still owe?

9.3 Markup

A. Basic concepts and calculations

The primary purpose of operating a business is to generate profits. Businesses engaged in merchandising generate profits through their buying and selling activities. The amount of profit depends on many factors, one of which is the pricing of goods. The selling price must cover

 (i) the cost of buying the goods;
 (ii) the operating expenses (or overhead) of the business;
(iii) the profit required by the owner to stay in business.

> SELLING PRICE = COST OF BUYING + EXPENSES + PROFIT

$$S = C + E + P \quad \longleftarrow Formula\ 9.9$$

Example 9.3a   Sheridan Service buys a certain type of battery for $84.00 each. Operating expenses of the business are 25% of cost and the owner requires a profit of 10% of cost. For how much should the batteries be sold?

Solution

Selling Price = Cost of Buying + Expenses + Profit
$$\begin{aligned} &= 84.00 + 25\%\ of\ 84.00 + 10\%\ of\ 84.00 \\ &= 84.00 + 0.25(84.00) + 0.10(84.00) \\ &= 84.00 + 21.00 + 8.40 \\ &= \$113.40 \end{aligned}$$

The batteries should be sold for $113.40 to cover the cost of buying, the operating expenses and the required profit.

Note In Example 9.3a the selling price is $113.40 while the cost is $84.00. The difference between selling price and cost = 113.40 − 84.00 = $29.40. This difference covers operating expenses of $21.00 and a profit of $8.40 and is referred to as **markup** or **margin** or **gross profit**.

> MARKUP = EXPENSES + PROFIT

$$M = E + P \quad \longleftarrow Formula\ 9.10$$

Using this relationship between markup, expenses and profit, the relationship stated in Formula 9.9 becomes

> SELLING PRICE = COST OF BUYING + MARKUP

$$S = C + M \quad \longleftarrow Formula\ 9.9A$$

The relationships established in Formulae 9.9, 9.9A and 9.10 are illustrated in the diagram below.

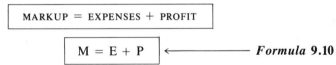

Example 9.3b Friden Business Machines bought two types of electronic calculators for resale. Model A cost $42.00 and sells for $56.50. Model B cost $78.00 and sells for $95.00. Business overhead is 24% of cost. For each model determine

(i) the markup (or margin or gross profit);

(ii) the operating expenses (or overhead);

(iii) the profit.

Solution

	Model A	*Model B*

(i)
$$C + M = S$$
$$42.00 + M = 56.50$$
$$M = 56.50 - 42.00$$
$$M = \$14.50$$
The markup on Model A is $14.50.

$$C + M = S \quad \longleftarrow \text{ using Formula 9.9}$$
$$78.00 + M = 95.00$$
$$M = 95.00 - 78.00$$
$$M = \$17.00$$
The markup on Model B is $17.00.

(ii) Expenses (or overhead)
$$= 24\% \text{ of } 42.00$$
$$= 0.24(42.00)$$
$$= \$10.08$$
Overhead for Model A is $10.08.

Expenses (or overhead)
$$= 24\% \text{ of } 78.00$$
$$= 0.24(78.00)$$
$$= \$18.72$$
Overhead for Model B is $18.72.

(iii)
$$E + P = M$$
$$10.08 + P = 14.50$$
$$P = 14.50 - 10.08$$
$$P = \$4.42$$
Profit on Model A is $4.42

$$E + P = M \longleftarrow \text{ using Formula 9.10}$$
$$18.72 + P = 17.00$$
$$P = 17.00 - 18.72$$
$$P = -\$1.72$$
Profit on Model B is −$1.72, that is, a loss of $1.72.

Example 9.3c A ski shop bought 100 pairs of a type of skis for $105.00 per pair and sold 60 pairs for the regular selling price of $295.00 per pair. The remaining skis were sold during a clearance sale for $180.00 per pair. Overhead is 40% of regular selling price. Determine

(i) the markup, the overhead and the profit per pair of skis sold at the regular selling price;

(ii) the markup, the overhead and the profit per pair of skis sold during the clearance sale;

(iii) the total profit realized.

Solution

(i) *At Regular Selling Price*

Markup

$$C + M = S$$
$$105.00 + M = 295.00$$
$$M = \$190.00$$

Overhead

$$E = 40\% \text{ of Regular}$$
$$\text{Selling Price}$$
$$= 0.40(295.00)$$
$$= \$118.00$$

Profit

$$E + P = M$$
$$118.00 + P = 190.00$$
$$P = \$72.00$$

(ii) *At Clearance Price*

Markup

$$C + M = S$$
$$105.00 + M = 180.00$$
$$M = \$75.00$$

Overhead

$$E = 40\% \text{ of Regular}$$
$$\text{Selling Price}$$
$$= 0.40(295.00)$$
$$= \$118.00$$

Profit

$$E + P = M$$
$$118.00 + P = 75.00$$
$$P = -\$43.00$$

(iii) Profit from sale of 60 pairs
at regular selling price $= 60(72.00) = \$4320.00$
Profit from sale of 40 pairs
during clearance sale $= 40(-43.00) = -1720.00$

Total profit $\underline{\$2600.00}$

B. Rate of markup

A markup may be stated in either one of two ways

1. as a percent of cost;
2. as a percent of selling price.

Since the two methods produce different results, the use of the two methods creates some difficulties in dealing with markups. Accordingly great care must be taken to pay attention to whether the markup is based on the cost or on the selling price.

Finding the rate of markup, as in finding any rate, involves the comparison of two numbers. One is used as the base while the second number is to be expressed as a fraction (percent) of the base.

$$\text{RATE OF MARKUP BASED ON COST} = \frac{\text{MARKUP}}{\text{COST}} = \frac{M}{C} \quad \longleftarrow \textit{Formula 9.11}$$

$$\text{RATE OF MARKUP BASED ON SELLING PRICE} = \frac{\text{MARKUP}}{\text{SELLING PRICE}} = \frac{M}{S} \quad \longleftarrow \textit{Formula 9.12}$$

Example 9.3d Compute (a) the missing value (cost, selling price, markup), (b) the rate of markup based on cost, (c) the rate of markup based on selling price, for each of the following.

  (i) cost, $60.00, selling price, $75.00

 (ii) cost, $48.00, markup, $16.00

(iii) selling price, $88.00, markup, $33.00

(iv) cost, $8.00, markup, $8.00

 (v) selling price, $24.00, markup, $18.00

Solution

Problem number	(a) *Missing value*	(b) *Rate of markup based on cost*	(c) *Rate of markup based on selling price*
(i)	Markup $= 75.00 - 60.00$ $= \$15.00$	$\dfrac{15}{60} = 0.25 = 25\%$	$\dfrac{15}{75} = 0.20 = 20\%$
(ii)	Selling Price $= 48.00 + 16.00$ $= \$64.00$	$\dfrac{16}{48} = \dfrac{1}{3} = 33\dfrac{1}{3}\%$	$\dfrac{16}{64} = 0.25 = 25\%$
(iii)	Cost $= 88.00 - 33.00$ $= \$55.00$	$\dfrac{33}{55} = 0.60 = 60\%$	$\dfrac{33}{88} = 0.375$ $= 37.5\%$
(iv)	Selling Price $= 8.00 + 8.00$ $= \$16.00$	$\dfrac{8}{8} = 1.00 = 100\%$	$\dfrac{8}{16} = 0.50 = 50\%$
(v)	Cost $= 24.00 - 18.00$ $= 6.00$	$\dfrac{18}{6} = 3.00 = 300\%$	$\dfrac{18}{24} = 0.75 = 75\%$

C. Finding the cost or selling price

When the rate of markup is given and either the cost or the selling price is known, the missing value may be found using Formula 9.9A.

$$\boxed{\text{COST} + \text{MARKUP} = \text{SELLING PRICE}} \qquad \boxed{C + M = S}$$

When using this formula, special attention must be given to the base for the markup, that is, whether it is based on cost or based on selling price.

While in real life situations it is usually clearly understood what the base is because only one of the two methods is used, in this text, to avoid confusion, the markup is assumed to be based on cost if the base is not stated. Thus, a statement such as "markup is 40%" means markup is 40% of *cost*.

Example 9.3e What is the selling price of an article costing $72.00 if the markup is

(i) 40% of cost? (ii) 40% of selling price?

Solution

(i)

$$C + M = S \longleftarrow \text{using Formula 9.9A}$$
$$C + 40\% \text{ of } C = S \longleftarrow \text{the replacement of M by}$$
$$72.00 + 0.40(72.00) = S \qquad \begin{array}{l}40\% \text{ of C is the crucial} \\ \text{step in the solution}\end{array}$$
$$72.00 + 28.80 = S$$
$$S = \$100.80$$

If the markup is 40% based on cost, the selling price is $100.80.

(ii)

$$C + M = S$$
$$C + 40\% \text{ of } S = S$$
$$72.00 + 0.40 S = S$$
$$72.00 = S - 0.40 S$$
$$72.00 = 0.60S$$
$$S = \frac{72.00}{0.60}$$
$$S = \$120.00$$

If the markup is 40% based on selling price, the selling price is $120.00.

Note In problems of this type the student is advised to replace M by X% of C or X% of S before using specific numbers. This approach has been used in the preceding problem and in the following worked examples.

Example 9.3f What is the cost of an article selling for $65.00 if the markup is

(i) 30% of selling price? (ii) 30% of cost?

Solution

(i)
$$C + M = S$$
$$C + 30\% \text{ of } S = S \longleftarrow \text{ replace M by 30\% of S}$$
$$C + 0.30(65.00) = 65.00$$
$$C + 19.50 = 65.00$$
$$C = 65.00 - 19.50$$
$$C = \$45.50$$

If the markup is 30% based on selling price,
the cost is $45.50.

(ii)
$$C + M = S$$
$$C + 30\% \text{ of } C = S \longleftarrow \text{ replace M by 30\% of C}$$
$$C + 0.30\,C = 65.00$$
$$1.30\,C = 65.00$$
$$C = \frac{65.00}{1.30}$$
$$C = \$50.00$$

If the markup is 30% based on cost,
the cost is $50.00.

Example 9.3g Find the missing value in each of the following.

Problem	(i)	(ii)	(iii)	(iv)	(v)
Cost	$45.00	$84.00	?	?	?
Selling price	?	?	$3.24	$23.10	$42.90
Markup	$33\frac{1}{3}\%$	40% of S	$16\frac{2}{3}\%$ of S	37.5% of C	50%

Solution

(i)
$$C + M = S$$
$$C + 33\tfrac{1}{3}\% \text{ of } C = S \longleftarrow \text{ when the base is not stated,}$$
$$45.00 + \tfrac{1}{3}(45.00) = S \qquad \text{the markup is assumed to be}$$
$$\qquad\qquad\qquad\qquad \text{a percent of } cost$$
$$45.00 + 15.00 = S$$
$$S = \$60.00$$

(ii)
$$C + M = S$$
$$C + 40\% \text{ of } S = S$$
$$84.00 + 0.40\ S = S$$
$$84.00 = 0.60\ S$$
$$S = \frac{84.00}{0.60}$$
$$S = \$140.00$$

(iii)
$$C + M = S$$
$$C + 16\tfrac{2}{3}\% \text{ of } S = S$$
$$C + (\tfrac{1}{6})(3.24) = 3.24$$
$$C + 0.54 = 3.24$$
$$C = \$2.70$$

(iv)
$$C + M = S$$
$$C + 37.5\% \text{ of } C = S$$
$$C + 0.375\ C = 23.10$$
$$1.375\ C = 23.10$$
$$C = \frac{23.10}{1.375}$$
$$C = \$16.80$$

(v)
$$C + M = S$$
$$C + 50\% \text{ of } C = S$$
$$C + 0.50\ C = 42.90$$
$$1.50\ C = 42.90$$
$$C = \$28.60$$

Example 9.3h The Beaver Ski Shop sells ski vests for $98.00. The markup is 75%.

(i) For how much did the Ski Shop buy the vest?

(ii) What is the rate of markup based on the selling price?

Solution

(i)
$$C + M = S$$
$$C + 75\% \text{ of } C = S \longleftarrow \text{the markup is assumed to be}$$
$$C + 0.75\ C = 98.00 \qquad \text{based on cost}$$
$$1.75\ C = 98.00$$
$$C = 56.00$$
The Ski Shop paid $56.00 for the vest.

(ii) Rate of markup based on selling price $= \dfrac{\text{markup}}{\text{selling price}} = \dfrac{98.00 - 56.00}{98.00}$

$$= \dfrac{42.00}{98.00} = 0.4285714 = 42.86\%$$

Example 9.3i   Sheridan Service bought four Michelin tires from Canadian Tire at $343.00 and sold the tires at a markup of 30% of the selling price.

(i) For how much were the tires sold?

(ii) What is the rate of markup based on cost?

Solution

(i)
$$C + M = S$$
$$C + 30\% \text{ of } S = S$$
$$343.00 + 0.30\ S = S$$
$$343.00 = 0.70\ S$$
$$S = 490.00$$

The tires were sold for $490.00

(ii) Rate of markup based on cost $= \dfrac{\text{markup}}{\text{cost}} = \dfrac{490.00 - 343.00}{343.00}$

$$= \dfrac{147.00}{343.00} = 0.4285714 = 42.86\%$$

Example 9.3j   The gross profit on each of two articles is $25.80. If the rate of markup for Article A is 40% of cost while the rate is 40% of selling price for Article B, determine the cost and the selling price of each.

Solution

For Article A

Gross Profit (or Markup) = 40% of Cost
$$25.80 = 0.40\ C$$
$$C = 64.50$$

The cost of Article A is $64.50.
The selling price is 64.50 + 25.80 = $90.30.

For Article B

Gross Profit (or Markup) = 40% of Selling Price
$$25.80 = 0.40\ S$$
$$S = 64.50$$

The selling price of Article B is $64.50.
The cost = 64.50 − 25.80 = $38.70.

Exercise 9.3

A. For each of the following determine

  (a) the amount of markup
  (b) the amount of overhead
  (c) the profit or loss realized on the sale
  (d) the rate of markup based on cost
  (e) the rate of markup based on selling price.

Problem number	Cost	Selling price	Overhead
1.	$24.00	$30.00	16% of Cost
2.	$72.00	$96.00	15% of Selling Price
3.	$52.50	$87.50	36% of Selling Price
4.	$42.45	$67.92	60% of Cost
5.	$27.00	$37.50	34% of Selling Price
6.	$36.00	$42.30	21% of Cost

B. For each of the following compute the missing values as indicated.

Problem number	Cost	Selling price	Markup	Rate of Markup based on Cost	Rate of Markup based on Selling price
1.	$25.00	$31.25	?	?	?
2.	$63.00	$84.00	?	?	?
3.	$64.00	?	$38.40	?	?
4.	?	$162.00	$27.00	?	?
5.	$54.25	?	?	40%	?
6.	?	$94.50	?	?	30%
7.	?	$66.36	?	50%	?
8.	?	$133.25	?	$66\frac{2}{3}\%$	?
9.	$31.24	?	?	?	60%
10.	$87.74	?	?	?	$33\frac{1}{3}\%$
11.	?	?	$22.26	?	$16\frac{2}{3}\%$
12.	?	?	$90.75	125%	?

C. Answer each of the following questions.

  1. A hardware store buys outdoor lights for $5.00 per dozen less 20%, 20%. The store's overhead is 45% of cost and the required profit is 15% of cost. For how much per dozen should the lights be sold?

2. A merchant buys an item listed at $96.00 less $33\frac{1}{3}$% from a distributor. Overhead is 32% of cost and profit is 27.5% of cost. For how much should the item be retailed?

3. A shoe store bought a shipment of 200 pairs of ladies shoes for $42.00 per pair. The store sold 120 pairs at the regular selling price of $125.00 per pair. 60 pairs were sold at a clearance sale at a discount of 40% and the remaining pairs during an inventory sale at a break-even price. The store's overhead is 50% of cost.

   (a) What was the price at which the shoes were sold during the clearance sale?

   (b) What was the price during the inventory sale?

   (c) What was the total profit realized on the shipment?

   (d) What was the average rate of markup based on cost that was realized on the shipment?

4. The Pottery purchased 600 pans auctioned off en bloc for $4950.00. Upon inspection the pans were classified normal quality, seconds and substandard. The 360 normal quality pans were sold at a markup of 80%, the 190 pans classified as seconds were sold at a markup of 20% and the pans classified as substandard were disposed of at a loss of 20% of their auctioned price.

   (a) What was unit price at which each of the three classifications were sold?

   (b) If overhead is $33\frac{1}{3}$% of cost, what was the amount of profit realized on the purchase?

   (c) What was the average rate of markup based on the selling price at which the pans were sold?

5. Tennis rackets are listed at $55.00 less 40%, 25%. They were sold for $54.45.

   (a) What is the markup as a percent of cost?

   (b) What is the markup as a percent of selling price?

6. Micro-computers were purchased by a dealer for $1240.00 less 50%, 10%. They were sold for $1395.00.

   (a) What was the markup as a percent of cost?

   (b) What was the markup as a percent of selling price?

7. A bookstore makes a gross profit of $3.42 on a text book. The store's markup is 15% of cost.

   (a) For how much did the bookstore buy the textbooks?

   (b) What is the selling price of the textbooks?

   (c) What is the rate of markup based on the selling price?

8. An appliance store sells electric kettles at a markup of 18% of the selling price. The store's margin on a particular model is $6.57.

   (a) What was the cost of the kettles to the store?

   (b) For how much does the store sell the kettles?

   (c) What is the percent markup based on cost?

9. The markup on an item selling for $74.55 is 40%.

   (a) What is the cost of the item?

   (b) What is the rate of markup based on the selling price?

10. Sheridan Service sells oil at a markup of 40% of the selling price. If Sheridan paid $0.99 per litre of oil

   (a) what is the selling price per litre?

   (b) what is the rate of markup based on cost?

11. The Ski Shop purchased ski poles for $12.80 per pair. The poles are marked up 60% of the selling price.

   (a) For how much does the Ski Shop sell a pair of ski poles?

   (b) What is the percent markup based on cost?

12. Nippon Photographic Supplies sells a make of camera for $444.98. The markup is 90% of cost.

   (a) How much does the store pay for the cameras?

   (b) What is the rate of markup based on the selling price?

9.4 Problems involving markup, markdown, discount

A. Markdown

A **markdown** is a reduction in the price of an article. Markdowns are used for a variety of purposes, such as sales promotions, meeting competitors' prices, reducing excess inventories, clearing out seasonal merchandise and selling off discontinued items. A markdown, unlike a markup, is always stated as a percent of the price which is to be reduced and is computed as if it were a discount.

While markdowns are simple to calculate, the rather wide variety of terms used to identify the price to be reduced (such as selling price, regular selling price, list price, marked price, price tag) and the reduced price (such as sale price or clearance price) introduces an element of confusion.

In general

> REDUCED PRICE = PRICE TO BE REDUCED − MARKDOWN

However, since the markdown is a percent of the price that is to be reduced, the net cost factor approach used with discounts is applicable (see Formula 9.4).

> REDUCED PRICE = NCF × PRICE TO BE REDUCED
> where NCF = 100% − % markdown

Example 9.4a   A ski suit regularly selling for $280.00 is marked down 45% during the Beaver Ski Shop's annual clearance sale. For how much was the ski suit sold?

Solution
Sale Price = Regular Selling Price − Markdown
    = 280 − 45% of 280.00
    = 280.00 − 0.45(280.00)
    = 280.00 − 126.00
    = $154.00

Alternatively

Sale Price = NCF × Regular Selling Price
    = (100% − 45%)(280.00)
    = 0.55(280.00)
    = $154.00
The ski suit was sold for $154.00.

Example 9.4b   Solomon 555 ski bindings bought for $57.75 were marked up 45% of selling price. When the binding was discontinued, it was marked down 40%. For how much was the binding put on sale?

Solution
First determine the regular selling price (marked price).
$$C + M = S$$
$$C + 45\% \text{ of } S = S$$
$$57.75 + 0.45\,S = S$$
$$57.75 = 0.55\,S$$
$$S = \$105.00$$

The marked price is $105.00.

Sale Price = Marked Price − Markdown *or* (= NCF × Marked Price)
    = 105.00 − 40% of 105.00   (= 0.60 × 105.00)
    = 105.00 − 42.00   (= $63.00)
    = $63.00
The Sale price is $63.00.

Example 9.4c   Lund Sporting Goods sold a bicycle regularly priced $195.00 for $144.30.

(i) What is the amount of markdown?

(ii) What is the rate of markdown?

Solution

(i) Markdown = Price to be Reduced − Reduced Price
$\qquad$ = Regular Selling Price − Sale Price
$\qquad$ = 195.00 − 144.30
$\qquad$ = $50.70

(ii) Rate of Markdown $= \dfrac{\text{Markdown}}{\text{Price to be Reduced}}$

$\qquad = \dfrac{50.70}{195.00} = 0.26 = 26\%$

B. Further problems

The pricing relationship SELLING PRICE = COST + EXPENSE + PROFIT ($S = C + E + P$) plays an important role in pricing. It indicates how big a markup is needed to cover cost, overhead and a reasonable profit, and how large a markdown can be tolerated. The relationship should be used as a guide in considering the effect of markdown decisions on the operating results of a business.

The cost of buying an article plus the overhead represents the total handling cost of the article.

> TOTAL COST = COST OF BUYING + OVERHEAD

If an article is sold at a price which equals the **total cost** the business makes no profit nor does it suffer a loss. This price is referred to as the breakeven point (as discussed in Chapter 7). Any business, of course, prefers to sell at least at a breakeven price. If the price is insufficient to recover the total cost, the business will suffer an operating loss. If the price does not even cover the cost of buying, the business suffers an absolute loss. To determine the profit or loss, the accounting relationship

> PROFIT = REVENUE − TOTAL COST

is used.

Example 9.4d During its annual Midnight Madness Sale the Ski Shop sold a pair of ski boots, regularly priced at $245.00, at a discount of 40%. The boots cost $96.00 and expenses are 26% of regular selling price.

(i) For how much were the ski boots sold?

(ii) What was their total handling cost?

(iii) What operating profit or loss was made on the sale?

Solution

(i) Sale Price $= 0.60(245.00) = \$147.00$

(ii) Total Cost $=$ Cost of Buying $+$ Expenses
$$= 96.00 + 0.26(245.00)$$
$$= 96.00 + 63.70$$
$$= \$159.70$$

(iii) Profit $\quad=$ Revenue $-$ Total Cost
$$= 147.00 - 159.70$$
$$= -\$12.70 \text{ (a loss)}$$

Since the total cost was higher than the revenue received from the sale of the skiboots, the Ski Shop had an operating loss of $12.70.

Example 9.4e The Cook Nook paid \$115.24 for a set of dishes. Expenses are 18% of selling price and the required profit is 15% of selling price. During an inventory sale the set of dishes was marked down 30%.

(i) What was the sale price?

(ii) What was the operating profit or loss?

Solution

(i) First determine the selling price.

Selling Price $\quad=$ Cost $+$ Expenses $+$ Profit
$$S = C + 18\% \text{ of } S + 15\% \text{ of } S$$
$$S = C + 0.18\,S + 0.15\,S$$
$$S = 115.24 + 0.33\,S$$
$$0.67\,S = 115.24$$

$$S = \frac{115.24}{0.67} = \$172.00$$

Sale Price $=$ Selling Price $-$ Markdown
$$= S - 30\% \text{ of } S$$
$$= S - 0.30\,S$$
$$= 0.70\,S$$
$$= 0.70(172.00)$$
$$= \$120.40$$

The sale price is $120.40.

(ii) Total cost $=$ Cost of Buying $+$ Expenses
$$= C + 18\% \text{ of } S$$
$$= 115.24 + 0.18(172.00)$$
$$= 115.24 + 30.96$$
$$= \$146.20$$

Profit = Revenue − Total Cost
$$= 120.40 − 146.20$$
$$= −\$25.80$$

The dishes were sold at an operating loss of $25.80.

Example 9.4f The Winemaker sells California concentrate for $22.50. The store's overhead is 50% and the owners require a profit of 30%.

(i) For how much does The Winemaker buy the concentrate?

(ii) What is the break-even price?

(iii) What is the highest rate of markdown at which the store will still break even?

(iv) What is the highest rate of discount which can be advertised on a special sale without incurring an absolute loss?

Solution

(i)   S = C + E + P
S = C + 50% of C + 30% of C
S = C + 0.50 C + 0.30 C
22.50 = 1.80 C

$$C = \frac{22.50}{1.80} = \$12.50$$

The Winemaker bought the concentrate for $12.50.

(ii) Total Cost = C + 50% of C
= 1.50 C
= 1.50(12.50)
= $18.75

To break even, the concentrate must be sold for $18.75.

(iii) To break even, the maximum markdown is 22.50 − 18.75 = $3.75

$$\text{rate of markdown} = \frac{3.75}{22.50} = 0.1666667 = 16\tfrac{2}{3}\%$$

The highest rate of markdown to break even is $16\tfrac{2}{3}\%$.

(iv) The lowest price at which the concentrate can be offered for sale without incurring an absolute loss is the cost at which the concentrate was bought, that is $12.50. The maximum amount of discount = 22.50 − 12.50 = $10.00.

$$\text{Rate of discount} = \frac{10.00}{22.50} = 0.4444444 = 44\tfrac{4}{9}\%$$

The maximum rate of discount which can be advertised without incurring an absolute loss is $44\tfrac{4}{9}\%$.

Example 9.4g Big Sound Electronics purchased stereo equipment for $960.00 less 30%, 15%. Overhead is 25% of regular selling price. Big Sound marks all merchandise at a price which allows the store to offer a discount of 20% while still making the usual profit of 15% of regular selling price. During its annual mid-summer sale, the usual discount of 20% was replaced by a markdown of 45% and the equipment was sold during the sale. What operating profit or loss was made on the sale?

Solution

Complex problems of this type are best solved by a systematic approach which considers the information given step by step. The following computations should be made to determine the profit.

(i) the purchase price to the store;

(ii) the regular selling price required to cover cost, expenses and the usual profit;

(iii) the marked price from which the 20% discount is offered;

(iv) the mid-summer sale price;

(v) the total handling cost;

(vi) the operating profit or loss.

Step-by-step computations

(i) Cost = NCF × List Price = $0.70(0.85)(960.00) = \$571.20$

(ii) $S = C + E + P$
$S = C + 25\%$ of $S + 15\%$ of S
$S = C + 0.25S + 0.15S$
$S = 571.20 + 0.40S$
$0.60S = 571.20$

$$S = \frac{571.20}{0.60} = \$952.00$$

The regular selling price is $952.00.

(iii) Marked Price − Discount = Regular Selling Price
$X - 20\%$ of $X = 952.00$
$X - 0.20X = 952.00$
$0.80X = 952.00$

$$X = \frac{952.00}{0.80} = \$1190.00$$

The marked price was $1190.00.

(iv) Sale Price = Marked Price − Markdown

$$= X - 45\% \text{ of } X$$
$$= X - 0.45\,X$$
$$= 0.55\,X$$
$$= 0.55(1190.00)$$
$$= \$654.50$$

(v) Total Cost = Cost of Buying + Overhead

$$= C + 25\% \text{ of } S$$
$$= 571.20 + 0.25(952.00)$$
$$= 571.20 + 238.00$$
$$= \$809.20$$

(vi) Profit = Revenue − Total Cost

$$= 654.50 - 809.20$$
$$= -\$154.70$$

The equipment was sold at an operating loss of $154.70.

Example 9.4h A furniture store bought a dining room suite which must be retailed for $5250.00 to cover the wholesale price, overhead of 50% of the wholesale price and a normal profit of 25% of the wholesale price. The suite is marked so that the store can allow a 20% discount while still receiving the required retail price.

When the suite remained unsold the store owner decided to mark the suite down for an inventory clearance sale. To arrive at the rate of markdown, the owner decided that the store's profit should have to be no less than 10% of the normal profit and that part of the markdown would be covered through a reduction in the commission paid to the salesperson. This was done by reducing the normal commission (which accounts for 40% of the overhead) by $33\frac{1}{3}\%$.

What is the maximum rate of markdown that can be advertised instead of the usual 20%?

Solution

Step 1 Determine the wholesale cost.

$$S = C + E + P$$
$$S = C + 50\% \text{ of } C + 25\% \text{ of } C$$
$$S = C + 0.50\,C + 0.25\,C$$
$$5250.00 = 1.75\,C$$

$$C = \frac{5250.00}{1.75} = \$3000.00$$

Step 2 Determine the marked price.

Marked Price $-$ Discount $=$ Selling Price

$$X - 20\% \text{ of } X = S$$
$$X - 0.20X = S$$
$$0.80X = 5250.00$$

$$X = \frac{5250.00}{0.80} = \$6562.50$$

Step 3 Determine the required profit.

Normal Profit $=$ 25% of Wholesale Cost
$$= 0.25(3000.00)$$
$$= \$750.00$$

Required Profit $=$ 10% of Normal Profit
$$= 0.10(750.00)$$
$$= \$75.00$$

Step 4 Determine the amount of overhead to be recovered.

Normal Overhead $=$ 50% of Wholesale Cost
$$= 0.50(3000.00)$$
$$= \$1500.00$$

Normal Commisson $=$ 40% of Normal Overhead
$$= 0.40(1500.00)$$
$$= \$600.00$$

Reduction in Overhead $=$ $33\frac{1}{3}\%$ of Commission
$$= (\tfrac{1}{3})(600.00)$$
$$= \$200.00$$

Overhead to be Recovered $=$ $1500.00 - 200.00 = \$1300.00$

Step 5 Determine the Sale Price.

Sale Price $=$ Cost $+$ Overhead $+$ Profit
$$= 3000.00 + 1300.00 + 75.00$$
$$= \$4375.00$$

Step 6 Determine the amount of markdown.

Markdown $=$ Marked Price $-$ Sale Price
$$= 6562.50 - 4375.00$$
$$= \$2187.50$$

Step 7 Determine the rate of markdown.

$$\text{Rate of Markdown} = \frac{\text{Amount of Markdown}}{\text{Marked Price}}$$

$$= \frac{2187.50}{6562.50}$$

$$= 0.3333333$$

$$= 33\tfrac{1}{3}\%$$

Instead of the usual 20%, a markdown of $33\tfrac{1}{3}\%$ can be advertised.

Exercise 9.4

A. Compute the missing values assuming that all items carry a marked price such that a discount may be allowed to obtain the selling price.

Problem number	Cost	Markup	Selling price	Discount	Marked price	Mark down	Sale price
1.	$51.00	25% of S	?	20%	?	26%	?
2.	?	50% of C	$105.00	25%	?	?	$84.00
3.	$40.00	? of C	?	$16\tfrac{2}{3}\%$	$144.00	?	$90.00
4.	$29.16	? of S	?	10%	$72.00	35%	?
5.	?	60% of C	$72.80	?	?	36%	$61.60
6.	?	$33\tfrac{1}{3}\%$ of C	?	16%	?	40%	$45.00

B. Compute the missing values for each of the following.

Problem Number	Regular Selling Price	Markdown	Sale Price	Cost	Overhead	Total Cost	Operating Profit (Loss)
1.	$85.00	40%	?	$42.00	20% of S	?	?
2.	?	$33\tfrac{1}{3}\%$	$42.00	$34.44	12% of S	?	?
3.	?	35%	$62.66	?	25% of S	$54.75	?
4.	$72.80	$12\tfrac{1}{2}\%$	?	$54.75	20% of C	?	?
5.	$	25%	$120.00	$105.00	? of S	?	($4.20)
6.	$92.40	$16\tfrac{2}{3}\%$	?	?	15% of C	?	$8.46

C. Answer each of the following questions.

1. A cookware set which cost a dealer $440.00 less 55%, 25% is marked up 180%. For quick sale the cookware was reduced 45%.

(a) What is the sale price?

(b) What rate of markup based on cost was realized?

2. A gas barbecue which cost a retailer $420.00 less $33\frac{1}{3}\%, 20\%, 5\%$ carries a price tag at a markup of 60% of the regular selling price. During the end-of-season sale the barbecue is marked down 45%.

(a) What is the sale price?

(b) What rate of markup based on cost will be realized?

3. A discount clothing store purchased raincoats for $36.75. The store requires a gross profit of 30% of the regular selling price. What price should be marked on the raincoats if the store wants to offer a 25% discount without reducing its gross profit?

4. The Outdoor Shop buys tents for $264.00 less 25%. The store operates on a margin of $33\frac{1}{3}\%$ of regular selling price and advertises that all merchandise is sold at a discount of 20% of the marked price. What is the marked price of the tents?

5. The Stereo Shop sold a radio regularly priced $125.00 for $75.00. The radio was originally purchased for $120.00 less $33\frac{1}{3}\%, 15\%$. The store's overhead is 12% of the regular selling price.

(a) What was the rate of markdown at which the radio was sold?

(b) What was the operating profit or loss?

(c) What rate of markup based on cost was realized?

(d) What was the rate of markup based on the sale price?

6. An automatic dishwasher which cost a dealer $620.00 less $37\frac{1}{2}\%, 4\%$ is regularly priced at $558.00. The dealer's overhead is 15% of the regular selling price and the dishwasher was cleared out for $432.45.

(a) What was the rate of markdown at which the dishwasher was sold?

(b) What is the regular markup based on selling price?

(c) What was the operating profit or loss?

(d) What rate of markup based on cost was realized?

7. A jewelry store paid $36.40 for a ladies watch. Store expenses are 24% of regular selling price and the normal net profit is 20% of regular selling price. During a Special Bargain Day Sale the watch was sold at a discount of 30%. What operating profit or loss was realized on the sale?

8. A hardware store paid $33.45 for a set of cookware. Overhead is 15% of regular selling price and profit is 10% of regular selling price. During a clearance sale the set was sold at a markdown of 15%. What is the operating profit or loss on the sale?

9. A clothing store buys shorts for $24.00 less 40%, $16\frac{2}{3}\%$. The shorts are marked up to cover overhead of 25% of cost and a profit of $33\frac{1}{3}\%$ of cost.

(a) What is the regular selling price of the shorts?

(b) What is the maximum amount of markdown to break even?

(c) What is the rate of markdown if the shorts are sold at the break-even price?

10. A furniture store bought chairs for $75.00 less $33\frac{1}{3}\%, 20\%, 10\%$. The store's overhead is 75% of cost and normal profit is 25% of cost.

   (a) What is the marked price of the chairs?

   (b) At what price can the chairs be put on sale so that the store incurs an operating loss of no more than $33\frac{1}{3}\%$ of the overhead?

   (c) What is the maximum rate of markdown at which the chairs can be offered for sale in (b)?

11. A department store bought stereo equipment listed at $900.00 less 60%, $16\frac{2}{3}\%$. Expenses are 45% of regular selling price and normal profit is 15% of regular selling price. The equipment was marked so that the store could advertise a 37.5% discount while still maintaining its usual markup. During the annual inventory sale the unsold equipment was marked down 55%. What operating profit or loss was realized on the equipment sold during the sale?

12. Lund's Pro Shop purchased sets of golf clubs for $500.00 less 40%, $16\frac{2}{3}\%$. Expenses are 20% of regular selling price and the required profit is 17.5% of the regular selling price. The sets were marked so that the shop can offer a 36% discount without affecting its margin. At the end of the season the unsold sets were advertised at a discount of 54%. What operating profit or loss was realized on the sets sold at the reduced price?

13. Bad Boy Appliances bought micro-wave ovens for $900.00 less $33\frac{1}{3}\%$, 5%. Expenses are 15% of regular selling price and profit is 9% of regular selling price. For competitive reasons the store marks all merchandise so that a discount of 25% can be advertised without affecting the margin. To promote sales the ovens were marked down 40%. What operating profit or loss was made on the ovens sold during the sales promotion?

14. Blue Lake Marina sells a make of cruiser for $16 800.00. The selling price covers overhead of 15% of cost and a normal profit of 10% of cost. The cruisers were marked so that the marina can offer a 20% discount while still maintaining its regular gross profit. At the end of the boating season the cruiser was marked down so that the marina would make 25% of its usual profit after having the marina's overhead reduced by $33\frac{1}{3}\%$ of the usual commission paid to the sales personnel. The normal commission accounts for 50% of the normal overhead. What was the rate of markdown?

Review exercise

1. A tool box is listed for $56.00 less 25%, 20%, 5%.

   (a) What is the net price of the tool box?

   (b) What is the amount of discount?

   (c) What is the single rate of discount that was allowed?

2. Compute the exact rate of discount allowed on a lawn mower which lists for $168.00 and is sold for $105.00.

3. Determine the exact single rate of discount which is equivalent to the discount series 35%, 12%, 5%.

4. A 40% discount allowed on an article amounts to $1.44. What is the net price?

5. Baton Construction Supplies have been selling wheelbarrows for $112.00 less 15%. What additional discount percent must the company offer to meet a competitor's price of $80.92?

6. A freezer was sold during a clearance sale for $387.50. If the freezer was sold at a discount of $16\frac{2}{3}$%, what was the list price?

7. The net price of a snow shovel is $20.40 after discounts of 20%, 15%. What is the list price?

8. On May 18 an invoice dated May 17 for $4000.00 less 20%, 15%, terms 5/10 E.O.M., was received by Aldo Distributors.

   (a) What is the last day of the discount period?

   (b) What is the amount due if the invoice is paid within the discount period?

9. What amount must be remitted if the following invoices, all with terms 5/10, 2/30, n/60, are paid together on December 8.

    Invoice No. 312 dated November 2 for $923.00
    Invoice No. 429 dated November 14 for $784.00
    Invoice No. 563 dated November 30 for $873.00

10. Delta Furnishings received an invoice dated May 10 for a shipment of goods received June 21. The invoice was for $8400.00 less $33\frac{1}{3}$%, $12\frac{1}{2}$% with terms 3/20 R.O.G. How much must Delta pay on July 9 to reduce their debt

    (a) by $2000.00?   (b) to $2000.00?

11. The Peel Trading Company received an invoice dated September 20 for $16 000.00 less 25%, 20%, terms 5/10, 2/30, n/60. Peel made a payment on September 30 to reduce the debt to $5000.00 and a payment on October 20 to reduce the debt by $3000.00

    (a) What amount must Peel forward to pay the balance of the debt at the end of the credit period?

    (b) What is the total amount paid by Peel?

12. Emco Ltd. received an invoice dated May 5 for $4000.00 less 15%, $7\frac{1}{2}$%, terms 3/15 E.O.M. A cheque for $1595.65 was mailed by Emco on June 15 as part payment of the invoice.

    (a) By how much did Emco reduce the amount due on the invoice?

    (b) How much does Emco still owe?

13. Home Hardware buys cat litter for $6.00 less 20% per bag. The store's overhead is 45% of cost and the owner requires a profit of 20% of cost.

   (a) For how much should the bags be sold?

   (b) What is the amount of markup included in the selling price?

   (c) What is the rate of markup based on selling price?

   (d) What is the rate of markup based on cost?

   (e) What is the break-even price?

   (f) What operating profit or loss is made if a bag is sold for $6.00?

14. A merchant realizes a gross profit of $31.50 if he sells an article at a margin of 35% of the selling price.

   (a) What is the regular selling price?

   (b) What is the cost?

   (c) What is the rate of markup based on cost?

   (d) If overhead is 28% of cost what is the break-even price?

   (e) If the article is sold at a markdown of 24% what is the operating profit or loss?

15. Using a margin of 35% of cost, a store priced an item at $8.91.

   (a) What was the cost of the item?

   (b) What is the margin as a percent of selling price?

16. An article costing $54.25 was marked up to realize a gross profit of 30% of the selling price.

   (a) What was the selling price?

   (b) What was the gross profit as a percent of cost?

17. A bedroom suite which cost a dealer $1800.00 less 37.5%, 18% carries a price tag at a markup of 120% of cost. For quick sale the bedroom suite was marked down 40%.

   (a) What was the sale price?

   (b) What rate of markup based on cost was realized?

18. Gino's purchased men's suits for $195.00 less $33\frac{1}{3}$%. The store operates at a normal gross profit of 35% of regular selling price. The owner marks all merchandise so that the store can offer a $16\frac{2}{3}$% discount. What is the marked price?

19. An appliance store sold G.E. coffee perculators for $22.95 during a promotional sale. The store bought the perculators for $36.00 less 40%, 15%. Overhead is 25% of regular selling price.

   (a) If the store's margin is 40% of selling price what was the rate of markdown?

   (b) What operating profit or loss was made during sale?

   (c) What rate of markup based on cost was realized?

20. Harvey and Billnot buy men's shirts for $21.00 less 25%, 20%. The shirts are priced to cover expenses of 20% of selling price and a profit of 17% of selling price. For a special weekend sale shirts were marked down 20%.

(a) What was the operating profit or loss on the shirts sold during the weekend sale?

(b) What rate of markup was realized based on the sale price?

21. A jewelry store paid a unit price of $250.00 less 40%, $16\frac{2}{3}$%, 8% for a shipment of watches. The store's overhead is 65% of cost and the normal profit is 55% of cost.

(a) What is the regular selling price of the watches?

(b) What is the selling price for the store to break even?

(c) What is the rate of markdown to sell the watches at the break-even price?

22. Sight and Sound bought colour TV sets for $1080.00 less $33\frac{1}{3}$%, $8\frac{1}{3}$%. Overhead is 18% of selling price and required profit is $15\frac{1}{3}$% of selling price. The TV sets were marked so that the store was able to advertise a discount of 25% while still maintaining its margin. To clear the inventory the remaining TV sets are marked down $37\frac{1}{2}$%.

(a) What operating profit or loss will be realized at the reduced price?

(b) What is the realized rate of markup based on cost?

23. Ward Machinery list a log splitter at $1860.00 less $33\frac{1}{3}$%, 15%. To meet competition Ward wants to reduce their net price to $922.25. What additional percent discount must Ward allow?

24. West End Appliances bought foodmixers for $180.00 less 40%, $16\frac{2}{3}$%, 10%. The store's overhead is 45% of selling price and profit required is $21\frac{1}{4}$% of selling price.

(a) What is the break-even price?

(b) What is the maximum rate of markdown that the store may offer to break even?

(c) What is the rate of markup based on cost which is realized if the foodmixers are sold at the break-even price?

25. A merchant realizes a margin of $42.00 if he sells an article at a markup of 37.5% of cost.

(a) What is the regular selling price?

(b) What is the rate of markup based on selling price?

(c) If the merchant's expenses are 17.5% of selling price what is his break-even price?

(d) If the article is reduced for sale to $121.66 what is the rate of markdown?

26. The Knit Shoppe bought 250 sweaters for $3100.00. 50 sweaters were sold at a markup of 150% and 120 sweaters at a markup of 75%. 60 of the sweaters were sold during a clearance sale for $15.00 each and the remaining sweaters were disposed of at 20% below cost.

(a) What was the margin realized on the purchase?

(b) What was the percent markup realized based on cost?

(c) What was the gross profit realized based on selling price?

Self-test

1. Determine the net cost of an article listed at $590.00 less 37.5%, 12.5%, $8\frac{1}{3}$%.

2. What rate of discount has been allowed if an item which lists for $270.00 is sold for $168.75?

3. Compute the single discount percent equivalent to the discount series 40%, 10%, $8\frac{1}{3}$% (rate must be exact).

4. A discount store lists an article for $1020.00 less 25% and 15%. A competitor carries the same article for $927.00 less 25%. What further discount (correct to the nearest 1/10 of 1%) must the competitor allow so that their net price will be the same as the discount store?

5. What amount must be remitted if the following invoices, all with terms 4/10, 2/30, n/60, are paid on May 10?

    $850.00 less 20%, 10% dated March 21

    $960.00 less 30%, $16\frac{2}{3}$% dated April 10

    $1040.00 less $33\frac{1}{3}$%, 25%, 5% dated April 30

6. An invoice for $3200.00, dated March 20, terms 3/10 E.O.M., was received March 23. What payment must be made on April 10 to reduce the debt to $1200.00?

7. On January 15 Sheridan Service received an invoice dated January 14, terms 4/10 E.O.M., for $2592.00. On February 9 Sheridan Service mailed a cheque for $1392.00 in partial payment of the invoice. By how much did Sheridan Service reduce its debt?

8. What is the selling price of an item bought for $1270.00 if the markup is 20% of the selling price?

9. The regular selling price of merchandise sold in a store includes a markup of 40% based on selling price. During a sale an item which cost the store $180.00 was marked down 20%. For how much was the item sold?

10. The net price of an article is $727.20 after discounts of 20% and 10% have been allowed. What was the list price?

11. An item which cost the dealer $350 less 35%, 12.5% carries a price tag at a markup of 150% on cost. For quick sale the item was reduced 30%. What was the sale price?

12. Find the cost of an item which was sold for $1904.00 in order to realize a markup of 40% based on cost.

13. An article cost $900.00 and sold for $2520.00. What was the percent markup (to the nearest $\frac{1}{100}$ of 1%) based on cost?

14. A gross profit of $90.00 is made on a sale. If the gross profit was 45% based on selling price, what was the cost?

15. An appliance shop reduces the price of an appliance for quick sale from $1560.00 to $1195.00. Compute the markdown correct to the nearest $\frac{1}{100}$ of 1%.

16. An invoice shows a net purchase price of $552.44 after subtraction of discounts of $33\frac{1}{3}\%$, 20%, $8\frac{1}{3}\%$. What was the list price?

17. A retailer buys an appliance for resale at $1480.00 less 25%, 15%. The store marks the merchandise to cover expenses of 40% of the regular selling price and a net profit of 10% of the regular selling price. During a clearance sale the appliance was sold at a markdown of 45%. What was the operating profit or loss?

18. A discount store buys stereos for $830.00 less 37.5%, 12.5%. Expenses are 20% of normal selling price and the required profit is 15% of normal selling price. All merchandise is marked so that the store can advertise a discount of 30% while still maintaining its regular markup. During the annual clearance sale the marked price of the unsold items is marked down 50%. What operating profit or loss is made by the store on items sold during the sale?

Summary of formulae used

Formula 9.1

$$\text{AMOUNT OF DISCOUNT} = \text{RATE OF DISCOUNT} \times \text{LIST PRICE}$$

Finding the amount of discount when the list price is known

Formula 9.2

$$\text{NET PRICE or NET COST} = \text{LIST PRICE} - \text{AMOUNT OF TRADE DISCOUNT}$$

Finding the net amount when the amount of discount is known

Formula 9.3

$$\text{NET COST FACTOR (NCF)} = 100\% - \%\text{ DISCOUNT}$$

Finding the net cost factor (NCF)

Formula 9.3A

$$\text{NET COST FACTOR (NCF)} = 1 - d$$

where d = rate of discount in decimal form

Restatement of Formula 9.3 in algebraic terms

Formula 9.4

$$\text{NET PRICE or NET COST} = \text{NET COST FACTOR (NCF)} \times \text{LIST PRICE}$$

Finding the net amount directly without computing the amount of discount

Formula 9.4A

$N = (1 - d) L$ or $N = L(1 - d)$

    where N = net cost or net price

        L = list price

        d = rate of discount in
            decimal form

Restatement of Formula
9.4 in algebraic terms

Formula 9.5

NET COST FACTOR   NCF FOR   NCF FOR   NCF FOR

   (NCF) FOR   = THE 1st   × THE 2nd X . . . X THE LAST

A DISCOUNT SERIES   DISCOUNT   DISCOUNT   DISCOUNT

*Commercial
discount,
markup and
markdown*

Formula 9.5A

NCF FOR A

DISCOUNT $= (1 - d_1)(1 - d_2)(1 - d_3). . . . . (1 - d_n)$

SERIES

Restatement of Formula
9.5 in algebraic terms

Formula 9.6

NET COST   NET COST FACTOR FOR   LIST

  or   =   THE DISCOUNT SERIES × PRICE

NET PRICE

Finding the net amount
directly when a list
price is subject to a
series of discounts

Formula 9.6A

NET PRICE

  or $= (1 - d_1)(1 - d_2)(1 - d_3). . . .(1 - d_n)L$

NET COST

Restatement of Formula
9.6 in algebraic terms

Formula 9.7

RATE OF   AMOUNT OF DISCOUNT

DISCOUNT   =   LIST PRICE

Finding the rate of
discount

Formula 9.8

SINGLE EQUIVALENT RATE OF DISCOUNT

FOR A DISCOUNT SERIES

   $= 1 -$ NCF FOR THE DISCOUNT SERIES

   $= 1 - \left[(1 - d_1)(1 - d_2)(1 - d_3). . . .(1 - d_n) \right]$

Finding the single rate
of discount which has
the same effect as a
given series of discounts

Formula 9.9

SELLING PRICE $=$ COST $+$ EXPENSES $+$ PROFIT

        or

       $S = C + E + P$

Basic relationship
between selling price, cost,
overhead and profit

Formula 9.9A

SELLING PRICE $=$ COST $+$ MARKUP

        or

       $S = C + M$

Basic relationship
between selling price,
cost and markup
where the markup is as
defined in Formula 9.10

Formula 9.10

$$\text{MARKUP} = \text{EXPENSES} + \text{PROFIT}$$

or

$$M = E + P$$

Relationship between markup, overhead and profit

Formula 9.11

$$\frac{\text{RATE OF MARKUP}}{\text{BASED ON COST}} = \frac{\text{MARKUP}}{\text{COST}}$$

Finding the rate of markup as a percent of cost

Formula 9.12

$$\frac{\text{RATE OF MARKUP}}{\text{BASED ON}} = \frac{\text{MARKUP}}{\text{SELLING PRICE}}$$

Finding the rate of markup as a percent of selling price

Glossary of terms used

Cash Discount   a reduction in the amount of an invoice

Discount series   two or more discounts taken off a list price in succession

End-of-month-dating   payment terms based on the last day of the month in which the invoice is dated

Gross profit   see *Markup*

Margin   see *Markup*

Markdown   a reduction in a price

Markup   the difference between the cost of merchandise and the selling price

Net cost   the difference between a list price and the amount of discount

Net cost factor   the difference between 100% and a percent discount—the net cost expressed as a fraction of the list price

Payment terms   a statement of the conditions under which a cash discount may be taken

Partial payment   part payment of an invoice

Ordinary dating   payment terms based on the date of an invoice

Proximo dating   see *End-of-month dating*

Receipt-of-goods dating   payment terms based on the date of the receipt of merchandise

Single equivalent rate of discount   the single rate of discount which has the same effect as a specific series of discounts

Total cost   the cost at which merchandise is bought plus the overhead

Trade discounts   a reduction of a catalogue or list price

10 *Simple interest*

Introduction

The use of money as a means of exchange has led to the practice of lending and borrowing money. Lenders usually require compensation for their services in the form of interest. The amount of such interest is based on three factors: the amount of money borrowed, the rate of interest at which it is borrowed and the time period for which it is borrowed.

Objectives

Upon completion of this chapter, you will be able to

1. interpret the letter symbols used in the formula $I = Prt$;
2. determine the exact time in days between two dates;
3. compute the exact simple interest by means of the formula $I = Prt$;
4. find the principal, rate or time from the formula $I = Prt$;
5. use the formula $S = P(1 + rt)$ to find the amount (or maturity value) when the principal, rate and time are given;
6. use the formula $P = \frac{S}{1 + rt}$ to compute the principal (or present value) when the maturity value, rate and time are given;
7. compute equivalent values for specified focal dates.

10.1 Basic concepts and formula

A. Formula

Interest is the rent charged for the use of money. The amount of **simple** interest is determined by the relationship

$$\boxed{\begin{array}{c} \text{Interest} = \text{Principal} \times \text{Rate} \times \text{Time} \\ I = Prt \end{array}} \longleftarrow \textit{Formula } \textbf{10.1}$$

where   I is the amount of interest earned;

          P is the principal sum of money earning the interest;

          r is the annual (yearly) rate of interest;

          t is the time period in years.

B. *Matching* r *and* t

While the time may be stated in days, months or years, the rate of interest is a yearly charge unless otherwise stated. In using the simple interest formula it is imperative that the time t corresponds to the interest rate r. This often requires conversion of months or days into years.

Example 10.1a State r and t for each of the following.

(i) Rate 9%; time 3 years

    Solution

    The annual rate $r = 9\% = 0.09$

    The time in years $t = 3$

(ii) Rate 8.5%; time 18 months

    Solution

    The annual rate $r = 8.5\% = 0.085$

    The time in years $t = \dfrac{18}{12}$

    Note To convert months into years, divide by 12.

(iii) Rate $11\frac{1}{4}\%$; time 243 days

    Solution

    The annual rate $r = 11.25\% = 0.1125$

    The time in years $t = \dfrac{243}{365}$

    Note To convert days into years, divide by 365.

Exercise 10.1

A. State r and t for each of the following.

    1. Rate is $12\frac{1}{2}\%$; time is $1\frac{1}{4}$ years

    2. Rate is $9\frac{3}{4}\%$; time is 21 months

    3. Rate is 10.25%; time is 165 days

    4. Rate is $15\frac{1}{2}\%$; time is 332 days

10.2 Determining the number of days

A. Counting exact time

When the **interest period** involves two dates the number of days between the two dates must be determined. To count the number of days the usual practice is to count the ending date but *not* the beginning date.

Counting days requires a knowledge of the order of the twelve months in the year and the number of days in each month. The number of days in each of the twelve months in order (ignoring leap years) is listed below.

1. January	31	2. February	28	3. March	31
4. April	30	5. May	31	6. June	30
7. July	31	8. August	31	9. September	30
10. October	31	11. November	30	12. December	31

Example 10.2a Find the number of days between January 30 and June 1.

Solution

The beginning date is January 30 ← do *not* count

The ending date is June 1 ← to be counted

Number of days	January	1	← (31 − 30)
	February	28	
	March	31	
	April	30	
	May	31	
	June	1	
	Total	122	

Example 10.2b Find the number of days between November 12, 1985 and May 5, 1986.

Solution

The beginning date is November 12 ← do *not* count

The ending date is May 5 ← to be counted

Number of days	November 1985	18	←(30 − 12)
	December	31	
	January 1986	31	
	February	28	
	March	31	
	April	30	
	May	5	
	Total	174	

B. Using a table

If available, exact time may also be obtained from a table listing the number of each day of the year. (See Table 10.1). When using such a table care must be taken to distinguish two cases:

(i) the beginning date and the ending date are in the *same* year;

(ii) the ending date is in the year *following* the beginning date or later years.

TABLE 10.1 *The number of each day of the year*

Day of Month	Jan.	Feb.	Mar.	Apr.	May	June	July	Aug.	Sept.	Oct.	Nov.	Dec.	Day of Month
1	1	32	60	91	121	152	182	213	244	274	305	335	1
2	2	33	61	92	122	153	183	214	245	275	306	336	2
3	3	34	62	93	123	154	184	215	246	276	307	337	3
4	4	35	63	94	124	155	185	216	247	277	308	338	4
5	5	36	64	95	125	156	186	217	248	278	309	339	5
6	6	37	65	96	126	157	187	218	249	279	310	340	6
7	7	38	66	97	127	158	188	219	250	280	311	341	7
8	8	39	67	98	128	159	189	220	251	281	312	342	8
9	9	40	68	99	129	160	190	221	252	282	313	343	9
10	10	41	69	100	130	161	191	222	253	283	314	344	10
11	11	42	70	101	131	162	192	223	254	284	315	345	11
12	12	43	71	102	132	163	193	224	255	285	316	346	12
13	13	44	72	103	133	164	194	225	256	286	317	347	13
14	14	45	73	104	134	165	195	226	257	287	318	348	14
15	15	46	74	105	135	166	196	227	258	288	319	349	15
16	16	47	75	106	136	167	197	228	259	289	320	350	16
17	17	48	76	107	137	168	198	229	260	290	321	351	17
18	18	49	77	108	138	169	199	230	261	291	322	352	18
19	19	50	78	109	139	170	200	231	262	292	323	353	19
20	20	51	79	110	140	171	201	232	263	293	324	354	20
21	21	52	80	111	141	172	202	233	264	294	325	355	21
22	22	53	81	112	142	173	203	234	265	295	326	356	22
23	23	54	82	113	143	174	204	235	266	296	327	357	23
24	24	55	83	114	144	175	205	236	267	297	328	358	24
25	25	56	84	115	145	176	206	237	268	298	329	359	25
26	26	57	85	116	146	177	207	238	269	299	330	360	26
27	27	58	86	117	147	178	208	239	270	300	331	361	27
28	28	59	87	118	148	179	209	240	271	301	332	362	28
29	29		88	119	149	180	210	241	272	302	333	363	29
30	30		89	120	150	181	211	242	273	303	334	364	30
31	31		90		151		212	243		304		365	31

Note For leap years, February 29 becomes day 60 and the numbers in the table must be increased by 1 for all following days.

***Example* 10.2c** Find the number of days between May 29 and August 3.

Solution

The beginning date is May 29 ———————→ Day 149
The ending date is August 3 ———————→   Day 215
    The difference in days is (215 − 149)   66

***Example* 10.2d** Find the number of days between September 1, 1986 and April 1, 1987.

Solution

The beginning date is September 1, 1986 ———→ Day 244
Number of days in 1986 is 365
Number of days remaining in 1986 is (365 − 244) = 121
The ending date is April 1, 1987 ————→ Day 91
    The total number of days is (121 + 91)   212

C. Leap years

Leap years are divisible by 4, such as 1980, 1984, 1988, 1992 and 1996. An extra day is added to February if a year is a **leap year**.

However, the last year of a century is *not* a leap year unless the number is divisible by 400. This means that while the year 1900 was not a leap year, the year 2000 will have the extra day.

***Example* 10.2e** Find the number of days between December 12, 1987 and April 1, 1988

(i) by counting;   (ii) by using Table 10.1.

Solution

  (i) The beginning date is December 12, 1987
      The ending date is April 1, 1988

Number of days	December 1987	19 ←——— (31 − 12)
	January 1988	31
	February	29 ←——— Leap year
	March	31
	April	1
	Total	111

  (ii) The beginning date is December 12, 1987 ————→ Day 346
      The number of days in 1987 is 365
      The number of days remaining in 1987 is (365 − 346) = 19
      The ending date is April 1, 1988 ————→ Day 92
      (for a leap year increase the table number 91 by 1 to 92)
        Total   111

Exercise 10.2

A. Determine the exact time by counting days for each of the following
1. January 18, 1987 to May 10, 1987
2. August 30, 1988 to April 1, 1989
3. November 1, 1987 to April 15, 1988
4. December 24, 1986 to February 5, 1988

B. Determine the exact time using a table (See Table 10.1).
1. April 1, 1986 to December 1, 1986
2. July 30, 1986 to March 30, 1987
3. April 5, 1987 to March 11, 1988
4. August 25, 1986 to May 20, 1988

10.3   Computing the amount of interest

If the principal, rate and time are known the amount of interest can be determined
by substitution in the formula $I = Prt$.

A.

Example 10.3a   Compute the amount of interest for
(i) $3600.00 at 9% p.a. (per annum) for 3 years;
(ii) $5240.00 at 10.5% p.a. for 16 months;
(iii) $1293.60 at 11.75% p.a. for 215 days.

Solution

(i) $P = 3600.00; r = 9\% = 0.09; t = 3$
$\quad I = Prt = (3600.00)(0.09)(3) = \$972.00$

(ii) $P = 5240.00; r = 10.5\% = 0.105; t = 16 \text{ months} = \dfrac{16}{12}$
$\quad I = Prt = (5240.00)(0.105)\left(\dfrac{16}{12}\right) = \$733.60$

(iii) $P = 1293.60; r = 11.75 = 0.1175; t = 215 \text{ days} = \dfrac{215}{365}$
$\quad I = Prt = (1293.60)(0.1175)\left(\dfrac{215}{365}\right) = \$89.53$

B.

Example 10.3b Find the amount of interest earned by $785.95 invested at 9.25% from January 30, 1987 to April 21, 1987.

Solution

Number of days

January	1	⟵ (31 − 30)
February	28	
March	31	
April	21	

Total   81

$P = 785.95$; $r = 9.25\% = 0.0925$; $t = \frac{81}{365}$

$I = (785.95)(0.0925)(\frac{81}{365}) = \$16.13$

C.

Example 10.3c Compute the exact interest on $1240.00 earning 10.75% p.a. from September 30, 1987 to May 15, 1988.

Solution

The beginning date is September 30, 1987   ⟶   Day 273
The number of days remaining in 1987 is $(365 - 273) =$ 92
The ending date is May 15, 1988 (Day 135 + 1)   136 ⟵ leap year
Total   228

$P = 1240.00$; $r = 10.75\% = 0.1075$; $t = \dfrac{228}{365}$

$I = (1240.00)(0.1075)\left(\dfrac{228}{365}\right) = \$83.27$

Note 365 is used to convert the number of days into years even if the year involved is a leap year.

Exercise 10.3

A. Compute the exact interest for each of the following.

1. $4000.00 at $10\frac{1}{2}\%$ for $2\frac{1}{4}$ years
2. $645.00 at $13\frac{1}{4}\%$ for $1\frac{3}{4}$ years
3. $1660.00 at 9.75% for 16 months
4. $742.40 at 10.9% for 9 months
5. $980.00 at 11.5% for 244 days
6. $465.40 at 12.4% for 163 days

B. Compute the exact interest for each of the following.

    1. $275.00 at 9.25% from November 30, 1986 to May 5, 1987

    2. $1090.60 at 11.8% from October 12, 1987 to April 24, 1988

    3. $424.23 at $12\frac{3}{4}$% from April 4, 1988 to November 4, 1988

    4. $724.85 at 10.4% from August 30, 1986 to March 30, 1987

10.4 *Finding the principal, rate, or time*

A. *Problems derived from the simple interest formula*

The simple interest formula I = Prt contains the four variables I, P, r, t. If any *three* of the four are given, the value of the unknown variable can be computed by substituting the known values in the formula or by solving for the unknown variable first and then substituting in the resulting derived formula.

The three derived formulae are

(i) To find the principal P $P = \dfrac{I}{rt}$ ⟵ *Formula* **10.2a**

(ii) To find the rate of interest r $r = \dfrac{I}{Pt}$ ⟵ *Formula* **10.2b**

(iii) To find the time period t $t = \dfrac{I}{Pr}$ ⟵ *Formula* **10.2c**

Note (a) In Formula 10.2b, if the time period t is expressed *in years*, the value of r represents an *annual* rate of interest in decimal form.

      (b) In Formula 10.2c, if the rate of interest r is an *annual* rate, the value of t represents *years* in decimal form.

B. *Finding the principal*

If the amount of interest, the rate of interest and the time period are known the principal can be determined.

***Example* 10.4a** What principal will earn interest of $57.40 at 10.25% in 8 months?

Solution

$$I = 57.40; \; r = 10.25\%; \; t = \frac{8}{12}$$

(i) Using the formula $I = Prt$

$$57.40 = (P)(0.1025)\left(\frac{8}{12}\right) \longleftarrow \text{by substitution}$$

$$57.40 = (P)(0.0683333) \longleftarrow (0.1025)\left(\frac{8}{12}\right)$$

$$P = \frac{57.40}{0.0683333} \longleftarrow \text{divide 57.40 by the coefficient of P}$$

$$= \$840.00$$

(ii) Using the derived formula $P = \dfrac{I}{rt}$

$$P = \frac{57.40}{(0.1025)(\frac{8}{12})} \longleftarrow \text{by substitution}$$

$$= \frac{(57.40)(12)}{(0.1025)(8)} \longleftarrow \text{move the 12 into the numerator}$$

$$= \$840.00$$

Note

(1) When the time is given in months, the formula may be modified to

$$P = \frac{(I)(12)}{(r)(t \text{ in months})}$$

(2) When the time is given in days, the formula may be modified to

$$P = \frac{(I)(365)}{(r)(t \text{ in days})}$$

Example 10.4b   Determine the sum of money that must be invested for 245 days at 9.75% to earn $71.99.

Solution

$$I = 71.99; \ r = 9.75\% = 0.0975; \ t = \frac{245}{365}$$

(i) Using the formula $I = Prt$

$$71.99 = (P)(0.0975)\left(\frac{245}{365}\right)$$

$$71.99 = (P)(0.0654452)$$

$$P = \frac{71.99}{0.0654452}$$

$$= \$1100.00$$

(ii) Using the derived formula $P = \dfrac{I}{rt}$

$$P = \frac{71.99}{(0.0975)(\frac{245}{365})}$$

$$= \frac{(71.99)(365)}{(0.0975)(245)} \quad \longleftarrow \quad \begin{array}{l}\text{move the 365 into the} \\ \text{numerator}\end{array}$$

$$= \$1100.00$$

C. Finding the rate

If the amount of interest, the principal and the time period are known, the rate of interest can be determined.

***Example* 10.4c** Find the annual rate of interest required for \$744.00 to earn \$75.95 in 14 months.

Solution

$$I = 75.95; \quad P = 744.00; \quad t = \frac{14}{12}$$

(i) Using the formula $I = Prt$

$$75.95 = (744)(r)\left(\frac{14}{12}\right)$$

$$75.95 = (868)(r)$$

$$r = \frac{75.95}{868}$$

$$= 0.0875$$

$$= 8.75\% \quad \longleftarrow \quad \text{convert to a percent}$$

(ii) Using the derived formula $r = \dfrac{I}{Pt}$

$$r = \frac{75.95}{(744.00)(\frac{14}{12})}$$

$$= \frac{(75.95)(12)}{(744.00)(14)}$$

$$= 0.0875$$

$$= 8.75\%$$

Note

(1) When the time is given in months, the formula may be modified to

$$r = \frac{(I)(12)}{(P)(t \text{ in months})}$$

(2) When the time is given in days, the formula may be modified to

$$r = \frac{(I)(365)}{(P)(t \text{ in days})}$$

Example 10.4d Find the yearly rate of interest on a principal of $1600.00 earning interest of $59.18 in 120 days.

Solution

$$I = 59.18; \qquad P = 1600.00; \qquad t = \frac{120}{365}$$

(i) Using the formula $I = Prt$

$$59.18 = (1600.00)(r)\left(\frac{120}{365}\right)$$

$$59.18 = (526.0274)(r)$$

$$r = \frac{59.18}{526.0274}$$

$$= 0.1125$$

$$= 11.25\%$$

(ii) Using the derived formula $r = \dfrac{I}{Pt}$

$$r = \frac{59.18}{(1600.00)(\frac{120}{365})}$$

$$= \frac{(59.18)(365)}{(1600.00)(120)}$$

$$= 0.1125$$

$$= 11.25\%$$

D. Finding the time

If the amount of interest, the principal and the rate of interest are known, the time period can be determined.

Example 10.4e Find the number of years required for $745.00 to earn $178.80 simple interest at 12% p.a.

Solution

$$I = 178.80; \qquad P = 745.00; \qquad r = 12.0\% = 0.12$$

(i) Using the formula $I = Prt$

$$178.80 = (745.00)(0.12)(t)$$

$$178.80 = (89.40)(t)$$

$$t = \frac{178.80}{89.40}$$

$$= 2.00 \text{ (years)}$$

(ii) Using the derived formula $t = \dfrac{I}{Pr}$

$$t = \frac{178.80}{(745.00)(0.12)}.$$

$$= 2.00 \text{ (years)}$$

Note

(1) The value of t in the formula $I = Prt$ will be in years. If the time period is to be stated in months or in days it is necessary to multiply by 12 or 365 respectively.

(2) If the time is to be shown in months, the derived formula may be modified to

$$t = \frac{(I)(12)}{Pr}$$

(3) If the time is to be shown in days, the derived formula may be modified to

$$t = \frac{(I)(365)}{Pr}$$

Example 10.4f Determine the number of months required for a deposit of $1320.00 to earn $51.70 interest at 11.75%.

Solution

$$I = 51.70; \qquad P = 1320.00; \qquad r = 11.75\% = 0.1175$$

(i) Using the formula $I = Prt$

$$51.70 = (1320.00)(0.1175)(t)$$

$$51.70 = (155.10)(t)$$

$$t = \frac{51.70}{155.10}$$

$= 0.3333333$ years

$= (0.3333333)(12)$ months

$= 4$ months

(ii) Using the derived formula $t = \dfrac{I}{Pr}$

$$t = \frac{51.70}{(1320.00)(0.1175)} \text{ years}$$

$$= \frac{(51.70)(12)}{(1320.00)(0.1175)} \text{ months}$$

$= 4$ months

Example 10.4g How many days are needed for $1500.00 to earn $69.04 at 10.5% p.a.?

Solution

$$I = 69.04; \quad P = 1500.00; \quad r = 10.5\% = 0.105$$

(i) Using the formula $I = Prt$

$69.04 = (1500.00)(0.105)(t)$

$69.04 = (157.50)(t)$

$$t = \frac{69.04}{157.50}$$

$= 0.438\ 3492$ years

$= (0.438\ 3492)(365)$ days

$= 160$ days

(ii) Using the derived formula $t = \dfrac{I}{Pr}$

$$t = \frac{69.04}{(1500.00)(0.105)} \text{ years}$$

$$= \frac{(69.04)(365)}{(1500.00)(0.105)} \text{ days}$$

$= 160$ days

Exercise 10.4

A. Determine the missing value for each of the following.

Problem number	Interest	Principal	Rate	Time
1.	$67.83	?	9.5%	7 months
2.	$256.25	?	10.25%	250 days
3.	$215.00	$2400.00	?	10 months
4.	$53.40	$750.00	?	315 days
5.	$136.34	$954.00	$12\frac{1}{4}\%$	? (months)
6.	$52.64	$1295.80	$9\frac{3}{4}\%$	? (months)
7.	$15.30	$344.75	11.25%	? (days)
8.	$68.96	$830.30	10.75%	? (days)

B. Find the value indicated for each of the following.

1. Find the principal which will earn $148.32 at 13.5% in 8 months.
2. Determine the deposit that must be made to earn $39.27 in 255 days at 11%.
3. A loan of $880.00 can be repaid in 15 months by paying the principal sum borrowed plus $104.50 interest. What was the rate of interest charged?
4. At what rate of interest will $1387.00 earn $101.84 in 200 days?
5. In how many months will $1290.00 earn $156.68 interest at $13\frac{1}{4}\%$?
6. Determine the number of days it will take $564.00 to earn $22.39 at 11.5%.
7. What principal will earn $39.96 from June 18, 1987 to December 15, 1987 at 9.25%?
8. What rate of interest is required for $740.48 to earn $42.49 interest from September 10, 1987 to March 4, 1988?

10.5   The amount of a sum of money

A.   Basic concept

The **amount of a sum of money** (or **maturity value**) is the value obtained by adding the original principal and the interest due.

$$\text{AMOUNT (or MATURITY VALUE)} = \text{PRINCIPAL} + \text{INTEREST}$$
$$S = P + I$$

←*Formula* **10.3**

Example 10.5a   Determine the amount (maturity value), principal or interest as indicated.

(i) Principal is $2200.00; the interest is $240; find the amount.

Solution

$$P = 2200.00; \quad I = 240.00$$

S = P + I
  = 2200.00 + 240.00
  = $2440.00

(ii) Principal is $850.00; the amount is $920.00; find the interest.

Solution

$$S = P + I; \quad P = 850.00; \quad S = 920.00$$

920.00 = 850.00 + I
920.00 − 850.00 = I
    I = $70.00

(iii) Amount is $430.00; the interest is $40.00; find the principal.

Solution

$$S = P + I; \quad S = 430.00; \quad I = 40.00$$

430.00 = P + 40.00
430.00 − 40.00 = P
    P = $390.00

B. The amount formula S = P(1 + rt)

The two formulas $I = Prt$ and $S = P + I$ are combined to obtain the amount formula for simple interest.

S = P + I

S = P + Prt ⟵ substitute Prt for I

$\boxed{S = P(1 + rt)}$ ⟵ take out the common factor P ⟵ *Formula* **10.4**

Example **10.5b** Find the amount of $720.00 earning 11% p.a. for 146 days.

Solution

$$P = 720.00; \quad r = 11\% = 0.11; \quad t = \frac{146}{365}$$

$S = P(1 + rt)$

$= (720.00)\left[1 + (0.11)\left(\frac{146}{365}\right)\right]$

$= (720.00)(1 + 0.044)$

$= (720.00)(1.044)$

$= \$751.68$

Example 10.5c Find the maturity value of a deposit of $1250.00 invested at 9.75% p.a. from October 15, 1986 to May 1, 1987.

Solution

The time period in days $= 16 + 30 + 31 + 31 + 28 + 31 + 30 + 1 = 198$

$$P = 1250.00; \quad r = 9.75\% = 0.0975; \quad t = \frac{198}{365}$$

$S = P(1 + rt)$

$$= (1250.00)\left[1 + (0.0975)\left(\frac{198}{365}\right)\right]$$

$$= (1250.00)(1 + 0.0528904)$$

$$= (1250.00)(1.0528904)$$

$$= \$1316.11$$

Exercise 10.5

A. Use the amount formula to answer each of the following.

1. Find the amount of $480.00 at $12\frac{1}{2}\%$ for 220 days.
2. Find the maturity value of $732.00 invested at 9.8% from May 20, 1988 to November 23, 1988.
3. Compute the accumulated value of $820.00 over 9 months at $11\frac{3}{4}\%$.
4. What payment is required to pay off a loan of $1200.00 at 14% seven months later?

10.6 *Present value*

A. *Finding the principal when the amount is known*

The formula $S = P(1 + rt)$ permits the determination of the principal when the maturity value, the rate and the time are given.

Example 10.6a Find the principal which will amount to $1294.50 in 9 months at 10.5% per annum.

Solution

$$S = 1294.50; \quad r = 10.5\% = 0.105; \quad t = \frac{9}{12}$$

$S = P(1 + rt)$ ⟵―――――― use the amount formula when S is known

$$1294.50 = (P)\left[1 + (0.105)\left(\frac{9}{12}\right)\right]$$

$$1294.50 = (P)(1 + 0.07875)$$

$$1294.50 = (P)(1.07875)$$

$$P = \frac{1294.50}{1.07875}$$

$$P = \$1200.00$$

***Example* 10.6b**   What sum of money must be invested on January 31, 1988 to amount to $7700.00 on August 18, 1988 at 10% p.a.?

Solution

The time period in days = 29 (leap year) + 31 + 30 + 31 + 30 + 31 + 18 = 200

$$S = 7700.00; \quad r = 10\% = 0.10; \quad t = \frac{200}{365}$$

$$7700.00 = (P)\left[1 + (0.10)\left(\frac{200}{365}\right)\right] \longleftarrow \text{using Formula 10.4}$$

$$7700.00 = (P)(1 + 0.0547945)$$

$$7700.00 = (P)(1.0547945)$$

$$P = \frac{7700.00}{1.0547945}$$

$$P = \$7300.00$$

Note   (1) The total interest earned is $7700 − $7300 = $400.00.

(2) The daily amount of interest is $\dfrac{\$400.00}{200} = \$2.00.$

B. The present value concept and formula

In an economy in which interest is paid for the use of money, the value of any sum of money subject to interest changes with time. This is referred to as the **time value of money**.

FIGURE 10.1   *Time graph for Example 10.6b*

Jan. 31, 1988	$r = 10\%$	August 18, 1988
Original Principal $7300		Maturity Value $7700

To illustrate the concept of time value of money Example 10.6b is represented on the time graph shown in Figure 10.1

As indicated the original principal of $7300 will grow to $7700 at 10% in 200 days. This means $400 interest is earned by the original principal in 200 days; that is, the original principal of $7300 will grow by $2.00 per day. Accordingly, the value of the investment changes day by day and if the value of the investment on a particular date is considered, it is referred to as the **present value** of the amount (or maturity value) on that date.

Hence the original principal of $7300 is the present value of $7700 on January 31, 1988.

The present value of an amount at any given point in time may be defined to be the principal needed to grow to the amount at a given rate of interest over a given period of time.

Since the problem of finding the present value is equivalent to finding the principal when the amount, rate and time are given, the amount formula $S = P(1 + rt)$ is applicable. However, as the problem of finding the present value of an amount is one of the frequently recurring problems in financial analysis, it is useful to solve the amount formula for P to obtain the present value formula.

$$S = P(1 + rt) \longleftarrow \text{starting with the amount formula}$$

$$\frac{S}{(1 + rt)} = \frac{P(1 + rt)}{(1 + rt)} \longleftarrow \text{divide both sides by } (1 + rt)$$

$$\frac{S}{(1 + rt)} = P \longleftarrow \text{reduce the fraction } \frac{(1 + rt)}{(1 + rt)} \text{ to } 1$$

$$\boxed{P = \frac{S}{1 + rt}} \longleftarrow \begin{array}{l} \text{present value formula} \\ \text{for simple interest} \end{array} \longleftarrow \textbf{Formula 10.5}$$

Example 10.6c Find the present value of an investment with a maturity value of $918.00 eight months before the due date at 12% p.a.

Solution

$$S = 918.00; \quad r = 12\% = 0.12; \quad t = \frac{8}{12}$$

$$P = \frac{S}{1 + rt}$$

$$P = \frac{918.00}{1 + (0.12)(\frac{8}{12})} \longleftarrow \text{using Formula 10.5}$$

$$= \frac{918.00}{1 + 0.08}$$

$$= \frac{918.00}{1.08}$$

$$= \$850.00$$

Example 10.6d Find the sum of money which deposited in an account on April 1 will grow to $674.73 by September 10 at 10.75% p.a.

Solution

The time in days $= 29 + 31 + 30 + 31 + 31 + 10 = 162$

$$S = 674.73; \qquad r = 10.75\% = 0.1075; \qquad t = \frac{162}{365}$$

$$P = \frac{674.73}{1 + (0.1075)(\frac{162}{365})} = \frac{674.73}{1 + 0.0477123} = \frac{674.73}{1.0477123} = \$644.00$$

345

Simple interest

Exercise 10.6

A. Find the principal and the missing value in each of the following.

Problem number	Amount	Interest	Rate	Time
1.	$305.90	—	12%	15 months
2.	$729.30	$117.30	—	20 months
3.	—	$29.67	12.9%	8 months
4.	—	$27.11	9.5%	240 days
5.	$2195.10	$170.10	10.5%	—
6.	$1079.68	—	13.5%	275 days

B. Solve each of the following.

1. What principal will amount to $1276.99 at 10.8% in 5 months?
2. What sum of money will accumulate to $492.67 in 93 days at 14.6%?
3. Determine the present value of a debt of $1760.00 due in 4 months if interest at $9\frac{3}{4}\%$ is allowed.
4. Find the present value of a debt of $460.00 ninety days before it is due if money is worth 12%.

10.7 Equivalent values

A. Dated values

If a sum of money is subject to a rate of interest it will grow over a period of time. Thus the value of the sum of money changes with time, a fact referred to as the time value of money.

For example, a sum of $1000.00 invested today at 12% p.a. simple interest has a value of $1000.00 today, $1030.00 in three months, $1060.00 in six months and $1120.00 in one year.

The value of the original sum at any particular point is a **dated value** of that sum and the various dated values at different points in time are equivalent to the original sum of money.

Point in time	Dated value
Today	$1000.00
3 months from now	$1030.00
6 months from now	$1060.00
1 year from now	$1120.00

To further illustrate the concept of a dated value consider the case of an obligation of $500.00 payable today. Suppose the debtor requests an extension of four months of the obligation. How much should he expect to pay then if money is worth 18% p.a.?

Since the lender could invest the $500.00 at 18% p.a., the debtor should be prepared to pay the dated value. This dated value includes interest for the additional time period and thus represents the amount to which the $500.00 will grow in four months. It is found using Formula 10.4.

$$S = P(1 + rt)$$

$$= 500.00 \left(1 + (0.18)\left(\frac{4}{12}\right)\right)$$

$$= 500.00(1 + 0.06)$$

$$= \$530.00$$

Also consider the case of an obligation of $1090.00 due six months from now. Suppose the debtor offers to pay the debt today. How much should the payment be if money is worth 18% p.a.?

Since the payment could be invested at 18% p.a., the payment should be the sum of money which will grow to $1090.00 in six months at 18% p.a. By definition this sum of money is the present value of the $1090.00. The present value represents the dated value of the $1090.00 today, and is found using Formula 10.5.

$$P = \frac{S}{1 + rt}$$

$$= \frac{1090.00}{1 + (0.18)\left(\frac{6}{12}\right)}$$

$$= \frac{1090.00}{1 + 0.09}$$

$$= \$1000.00$$

Due to the time value of money, sums of money located at different points in time are *not* directly comparable. For example, given a choice between $2000.00

today and $2200.00 one year from now, it does not automatically follow, from the point of view of investing money, that the larger sum of money is preferable; nor does it automatically follow that the chronologically earlier sum of money should be taken.

To make a rational choice, we must allow for the rate money is worth and select a comparison date or **focal date** to obtain the dated values of the sums of money at a specific point in time.

Dated values at the *same* point in time are directly comparable and may be obtained for simple interest by using either the amount formula, Formula 10.4, $S = P(1 + rt)$, or the present value formula, Formula 10.5, $P = \frac{S}{(1 + rt)}$.

B. Choosing the appropriate formula

The choice of formula for finding dated values depends on the due date of the sum of money relative to the selected focal (or comparison) date.

(a) If the due date falls before the focal date, use the amount formula.

FIGURE 10.2 *Diagram indicating when to use the amount formula*

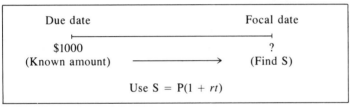

Due date   Focal date

$1000   ?
(Known amount)   ⟶   (Find S)

Use S = P(1 + rt)

Explanation of diagram We are looking for a future value relative to the given value. This future value will be higher than the known value by the interest which accumulates on the known value from the due date to the focal date. This is an amount problem (note that the arrow points to the right) so that the amount formula $S = P(1 + rt)$ is applicable.

(b) If the due date falls after the focal date, use the present value formula.

FIGURE 10.3 *Diagram indicating when to use the present value formula*

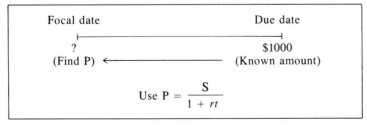

Focal date   Due date

? $1000
(Find P) ⟵   (Known amount)

Use P = $\dfrac{S}{1 + rt}$

Explanation of diagram We are looking for an earlier value relative to the given value. This earlier value will be less than the given value by the interest which would accumulate on the unknown earlier value from the focal date to the due date. We are, in fact, looking for the principal which will grow to the given value. This is a present value problem (note that the arrow points to the left) so that the present value formula $P = \dfrac{S}{1 + rt}$ is appropriate.

C. Finding the equivalent single payment

Example 10.7a A debt can be paid off by payments of $920.00 one year from now and $1300.00 two years from now. Determine the single payment now which would settle the debt allowing for simple interest at 15% p.a.

Solution

See Figure 10.4 for the graphical representation of the dated values as suggested in Figures 10.2 and 10.3 to determine which formula is appropriate.

FIGURE 10.4 *Graphical representation of the dated values*

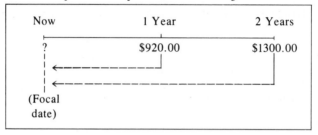

Since the focal date is *earlier* relative to the dates for the given sums of money (arrows point to the left) the present value formula $P = \dfrac{S}{1 + rt}$ is appropriate.

(i) The present value of the $920.00 at the focal date

$$P = \frac{920.00}{1 + (0.15)(1)}$$

$$= \frac{920.00}{1.15}$$

$$= 800.00$$

(ii) The present value of the $1300.00 at the focal date

$$P = \frac{1300.00}{1 + (0.15)(2)} = \frac{1300.00}{1.30} = 1000.00$$

(iii) Single payment required now $= 800.00 + 1000.00 = \$1800.00$

***Example* 10.7b** Debt payments of $400 due today, $500 due in 5 months and $618 due in one year, are to be combined into a single payment to be made 9 months from now with interest allowed at 12% p.a.

Solution

FIGURE 10.5 *Graphical representation of the dated values*

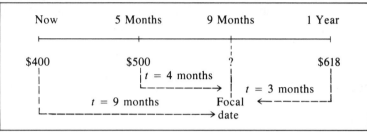

Since the focal date is in the *future* relative to the $400 now and the $500 five months from now (arrows point to the right) the amount formula $S = P(1 + rt)$ is appropriate for these two amounts. However, since the focal date is *earlier* relative to the $618 one year from now (the arrow points to the left) the present value formula $P = \dfrac{S}{1 + rt}$ is applicable for this amount.

(i) The amount of $400 at the focal date

$$P = 400.00; \quad r = 12\% = 0.12; \quad t = \frac{9}{12}$$

$$S = 400\left[1 + (0.12)\left(\frac{9}{12}\right)\right] = 400(1 + 0.09) = 400(1.09) = 436.00$$

(ii) The amount of $500 at the focal date

$$P = 500.00; \quad r = 12\% = 0.12; \quad t = \frac{4}{12}$$

$$S = 500\left[1 + (0.12)\left(\frac{4}{12}\right)\right] = 500(1 + 0.04) = 500(1.04) = 520.00$$

(iii) The present value of $618 at the focal date

$$S = 618.00; \quad r = 12\% = 0.12; \quad t = \frac{3}{12}$$

$$P = \frac{618.00}{1 + (0.12)(\frac{3}{12})} = \frac{618.00}{1 + 0.03} = \frac{618.00}{1.03} = 600.00$$

(iv) The single payment needed = 436.00 + 520.00 + 600.00 = $1556.00

D. Finding the value of two or more equivalent payments

The **equivalent values** obtained when using simple interest formulae are influenced by the selection of the focal date. Although the differences in the values obtained are small, agreement concerning the selection of the focal date should be made by the parties to the financial transaction.

Example 10.7c Debts of $400.00 due now and $700 due in 5 months are to be settled by a payment of $500.00 in 3 months and a final payment in 8 months. Determine the value of the final payment at 15% p.a. with a focal date 8 months from now.

Solution

Let the value of the final payment be represented by $x.

(i) Represent the data given in a time diagram

FIGURE 10.6 *Graphical representation of data*

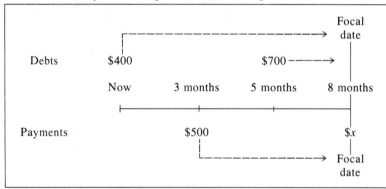

(ii) Dated value of the debts

(a) The value at the focal date of the $400 due 8 months before the focal date is found by using the amount formula.

$$S = 400\left[1 + (0.15)\left(\frac{8}{12}\right)\right] = 400(1 + 0.10) = 400(1.10) = \$440.00$$

(b) The value at the focal date of the $700 due 3 months before the focal date is found by using the amount formula.

$$S = 700\left[1 + (0.15)\left(\frac{3}{12}\right)\right] = 700(1 + 0.0375) = 700(1.0375) = \$726.25$$

(iii) Dated value of the payments

(a) The value at the focal date of the $500 payment made 5 months before the focal date is found by using the amount formula.

$$S = 500\left[1 + (0.15)\left(\frac{5}{12}\right)\right] = 500(1 + 0.0625) = 500(1.0625) = \$531.25$$

(b) The value at the focal date of the final payment is $x (no adjustment for interest is necessary for a sum of money located at the focal date).

(iv) The so-called **equation of values** at the focal date is now set up by matching the dated values of the debts to the dated values of the payments.

> THE SUM OF THE DATED VALUES OF PAYMENTS =
>
> THE SUM OF THE DATED VALUES OF DEBTS

$$500\left[1 + (0.15)\left(\frac{5}{12}\right)\right] + x = 400\left[1 + (0.15)\left(\frac{8}{12}\right)\right] + 700\left[1 + (0.15)\left(\frac{3}{12}\right)\right]$$

$$531.25 + x = 440.00 + 726.25$$

$$531.25 + x = 1166.25$$

$$x = 1166.25 - 531.25$$

$$x = 635.00$$

The final payment to be made in 8 months is $635.00.

Example 10.7d   Debts of $2000 due 60 days ago and $1800 due in 30 days are to be settled by three equal payments due now, 60 days from now and 120 days from now. Find the size of the equal payments at 10% p.a. with the agreed focal date now.

Solution

Let the size of the equal payments be represented by $x.

(i) Graphical representation of data

FIGURE 10.7   *Graphical representation of data*

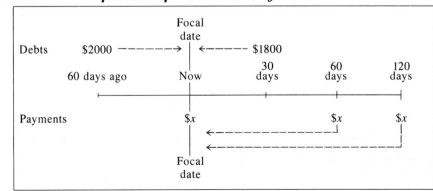

(ii) Dated value of the debts at the focal date

(a) The $2000 debt is due 60 days before the focal date, hence the amount formula is appropriate.

$$S = 2000\left[1 + (0.10)\left(\frac{60}{365}\right)\right] = 2000(1 + 0.0164384) = \$2032.88$$

(b) The $1800 debt is due 30 days after the focal date, hence the present value formula is appropriate.

$$P = \frac{1800}{1 + (0.10)(\frac{30}{365})} = \frac{1800}{1 + 0.0082192} = \$1785.33$$

(iii) Dated value of the payments at the focal date

(a) Since the first payment is to be made at the focal date its value is x.

(b) The second payment is to be made 60 days after the focal date, hence the present value formula is appropriate.

$$P = \frac{x}{1 + (0.10)(\frac{60}{365})} = \frac{x}{1 + 0.0164384}$$

$$= \frac{1}{1.0164384}(x) = \$0.9838275x$$

(c) The third payment is to be made 120 days after the focal date, hence the present value formula is appropriate.

$$P = \frac{x}{1 + (0.10)(\frac{120}{365})} = \frac{x}{1 + 0.0328767}$$

$$= \frac{1}{1.0328767}(x) = \$0.9681698x$$

(iv) The equation of values (dated value of payments = dated value of debts)

$$x + 0.9838275x + 0.9681698x = 2032.88 + 1785.33$$
$$2.9519973x = 3818.21$$

$$x = \frac{3818.21}{2.9519973}$$

$$x = 1293.43$$

The size of each of the three equal payments is $1293.43.

Example 10.7e A loan of $2000 made at 13.5% p.a. is to be repaid in four equal payments due at the end of the next four quarters respectively. Determine the size of the quarterly payments if the agreed focal date is the date of the loan.

Solution

Let the size of the equal quarterly payments be represented by $x.

(i) Graphical representation of data

FIGURE 10.8 *Graphical representation of data*

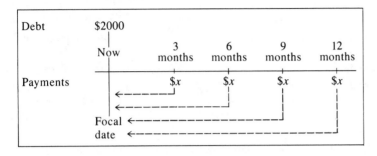

(ii) Dated value of debt at the focal date is $2000.00.

(iii) Dated value of payments at the focal date
The payments are due 3, 6, 9 and 12 months after the focal date respectively, hence their values are

(a) $P_1 = \dfrac{x}{1 + (0.135)(\frac{3}{12})} = \dfrac{x}{1 + 0.03375} = \dfrac{1}{1.03375}(x) = 0.9673519x$

(b) $P_2 = \dfrac{x}{1 + (0.135)(\frac{6}{12})} = \dfrac{x}{1 + 0.06750} = \dfrac{1}{1.06750}(x) = 0.9367682x$

(c) $P_3 = \dfrac{x}{1 + (0.135)(\frac{9}{12})} = \dfrac{x}{1 + 0.10125} = \dfrac{1}{1.10125}(x) = 0.9080590x$

(d) $P_4 = \dfrac{x}{1 + (0.135)(\frac{12}{12})} = \dfrac{x}{1 + 0.13500} = \dfrac{1}{1.13500}(x) = 0.8810573x$

(iv) $0.9673519x + 0.9367682x + 0.9080590x + 0.8810573x = 2000.00$
$$3.6932364x = 2000.00$$
$$x = 541.53$$

The size of the quarterly payment is $541.53

Exercise 10.7

A. Find the equivalent payments indicated for each of the following debts.

Problem number	Old debt	Equivalent payment	Focal date	Rate
1.	$800 due today	In full	4 months hence	11%
2.	$1200 due 3 months ago	In full	today	12%
3.	$600 due in 2 months	In full	7 months hence	13%
4.	$900 due in 8 months	In full	2 months hence	10%
5.	$500 due 4 months ago, $600 due in 2 months	In full	today	12%
6.	$800 due today and $700 due in 2 months	In full	4 months hence	9%
7.	$2000 due today	$1200 in 3 months and the balance in 6 months	today	12%
8.	$400 due 1 month ago, $600 due in 3 months	$500 today and the balance in 6 months	today	11%
9.	$1200 due today	Two equal payments due in 3 and 6 months	today	10%
10.	$1800 due 30 days ago	Three equal payments due today, in 30 days and in 60 days	today	9%

B. Solve each of the following problems.

1. Debt payments of $600 each are due 3 months and 6 months from now respectively. If interest at 10% is allowed what single payment is required to settle the debt today?

2. A loan payment of $1000 was due 60 days ago and another payment of $1200 is due in 30 days. What single payment 90 days from now is required to pay off the two obligations if interest is to be 12% and the agreed focal date is 90 days from now?

3. Loans of $400 due 3 months ago and $700 due today are to be repaid by a payment of $600 in one month and the balance in 4 months. If money is worth 12% and the agreed focal date is today, what is the size of the final payment?

4. Two obligations of $800 each due 60 days ago and 30 days ago respectively, are to be settled by two equal payments to be made today and 60 days from now respectively. If interest allowed is 15% and the agreed focal date is 60 days hence, what is the size of the equal payments?

5. A loan of $4000 is to be repaid by 3 equal payments due in 4, 8 and 12 months respectively. Determine the size of the equal payments at 12% with a focal date today.

6. A loan of $1500 taken out on March 1 requires equal payments on April 30, June 20 and August 10 and a final payment of $400 on September 30. If the focal date is September 30, what is the size of the equal payments at 13%?

Review exercise

1. Determine the exact time for
   (a) April 25 to October 14;
   (b) July 30 to February 1.

2. Compute the exact interest for
   (a) $1975.00 at 14.5% for 215 days;
   (b) $844.65 at 13.25% from May 30 to January 4.

3. What principal will earn
   (a) $83.52 interest at 12% in 219 days?
   (b) $34.40 interest at $9\frac{3}{4}$% from October 30, 1986 to June 1, 1987?

4. Answer each of the following.
   (a) What was the rate of interest if the interest on a loan of $675 for 284 days was $39.39?
   (b) How long will it take for $2075 to earn $124.29 interest at $8\frac{1}{4}$% p.a.? (State your answer in days).
   (c) If $680 is worth $698.70 after three months, what interest rate was charged?
   (d) How many months will it take $750 to grow to $805 at 11% p.a.?

5. Solve each of the following.
   (a) What principal will have a maturity value of $665.60 at 10% in 146 days?
   (b) What is the present value of $6300 due in 16 months at $7\frac{3}{4}$%?

6. What principal will earn $61.52 at 11.75% in 156 days?

7. What sum of money will earn $112.50 from September 1, 1988 to April 30, 1989 at 14.5%?

8. At what rate of interest must a principal of $1435.00 be invested to earn interest of $67.57 in 125 days?

9. At what rate of interest will $1500.00 grow to $1622.21 from June 1 to December 1?

10. In how many months will $2500.00 earn $182.29 interest at 12.5%?

11. In how many days will $3100.00 grow to $3426.39 at 15.75%?

12. Compute the accumulated value of $4200.00 at 11.5% after eleven months.

13. What is the amount to which $1550.00 will grow from June 10 to December 15 at 14%?

14. What sum of money will accumulate to $1460.80 in eight months at 16%?

15. What principal will amount to $3441.62 if invested at 13% from November 1, 1987 to May 31, 1988?

16. What is the present value of $3780.00 due in nine months if interest is 12%?

17. Find the present value on June 1 of $1785.00 due on October 15 if interest is 15%.

18. Debt payments of $1750.00 and $1600.00 are due four months from now and nine months from now respectively. What single payment is required to pay off the debt today if interest is 13.5%?

19. A loan payment of $1450.00 was due 45 days ago and a payment of $1200.00 is due in 60 days. What single payment made 30 days from now is required to settle the two payments if interest is 16% and the agreed focal date is 30 days from now?

20. Debt obligations of $800.00 due two months ago and $1200.00 due in one month are to be repaid by a payment of $1000.00 today and the balance in three months. What is the size of the final payment if interest is 15.5% and the agreed focal date is one month from now?

21. An obligation of $10 000.00 is to be repaid by equal payments due in 60 days, 120 days and 180 days respectively. What is the size of the equal payments if money is worth 13% and the agreed focal date is today?

22. Payments of $4000 each due in four, eight and twelve months respectively are to be settled by five equal payments due today, three months from now, six months from now, nine months from now and twelve months from now. What is the size of the equal payments if interest is 12.75% and the agreed focal date is today?

23. A loan of $5000.00 due in one year is to be repaid by three equal payments due today, six months from now and one year from now respectively. What is the size of the equal payments if interest is 14% and the agreed focal date is today?

24. Three debts, the first for $1000 due two months ago, the second for $1200 due in 2 months and the third for $1400 due in 4 months, are to be paid by a single payment today. How much is the single payment if money is worth 11.5% p.a. and the agreed focal date is today?

25. Debts of $700 due 3 months ago and of $1000 due today are to be paid by payment of $800 in two months and a final payment in five months. If 15% interest is allowed and the focal date is five months from now, what is the size of the final payment?

26. A loan of $3000 is to be repaid in three equal instalments due 90, 180 and 300 days respectively after the date of the loan. If the focal date is the date of the loan and interest is 10.9% p.a., find the size of the instalments.

Self test

1. Find the exact interest earned by $1290.00 at 10.5% p.a. in 173 days.

2. In how many months will $8500.00 grow to $9491.67 at 20% p.a.?

3. What interest rate is paid if the interest on a loan of $2500.00 for 6 months is $156.25?

4. What principal will have a maturity value of $10 000.00 at 8.25% p.a. in 3 months?

5. What is the amount to which $5500.00 will grow at 8.75% p.a. in 10 months?

6. What principal will earn $67.14 interest at 19.25% p.a. for 82 days?

7. What is the present value of $5000.00 due at 17.25% p.a. in 243 days?

8. What rate of interest is paid if the interest on a loan of $2500.00 is $179.32 from November 14, 1988 to May 20, 1989?

9. How many days will it take for $8500.00 to earn $1024.13 at 12.25% p.a.?

10. What principal will earn $113.66 interest at 19.75% p.a. from February 4, 1988 to July 6, 1988.

11. What sum of money will accumulate to $7500.00 at 11.75% p.a. in 88 days?

12. Find the exact interest on $835.00 at 22.5% p.a. from October 9, 1987 to August 4, 1988.

13. A loan of $3320.00 is to be repaid by 3 equal payments due in 92 days, 235 days and 326 days respectively. Determine the size of the equal payments at 8.75% p.a. with a focal date today.

14. Debt payments of $1725.00 due today, $510.00 due in 75 days and $655 due in 323 days, are to be combined into a single payment to be made 115 days from now. What is that single payment, if money is worth 20% p.a. and the agreed focal date is 115 days from now?

15. Debt payments of $1010.00 due 5 months ago and $1280.00 due today are to be repaid by a payment of $615.00 in 4 months and the balance in 7 months. If money is worth 17.75% p.a. and the agreed focal date is in 7 months, what is the size of the final payment?

16. A debt of $1310.00 due 5 months ago and a second debt of $1225.00 due in 3 months with interest at 12% p.a. are to be settled by 2 equal payments due now and 7 months from now respectively. Find the size of the equal payments at 10.25% p.a. with the agreed focal date now.

Summary of formulae used

Formula 10.1 $I = Prt$ Finding the amount of interest when the principal, the rate and the time are known

Formula 10.2a $P = \dfrac{I}{rt}$ Finding the principal directly when the amount of interest, the rate of interest and the time are known

Formula 10.2b $r = \dfrac{I}{Pt}$ Finding the rate of interest directly when the amount of interest, the principal and the time are known

Formula 10.2c $t = \dfrac{I}{Pr}$ Finding the time directly when the amount of interest, the principal and the rate of interest are known

Formula 10.3 $S = P + I$ Finding the amount (maturity value) when the principal and the amount of interest are known

Formula 10.4 $S = P(1 + rt)$ Finding the amount (maturity value) at simple interest directly when the principal, rate of interest and time are known

Formula 10.5 $P = \dfrac{S}{1 + rt}$ Finding the present value at simple interest when the amount, the rate of interest and the time are known

Glossary of terms used

Amount of a sum of money the value obtained when adding the amount of interest to the original principal

Dated value the value of a sum of money at a specific point in time relative to its due date allowing for interest

Equivalent values the dated values of an original sum of money

Exact time the time period in days between two calendar dates

Focal date a specific point in time selected to compare the time value of one or more dated sums of money

Interest rent paid for the use of money

Interest period the time period for which interest is charged

Leap year a year which has an extra day in February

Maturity value see amount

Present value the principal which grow to a given amount (maturity value) over a given period of time at a given rate of interest

Simple interest interest calculated on the original principal by the formula $I = Prt$

Time value of money a concept of money value which allows for a change in the value of a sum of money over time if the sum of money is subject to a rate of interest

11 Promissory notes, simple discount and bank discount

Introduction

Lenders require borrowers to attest to the fact that money was provided. Informally, this may be done by signing an I.O.U. However, to meet the legal requirements of the business and financial community, formal written promises to pay, called Promissory Notes, are used.

Objectives

Upon completion of this chapter, you will be able to

1. recognize promissory notes and interpret correctly related terms such as maker, payee, face value, term of a note, three-days of grace, due date, interest period and maturity value;
2. determine the maturity value of interest-bearing notes by means of the formula $S = P(1 + rt)$;
3. determine the present value of promissory notes;
4. discount promissory notes using simple discount;
5. discount promissory notes using bank discount;
6. examine the relationship between the simple discount rate and the bank discount rate.

11.1 Basic concepts and computations

A. Nature of promissory notes and illustration

A **promissory note** is a written promise by one party to pay a certain sum of money, with or without interest, at a specific date to another party. (See the illustration that follows.)

FIGURE 11.1 *Promissory note illustrated*

$650.00	MISSISSAUGA, ONTARIO,	OCTOBER 30, 1986

___FOUR MONTHS___ after date ___I___ promise to pay to the order of

CREDIT VALLEY NURSERY

SIX-HUNDRED-FIFTY and 00/100 ------------------------ Dollars

at _____SHERIDAN CREDIT UNION LIMITED_____ for value received

with interest at ___10.5%___ per annum.

Due *March 3, 87*   Signed *D. Peel*

B. Related terms explained

The following information is directly available in the promissory note (see items a, b, c, d, e, f below) or can be determined (see items g, h, i, j).

(a) The **maker** of the note is the party making the promise to pay. ⟶ (D. Peel)

(b) The **payee** of the note is the party to whom the promise is made. ⟶ (Credit Valley Nursery)

(c) The **face value** of the note is the sum of money (principal) specified. ⟶ ($650.00)

(d) The **rate of interest** is stated as a simple annual rate based on the face value. ⟶ (10.5%)

(e) The **issue date** is the date on which the note was made. ⟶ (October 30, 1982)

(f) The **term** of the note is the length of time before the note matures (becomes payable). ⟶ (4 months)

(g) The **due date** or **date of maturity** is the date on which the note is to be paid. ⟶ (See Subsection C)

(h) The **interest period** is the time period from the date of issue to the legal due date. ⟶ (See Subsection C)

(i) The **amount of interest** is payable together with the face value at the legal due date. ⟶ (See Subsection C)

(j) The **maturity value** is the amount payable at the due date (face value plus interest) ⟶ (See Subsection C)

C. Computed values

Example 11.1a For the promissory note illustrated in Figure 11.1 determine
(i) the due date; (ii) the interest period;
(iii) the amount of interest; (iv) the maturity value.

Solution
(i) *Finding the due date*

The Canadian law relating to promissory notes adds **three days of grace** to the term of the note to obtain the **legal due date** (Bills of Exchange Act, Section 42). Since calendar months vary in length, the month in which the term ends does not necessarily have a date corresponding to the date of issue. In such cases the last day of the month is used as the end of the term of the note and three days of grace are added to determine the legal due date.

With reference to the promissory note under consideration

the date of issue is October 30,
the term of the note is 4 months
the month in which the term ends is February,
the end of the term is February 28, (since February has no day corresponding to day 30, the last day of the month is used to establish the end of the term of the note)
the legal due date (adding 3 days) is March 3.

(ii) *Determining the interest period*

If the note bears interest, the interest period covers the number of days from the date of issue of the note to the legal due date.

October 30 to March 3 $\longrightarrow$ $(1 + 30 + 31 + 31 + 28 + 3) = 124$ days

(iii) *Computing the amount of interest*

The interest payable on the note is the simple interest based on the face value of the note for the interest period at the stated rate and is found using

the simple interest formula $\boxed{I = Prt}$ $\longleftarrow$ ***Formula 10.1***

$I = (650.00)(0.105)(\frac{124}{365}) = \$23.19$

(iv) *Finding the maturity value of the note*

The maturity value of a promissory note is the total amount payable at the legal due date.

Face Value + Interest $= 650.00 + 23.19 = \$673.19$

Exercise 11.1

A. Determine each of the items listed from the information provided in the promissory note below.

$530.00   OAKVILLE, ONTARIO   OCTOBER 30, 1988

FIVE MONTHS   after date   I   promise to pay

to the order of   JANE WELTON

FIVE-HUNDRED-THIRTY AND 00/000---------------- Dollars

at   SHERIDAN CENTRAL BANK   for value received

with interest at   13.5%   per annum.

Due *April 2, 1989*   Signed *E. Salt*

---

1. Date issued: _____

2. Due date: _____

3. Face value: _____

4. Interest rate: _____

5. Interest period (days): _____

6. Amount of interest: _____

7. Maturity value: _____

B. For each of the following notes, determine

  (a) the due date;

  (b) the interest period (in days);

  (c) the amount of interest;

  (d) the maturity value.

1. The face value of a five-months, 12 percent note dated September 30, 1987 is $840.

2. A note for $760 dated March 20, with interest at 14% per annum, is issued for 120 days.

3. A 60-day 10.5 percent note for $1250 is issued January 31, 1988.

4. A four-months 13 percent note for $2000 is issued July 31.

11.2   *Maturity value of promissory notes*

A.   *Using the formula* **S = P(1 + rt)**

Since the maturity value of a promissory note is the principal (face value) plus the interest accumulated to the legal due date, the amount formula for simple interest may be used to determine the maturity value directly.

$$S = P(1 + rt)$$ ⟵ *Formula* **10.4**

S = the maturity value of the promissory note;
P = the face value of the note;
r = the rate of interest on the note;
t = the interest period (the number of days between the *date of issue* and the *legal due date*).

B. Worked examples

Example 11.2a   For the promissory note illustrated in Figure 11.1 determine the maturity value using the amount formula $S = P(1 + rt)$.

Solution

$$P = 650.00; \qquad r = 0.105; \qquad t = \frac{124}{365}$$

$$S = 650.00\left[1 + (0.105)\left(\frac{124}{365}\right)\right] = 650.00(1 + 0.0356712) = \$673.19$$

Example 11.2b   Find the maturity value of an $800, 6-months note with interest at 12.5% dated May 31.

Solution

The date of issue is May 31;
the term of the note is 6 months;
the term ends November 30;
the legal due date is December 3;
the interest period (May 31 to December 3) has 186 days.

$$P = 800.00; \qquad r = 0.125; \qquad t = \frac{186}{365}$$

$$S = 800.00\left[1 + (0.125)\left(\frac{186}{365}\right)\right] = 800.00(1 + 0.0636986) = \$850.96$$

Example 11.2c   Determine the maturity value of a 90-day, $750 note dated December 15, 1987 with interest at 11%.

Solution

The date of issue is December 15, 1987;
the term is 90 days;
the term ends March 14, 1988;
   (from 90 days take away 16 days remaining
   in December, 31 days for January, 29 days
   for February 1988 being a leap year, which
   leaves 14 days for March)
the legal due days (adding the three days of grace) is March 17;
the interest period (December 15 to March 17) has 93 days.

$$P = 750.00; \qquad r = 0.11; \qquad t = \frac{93}{365}$$

should be

$$S = 750.00\left[1 + (0.11)\left(\frac{93}{365}\right)\right] = 750.00(1 + 0.0280274) = \$771.02$$

Exercise 11.2

A. Use the amount formula to compute the maturity value of each of the following promissory notes.

1. A four-months 11.5 percent note for $620 is issued May 25.

2. A $350 note is issued on October 30 at 13% for 90 days.

3. A 150-day note for $820 with interest at 15% is dated June 28.

4. A seven-months $420 note dated November 1, 1987 earns interest at 9.5%.

11.3   Present value of promissory notes

A.   Finding the face value

The face value (or principal or **present value at the date of issue**) **of promissory notes** may be obtained by solving the amount formula, $S = P(1 + rt)$ for P; that is,

by using the present value formula $\boxed{P = \dfrac{S}{1 + rt}}$ ⟵ *Formula* **10.5**

P = is the face value (or present value) of the note at the date of issue;
S = is the maturity value;
r = is the rate of interest;
t = is the interest period.

Example 11.3a   A 5-months note dated January 31, 1986 and bearing interest at 12% p.a. has a maturity value of $567.16. Find the face value of the note.

Solution

FIGURE 11.2 *Graphical representation of data*

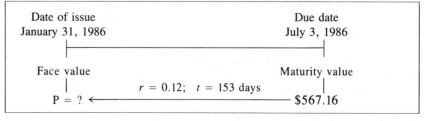

The term of the note ends June 30;
the legal due date is July 3;
the interest period (January 31 to July 3) has 153 days.

$$S = 567.16; \qquad r = 0.12; \qquad t = \frac{153}{365}$$

$$P = \frac{567.16}{1 + (0.12)(\frac{153}{365})} = \frac{567.16}{1 + 0.0503014} = \$540.00$$

B. Present value of non-interest-bearing notes

If a promissory note is *non*-interest bearing, the maturity value of the note is the same as the face value of the note. However, since the time value of money is considered, allowance must be made for the prevailing rate of interest (referred to as the **rate money is worth**) to determine the dated value of the note at a specific point in time (see sub-section 10.7) and the interest period consists of the number of days from the focal date to the due date of the note. As the focal date (the date of issue or a selected date prior to the due date) falls before the due date, the present value formula is applicable.

Example **11.3b**   Find the present value on the date of issue of a non-interest-bearing $950, three-months promissory note, dated April 30, if money is worth 13.5%.

Solution

FIGURE 11.3 *Graphical representation of data*

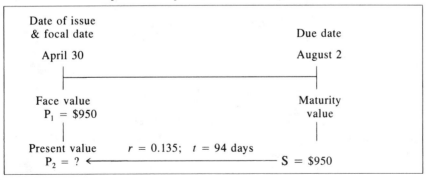

The term of the note ends July 30;
the legal due date is August 2;
the interest period (April 30 to August 2) has 94 days;
the maturity value of the note is the face value $950.00

$$S = 950.00; \qquad r = 0.135; \qquad t = \frac{94}{365}$$

$$P = \frac{950.00}{1 + (0.135)(\frac{94}{365})} = \frac{950.00}{1 + 0.0347671} = \$918.08$$

Example 11.3c Find the value of a non-interest-bearing \$400, 120-day note dated March 2, on May 15 if money is worth 13%.

Solution

The 120-day term ends June 30;
the legal due date is July 3;
the focal date is May 15;
the interest period (May 15 to July 3) has 49 days;
the maturity value of the note is its face value \$400.00.

FIGURE 11.4 Graphical representation of data

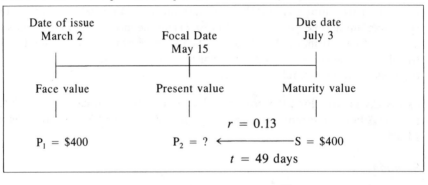

$$S = 400.00; \quad r = 0.13; \quad t = \frac{49}{365}$$

$$P = \frac{400.00}{1 + (0.13)(\frac{49}{365})} = \frac{400.00}{1 + 0.0174521} = \$393.14$$

C. Present value of interest-bearing notes

The present value of an **interest-bearing promissory note** is its value any time prior to the due date allowing for the rate money is worth. Hence it is the present value of the maturity value of the promissory note.

To determine the present value we need to know the maturity value of the note. In computing the maturity value and the present value *two* rates of interest must be considered:

(a) the rate of interest stated on the promissory note which is the rate needed to determine the maturity value;

(b) the rate money is worth, required to determine the present value of the note at the date specified (the focal date).

As the two rates are likely to be *different*, care must be taken in using them.

Example 11.3d A 7-months note for $1500 is issued on March 31 bearing interest at 9%. Find the present value of the note on the date of issue if money is worth 12%.

Solution

(i) First, determine the *maturity value* of the note.
   The term of the note ends October 31;
   the legal due date is November 3;
   the interest period (March 31 to November 3) has 217 days.

FIGURE 11.5 *Graphical representation of data*

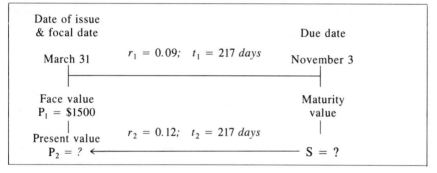

$$P_1 = 1500.00; \qquad r_1 = 0.09; \qquad t_1 = \frac{217}{365}$$

$$S = 1500\left[1 + (0.09)\left(\frac{217}{365}\right)\right] = 1500(1 + 0.0535069) = \$1580.26$$

(ii) Secondly, use the maturity value found in (i) to determine the *present value* at the specified date.

   The focal date (date of issue) is March 31;
   the legal due date is November 3;
   the interest period (March 31 to November 3) has 217 days.

$$S = 1580.26; \qquad r_2 = 0.12; \qquad t_2 = \frac{217}{365}$$

$$P_2 = \frac{1580.26}{1 + (0.12)(\frac{217}{365})} = \frac{1580.26}{1 + 0.0713425} = \$1475.03$$

Note The present value at the date of issue is less than the face value of the note since the interest rate on the note (9.0%) is less than the rate money is worth (12.0%).

Example 11.3e A 180-day note for $2000 with interest at 15% is dated September 18, 1986. Find the value of the note on December 1, 1986 if money is worth 11.5%.

Solution

(i) Find the maturity value of the note.

> The 180-day term ends March 17, 1987;
> the legal due date is March 20, 1987;
> the interest period (September 18 to March 20) has 183 days.

FIGURE 11.6 *Graphical representation of data*

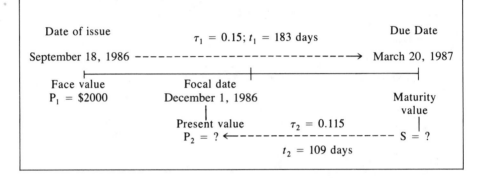

$$P_1 = 2000; \qquad \tau_1 = 0.15; \qquad t_1 = \frac{183}{365}$$

$$S = 2000\left[1 + (0.15)\left(\frac{183}{365}\right)\right] = 2000(1 + 0.0752055) = \$2150.41$$

(ii) Find the present value.

> The focal date is December 1, 1986;
> the interest period (December 1 to March 20) has 109 days.

$$S = 2150.41; \qquad \tau_2 = 0.115; \qquad t_2 \frac{109}{365}$$

$$P_2 = \frac{2150.41}{1 + (0.115)(\frac{109}{365})} = \frac{2150.41}{1 + 0.0343425} = \$2079.01$$

Exercise 11.3

A. Compute the face value of each of the following promissory notes.

> **1.** A six-months note dated April 9 with interest at 13% has a maturity value of $485.15.

2. The maturity value of a 150-day 12.5 percent note dated March 25 is $1641.74.

B. Find the present value at the date indicated of each of the following promissory notes.

1. a non-interest-bearing note for $1200 issued August 10 for three months if money is worth 11% on the date of issue;

2. a non-interest-bearing note for $750 issued February 2, 1988 for 180 days if money is worth 12.5%, on June 1, 1988;

3. a 60-day 14% note for $1600 issued October 28 if money is worth 12%, on November 30;

4. a four-months note for $930 dated April 1 with interest at 10.5% if money is worth 12%, on June 20.

11.4 *The simple discount method of discounting promissory notes*

A. *Discounting promissory notes*

Promissory notes are negotiable; that is, they can be transferred or sold by one party (the holder of the note) to another party (the buyer). The act of selling (buying) a promissory note is called **discounting**.

The buyer of the note purchases its maturity value. The purchase price offered by the buyer is agreed upon by the two parties to the transaction at a rate of interest satisfactory to the buyer.

The following terms are important in computing the discounted value of a note.

(a) The **rate of discount** is the rate of interest to be used in discounting.

(b) The **date of discount** is the date on which the discounting takes place.

(c) The **discount period** is the time period from the date of discount to the legal due date.

(d) The **proceeds** of the note is the amount paid by the buyer.

(e) The amount of discount is the difference between the maturity value and the proceeds of the note.

B. *Simple Discount*

When the simple discount method is used, the proceeds of a promissory note are the present value of the note at the date of discount. Hence the present value formula

$$P = \frac{S}{(1 + rt)}$$ is applicable,

P is the proceeds of the note;
S is the maturity value;
r is the discount rate to be used;
t is the discount period.

Using this formula means that the amount of discount is the same as the amount of simple interest based on the present value of the note on the date of discount. Hence discounting promissory notes by the simple discount method requires the same formulas and computations used in sub-section 11.3, B and C.

C. Discounting non-interest-bearing notes

Example 11.4a A 2-months non-interest-bearing promissory note for $700.00 is dated June 30. Find the proceeds of the note and the amount of discount if the note is discounted on July 31 at 16%.

Solution

The maturity value is the face value of the note $700.00;
the term of the notes ends August 30;
the legal due date of the note is September 2;
the discount date is July 31;
the discount period (July 31 to September 2) has 33 days.

$$S = 700.00; \qquad r = 0.16; \qquad t = \frac{33}{365}$$

$$P = \frac{700.00}{1 + (0.16)(\frac{33}{365})} = \frac{700.00}{1 + 0.0144658} = \$690.02$$

The proceeds of the note on July 31 are $690.02.
The amount of simple discount (simple interest) is (700.00 − 690.02) = $9.98.

Note The buyer of the promissory note invests $690.02 for 33 days and will make 16% p.a. simple interest. This can be verified by computing the amount of simple interest.

$$I = Prt = (690.02)(0.16)\left(\frac{33}{365}\right) = \$9.98$$

D. Discounting interest-bearing notes

Example 11.4b A 150-day, 10% promissory note for $1200 dated October 28, 1987 is sold January 31, 1988 to yield 13%. Determine the proceeds of the note and the amount of discount.

Solution

(i) *Diagram* The information needed in discounting interest-bearing notes is essentially the same as used in computing the present value of such notes as illustrated in Figure 11.7.

FIGURE 11.7 *Graphical representation of data*

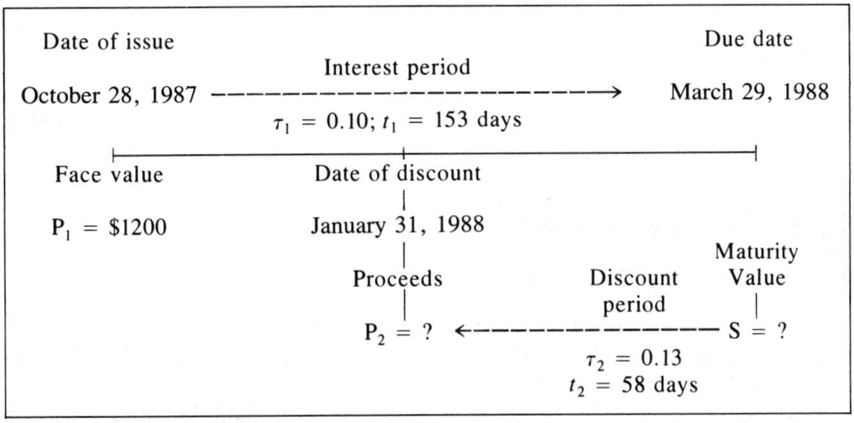

Date of issue   Due date

Interest period

October 28, 1987 $- - - - - - - - - - - - - - - - - - \rightarrow$ March 29, 1988

$\tau_1 = 0.10; t_1 = 153$ days

Face value   Date of discount

$P_1 = \$1200$ January 31, 1988

                                                                    Maturity
                              Proceeds   Discount   Value
                                                    period
                              $P_2 = ?$ $\leftarrow - - - - - - - - - - - - -$ $S = ?$
                                                    $\tau_2 = 0.13$
                                                    $t_2 = 58$ days

(ii) *Find the maturity value*

The 150-day term of the note ends March 26;
   (note that 1988 is a leap year; February has 29 days)
the legal due date is March 29;
the interest period (October 28 to March 29) has 153 days.

$$P_1 = 1200; \qquad \tau_1 = 0.10; \qquad t_1 = \frac{153}{365}$$

$$S = 1200\left[1 + (0.10)\left(\frac{153}{365}\right)\right] = 1200(1 + 0.0419178) = \$1250.30$$

(iii) *Find the proceeds* (present value on January 31, 1988)

The date of discount is January 31, 1988;
the discount period (January 31 to March 29) has 58 days.

$$S = 1250.30; \qquad \tau = 0.13; \qquad t_2 = \frac{58}{365}$$

$$P_2 = \frac{1250.30}{1 + (0.13)(\frac{58}{365})} = \frac{1250.30}{1 + 0.0206575} = \$1224.99$$

The proceeds of the note on January 31, 1988 are \$1224.99.
The amount of simple discount is $1250.30 - 1224.99 = \$25.31$, the same
amount as the simple interest on \$1224.99 at 13% for 58 days
$\left[\text{found by } (1224.99)(0.13)(\frac{58}{365})\right]$.

Exercise 11.4

A. Find the proceeds and the amount of discount for each of the following using the
simple discount method.

1. A 90-day non-interest bearing note for \$1000 dated May 1 is discounted June 10 at
15%.

2. A five-months non-interest-bearing note for $680 issued December 2, 1985 is discounted at 12% on February 15, 1986.

3. A three-months $850 note with interest at 9% dated June 1 is discounted at 11.5% on July 20.

4. A 120-day note for $1300 with interest at 13.5 percent issued August 12 is discounted September 30 at 12 percent.

11.5 Bank discount

A. Nature of bank discount and terminology

When a chartered bank discounts short-term promissory notes, the amount of interest charged by the bank is based on the maturity value rather than the present value at the date of discount.

The amount deducted is referred to as interest paid in advance or **bank discount** and is always slightly *higher* than the **simple discount** which is based on the present value of the promissory note.

Since the bank discount is based on the maturity value of the note rather than its present value at the time of discount, the rate of discount used by the bank is not a true rate of interest. To distinguish this type of discount rate from a rate of interest, the symbol d is normally used to designate the rate of discount in formulae dealing with bank discount calculations.

The following terms and symbols are normally used in dealing with bank discount.

P the proceeds of the note;
S the maturity value of the note;
D the amount of bank discount;
d the **rate of bank discount**;
t the discount period.

B. Bank discount formulae

The following formulae are used for computations involving bank discount

(a) *Finding the amount of bank discount*

$$D = Sdt$$ ⟵ ─────── *Formula* **11.1**

D is the amount of bank discount;
S is the maturity value;
d is the rate of bank discount;
t is the discount period.

(b) *Finding the proceeds of a promissory note*

$$P = S - D$$ ⟵ ─────── *Formula* **11.2**

P are the proceeds of the note;
S is the maturity value;
D is the amount of bank discount.

(c) *Direct formula for finding the proceeds*

$P = S - D$ ⟵————————— *Formula* **11.2**

$D = Sdt$ ⟵————————— *Formula* **11.1**

$P = S - Sdt$ ⟵———— substitute Sdt for D and take
out the common factor S

$$\boxed{P = S(1 - dt)}$$ ⟵———— *Formula* **11.3**

(d) *Finding the maturity value from the proceeds*

$P = S(1 - dt)$ ⟵—— starting with the formula for the proceeds

$$\frac{P}{1 - dt} = \frac{S(1 - dt)}{(1 - dt)}$$ ⟵—— divide both sides
by $(1 - dt)$

$$\frac{P}{1 - dt} = S$$ ⟵—— reduce the fraction $\frac{(1 - dt)}{(1 - dt)}$ *to* 1

$$\boxed{S = \frac{P}{1 - dt}}$$ ⟵————————— *Formula* **11.4**

C. *Finding the proceeds of promissory notes payable to a bank*

Bank loans made for a specified period of time are sometimes secured by promissory notes of the type illustrated in Figure 11.8.

FIGURE 11.8 *Promissory note illustrated*

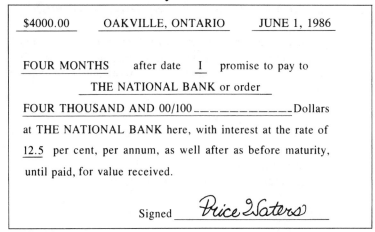

$4000.00   OAKVILLE, ONTARIO   JUNE 1, 1986

FOUR MONTHS   after date   I   promise to pay to

THE NATIONAL BANK or order

FOUR THOUSAND AND 00/100 _____Dollars

at THE NATIONAL BANK here, with interest at the rate of

12.5 per cent, per annum, as well after as before maturity,

until paid, for value received.

Signed   *Price Waters*

Note The type of note illustrated (called a time note) is not used as much any more as it used to be. The current trend is toward the use of demand notes referred to in Chapter 12.

Example 11.5a Determine the bank discount and the proceeds for the note illustrated.

Solution

(i) *By first finding the amount of bank discount*

The maturity value is the face value $4000.00;
the date of issue is June 1;
the term of the note ends October 1;
the legal due date is October 4;
the discount period (June 1 to October 4) has 125 days.

$$S = 4000.00; \qquad d = 0.125; \qquad t = \frac{125}{365}$$

$$D = Sdt = (4000)(0.125)\left(\frac{125}{365}\right) = \$\ 171.23$$

$$P = S - D = 4000.00 - 171.23 = \$3828.77$$

(ii) *By first finding the proceeds*

$$P = S(1 - dt) = 4000\left[1 - (0.125)\left(\frac{125}{365}\right)\right]$$

$$= 4000(1 - 0.0428082) = 4000(0.9571918) = \$3828.77$$

$$D = S - P = 4000.00 - 3828.77 = \$171.23$$

D. Discounting non-interest-bearing notes at a bank

Example 11.5b A 2-months non-interest-bearing note for $700 is dated June 30. Find the proceeds of the note and the amount of discount if it is discounted on July 31 at 16% at a bank. (This is the same note as in Example 11.4a except that it is discounted at a bank).

Solution

The maturity value is the face value of $700.00;
the term of the note ends August 30;
the legal due date is September 2;
the discount period (July 31 to September 2) has 33 days.

$$S = 700.00; \qquad d = 0.16; \qquad t = \frac{33}{365}$$

$$P = S(1 - dt) = 700\left[1 - (0.16)\left(\frac{33}{365}\right)\right]$$

$$= 700(1 - 0.0144658) = 700(0.9855342) = \$689.87$$

$$D = S - P = 700.00 - 689.87 = \$10.13$$

Note The proceeds by the simple discount method (see Example 11.4a) were $690.02 for a discount of $9.98 while the bank discount is $10.13—a difference of $0.15.

E. *Discounting interest-bearing notes at a bank*

Example 11.5c   A 150-day, 10% promissory note for $1200 dated October 28, 1987 is discounted at a bank on January 31, 1988 at 13%. Determine the proceeds of the note and the amount of bank discount. (This is the same note as in Example 11.4b except that it is discounted at a bank).

Solution

(i) *Find the maturity value* (same as Example 11.4b)

The 150-day term ends March 26;
the legal due date is March 29;
the interest period (October 28 to March 29) has 153 days.

$$P_1 = 1200; \quad \tau = 0.10; \quad t_1 = \frac{153}{365}$$

$$S = 1200\left[1 + (0.10)\left(\frac{153}{365}\right)\right] = 1200(1 + 0.0419178) = \$1250.30$$

(ii) *Find the proceeds of the note*

The date of discount is January 31;
the discount period (January 31 to March 29) has 58 days.

$$S = 1250.30; \quad d = 0.13; \quad t_2 = \frac{58}{365}$$

$$P_2 = S(1 - dt) = 1250.30\left[1 - (0.13)\left(\frac{58}{365}\right)\right]$$

$$= 1250.30(1 - 0.0206575)$$
$$= 1250.30(0.9793425) = \$1224.47$$

$$D = S - P = 1250.30 - 1224.47 = \$25.83$$

Note   The simple discount (Example 11.4b) is $25.31—a difference of $0.52. Because the base for the bank discount is greater than the base for the simple discount, the amount of bank discount is greater than the amount of simple discount.

F. Finding the maturity value from the proceeds

If the proceeds of a promissory note discounted at a bank are known, the maturity value of the note may be found by substituting in the proceeds formula $P = S(1 - dt)$ or by using the amount formula $S = \dfrac{P}{1 - dt}$

Example 11.5d You wish to borrow $2000 from a bank on a 3-months time note. Determine the amount for which the note will be written and the interest paid in advance if the bank discounts your note at 14% on March 31.

Solution

The date of issue of the note is March 31;
the term of the note ends June 30;
the legal due date is July 3;
the discount period (March 31 to July 3) has 94 days.

$$P = 2000; \qquad d = 0.14; \qquad t = \frac{94}{365}$$

$$S = \frac{P}{1 - dt} = \frac{2000.00}{1 - (0.14)(\frac{94}{365})} = \frac{2000.00}{1 - 0.0360548}$$

$$= \frac{2000.00}{0.9639452} = \$2074.81$$

Exercise 11.5

A. Find the proceeds and the amount of discount for each of the following using the bank discount method.

1. A three-months non-interest-bearing note for $950 dated November 1 is discounted at a bank at 11% on the date issued.

2. A 150-day $700 note payable to the Local Bank of Milton dated January 15, 1987 is discounted by the bank at 14 percent.

3. A 60-day $2500 note with interest at 11% issued April 30 is discounted at a bank at 12.5% on May 12.

4. A five-months 15 percent note for $1800 dated July 14 is discounted at a bank on November 3 at 13 percent.

B. Find the maturity value and the amount of discount for each of the following.

1. The proceeds of a bank loan secured by a four-months note dated October 20 and discounted at 10% are $1600.

2. A 90-day note payable to a bank dated August 1 is discounted by the bank at 13% to yield proceeds of $1150.

11.6 Simple discount versus bank discount

A. Comparison of r and d

The solutions to Example 11.5b and 11.5c indicate that when the simple discount rate r and the bank discount rate d are equal, then the amount of bank discount is *greater* than the amount of simple discount. This implies that if the amount of discount by the two methods is the same (that is, the proceeds of a promissory note are to be the same) then the bank discount rate d must be smaller than the simple discount rate r.

Example 11.6a   The proceeds of a promissory note with a maturity value of $2000 discounted 73 days before maturity were $1940. What was

(i) the simple discount rate (simple interest)?

(ii) the bank discount rate (interest paid in advance)?

Solution

(i) The simple discount rate r is found using the simple interest formula
$I = Prt$ or $r = \frac{I}{Pt}$.

$$I = 2000 - 1940 = 60; \qquad P = 1940; \qquad t = \frac{73}{365}$$

$$r = \frac{I}{Pt} = \frac{60}{(1940)(\frac{73}{365})} = \frac{(60)(365)}{(1940)(73)} = 0.1546392 = 15.464\%$$

(ii) The bank discount rate d is found using the formula for the amount of bank discount $D = Sdt$ or $d = \frac{D}{St}$.

$$D = 2000 - 1940 = 60; \qquad S = 2000; \qquad t = \frac{73}{365}$$

$$d = \frac{D}{St} = \frac{60}{(2000)(\frac{73}{365})} = \frac{(60)(365)}{(2000)(73)} = 0.15 = 15.000\%$$

Note $r - d = 15.464\% - 15.000\% = 0.464\%$. This means that the simple discount rate is 0.464% greater than the bank discount rate; that is, a bank discount rate of 15% for 73 days is equivalent to a simple interest rate of 15.464% for the same time period.

B. Relationship between d and r

If, as in Example 11.6a, the proceeds of a promissory note are the same, the following relationships between d and r exist.

(a) The simple interest rate r stated in terms of the bank discount rate d is

$$r = \frac{d}{1 - dt} \qquad \longleftarrow \quad \textbf{\textit{Formula 11.5}}$$

The formula may be obtained from the two amount formulae, $S = P(1 + rt)$

and $S = \dfrac{P}{1 - dt}$.

$$P(1 + rt) = \frac{P}{1 - dt} \qquad \longleftarrow \qquad \text{both sides are equal to S}$$

$$1 + rt = \frac{1}{1 - dt} \qquad \longleftarrow \qquad \text{divide both sides by P}$$

$$rt = \frac{1}{1 - dt} - 1 \longleftarrow \qquad \text{subtract 1 from both sides}$$

$$rt = \frac{1 - 1(1 - dt)}{1 - dt} \qquad \longleftarrow \qquad \text{use the common denominator } 1 - dt$$

$$rt = \frac{1 - 1 + dt}{1 - dt} = \frac{dt}{1 - dt} \qquad \longleftarrow \qquad \text{to simplify divide both sides by } t$$

$$r = \frac{d}{1 - dt}$$

(b) The bank discount rate d stated in terms of the simple discount (interest) rate r is

$$d = \frac{r}{1 + rt} \qquad \longleftarrow \qquad \textbf{\textit{Formula 11.6}}$$

This formula may be obtained from the preceding formula $r = \dfrac{d}{1 - dt}$.

$$r(1 - dt) = d \longleftarrow \qquad \text{multiply both sides by } (1 - dt)$$
$$r - rdt = d \longleftarrow \qquad \text{simplify}$$
$$r = d + rdt \longleftarrow \qquad \text{add } rdt \text{ to both sides}$$
$$r = d(1 + rt) \longleftarrow \qquad \text{take out the common factor } d$$

$$\frac{r}{1 + rt} = d \longleftarrow \qquad \text{divide both sides by } (1 + rt)$$

Note The relationship between r and d in the two formulae is *independent* of the maturity value, proceeds or amount of discount of the promissory note, but is *influenced* by the length of the discount period.

Example 11.6b A bank discounts a promissory note 95 days before maturity at 12%. What is the equivalent simple rate of interest earned?

Solution

$$d = 0.12; \qquad t = \frac{95}{365}$$

$$r = \frac{d}{1 - dt} = \frac{0.12}{1 - (0.12)(\frac{95}{365})} = \frac{0.12}{1 - 0.0312329} = \frac{0.12}{0.9687671} = 0.1238688 = 12.39\%$$

Example 11.6c Current policy at a local bank branch requires that the yield on discounted notes be 12.75% simple interest. At what rate should a note be discounted if the note matures?

(i) in 90 days?   (ii) in 180 days?   (iii) in one year?

Solution

(i) $$r = 0.1275; \qquad t = \frac{90}{365}$$

$$d = \frac{r}{1 + rt} = \frac{0.1275}{1 + (0.1275)(\frac{90}{365})} = \frac{0.1275}{1 + 0.0314384} = 0.1236138 = 12.36\%$$

(ii) $$r = 0.1275; \qquad t = \frac{180}{365}$$

$$d = \frac{r}{1 + rt} = \frac{0.1275}{1 + (0.1275)(\frac{180}{365})} = \frac{0.1275}{1 + 0.0628767} = 0.1199575 = 12.00\%$$

(iii) $$r = 0.1275; \qquad t = \frac{365}{365}$$

$$d = \frac{r}{1 + rt} = \frac{0.1275}{1 + (0.1275)(1)} = 0.1130820 = 11.31\%$$

Note for 90 days the difference in rates, $r - d = 0.39\%$;
for 180 days the difference in rates, $r - d = 0.75\%$;
for 365 days the difference in rates, $r - d = 1.44\%$.
The *longer* the discount period, the *larger* the difference between d and r.

Exercise 11.6

A. Determine the simple discount rate and the bank discount rate for each of the following.

1. The proceeds of a promissory note with a maturity value of $960 discounted 125 days before maturity were $930.

2. After a discount of $50 the proceeds of a promissory note discounted 85 days before maturity were $1650.

B. Answer each of the following.

1. A promissory note with a maturity value of $980 is discounted at a simple discount rate of 13.5 percent 60 days before maturity. What is the equivalent bank discount rate?

2. A 90-day promissory note given as security for a bank loan of $1000 is discounted by the bank at 11.5 percent. What is the equivalent simple discount rate?

3. What simple interest rate is earned by a bank discounting 60-day notes at 13 percent?

4. A note is discounted by a bank at 11.5 percent 105 days before maturity. What is the simple interest rate earned by the bank?

5. What discount rate is required for a bank to earn 14 percent simple interest on **(a)** 60-day **(b)** 120-day **(c)** 180-day **(d)** 270-day promissory notes?

6. If a bank uses a 12 percent discount rate for short-term promissory notes, what simple rate of interest will the bank earn on **(a)** 60-day **(b)** 90-day **(c)** 180-day **(d)** 270-day promissory notes?

Review exercise

1. A four-months promissory note for $1600.00 dated June 30 bears interest at 14.5%.

   (a) What is the due date of the note?

   (b) What is the amount of interest payable at the due date?

   (c) What is the maturity value of the note?

2. Determine the maturity value of a 120-day note for $1250.00 dated May 23 and bearing interest at 15.75%?

3. Compute the face value of a 90-day note dated September 10 bearing interest at 17.25% whose maturity value is $767.93.

4. The maturity value of a seven-months promissory note issued July 31, 1988 is $3275.00. What is the present value of the note on the date of issue if interest is 13.75%?

5. Compute the maturity value of a 150-day, 12 percent promissory note with a face value of $5000.00 dated August 5.

6. What is the face value of a three-months promissory note dated November 30, 1987 with interest at 11.5 percent if its maturity value is $967.84?

7. A 90-day, $800 promissory note was issued July 31 with interest at 14%. What is the present value of the note on October 20?

8. A \$1850, four-months promissory note with interest at 12.5% issued June 1 is discounted on August 28 at 15.5%. Find the amount of discount and the proceeds of the note

(a) using the simple discount method;

(b) using the bank discount method.

9. A 150-day note for \$625.00 dated March 15 and bearing interest at 16.5% is discounted April 30 at 14%. Find the proceeds of the note

(a) using the simple discount method;

(b) using the bank discount method.

10. The proceeds of a bank loan secured by a six-months promissory note dated March 31 at 15.5% are \$3223.55. What was the amount of the loan?

11. Determine the present value on the date of issue of a non-interest-bearing promissory note for \$1300 dated March 10 for four months if money is worth 19.5%.

12. Find the proceeds and the discount of a five-months, \$700 promissory note dated September 6 with interest at 10.5 percent discounted on November 28 at 13.5 percent by the simple discount method.

13. A 60-day, 15 percent promissory note for \$2400 dated October 20 was discounted at a bank on November 5 at 12 percent. What were the proceeds of the note?

14. What is the maturity value of a six-months promissory note payable to a bank dated April 30 if the bank discounts the note at 13% to yield proceeds of \$1600?

15. The proceeds of a promissory note with a maturity value of \$1545.00 discounted 146 days before maturity were \$1446.63. What was the discount rate if the note was discounted

(a) by the simple discount method?

(b) by the bank discount method?

16. A promissory note with a maturity value of \$1385.00 is discounted at 16.5% by the bank discount method 120 days before maturity. What is the equivalent simple rate of discount?

17. What discount rate must a bank charge to earn 16% simple interest on a promissory note discounted

(a) 90 days before maturity?

(b) 180 days before maturity?

18. If a bank discounts notes at 14.5%, what simple rate of interest will the bank earn

(a) on a 150-day note?

(b) on a 270-day note?

19. What simple interest rate is earned by a bank discounting a 90-day promissory note at 12.5 percent?

20. A bank discounts a promissory note 183 days before maturity. What rate of discount should the bank use to earn a simple interest rate of 14.4%?

Self-test

1. For the following promissory note, determine the amount of interest due at maturity.

$565.00　　　TORONTO, ONTARIO　　　JANUARY 10, 1988

　FIVE MONTHS　 after date　we　promise to pay to the order of

WILSON LUMBER COMPANY

EXACTLY FIVE-HUNDRED-SIXTY-FIVE and 00/100⸺⸺⸺ Dollars

at　　　　WILSON LUMBER COMPANY　　　　for value received

with interest at　　　22.25%　　　per annum.

Due ⸻⸻⸻⸻　　　　　　　　　　　(seal) ⸻⸻⸻⸻

　　　　　　　　　　　　　　　　　　(seal) ⸻⸻⸻⸻

---

2. Find the maturity value of a $1140.00 — 17.75%, 120-day — note dated February 19, 1987.

3. Determine the face value of a four-months promissory note dated May 20, 1986 with interest at 11.5% p.a. if the maturity value of the note is $1206.05.

4. Compute the proceeds of a bank loan secured by a 180-day, $2400 promissory note discounted by the bank at 13.25% p.a.

5. Find the present value of a non-interest-bearing seven-months promissory note for $1800 dated August 7, 1988 on December 20, 1987 if money is then worth 13.75%.

6. A 180-day note dated September 14, 1988, is made at 19.25% for $1665.00. What is the present value of the note on October 18, 1988 if money is worth 15.5%?

7. What discount rate is required for a bank to earn 20% simple interest on a 270-day promissory note (correct to the nearest 1/1000 of 1%)?

8. A bank discounts a promissory note with a maturity value of $1672.50 eighty days before maturity at 13%. What simple rate of interest did the bank earn (correct to the nearest 1/100 of 1%)?

9. A $2100, five-months promissory note with interest at 10.5% dated August 6 is discounted on October 28 yielding proceeds of $2136.55. Compute the simple rate of discount (correct to 1/100 of 1%).

10. A $3000, six-months promissory note with interest at 14% p.a. dated March 15 is discounted at a bank 120 days after the date of issue at 16%. What are the proceeds of the note?

Summary of formulae used

Formula 10.1 $I = Prt$ Finding the amount of interest on promissory notes

Formula 10.4 $S = P(1 + rt)$ Finding the maturity value of promissory notes directly

Formula 10.5 $P = \dfrac{S}{1 + rt}$ Finding the present value of promissory notes given the maturity value

Formula 11.1 $D = Sdt$ Finding the amount of bank discount given the maturity value of a promissory note, the rate of bank discount and the discount period

Formula 11.2 $P = S - D$ Finding the proceeds of a promissory note given the maturity value and the amount of bank discount

Formula 11.3 $P = S(1 - dt)$ Finding the proceeds of promissory notes directly when the bank discount method is used given the maturity value of the note, the rate of bank discount and the discount period

Formula 11.4 $S = \dfrac{P}{1 - dt}$ Finding the maturity value of a promissory note when the bank discount method is used given the proceeds, rate of bank discount and discount period

Formula 11.5 $r = \dfrac{d}{1 - dt}$ Finding the rate of simple discount when the bank discount rate is known

Formula 11.6 $d = \dfrac{r}{1 + rt}$ Finding the bank discount rate when the simple discount rate is known

Glossary of terms used

Amount of discount   the difference between the maturity value of a promissory note and its proceeds when discounted

Bank discount   the method of discounting used by the chartered banks whereby interest is collected in advance; the amount of money deducted by the bank from the maturity value of a promissory note when discounting the note

Bank discount rate   see Rate of bank discount

Date of discount the date at which a promissory note is bought or sold

Date of issue the date on which a promissory note is made

Date of maturity see Legal due date

Discount see Amount of discount

Discounting the act of buying or selling promissory notes

Discount period the time, in days, from the date of discount to the legal due date

Due date see Legal due date

Face value the sum of money specified on the promissory note

Interest-bearing promissory notes notes which are subject to the rate of interest stated on the note

Interest paid in advance interest based on the maturity value of a loan secured by a promissory note and deducted from the maturity value of the note
Also see Bank discount

Interest period the time, in days, from the date of issue to the legal due date for promissory notes

Issue date see date of issue

Legal due date the date on which the promissory note is to be paid

Maker the party making the promise to pay by signing the promissory note

Maturity value the amount (face value plus interest) which must be paid on the legal due date to honour the note

Non-interest-bearing promissory notes notes which do not require the payment of interest (the maturity value of such notes is the same as their face value)

Payee the party to whom the promise to pay is made

Present value of a promissory note the value of a promissory note at a specified date before the legal due date determined on the basis of a specified rate of interest or rate of discount or the rate money is worth

Proceeds the sum of money for which a promissory note is bought or sold at the date of discount

Promissory note a written promise to pay a specified sum of money after a specified period of time with or without interest as specified

Rate money is worth the prevailing rate of interest

Rate of bank discount a rate used by the chartered banks to collect interest in advance when discounting promissory notes

Rate of discount the rate used to determine the proceeds of a promissory note; the rate may be a simple discount rate or a bank discount rate depending on whether the discounter is a chartered bank or not

Rate of interest the simple annual rate of interest based on the face value

Simple discount the method of discounting promissory notes using the present value approach (simple interest) to determine the proceeds; the amount of discount deducted from the maturity value to find the proceeds when using the simple discount method

Term of a promissory note the time period for which the note was written (in days or months)

Three days of grace the number of days added to the term of a note in Canada to determine the legal due date

12 *Consumer credit—periodic loan repayment plans*

Introduction

Consumer credit is an important factor in the Canadian economic system. Directly or indirectly it affects the everyday lives of most Canadians.

A wide variety of financial intermediaries are involved in providing credit facilities to Canadian consumers. This variety results in different approaches to credit granting and a range of different interest rates charged for the use of credit.

While Consumer Protection Legislation protects the user of credit from abuses, a prudent use of consumer credit requires knowledge on the part of the consumer.

Objectives

Upon completion of this Chapter, you will be able to

1. correctly interpret and apply terminology commonly used by Canadian credit granting institutions;
2. distinguish between the commonly used rates of interest and compute rates of interest for given instalment plans;
3. compute rebates and payoff figures using the sum-of-the-digits method (Rule of 78);
4. compare the cost of credit for different instalment plans;
5. compute the cost of credit and the balance that should appear on a monthly statement for revolving charge accounts;
6. compute interest and balances for demand loans;
7. develop repayment schedules for amortized loans.

12.1 *Basic concepts and computations*

A. *Consumer credit in Canada*

Consumer credit represents funds borrowed by individuals for personal consumption or personal financing purposes. The rapid growth in the amount of outstanding consumer credit in Canada is due to rapid increases in population, employment, incomes and changing spending and savings patterns. This growth is reflected in the rapid development and expansion of the consumer credit industry.

The main sources of consumer credit in Canada are the Chartered Banks, Credit Unions, Trust Companies, Consumer Loan Companies, Sales Finance Companies, Retailers and Department Stores.

Regulation of consumer credit in Canada has been a concern of governments as far back as 1906 when the *Money Lenders Act* was passed. This initial attempt at regulation was followed by the more comprehensive *Small Loans Act* passed in 1939, amended in 1956, but repealed in December 1980. The rapid expansion of consumer credit in recent years has been accompanied by increased attention to the activities of the consumer credit industry by provincial and federal legislative bodies.

Regulation of the industry is a complex issue because of constitutional problems regarding the jurisdiction of the main issues:

(a) the contract between the borrower and the lender which is subject to provincial legislation;

(b) the interest rate which is governed by federal legislation.

Federal legislation essentially has taken the form of requiring disclosure of the cost of credit in dollar terms as well as in terms of the simple annual rate of interest.

While legislation provides some protection for the user of consumer credit the ease with which credit can be obtained from the variety of credit granting institutions makes it important that the user be knowledgeable in a field that so directly affects him.

B. Commonly used terms

The diversity of situations encountered together with the variety of institutions granting cedit to individuals has resulted in a proliferation of terms used in the field. Not surprisingly many of the users have only a vague understanding of the terms used. Some of the more commonly used terms are listed below.

(a) The **cash price** is the amount of cash for which a commodity can be bought.

(b) A **down payment** is a partial cash payment often required when making an instalment purchase.

(c) The **amount financed** is the outstanding balance after deducting any down payment from the cash price.

(d) The **carrying charge** (or **cost of credit** or **cost of financing**) is the total extra money paid for the privilege of buying on credit.

(e) The **amount paid in instalments** is the total sum of money needed to repay the amount financed plus the carrying charge.

(f) A **periodic instalment payment** is the periodic (usually monthly) amount required to repay the total amount to be paid in instalments by a given number of payments.

(g) The **instalment period** is the number of periods (usually months) in which the instalment purchase has to be paid.

C. Instalment plans—basic computations

Example 12.1a A stereo set can be bought for $660 cash; or 25% down with a carrying charge of $99 and equal monthly payments for 22 months. Determine

(i) the down payment;
(ii) the amount financed;
(iii) the total instalment plan cost;
(iv) the monthly instalment payment.

Solution

(i) The down payment = 25% of 660 = (0.25)(660) = $165

(ii) The amount financed = Cash price − Down Payment = 660 − 165 = $495

(iii) The total instalment plan cost = Amount financed + Carrying charge
$$= 495 + 99 = \$594$$

(iv) The monthly payment = Total instalment plan cost ÷ Number of payments
$$= 594 \div 22 = \$27$$

Example 12.1b Terri bought a car priced $6000. She made a down payment of 15% and signed an instalment contract for 30 months including a finance cost of 10% simple interest. Determine the monthly payment

Solution

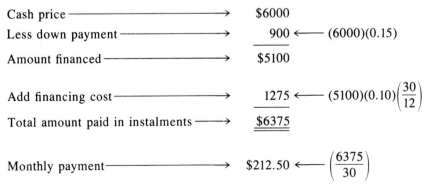

Cash price ⟶	$6000
Less down payment ⟶	900 ⟵ (6000)(0.15)
Amount financed ⟶	$5100
Add financing cost ⟶	1275 ⟵ $(5100)(0.10)\left(\dfrac{30}{12}\right)$
Total amount paid in instalments ⟶	$6375
Monthly payment ⟶	$212.50 ⟵ $\left(\dfrac{6375}{30}\right)$

Example 12.1c   Robin traded his old refrigerator for a new one valued $750. He received a trade-in allowance of $75, made a cash payment of 10% of the value of the refrigerator and agreed to make 20 payments of $34.50. What was the interest cost?

Solution

Cash price ⟶		$750
Less Trade-in allowance ⟶	$75	
Down payment ⟶	75	150
Amount financed ⟶		$600
Amount paid in instalments ⟶		690 ⟵ (34.50)(20)
Interest cost ⟶		$ 90

Exercise 12.1

A.   For each of the following determine

> **(a)** the down payment;
>
> **(b)** the amount financed;
>
> **(c)** the carrying charge;
>
> **(d)** the total amount paid in instalments;
>
> **(e)** the monthly payment.

1. A TV set is advertised by a store for $800.00. The set may be bought on credit for 20% down, a simple interest charge of 11.25% and 16 equal monthly payments.

2. The Westmans bought a refrigerator priced at $720.00 on the instalment plan for 10% down and 20 equal monthly payments. Interest is at the nominal annual rate of 15%.

B.   Answer each of the following

1. Joni financed her Sunflight Holiday valued $1620.00 by paying 30% down and signing a contract requiring 15 equal monthly payments including interest at an annual rate of 18%. What is the monthly payment?

2. Bud's Ski Shop advertises a complete downhill equipment package for $480.00. The package is available on credit for 5% down, a simple interest charge of 8% and 24 equal monthly payments. What is the monthly payment?

3. Laurin traded his old car for a new one priced $5400.00. He received a trade-in allowance of $550.00, made a cash payment of 5% of the balance and agreed to make 36 monthly payments of $157.50 each. What was the cost of financing?

4. Bruce traded his service station's compressor for a new one having a cash price of $2460.00. He made a down payment of 10% of the cash price, received a trade-in allowance of $200.00 and signed a contract requiring 21 monthly payments of $112.50 each. Determine the amount of interest charged.

389

*Consumer
credit–
periodic loan
repayment
plans*

12.2 *Interest on instalment purchases and instalment loans*

A. *Rates of interest*

The cost of financing an instalment purchase or instalment loan is usually stated as a **rate of interest**. Since interest rates may be stated in a variety of ways, some of them misleading, consumer protection legislation requires disclosure of the **true rate of interest** as well as the total amount of interest. While such legislation provides a measure of protection against abuse, in his own best interest the user of consumer credit should be familiar with the two commonly used rates of interest discussed below.

(a) **Nominal rate** The carrying charge is stated as a simple rate of interest based on the original amount financed. As a simple rate of interest it is found by dividing the interest cost (carrying charge) by the product of principal (original amount financed) and time (repayment period in years).

$$\text{NOMINAL RATE} = \frac{\text{CARRYING CHARGE}}{(\text{ORIGINAL AMOUNT FINANCED})(\text{TIME})} \qquad \leftarrow \textit{Formula 12.1}$$

(b) **Effective (or true) rate** Since the nominal rate of interest is based on the original amount financed, it does not allow for the fact that the principal balance is reduced by every payment. It is a deceptive rate as it appears to be low when compared to the true rate of interest which is computed on the unpaid balance.

The effective rate which must be disclosed under consumer protection legislation must allow for the reduction in the principal as the instalment payments are made; that is, it is a rate based on the unpaid balance and may be determined for periodic instalment plans by using the formula below.

$$R = \frac{2NC}{P(n+1)} \qquad \leftarrow \textit{Formula 12.2}$$

R = the effective rate of interest per year;
C = the carrying charge (interest cost);
N = the number of payment periods in one year;
P = the original balance financed;
n = the number of instalment payments;

For instalment plans requiring *monthly* payments, N = 12. In this case 2NC becomes 2(12)(C), that is 24C. Since most periodic instalment plans require monthly payments, the formula used is often shown as

$$R = \frac{24C}{P(n + 1)} \quad \longleftarrow use\ only\ when\ N = 12 \longleftarrow Formula\ \textbf{12.3}$$

B. Effective rate of interest formula for periodic instalment plans derived

The periodic instalment plan formula $R = \frac{2NC}{P(n + 1)}$ may be derived from the simple interest formula $R = \frac{I}{Pt}$ by converting the periodic instalment problem into a simple interest problem with a constant principal as in the following example.

Example 12.2a   A loan of $600 is to be repaid in 5 monthly instalments of $126 each. Determine the effective (true) rate of interest.

Solution

Total amount paid in instalments $\longrightarrow$	$630 $\longleftarrow$	5 times 126
Less Original amount financed $\longrightarrow$	600	
Total interest cost (carrying charge) $\longrightarrow$	$ 30	

Having determined the carrying charge, we may now convert the instalment problem into a simple interest problem by considering the periodic payment needed to repay the original principal.

To repay a debt of $600 in five monthly instalments requires a monthly payment of $120 to just retire the principal without consideration of any interest. Each of the five payments of $120 may now be considered as separate principals with regard to interest.

On the first instalment of $120 interest is owed for 1 month;
on the second instalment of $120 interest is owed for 2 months;
on the third instalment of $120 interest is owed for 3 months;
on the fourth instalment of $120 interest is owed for 4 months;
on the fifth instalment of $120 interest is owed for 5 months;

This means that repaying a loan of $600 in five equal monthly instalments is equivalent to having a loan of $120 for (1 + 2 + 3 + 4 + 5) months; that is, 15 months.

The rate of interest on a $120 loan for 15 months costing $30 (the carrying charge determined previously) may now be computed by using the formula

$$r = \frac{I}{P_1 t_1} = \frac{30}{(120)(\frac{15}{12})} = 0.20 = 20\%.$$

Note The symbol P_1 is used to distinguish the $120 principal repayment from the original loan balance of $600 designated by the symbol P; the symbol t_1 is used to distinguish the 15 interest periods related to the $120 principal repayment from the 5 instalment periods designated by the symbol n in the formula for finding the effective rate of interest.

The rate found by means of the above computations is more readily determined by using the special formula. $C = 30$; $P = 600$; $N = 12$; $n = 5$

$$R = \frac{2NC}{P(n + 1)} = \frac{2(12)(30)}{600(5 + 1)} = \frac{(24)(30)}{(600)(6)} = 0.20 = 20\%$$

Referring back to the two alternate ways of finding the effective rate of interest, note that

(a) $P_1 = 120 = \dfrac{600}{5} = \dfrac{P}{n}$

(b) $t_1 = \dfrac{15}{12} = \dfrac{1 + 2 + 3 + 4 + 5}{12} = \dfrac{(\frac{1}{2})(n)(n + 1)}{\text{Number of Months in one year}}$ ⟵ see Formula 12.6

         ⟵ represented by N

$$= \frac{(\frac{1}{2})(n)(n + 1)}{N}$$

$$= \frac{(n)(n + 1)}{2N}$$

(c) $I = 30 = C$

Substituting in the formula $r = \frac{I}{P_1 t_1}$ we obtain

$$r = \frac{C}{(\frac{P}{n})(\frac{(n)(n + 1)}{2N})}$$ ⟵ replace P_1, t_1 and I as shown above

$$= \frac{C}{\frac{P(n + 1)}{2N}}$$

$$= \left(\frac{C}{1}\right)\left(\frac{2N}{P(n + 1)}\right)$$ ⟵ change the division to a multiplication by inverting $\dfrac{P(n + 1)}{2N}$

$$\boxed{r = \frac{2NC}{P(n + 1)}}$$ ⟵ simplify

Example 12.2b An instalment purchase of $900 is financed by making 25 weekly payments of $38.88 each. Determine the true rate of interest by using

(i) the formula $r = \dfrac{I}{P_1 t_1}$ (as used in Example 12.2a);

(ii) the formula $r = \dfrac{2NC}{P(n + 1)}$.

Solution

Total amount paid in instalments ⟶ $972 ⟵ (25)(38.88)

Less Original amount financed ⟶ 900

Carrying charge (interest) ⟶ $ 72

Original amount financed ⟶ P = 900

Carrying charge ⟶ C = 72

Number of payment periods in one year ⟶ N = 52

Actual number of instalment payments ⟶ n = 25

(i) $I = C = 72$

$$P_1 = \frac{P}{n} = \frac{900}{25} = 36$$

$$t_1 = \frac{1+2+3+4+5+6+7+8+9+10+11+12+13+14+15+16+17+18+19+20+21+22+23+24+25}{\text{Number of weeks in one year}}$$

found more readily by

$$t_1 = \frac{n(n+1)}{2N} = \frac{(25)(25+1)}{(2)(52)} = \frac{(25)(26)}{(2)(52)} = \frac{25}{4} = 6.25$$

$$r = \frac{I}{P_1 t_1} = \frac{72}{(36)(6.25)} = 0.32 = 32\%$$

(ii) Alternatively and more directly

$$R = \frac{2NC}{P(n+1)} = \frac{2(52)(72)}{900(25+1)} = \frac{2(52)(72)}{900(26)} = 0.32 = 32\%$$

C. Computing interest rates

Example 12.2c A TV-set is offered for $960 cash or on the instalment plan for 25% down and 24 monthly payments of $36 each. Determine

(i) the nominal rate of interest;

(ii) the effective (true) rate of interest.

Solution

Cash price ⟶ $960.00

Less Down payment ⟶ 240.00

Original amount financed ⟶ $720.00

Total paid in instalments ⟶ 864.00

Carrying Charge ⟶ $144.00

(i) Nominal rate $= \dfrac{\text{Carrying charge}}{\text{Original amount} \times \text{time}} = \dfrac{144}{(720)(\frac{24}{12})} = 0.10 = 10\%$

(ii) Effective rate $= \dfrac{2NC}{P(n+1)} = \dfrac{(2)(12)(144)}{720(24+1)} = 0.192 = 19.2\%$

Example 12.2d Jim Stone traded his car for a new car priced $7200. He received a trade-in allowance of $1500 and signed an instalment contract to pay the balance and nominal interest at 12% p.a. in 30 equal monthly instalments. Determine

(i) the monthly payment;

(ii) the true rate of interest.

Solution

Cash price ⟶ $7200.00

Less Trade-in allowance ⟶ 1500.00

Original amount financed ⟶ $5700.00

Carrying charge ⟶ 1710.00 ⟵ $(5700)(0.12)\left(\dfrac{30}{12}\right)$

Amount paid in instalments ⟶ $7410.00

(i) Monthly payment $= \dfrac{7410}{30} = \$247.00$

(ii) True rate $= \dfrac{2NC}{P(n+1)} = \dfrac{(2)(12)(1710)}{5700(30+1)} = 0.2322581 = 23.23\%$

Example 12.2e During a clearance sale a set of golf clubs was listed at $400 less 25%. The set could be bought on time for a down payment of 10% and 18 equal monthly instalments at a carrying charge of $43.20. Determine

(i) the monthly payment;

(ii) the nominal rate of interest;

(iii) the true rate of interest.

Solution

Cash price ⟶	$300.00
Less Down payment ⟶	30.00
Amount financed ⟶	$270.00
Carrying charge ⟶	43.20
Amount paid in instalments ⟶	$313.20

(i) Monthly payment $= \dfrac{313.20}{18} = \$17.40$

(ii) Nominal rate $= \dfrac{43.20}{(270)(\frac{18}{12})}$ $0.1066667 = 10.67\%$

(iii) True rate $= \dfrac{2NC}{P(n+1)} = \dfrac{(2)(12)(43.20)}{270(18+1)} = 0.2021053 = 20.21\%$

Exercise 12.2

A. For each of the following determine

  (a) the nominal rate of interest;

  (b) the effective (true) rate of interest.

1. A loan of $940.00 is to be repaid in 21 monthly instalments of $53.25 each.

2. An instalment purchase of $345.00 is financed by making 8 monthly payments of $46.40 each.

3. A principal of $1244.00 is repaid in 36 semi-monthly payments of $39.93 each.

4. An instalment balance of $772.00 is repaid in 48 bi-weekly payments of $18.77 each.

B. Answer each of the following

1. Teli contracted to pay for her Austrian Skitour by a down payment of 20% of the cost of $990.00 and nine equal monthly payments including interest of $95.04.
   Determine **(a)** the monthly payment;

   (b) the true rate of interest.

2. Milos bought radio equipment valued $1250.00. He made a down payment of 16% and borrowed the balance at a nominal rate of 14%. He also agreed to repay the loan in 25 equal monthly payments.

   Determine **(a)** the monthly payment;

   (b) the true rate of interest.

3. During its annual August sale the Kenora Marina sold a sailboat listed at $1280.00 less 20% on credit for 25% down and 15 equal monthly payments including interest at a nominal rate of 10%.

   Determine **(a)** the monthly payment;

   (b) the effective rate of interest.

4. Jerry bought a motorcycle listed at $1440.00 less 12.5% for 15% down and 21 equal monthly payments including $171.36 interest.

   Determine **(a)** the monthly payment;

   (b) the nominal rate of interest;

   (c) the true rate of interest.

12.3 Instalment loans —rebates and payout balances

A. Early payoff of instalment loans

When an instalment loan is paid off early, the principal balance (**payoff figure**) must be determined. The method used to compute the payoff figure requires the determination of the unearned interest included in the outstanding instalment payments which are to be cancelled by the early lump sum payment. The amount of unearned interest is the **rebate** which is deducted from the sum of the outstanding instalment payments to obtain the payoff figure.

The method used to determine the rebate is known as the **Sum-of-the-Digits Method** (often referred to as the **Rule of 78**).

B. The rule of 78

The label *Rule of 78* is accurate when using the Sum-of-the-Digits Method for computing the rebate on any 12-months loan. Under this rule it is assumed that parts of the loan principal are outstanding over the 12-months period.

For the first month .... 12 parts;

for the second month .... 11 parts;

for the third month .... 10 parts;

for the fourth month .... 9 parts;

. .

. .

. .

for the last (12th) month .... 1 part.

The details of using the Rule of 78 for any 12-months loans may be summarized as shown in Table 12.1.

TABLE 12.1 *Details of calculation of rebate for a twelve-months loan by the "rule of 78"*

Month	Digit assigned to month	Number of parts of principal assigned to month	Fraction of interest earned during month	Rebate as a fraction of total interest at the end of the month
first	1	12	$\frac{12}{78}$	$\frac{66}{78}$
second	2	11	$\frac{11}{78}$	$\frac{55}{78}$
third	3	10	$\frac{10}{78}$	$\frac{45}{78}$
fourth	4	9	$\frac{9}{78}$	$\frac{36}{78}$
fifth	5	8	$\frac{8}{78}$	$\frac{28}{78}$
sixth	6	7	$\frac{7}{78}$	$\frac{21}{78}$
seventh	7	6	$\frac{6}{78}$	$\frac{15}{78}$
eighth	8	5	$\frac{5}{78}$	$\frac{10}{78}$
ninth	9	4	$\frac{4}{78}$	$\frac{6}{78}$
tenth	10	3	$\frac{3}{78}$	$\frac{3}{78}$
eleventh	11	2	$\frac{2}{78}$	$\frac{1}{78}$
twelfth	12	1	$\frac{1}{78}$	Nil
Total number of parts		78 ⟵ *Rule of 78*		

Example 12.3a What is the rebate as a fraction of the total loan interest for a 12-months loan repaid in full after

(i) the fourth instalment?   (ii) the ninth instalment?

Solution

(i) The outstanding instalments after the fourth are for the fifth to the twelfth month. The number of parts of principal assigned to these months are 8, 7, 6, 5, 4, 3, 2 and 1 respectively. The sum of $8 + 7 + 6 + 5 + 4 + 3 + 2 + 1$ is 36. Hence the rebate is $\frac{36}{78}$ of the total interest (as indicated in the table).

(ii) The outstanding instalments after the ninth are for the tenth, eleventh and twelfth month. The number of parts assigned to these months are 3, 2 and 1 respectively. The sum of these parts is 6. Hence the rebate is $\frac{6}{78}$ of the total interest (as indicated in the table).

Example 12.3b A loan of $2010 is repaid in twelve monthly instalments of $200 each. What sum of money is needed to pay off the loan after the eighth month?

Solution

Amount to be paid in instalments ⟶ $2400.00 ⟵ (12)(200)

Original amount financed ⟶ 2010.00

Carrying charge ⟶ $ 390.00

Amount to be paid in instalments ⟶ $2400.00

Amount paid in the first eight months ⟶ 1600.00 ⟵ (8)(200)

Balance outstanding ⟶ $ 800.00

The outstanding payments are for	Month 9	Month 10	Month 11	Month 12
The number of parts of principal assigned to these months are	4	3	2	1
The fraction of total interest included in the payments are	$\frac{4}{78}$	$\frac{3}{78}$	$\frac{2}{78}$	$\frac{1}{78}$

The unearned fraction of total interest in the outstanding payments is $\dfrac{4 + 3 + 2 + 1}{78} = \dfrac{10}{78}$ (as per table)

The rebate is $\frac{10}{78}$ of the total interest, that is $(\frac{10}{78})(390) = \underline{\$50.00}$

Balance owed in instalments ⟶ $800.00

Less Rebate ⟶ 50.00

Payoff figure ⟶ $750.00

C. Formula for finding the unearned finance charge (rebate)

In Example 12.3b, the unearned finance charge (rebate) is $(\frac{10}{78})(390) = \$50.00$.

Note The 10 is the sum of the digits of the outstanding (cancelled) payments; the 78 is the sum of the digits of all twelve payments; the 390 is the total financing cost.

This information can be used to obtain a generalized formula for finding the unearned finance charge (rebate).

$$\begin{array}{l} \text{UNEARNED} \\ \text{FINANCE} \\ \text{CHARGE} \end{array} = \dfrac{\begin{array}{c}\text{SUM OF THE DIGITS OF THE}\\ \text{OUTSTANDING PAYMENTS}\end{array}}{\begin{array}{c}\text{SUM OF THE DIGITS OF ALL}\\ \text{PAYMENTS}\end{array}} \times \begin{array}{l}\text{TOTAL}\\ \text{FINANCE}\\ \text{CHARGE}\end{array}$$

⟵ *Formula 12.4*

Example 12.3c An instalment contract requires the repayment of $900.00 plus nominal interest of 13% p.a. in twelve equal monthly instalments. Determine the unearned finance charge (rebate) and the balance (payoff figure)
(i) after 5 months;   (ii) after 9 months.

Solution

Original amount financed ⟶ $900.00

Add Carrying charge ⟶ 117.00 ⟵ $(900)(0.13)\left(\dfrac{12}{12}\right)$

Total to be paid in instalments ⟶ $\underline{\underline{\$1017.00}}$

Monthly payment $= \dfrac{1017}{12} = \$84.75$

(i)   Number of payments outstanding ⟶ 7

Sum of the digits of these payments ⟶ $7+6+5+4+3+2+1 = 28$

Sum of the digits of all payments ⟶ 78

Unearned finance charge ⟶ $42 ⟵ $\dfrac{28}{78}(117)$

Balance owed in instalments ⟶ $593.25 ⟵ $(7)(84.75)$

Rebate ⟶ 42.00

Payoff figure ⟶ $\underline{\underline{\$551.25}}$

(ii)   Number of payments outstanding ⟶ 3

Sum of the digits of these payments ⟶ $3 + 2 + 1 = 6$

Unearned finance charge ⟶ $9.00 ⟵ $\dfrac{6}{78}(117)$

Balance owed in instalments ⟶ $254.25 ⟵ $(3)(84.75)$

Rebate ⟶ 9.00

Payoff figure ⟶ $\underline{\underline{\$245.25}}$

D. Sum-of-the-digits method

The Rule of 78 for 12-months loans can be expanded to cover any other repayment period. The method is then referred to as the **Sum-of-the-Digits Method**. The details of computations are similar to those when using the Rule of 78. The number of parts into which the original principal is divided depends on the term of the loan. Table 12.2 indicates the number of parts assigned to each month for three representative loan terms (12-months, 24-months and 30-months).

TABLE 12.2 *Number of parts assigned to each month for three selected loan terms*

Month	Number of parts of principal assigned to month		
	12-months loan	*24-months loan*	*30-months loan*
1	12	24	30
2	11	23	29
3	10	22	28
.	.	.	.
.	.	.	.
11	2	14	20
12	1	13	19
13		12	18
.		.	.
.		.	.
23		2	8
24		1	7
25			6
.			.
.			.
29			2
30			1
Total	78	300	465

The unearned finance charge (rebate) as a fraction of total interest at the end of any particular month is obtained as

SUM OF THE DIGITS OF THE OUTSTANDING PAYMENTS
SUM OF THE DIGITS OF ALL PAYMENTS

To avoid the addition of the digits, the sum of the digits may be obtained by using the formula for finding the sum of the first *n* digits.

$$\frac{n(n + 1)}{2} \quad \text{where } n \text{ is the highest digit}$$ ⟵ **Formula 12.5**

Example 12.3d Use the formula $\frac{(n)(n+1)}{2}$ to determine the sum of the digits of all payments for

   (i) a 12-months loan; (ii) a 24-months loan; (iii) a 30-months loan.

Solution

(i) For a 12-months loan the highest digit is 12 $\longrightarrow n = 12$

$$\text{the sum-of-the-digits} = \frac{(n)(n+1)}{2} = \frac{(12)(12+1)}{2} = \frac{(12)(13)}{2} = 78$$

(ii) For a 24-months loan the highest digit is 24 $\longrightarrow n = 24$

$$\text{the sum-of-the-digits} = \frac{(n)(n+1)}{2} = \frac{(24)(24+1)}{2} = \frac{(24)(25)}{2} = 300$$

(iii) For a 30-months loan the highest digit is 30 $\longrightarrow n = 30$

$$\text{the sum-of-the-digits} = \frac{(n)(n+1)}{2} = \frac{(30)(30+1)}{2} = \frac{(30)(31)}{2} = 465$$

Example 12.3e Use the formula $\frac{(n)(n+1)}{2}$ to determine the sum-of-the-digits for (i) 7 outstanding payments; (ii) 22 outstanding payments.

Solution

(i) $n = 7$; hence $\dfrac{(n)(n+1)}{2} = \dfrac{(7)(7+1)}{2} = \dfrac{(7)(8)}{2} = 28$

(ii) $n = 22$; hence $\dfrac{(n)(n+1)}{2} = \dfrac{(22)(22+1)}{2} = \dfrac{(22)(23)}{2} = 253$

Example 12.3f Determine the rebate as a fraction of the total interest for

(i) a 21-months loan if 9 payments are outstanding;

(ii) a 36-months loan if 15 payments are outstanding.

Solution

(i) The sum-of-the-digits for 9 outstanding payments is $\dfrac{(9)(9+1)}{2} = 45$;

the sum-of-the-digits for a 21-months loan is $\dfrac{(21)(21+1)}{2} = 231$;

the rebate as a fraction of the total interest $= \dfrac{45}{231}$.

(ii) The sum-of-the-digits for 15 outstanding payments is $\dfrac{(15)(15 + 1)}{2} = 120$;

the sum-of-the-digits for a 36-months loan is $\dfrac{(36)(36 + 1)}{2} = 666$;

the rebate as a fraction of the total interest $= \dfrac{120}{666}$.

Example 12.3g   Mira Sonic bought a stereo system valued $1600. She paid 15% down and contracted to pay the balance and interest at 14% p.a. in 30 monthly instalments. Determine the payoff figure just after she made the 20th instalment payment.

Solution

Cash price $\longrightarrow$ $1600.00

Less Down payment $\longrightarrow$ 240.00

Amount financed $\longrightarrow$ $1360.00

Add Interest cost $\longrightarrow$ 476.00 $\longleftarrow$ $(1360)(0.14)\left(\dfrac{30}{12}\right)$

Amount to be paid in instalments $1836.00

Monthly instalment payment $= \dfrac{1836.00}{30} = \$61.20$

Number of outstanding payments $\longrightarrow$ 10 $\longleftarrow$ $(30 - 20)$

Sum-of-the-digits of the outstanding payments $= \dfrac{(10)(10 + 1)}{2} = 55$

Sum-of-the-digits for a 30-months loan $= \dfrac{(30)(30 + 1)}{2} = 465$

Rebate after 20 payments $= \left(\dfrac{55}{465}\right)(476) = \$56.30$

Balance owed in instalments $\longrightarrow$ $612.00 $\longleftarrow$ $(10)(61.20)$

Less Rebate $\longrightarrow$ 56.30

Payoff figure $\longrightarrow$ $555.70

Example 12.3h   Bart Fast traded his car for a new car valued $8000.00. He received a trade-in allowance of 25%, made a cash payment of $1000.00 and agreed to repay the balance in 48 monthly instalments of $145.00. How much will the payoff figure be if he decides to trade again after making 21 payments?

Solution

Cash price ⟶ $8000.00

Less Trade-in allowance ⟶ $2000.00

Cash payment ⟶ 1000.00 3000.00

Amount financed ⟶ $5000.00

Amount paid in instalments ⟶ $6960.00

Interest cost ⟶ $1960.00

Number of outstanding payments ⟶ 27

Sum-of-the-digits of the oustanding payments $= \dfrac{(27)(27+1)}{2} = 378$

Sum-of-the-digits for a 48-months loan $= \dfrac{(48)(48+1)}{2} = 1176$

Rebate $= \left(\dfrac{378}{1176}\right)(1960.00) = \$630.00$

Balance owed in instalments ⟶ $3915.00 ⟵ (27)(145.00)

Less Rebate ⟶ 630.00

Payoff figure ⟶ $3285.00

Exercise 12.3

A. Determine the rebate as a fraction of the total loan interest using the Sum-of-the-Digits Method for each of the following

1. A 12-months loan
   (a) repaid in full after the fifth instalment;
   (b) if two payments are outstanding.

2. An 18-months loan
   (a) repaid in full after the seventh instalment;
   (b) if four payments are outstanding.

3. A 27-months loan
   (a) repaid in full after the 16th instalment;
   (b) if 14 payments are outstanding.

4. A 42-months loan
   (a) repaid in full after the 36th payment;
   (b) if 18 instalments are outstanding.

B. Answer each of the following

1. A 12-months loan of $1200.00 is repaid in monthly instalments of $116.25 each. What is the payoff figure after nine months?

2. A 36-months loan of $4792.50 is repaid in monthly instalments of $156.25 each. What is the payoff figure after 27 months?

3. Keri Grimm paid 20% down on a fur coat priced $4500.00. He financed the balance and $360 interest over 32 months in equal monthly payments. Determine the payoff figure just after the 24th instalment.

4. Rick bought an outboard motor valued $2400.00. He paid 5% down and financed the balance plus interest at the nominal rate of 8% over 20 equal monthly payments. What sum of money does he need to pay off the loan balance after 15 instalments?

5. You traded your car for a new one valued $5750.00. You received a trade-in allowance of 16%, made a cash payment of $300.00 and financed the balance through equal monthly payments over 40 months with nominal interest of 10%. What is the payoff figure when 10 payments are outstanding?

6. Joe Rite bought a powerboat listed at $7200 less 15%. He made a down payment of 25% and signed an instalment contract requiring 25 equal monthly payments including $688.50 interest. How much money does he need to pay off the contract when 15 payments are outstanding?

12.4   Comparing the cost of credit

A.   Shopping for credit

Consumer credit is available from a variety of institutions offering a variety of credit plans at interest rates which are not directly comparable. It is in the user's interest to shop around for credit and to compare the cost of credit in dollars as well as in terms of the rate of interest.

Example 12.4a   Jim and Jane bought identical home entertainment systems at the same store marked for sale at $1600 less 25%. Jim used the store's instalment plan requiring a 5% down payment and 30 monthly payments of $52 each. Jane also paid 5% down to hold the equipment but borrowed the balance from a trust company at a nominal annual rate of 10% to be repaid in 30 monthly instalments.

 (i) How much did Jane save by borrowing from the trust company?

 (ii) What is the nominal annual rate of interest charged by the store?

(iii) What is the true rate of interest paid   (a) by Jim;   (b) by Jane?

(iv) Using the sum-of-the-digits method, what are the respective payoff figures after 12 payments?

Solution

(i) *Jim's contract*

Cash price	$1200.00	←— (0.75)(1600)
Less Down payment	60.00	←— (0.05)(1200)
Amount financed	$1140.00	
Paid in instalments	1560.00	←—(30)(52)
Interest cost	$ 420.00	

Jane's contract

Cash price	$1200.00	
Less Down payment	60.00	
Amount financed	$1140.00	
Interest cost	285.00	←—$(1140)(0.10)\left(\dfrac{30}{12}\right)$
Paid in instalments	$1425.00	

Monthly instalment payment $= \dfrac{1425}{30} = \$47.50$

Jim's interest cost	$420.00
Less Jane's interest cost	285.00
Amount saved by Jane	$135.00

(ii) $I = 420.00;$ $P = 1140.00;$ $t = \dfrac{30}{12}$

Nominal rate of interest charged by store

$$= \frac{I}{Pt} = \frac{420}{(1140)(\frac{30}{12})} = 0.1473684 = 14.7\%$$

(iii) (a) True rate of interest paid by Jim

$$N = 12; \qquad C = 420.00; \qquad P = 1140.00; \qquad n = 30$$

$$r = \frac{2NC}{P(n+1)} = \frac{(2)(12)(420.00)}{(1140.00)(30+1)} = 0.285229 = 28.52\%$$

(b) True rate of interest paid by Jane

$$N = 12; \qquad C = 285.00; \qquad P = 1140.00; \qquad n = 30$$

$$r = \frac{2NC}{P(n+1)} = \frac{(2)(12)(285.00)}{(1140.00)(30+1)} = 0.1935484 = 19.35\%$$

(iv) Number of outstanding payments $= (30 - 12) = 18$

Sum-of-the-digits of the outstanding payments $= \dfrac{(18)(18 + 1)}{2} = 171$

Sum-of-the-digits of all payments $= \dfrac{(30)(30 + 1)}{2} = 465$

Rebate as a fraction of total interest cost $= \dfrac{171}{465}$

(a) Payoff figure for Jim

Balance owed in instalments $\longrightarrow$ \$936.00 $\longleftarrow$ (18)(52.00)

Rebate $\longrightarrow$ \$154.45 $\longleftarrow$ $\left(\dfrac{171}{465}\right)$(420.00)

Payoff figure after 12 payments $\longrightarrow$ \$781.55

(b) Payoff figure for Jane

Balance owed in instalments $\longrightarrow$ \$855.00 $\longleftarrow$ (18)(47.50)

Rebate $\longrightarrow$ \$104.81 $\longleftarrow$ $\left(\dfrac{171}{465}\right)$(285.00)

Payoff figure after 12 payments $\longrightarrow$ \$750.19

Exercise 12.4

A. Answer each of the following

1. Sean arranged an Hawaiian holiday for \$2200.00 with Coconut Tours. He made a cash payment of 30% and was offered the chance to finance the balance plus \$308.00 interest over 15 months in equal monthly payments. Upon discussion with the manager of his Credit Union he borrowed the balance from the Credit Union over the same period of time repaying the loan in blended monthly payments including interest at a nominal rate of 8%.

   (a) How much did Sean save by borrowing from the Credit Union?

   (b) What is the nominal rate of interest charged by Coconut Tours?

   (c) What is the true rate of interest charged by the Coconut Tours?

   (d) What is the true rate of interest charged by the Credit Union?

2. Ron Baka wants to purchase a motorcycle for \$1440.00. He has the 20% down payment and can finance the balance through Suzuki Motors by making 18 monthly payments of \$74.56 each. Alternatively he can borrow the balance from his bank for the same period of time and repay the loan in equal monthly payments including interest at the nominal rate of 9%.

   (a) How much will Ron save by borrowing from the bank?

(b) What is the nominal rate of interest charged by Suzuki Motors?

(c) What is the effective rate of interest charged by Suzuki Motors?

(d) What is the effective rate of interest charged by the bank?

B. Answer each of the following

1. Smith and Stone signed agreements to purchase equally priced cars from Wang Motors. Each made the required cash payment of 10% of the purchase price of $6400.00. Smith financed the balance through Wang Motors over 36 months agreeing to monthly payments of $217.60 each. Stone borrowed the balance from the local branch of the Royal Trust Company to be repaid in 36 equal monthly payments including interest at the nominal rate of 8%.

(a) How much did Stone save by borrowing from Royal Trust?

(b) What is the nominal rate of interest charged by Wang Motors?

(c) What is the true rate of interest paid by Smith?

(d) What is the true rate of interest paid by Stone?

(e) Using the Sum-of-the-Digits Method, what is Smith's payoff figure if 9 payments are outstanding?

(f) Using the Sum-of-the-Digits Method, what is Stone's payoff figure after 24 payments?

2. Peter bought a sailboat worth $2880.00 for 15% down and financed the balance through Marine Finance Corporation in 21 monthly payments of $144.10 each. Paul purchased an equally priced powerboat, also paid 15% down, but negotiated a loan for the balance through his Credit Union. He agreed to repay the loan plus interest of $353.40 in 21 equal monthly payments.

(a) How much did Paul save by borrowing from the Credit Union?

(b) What is the nominal rate of interest charged by Marine Finance?

(c) What is the true rate of interest paid by Peter?

(d) What is the true rate of interest charged by the Credit Union?

(e) What is Peter's payoff figure if 7 payments are outstanding?

(f) What is Peter's payoff figure after 16 payments?

12.5 Charge Accounts

A. Credit cards

Credit cards are used to buy goods and services on credit. Presentation of a credit card indicates that the authorized holder has a *revolving* charge account with the issuer—such as a department store, chain store, oil company or bank credit system. The credit card represents an account that is portable from department to department, from one store location to another or between the various retail outlets associated with a particular credit card system.

B. Carrying charges

Most credit card accounts are one-month accounts with optional payment plans. Purchases are charged to the account and each month a statement of the account is sent to the cardholder. If the account is paid in full before the next statement date no finance charges are added to the account. If the account is not paid in full, the cardholder is required to pay a minimum amount shown on the statement and a carrying charge, usually based on the previous unpaid balance, is added to the account. As a rule, interest is not charged on purchases made during the current month. However, in the case of bank charge accounts, if the credit card is used to borrow money or to cover chequing account overdrafts the carrying charge (interest) is computed by the bank card system from the date of the cash advance.

No uniform method for computing the carrying charge exists. The exact details of computing the carrying charge depends on the conditions established by the issuer of the credit card. These conditions are stated on the monthly statement.

Example 12.5a Some of the information shown on the most current monthly statement received by you from the Hudson's Bay Company was as follows: Previous balance, $712.14; Purchases, $73.57; Payment, $43.16. The Bay adds a charge for cost of credit monthly based on the previous month's balance at the rate of 21% per annum. Determine

  (i) the cost of credit shown;   (ii) the new balance;

(iii) the cost of credit that will appear on next month's statement.

Solution

  (i) The monthly rate of interest is $\longrightarrow$ $1.75\% \longleftarrow \dfrac{21\%}{12}$

        Cost of credit $\longrightarrow$ $\$12.46 \longleftarrow (0.0175)(712.14)$

  (ii) Previous balance $\longrightarrow$ $\$712.14$

      Add Purchases $\longrightarrow \$73.57$

          Cost of credit $\longrightarrow$ 12.46 86.03

                                  $\$798.17$

      Less Payment $\longrightarrow$ 43.16

        New balance $\longrightarrow$ $\underline{\underline{\$755.01}}$

(iii) Cost of credit (next month) $\longrightarrow$ $\$13.21 \longleftarrow (0.0175)(755.01)$

Example 12.5b Based on the T. Baton Company account statement (Figure 12.1) determine

  (i) the service charge (at the date of the statement Baton's charged interest at 21% p.a. based on the previous balance);

(ii) the total charges;

(iii) the total credits;

(iv) the new balance;

(v) the service charge that will appear on next month's statement.

FIGURE 12.1 *T. Baton account statement*

ANY ENQUIRIES CONCERNING YOUR ACCOUNT SHOULD BE DIRECTED TO	BATON'S CREDIT BRANCH 413 P.O. BOX 4000, TORONTO, ONTARIO M5W 1S2 (416)591-2232			
ACCOUNT NUMBER 768-346-44	**CREDIT AVAILABLE** 2,848.70	**LINE OF CREDIT** 3,000.00		**DUE DATE** OCT. 14/85
STATEMENT DATE SEP. 14/85	**PREVIOUS BALANCE** 79.02 +	**TOTAL CHARGES** ? −	**TOTAL CREDITS** ? =	**NEW BALANCE** ?	**PAYMENT REQUIRED** .00

DATE	REFERENCE	GENERAL DESCRIPTION	AMOUNT
		CREDITS	
AUG. 2	S218016 BOX 4000	PAYMENT THANK YOU	11.65CR
		CHARGES	
AUG.22	E108651 BTN CTR 228	7 - 16 BOYS WEAR	38.07
SEP. 6	D405769 BTN CTR 79	7 - 14 GIRLS WEAR	19.98
SEP. 6	D405769 BTR CTR 214	BRASSIERES	22.90
SEP.14		SALES TAX	1.60
		SERVICE CHARGE	?

YOUR PAYMENT MUST REACH US BY THE DUE DATE IN ORDER TO
APPEAR IN YOUR NEXT STATEMENT. PLEASE ALLOW FIVE DAYS FOR
MAILING AND PROCESSING TIME - OR YOU MAY MAKE YOUR PAYMENT
AT ANY BATON STORE UP TO THE DUE DATE ON THIS STATEMENT.

PLEASE SEE REVERSE SIDE FOR IMPORTANT INFORMATION   **BATON'S**

Solution

(i) The monthly rate of interest $= \frac{21.00\%}{12} = 1.75\% = 0.0175$
the previous balance as per statement $= \$79.02$
the service charge $= (0.0175)(79.02) = \$1.38$

(ii) The total charges are
$38.07 + 19.98 + 22.90 + 1.60 + 1.38 = \$83.93$

(iii) The total credits $= \$11.65$

(iv) The new balance $=$ Previous balance $+$ Charges $-$ Credits
$= 79.02 + 83.93 - 11.65 = \$151.30$

(v) Next month's service charge will $= (0.0175)(151.30) = \$2.65$

Exercise 12.5

A. For each of the following statements determine

    (a) the finance charge shown;
    (b) the new balance;
    (c) the finance charge that will appear on next month's statement

1. June's Simpsons-Sears statement for July contained the following information: Previous balance, $156.22; Purchases, $64.78; Purchases returns, $15.25; Payment received, $22.50. Simpsons-Sears added a finance charge based on the previous month's balance at the rate of 21% per annum.

2. Bill's Gulf Oil Company statement for October showed six gasoline purchases totalling $84.70 and two payments of $24.00 and $36.00 respectively. The previous balance was $372.60. At the time of the statement Gulf Oil added a service charge of 18% per annum based on the previous month's balance.

B. For each of the following excerpts from monthly charge account statements determine

    (a) the service charge;
    (b) the total charges;
    (c) the total credits;
    (d) the new balance;
    (e) the service charge that will appear on next month's statement.

1.

Statement date	Previous balance	Total charges	Total credits	New balance
July 14/85	566.22	?	?	?

Date	Reference	General Description	Amount
		Credits	
Jul 4	8513 Box 2000	Payment—Thank you	56.22 CR
Jul 9	C066 Square 180	Return—Hobbies and Crafts	7.00 CR
Jul 9	C066 Square 180	Return—Sales Tax	.49 CR
		Charges	
Jun 22	D267 Centre 245	Pre School Toys	15.99
Jun 22	D267 Centre 245	Pre School Toys	19.99
Jun 22	D267 Centre 245	Hobbies & Crafts	24.99
Jun 22	D267	Sales Tax	4.27
Jun 29	G310 York 056	Sportswear	63.95
Jun 29	G310	Sales Tax	4.48
Jul 14		Service Charge	?

The current credit service charge is 21% per annum based on the previous month's balance.

2.

Date	Dept.	Reference	Description	Additions	Deductions
Sep 13	420	823-1045	Girls' Wear 7-14	24.99	
Sep 14		777-0013	Returned Cheque	32.86	
Sep 22	636	821-2745	Food Prep/Housewares	148.72	
Sep 22	132	831-1741	Ladies Sportswear	12.36	
Oct 5		028-2867	Payment—Thank You		32.09
Oct 6	277	833-1894	Fabrics	13.50	
Oct 10	277	833-1894	Return—Fabrics		5.90

Statement date	Previous balance	Cost of credit	Payments credits	Purchases charges	New balance
Oct 11	1588.92	?	?	?	?

A charge for cost of credit will be added to your account each month based on your previous month's balance and is calculated at the rate of 24% per annum.

12.6 Demand loans

A. Nature of demand loans

When borrowing on a *demand* note, the borrower receives the full face value of the note. The lender may demand payment of the loan in full or in part at any time. Conversely, the borrower may repay all of the loan or any part at any time without notice and without interest penalty. Interest, based on the unpaid balance, is usually payable monthly. The interest rate on such loans is normally not fixed for the duration of the loan but fluctuates with market conditions and thus the total interest cost cannot be predicted with certainty.

B. Examples

Example 12.6a Penny Rose borrowed $1200.00 from her bank on a demand note. She agreed to repay the loan in six equal monthly instalments and also authorized the bank to collect interest monthly from her bank account at 15% p.a. calculated on the unpaid balance. What will the loan cost?

Solution

$$\text{Monthly payment of principal} = \frac{1200.00}{6} = \$200.00$$

$$\text{Monthly rate of interest} = \frac{15\%}{12} = 1.25\%$$

Month	Loan amount owing during month	Interest collected for month
1	$1200.00 ⟵ Original	$15.00 ⟵ (1200)(0.0125)
2	$1000.00 ⟵ 1200 - 200	$12.50 ⟵ (1000)(0.0125)
3	$ 800.00 ⟵ 1000 - 200	$10.00 ⟵ (800)(0.0125)
4	$ 600.00 ⟵ 800 - 200	$ 7.50 ⟵ (600)(0.0125)
5	$ 400.00 ⟵ 600 - 200	$ 5.00 ⟵ (400)(0.0125)
6	$ 200.00 ⟵ 400 - 200	$ 2.50 ⟵ (200)(0.0125)

Total interest cost ⟶ $52.50

411

*Consumer
credit–
periodic loan
repayment
plans*

Example 12.6b On August 17 Sheridan Toy Company borrowed $30 000.00 from Peel Credit Union on a demand note to finance its inventory. Interest on the loan, calculated on the daily balance, is charged against the borrower's current account on the 17th of each month while the loan is in force. A payment of $5000.00 was made on September 24, a further payment of $10 000.00 on October 20 and the balance was paid on December 10. The interest on demand loans on August 17 was 12% p.a. The rate was changed to 13% effective October 1, to 14.5% effective November 1 and to 14% effective December 1. Determine the cost of financing the loan.

Solution

Payment Date	Interest period	Principal	Rate	Amount of interest due
Sept. 17	Aug. 17 - Sept. 17	$30000.00	12.0%	$305.75 ⟵ $(30000)(0.12)(\frac{31}{365})$
Oct. 17	Sept. 17 - Sept. 24	$30000.00	12.0%	$ 69.04 ⟵ $(30000)(0.12)(\frac{7}{365})$
	Sept. 24. - Sept. 30	$25000.00	12.0%	49.32 ⟵ $(25000)(0.12)(\frac{6}{365})$
	Sept. 30 - Oct. 17	$25000.00	13.0%	151.37 ⟵ $(25000)(0.13)(\frac{17}{365})$
				$269.73
Nov. 17	Oct. 17 - Oct. 20	$25000.00	13.0%	$ 26.71 ⟵ $(25000)(0.13)(\frac{3}{365})$
	Oct. 20 - Oct. 31	$15000.00	13.0%	58.77 ⟵ $(15000)(0.13)(\frac{11}{365})$
	Oct. 31 - Nov. 17	$15000.00	14.5%	101.30 ⟵ $(15000)(0.145)(\frac{17}{365})$
				$186.78
Dec. 10	Nov. 17 - Nov. 30	$15000.00	14.5%	$ 77.47 ⟵ $(15000)(0.145)(\frac{13}{365})$
	Nov. 30 - Dec. 10	$15000.00	14.0%	57.53 ⟵ $(15000)(0.14)(\frac{10}{365})$
				$135.00

Total Cost of Financing ⟶ $897.26

C. Partial payments

Demand loans and debts of a similar nature are sometimes paid off by a series of **partial payments**. The commonly used approach to dealing with this type of loan repayment, referred to as **Declining Balance Method**, requires that each partial payment is first applied to pay the accumulated interest. Any remainder is then used to reduce the outstanding principal. Thus, interest is always calculated on the unpaid balance and the new unpaid balance is determined after each partial payment.

The following step-by-step procedure may be used in dealing with such problems.

(a) Compute the interest due to the date of the partial payment.

(b) Compare the interest due computed in (a) with the partial payment received and do (c) if the partial payment is greater than the interest due or do (d) if the partial payment is less than the interest due.

(c) *Partial payment greater than interest due*

   (i) Deduct the interest due from the partial payment.

   (ii) Deduct the remainder in (i) from the principal balance to obtain the new unpaid balance.

(d) *Partial payment less than interest due*

   In this case, the partial payment is not large enough to cover the interest due.

   (i) Deduct the partial payment from the interest due to determine the unpaid interest due at the date of the principal payment.

   (ii) Keep a record of this balance and apply any future partial payments to this unpaid interest first.

Example 12.6c On April 20 Bruce borrowed $4000.00 at 13% on a note requiring payment of principal and interest on demand. Bruce paid $600.00 on May 10 and $1200.00 on July 15. What payment is required on September 30 to pay the note in full?

Solution

April 20

Original Loan Balance ⟶ $4000.00

May 10

Deduct

First partial payment ⟶ $ 600.00

Less interest
April 20 - May 10 ⟶ 28.49   ⟵ $(4000.00)(0.13)\left(\dfrac{20}{365}\right)$

571.51

Unpaid balance ⟶ $3428.49

July 15

Deduct

413

*Consumer
credit–
periodic loan
repayment
plans*

Second partial payment ⟶ $1200.00

Less interest
May 10 - July 15 ⟶ 80.59   ⟵ $(3428.49)(0.13)\left(\dfrac{66}{365}\right)$

1119.41

Unpaid balance ⟶ $2309.08

Sept. 30

Add

Interest
July 15 - Sept. 30 ⟶ 63.33 ⟵ $(2309.08)(0.13)\left(\dfrac{77}{365}\right)$

Payment required to pay
the note in full ⟶ $2372.41

Example 12.6d   Provincial Bank lent $20 000.00 to the owner of the Purple Pelican on April 1 for commercial improvements. The loan was secured by a demand note subject to a variable rate of interest which was 12% on April 1. The rate of interest was raised to 14% effective August 1 and to 16% effective November 1. Partial payments, applied to the loan by the Declining Balance Method, were made as follows: June 10, $1000.00; September 20, $500.00; November 15, $1200.00. How much interest is due to the Credit Union on December 31?

Solution

April 1
Original loan balance ⟶ $20000.00

June 10
Deduct

First partial payment ⟶ $1000.00

Less Interest
April 1 - June 10 ⟶ 460.27   ⟵ $(20000.00)(0.12)\left(\dfrac{70}{365}\right)$

539.73

Unpaid loan balance ⟶ $19460.27

Sept. 20
Deduct

    Second partial payment → $ 500.00

    Less Interest
      June 10 - Sept. 20
    June 10 - July 31——→ $326.29   ←—— $(19460.27)(0.12)(\frac{51}{365})$
    July 31 - Sept 20——→ 380.67   706.96   ←—— $(19460.27)(0.14)(\frac{51}{365})$

Unpaid interest to Sept. 20 → $ 206.96

Unpaid loan balance ————————→ $19460.27

Nov. 15
    Third partial payment——→ $1200.00
    Less Unpaid interest
    to Sept 20   → $206.96   ←—— (see above)
    Sept 20 - Oct 31 → 306.03   ←—— $(19460.27)(0.14)(\frac{41}{365})$
    Oct 31 - Nov 15 → 127.96   ←—— $(19460.27)(0.16)(\frac{15}{365})$

                      640.95

                            559.05

Unpaid loan balance ————————→ $18901.22
Dec. 31
Interest due Nov 15 - Dec 31 → $381.13 ←————————$(18901.22)(0.16)(\frac{46}{365})$

Exercise 12.6

A. Determine the total interest cost for each of the following loans.

    1. Ted borrowed $1500.00 from his bank secured by a demand note. He agreed to repay the loan in five equal monthly instalments and authorized the bank to collect the interest monthly from his bank account at 16.5% per annum calculated on the unpaid balance.

    2. Jamie borrowed $900.00 from her Credit Union. The line of credit agreement provided for repayment of the loan in four equal monthly payments plus interest at 19% per annum calculated on the unpaid balance.

    3. Erindale Automotive borrowed $8000.00 from the Bank of Montreal on a demand note on May 10. Interest on the loan, calculated on the daily balance, is charged to Erindale's current account on the 10th of each month. Erindale made a payment of $2000.00 on July 20, a payment of $3000.00 on September 30 and repaid the balance on December 1. The rate of interest on the loan on May 10 was 18% per annum. The rate was changed to 19.5% on August 1 and to 18.5% on October 1.

4. The Tomac Swim Club arranged short-term financing of $12 500.00 on July 20 with the Bank of Commerce and secured the loan with a demand note. The club repaid the loan by payments of $6000.00 on September 15, $3000.00 on November 10 and the balance on December 30. Interest, calculated on the daily balance and charged to the club s current account on the last day of each month, was at 15.5% per annum on July 20. The rate was changed to 14.5% effective September 1 and to 15% effective December 1.

B. Use the *Declining Balance Method* to answer each of the following.

1. A loan of $6000.00 made at 16% per annum on March 10 is repaid in full on November 15. A payment of $2000.00 was made on June 30 and of $2500.00 on September 5. What was the final payment?

2. D. Slipp borrowed $15 000.00 on August 12. He paid $6000.00 on November 1, $5000.00 on December 15 and the balance on February 20. The rate of interest on the loan was 20.5%. How much did he pay on February 20?

3. The Continental Bank made a loan of $20 000.00 on March 25 to Dr. Hirsch to purchase equipment for his office. The loan was secured by a demand loan subject to a variable rate of interest which was 14% on March 25. Subsequently the rate of interest was raised to 15.5% effective July 1 and to 16.5% effective September 1. Dr. Hirsch made partial payments on the loan as follows: $600.00 on May 15; $800.00 on June 30; and $600.00 on October 10. The terms of the note require payment of any accrued interest on October 31. How much must Dr. Hirsch pay on October 31?

4. Dirk Ward borrowed $12 000.00 for investment purposes on May 10 on a demand note providing for a variable rate of interest and payment of any accrued interest on December 31. He paid $300.00 on June 25, $350 on September 20 and $400.00 on November 5. How much is the accrued interest on December 31 if the rate of interest was 19.5% on May 10, 18% effective August 1 and 16.5% effective November 1?

12.7 *Loan repayment schedules*

A. *Purpose*

In the case of loans repaid in fixed instalments (often referred to as **blended payment**) the constant periodic payment is first applied to pay the accumulated interest. The remainder of the payment is then used to reduce the unpaid balance of principal.

While lenders are obliged to disclose to the borrower the total cost of borrowing as well as the interest rate (see FIGURE 12.2) a detailed statement of the cost of borrowing as well as the effect of the periodic payments on the principal may be obtained by constructing a loan repayment schedule, often referred to as an amortization schedule.

415

Consumer
credit–
periodic loan
repayment
plans

FIGURE 12.2 *Statement of disclosure*

STATEMENT OF DISCLOSURE

(COST OF LOAN AND ANNUAL INTEREST RATE)   **PURSUANT TO THE CONSUMER PROTECTION ACT**

Name of Credit Union _____ *SHERIDAN* _____ Account No. _*2000*___

1) Balance of existing loan (if any) $ *2000·00*

4) Cost of Borrowing expressed in dollars and cents
(Interest calculated on full amount of loan (Item 3) $ *2604·00*

2) Add new amount loaned $ *4000·00*

5) Annual Interest Rate charged (calculated in
accordance with the Consumer Protection Act) ___*15·0*___ %

3) Full amount of loan $ *6000·00*

6) If any charge is made to the borrower in addition to interest herein noted, it must be disclosed here. $ _____
(Description) ....
Frequency of Instalments *60 MONTHS* Amount of Instalments $ *143·40* _____ First Instalment due_____ 19__

I, the undersigned, acknowledge receipt of this statement of cost of loan and annual interest rate, prior to the advance of the credit.

DATE _____   X..
COMPLETE IN DUPLICATE   SIGNATURE OF BORROWER
  Original to Borrnwer.   NOTE: Where more than one maker or co-maker, separate Disclosure Forms should be signed for individually.

Courtesy Peel Sheridan Dufferin Educational Credit Union Limited

The information usually contained in such a schedule includes

(a) the payment number or payment date;

(b) the amount paid at each payment date;

(c) the interest paid by each payment;

(d) the principal repaid by each payment;

(e) the unpaid loan balance after each payment.

A possible design for such schedules is provided in Figure 12.3 and the same design is used in the solution to Example 12.7a.

FIGURE 12.3 *Basic design of a loan repayment schedule*

①	②	③	④	⑤	⑥
Payment number	*Balance before payment*	*Amount paid*	*Interest paid*	*Principal repaid*	*Balance after payment*

B. Construction of loan repayment schedules illustrated

Example 12.7a You borrowed $1600.00 from Sheridan Credit Union at 15% p.a. and agreed to repay the loan in monthly instalments of $300.00 each, such payments to cover interest due and repayment of principal. Use the design shown in Figure 12.3 to construct a complete repayment schedule including the totalling of Columns ③, ④ and ⑤ ("Amount paid", "Interest paid" and "Principal repaid").

Solution

See *Figure* 12.4 and the *explanatory notes* that follow.

Explanatory Notes

(1) The Amount Paid shown in column ③ is the agreed upon monthly payment of $300.00.

(2) The Interest Paid shown in column ④ is at 15% per annum, converted into a periodic (monthly) rate of $\frac{15\%}{12}$ (1.25% per month) to facilitate the computation of the monthly amount of interest paid. (See notes (6) and (9)).

FIGURE 12.4 *Loan repayment schedule for example 12.7a*

①	②	③	④	⑤	⑥
Payment number	Balance before payment	Amount paid (1)	Interest paid (2)	Principal repaid (3)	Balance after payment (4)
0					1600.00(5)
1	1600.00	300.00	20.00 (6)	280.00(7)	1320.00(8)
2	1320.00	300.00	16.50 (9)	283.50(10)	1036.50(11)
3	1036.50	300.00	12.96	287.04	749.46
4	749.46	300.00	9.37	290.63	458.83
5	458.82	300.00	5.74	294.26	164.57(12)
6	164.55	166.63(15)	2.06(14)	164.57(13)	–.– –
Totals (16)		1666.63(18)	66.63(19)	1600.00(17)	

(3) The amount of Principal repaid each month shown in column ⑤ is found by subtracting the Interest paid for the month (column ④) from the Amount paid for the month (column ③). (See notes (7) and (10)).

(4) The Balance after payment for a month shown in column ⑥ is found by subtracting the Principal repaid for the month (column ⑤) from the balance before payment for the month (column ②) OR from the previous Balance after payment figure (column ⑥). (See notes (8) and (11)).

(5) The original loan balance of $1600.00 is introduced as the starting amount for the schedule and is the only amount shown in Line 0.

(6) Interest paid in Payment number 1
= 1.25% of 1600.00 = (0.0125)(1600.00) = $20.00

(7) Principal repaid by Payment number 1
= 300.00 − 20.00 = $280.00

(8) Balance after payment for Payment number 1
= 1600.00 − 280.00 = $1320.00

(9) Interest paid in Payment number 2
= 1.25% of 1320.00 = (0.0125)(1320.00) = $16.50

(10) Principal repaid by Payment number 2
= 300.00 − 16.50 = $283.50

(11) Balance after payment for Payment number 2
= 1320.00 − 283.50 = $1036.50

(12) The Balance after payment for Payment number 5 of $164.57 is smaller than the regular monthly payment of $300.00. Hence the next payment need only be sufficient to pay the outstanding balance of $164.57 plus the interest due. (See notes (13), (14) and (15)).

(13) Principal repaid in Payment number 6 must be $164.57 to pay off the outstanding loan balance.

(14) Interest paid in Payment number 6 is the interest due on $164.57 = 1.25% of 164.57 = (0.0125) (164.57) = $2.06.

(15) Amount paid in Payment number 6 = 164.57 + 2.06 = $166.63.

(16) The Totals of columns ③, ④ and ⑤ serve as a check of the arithmetic accuracy of the repayment schedule. (See notes (17), (18) and (19)).

(17) Principal repaid, the total of column ⑤, must equal the original loan balance of $1600.00.

(18) Amount paid, the total of column ③, must equal the total of all the payments made (5 payments of $300.00 each plus the final payment of $166.63).

(19) Interest paid, the total of column ④, must be the difference between the totals of columns ③ and ⑤ = 1666.63 − 1600.00 = $66.63.

C. Computer application 2—Loan repayment schedule

Computers are ideally suited for the construction of repayment schedules because of the iterative nature of the mathematical processes used in developing the schedules.

Program 2—Loan repayment schedule—provides a computer solution similar to Figure 12.4 (see Appendix p. 845).

Exercise 12.7

A. Use the design shown in Figure 12.3 to construct a complete repayment schedule including the totalling of the *Amount paid, Interest paid* and *Principal Repaid* columns for each of the following loans.

1. Carla borrowed $1200.00 from the Royal Bank at 16.5% per annum calculated on the monthly unpaid balance. She agreed to repay the loan in blended payments of $180.00 per month.

2. Julio borrowed $900.00 from Sheridan Credit Union at 15% per annum calculated on the daily balance on March 15. He gave the Credit Union six cheques for $135.00 dated the 15th of each of the next six months starting April 15 and a cheque dated October 15 for the remaining balance to cover payment of interest and repayment of principal.

Review exercise

1. Laird offers a set of appliances for $1680 cash. The appliances may be bought on credit for 10% down and 30 equal monthly payments including interest at the nominal annual rate of 14%. Determine

   (a) the down payment;

   (b) the amount financed;

   (c) the cost of financing;

   (d) the total amount paid in instalments;

   (e) the monthly payments;

   (f) the true rate of interest.

2. George traded his pickup truck for a new one valued $9400. He received a trade-in allowance of one-quarter of the purchase price, made a cash payment of 16% of the remaining balance and financed the remainder by monthly payments of $268.70 for 27 months.

   (a) What was the cost of financing?

   (b) What was the nominal annual rate of interest?

   (c) What was the effective rate of interest?

3. Gina bought a dining room suite priced at $1320.00 on credit. She paid 15% down and agreed to pay the balance in 20 equal monthly payments including interest at a nominal rate of 10% per annum. What is the monthly payment?

4. The Bad Guy Appliance Store offers a set of home appliances for $1750.00 less 20% for 12.5% down and 21 monthly payments of $71.50 each.

   Determine (a) the nominal rate of interest;
                      (b) the true rate of interest.

5. Ken purchased tools listed for $1260 less $16\frac{2}{3}$%, 10% on credit and agreed to pay for the tools in eight equal monthly instalments including $113.40 interest.

   (a) How much is the carrying charge?

   (b) How much is the monthly payment?

   (c) What is the nominal annual rate of interest?

   (d) What is the true rate of interest?

6. Determine the rebate as a fraction of the total loan interest using the Sum-of-the-Digits Method for

   (a) a 12-month loan repaid in full after eight payments;
   (b) a 30-month loan if eight payments remain outstanding.

7. A 21-months loan of $2500.00 is repaid in monthly instalments of $139.66 each. What is the payoff figure after twelve months?

8. Gillian bought a furcoat for $7500.00. She paid 20% down and financed the balance over twenty-four equal monthly payments including interest at the nominal annual rate of 12%. What is the payoff figure when seven payments remain outstanding?

9. Pierre bought a car for $7250.00. He received a trade-in allowance of 16% and made a cash payment of $450.00. He financed the balance over 48 months in equal monthly payments including interest at the nominal rate of 7.5% per annum. What is the payoff figure on the loan after 27 payments?

10. Joni bought a furcoat worth $4650.00. She paid 20% down and decided to finance the balance. The store offered financing in equal monthly payments over 30 months including a flat rate charge of 30%. Joni decided to shop around for credit and obtained a loan for the balance from her bank. She agreed to repay the loan in 30 monthly payments of $150.45 each.

    (a) How much did Joni save by borrowing from the bank?

    (b) What is the nominal rate of interest charged by the store?

    (c) What is the effective rate of interest charged by the store?

    (d) What is the true rate of interest charged by the bank?

    (e) What is the payoff figure on the bank loan after 18 payments?

    (f) What is the payoff figure on the bank loan if 7 payments are outstanding?

11. The Adams and the Fords bought identical living room suites from Turin Furniture for $4500.00. The Adams financed the purchase through the credit plan offered by

the furniture store over three years by making equal monthly payments including nominal annual interest of 15%. The Fords borrowed the money from their Credit Union repaying the loan in equal monthly payments of $160.44 over three years.

(a) How much did the Fords save by borrowing from the Credit Union?

(b) What is the true rate of interest paid
   (i) by the Adams?
   (ii) by the Fords?

(c) Using the Sum-of-the-Digits Method, what is the payoff figure
   (i) for the Fords after eighteen months?
   (ii) for the Adams when nine payments remain outstanding?

12. Tryman borrowed $10 000 on March 10 on a demand note. The loan was repaid by payments of $3000 on June 20, $4000 on August 31 and the balance on November 15. Interest, calculated on the daily balance and charged to Tryman's current account on the last day of each month, was at 19% on March 10 but was changed to 20% effective June 1 and to 18% effective October 1. How much did the loan cost?

13. Quick Print Press borrowed $20 000 from the Provincial Bank on May 25 at 17.5% and secured the loan by signing a promissory note subject to a variable rate of interest. Quick Print made partial payments of $5000 on July 10 and $8000 on September 15. The rate of interest was increased to 18% effective August 1 and to 18.5% effective October 1. What payment must be made on October 31 if under the terms of the loan agreement, any interest accrued as of October 31 is to be paid on October 31?

14. You borrowed $3000 at 18% per annum calculated on the unpaid monthly balance and agreed to repay the principal together with interest in monthly payments of $500 each. Construct a complete repayment schedule.

Self-test

1. A bedroom suite costs $972.80 cash; or 25% down, a carrying charge of $115.20 and the balance in 22 monthly instalments. What is the monthly payment?

2. Rob bought a refrigerator for $1792.00 requiring a down payment of 25% and 32 monthly payments of $48.00. What is the carrying charge?

3. You bought a fur coat for $1105.92 requiring a down payment of $16\frac{2}{3}$% and 37 monthly payments of $28.80. What is the nominal rate of interest (correct to the nearest 1/10 of 1%)?

4. The cash price of an automobile is $14 652.00. The automobile may be bought on the instalment plan for $33\frac{1}{3}$% down and 42 monthly payments which include a carrying charge at a nominal rate of 6%. What is the true rate of interest (correct to the nearest 1/10 of 1%)?

5. A refrigerator costs $999.00 cash; or 20% down, a carrying charge of $108.00 and the balance in 42 monthly instalments. How much is the payout figure when 8 payments remain outstanding?

6. The cash price of a colour T.V. set is $651.00. The colour T.V. set may be bought on the instalment plan for 20% down and 35 monthly payments which include a carrying charge at a nominal rate of 18%. How much is the payout figure after 10 payments?

7. Ted received a statement for the current month from the T. Baton Company containing the following information: Previous balance, $842.50; Purchases, $98.60; Purchase returns, $15.40; Payment received, $48.00. The T. Baton Company added a service charge of 21% per annum based on the previous month's balance.
Determine **(a)** the service charge shown on the statement;
          (b) the new balance shown on the statement;
          (c) the service charge that will appear on next month's statement.

8. The owner of Jane's Boutique borrowed $6000.00 from Halton Community Credit Union on June 5. The loan was secured by a demand note with interest calculated on the daily balance and charged to the store's account on the 5th day of each month. The loan was repaid by payments of $1500.00 on July 15, $2000.00 on October 10 and $2500.00 on December 30. The rate of interest charged by the Credit Union was 14.5% on June 5. The rate was changed to 15.5% effective July 1 and to 16% effective October 1. Determine the total interest cost on the loan.

9. Herb's Restaurant borrowed $24 000.00 on March 1 on a demand note providing for a variable rate of interest. While repayment of principal is open, any accrued interest is to be paid on November 30. Payments on the loan were made as follows: $600.00 on April 15, $500.00 on July 20 and $1000.00 on October 10. The rate of interest was 14% on March 1, but was changed to 15.5% effective August 1 and to 14.5% effective November 1. Using the Declining Balance Method to record the partial payments, determine the accrued interest on November 30.

10. Use the design shown in Figure 12.3 to construct a complete repayment schedule, including the totalling of the Amount paid, Interest paid, and Principal repaid columns, for a loan of $4000 repaid in monthly instalments of $750.00 each including interest of 13.5% per annum calculated on the unpaid balance.

Summary of formulae used

Formula 12.1   NOMINAL RATE $= \dfrac{\text{CARRYING CHARGE}}{(\text{ORIGINAL AMOUNT FINANCED})\,(\text{TIME})}$

Finding the simple rate of interest based on the original amount financed

Formula 12.2 EFFECTIVE (TRUE) RATE $= \dfrac{2NC}{P(n + 1)}$

Finding the true rate of interest for instalment purchases which allows for the reduction in principal by periodic equal payments

Formula 12.3 EFFECTIVE (TRUE) RATE $= \dfrac{24C}{P(n + 1)}$

Finding the true rate of interest for instalment purchases when the instalment payments are made monthly

Formula 12.4 $\dfrac{\text{UNEARNED FINANCE CHARGE}}{} = \dfrac{\text{SUM OF THE DIGITS OF THE OUTSTANDING PAYMENTS}}{\text{SUM OF THE DIGITS OF ALL PAYMENTS}} \times \dfrac{\text{TOTAL FINANCE CHARGE}}{}$

Finding the unearned finance charge (rebate) in case of early repayment of an instalment loan

Formula 12.5 SUM-OF-THE-DIGITS $= \dfrac{n(n + 1)}{2}$

Finding the sum of the first n digits to find the sum of the digits of the payments in a loan

Glossary of terms used

Amount financed the outstanding balance on an instalment purchase after deducting any down payment or trade-in allowance from the cash price

Amount paid in instalments the total sum of money that will be paid in instalments to repay the original amount financed plus the carrying charge

Blended payments the usual method of repaying a personal consumer loan by fixed periodic (monthly) payments which cover payment of interest and repayment of principal

Carrying charge the total extra money paid for the privilege of buying on credit
See also *Cost of credit* and *Cost of financing*

Cash price the amount of cash for which a commodity can be bought

Charge accounts accounts maintained by consumers with department stores and other retailers to charge purchases

Consumer credit funds borrowed by individuals for personal consumption or personal financing purposes

Cost of credit see *Carrying charge*

Cost of financing see *Carrying charge*

Credit cards portable accounts used to buy goods and services on credit

Declining balance method the commonly used approach to applying partial payments to demand loans whereby each partial payment is first applied to pay the accumulated interest and any remainder is then used to reduce the oustanding principal

Demand loan   a loan for which repayment in full or in part may be required at any time

Down payment   a partial cash payment often required at the time of an instalment purchase

Effective rate of interest   the rate of interest which properly represents the cost of financing instalment loans by allowing for the declining principal balance

Instalment period   the length of time (usually months) over which an instalment purchase has to be repaid

Loan repayment schedule   a detailed statement of instalment payments, interest cost, repayment of principal and outstanding balance of principal for an instalment plan

Nominal rate of interest   the rate of interest which expresses the cost of financing an instalment purchase as a simple rate of interest based on the original loan balance; this rate allows for the time element but not for the reduction in principal balance

Partial payments   fractional payments to repay a debt (usually of the demand loan type)

Payoff figure   the amount required to pay off the principal balance on an instalment loan

Periodic instalment plan   a financing plan whereby a consumer debt including interest and principal is repaid in equal periodic payments

Rates of interest   see *Nominal rate of interest* and *Effective rate of interest*

Rebate   the amount of unearned interest deducted from the sum of the outstanding instalment payments to obtain the payoff figure in the case of an early repayment of the loan principal

Rule of 78   the label used for the Sum-of-the-Digits Method of finding the rebate; this label is appropriate in computing the rebate for a 12-months loan

Sum-of-the-digits method   the method usually used to compute the rebate in case of early repayment of an instalment loan

True rate of interest   see *Effective rate of interest*

PART THREE

Mathematics of finance and investment

13 Compound interest— amount and present value

Introduction

The simple interest method discussed in Chapter 10 is usually used only for time period less than one year in length. For longer terms the compound interest method, whereby interest is added periodically to the principal, is generally used.

As in the case of simple interest, the two basic problems centre around the determination of *Amount* and *Present Value*. This involves computation of the compounding factor $(1 + i)^n$. The arithmetic difficulties associated with computing the numerical value of $(1 + i)^n$ have disappeared with the availability of electronic calculators equipped with an exponential function (universal power key and universal root key).

Objectives

Upon completion of this chapter you will be able to

1. determine the rate per compounding period i and the number of compounding periods n, set up the compounding factor $(1 + i)^n$ in exponential form and compute the numerical value of $(1 + i)^n$;
2. use the compound amount formula $S = P(1 + i)^n$ to compute future values, including problems involving changes in rate of interest and principal;
3. use the present value formula $P = \frac{S}{(1 + i)^n}$ to compute the present value of future sums of money;
4. discount long-term promissory notes;
5. solve problems involving the use of equations of value.

13.1 Basic concepts and computations

A. Basic procedure for computing compound interest

The term **Compound Interest** refers to a procedure for computing interest whereby the interest for a specified time period is added to the original principal. The resulting amount becomes the new principal for the next time period. Thus the interest earned in prior periods earns interest in future periods.

The compound interest method is generally used to calculate interest for long-term investments. While the amount of compound interest for the first interest period is the same as the amount of simple interest, for further interest periods the amount of compound interest becomes increasingly greater than the amount of simple interest.

The basic procedure for computing compound interest and the effect of compounding is illustrated in Table 13.1. The table also provides a comparison of compound interest and simple interest for an original principal of $10 000.00 invested at 10% per annum for six years.

TABLE 13.1 *Compound interest versus simple interest for a principal of $10 000.00 invested at 10% per annum for 6 years*

Year		At compound interest		At simple interest	
		Interest computation	*Amount*	*Interest Computation*	*Amount*
1	Original Principal		10 000.00		10 000.00
	Add Interest	(0.10)(10 000.00)	1 000.00	(0.10)(10 000.00)	1 000.00
2	Amount End Year 1		11 000.00		11 000.00
	Add Interest	(0.10)(11 000.00)	1 100.00	(0.10)(10 000.00)	1 000.00
3	Amount End Year 2		12 100.00		12 000.00
	Add Interest	(0.10)(12 100.00)	1 210.00	(0.10)(10 000.00)	1 000.00
4	Amount End Year 3		13 310.00		13 000.00
	Add Interest	(0.10)(13 310.00)	1 331.00	(0.10)(10 000.00)	1 000.00
5	Amount End Year 4		14 641.00		14 000.00
	Add Interest	(0.10)(14 641.00)	1 464.10	(0.10)(10 000.00)	1 000.00
6	Amount End Year 5		16 105.10		15 000.00
	Add Interest	(0.10)(16 105.10)	1 610.51	(0.10)(10 000.00)	1 000.00
	Amount End Year 6		17 715.61		16 000.00

The method of computation used in Table 13.1 represents the step-by-step approach used in maintaining a savings account record and may be referred to as the *Bank-Book* Method of computing compound interest. Note that the amount of interest is determined for each interest period based on the previous balance and added to that balance.

The following should be noted about the end results after six years.

	At compound interest	At simple interest
Amount after six years	$17 715.61	$16 000.00
Less Original principal	10 000,00	10 000.00
Amount of interest	$ 7 715.61	6 000.00

In this case the compound interest exceeds the simple interest by $1715.61. This difference represents the amount of interest earned by interest added to the principal at the end of each compounding period.

B.   *Computer application 3—Accumulation of principal*

The Bank Book Method of accumulating a sum of money at compound interest is an iterative process illustrated in Computer Program 3 (see Appendix p. 845).

C.   *The amount formula for compound interest*

While the Bank Book method is useful in maintaining a savings account record, it is impractical for computational purposes. As in the case of simple interest the **amount** or **future value** can be found by using the amount formula.

For simple interest the amount formula is $S = P(1 + rt)$—see Chapter 10, Formula 10.4.

For compound interest, the amount formula is

$$S = P(1 + i)^n \qquad \longleftarrow \textit{Formula } \textbf{13.1}$$

S is the Amount or Future Value;
P is the Original Principal;
i is the Periodic Rate of Interest;
n is the Number of Compounding Periods.

The results of Table 13.1 could have been obtained by using the two amount formulae.

For simple interest
$$\begin{aligned} S = P(1 + rt) &= 10000.00\big[1 + (0.10)(6)\big] \\ &= 10000.00(1 + 0.60) \\ &= 10000.00(1.60) \\ &= \$16000.00 \end{aligned}$$

For compound interest

$$S = P(1 + i)^n = 10000.00(1 + 0.10)^6$$
$$= 10000.00(1.10)^6$$
$$= 10000.00(1.10)(1.10)(1.10)(1.10)(1.10)(1.10)$$
$$= 10000.00(1.771561)$$
$$= \$17715.61$$

D. Finding i and n

When using the compound interest formula the determination of the factor $(1 + i)^n$ is the main computational problem. The value of this factor, called the **compounding factor** or **accumulation factor** depends on the values of i and n.

The value of i, the periodic rate of interest, is determined from the stated rate of interest to be used in compounding, referred to as the **nominal rate of interest**. Since the nominal rate of interest is usually stated as an annual rate, the value of i is obtained by dividing the nominal rate by the number of **conversion periods** per year.

The commonly used conversion periods cover a number of months which is an exact divisor of twelve, namely

(a) 12 months, referred to as annual compounding

$\longrightarrow$ 1 conversion per year;

(b) 6 months, referred to as semi-annual compounding

$\longrightarrow$ 2 conversions per year;

(c) 3 months, referred to as quarterly compounding

$\longrightarrow$ 4 conversions per year;

(d) 1 month, referred to as monthly compounding

$\longrightarrow$ 12 conversions per year.

The number of **compounding periods** n must correspond to the time interval used for i, which means that the total time period expressed in years must be multiplied by the number of possible conversion periods per year to obtain n.

Example 13.1b Determine i and n for

  (i) 19% p.a. compounded annually for 14 years;

 (ii) 17% p.a. compounded semi-annually for 15 years;

(iii) 14% p.a. compounded quarterly for 12.5 years;

(iv) 18% p.a. compounded monthly for 10.75 years;

 (v) 15% p.a. compounded quarterly for 30 months;

(vi) 13.5% p.a. compounded semi-annually for 42 months.

Solution

(i) $i = \dfrac{19\%}{1} = 19\% = 0.19 \longleftarrow$ 1 conversion period per year

$n = (14)(1) = 14$

(ii) $i = \dfrac{17\%}{2} = 8.5\% = 0.085 \longleftarrow$ 2 conversion periods per year

$n = (15)(2) = 30$

(iii) $i = \dfrac{14\%}{4} = 3.5\% = 0.035 \longleftarrow$ 4 conversion periods per year

$n = (12.5)(4) = 50$

(iv) $i = \dfrac{18\%}{12} = 1.5\% = 0.015 \longleftarrow$ 12 conversion periods per year

$n = (10.75)(12) = 129$

(v) $i = \dfrac{15\%}{4} = 3.75\% = 0.0375$

$n = \left(\dfrac{30}{12}\right)(4) = (2.5)(4) = 10 \longleftarrow$ divide by 12 to convert months into years

(vi) $i = \dfrac{13.5\%}{2} = 6.75\% = 0.0675$

$n = \left(\dfrac{42}{12}\right)(2) = (3.5)(2) = 7 \longleftarrow$ divide by 12 to convert months into years

E. Computing the compounding factor $(1 + i)^n$

Once the numerical values of i and n have been determined, the exponential form of the compounding factor is obtained by substituting in the general form $(1 + i)^n$.

In Example 13.1b the exponential form of the factor is

(i) for $i = 0.19$, $n = 14 \longrightarrow (1 + 0.19)^{14} \longrightarrow (1.19)^{14}$

(ii) for $i = 0.085$, $n = 30 \longrightarrow (1 + 0.085)^{30} \longrightarrow (1.085)^{30}$

(iii) for $i = 0.035$, $n = 50 \longrightarrow (1 + 0.035)^{50} \longrightarrow (1.035)^{50}$

(iv) for $i = 0.015$, $n = 129 \longrightarrow (1 + 0.015)^{129} \longrightarrow (1.015)^{129}$

(v) for $i = 0.0375$, $n = 10 \longrightarrow (1 + 0.0375)^{10} \longrightarrow (1.0375)^{10}$

(vi) for $i = 0.0675$, $n = 7 \longrightarrow (1 + 0.0675)^{7} \longrightarrow (1.0675)^{7}$

The numerical value of any of these factors can now be computed using electronic calculators.

For calculators equipped with the exponential function feature $\boxed{Y^X}$, the numerical value of the compounding factor can be computed directly.

Step 1   Enter the numerical value of $(1 + i)$ in the keyboard.

Step 2   Press the function key $\boxed{Y^X}$.

Step 3   Enter the numerical value of n in the keyboard.

Step 4   Press $\boxed{=}$.

Step 5   Read the answer in the display.

The numerical value of the compounding factors in Example 13.1b are obtained as follows

	(i)	(ii)	(iii)	(iv)	(v)	(vi)
Step 1 Enter	1.19	1.085	1.035	1.015	1.0375	1.0675
Step 2 Press	Y^X	Y^X	Y^X	Y^X	Y^X	Y^X
Step 3 Enter	14	30	50	129	10	7
Step 4 Press	=	=	=	=	=	=
Step 5 Read	11.419773	11.558252	5.5849268	6.8252638	1.4450439	1.5797021

With the increasing availability of inexpensive electronic calculators the two traditional methods of determining the compounding factor $(1 + i)^n$ are rapidly falling into disuse. The use of logarithms for this purpose has virtually disappeared and the use of tables is diminishing. Neither method is used in this text.

Exercise 13.1

A. Determine i and n for each of the following.

  1. 12% compounded annually for 5 years

  2. 14.4% compounded semi-annually for 8 years

  3. 13.5% compounded quarterly for 9 years

  4. 17% compounded monthly for 4 years

  5. 15.5% compounded semi-annually for 13.5 years

  6. 11.5% compounded quarterly for five and three-quarter years

  7. 15% compounded monthly for 12.5 years

  8. 10.75% compounded quarterly for three years, nine months

  9. 12.25% compounded semi-annually for 54 months

  10. 16.2% compounded monthly for 15.5 years

B. Set up and compute the compounding factor $(1 + i)^n$ for each of the questions in A.

C.

1. For a sum of money invested at 14% compounded quarterly for 12 years, state
   (a) the number of compounding periods;
   (b) the periodic rate of interest;
   (c) the compounding factor in exponential form;
   (d) the numerical value of the compounding factor.

2. For each of the following periodic rates of interest determine the nominal annual compounding rate.
   (a) $i = 2\%$; compounding is quarterly
   (b) $i = 1.5\%$; compounding is monthly
   (c) $i = 6.5\%$; compounding is semi-annual
   (d) $i = 9.75\%$; compounding is annual

13.2 Using the compound amount formula $S = P(1 + i)^n$

A. Finding the compound amount (maturity value)

Example 13.2a Find the amount to which $6000.00 will grow if invested at 10% per annum compounded quarterly for 5 years.

Solution
The original principal P $= 6000.00$;

the quarterly rate of interest $i = \dfrac{10\%}{4} = 2.5\% = 0.025$;

the number compounding periods (quarters) $n = (5)(4) = 20$.

$$S = P(1 + i)^n \longleftarrow \text{using Formula 13.1}$$
$$= 6000.00(1 + 0.025)^{20} \longleftarrow \text{substituting for P, } i, n$$
$$= 6000.0(1.025)^{20} \longleftarrow \text{exponential form of factor}$$
$$= 6000.00(1.638\ 616\ 4) \longleftarrow \text{using a calculator}$$
$$= \$9831.70$$

Example 13.2b What is the amount after 78 months of $2500 invested at 14.25% p.a. compounded semi-annually?

Solution
The original principal P $= 2500.00$;

the semi-annual rate of interest $i = \dfrac{14.25\%}{2} = 7.125\% = 0.07125$;

the number of compounding periods (six-months)

$$n = \left(\frac{78}{12}\right)(2) = (6.5)(2) = 13.$$

$$\begin{aligned} S &= P(1 + i)^n \\ &= 2500.00(1 + 0.07125)^{13} \\ &= 2500.00(1.07125)^{13} \\ &= 2500.00(2.446\ 700\ 7) \\ &= \$6116.75 \end{aligned}$$

Example 13.2c Accumulate a deposit of $1750.00 made into a Registered Retirement Savings Plan from March 1, 1982 to December 1, 2000 at 11.5% p.a. compounded quarterly.

Solution

The original principal P = 1750.00;

the quarterly rate of interest $i = \dfrac{11.5\%}{4} = 2.875\% = 0.02875$;

the time period from March 1, 1982 to December 1, 2000, contains 18 years and 9 months, that is 18.75 years: $n = (18.75)(4) = 75$.

$$\begin{aligned} S &= P(1 + i)^n \\ &= 1750.00(1 + 0.02875)^{75} \\ &= 1750.00(1.02875)^{75} \\ &= 1750.00(8.379\ 895\ 8) \\ &= \$14664.82 \end{aligned}$$

B. Using preprogrammed financial calculators

Preprogrammed financial calculators may be used efficiently to solve compounding problems by selecting the compound interest mode, entering the given values and retrieving the answer.

Slight variations in the programming of the various available models exist, particularly in distinguishing between compound interest calculations and annuity calculations. Reference in this regard should be made to the instruction booklet for the particular model used. Throughout this text the explanations regarding the operation of a preprogrammed financial calculator are based on the use of a Texas Instrument Business Analyst II model.

The four variables used in compound interest calculations—P, S, i, n—are programmed into the calculator and are addressed by using keys as follows provided that the calculator is set in the financial mode.

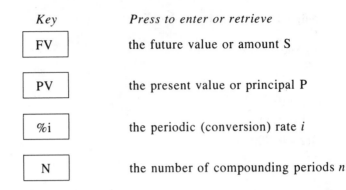

Key	Press to enter or retrieve
FV	the future value or amount S
PV	the present value or principal P
%i	the periodic (conversion) rate i
N	the number of compounding periods n

A fifth key, the periodic payment key | PMT |, is not needed for compound interest calculations. However on the T.I. Business Analyst II this key is useful in assuring that the compound interest mode is used since the calculator is programmed to perform compound interest calculations when zero is entered as payment.

To begin a compound interest calculation enter a zero payment; that is, press 0 | PMT |. If now values are entered in any order for any three of the four compound interest variables, the value of the fourth variable is retrieved by pressing | 2nd | followed by the key representing the unknown fourth variable.

To solve Example 13.2a in which P = 6000, i = 2.5% and n = 20, the following procedure may be used.

Press	Display shows	
0 PMT	0	← this assures that the calculator performs a compound interest calculation
6000 PV	6000	← this enters the present value (principal) P
2.5 %i	2.5	← this enters the conversion rate i
20 N	20	← this enters the number of compounding periods n
2nd FV	9831.6986	← this retrieves the wanted amount S

The amount is $9831.70.

Note   The answer shown in the display is the result of using the floating point decimal. However a fixed number of decimals may be set by pressing ⃞ FIX ⃞ and the desired number of decimal digits such as ⃞ FIX ⃞ ⃞ 2 ⃞ . To return to the floating decimal point press ⃞ FIX ⃞ ⃞ 8 ⃞ or ⃞ FIX ⃞ ⃞ 9 ⃞ .

C.   *Applications involving changes in interest rate or principal*

Example 13.2d   A deposit of $2000.00 earns interest at 12% p.a. compounded monthly for four years. At that time the interest rate is changed to 13% p.a. compounded quarterly. What is the value of the deposit three years after the change in the rate of interest?

Solution

The data given may be represented on a time diagram as shown in Figure 13.1.

FIGURE 13.1   *Graphical representation of data*

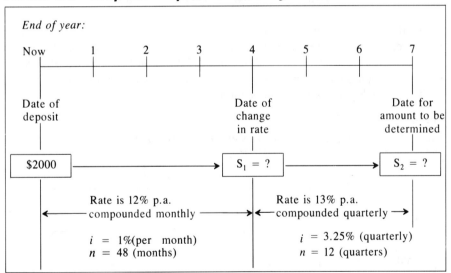

Step 1   Determine the accumulated value of the original deposit at the point in time when the interest rate changes; that is, after 4 years.

$$P = 2000.00; \qquad i = 1\% = 0.01; \qquad n = 48$$
$$S_1 = 2000.00(1 + 0.01)^{48} = 2000.00(1.6122261) = \$3224.45$$

Step 2 Use the accumulated value after four years as new principal and determine its accumulated value three years later using the new rate of interest.

$$P = 3224.45; \qquad i = 3.25\% = 0.0325; \qquad n = 12$$
$$S_2 = 3224.45(1 + 0.0325)^{12} = 3224.45(1.4678468) = \$4733.00$$

Example 13.2e A debt of $500 accumulates interest at 12% p.a. compounded quarterly from April 1, 1983 to July 1, 1984 and 9% p.a. compounded monthly thereafter. Determine the compound amount of the debt on December 1. 1985.

Solution

Step 1 Determine the accumulated value of the debt on July 1, 1984.

$P = 500.00; \qquad i = 3\% = 0.03; \qquad$ the period April 1, 1983 to July 1, 1984 contains 15 months: $n = 5$

$$S_1 = 500.00(1.03)^5 = 500.00(1.1592741) = \$579.64$$

Step 2 Use the result of Step 1 as new principal and find its accumulated value on December 1, 1985.

$P = 579.64; \qquad i = 0.75\% = 0.0075; \qquad$ the period July 1, 1984 to December 1, 1985 contains 17 months: $n = 17$

$$S_2 = 579.64(1.0075)^{17} = 579.64(1.1354446) = \$658.15$$

Example 13.2f Jay opened a Registered Retirement Savings Plan account with his Credit Union on February 1, 1980 with a deposit of $2000.00. He added $1900.00 on February 1, 1981 and another $1700.00 on February 1, 1984. What will his account amount to on August 1, 1990 if the plan earns a fixed rate of interest of 11% p.a. compounded semi-annually?

Solution

FIGURE 13.2 *Graphical representation of data*

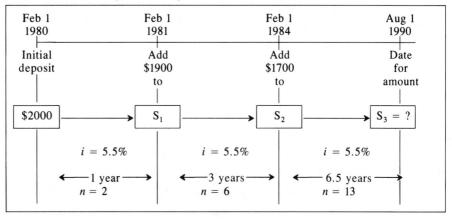

Step 1   Determine the amount of the initial deposit on February 1, 1981.

P = 2000.00; $i = 5.5\% = 0.055$;   the period Feb. 1, 1980 to Feb. 1, 1981 contains 1 year: $n = 2$

$S_1 = 2000.00(1.055)^2 = 2000.00(1.113025) = \$2226.05$

Step 2   Add the deposit of $1900.00 to the amount of $2226.05 to obtain the new principal as of February 1, 1981 and determine its amount on February 1, 1984.

P = 2226.05 + 1900.00 = 4126.05; $i = 0.055$;   the period Feb. 1, 1981 to Feb. 1, 1984 contains 3 years: $n = 6$

$S_2 = 4126.05(1.055)^6 = 4126.05(1.3788428) = \$5689.17$

Step 3   Add the deposit of $1700.00 to the amount of $5689.17 to obtain the new principal as of February 1, 1984 and determine its amount on August 1, 1990.

P = 5689.17 + 1700.00 = 7389.17; $i = 0.055$;   the period Feb. 1, 1984 to Aug. 1, 1990 contains 6.5 years: $n = 13$

$S_3 = 7389.17(1.055)^{13} = 7389.17(2.0057739) = \$14821.00$

Example 13.2g   A demand loan of $10 000.00 is repaid by payments of $5000.00 in one year, $6000.00 in four years and a final payment in six years. Interest on the loan is 16% p.a. compounded quarterly during the first year, 14% p.a. compounded semi-annually for the next three years and 13.5% p.a. compounded annually for the remaining years. Determine the final payment.

Solution

FIGURE 13.3   *Graphical representation of data*

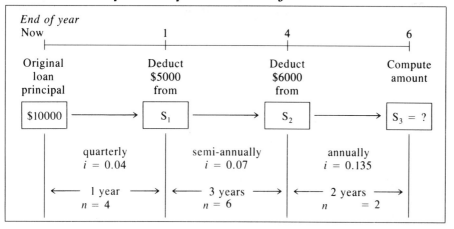

Step 1   Determine the accumulated value of the debt at the time of the first payment.

$$P = 10000.00; \qquad i = 4\% = 0.04; \qquad n = 4$$
$$S_1 = 10000.00(1.04)^4 = 10000.00(1.1698586) = \$11698.59$$

Step 2 Subtract the payment of $5000.00 from the accumulated value of $11 698.59 to obtain the debt balance and determine its accumulated value at the time of the second payment three years later.

$$P = 11698.59 - 5000.00 = 6698.59; \qquad i = 7\% = 0.07; \qquad n = 6$$
$$S_2 = 6698.59(1.07)^6 = 6698.59(1.5007304) = \$10052.78$$

Step 3 Subtract the payment of $6000.00 from the accumulated value of $10 052.78 to obtain the debt balance and determine its accumulated value two years later.

$$P = 10052.78 - 6000.00 = 4052.78; \qquad i = 13.5\% = 0.135; \qquad n = 2$$
$$S_3 = 4052.78(1.135)^2 = 4052.78(1.288225) = \$5220.89$$

The final payment after six years is $5220.89.

Exercise 13.2

A. Find the compound amount for each of the following.

Problem number	Principal	Nominal rate	Frequency of conversion	Time
1.	$ 400.00	13.5%	Annually	8 years
2.	1000.00	12.5%	Semi-annually	12 years
3.	1250.00	16.5%	Quarterly	9 years
4.	500.00	12%	Monthly	3 years
5.	1700.00	18%	Quarterly	14.75 years
6.	840.00	15%	Semi-annually	8.5 years
7.	2500.00	16%	Monthly	12.25 years
8.	150.00	13.25%	Quarterly	27 months
9.	480.00	15.75%	Semi-annually	42 months
10.	1400.00	14.4%	Monthly	18.75 years

B. Answer each of the following questions.

1. What is the maturity value of a five-year term deposit of $5000.00 at 12.5% compounded semi-annually? How much interest did the deposit earn?

2. To what sum of money will a registered retirement savings deposit of $1500.00 amount in 15 years at 12% compounded quarterly? How much of the amount is interest?

3. You made a registered retirement savings plan deposit of $1000.00 on December 1, 1982 at a fixed rate of 11% compounded monthly. If you withdraw the deposit on August 1, 1989, how much will you receive?

4. Roy's father made a trust deposit of $500.00 on October 31, 1978 to be withdrawn on Roy's 18th birthday on July 31, 1996. To what will the deposit amount on that date at 13% compounded quarterly?

5. What is the accumulated value of $100.00 invested for eight years at 15% p.a. compounded
   (a) annually? (b) semi-annually? (c) quarterly? (d) monthly?

6. To what will a principal of $500.00 amount in five years at 13% p.a. compounded
   (a) annually? (b) semi-annually? (c) quarterly? (d) monthly?

7. What is the accumulated value and the amount of compound interest of $100.00 invested at 14% compounded quarterly for
   (a) five years? (b) 10 years? (c) 20 years?

8. Find the compound amount and the compound interest on $500.00 invested at 12% compounded monthly for
   (a) 3.5 years; (b) 6 years; (c) 11.5 years.

9. The Canadian consumer price index was approximately 200 at the beginning of 1980. If inflation was to continue at an average annual rate of 10% what would the index be at the beginning of 1990?

10. Peel Credit Union expects an average annual growth rate of 20% for the next five years. If the assests of the Credit Union currently amount to $2.50 million, what will the forecasted assests amount to five years hence?

11. A local bank offers $5000.00 five-year certificates at 13.75% compounded semi-annually. Your Credit Union makes the same type of deposit available at 13.5% compounded monthly.
    (a) Which investment is preferable from the point of view of interest?
    (b) What is the difference in the amount of interest?

12. The Continental Bank advertises capital savings at 12.25% compounded semi-annually while National Trust offers premium savings at 12% compounded monthly. If you have $1000.00 to invest for two years
    (a) which deposit will earn more interest?
    (b) what is the difference in the amount of interest?

C. Answer each of the following questions.

1. A deposit of $2000.00 earns interest at 14% p.a. compounded quarterly. After two and a half years the interest rate is changed to 13.5% compounded monthly. How much is the account after six years?

2. An investment of $2500.00 earns interest at 15% p.a. compounded monthly for 3

years. At that time the interest rate is changed to 15.5% compounded quarterly. How much will be the accumulated value one and a half years after the change?

3. A debt of $800.00 accumulates interest at 13% compounded semi-annually from February 1, 1984 to August 1, 1986 and 14% compounded quarterly thereafter. Determine the amount of the debt on November 1, 1989.

4. Accumulate $1300.00 at 13.5% p.a. compounded monthly from March 1, 1986 to July 1, 1988 and thereafter at 13% p.a. compounded quarterly. What is the amount on April 1, 1992?

5. Pat opened an RRSP deposit account on December 1, 1985 with a deposit of $1000.00. He added $1000.00 on July 1, 1986 and $1000.00 on November 1, 1987. How much is in his account on January 1, 1989 if the deposit earns 12% p.a. compounded monthly?

6. Terri started an RRSP on March 1, 1985 with a deposit of $2000.00. She added $1800.00 on December 1, 1987 and $1700.00 on September 1, 1989. What is the accumulated value of her account on December 1, 1992 if interest is 11.5% compounded quarterly?

7. A debt of $4000.00 is repaid by payments of $1500.00 in nine months, $2000.00 in 18 months and a final payment in 27 months. If interest was 10% compounded quarterly, what was the amount of the final payment?

8. Sheridan Service has a line of credit loan with the Bank of Nova Scotia. The initial loan balance was $6000.00 and payments of $2000.00 and $3000.00 were made after four months and nine months respectively. At the end of one year Sheridan Service borrowed an additional $4000.00. Six months later the line of credit loan was converted into a collateral mortgage loan. For how much was the mortgage if interest was 18% compounded monthly?

9. A demand loan of $3000.00 is repaid by payments of $1500.00 after two years, $1500.00 after four years and a final payment after seven years. Interest is 14% compounded quarterly for the first year, 15% compounded semi-annually for the next three years and 15% compounded monthly thereafter. What is the size of the final payment?

10. A variable rate demand loan showed an initial balance of $12 000.00, payments of $5000.00 after eighteen months, $4000.00 after thirty months and a final payment after five years. Interest was 13% compounded semi-annually for the first two years and 15% compounded monthly for the remaining time period. How much was the size of the final payment?

13.3 Present value and compound discount

A. The present value concept and related terms

Example **13.3a** Find the principal which will amount to $17 715.61 at 10% p.a. compounded annually, in six years.

Solution

The problem may be graphically represented as shown in Figure 13.4

FIGURE 13.4 *Graphical representation of data*

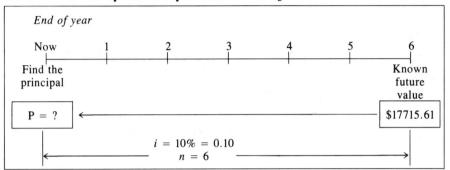

This problem is the inverse of the problem used to illustrate the meaning of compound interest. Instead of knowing the value of the principal and finding its future value, we know that the future value is $17 715.61 and we wish to determine the value of the principal.

To solve the problem we may use the amount formula $S = P(1 + i)^n$ and substitute the known values.

$$S = 17715.61; \quad i = 10\% = 0.10; \quad n = 6$$

$17715.61 = P(1.10)^6 \longleftarrow$ by substitution in $S = P(1 + i)^n$

$17715.61 = P(1.771561) \longleftarrow$ computing $(1.10)^6$

$$P = \frac{17715.61}{1.771561} \longleftarrow \begin{array}{l} \text{solve for P by dividing both} \\ \text{sides by 1.771561} \end{array}$$

$$P = \$10000.00$$

The principal which will grow to $17 715.61 in 6 years at 10% p.a. compounded annually is $10 000.00.

This principal is referred to as **present value** or **discounted value** or **proceeds** of the known future amount.

The difference between the known future amount of $17 715.61 and the computed present value (principal) of $10 000.00 is referred to as the **compound discount** and represents the compound interest accumulating on the computed present value.

The process of computing the present value or discounted value or proceeds is referred to as **discounting**.

B.   The present value formula

The present value of an amount at a given point in time at compound interest may be defined to be the principal which will grow to the given amount if compounded at a given periodic rate of interest over a given number of conversion periods.

Since the problem of finding the present value is equivalent to finding the principal when the amount, the periodic rate of interest and the number of conversion periods are given, the compound amount formula $S = P(1 + i)^n$ is applicable.

However, as the problem of finding the present value of an amount is a frequently encountered problem in financial analysis, it is useful to solve the compound amount formula for P to obtain the present value formula.

$$S = P(1 + i)^n \quad \longleftarrow \quad \text{starting with the compound amount formula, Formula 13.1.}$$

$$\frac{S}{(1 + i)^n} = \frac{P(1 + i)^n}{(1 + i)^n} \quad \longleftarrow \quad \text{divide both sides by the compounding factor } (1 + i)^n$$

$$\frac{S}{(1 + i)^n} = P \quad \longleftarrow \quad \text{reduce the fraction } \frac{(1 + i)^n}{(1 + i)^n} \text{ to 1}$$

$$\boxed{P = \frac{S}{(1 + i)^n}} \quad \longleftarrow \quad \begin{array}{l}\text{Present value formula} \\ \text{for compound interest}\end{array} \quad \longleftarrow \quad \textbf{\textit{Formula 13.2}}$$

Example 13.3b   Find the present value of $11 593.11 due in nine years at 12% p.a. compounded quarterly.

Solution

$$S = 11593.11; \qquad i = 3\% = 0.03; \qquad n = 36$$

$$P = \frac{S}{(1 + i)^n} \quad \longleftarrow \quad \text{using the present value formula}$$

$$= \frac{11593.11}{(1 + 0.03)^{36}} \quad \longleftarrow \quad \text{by substitution}$$

$$= \frac{11593.11}{2.8982783}$$

$$= \$4000.00$$

Note   The division of 11593.11 by 2.8982783, like any division, may be changed to a multiplication by using the reciprocal of the divisor.

$$\frac{11593.11}{2.8982783} \quad \longleftarrow \quad \begin{array}{l}\text{the division to be changed into a} \\ \text{multiplication}\end{array}$$

$$= 11593.11\left(\frac{1}{2.8982783}\right) \quad \longleftarrow \quad \begin{array}{l}\text{the reciprocal of the divisor 2.8982783} \\ \text{is found by dividing 1 by 2.8982783}\end{array}$$

$$= 11593.11(0.3450324) \quad \longleftarrow \quad \text{computed value of the reciprocal}$$

$$= \$4000.00$$

For calculators equipped with the reciprocal function key $\boxed{\dfrac{1}{x}}$ the conversion of the division into a multiplication is readily accomplished by first computing the compounding factor and then using the $\boxed{\dfrac{1}{x}}$ key to obtain the reciprocal.

Example 13.3c   What principal will amount to $5000.00 seven years hence if interest is 9% p.a. compounded monthly?

Solution

Finding the principal which amounts to a future sum of money is equivalent to finding the present value.

$$S = 5000.00; \qquad i = 0.75\% = 0.0075; \qquad n = 84$$

$$P = \frac{5000.00}{(1.0075)^{84}} \quad \longleftarrow \quad \text{using Formula 13.2}$$

$$= \frac{5000.00}{1.8732019} \quad \longleftarrow \quad \text{computing the factor } (1.0075)^{84}$$

$$= 5000.00(0.5338453) \quad \longleftarrow \quad \text{using the reciprocal function key}$$

$$= \$2669.23$$

The common procedure using the reciprocal of the divisor to change division into multiplication is reflected in the practice of stating the present value formula with a *negative* exponent.

$$\frac{1}{a^n} = a^{-n} \quad \longleftarrow \quad \text{negative exponent rule}$$

$$\frac{1}{(1 + i)^n} = (1 + i)^{-n}$$

$$\frac{S}{(1 + i)^n} = S(1 + i)^{-n}$$

Thus Formula 13.2, the present value formula, may be restated in multiplication form using a negative exponent.

$$\boxed{P = S(1 + i)^{-n}} \quad \longleftarrow \quad \textbf{\textit{Formula} 13.2a}$$

The factor $(1 + i)^{-n}$ is referred to as the **discount factor** and is the reciprocal of the compounding factor $(1 + i)^n$.

C. Using preprogrammed financial calculators to find present value

As explained in Section 13.2, sub-section B, preprogrammed calculators provide quick solutions to compound interest calculations by entering values for three of the four variables and retrieving the value of the fourth variable.

To solve Example 13.3c in which S = 5000, i = 0.75%, n = 84 and P is to be determined, use the following procedure.

Press		Display shows	
0	PMT	0	← this assures that the calculator performs a compound interest calculation
5000	FV	5000	← this enters the future value (amount) S
0.75	%i	0.75	← this enters the conversion rate i
84	N	84	← this enters the number of compounding periods n
2nd	PV	2669.2264	← this retrieves the wanted principal (present value) P

The principal is $2669.23.

Exercise 13.3

A. Find the present value of each of the following amounts.

Problem number	Amount	Nominal rate	Frequency of conversion	Time
1.	$1000.00	14%	Quarterly	7 years
2.	1500.00	13.5%	Semi-annually	10 years
3.	600.00	15%	Monthly	6 years
4.	350.00	11.5%	Annually	8 years
5.	1200.00	15.5%	Monthly	12 years
6.	3000.00	12.25%	Semi-annually	5 years 6 months
7.	900.00	16.4%	Quarterly	9 years 3 months
8.	500.00	15.6%	Monthly	15 years

B. Answer each of the following questions.

1. Find the present value and the compound discount of $1600.00 due four and a half years from now if money is worth 18.5% compounded semi-annually.

2. Find the present value and the compound discount of $2500.00 due in six years, three months if interest is 16% compounded quarterly.

3. Find the principal which will amount to $1250.00 in four years at 20% p.a. compounded quarterly.

4. What sum of money will grow to $2000.00 in seven years at 15% compounded monthly?

5. A debt of $5000.00 is due November 1, 1990. What is the value of the obligation on February 1, 1984 if money is worth 22% compounded quarterly?

6. How much would you have to deposit in an account today to have $3000.00 in a five-year term deposit at maturity if interest is 12.75% compounded annually?

13.4 Discounting promissory notes at compound interest

A. Discounting long-term promissory notes

Long-term promissory notes (written for a term longer than one year) are usually subject to compound interest. As with short-term promissory notes, long-term promissory notes are negotiable and can be bought and sold, that is *discounted*, at any time before maturity.

The principles involved in discounting long-term promissory notes are similar to those used in discounting short-term promissory notes by the simple discount method except that there is no requirement to add three days of grace in determining the legal due date of a long-term promissory note.

The discounted value or proceeds of a long-term promissory note is the present value at the date of discount of the maturity value of the note and is found using the present value formulae $P = \frac{S}{(1 + i)^n}$ or $P = S(1 + i)^{-n}$. This method of discounting long-term promissory notes is generally used even by the chartered banks.

For non-interest bearing notes the maturity value is the face value. However, for interest bearing promissory notes the maturity value must be determined first by means of the amount formula $S = P(1 + i)^n$.

B. Discounting non-interest bearing promissory notes

Since the face value of a non-interest bearing note is also its maturity value, the proceeds of a non-interest bearing note is the present value of its face value at the date of discount.

Example 13.4a Determine the proceeds of a non-interest bearing note for $1500.00 discounted two and a quarter years before its due date at 15% p.a. compounded monthly.

Solution

The maturity value S = 1500.00;

the rate of discount $i = \left(\dfrac{15}{12}\right)\% = 1.25\% = 0.0125$;

the number of conversion periods $n = (2.25)(12) = 27$.

$P = S(1 + i)^{-n} \longleftarrow \text{————————————}$ using Formula 13.2A

$= 1500.00(1 + 0.0125)^{-27}$

$= 1500.00\left(\dfrac{1}{1.3985109}\right)$

$= 1500.00(0.7150463)$

$= \$1072.57$

C. Discounting interest bearing promissory notes

The proceeds of an interest bearing note is the present value at the date of discount of the value of the note at maturity. Hence the maturity value of an interest bearing promissory note must be determined first when finding the discounted value.

Example 13.4b Determine the proceeds of a promissory note for $3600.00 with interest at 12% p.a. compounded quarterly, issued September 1, 1986, due on June 1, 1992 and discounted on December 1, 1988 at 15% p.a. compounded semi-annually.

Solution

Step 1 Find the maturity value of the note using Formula 13.1, $S = P(1 + i)^n$.
P = 3600; the interest rate $i = 3\% = 0.03$; the interest period, September 1, 1986 to June 1, 1992, contains 5 years and 9 months:

$n = \left(5\dfrac{9}{12}\right)(4) = 23$.

$S = 3600.00(1 + 0.03)^{23}$

$= 3600.00(1.9735865)$

$= \$7104.91$

Step 2 Find the present value at the date of discount of the maturity value found in Step 1 using $P = S(1 + i)^{-n}$.

$S = 7104.91$;   the rate of discount, $i = 7.5\% = 0.075$;   the discount period, December 1, 1988 to June 1, 1992, contains 3 years and

6 months: $n = \left(3\dfrac{6}{12}\right)(2) = 7.$

$P = 7104.91(1 + 0.075)^{-7}$

   $= 7104.91(0.6027549)$

   $= \$4282.52$

The proceeds of the note on December 1, 1988 are \$4282.52. The method and the data may be represented graphically as shown in Figure 13.5.

FIGURE 13.5 *Graphical representation of method and data*

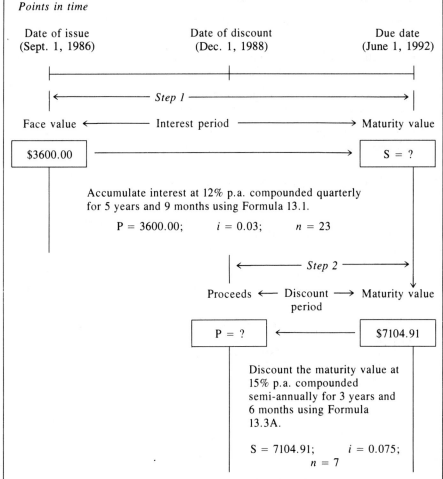

Exercise 13.4

A. Find the proceeds and the compound discount for each of the following long-term promissory notes.

No	Face value	Date issue	Term	Int. rate	Frequency of conversion	Date of discount	Disct rate	Frequency of conversion
1.	$2000	1986-06-30	5 years	−	−	1988-12-31	12%	semi-annual
2.	700	1984-04-01	10 years	−	−	1989-07-01	15%	quarterly
3.	1500	1985-05-31	8 years	13.5%	annually	1990-05-31	16%	semi-annual
4.	4000	1987-09-30	4 years	11%	semi-annual	1989-03-31	15%	quarterly
5.	800	1986-02-01	7 yrs 9 mo	14%	quarterly	1991-11-01	12%	monthly
6.	2200	1984-10-31	8.25 years	12%	monthly	1987-01-31	10%	quarterly

B. Find the proceeds of each of the following promissory notes.

1. A non-interest bearing promissory note for $6000.00 discounted 54 months before its due date at 11% compounded quarterly

2. A $4200.00 non-interest bearing note due August 1, 1992, discounted on March 1, 1988 at 13.5% compounded monthly

3. A promissory note with a maturity value of $1800.00 due on September 30, 1990, discounted at 15% compounded semi-annually on March 31, 1987

4. A fifteen-year promissory note discounted after six years at 9% compounded quarterly with a maturity value of $7500.00

5. A five-year promissory note for $3000.00 with interest at 12% compounded semi-annually, discounted 21 months before maturity at 14% compounded quarterly

6. A $5000.00 seven-year note bearing interest at 15% compounded quarterly, discounted two and a half years after the date of issue at 13.5% compounded monthly

7. A six-year $900.00 note bearing interest at 10% compounded quarterly, issued June 1, 1984, discounted on December 1, 1989, to yield 12.5% compounded semi-annually

8. A ten-year promissory note dated April 1, 1987 with a face value of $1300.00 bearing interest at 13% compounded semi-annually, discounted seven years later when money was worth 15% compounded quarterly

13.5 Equivalent values

A. Equations of value

As indicated in Chapter 10, sums of money have different values at different points in time. Because of their time value, sums of money coming due at different points in time are not directly comparable. To make such sums of money comparable a specific point in time, the **comparison date** or **focal date** must be selected and allowance must be made for interest from the due dates of the sums of money to the selected focal date; that is, the dated values of the sums of money must be determined.

For compound interest the dated values are equivalent and equations of value can be set up using the amount formula $S = P(1 + i)^n$ or the present value formula $P = S(1 + i)^{-n}$.

As with simple interest the selection of the appropriate formula depends on the position of the due dates relative to the focal date and should be made as follows

(a) if the due date falls *before* the focal date use the *amount* formula;

(b) if the due date falls *after* the focal date use the *present value* formula.

B. Finding the equivalent single payment

Example **13.5a** $4000.00 is payable three years from now. If money is worth 14% p.a. compounded semi-annually determine the equivalent value

(i) seven years from now;   (ii) now.

Solution

(i) The method and the data may be represented graphically as shown in Figure 13.6.

FIGURE 13.6   *Graphical representation of method and data*

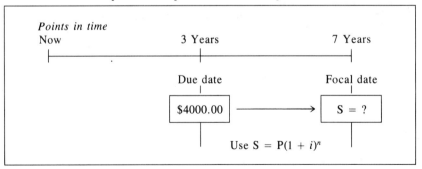

Since the due date falls *before* the focal date use the amount formula.

$$P = 4000.00; \qquad i = \frac{14\%}{2} = 0.07; \qquad n = 4(2) = 8$$

$$S = 4000.00(1 + 0.07)^8 = 4000.00(1.7181862) = \$6872.74$$

The equivalent value of the $4000.00 seven years from now is $6872.74.

(ii) The method and the data may be represented graphically as shown in Figure 13.7.

FIGURE 13.7 *Graphical representation of method and data*

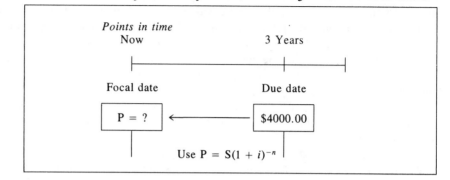

Since the due date falls *after* the focal date, use the present value formula.

$$S = 4000.00; \qquad i = \frac{14\%}{2} = 0.07; \qquad n = 3(2) = 6$$

$$P = 4000.00(1 + 0.07)^{-6} = 4000.00(0.6663422) = \$2665.37$$

The equivalent of the $4000.00 now is $2665.37.

Example 13.5b   A debt can be paid off by payments of $1600.00 one year from now, $1800.00 eighteen months from now and $2000.00 thirty months from now. Determine the single payment now which would settle the debt if money is worth 16% p.a. compounded quarterly.

Solution

While any date may be selected as the focal date, the logical selection for the focal date is the point in time designated 'now'. As is indicated in Figure 13.8, the due dates of the three payments are *after* the focal date. Hence the present value formula $P = S(1 + i)^{-n}$ is appropriate for finding the equivalent values of the three payments.

The equivalent values of the three payments at the selected focal date are

$$P_1 = 1600.00(1 + 0.04)^{-4} = 1600.00(0.8548042) = \$1367.69$$
$$P_2 = 1800.00(1 + 0.04)^{-6} = 1800.00(0.7903145) = \$1422.57$$
$$P_3 = 2000.00(1 + 0.04)^{-10} = 2000.00(0.6755642) = \$1351.13$$

The equivalent single payment to settle the debt now is $4141.39.

FIGURE 13.8 *Graphical representation of method and data*

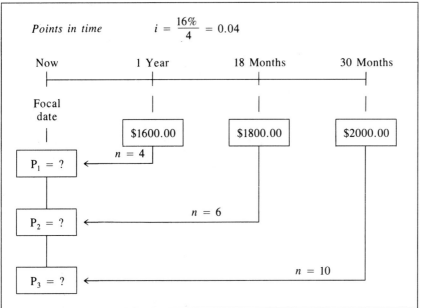

Example 13.5c Debt payments of $400.00 due five months ago, $600.00 due today and $800 due in nine months are to be combined into one payment due three months from today at 15% p.a. compounded monthly.

Solution

The logical selection for the focal date is the date referred to as '3 months from now', the date when the equivalent single payment is to be made.

As indicated in Figure 13.9, the first two payments are due *before* the focal date and the amount formula $S = P(1 + i)^n$ should be used. However, the third payment is due *after* the focal date which means that for it the present value formula $P = S(1 + i)^{-n}$ is applicable.

The equivalent values (designated E_1, E_2, E_3) of the debt payments at the selected focal date are

$$E_1 = 400.00(1 + 0.0125)^8 = 400.00(1.1044861) = \$ 441.79$$
$$E_2 = 600.00(1 + 0.0125)^3 = 600.00(1.0379707) = \$ 622.78$$
$$E_3 = 800.00(1 + 0.0125)^{-6} = 800.00(0.9281749) = \$ 742.54$$

The equivalent single payment to settle the debt three months from now is $1807.11.

FIGURE 13.9 *Graphical representation of method and data*

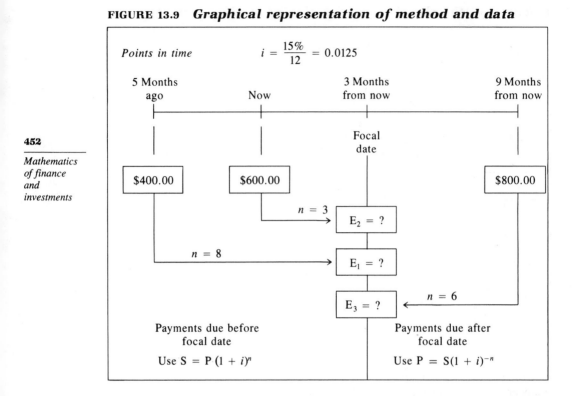

Example 13.5d Payments of $500.00 are due at the end of each of the next five years. Determine the equivalent single payment five years from now (just after the last payment is due) if money is worth 13% p.a. compounded annually.

Solution

Select as focal date the point in time referred to as 'five years from now'.

Let the equivalent single payment be represented by E and the dated values of the first four payments be represented by E_1, E_2, E_3, E_4 as indicated in Figure 13.10. Then the following equation of values may be setup

$$E = 500.00 + E_4 + E_3 + E_2 + E_1$$
$$= 500.00 + 500.00(1.13) + 500.00(1.13)^2 + 500.00(1.13)^3 + 500.00(1.13)^4$$
$$= 500.00\left[1 + (1.13) + (1.13)^2 + (1.13)^3 + (1.13)^4\right]$$
$$= 500.00(1 + 1.13 + 1.2769 + 1.442897 + 1.6304736)$$
$$= 500.00(6.4802706)$$
$$= 3240.14$$

The equivalent single payment after five years is $3240.14.

FIGURE 13.10 *Graphical representation of method and data*

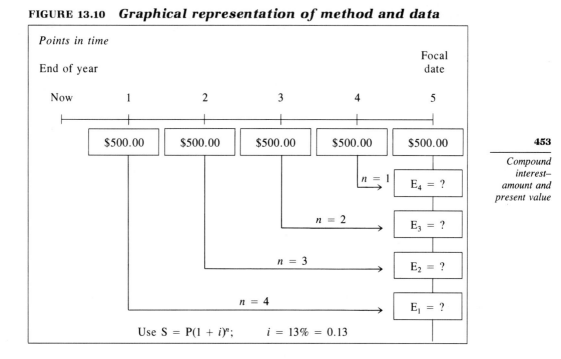

Example 13.5e Payments of $200.00 are due at the end of each of the next five quarters. Determine the equivalent single payment which would settle the debt payments now if interest is 15% p.a. compounded quarterly.

Solution

Select as focal date the point in time referred to as 'now'.

Let the equivalent single payment be represented by E and the dated values of the five payments by E_1, E_2, E_3, E_4, E_5 respectively as indicated in Figure 13.11. Then the following equation of values may be set up.

$$E = E_1 + E_2 + E_3 + E_4 + E_5$$
$$= 200.00(1.0375)^{-1} + 200.00(1.0375)^{-2} + 200.00(1.0375)^{-3}$$
$$\qquad + 200.00(1.0375)^{-4} + 200.00(1.0375)^{-5}$$
$$= 200.00[(1.0375)^{-1} + (1.0375)^{-2} + (1.0375)^{-3} + (1.0375)^{-4} + (1.0375)^{-5}]$$
$$= 200.00(0.9638554 + 0.9290173 + 0.8954383 + 0.8630731 + 0.8318777)$$
$$= 200.00(4.4832618)$$
$$= 896.65$$

The equivalent single payment now is $896.65.

FIGURE 13.11 **Graphical representation of method and data**

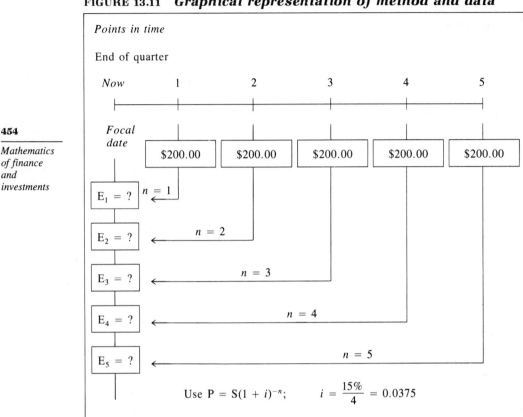

Points in time

End of quarter

| *Now* | 1 | 2 | 3 | 4 | 5 |

*Focal
date*

$$\text{Use } P = S(1 + i)^{-n}; \qquad i = \frac{15\%}{4} = 0.0375$$

C. *Finding the value of two or more equivalent payments*

When two or more equivalent payments are required an equation of values matching the dated values of the original debt payments against the dated values of the proposed replacement payments on a selected focal date should be setup. This is similar to the procedure used for simple interest in Chapter 10.

Example 13.5f   Debt payments of $1000.00 due today and $2000.00 due one year from now are to be settled by a payment of $1500.00 three months from now and a final payment eighteen months from now. Determine the size of the final payment if interest is 18% p.a. compounded quarterly.

Solution

Let the size of the final payment be x. The logical focal date is the date of the final payment.

FIGURE 13.12 *Graphical representation of method and data*

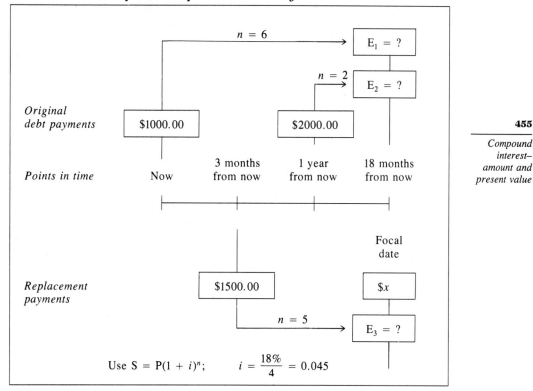

As indicated in Figure 13.12, the two original debt payments and the first replacement payment are due before the selected focal date, hence the amount formula $S = P(1 + i)^n$ is applicable. The final payment is dated on the focal date, hence its dated value is x.

The equivalent values of the original debt payments at the selected focal date, designated E_1 and E_2, are matched against the equivalent values of the replacement payments, designated E_3 and x, giving rise to the equation of values.

$$E_1 + E_2 = x + E_3$$
$$1000.00(1.045)^6 + 2000.00(1.045)^2 = x + 1500.00(1.045)^5$$
$$1000.00(1.3022601) + 2000.00(1.0920250) = x + 1500.00(1.2461819)$$
$$1302.26 + 2184.05 = x + 1869.27$$
$$x = 1617.04$$

The final payment is $1617.04.

Example 13.5g Debt payments of $750.00 due seven months ago, $600.00 due two months ago and $900.00 due in five months are to be settled by two equal payments due now and three months from now respectively. Determine the size of the equal payments at 15% p.a. compounded monthly.

Solution

Let the size of the equal payments be represented by $x and select 'now' as the focal date.

$$i = \frac{15\%}{12} = 0.0125.$$

First consider the dated values of the original debt payments at the selected focal date.

The due dates of the debt payments of $750.00 and $600.00 are seven months and two months respectively before the focal date, hence their dated values at the selected focal date are $750.00(1.0125)^7$ and $600.00(1.0125)^2$ respectively.

The due date of the $900.00 payment is five months after the selected focal date, hence its dated value is $900.00(1.0125)^{-5}$.

Secondly, consider the dated values of the replacement payments at the selected focal date.

The first replacement payment due at the focal date is $x. The second replacement payment is due three months after the selected due date, hence its dated value is $x(1.0125)^{-3}$.

Now equate the dated values of the replacement payments to the dated values of the original debt payments to set up the equation of values.

$$x + x(1.0125)^{-3} = 750.00(1.0125)^7 + 600.00(1.0125)^2 + 900.00(1.0125)^{-5}$$

$$x + 0.9634183x = 750.00(1.0908505) + 600.00(1.0251563)$$
$$+ 900.00(0.9397771)$$

$$1.9634183x = 818.14 + 615.09 + 845.80$$

$$1.9634183x = 2279.03$$

$$x = \frac{2279.03}{1.9634183}$$

$$x = 1160.75$$

The size of the two equal payments is $1160.75.

Example 13.5h Two debts, one of $4000 due in three months with interest at 17% compounded quarterly and the other of $3000 due in eighteen months with interest at 16.5% compounded semi-annually, are to be discharged by making two equal payments. What is the size of the equal payments if the first is due one year from now, the second two years from now and money is worth 18% compounded monthly?

Solution

Let the size of the equal payments be represented by x and select 'one year from now' as the focal date.

Since the two debts are interest bearing the maturity value of the two debts needs to be determined first.

The maturity value of $4000 due in three months at 17% compounded quarterly $= 4000(1.0425)^1 = \$4170.00$.

The maturity value of $3000 due in eighteen months at 16.5% compounded semi-annually $= 3000(1.0825)^3$
$$= 3000(1.2684803) = \$3805.44$$

Now determine the dated values of the two maturity values at the selected focal date subject to 18% compounded monthly.

The first debt matures nine months before the selected focal date, hence its dated value
$$= 4170.00(1.015)^9 = 4170.00(1.14339) = \$4767.94$$

The second debt matures six months after the selected focal date, hence its dated value
$$= 3805.44(1.015)^{-6} = 3805.44(0.9145422) = \$3480.24$$

The dated values of the two replacement payments at the selected focal date are x and $x(1.015)^{-12}$.

Therefore the equation of values is
$$x + x(1.015)^{-12} = 4767.94 + 3480.24$$
$$x + 0.8363874x = 8248.18$$

$$x = \frac{8248.18}{1.8363874}$$

$$x = 4491.53$$

The size of the two equal payments is $4491.53.

Example 13.5i What is the size of the equal payments which must be made at the end of each of the next five years to settle a debt of $5000.00 due in five years if money is worth 14% p.a. compounded annually?

Solution

Select as focal date the point in time referred to as 'five years from now'. Let the equal payments be represented by x and let the dated values of the first four payments be represented by E_1, E_2, E_3, E_4 respectively as indicated in Figure 13.13.

FIGURE 13.13 *Graphical representation of method and data*

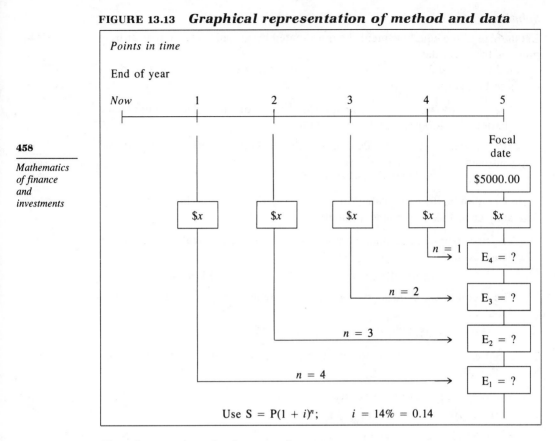

Then the equation of values may be set up.

$$5000.00 = x + E_4 + E_3 + E_2 + E_1$$

$$5000.00 = x + x(1.14) + x(1.14)^2 + x(1.14)^3 + x(1.14)^4$$

$$5000.00 = x[1 + (1.14) + (1.14)^2 + (1.14)^3 + (1.14)^4]$$

$$5000.00 = x(1 + 1.14 + 1.2996 + 1.481544 + 1.6889602)$$

$$5000.00 = 6.6101042x$$

$$x = \frac{5000.00}{6.6101042}$$

$$x = 756.42.$$

The size of the equal payments is $756.42.

Example 13.5j   What is the size of the equal payments which must be made at the end of each of the next five quarters to settle a debt of $3000.00 due now if money is worth 16% p.a. compounded quarterly?

Solution
Select as focal date the point in time referred to as 'now'. Let the size of the equal

payments be represented by $x and let the dated values of the five payments be represented by E_1, E_2, E_3, E_4, E_5 respectively as indicated in Figure 13.14.

Then the equation of values may be set up.

$$3000.00 = E_1 + E_2 + E_3 + E_4 + E_5$$

$$3000.00 = x(1.04)^{-1} + x(1.04)^{-2} + x(1.04)^{-3} + x(1.04)^{-4} + x(1.04)^{-5}$$

FIGURE 13.14 *Graphical representation of method and data*

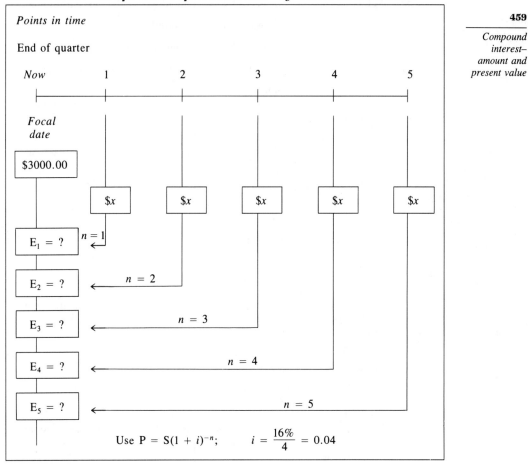

$$3000.00 = x[(1.04)^{-1} + (1.04)^{-2} + (1.04)^{-3} + (1.04)^{-4} + (1.04)^{-5}]$$

$$3000.00 = x(0.9615385 + 0.9245562 + 0.8889964 + 0.8548042$$
$$+ 0.8219271)$$

$$3000.00 = 4.4518223x$$

$$x = \frac{3000.00}{4.4518223}$$

$$x = 673.88$$

The size of the equal payments is $673.88.

Exercise 13.5

A. Find the equivalent single payment on the given focal date for each of the following.

Problem number	Original payments	Int. rate	Frequency of conversion	Focal date
1.	$5000.00 due in 2 years	12%	monthly	5 years from now
2.	$1600.00 due in 18 months	14%	quarterly	42 months from now
3.	$3400.00 due in 4 years	10%	semi-annually	one year from now
4.	$2700.00 due in 60 months	15%	quarterly	6 months from now
5.	$800.00 due in 6 months and $700.00 due in 15 months	13%	monthly	2 years from now
6.	$1000.00 due in 9 months and $1200.00 due in 18 months	16%	quarterly	3 years from now
7.	$400.00 due in 3 years and $600.00 due in 5 years	11%	semi-annually	now
8.	$2000.00 due in 20 months and $1500.00 due in 40 months	15%	monthly	9 months from now
9.	$800.00 due today and $1400.00 due in 3 years with interest at 16% compounded annually	13.5%	quarterly	one year from now
10.	$500.00 due in 6 months with interest at 14% compounded quarterly and $800.00 due in 18 months with interest at 16% compounded semi-annually	18%	monthly	9 months from now

B. Find the equivalent replacement payments for each of the following.

No.	Original payments	Int. rate	Frequency of conversion	Replacement payments	Focal date
1.	$2000.00 due now and $2000.00 due in 4 years	14.5%	annually	$2000.00 due in 2 years, a second payment due in 7 years	7 years from now
2.	$1500.00 due in 6 months and $1900.00 due in 21 months	17%	quarterly	$2000.00 due in 3 years, the remainder due in 45 months	45 months from now
3.	$800.00 due 2 years ago and $1000.00 due in 5 years	12%	semi-annually	2 equal payments; first payment due in 4 years, second payment due in 8 years	4 years from now
4.	$3000.00 due 1 year ago and $2500.00 due in 4 years	15%	monthly	2 equal payments; first due now, second payment due in 6 years	now
5.	$900.00 due in 3 months and $800.00 due in 30 months with interest at 15% compounded quarterly	21%	monthly	2 equal payments; first due today, second due in 3 years	today
6.	$1400.00 due today and $1600.00 due in 5 years with interest at 14.5% compounded annually	14%	quarterly	2 equal payments; first due in 18 months, second due in 4 years	18 months from now

C. Solve each of the following problems.

1. $4000.00 is due in five years. If money is worth 12% compounded annually, find the equivalent payment which would settle the debt

(a) now;   (b) in 2 years;   (c) in 5 years;   (d) in 10 years.

2. A debt payment of $5500 is due in 27 months. If money is worth 16% p.a. compounded quarterly, what is the equivalent payment

   (a) now; (b) 15 months from now? (c) 27 months from now; (d) 36 months from now?

3. A debt can be paid by payments of $2000.00 today, $2000.00 in three years and $2000.00 in six years. What single payment would settle the debt four years from now if money is worth 10% compounded semi-annually?

4. $600.00, $800.00 and $1200.00 are due in one year, three years and six years respectively. What is the equivalent single sum of money due two and a half years from now if interest is 12% compounded monthly?

5. Debt payments of $400.00 due today and $700.00 due in eight months with interest at 12% compounded monthly are to be settled by a payment of $500.00 six months from now and a final payment in fifteen months. Determine the size of the final payment if money is worth 15% compounded monthly.

6. Payments of $1200.00 due one year ago and $1000.00 due six months ago are to be replaced by a payment of $800.00 now, a second payment of $1000.00 nine months from now and a final payment eighteen months from now. What is the size of the final payment if interest is 14% compounded quarterly?

7. An obligation of $8000.00 due one year ago is to be settled by four equal payments due at the beginning of each of the next four years respectively. What is the size of the equal payments if interest is 12% compounded semi-annually?

8. A loan of $3000.00 made today is to be repaid in three equal instalments due in one year, three years and five years respectively. What is the size of the equal instalments if money is worth 12% compounded monthly?

9. Payments of $500.00 each are due at the end of each of the next five years. If money is worth 11% compounded annually what is the single equivalent payment

   (a) five years from now? (b) now?

10. Rework Problem 9 with payments due at the beginning of each of the next five years (The solution can be obtained directly from your solution to Problem 9).

11. What is the size of the equal payments which must be made at the end of each of the next four years to settle a debt of $3000.00 subject to interest at 10% p.a. compounded annually

    (a) due four years from now? (b) due now?

12. Rework Problem 11 with payments made at the beginning of each of the next four years (The solution can be obtained directly from your solution to Problem 11).

Review exercise

1. What is the accumulated value of $500.00 in fifteen years at 13.5% compounded

   (a) annually? (b) quarterly? (c) monthly?

2. What is the amount of $10 000.00 at 16.5% compounded monthly

(a) in four years?　　(b) in eight and one-half years?　　(c) in twenty years?

3. Landmark Trust offers 5-year investment certificates at 15% compounded semi-annually.

(a) What is the value of a $2000 certificate at maturity?

(b) How much of the maturity value is interest?

4. Western Savings offers three-year term deposits at 15.25% compounded annually while your Credit Union offers such deposits at 14.5% compounded quarterly. If you have $5000 to invest what is the maturity value of your deposit

(a) at Western Savings?　　(b) at your Credit Union?

5. Find the compound amount and the compound interest of

(a) $1800.00 invested at 14% compounded quarterly for 15.5 years;

(b) $1250.00 invested at 13.5% compounded monthly for 15 years.

6. Find the present value and the compound discount of

(a) $3600.00 due in 9 years if interest is 15% compounded semi-annually;

(b) $9000.00 due in 5 years if money is worth 16.8% compounded quarterly.

7. The Peel Company borrowed $20 000.00 at 10% compounded semi-annually and made payments toward the loan of $8000.00 after two years and $10 000.00 after three and a half years. How much is required to pay the loan off one year after the second payment?

8. Ted deposited $1750.00 in an RRSP on March 1, 1982 at 10% compounded quarterly. Subsequently the interest rate was changed to 12% compounded monthly on September 1, 1984 and to 11% compounded semi-annually on June 1, 1986. What will the value of the RRSP deposit be on December 1, 1992 if no further changes in interest are made?

9. A non-interest bearing note for $1500.00 is due on June 30, 1994. The note is discounted at 15% compounded quarterly on September 30, 1988. What are the proceeds of the note?

10. An investment of $2500 is accumulated at 14% compounded quarterly for two and one-half year. At that time the interest rate is changed to 13.5% compounded monthly. How much is the amount of the investment two years after the change in interest rate?

11. To assure that funds are available to repay the principal at maturity a borrower deposits $2000 each year for three years. If interest is 13% compounded quarterly, how much will the borrower have on deposit four years after the first deposit was made?

12. Cindy started a registered retirement savings plan on February 1, 1984 with a deposit of $2500. She added $2000 on February 1, 1985 and $1500 on February 1, 1986. What is the accumulated value of her RRSP account on August 1, 1994 if interest is 14% compounded quarterly?

13. A demand loan of $8000 is repaid by payments of $3000 after fifteen months, $4000 after thirty months and a final payment after four years. If interest was 15% for the first two years and 16% for the remaining time period and compounding is quarterly, what is the size of the final payment?

14. Find the present value and the compound discount of $4000 due in seven years and six months if interest is 14.8% compounded quarterly?

15. Find the principal which will accumulate to $6000 in fifteen years at 15% compounded monthly.

16. Find the proceeds of a non-interest bearing promissory note for $75 000 discounted 42 months before maturity at 16.5% compounded semi-annually.

17. A ten-year promissory note for $1750.00 dated May 1, 1984, bearing interest at 13% compounded semi-annually is discounted on August 1, 1990 to yield 14% compounded quarterly. Determine the proceeds of the note.

18. A seven-year $10 000 promissory note bearing interst at 12% compounded quarterly is discounted four years after the date of issue at 16% compounded semi-annually. What are the proceeds of the note?

19. A $40 000, 15-year promissory note dated June 1, 1986, bearing interest at 15% compounded semi-annually is discounted on September 1, 1990 at 17% compounded quarterly. What are the proceeds of the note?

20. A sum of money has a value of $3000 eighteen months from now. If money is worth 18% compounded monthly what is its equivalent value

    (a) now?   (b) one year from now?   (c) three years from now?

21. Payments of $1000, $1200 and $1500 are due in six months, eighteen months and thirty months from now respectively. What is the equivalent single payment two years from now if money is worth 16% compounded quarterly?

22. An obligation of $10 000 is due one year from now with interest at 13% compounded semi-annually. The obligation is to be settled by a payment of $6000 in six months and a final payment in fifteen months. What is the size of the second payment if interest is 18% compounded monthly?

23. Joe owes $3000 due in two years with interest at 16% compounded semi-annually and $2500 due in fifteen months at 13% compounded quarterly. If Joe wants to discharge these debts by making two equal payments, the first one now and the second eighteen months from now, what is the size of the two payments if money is worth 15% compounded monthly?

24. Debt payments of $400.00 due today, $500.00 due in eighteen months and $900.00 due in three years are to be combined into a single payment due two years from now. What is the size of the single payment if interest is 16% p.a. compounded quarterly?

25. Debt payments of $2600.00 due one year ago and $2400.00 due two years from now are to be replaced by two equal payments due one year from now and four years from

now respectively. What is the size of the equal payments if money is worth 13.5% p.a. compounded semi-annually?

26. A loan of $7000.00 taken out two years ago is to be repaid by three equal instalments due now, two years from now and three years from now respectively. What is the size of the equal instalments if interest on the debt is 12% p.a. compounded monthly?

Self-test

1. What sum of money invested at 12% compounded quarterly will grow to $3300 in 11 years?

2. Find the compound interest earned by $1300 invested at 13.5% compounded monthly for seven years.

3. Determine the compounding factor for a sum of money invested for 14.5 years at 13% compounded semi-annually.

4. Five years after Mr. T. deposited $3600 in a savings account which earned interest at 10.2% compounded monthly, the rate of interest was changed to 9% compounded semi-annually. How much was in the account 12 years after the deposit was made?

5. A debt can be repaid by payments of $4000 today, $4000 in five years and $3000 in six years. What single payment would settle the debt one year from now if money is worth 19% compounded semi-annually?

6. A $10 200 debt will accumulate for five years at 21% compounded semi-annually. For how much will the debt sell three years after it was incurred if the buyer of the debt charges 18% compounded quarterly?

7. What is the present value of $5900 payable in 15 years if the current interest rate is 14% compounded semi-annually?

8. Determine the compound discount on $8800 due in 7.5 years if interest is 16.5% compounded monthly.

9. Two debt payments, the first in the amount of $800 due today, and the second in the amount of $600 due in nine months with interest at 10.5% compounded monthly, are to be settled by a payment of $800 six months from now and a final payment in 24 months. Determine the size of the final payment if money is worth 13.5% compounded quarterly.

10. A note dated July 1, 1986 promises the payment of $8000 with interest at 16.5% compounded quarterly on January 1, 1995. Find the proceeds from the sale of the note on July 1, 1990 if money was then worth 12% compounded semi-annually.

11. Mr. S. borrowed $5000 at 13% compounded semi-annually. He repaid $2000 after two years and $2500 after three years. How much will he owe after five years?

12. A debt of \$7000 due today is to be settled by three equal payments due three months from now, 15 months from now and 27 months from now respectively. What is the size of the equal payments at 21% compounded quarterly?

Summary of formulae used

Formula 13.1 $\quad S = P(1 + i)^n$

Finding the compound amount (future value, maturity value) when the original principal, the rate of interest and the time period are known

Formula 13.2 $\quad P = \dfrac{S}{(1 + i)^n}$

Finding the present value (principal, proceeds, discounted value) when the compound amount, the rate of interest and the time period are known

Formula 13.2A $\quad P = S(1 + i)^{-n}$

Finding the present value by means of the discount factor (the reciprocal of the compounding factor)

Glossary of terms used

Accumulation factor see *Compounding factor*

Amount see *Compound Amount*

Comparison date see *Focal date*

Compound amount the sum of money to which a principal will grow at compound interest in a specific number of compounding or conversion periods at a specified periodic rate of interest

Compound discount the difference between a given amount and its present value (or proceeds or discounted value) at a specified point in time

Compound interest a procedure for computing interest whereby interest earned during an interest period is added onto the principal at the end of the interest period

Compounding factor the factor $(1 + i)^n$ found in compound interest formulae

Compounding period the time between two successive interest dates

Conversion period see *Compounding period*

Discount factor the factor $(1 + i)^{-n}$ which is the reciprocal of the compounding factor

Discounted value see *Present value*

Discounting the process of computing the present value (or proceeds or discounted value) of a future sum of money

Equivalent values the dated values of an original sum of money

Focal date a specific point in time selected to compare the time values of one or more dated sums of money

Future value see *Compound amount*

Maturity value see *Compound amount*

Nominal rate of interest the stated rate at which the compounding is done one or more times per year; usually stated as an annual rate

Present value the principal at any point in time which will grow at compound interest to a given amount over a given number of compounding periods at a given rate of interest

Proceeds see *Present value*

14 Compound interest— further topics

Introduction

The two basic problems of computing compound amount and present value have been considered in the previous chapter. Additional problems involving compound interest are considered in this chapter. The topics involve computations with fractional conversion periods, finding interest rates, finding the number of conversion periods, computing equated dates and equivalent rates and using continuous compounding.

In this and the following chapters you will use the power function and the natural logarithm function to determine values which will be used for further computation. You are encouraged to use the memory to retain such values. When doing so, you need to be aware that the number of digits retained in the registers is greater than the number of digits displayed. Thus, depending on whether the memory or the displayed digits are used, slight differences may result. Any such differences are insignificant and should not concern you. For the worked examples in this text the memory was used whenever it was convenient to do so.

Objectives

Upon completion of this chapter using an electronic calculator equipped with the universal power and universal root function, the natural logarithm and anti-logarithm function you will be able to

1. find the compound amount when n is a fractional value;
2. find discounted values for fractional compounding periods;
3 discount promissory notes involving fractional compounding periods;
4. compute periodic, nominal and effective rates of interest and determine the number of conversion periods;
5. find equated dates, equivalent rates and solve problems involving continuous compounding.

14.1 Finding the compound amount when n is a fractional value

A. Two methods for solving the problem

The value of n in the compounding factor $(1 + i)^n$ is not restricted to integral values, but may take any *fractional* value. The compound amount may be determined by means of the formula $S = P(1 + i)^n$ whether the time period contains an integral number of conversion periods or not.

Using the formula with n as a fractional value is the theoretically correct method giving the exact accumulated value. Historically, however, the computation when using a fractional n was laborious and required the use of logarithms. To avoid the use of logarithms, an *approximation* method using simple interest for the fractional conversion period was used in practice.

With the advent of electronic calculators equipped with an exponential function the problem of computation with fractional values of n no longer exists. In fact, using the exact method with an electronic calculator is more direct than the practical method. Except for the specific application of the practical method used in bond valuation (see Chapter 19), only the exact method is used in this text.

B. Examples using the exact method

Use Formula 13.1 $S = P(1 + i)^n$ where n is a fractional value representing the entire time period.

Example 14.1a Find the accumulated value of $1000.00 invested for two years and nine months at 15% p.a. compounded annually using the exact method.

Solution

The entire time period is 2 years and 9 months; the number of whole conversion periods is 2; the fractional conversion period is $\frac{9}{12}$ of a year.

$$P = 1000.00; \qquad i = 15\% = 0.15; \qquad n = 2\frac{9}{12} = 2.75$$

$$S = 1000.00(1.15)^{2.75} = 1000.00(1.4686525) = \$1468.65$$

Example 14.1b Determine the compound amount of $400.00 invested at 14% p.a. compounded quarterly for three years and five months using the exact method.

Solution

$$P = 400.00; \qquad i = 3.5\% = 0.035;$$

$$n = \left(3\frac{5}{12}\right)(4) = \left(\frac{41}{12}\right)(4) = \frac{41}{3} = 13\frac{2}{3} = 13.666667$$

$$S = 400.00(1.035)^{13.666667} = 400.00(1.6002388) = \$640.10$$

Example 14.1c Find the maturity value of a promissory note for $2000.00 dated February 1, 1986 and due on October 1, 1990 if interest is 13% p.a. compounded semi-annually.

Solution

P = 2000.00; i = 6.5% = 0.065; the time period February 1, 1986 to October 1, 1990 contains 4 years and 8 months:

$$n = \left(4\frac{8}{12}\right)(2) = \left(\frac{56}{12}\right)(2) = 9.3333333.$$

S = $2000.00(1.065)^{9.3333333}$ = 2000.00(1.7999606)
  = $3599.92

Example 14.1d A debt of $3500.00 dated August 31, 1985 is payable together with interest at 15% p.a. compounded quarterly on June 30, 1988. Determine the amount to be paid.

Solution

P = 3500.00; i = 3.75% = 0.0375; the time period August 31, 1985 to June 30, 1988 contains 2 years and 10 months: the number of quarters
n = 11.333333

S = $3500.00(1.0375)^{11.333333}$

  = 3500.00(1.517744)
  = $5312.10

Exercise 14.1

A. 1. Find the accumulated value of each of the following.

Problem number	Principal	Rate	Frequency of conversion	Time
(a)	$2500.00	20%	annually	7 years 6 months
(b)	400.00	14%	quarterly	3 years 8 months
(c)	1300.00	12%	semi-annually	9 years 3 months
(d)	4500.00	15%	monthly	7.5 months

2. Find the compound interest for each of the following.

Problem number	Principal	Rate	Frequency of conversion	Time
(a)	$ 600.00	12.5%	annually	4 years 7 months
(b)	1400.00	17.5%	semi-annually	15 years 2 months
(c)	950.00	16.0%	quarterly	9 years 10 months
(d)	3000.00	20.5%	annually	50 months

B. Solve each of the following problems:

1. A demand loan for $5000.00 with interest at 15% compounded semi-annually is repaid after five years ten months. What is the amount of interest paid?

2. $4000.00 is invested for four years eight months at 18.5% compounded annually. What is the compound amount?

3. Determine the maturity value of a $600.00 promissory note dated August 1, 1986 and due on June 1, 1991 if interest is 13% p.a. compounded semi-annually.

4. Find the maturity value of a promissory note for $3200.00 dated March 31, 1987 and due on August 31, 1993 if interest is 14% compounded quarterly.

5. A debt of $8000.00 is payable in seven years and five months. Determine the accumulated value of the debt at 22% p.a. compounded annually.

6. A $6000.00 investment matures in three years eleven months. Find the maturity value if interest is 15% p.a. compounded quarterly.

14.2 *Discounted value for a fractional compounding period*

A. *Exact method for solving the problem*

The comments made in Section 14.1 regarding fractional values of n when finding the compound amount are relevant when finding the present value or discounted value of a future sum of money for a fractional time period. Only the exact method is used in this text.

Use Formula 13.1, $S = P(1 + i)^n$ or Formula 13.2, $P = \dfrac{S}{(1 + i)^n}$ or Formula 13.2A, $P = S(1 + i)^{-n}$ where n is a fractional value representing the *entire* time period, S is a known value and P is to be determined.

B. Examples

Example 14.2a Find the present value of $2000.00 due in three years and eight months if money is worth 13% p.a. compounded quarterly.

Solution

$$S = 2000.00; \quad i = \frac{13\%}{4} = 3.25\% = 0.0325; n = \left(3\frac{8}{12}\right)(4) = 14\frac{2}{3} = 14.666667$$

$$P = \frac{S}{(1 + i)^n} \longleftarrow \text{using Formula 13.2}$$

$$= \frac{2000.00}{(1 + 0.0325)^{14.666667}} \longleftarrow \begin{array}{l}\text{use as many decimals as are}\\ \text{available in your calculator}\end{array}$$

$$= \frac{2000.00}{1.5985303}$$

$$= 2000.00(0.6255746) \longleftarrow \text{multiply by the reciprocal}$$

$$= \$1251.15$$

Example 14.2b Determine the principal that will accumulate to $3358.33 from September 1, 1987 to April 1, 1991 at 15% p.a. compounded semi-annually.

Solution

Finding the principal which will grow to the given amount of $3358.33 is equivalent to finding the present value or discounted value of this amount.

The time period September 1, 1987 to April 1, 1991 contains 3 years and 7 months; that is, it consists of 7 whole conversion periods of six months each and a fractional conversion period of 1 month.

$$\text{Use } P = \frac{S}{(1 + i)^n}$$

$$S = 3358.33; \quad i = 7.5\% = 0.075; \quad n = \left(3\frac{7}{12}\right)(2) = 7\frac{1}{6} = 7.1666667$$

$$P = \frac{3358.33}{(1.075)^{7.1666667}}$$

$$= \frac{3358.33}{1.6791674}$$

$$= 3358.33(0.5955332)$$

$$= \$2000.00$$

Exercise 14.2

A. 1. Find the present value of each of the following.

Problem number	Amount	Rate	Frequency of conversion	Time due
(a)	$1500.00	15.5%	annually	in 15 years 9 months
(b)	900.00	21.5%	semi-annually	in 8 years 10 months
(c)	6400.00	17%	quarterly	in 5 years 7 months
(d)	7200.00	18%	monthly	in 21.5 months

2. Find the compound discount for each of the following.

Problem number	Amount	Rate	Frequency of conversion	Time due
(a)	$7500.00	12%	quarterly	in 4 years 5 months
(b)	4800.00	14.5%	semi-annually	in 9 years 9 months
(c)	870.00	18%	monthly	in 45.5 months
(d)	1250.00	15.5%	annually	in 12 years 4 months

B. Solve each of the following problems.

1. What is the principal which will grow to $3000.00 in eight years eight months at 15% compounded semi-annually?

2. Find the sum of money which accumulates to $1600.00 at 22% compounded quarterly in six years four months.

3. Determine the proceeds of an investment with a maturity value of $10 000.00 if discounted at 15% compounded monthly 22.5 months before the date of maturity.

4. Compute the discounted value of $7000.00 due in three years five months if money is worth 16% compounded quarterly.

5. Find the discounted value of $3800.00 due in six years eight months if interest is 17.5% compounded annually.

6. Calculate the proceeds of $5500 due in seven years eight months discounted at 13.5% compounded semi-annually.

14.3 Discounting promissory notes involving fractional conversion periods

A. Non-interest-bearing notes

Example 14.3a A four year non-interest-bearing promissory note for $6000.00 dated August 31, 1986 is discounted on October 31, 1987 at 14% p.a. compounded quarterly. Determine the proceeds of the note.

Solution

The due date of the note is August 31, 1990; the discount period October 31, 1987 to August 31, 1990 contains 2 years and 10 months.

$$S = 6000.00; \qquad i = 3.5\% = 0.035;$$

$$n = \left(2\frac{10}{12}\right)(4) = 11\frac{1}{3} = 11.333333$$

$P = S(1 + i)^{-n}$
$= 6000.00(1 + 0.035)^{-11.333333}$
$= 6000.00(0.6771362)$
$= \$4062.82$

Example 14.3b You signed a promissory note at the Continental Bank for $3000.00 due in 27 months. If the bank charges interest at 16% p.a. compounded semi-annually, determine the proceeds of the note.

Solution

The amount shown on the note is the sum of money due in 27 months; that is, the maturity value of the note.

$$S = 3000.00; \qquad i = 8\% = 0.08; \qquad n = \left(\frac{27}{12}\right)(2) = 4.5$$

$P = S(1 + i)^{-n}$
$= 3000.00(1 + 0.08)^{-4.5}$
$= 3000.00(0.7072828)$
$= \$2121.85$

B. Interest-bearing notes

Example 14.3c A five-year note for $8000.00 bearing interest at 12% p.a. compounded monthly is discounted two years and five months before the due date at 14% p.a. compounded semi-annually. Determine the proceeds of the note.

Solution

Step 1 Find the maturity value using $S = P(1 + i)^n$

$$P = 8000.00; \qquad i = 1\% = 0.01; \qquad n = 60$$

$$S = 8000.00(1.01)^{60}$$

$$= 8000.00(1.8166967)$$

$$= \$14533.57$$

Step 2 Find the present value of the maturity value found in Step 1 using $P = S(1 + i)^{-n}$

$$S = 14533.57; \qquad i = 7\% = 0.07; \qquad n = \left(\frac{29}{12}\right)(2) = 4.8333333$$

$$P = 14533.57(1.07)^{-4.8333333}$$

$$= 14533.57(0.7210716)$$

$$= \$10479.75$$

Exercise 14.3

A. Find the proceeds of each of the following promissory notes.

No	Face value	Date of issue	Term	Int. rate	Frequency of conversion	Date of discount	Disct rate	Frequency of conversion
1	$5000	1986-04-01	10 years	—	—	1991-08-01	15%	annually
2	900	1985-08-31	8 years	—	—	1990-06-30	12%	quarterly
3	$3200	1988-03-31	6 years	—	—	1991-10-31	20%	quarterly
4	1450	1987-10-01	9 years	—	—	1992-12-01	14%	semi-annually
5	780	1986-09-30	10 years	14%	annually	1990-04-30	16%	quarterly
6	2100	1985-02-01	12 years	15%	monthly	1989-07-01	17%	semi-annually
7	1850	1987-11-01	5 years	12%	quarterly	1989-10-01	14%	semi-annually
8	3400	1988-01-31	7 years	18%	monthly	1992-12-31	16%	quarterly

B. Solve each of the following problems.

1. A four-year non-interest-bearing promissory note for $3750.00 is discounted thirty-two months after the date of issue at 13.5% compounded semi-annually. Find the proceeds of the note.

2. A seven-year non-interest-bearing note for $5200.00 is discounted three years eight months before its due date at 16% compounded quarterly. Find the proceeds of the note.

3. A non-interest-bearing eight-year note for $4500.00 issued August 1, 1986 is discounted April 1, 1990 at 14.5% compounded annually. Find the compound discount.

4. A $2800.00 promissory note issued without interest for five years on September 30, 1988 is discounted on July 31, 1991 at 18% compounded quarterly. Find the compound discount.

5. A six-year note for $1750.00 issued on December 1, 1986 with interest at 13.5% compounded annually is discounted on March 1, 1989 at 15% compounded semi-annually. What are the proceeds of the note?

6. A ten-year note for $1200.00 bearing interest at 15% compounded monthly is discounted at 16% compounded quarterly three years ten months after the date of issue. Find the proceeds of the note.

7. Four years seven months before its due date a seven-year note for $2650.00 bearing interest at 22% compounded quarterly is discounted at 18% compounded semi-annually. Find the compound discount.

8. On April 15, 1992 a ten-year note dated June 15, 1987 is discounted at 18% compounded quarterly. If the face value of the note is $4000.00 and interest is 16% compounded quarterly, find the compound discount.

14.4 Finding i and n

A. Finding the nominal rate of interest

If the original principal P, the compound amount S and the number of conversion periods n are known, the periodic rate of interest (conversion rate) i may be determined by substituting in Formula 13.1, $S = P(1 + i)^n$ and solving for i.

Example 14.4a   What is the annual compounding rate if $200 accumulates to $495.19 in eight years?

Solution

$$P = 200.00; \qquad S = 495.19; \qquad n = 8$$

$495.19 = 200.00(1 + i)^8 \quad \longleftarrow i \text{ is an } annual \text{ rate}$

$(1 + i)^8 = 2.47595$

$[(1 + i)^8]^{\frac{1}{8}} = 2.47595^{\frac{1}{8}} \qquad \longleftarrow \quad \text{raise each side to the power } \frac{1}{8}$

$1 + i = 2.47595^{0.125}$

$1 + i = 1.1199993$

$i = 0.1199993$

$\quad = 11.99993\% \quad \longleftarrow \text{the desired annual rate}$

The annual compounding rate is 12.0%.

Example 14.4b   Find the nominal annual rate of interest compounded quarterly if $1200.00 accumulates to $2505.78 in five years.

Solution

$$P = 1200.00; \qquad S = 2505.78; \qquad n = 20$$

$2505.78 = 1200.00(1 + i)^{20} \quad \longleftarrow i \text{ is a } quarterly \text{ rate}$

$(1 + i)^{20} = 2.08815$

$1 + i = 2.08815^{0.05} \qquad \longleftarrow \quad \text{raise both sides to the power } \frac{1}{20}, \text{ that is } 0.05$

$1 + i = 1.0374999$

$i = 0.374999$

$\quad = 3.74999\%$

The nominal annual rate of interest is $(3.75\%)(4) = 15.0\%$.

Example 14.4c   At what nominal rate of interest compounded quarterly will money double in four years?

Solution

While neither P nor S are given any sum of money may be used as principal. For purposes of the calculation a convenient value for the principal is $1.00.

$$P = 1; \qquad S = 2; \qquad n = 16$$

$2 = 1(1 + i)^{16} \longleftarrow$ i is a *quarterly* rate

$(1 + i)^{16} = 2$

$1 + i = 2^{\frac{1}{16}}$

$1 + i = 2^{0.0625}$

$1 + i = 1.0442738$

$i = 0.0442738$

$\quad = 4.42738\%$

The nominal annual rate is $4(4.42738\%) = 17.71\%$ (approximately).

Example 14.4d If $1000.00 earns interest of $195.62 in one year
  (i) what is the annual rate of interest?
  (ii) what is the nominal annual rate of interest compounded monthly?

Solution

(i) $P = 1000.00; \qquad I = 195.62; \qquad S = P + I = 1195.62; \qquad n = 1$

$\quad 1195.62 = 1000.00(1 + i)^1 \longleftarrow$ i is an *annual* rate

$\quad 1 + i = 1.19562$

$\qquad i = 1.19562$

$\qquad i = 0.19562$

$\qquad\quad = 19.562\%$

The annual rate of interest is 19.562%.

(ii) $1195.62 = 1000.00(1 + i)^{12} \longleftarrow$ i is a *monthly* rate

$\quad (1 + i)^{12} = 1.19562$

$\quad 1 + i = 1.19562^{\frac{1}{12}}$

$\quad 1 + i = 1.19562^{0.0833333}$

$\quad 1 + i = 1.015$

$\qquad i = 0.015$

$\qquad\quad = 1.5\%$

The nominal annual rate of interest compounded monthly is $(1.5\%)(12) = 18.0\%$.

Example 14.4e Solve the compound amount formula $S = P(1 + i)^n$ for the rate of interest i.

Solution

$$S = P(1 + i)^n$$

$$(1 + i)^n = \frac{S}{P} \quad \longleftarrow \quad \text{divide both sides by P to isolate the compounding factor } (1 + i)^n$$

$$\left[(1 + i)^n\right]^{\frac{1}{n}} = \left(\frac{S}{P}\right)^{\frac{1}{n}} \quad \longleftarrow \quad \text{raise both sides to the power } \tfrac{1}{n}$$

$$1 + i = \left(\frac{S}{P}\right)^{\frac{1}{n}}$$

$$\boxed{\, i = \left(\frac{S}{P}\right)^{\frac{1}{n}} - 1 \,} \quad \longleftarrow \quad \textbf{\textit{Formula}} \ \textbf{14.1}$$

The nominal annual rate of interest can now be determined by multiplying the conversion rate i by the number of conversion periods per year.

Note The result obtained in Example 14.4e represents the general solution for finding the conversion rate i and may be used as a special formula. (See Formula 14.1)

The steps required in solving Formula $S = P(1 + i)^n$ for i are reflected in the steps required to compute i when using an electronic calculator equipped with a power function.

Step 1 Divide S by P to find the numerical value of $(1 + i)^n$.

Step 2 Raise the value obtained in Step 1 to the *reciprocal* of n to obtain the numerical value of $(1 + i)$.

Step 3 Subtract 1 to obtain the value of i in decimal form.

Preprogrammed financial calculators may be used to find i by the same procedure used in Chapter 13 to determine S or P, that is, by selecting the compound interest mode, entering the given variables S, P and n, and retrieving the fourth variable i.

Example 14.4f What is the nominal annual rate of interest compounded quarterly if $720.00 accumulates to $1293.02 in three years?

Solution

$$P = 720.00; \qquad S = 1293.02; \qquad n = 12$$

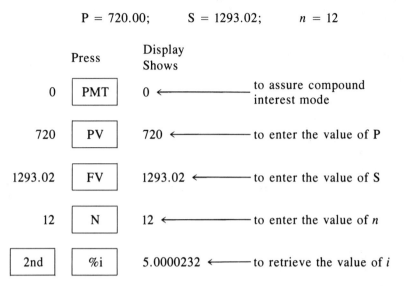

	Press	Display Shows	
0	PMT	0 ⟵————————	to assure compound interest mode
720	PV	720 ⟵————————	to enter the value of P
1293.02	FV	1293.02 ⟵————————	to enter the value of S
12	N	12 ⟵————————	to enter the value of n
2nd	%i	5.0000232 ⟵————————	to retrieve the value of i

The quarterly rate of interest is 5.0%. The nominal annual rate of interest compounded quarterly is 20%.

B. Effective rate of interest

In Example 14.4d compounding at an annual rate of interest of 19.562% has the same effect as compounding at 18% p.a. compounded monthly since in either case the interest amounts to $195.62.

The annual rate of 19.562% is referred to as the **effective rate of interest**. This rate may be defined as the rate of interest compounded annually which yields the same amount of interest as a nominal annual rate of interest compounded a number of times per year other than one.

A formula for finding the effective rate of interest may be obtained as follows.
Let the nominal annual rate of interest be compounded m times per year; let the interest rate per conversion period be i.
Then the accumulated amount after one year $S_1 = P(1 + i)^m$.
Let the corresponding effective annual rate of interest be f;
then the accumulated amount after one year $S_1 = P(1 + f)^1$.

$$P(1 + f)^1 = P(1 + i)^m \quad \longleftarrow \text{ the amounts are equal by definition}$$
$$1 + f = (1 + i)^m \quad \longleftarrow \text{ divide both sides by } P$$
$$\boxed{f = (1 + i)^m - 1} \quad \longleftarrow \textbf{\textit{Formula 14.2}}$$

Example 14.4g Determine the effective rate of interest corresponding to 18% p.a. compounded (i) monthly; (ii) quarterly; (iii) semi-annually; (iv) annually; (v) daily.

Solution

(i) $$i = \left(\frac{18\%}{12}\right) = 0.015; \qquad m = 12$$

$$
\begin{aligned}
f &= (1 + i)^m - 1 \longleftarrow \text{ using Formula 14.2} \\
&= (1 + 0.015)^{12} - 1 \\
&= 1.1956182 - 1 \\
&= 0.1956182 \\
&= 19.562\% \longleftarrow \text{ see Example 14.4d}
\end{aligned}
$$

(ii) $$i = \left(\frac{18\%}{4}\right) = 0.045; \qquad m = 4$$

$$
\begin{aligned}
f &= (1.045)^4 - 1 \\
&= 1.1925186 - 1 \\
&= 0.1925186 \\
&= 19.252\%
\end{aligned}
$$

(iii) $i = (\frac{18\%}{2}) = 0.09; \qquad m = 2$

$$
\begin{aligned}
f &= (1.09)^2 - 1 \\
&= 1.18810 - 1 \\
&= 18.810\%
\end{aligned}
$$

(iv) $$i = 18\% = 0.18; \qquad m = 1$$

$$
\begin{aligned}
f &= (1.18)^1 - 1 \\
&= 18.000\%
\end{aligned}
$$

(v) $i = (\frac{18\%}{365}) = 0.00049315; \qquad m = 365$

$$
\begin{aligned}
f &= (1.00049315)^{365} - 1 \\
&= 1.1971641 - 1 \\
&= 19.716\%
\end{aligned}
$$

Summary of Results

For a nominal annual rate of 18% p.a. effective rates are

when compounding annually ($m = 1$) $\longrightarrow f = 18.000\%$
when compounding semi-annually ($m = 2$) $\longrightarrow f = 18.810\%$
when compounding quarterly ($m = 4$) $\longrightarrow f = 19.252\%$
when compounding monthly ($m = 12$) $\longrightarrow f = 19.562\%$
when compounding daily ($m = 365$) $\longrightarrow f = 19.716\%$

Interpretation of Results

(a) The nominal annual rate is the effective rate of interest if the number of conversion periods per year is 1, that, is if compounding annually.

(b) For a given nominal annual rate, the effective rate of interest increases as the number of conversion periods per year increases.

Example **14.4h**   You have money to invest in interest-earning deposits. You have determined that suitable deposits are available at your Bank paying 13.5% p.a. compounded semi-annually, at a local Trust Company paying 14% p.a. and at your Credit Union paying 13.25% p.a. compounded monthly. What institution offers the best rate of interest?

Solution

Since the methods of conversion differ, the interest rates are not directly comparable. To make the rates comparable the effective rates of interest corresponding to the nominal annual rates should be determined.

For the Bank

$$i = \left(\frac{13.5\%}{2}\right) = 0.0675; \qquad m = 2$$

$$f = (1 + 0.0675)^2 - 1 = 1.1395563 - 1 = 0.1395563 = 13.956\%$$

For the Trust Company

$$i = 14\% = 0.14; \qquad m = 1$$

$$f = i = 14\%$$

For the Credit Union

$$i = \left(\frac{13.25\%}{12}\right) = 0.0110417; \qquad m = 12$$

$$f = (1.0110417)^{12} - 1 = 1.1408503 - 1 = 0.1408503 = 14.085\%$$

While the nominal rate offered by the Credit Union is lowest, the corresponding effective rate of interest is highest due to the higher frequency of conversion. Hence the rate offered by the Credit Union is marginally better.

C.   *Finding the number of conversion periods*

If the principal P, the compound amount S and the periodic rate of interest i are known, the number of conversion periods n may be determined by substituting the known values in $S = P(1 + i)^n$ and solving for n.

Example **14.4i**   In how many years will $2000.00 grow to $5306.60 at 20% compounded quarterly?

Solution

$$P = 2000.00; \qquad S = 5306.60; \qquad i = 5\% = 0.05$$

$5306.60 = 2000.00(1.05)^n$ ⟵——substituting in Formula 13.1

$(1.05)^n = 2.65330$

$n \ln 1.05 = \ln 2.65330$ ⟵————solve for n using natural logarithm

$0.0487902n = 0.9758041$ ⟵————obtain the numerical values

using the ⎡lnx⎤ key

$$n = \frac{0.9758041}{0.0487902}$$

$= 20.000018$

$= 20 \text{ (quarters)}$

Example 14.4j How long does it take for money to double
  (i) at 10% p.a.?
 (ii) at 12% p.a. compounded monthly?
(iii) at 16% p.a. compounded semi-annually?
 (iv) at 20% p.a. compounded quarterly?

Solution

While neither P nor S are given, any sum of money may be used as principal. For purposes of the calculation a convenient value for the principal is $1.00.

$$P = 1.00; \qquad S = 2.00$$

(i) At 10% p.a. $i = 10\% = 0.10$

$$2 = 1(1 + i)^n$$

$$1.10^n = 2$$

$$n \ln 1.10 = \ln 2$$

$$0.0953102n = 0.6931472$$

$$n = 7.2725409 \text{ (years)}$$

At 10% p.a. money doubles in approximately 7 years and 3 months

(ii) At 12% p.a. compounded monthly $i = 1\% = 0.01$

$$2 = 1(1.01)^n$$

$$1.01^n = 2$$

$$n \ln 1.01 = \ln 2$$

$$0.0099503 = 0.6931472$$

$$n = 69.660717 \text{ (months)}$$

At 12% p.a. compounded monthly money doubles in approximately 5 years and 10 months.

(iii) At 16% p.a. compounded semi-annually $i = 8\% = 0.08$

$$1.08^n = 2$$
$$n \ln 1.08 = \ln 2$$
$$0.0769610n = 0.6931472$$
$$n = 9.0064683 \text{ (half-year periods)}$$

At 16% p.a. compounded semi-annually money doubles in approximately 4.5 years.

(iv) At 20% p.a. compounded quarterly $i = 5\% = 0.05$

$$1.05^n = 2$$
$$n \ln 1.05 = \ln 2$$
$$0.0487902n = 0.6931472$$
$$n = 14.206699 \text{ (quarters)}$$

At 20% p.a. compounded quarterly money doubles in approximately 3.5 years.

Note A quick estimator of the number of conversion periods needed to double money in value is given by the **Rule of 70** which indicates that the number of conversion periods required to double money is 70 divided by the periodic rate of interest i. A comparison of the results when estimating using the rule of 70 with the computed values obtained in Example 14.4j is shown below.

	Periodic rate	*Estimated number of conversion periods*	*Computed number of conversion periods*
(i)	10%	$\dfrac{70}{10} = 7$	7.27
(ii)	1%	$\dfrac{70}{1} = 70$	69.66
(iii)	8%	$\dfrac{70}{8} = 8.75$	9.00
(iv)	5%	$\dfrac{70}{5} = 14$	14.21

Example 14.4k Solve the compound amount formula $S = P(1 + i)^n$ for the number of compounding periods n.

Solution

$$S = P(1 + i)^n$$

$$(1 + i)^n = \frac{S}{P}$$

$$n \ln(1 + i) = \ln\left(\frac{S}{P}\right) \longleftarrow \begin{array}{l}\text{take the natural logarithm}\\ \text{of both sides}\end{array}$$

$$\boxed{n = \frac{\ln\left(\frac{S}{P}\right)}{\ln(1 + i)}} \longleftarrow \textbf{\textit{Formula 14.3}}$$

Note The result obtained represents the general solution for finding the number of compounding periods n and may be used as a special formula. (See Formula 14.3)

The steps required in solving Formula 13.1, $S = P(1 + i)^n$, for n are reflected in the steps required to compute n when using an electronic calculator equipped with a natural logarithm function ($\boxed{\ln x}$ key).

Step 1 Divide S by P to find the numerical value of $(1 + i)^n$.

Step 2 Find the natural logarithm of $\frac{S}{P}$ and of $(1 + i)$.

Step 3 Divide the natural logarithm of $\frac{S}{P}$ by the natural logarithm of $(1 + i)$.

Preprogrammed financial calculators may be used to find n by the same procedure previously used to find S, P or i.

Example 14.41 How long will it take for money to triple at 21% compounded monthly?

Solution

Let P = 1;   then S = 3; $i = 1.75\%$

	Press	Display Shows
0	PMT	0
1	PV	1
3	FV	3
1.75	%i	1.75
2nd	N	63.325563 (months)

At 21% compounded monthly money triples in approximately 5 years and 3 months.

Exercise 14.4

A. Compute the rate of interest or the number of interest periods as indicated.

1. Compute the effective rate of interest for each of the following.

    (a) 19.5% compounded semi-annually

    (b) 14.5% compounded quarterly

    (c) 15.0% compounded monthly

    (d) 18.2% compounded monthly

    (e) 14.6% compounded quarterly

    (f) 21.2% compounded semi-annually

2. Find the nominal annual rate of interest for each of the following.

Problem number	Principal	Amount	Time	Frequency of conversion
(a)	$1400.00	$3192.98	7 years	annually
(b)	2350.00	4676.00	5 years	quarterly
(c)	690.00	1812.00	6 years	monthly
(d)	1240.00	4720.80	12 years	semi-annually
(e)	3160.00	5000.00	4 years 9 months	quarterly
(f)	785.00	1200.00	3 years 8 months	monthly

3. Determine the number of compounding periods for each of the following.

Problem number	Principal	Amount	Interest rate	Frequency of conversion
(a)	$2600.00	$6437.50	17%	annually
(b)	1240.00	3249.00	14%	quarterly
(c)	560.00	1350.00	18%	monthly
(d)	3480.00	4715.00	13%	semi-annually
(e)	950.00	1900.00	14%	quarterly
(f)	1300.00	3900.00	20%	semi-annually

B. Solve each of the following.

1. What is the nominal rate of interest compounded quarterly at which $420.00 will accumulate to $1000.00 in nine years six months?

2. A principal of $1250.00 compounded monthly amounts to $2800.00 in 7.25 years. What is the nominal annual rate of interest?

3. At what nominal rate of interest will money double itself in

    (a) six years nine months if compounded quarterly?

    (b) nine years two months if compounded monthly?

4. What is the nominal rate of interest at which money will triple itself in

   (a) twelve years if compounded annually?

   (b) seven years six months if compounded semi-annually?

5. What is the effective rate of interest if $100.00 grows to $150.00 in six years compounded quarterly?

6. If $1100.00 accumulates to $1850.00 in four years six months compounded semi-annually, what is the effective rate of interest?

7. Find the nominal annual rate of interest compounded quarterly which is equal to an effective rate of 19.25%.

8. If the effective rate of interest on an investment is 16.4%, what is the nominal rate of interest compounded monthly?

9. How long will it take $400.00 to accumulate to $760 at 17% p.a. compounded semi-annually?

10. In how many days will $540.00 grow to $600.00 at 13.5 p.a. compounded monthly?

11. In how many years will money quadruple at 17% compounded quarterly?

12. In how many months will money triple at 15% compounded semi-annually?

13. If an investment of $800.00 earned interest of $320.00 at 12% compounded monthly, for how many years was the money invested?

14. A loan of $2000.00 was repaid together with interest of $1164.00. If interest was 14% compounded quarterly, for how many months was the loan taken out?

15. If you borrowed $1000.00 on May 1, 1986 at 10% compounded semi-annually and interest on the loan amounts to $157.63, on what date is the loan due?

16. A promissory note for $600.00 dated May 15, 1987 requires an interest payment of $150.00 at maturity. If interest is at 15% compounded monthly, determine the due date of the note.

17. A non-interest-bearing promissory note for $1500.00 was discounted at 13% p.a. compounded quarterly. If the proceeds of the note were $1199.11, how many months before the due date was the note discounted?

18. A five-year $1000.00 note bearing interest at 11% compounded annually was discounted at 15% compounded semi-annually yielding proceeds of $1416.56. How many months before the due date was the discount date?

14.5 Special problems—equated date, equivalent rates, continuous compounding

A. Equated date

In Chapter 13 section 13.5, the concept of *equivalence* of values when using the compound interest method was considered. In solving problems of equivalence the unknown value was always the size of a payment at the selected focal date.

While this is the most frequently arising problem, occasionally the value to be found is the focal date or the interest rate.

The **equated date** may be defined as the date on which a single sum of money is equal to the sum of two or more dated sums of money. To find an equated date, an equation of value may be set up by the same technique used in Section 13.5. However, solving the equation for n requires the same technique as used in Section 14.4 sub-section C. Since this involves the use of logarithm, the problem can be solved using an electronic calculator provided the calculator is equipped with the natural logarithm function ($\boxed{lnx}$ key).

***Example* 14.5a**   A financial obligation requires the payment of $2000.00 in six months, $3000.00 in fifteen months and $5000.00 in 24 months. When can the obligation be discharged by the single payment equal to the sum of required payments if money is worth 15% p.a. compounded monthly?

Solution

The single payment equal to the sum of the required payments is $2000.00 plus $3000.00 plus $5000.00; that is $10 000.00. Select as focal date the point in time referred to as 'now', and let the number of compounding periods from the focal date to the equated date be represented by n. Since the compounding is done monthly, n will be a number of months and $i = \frac{15\%}{12} = 1.25\% = 0.0125$. The method and data may be represented graphically as shown in Figure 14.1.

Let E_1, E_2, E_3 represent the equivalent values of the original payments at the focal date as indicated in Figure 14.1.

Let E_4 represent the equivalent value of the single payment of $10 000.00 at the focal date.

Then the equation of values may be set up.

$$E_4 = E_1 + E_2 + E_3$$

$$10000.00(1.0125)^{-n} = 2000.00(1.0125)^{-6} + 3000.00(1.0125)^{-15} + 5000.00(1.0125)^{-24}$$

$$10000.00(1.0125)^{-n} = 2000.00(0.9281749) + 3000.00(0.8299932) + 5000.00(0.7421971)$$

$$10000.00(1.0125)^{-n} = 1856.35 + 2489.98 + 3710.99$$

$$10000.00(1.0125)^{-n} = 8057.32$$

$$(1.0125)^{-n} = \frac{8057.32}{10000.00}$$

$$(1.0125)^{-n} = 0.805732$$

$$-n(\ln 1.0125) = \ln 0.805732$$

$$-n(0.0124225) = -0.2160041$$

$$n = \frac{0.2160041}{0.0124225}$$

$$n = 17.388107$$

FIGURE 14.1 *Graphical representation of method and data*

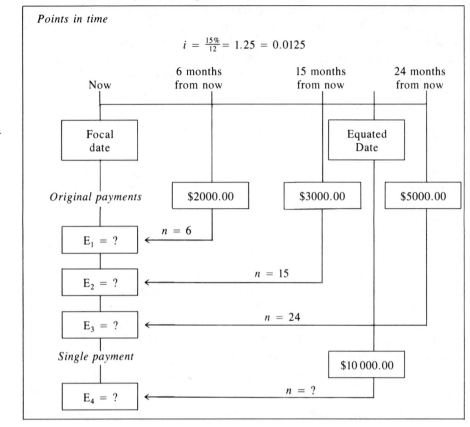

The equated date is about 17.4 months or 529 days from now. While the definition of equated date requires that the single sum of money be equal to the sum of the dated sums of money considered, the method used in solving the problem can be applied to problems in which the single sum of money need not be equal to the sum of the dated sums of money considered.

Example 14.5b A loan is to be repaid by three equal payments of $1500.00 due now, two years from now and four years from now respectively. When can the obligation be paid off by a single payment of $5010.00 if interest is 10% compounded annually?

Solution

Select as focal date the point in time referred to as 'now' and let the number of compounding periods from the focal date to the equated date be represented by n.

Since the compounding is done annually, n will be a number of years and $i = 10\% = 0.10$.

Let E_1, E_2, E_3 represent the equivalent values of the original payments at the focal date.

$$E_1 = 1500.00 \qquad\qquad\qquad\qquad = 1500.00$$
$$E_2 = 1500.00(1.10)^{-2} = 1500.00(0.8264463) = 1239.67$$
$$E_3 = 1500.00(1.10)^{-4} = 1500.00(0.6830135) = 1024.52$$
$$E_1 + E_2 + E_3 = 3764.19$$

Let E_4 represent the equivalent value of the single payment of \$5010.00 at the focal date.

$$E_4 = 5010.00(1.10)^{-n}$$
$$E_4 = E_1 + E_2 + E_3$$
$$5010.00(1.10)^{-n} = 3764.19$$
$$(1.10)^{-n} = 0.7513353$$
$$-n(\ln 1.10) = \ln 0.7513353$$
$$-0.0953102n = -0.2859033$$
$$n = 3$$

The single payment should be made three years from now.

Example 14.5c   A loan of \$2000.00 taken out today is to be repaid by a payment of \$1200.00 in six months and a final payment of \$1000.00. If interest is 15% compounded monthly, when should the final payment be made?

Solution

Let the focal point be 'now' and $i = \frac{15\%}{12} = 1.25\% = 0.0125$.

$$2000.00 = 1200.00(1.0125)^{-6} + 1000.00(1.0125)^{-n}$$
$$2000.00 = 1200.00(0.9281749) + 1000.00(1.0125)^{-n}$$
$$2000.00 = 1113.81 + 1000.00(1.0125)^{-n}$$
$$886.19 = 1000.00(1.0125)^{-n}$$
$$(1.0125)^{-n} = 0.88619$$
$$-n(\ln 1.0125) = \ln 0.88619$$
$$-0.0124225n = -0.1208239$$
$$n = 9.7261997 \text{ (months)}$$
$$n = 296 \text{ } days \longleftarrow \left(\frac{9.7261997}{12}\right)(365)$$

The final payment should be made in 296 days.

B. Equivalent rates

Interest rates which accumulate a given principal to the same compound amount over the same period of time are referred as being equivalent.

Example 14.5d Find the compound amount after one year of $100.00 accumulated at

(i) 12.55% compounded annually; (ii) 12.18% compounded semi-annually;
(iii) 12.00% compounded quarterly; (iv) 11.88% compounded monthly.

Solution

	(i)	(ii)	(iii)	(iv)
Principal	100.00	100.00	100.00	100.00
Nominal rate	12.55%	12.18%	12.00%	11.88%
i	0.1255	0.0609	0.03	0.0099
n	1	2	4	12
Amount	$100.00(1.1255)^1$	$100.00(1.0609)^2$	$100.00(1.03)^4$	$100.00(1.0099)^{12}$
	100.00(1.1255)	100.00(1.1255088)	100.00(1.1255088)	100.00(1.1254870)
	$112.55	$112.55	$112.55	$112.55

Note The four different nominal annual rates produce the same compound amount of $112.55 for the same principal of $100.00 over the same time period of one year. Hence, by definition, the four nominal rates are **equivalent rates**.

To find equivalent rates we need to equate the accumulated values of $1 for the rates under consideration based on a selected time period, usually one year.

Example 14.5e Find the nominal annual rate compounded semi-annually which is equivalent to an effective annual rate of 12%.

Solution

Let the semi-annual rate of interest be represented by i.
For $P = 1$, $n = 2$ the accumulated value $S_1 = (1 + i)^2$.
For the given effective rate the accumulated value $S_2 = (1 + i)^1$.
By definition to be equivalent $S_1 = S_2$

$$(1 + i)^2 = 1.12$$
$$1 + i = 1.12^{0.5}$$
$$1 + i = 1.0583005$$
$$i = 0.0583005 \longleftarrow \text{semi-annual rate}$$

The nominal annual rate is $2(0.0583005) = 0.1166010 = 11.66\%$.

Example 14.5f What nominal rate compounded quarterly is equivalent to 16.2% p.a. compounded monthly?

Solution

Let the quarterly rate be i; $P = 1$; $n = 4$.
The accumulated value of \$1 after one year $S_1 = (1 + i)^4$.
For the given rate $i = \frac{16.2\%}{12} = 1.35\% = 0.0135$; $n = 12$.
The accumulated value of \$1 after one year $S_2 = (1.0135)^{12}$.
To be equivalent $S_1 = S_2$

$$(1 + i)^4 = (1.0135)^{12}$$
$$1 + i = (1.0135)^3$$
$$1 + i = 1.0410492$$
$$i = 0.0410492 \longleftarrow \text{quarterly rate}$$

The nominal annual rate is $4(0.0410492) = 0.1641968 = 16.42\%$.

Example 14.5g Peel Credit Union offers premium savings deposits at 12% interest paid semi-annually. The Board of Directors wishes to change to monthly payment of interest. What nominal rate should the Board set to maintain the same effective rate?

Solution

Let the monthly rate be i; $n = 12$; $P = 1$.
The accumulated value of \$1 in one year $S_1 = (1 + i)^{12}$.
For the existing rate $n = 2$, $i = 0.06$.
The accumulated value of \$1 in one year $S_2 = (1.06)^2$.
To yield the same effective rate, the two rates must be equivalent.

$$(1 + i)^{12} = (1.06)^2$$
$$1 + i = (1.06)^{\frac{1}{6}}$$
$$1 + i = 1.0097588$$
$$i = 0.0097588 \longleftarrow \text{monthly rate}$$

The nominal rate is $12(0.0097588) = 0.117106 = 11.71\%$.

Note The effective annual rate of interests using Formula 14.4
$f = (1 + i)^m - 1$ are
for the existing rate
$f = (1 + 0.06)^2 - 1 = 1.1236 - 1 = 0.1236 = 12.36\%$
for the new nominal rate compounded monthly
$f = (1 + 0.0097588)^{12} - 1 = 1.1236001 - 1 = 0.1236001 = 12.36\%$

C. Continuous compounding

Compounding is not restricted to the commonly used annual, semi-annual, quarterly and monthly intervals but may be done at any time interval. Daily compounding has become quite feasible with the widespread installation of computers in financial institutions. Shorter and shorter time intervals could be used until the limiting case, known as **continuous compounding** is reached.

Formulae for continuous compounding have been developed and are listed below (formulae 14.4, 14.5 and 14.6). Problems involving continuous compounding can be solved using an electronic calculator equipped with an antilog function

($\boxed{e^x}$ key). This function is normally available on calculators equipped with an

$\boxed{lnx}$ key.

492

Mathematics of finance and investments

(a) *Finding the compound amount*

$$\boxed{S = Pe^{nj}} \longleftarrow \text{———————} \textbf{\textit{Formula 14.4}}$$

e = the universal constant 2.7182818 (approximately);
n = the number of years for compounding;
j = the nominal annual rate of interest.

(b) *Finding the present value*

$$\boxed{P = Se^{-nj}} \longleftarrow \text{———————} \textbf{\textit{Formula 14.5}}$$

(c) *Finding the effective rate of interest*

$$\boxed{f = e^{j} - 1} \longleftarrow \text{———————} \textbf{\textit{Formula 14.6}}$$

Example 14.5h To how much will \$100.00 grow at 10% compounded continuously in

(i) one year? (ii) two years? (iii) eight years?

Solution

(i) $\qquad\qquad P = 100.00; \qquad n = 1; \qquad j = 10\% = 0.10$

$\quad S = 100.00[e^{1(0.10)}] \longleftarrow$ substituting in Formula 14.4

$\quad\quad = 100.00(e^{0.10})$

$\quad\quad = 100.00(1.1051709) \longleftarrow$ enter 0.10 in keyboard and

$\quad\quad = \$110.52 \qquad\qquad\qquad$ use $\boxed{e^x}$ key

(ii) $\qquad\qquad P = 100.00; \qquad n = 2; \qquad j = 10\% = 0.10$

$\quad S = 100.00[e^{2(0.10)}] = 100.00(e^{0.20}) = 100.00(1.2214028) = \$122.14$

(iii) $\qquad\qquad P = 100.00; \qquad n = 8; \qquad j = 10\% = 0.10$

$\quad S = 100.00[e^{8(0.10)}] = 100.00(e^{0.80}) = 100.00(2.2255409) = \$222.55$

Example 14.5i What is the present value of $1000.00 at 12% compounded continuously due in   (i) 2.5 years?   (ii) 5 years 9 months? (iii) 12 years 8 months?

Solution

(i) $S = 1000.00$; $n = 2.5$; $j = 12\% = 0.12$

$\quad P = 1000.00\left[e^{-2.5(0.12)}\right]$ ⟵——— substituting in Formula 14.5

$\qquad = 1000.00(e^{-0.30})$

$\qquad = 1000.00(0.7408182)$

$\qquad = \$740.82$

(ii) $S = 1000.00$; $n = 5.75$; $j = 12\% = 0.12$

$\quad P = 1000.00\left[e^{-5.75(0.12)}\right] = 1000.00(e^{-0.69})$

$\qquad\qquad\qquad\qquad = 1000.00(0.5015761)$

$\qquad\qquad\qquad\qquad = \$501.58$

(iii) $S = 1000.00$; $n = 12.666667$; $j = 12\% = 0.12$

$\quad P = 1000.00\left[e^{-12.666667(0.12)}\right] = 1000.00(e^{-1.52})$

$\qquad\qquad\qquad\qquad\qquad = 1000.00(0.2187119)$

$\qquad\qquad\qquad\qquad\qquad = \$218.71$

Example 14.5j Find the effective rate of interest for each of the following nominal rates compounded continuously   (i) 10%   (ii) 15%

Solution

(i) $f = e^{j} - 1$ ⟵——— *Formula* **14.6**
$\quad = e^{0.10} - 1$
$\quad = 1.1051709 - 1$
$\quad = 0.1051709$
$\quad = 10.517\%$ (approximately)

(ii) $f = e^{0.15} - 1 = 1.1618342 - 1 = 0.1618342 = 16.18\%$ (approximately)

Example 14.5k How long will it take money to double if compounded continuously at   (i) 10%   (ii) 18%?

Solution

$$P = 1.00; \qquad S = 2.00$$

$$2.00 = 1.00(e^{nj}) \longleftarrow \text{substituting in Formula 14.4}$$

$$e^{nj} = 2$$

$$nj(\ln e) = \ln 2 \longleftarrow \text{using natural logarithm}$$

$$nj = \frac{\ln 2}{\ln e}$$

$$n = \frac{\ln 2}{j(\ln e)} \longleftarrow \text{a general solution for doubling money}$$

(i) $j = 10\% = 0.10$

$$n = \frac{\ln 2}{0.10(\ln e)}$$

$$= \frac{0.6931472}{0.10(1)} \longleftarrow \boxed{\ln e = 1}$$

$$= 6.9314718 \text{ (years)}$$

$$= 83 \text{ months approximately}$$

(ii) $j = 18\% = 0.18$

$$n = \frac{\ln 2}{0.18(\ln e)}$$

$$= \frac{0.6931472}{0.18(1)}$$

$$= 3.8508177 \text{ (years)}$$

$$= 46 \text{ months approximately}$$

Note   The rule of 70 referred to in Section 14.4 and used to estimate the number of conversion periods required to double money originates from the general solution for doubling money when compounding continuously. Since $\ln e = 1$, the general solution $n = \frac{\ln 2}{j(\ln e)}$ is simplified to $n = \frac{\ln 2}{j}$ and since $\ln 2 = 0.69314718$ or approximately 0.70, an estimate of n is given by $n = \frac{0.70}{j}$. To use the interest in percent form multiply 0.70 by 100—hence the rule of 70. Similar rules might have been established for tripling, quadrupling, etc.

To triple money, $n = \frac{\ln 3}{j} = \frac{1.0986123}{j}$ that is

$\frac{110}{\text{Rate of Interest}} \longrightarrow$ Rule of 110.

For $j = 10\%$, money triples in about $\frac{110}{10} = 11$ compounding periods.

To quadruple money, $n = \frac{\ln 4}{j} = \frac{1.3862944}{j}$ that is $\frac{139}{\text{Rate of interest}}$.

For $j = 10\%$, money quadruples in about $\frac{139}{10} = 14$ periods.

***Example* 14.51** What is the nominal rate compounded continuously which is equivalent to 12% compounded quarterly?

Solution

Let the nominal rate compounded continuously be represented by j.

For $P = 1$ and $n = 1$ the accumulated value in one year $S_1 = e^j$.

For 12% compounded quarterly, the accumulated value in one year $S_2 = (1.03)^4$.

To be equivalent $S_1 = S_2$

$$e^j = (1.03)^4$$
$$e^j = 1.1255088$$
$$j(ln\ e) = ln\ 1.1255088$$
$$j = 0.1182352 \longleftarrow ln\ e = 1$$
$$j = 11.82\%\ (\text{approximately})$$

Exercise 14.5

A. Answer each of the following

1. Find the equated date at which the original payments are equivalent to the single payment for each of the following.

No.	Original payments	Int. rate	Frequency of conversion	Single payment
(a)	$400 due in 9 months and $700 due in 21 months	12%	quarterly	$1256.86
(b)	$1200 due today and $2000 due in 5 years	14%	semi-annually	$3808.70
(c)	$1000 due 8 months ago $1200 due in 6 months and $1500 due in 16 months	15%	monthly	$3500.00
(d)	$600 due in 2 years, $800 due in 3.5 years and $900 due in 5 years	20%	quarterly	$1800.00

2. Find the nominal annual rate of interest compounded annually equivalent to each of the following.
   (a) 12.5% compounded semi-annually
   (b) 21% compounded monthly
   (c) 14.2% compounded quarterly
   (d) 16.2% compounded monthly

3. Find the accumulated value of each of the following sums of money compounded continuously.

(a) $400.00 at 21% for six years

(b) $2700.00 at 14.5% for 12 years

(c) $1800.00 at 16% for four years seven months

(d) $3700.00 at 13.4% for three years ten months

4. Find the present value of each of the following amounts if interest is compounded continuously.

(a) $6000.00 due in 18 years at 17.75%

(b) $3400.00 due in nine years six months at 19.8%

(c) $4500.00 due in two years five months at 16.25%

(d) $1000.00 due in one year nine months at $12\frac{3}{8}\%$

5. Find the effective rate of each of the following nominal rates compounded continuously.

(a) 22.5%

(b) 14.25%

B. Solve each of the following problems.

1. A contract requires payments of $4000.00 today, $5000.00 in three years and $6000.00 in five years. When can the contract be fulfilled by a single payment equal to the sum of the required payments if money is worth 15% p.a. compounded monthly?

2. A financial obligation requires the payment of $500.00 in nine months, $700.00 in fifteen months and $600.00 in 27 months. When can the obligation be discharged by a single payment of $1600.00 if interest is 17% compounded quarterly?

3. Bruce purchased Sheridan Service from Ken agreeing to make three payments of $6000.00 each in one year, three years and five years respectively. Because of initial cash flow difficulties Bruce offered to pay $8000.00 in two years and a second payment of $10 000.00 at a later date. When should the second payment be made if interest is 13% compounded semi-annually?

4. Leo sold a property and is to receive $3000.00 in six months, $4000.00 in 24 months and $5000.00 in 36 months. The deal was renegotiated after nine months at which time a payment of $7000.00 was received by Leo and a further payment of $6000.00 was to be received later. When should the second payment be received if money is worth 14% compounded quarterly?

5. The Central Bank pays 17.5% compounded semi-annually on certain types of deposits. If interest is to be compounded monthly what nominal rate of interest should be set to maintain the same effective rate of interest?

6. The treasurer of Sheridan Credit Union intends to propose a change in the method of compounding interest on premium savings accounts to daily com-

pounding. If the current rate is 12% compounded quarterly, what nominal rate should the treasurer suggest to the Board of Directors to maintain the same effective rate of interest?

7. You have invested $1000.00 for five years at 16% compounded quarterly. How much more interest would you earn if interest were compounded continuously?

8. A private lender requires interest of 16.5% compounded continuously. A local bank charges 16.5% compounded monthly. How much more is the private lenders interest on a loan of $8000.00 taken out for eight years?

9. What single payment made today would pay off two debt payments of $1600.00 each, due in 15 months and 30 months respectively, if interest is 14% compounded continuously?

10. A contract offers $4000.00 in three years, $7000.00 in six years and $9000.00 in eight years. What single sum of money paid today would satisfy the contract if money is worth 11.75% compounded continuously?

11. What is the nominal rate of interest compounded quarterly which is equivalent to 20% compounded continuously?

12. Compute the nominal rate of interest compounded monthly which is equivalent to 15.5% compounded continuously.

13. How long will it take money to double if compounded continuously at
    (a) 21.55%?
    (b) 15.4%?

14. What length of time will it take for money to
    (a) triple at 19% compounded continuously?
    (b) quadruple at 15.4% compounded continuously?

15. What is the nominal rate compounded continuously which is equivalent to 14% compounded quarterly?

16. Find the nominal rate compounded continuously which is equivalent to 17.25% compounded monthly.

Review exercise

1. $6000.00 is invested for six years and seven months at 15% compounded semi-annually. What is the interest earned by the investment?

2. Determine the sum of money which will grow to $14 000 in four years eight months at 15% compounded quarterly.

3. Compute the maturity value of a $5000 promissory note dated November 15, 1986 and due on June 15, 1996 if interest is 18% compounded quarterly.

4. Determine the proceeds of $9000 three years ten months before the due date if interest is 17% compounded semi-annually.

5. A fifteen-year promissory note for $16 500 bearing interest at 15% compounded monthly is discounted at 19% compounded semi-annually three years four months after the date of issue. Compute the proceeds of the note.

6. An eight-year promissory note for $20 000 dated May 2, 1986, bearing interest at 17% compounded quarterly, is discounted on September 2, 1988 at 16.5% compounded semi-annually. Determine the proceeds of the note.

7. An investment of $2000.00 is made for three years four months at 12.5% compounded semi-annually. What is the amount of interest?

8. Determine the discounted value of $5200.00 due in forty months at 13% compounded quarterly.

9. Compute the proceeds of a non-interest-bearing promissory note for $1600.00 two years and eight months before the due date if money is worth 17.5% compounded annually.

10. At what nominal rate of interest compounded monthly will $400.00 earn $300.00 interest in four years?

11. What is the nominal rate of interest compounded monthly which is equivalent to an effective rate of 16.2%?

12. Find the equated date at which two payments of $500.00 due six months ago and $600.00 due today could be settled by a payment of $1300.00 if interest is 15% compounded monthly.

13. Find the accumulated value of $700.00 at 18.5% compounded continuously for seven years.

14. Find the principal which will grow to $1450.00 at 21.2% compounded continuously in six years nine months.

15. In what period of time will money triple at 19% compounded semi-annually?

16. Find the effective rate equivalent to 16.75% compounded continuously.

17. Find the amount of
   (a) $3500 compounded continuously for six years at 24%;
   (b) $8400 compounded continuously for three years eight months at 28%.

18. Find the present value of
    (a) $10 000 due in ten years if interest is 20% compounded continuously;
    (b) $7000 due in four years four months if interest is 15.5% compounded continuously.

19. Find the nominal annual rate of interest correct to two decimals
    (a) at which $2500 will grow to $7000 in eight years compounded quarterly;
    (b) at which money will double in five years compounded semi-annually;
    (c) if the effective annual rate of interest is 24.6% and compounding is done monthly;
    (d) which is equivalent to 16% compounded quarterly;
    (e) which is equivalent to 16% compounded continuously.

20. Compute the effective annual rate of interest correct to two decimals
    (a) for 16.5% compounded monthly;
    (b) at which $2000 will grow the $6800 in seven years compounded quarterly;
    (c) for 19% compounded continuously.

21. (a) What is the nominal annual rate of interest compounded monthly which is equivalent to 18.5% compounded quarterly?
    (b) What is the nominal annual rate of interest compounded quarterly which is equivalent to an effective annual rate of 20%?

22. (a) How many years will it take for $7500 to accumulate to $23 855.95 at 15% compounded semi-annually?
    (b) Over what period of time will money triple at 18% compounded quarterly?
    (c) How long will it take for a loan of $10 000 to cost $6350 at 16.5% compounded monthly?
    (d) In how many years will money double if compounded continuously at 13%?

23. A financial obligation requires the payment of $2000 now, $2500 in six months and $4000 in one year. When can the obligation be discharged by a single payment of $8000 if interest is 18% compounded monthly?

24. Gitu owes two debt payments—a payment of $5000 due in six months and a payment of $6000 due in fifteen months. If Gitu makes a payment of $5000 now, when should he make a payment of $6000 if money is worth 17% compounded semi-annually?

25. Payment of a debt of $10 000 incurred on December 1, 1986 with interest at 15% compounded semi-annually is due on December 1, 1989. If a payment of $7500 is made on December 1, 1988, on what date should a second payment of $7500 be made if money is worth 18% compounded quarterly?

26. Debts of $700 due in six months, $500 due in fifteen months and $900 due in two years are to be settled by a single payment one year from now. What is the size of that single payment if interest is 14.5% compounded continuously?

27. Three years and five months after its date of issue a six-year promissory note for $3300.00 bearing interest at 18% compounded monthly is discounted at 17% compounded semi-annually. Find the proceeds of the note.

28. A seven-year $1500.00 promissory note with interest at 12.5% compounded semi-annually was discounted at 14% compounded quarterly yielding proceeds of $2150.00. How many months before the due date was the discount date?

29. A contract requires payments of $2000.00 in one year and $4000.00 in five years. The contract was renegotiated and met by a payment of $3000.00 in two years and a final payment of $4500.00. If interest was 15.5% compounded continuously, when was the second payment made?

30. What is the nominal rate compounded continuously which is equivalent to 17% compounded semi-annually?

Self-test

1. A ten-year, $9200 promissory note with interest at 21% compounded monthly is discounted at 15% compounded semi-annually yielding proceeds of $34 524.63. How many months before the due date was the date of discount?

2. Determine the maturity value of $1400 due in 71 months compounded annually at 17.75% p.a.

3. Determine the effective annual rate of interest equivalent to 15% compounded monthly.

4. What is the nominal rate of interest compounded continuously which is equivalent to 23.1% compounded quarterly?

5. How many months from now can a payment of $1000 due 12 months ago and a payment of $400 due six months from now be settled by a payment of $2213.44 if interest is 21% compounded monthly?

6. At what nominal rate of interest compounded semi-annually will $6900 earn $6400 interest in five years?

7. In how many years will money double at 13.2% compounded quarterly?

8. What is the nominal rate of interest compounded semi-annually which is equivalent to an effective rate of 20.25%?

9. Seven years and two months after its date of issue an eleven-year promissory note for $8200 bearing interest at 13.5% compounded monthly is discounted at 10.5% compounded semi-annually. Find the proceeds of the note.

10. Find the accumulated value of $5100 invested at 18.9% compounded continuously for ten years and six months.

11. Compute the proceeds of a non-interest-bearing note for $1100, three years seven months before the due date if the money is worth 21% p.a. compounded annually.

12. Find the principal which will grow to $7400 at 15% compounded continuously in ten years and eight months.

Summary of formulae used

Formula 13.1	$S = P(1 + i)^n$	Finding the compound amount when n is a fractional value using the exact method
Formula 13.2	$P = \dfrac{S}{(1 + i)^n}$	Finding the present value (discounted value or proceeds) when n is a fractional value using the exact method
Formula 13.2A	$P = S(1 + i)^{-n}$	
Formula 14.1	$i = \left(\dfrac{S}{P}\right)^{\frac{1}{n}} - 1$	Finding the periodic rate of interest i when P, S and n are known
Formula 14.2	$f = (1 + i)^m - 1$	Finding the effective rate of interest f for a nominal annual rate compounded m times per year
Formula 14.3	$n = \dfrac{\ln\left(\frac{S}{P}\right)}{\ln(1 + i)}$	Finding the number of conversion periods n when P, S and i are known
Formula 14.4	$S = Pe^{nj}$	Finding the compound amount when using continuous compounding
Formula 14.5	$P = Se^{-nj}$	Finding the present value when using continuous compounding
Formula 14.6	$f = e^{j} - 1$	Finding the effective rate of interest for a nominal rate compounded continuously

Glossary of terms used

Continuous compounding the limiting case in compounding with regard to the length of the conversion period

Effective rate of interest the annual rate of interest which yields the same amount of interest per year as a nominal rate compounded a number of times per year

Equated date the date at which a single sum of money is equal to the sum of two or more dated sums of money

Equivalent rates interest rates which accumulate a given principal to the same amount over the same period of time

Rule of 70 a quick estimator of the number of conversion periods needed to double money at a given periodic rate of interest

Mathematics of finance and investments

15 *Ordinary simple annuities*

Introduction

An annuity is a series of payments, usually of equal size, made at periodic time intervals. The word **annuity** implies yearly payments but the term applies to all periodic payment plans, the most frequent of which require annual, semi-annual, quarterly or monthly payments. Practical applications of annuities are widely encountered in the financial dealings of businesses and individuals alike. Payments or receipts of money relating to rent, leases, pensions, family allowances, wages and salaries, insurance premiums, mortgages, loans, interest on bonds and other investments are examples of annuities. Various types of annuities can be identified depending on the term of an annuity, the date of payment and the length of the conversion period. In this chapter we will deal only with ordinary simple annuities.

Objectives

Upon completion of this chapter you will be able to

1. distinguish between types of annuities on the basis of term, payment date and conversion period;
2. compute the amount (or accumulated value) of ordinary annuities;
3. compute the present value (or discounted value) of ordinary annuities;
4. find the periodic rent when either the amount or the present value of an ordinary annuity are known;
5. find the term of an annuity when either the amount or the present value of the annuity are known;
6. find the interest rate when either the amount or the present value of an ordinary annuity are known.

15.1 Introduction to annuities

A. Basic concepts

An annuity is a series of payments, usually of equal size, made at periodic intervals. The length of the time between the successive payments is called the **payment interval** or **payment period**. The length of time from the beginning of the first payment interval to the end of the last payment interval is called the **term of the annuity**. The size of each of the regular payments is referred to as the **periodic rent** and the sum of the periodic payments in one year is called the **annual rent**.

B. Types of annuities

Several time variables affect annuities and lead to a classification of annuities according to the time variable considered.

Depending on whether the term of the annuity is fixed or indefinite, annuities are classified as **annuities certain** or **contingent annuities**.

Typical examples of *annuities certain* (annuities for which the term is fixed; that is, for which both the beginning date and the ending date are known) include rental payments for real estate, lease payments on equipment, instalment payments on loans, mortgage payments and interest payments on bonds and debentures.

Examples of *contingent annuities* (annuities for which the beginning date or the ending date or both are uncertain) are life insurance premiums and pension payments or payments from an RRSP converted into a life annuity at the age of 70. For both of these the ending date is unknown since they terminate with the death of the recipient. Some contingent annuities are the result of clauses in wills, where the beginning date of periodic payments to a beneficiary is unknown, or payments from a trust fund for the remaining life of a surviving spouse since neither the beginning date nor the ending date is known.

A special type of annuity is the **perpetuity**, defined as an annuity for which the payments continue forever. Perpetuities result when the size of the periodic rent is equal to or less than the periodic interest earned by a fund, such as a scholarship fund or an endowment fund to a university.

Variations in the date of payment create another classification of importance to us in dealing with annuities certain.

If payments are made at the end of each payment period we are dealing with an **ordinary annuity**. On the other hand, if payments are made at the beginning of each payment period, we are dealing with an **annuity due**.

Typical examples of ordinary annuities are instalment payments on loans, mortgage payments and interest payments on bonds and debentures, while rent payments on real estate and lease payments on equipment rentals represent annuities due.

Deferring the first payment for a specified period of time gives rise to a

deferred annuity which may be either an ordinary annuity or an annuity due depending on whether the future payments are at the beginning or the end of each payment interval.

A third time variable which bears on the classification of annuities is the length of the conversion period relative to the payment period. We distinguish between **simple annuities** and **complex (or general) annuities** depending on whether or not the conversion period coincides with the payment interval.

An example of a simple annuity is the monthly payments on a loan for which the interest is compounded monthly, since the interest period coincides with the payment period. However, the typical mortgage on homes compounded semi-annually but repaid by monthly payments is an example of a complex (or general) annuity since the conversion period is different from the payment period.

Example **15.1a**   Classify each of the following by
(i) term   (ii) date of payment   (iii) conversion period.

(a) Deposits of $150.00 earning interest at 12% compounded quarterly are made at the beginning of each quarter for four years.

   Solution

    (i) Annuity Certain (the term is fixed: four years)

    (ii) Annuity Due (payments are at the beginning of each quarter)

    (iii) Simple Annuity (the quarterly conversion period equals the quarterly payment period)

(b) Payments of $200.00 are made at the end of each month for five years. Interest is 16% compounded semi-annually.

   Solution

    (i) Annuity Certain (the term is fixed: five years)

    (ii) Ordinary Annuity (payments are at the end of each month)

    (iii) Complex Annuity (semi-annual conversion period does not match the monthly payment period)

(c) A fund of $10 000.00 is deposited in a trust account earning interest compounded annually. Starting five years from the date of deposit, the interest earned for the year is to be paid out as a scholarship.

   Solution

    (i) Perpetuity (the payments can go on forever)

    (ii) Deferred Annuity (the first payment is deferred for 5 years)

    (iii) Simple Annuity (the annual conversion period equals the annual interest period)

(d) In his will, Dr. C. directed that part of his estate be invested in a trust fund earning interest compounded quarterly. His surviving wife was to be paid for the remainder of her life $2000.00 at the end of every three months starting three months after his death.

Solution

(i) Contingent Annuity (both the starting date and ending date are uncertain)

(ii) Ordinary Annuity (payments at the end of every three months)

(iii) Simple Annuity (the quarterly conversion period equals the quarterly payment period)

Note   In this chapter we will deal only with annuities that have a fixed term with payments at the end of each payment period and with conversion periods that coincide with the payment periods; that is, with ordinary simple annuities which are also annuities certain. We will use the word annuity to mean this type of annuity. Other types of annuities will be considered in Chapters 16 and 17.

Exercise 15.1

A.   Classify each of the following by (a) term (b) date (c) conversion period.

1. Payments of $50.00 are made at the beginning of each month for five years at 22% compounded semi-annually.

2. Deposits of $500.00 are made at the end of each quarter for nine years earning interest at 14% compounded quarterly.

3. A fund with an initial deposit of $50 000.00 iṣ set up to provide annual scholarships to eligible business students in an amount not exceeding the annual interest earned by the fund. Scholarship payments are to begin three years from the date of deposit. Interest earned by the fund is compounded semi-annually.

4. A Board of Education introduced a long-term disability plan for its employees. The provisions of the plan provide for monthly payments equal to 90 percent of regular salary starting one month after the beginning of the disability. Assume that the plan is subject to monthly compounding.

5. Gary invested $10 000.00 in an account paying interest compounded monthly with the provision that equal monthly payments be made to him from the account for fifteen years at the beginning of each month starting ten years from the date of deposit.

6. Mr. X set up a trust fund earning interest compounded semi-annually to provide equal monthly support payments for his surviving wife starting one month after his death.

15.2 Amount of an annuity

A. Amount of a series of payments—basic computation

Example 15.2a   Find the amount of deposits of $2000.00, $4000.00, $5000.00, $1000.00 and $3000.00 made at the end of each of five consecutive years respectively at 12% compounded annually just after the last deposit was made.

Solution

The series of deposits may be represented on a time graph as shown:

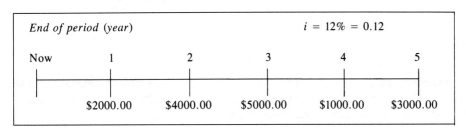

To find the amount of the series of deposits we need to determine the combined value of the five deposits including interest at the focal point *five years from now*. This can be done using Formula 13.1, $S = P(1 + i)^n$. A graphical representation of the method and data is shown in Figure 15.1 below.

FIGURE 15.1 *Grapical representation of method and data*

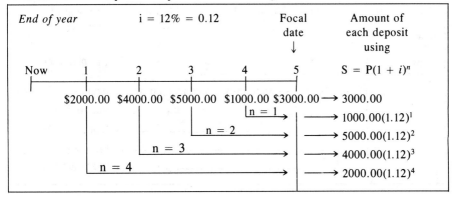

Explanations regarding the amount of each deposit:
The deposit of $3000.00 has just been made and has a value of $3000.00 at the focal date. The deposit of $1000.00 has been in for one year ($n = 1$) and has earned interest for one year at the focal date. Similarly, the deposit of $5000.00 has been in for two years ($n = 2$); the deposit of $4000.00 for three years ($n = 3$) and the deposit of $2000.00 for four years ($n = 4$).

The solution to the problem may now be completed by computing the amount of the individual deposits and adding.

Deposit 5 3000.00   = $3000.00

Deposit 4 1000.00(1.12)^1 = 1000.00(1.12)   =   1120.00

Deposit 3 5000.00(1.12)^2 = 5000.00(1.2544)   =   6272.00

Deposit 2 4000.00(1.12)^3 = 4000.00(1.4049280) =   5619.71

Deposit 1 2000.00(1.12)^4 = 2000.00(1.5735194) =   3147.04

                                                                      Total $19158.75

Example 15.2b   Find the amount of five deposits of $3000.00 each made at the end of each of five consecutive years respectively at 12% compounded annually, just after the last deposit has been made.

Solution

Note that this example is basically the same as Example 15.2a except that all deposits are equal in size. Hence the solution can be approached in the same way.

FIGURE 15.2 *Graphical representation of method and data*

End of year	$i = 12\% = 0.12$					Focal date ↓	Amount of each deposit using
Now	1	2	3	4	5		$S = P(1 + i)^n$
	$3000.00	$3000.00	$3000.00	$3000.00	$3000.00 →	3000.00
					$n = 1$ →	→ 3000.00(1.12)^1
				$n = 2$ →		→ 3000.00(1.12)^2
			$n = 3$ →			→ 3000.00(1.12)^3
		$n = 4$ →				→ 3000.00(1.12)^4

While the approach to solving the problem is fundamentally the same as in Example 15.2a, the fact that the deposits are *equal in size* permits a useful mathematical simplification. The equal deposit of $3000.00 can be taken out as common factor and the individual compounding factors can be added thus avoiding the computation of the amount of each of the individual deposits.

Deposit 5	3000.00(1)	(1)	(1.)
Deposit 4	$3000.00(1.12)^1$	$(1.12)^1$	$(1.12$)
Deposit 3	$3000.00(1.12)^2 =$	$3000.00(1.12)^2 =$	$3000.00(1.2544$)
Deposit 2	$3000.00(1.12)^3$	$(1.12)^3$	$(1.404928$)
Deposit 1	$3000.00(1.12)^4$	$(1.12)^4$	(1.5735194)

$$= 3000.00(6.3528474)$$
$$= \$19058.54$$

Since the deposits in Example 15.2b are equal in size and are made at the end of each period, the problem is an ordinary annuity. Because of the recurring nature of this type of problem it is useful to carry the mathematical simplification beyond just taking out the common factor. To illustrate the simplification the solution to Example 15.2b may be rewritten in equation form and manipulated as shown below.

The amount of the ordinary annuity

$$= 3000.00 + 3000.00(1.12)^1 + 3000.00(1.12)^2 + 3000.00(1.12)^3$$
$$+ 3000.00(1.12)^4$$

$$= 3000.00(1 + 1.12^1 + 1.12^2 + 1.12^3 + 1.12^4)$$

$= 3000.00$ (the sum of the first five terms of a geometric progression whose first term $t_1 = 1$, with a common ratio 1.12)

$$= 3000.00\left(\frac{1.12^5 - 1}{1.12 - 1}\right) \longleftarrow \text{see Chapter 6, Formula 6.9}$$

$$S = a\left(\frac{r^n - 1}{r - 1}\right) \text{ for } r > 1$$

$$= 3000.00\left(\frac{1.7623417 - 1}{0.12}\right)$$

$$= 3000.00\left(\frac{0.7623417}{0.12}\right)$$

$$= 3000.00(6.3528475)$$

$$= \$19058.54$$

Example 15.2c Use the geometric progression approach to determine the accumulated value of payments of $200.00 made at the end of each of six consecutive years if interest is 10% compounded annually.

Solution

Since the payments are equal in size and are made at the end of each compounding period the problem is an ordinary simple annuity and the accumulated value of the payments may be written in equation form.

Let the accumulated value be represented by S. Then

$$S = 200.00 + 200.00(1.10) + 200.00(1.10)^2 + 200.00(1.10)^3$$
$$+ 200.00(1.10)^4 + 200.00(1.10)^5$$

$$= 200.00(1 + 1.10 + 1.10^2 + 1.10^3 + 1.10^4 + 1.10^5)$$

$$= 200.00 \text{ (the sum of the first six terms of a geometric}$$
progression with the first term 1 and common ratio 1.10)

$$= 200.00\left(\frac{1.10^6 - 1}{1.10 - 1}\right)$$

$$= 200.00\left(\frac{1.7715610 - 1}{0.10}\right)$$

$$= 200.00\left(\frac{0.7715610}{0.10}\right)$$

$$= 200.00(7.71561)$$

$$= \$1543.12$$

B. Formula for finding the amount of an ordinary annuity

Because annuities are geometric progressions a general formula can be developed for finding the accumulated value of this type of series of payments.

Using the following generally adopted notation, the general problem is represented in Figure 15.3.

FIGURE 15.3 *Graphical representation of the general form of an ordinary annuity*

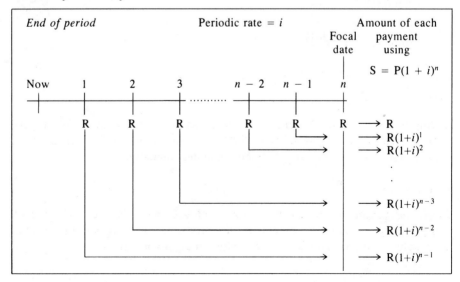

S_n = the amount (accumulated value) of an ordinary annuity;
R = the size of the periodic payment (rent);
i = the interest rate per conversion period;
n = the number of periodic payments (which for simple annuities is also the number of conversion periods).

The addition of the amount of the individual payments at the focal date gives rise to the equation

$$S_n = R + R(1 + i)^1 + R(1 + i)^2 + \ldots + R(1 + i)^{n-3} + R(1 + i)^{n-2} + R(1 + i)^{n-1}$$

$$= R\left[1 + (1 + i)^1 + (1 + i)^2 + \ldots + (1 + i)^{n-3} + (1 + i)^{n-2} + (1 + i)^{n-1}\right]$$

$= R$(the sum of the first n terms of a geometric progression with first term 1 and common ratio $1 + i$)

$$= R\left[\frac{(1 + i)^n - 1}{(1 + i) - 1}\right] \longleftarrow \qquad \text{substituting in Formula 6.9}$$

$$= \boxed{S_n = R\left(\frac{(1 + i)^n - 1}{i}\right)} \longleftarrow \qquad \textbf{Formula 15.1} \quad \textit{Amount of an ordinary annuity}$$

$$\boxed{\frac{(1 + i)^n - 1}{i} = s_{\overline{n}|\,i}}$$

$$\boxed{S_n = R\,s_{\overline{n}|\,i}} \longleftarrow \textbf{Formula 15.1A}$$

The factor $\dfrac{(1 + i)^n - 1}{i}$ is referred to as the **compounding** or **accumulation factor for annuities** or **the accumulated value of one dollar per period** and is customarily represented by the symbol $s_{\overline{n}|\,i}$ (read "s angle n at i").

Example 15.2d Find the accumulated value of quarterly payments of $50.00 made at the end of each quarter for ten years just after the last payment has been made if interest is 16% compounded quarterly.

Solution

Since the payments are of equal size made at the end of each quarter, the problem is an ordinary annuity.

$$R = 50.00; \qquad i = \frac{16\%}{4} = 4\% = 0.04; \qquad n = 10(4) = 40$$

$$S_n = 50.00\left(\frac{(1 + 0.04)^{40} - 1}{0.04}\right) \longleftarrow \text{substituting in Formula 15.1}$$

$$= 50.00\left(\frac{4.8010206 - 1}{0.04}\right)$$

$$= 50.00\left(\frac{3.8010206}{0.04}\right)$$

$$= 50.00(95.025515)$$

$$= \$4751.28$$

Example 15.2e   You deposit $10.00 at the end of each month for five years in an account paying 12% compounded monthly.

(i) How much will be the balance in your account at the end of the five-year term?

(ii) How much of the amount will you have contributed?

(iii) How much is interest?

Solution

(i) $R = 10.00;$ $i = 1\% = 0.01;$ $n = 60$

$$S_n = 10.00\, s_{\overline{60}\,|\,1\%}$$

$$= 10.00\left[\frac{(1.01^{60} - 1)}{0.01}\right]$$

$$= 10.00\left[\frac{(1.8166967 - 1)}{0.01}\right]$$

$$= 10.00(81.66967)$$

$$= \$816.70$$

(ii) Your contribution is $10.00 per month for 60 months; that, is $10.00(60) = \$600.00$.

(iii) Since your contribution is $600.00, the interest earned is $816.70 - 600.00 = \$216.70$.

C. Using preprogrammed financial calculators

Preprogrammed financial calculators may be used efficiently to solve annuity problems by selecting the financial mode, entering the given values and retrieving the answer.

The five variables used in annuity calculations S_n, A_n, R, i, n are programmed into the calculator and are addressed by using keys as follows provided that the calculator is set in the financial mode.

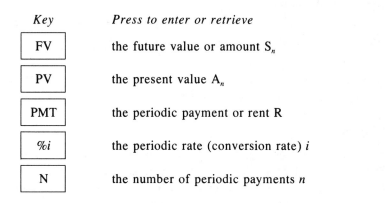

Key	Press to enter or retrieve
FV	the future value or amount S_n
PV	the present value A_n
PMT	the periodic payment or rent R
%i	the periodic rate (conversion rate) i
N	the number of periodic payments n

To begin an ordinary annuity calculation, enter the given values in any order. The value of the wanted variable is then retrieved by pressing | 2nd | followed by the key representing the unknown wanted variable.

When performing an annuity calculation only one of the present value A_n *or the* amount S_n is involved.

To solve Example 15.2e in which R = 10.00, i = 1% and n = 60 the following procedure may be used.

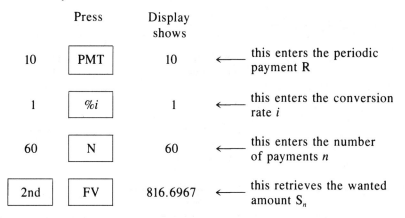

	Press	Display shows	
10	PMT	10	⟵ this enters the periodic payment R
1	%i	1	⟵ this enters the conversion rate i
60	N	60	⟵ this enters the number of payments n
2nd	FV	816.6967	⟵ this retrieves the wanted amount S_n

The future value is $816.70.

D. Applications

Example **15.2f** Jim West set up a savings plan with City Trust of Victoria whereby he deposits $300.00 at the end of each quarter for eight years. The amount in his account at that time will then become a term deposit withdrawable after a further five years. If interest throughout the total time period is 11% compounded quarterly

    (i) how much will be in Jim's account just after he made his last deposit?

    (ii) how much will the balance of his account be when he can withdraw the deposit?

    (iii) how much of the total at the time of withdrawal was contributed by Jim?

    (iv) how much is the interest earned?

Solution

As indicated in Figure 15.4, problems of this type may be solved in stages. The first stage involves finding the amount of an *ordinary annuity*. This amount becomes the principal for the second stage which involves finding the amount of a *single* sum of money invested for five years.

FIGURE 15.4 *Graphical representation of method and data*

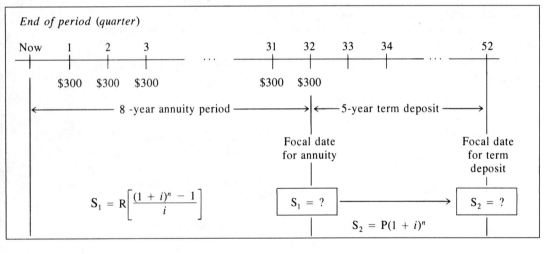

(i) $R = 300.00$; $i = \dfrac{11\%}{4} = 2.75\% = 0.0275$; $n = 8(4) = 32$

$$S_1 = 300.00\left[\frac{(1.0275^{32} - 1)}{0.0275}\right] \quad \longleftarrow \text{Formula 15.1}$$

$$= 300.00\left[\frac{(2.3824214 - 1)}{0.0275}\right]$$

$$= 300.00(50.269869)$$

$$= \$15080.96$$

(ii) $P = S_1 = 15080.96;$ $i = 0.0275;$ $n = 5(4) = 20$

$S_2 = 15080.96(1.0275)^{20}$ ⟵——— Formula 13.1

$= 15080.96(1.7204284)$

$= \$25945.71$

(iii) Jim's contribution $= 32(300.00) = \$9600.00.$

(iv) The amount of interest earned $= 25945.71 - 9600.00 = \$16345.71.$

Example 15.2g   The Gordon's saved for the purchase of their dream home by making deposits of \$1000.00 per year for ten consecutive years in an account with Cooperative Trust in Saskatoon earning interest at 10.75% compounded annually. At the end of the ten-year contribution period the deposit was left for a further six years earning interest at 11.5% compounded semi-annually.

(i) What down payment were the Gordon's able to make on their house?

(ii) How much of the down payment was interest?

Solution

(i) First find the amount of the yearly deposits of \$1000.00 at the end of the term of the ordinary annuity formed by the yearly deposits.

$$R = 1000.00;   i = 10.75\% = 0.1075;   n = 10$$

$$S_1 = 1000.00 \left[\frac{(1.1075^{10} - 1)}{0.1075} \right]$$

$$= 1000.00 \left[\frac{(2.7761143 - 1)}{0.1075} \right]$$

$$= 1000.00(16.521994)$$

$$= \$16521.99$$

Secondly, compute the accumulated value of S_1 in six years.

$$P = S_1 = 16521.99;   i = \frac{11.5\%}{2} = 5.75\% = 0.0575;   n = 12$$

$S_2 = 16521.99(1.0575)^{12}$

$= 16521.99(1.9559805)$

$= \$32316.69$

The Gordon's made a down payment of \$32 316.69.

(ii) Since the Gordon's contributed $(1000.00)(10) = \$10000.00$, the amount of interest in the down payment is \$22 316.69.

Example 15.2h Marcel has contributed $1500.00 per year for the last twelve years into an RRSP deposit account with his Caisse Populaire in Quebec City. Interest earned by these deposits was 9.5% compounded annually for the first eight years and 10.5% compounded annually for the last four years. Five years after the last deposit he converted his RRSP into a Registered Retirement Income Fund (RRIF). How much was the beginning balance in the RRIF if interest for those five years remained at 10.5%?

Solution

As indicated in Figure 15.5, the problem may be divided into two annuities. The first annuity covers the deposits for the first eight years; the second annuity covers the next four payments.

The focal date for the first annuity is at the end of year 8 (Focal date 1).

The accumulated value of this annuity is computed using Formula 15.1.

$$S_1 = 1500\left[\frac{(1.095^8 - 1)}{0.095}\right]$$

$$= 1500.00\left[\frac{(2.0668690 - 1)}{0.095}\right]$$

FIGURE 15.5 *Graphical representation of method and data*

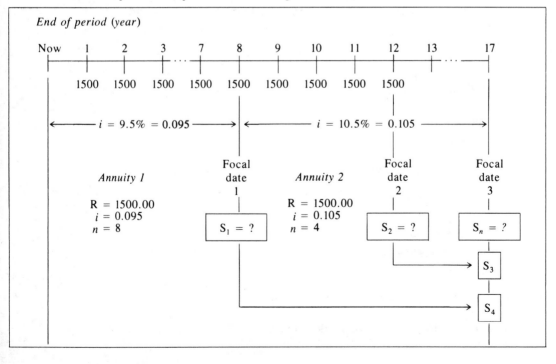

$$= 1500.00(11.230200)$$

$$= \$16845.30$$

S_1 is now accumulated for nine years (to the end of Year 17) at 10.5% to obtain S_4 at the focal date for the beginning balance in the RRIF (Focal date 3).

$$S_4 = 16845.30(1.105)^9$$

$$= 16845.30(2.4561818)$$

$$= \$41375.12$$

The focal date for the second annuity is at the end of Year 12 (Focal date 2).

$$S_2 = 1500.00\left[\frac{(1.105^4 - 1)}{0.105}\right]$$

$$= 1500.00\left[\frac{(1.4909021 - 1)}{0.105}\right]$$

$$= 1500.00(4.6752576)$$

$$= \$7012.89$$

S_2 is now accumulated for five years (to the end of Year 17) to obtain S_3 at Focal date 3.

$$S_3 = 7012.89(1.105)^5$$

$$= 7012.89(1.6474468)$$

$$= \$11553.36$$

The beginning balance S in the RRIF is now obtained by adding S_3 and S_4.

$$S_n = 11553.36 + 41375.12$$

$$= \$52928.48$$

Exercise 15.2

A. Use the geometric progression approach to find the amount of each of the following ordinary annuities.

Problem number	Periodic payment	Payment interval	Term	Interest rate	Conversion period
1.	$2000.00	1 year	4 years	18%	annually
2.	$80.00	1 month	6 months	12%	monthly
3.	$150.00	3 months	15 months	14%	quarterly
4.	$729.00	6 months	2 years	21%	semi-annually

B. Find the amount of the ordinary annuity for each of the following.

Problem number	Periodic payment	Payment interval	Term	Interest rate	Conversion period
1.	$1500.00	1 quarter	$7\frac{1}{2}$ years	13%	quarterly
2.	$20.00	1 month	6.75 years	12%	monthly
3.	$700.00	6 months	20 years	17%	semi-annually
4.	$10.00	1 month	15 years	15%	monthly
5.	$320.00	3 months	8 years 9 months	20.4%	quarterly
6.	$2000.00	$\frac{1}{2}$ year	11 years 6 months	18.8%	semi-annually

C. Answer each of the following questions.

1. Find the accumulated value of payments of $200.00 made at the end of every three months for twelve years if money is worth 13% compounded quarterly.

2. To what will deposits of $60.00 made at the end of each month amount to after six years if interest is 10.8% compounded monthly?

3. How much interest is included in the amount of an ordinary annuity of $1500.00 every six months at 12% compounded semi-annually if the term of the annuity is fifteen years?

4. Jane made ordinary annuity payments of $15.00 per month for sixteen years earning 9% compounded monthly. How much interest is included in the amount of the annuity?

5. Saving for his retirement 25 years from now, Mr. Olsen set up a savings plan whereby he will deposit $25.00 at the end of each month for the next 15 years. Interest is 12% compounded monthly.

   (a) How much money will be in Mr. Olsen's account at the date of his retirement?

   (b) How much will Mr. Olsen contribute?

   (c) How much is interest?

6. The Wolfs have each contributed $1000.00 per year for the last ten years into a joint RRSP account earning 16% compounded annually. If they leave their accumulated contributions for another five years in the RRSP at the same rate of interest.

   (a) how much will Mr. and Mrs. Wolf have in the RRSP?

   (b) how much was contributed by the Wolfs?

   (c) how much will be interest?

7. Mrs. Pitt has made quarterly payments of $1375.00 at the end of each quarter into an RRSP for the last seven years earning interest at 15% compounded quarterly. If

she leaves the accumulated money in the RRSP for another three years at 16% compounded semi-annually, how much will she be able to transfer at the end of the three years into a Registered Retirement Income Fund?

8. For the last six years Joe has made deposits of $300.00 at the end of every six months earning interest at 14% compounded semi-annually. If he leaves the accumulated balance for another ten years at 12% compounded quarterly, what will the balance be in Joe's account then?

15.3 *Present value of an annuity*

A. *Present value of a series of payments—basic computation*

Example 15.3a Find the single sum of money whose value now is equivalent to payments of $2000.00, $4000.00, $5000.00, $1000.00 and $3000.00 made at the end of each of five consecutive years respectively at 12% compounded annually.

Solution

The series of payments may be represented on a time graph.

End of period (year)	$i = 12\% = 0.12$				
Now	1	2	3	4	5
	$2000.0	$4000.00	$5000.00	$1000.00	$3000.00

To find the present value of the series of payments we need to determine the *combined* present value of the five payments at the focal point 'now'. This can be done using Formula 13.2A, $P = S(1 + i)^{-n}$. A graphical representation of the method and data is shown in Figure 15.6.

The solution to the problem may now be completed by computing the present value of the individual payments and adding.

Payment 1	$2000.00(1.12)^{-1} = 2000.00(0.8928571) =$	$1785.71
Payment 2	$4000.00(1.12)^{-2} = 4000.00(0.7971939) =$	3188.78
Payment 3	$5000.00(1.12)^{-3} = 5000.00(0.7117802) =$	3558.90
Payment 4	$1000.00(1.12)^{-4} = 1000.00(0.6355181) =$	635.52
Payment 5	$3000.00(1.12)^{-5} = 3000.00(0.5674269) =$	1702.28

Total $10871.19

FIGURE 15.6 **Graphical representation of method and data**

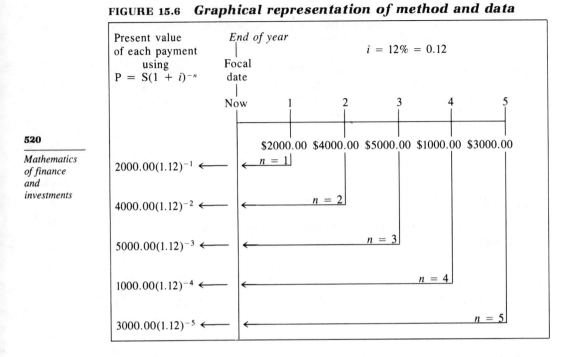

Example 15.3b Find the present value of five payments of $3000.00 made at the end of each of five consecutive years respectively if money is worth 12% compounded annually.

Solution

Note that this example is basically the same as Example 15.3a except that all payments are equal in size.

While the approach to solving the problem is fundamentally the same as in Example 15.3a, the fact that the payments are equal in size permits the same mathematical simplification used for Example 15.2b.

Payment 1	$3000.00(1.12)^{-1}$	$(1.12)^{-1}$	(0.8928571)
Payment 2	$3000.00(1.12)^{-2}$	$(1.12)^{-2}$	(0.7971939)
Payment 3	$3000.00(1.12)^{-3} = 3000.00(1.12)^{-3} = 3000.00(0.7117802)$		
Payment 4	$3000.00(1.12)^{-4}$	$(1.12)^{-4}$	(0.6355181)
Payment 5	$3000.00(1.12)^{-5}$	$(1.12)^{-5}$	(0.5674269)

$$= 3000.00(3.6047762)$$
$$= \$10814.33$$

Since the payments in Example 15.3b are equal in size and are made at the end of each period, the problem is an ordinary annuity. Since finding the sum of the present values of the individual payments at the beginning of the term of an annuity is a recurring problem definded as finding the **present value of an annuity**, it is useful to carry the mathematical simplification beyond just taking out the common factor 3000.00.

FIGURE 15.7 *Graphical representation of method and data*

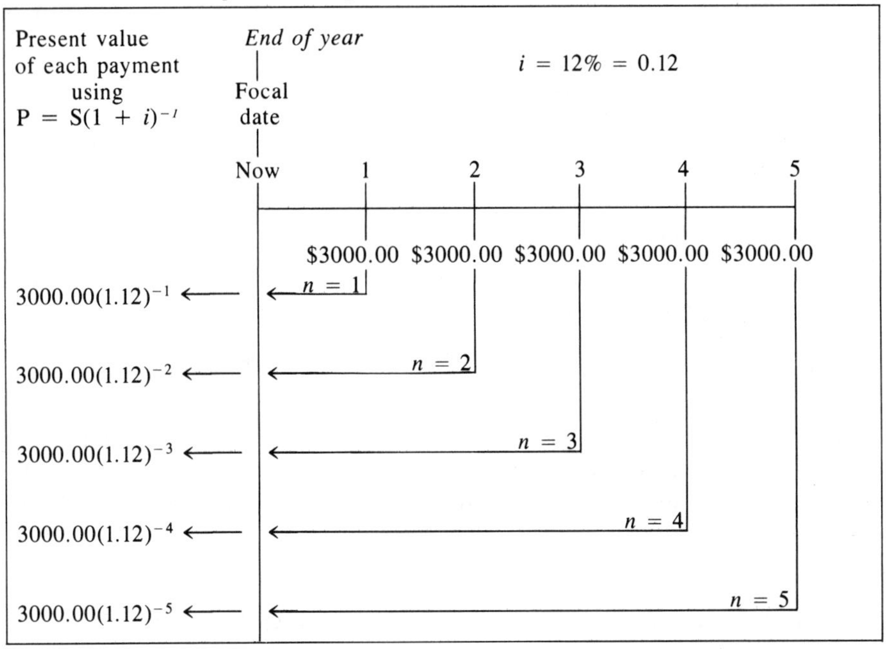

To illustrate the simplification, the solution to Example 15.3b may be rewritten in equation form and manipulated as shown below.

The present value of the ordinary annuity

$= 3000.00(1.12)^{-1} + 3000.00(1.12)^{-2} + 3000.00(1.12)^{-3}$

$\qquad + 3000.00(1.12)^{-4} + 3000.00(1.12)^{-5}$

$= 3000.00(1.12^{-1} + 1.12^{-2} + 1.12^{-3} + 1.12^{-4} + 1.12^{-5})$ ⟵ taking out the common factor 3000.00

$= 3000.00(1.12^{-1})(1 + 1.12^{-1} + 1.12^{-2} + 1.12^{-3} + 1.12^{-4})$ ⟵ taking out the common factor 1.12^{-1}

$= 3000.00(1.12^{-1})$ (the sum of the first five terms of a geometric progression with the first term 1 and common ratio 1.12^{-1})

$= 3000.00(1.12^{-1})\left[\dfrac{1 - (1.12^{-1})^5}{1 - (1.12^{-1})}\right]$ ⟵ see Chapter 6, Formula 6.9

$\qquad\qquad\qquad\qquad\qquad\qquad S = a\left(\dfrac{1 - r^n}{1 - r}\right)$ for $r < 1$

$$= 3000.00\left(\frac{1}{1.12}\right)\left[\frac{1 - 1.12^{-5}}{1 - \frac{1}{1.12}}\right] \longleftarrow \quad \text{convert } 1.12^{-1} \text{ to } \frac{1}{1.12}$$

$$= 3000.00\left(\frac{1}{1.12}\right)\left[\frac{1 - 1.12^{-5}}{\frac{1.12 - 1}{1.12}}\right] \longleftarrow \quad \text{convert } 1 - \frac{1}{1.12} \text{ to } \frac{1.12 - 1}{1.12}$$

$$= 3000.00\left(\frac{1}{1.12}\right)\left[\frac{(1.12)(1 - 1.12^{-5})}{1.12 - 1}\right] \longleftarrow \quad \text{simplify the complex fraction}$$

$$= 3000.00\left(\frac{1}{1}\right)\left[\frac{1 - 1.12^{-5}}{0.12}\right] \longleftarrow \quad \text{reduce by } 1.12$$

$$= 3000.00\left[\frac{(1 - 0.5674269)}{0.12}\right]$$

$$= 3000.00\left(\frac{0.4325731}{0.12}\right)$$

$$= 3000.00(3.6047762)$$

$$= \$10814.33$$

Example 15.3c Use the geometric progression approach to determine the present value at the beginning of the first deposit period of deposits of $600.00 made at the end of each of four consecutive years if money is worth 10% compounded annually.

Solution

Since the deposits are equal in size, made at the end of each period, and since the focal date is at the beginning of the first deposit period, the problem is an ordinary annuity. In equation form the combined present value of the deposits, represented by A_n *may be written as*

$$A_n = 600.00(1.10)^{-1} + 600.00(1.10)^{-2} + 600.00(1.10)^{-3} + 600.00(1.10)^{-4}$$

$$= 600.00(1.10^{-1} + 1.10^{-2} + 1.10^{-3} + 1.10^{-4}) \longleftarrow \text{common factor } 600.00$$

$$= 600.00(1.10^{-1})(1 + 1.10^{-1} + 1.10^{-2} + 1.10^{-3}) \longleftarrow \text{common factor } 1.10^{-1}$$

$$= 600.00(1.10^{-1})\left[\begin{array}{l}\text{the sum of the first four terms}\\ \text{of a geometric progression with}\\ \text{first term 1 and common ratio } 1.10^{-1}\end{array}\right]$$

$$= 600.00(1.10^{-1})\left[\frac{1 - 1.10^{-4}}{1 - 1.10^{-1}}\right] \longleftarrow \quad \text{using Formula 6.9}$$

$$= 600.00\left(\frac{1}{1.10}\right)\left[\frac{1 - 1.10^{-4}}{1 - \frac{1}{1.10}}\right]$$

$$= 600.00\left(\frac{1}{1.10}\right)\left[\frac{(1.10)(1 - 1.10^{-4})}{1.10 - 1}\right]$$

$$= 600.00\left(\frac{1 - 1.10^{-4}}{0.10}\right)$$

$$= 600.00 \left[\frac{(1 - 0.6830135)}{0.10} \right]$$

$$= 600.00(3.1698654)$$

$$= \$1901.92$$

B. Formula for finding the present value of an ordinary annuity

The fact that annuities are geometric progressions and that the present value of an annuity is the sum of the present values of the periodic payments at the beginning of the term of the annuity permits the development of a general formula for finding the present value of an annuity.

Using the following generally adopted notation the general problem is presented in Figure 15.8.

A_n = the present value (discounted value) of an ordinary annuity;

R = the size of the periodic payment (rent);

i = the interest rate per conversion period;

n = the number of periodic payments (which for simple annuities equals the number of conversion periods).

FIGURE 15.8 *Graphical representation of general problem of finding the present value of an ordinary annuity*

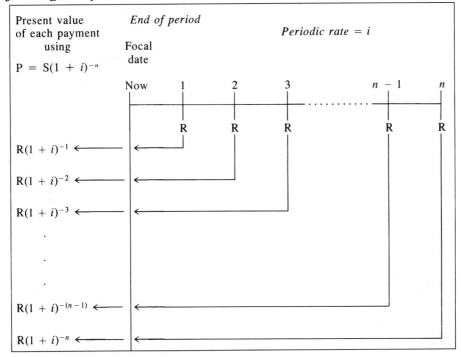

The addition of the present values of the individual payments at the focal date gives rise to the following equation.

$$A_n = R(1 + i)^{-1} + R(1 + i)^{-2} + R(1 + i)^{-3} + \ldots + R(1 + i)^{-(n-1)} + R(1 + i)^{-n}$$

$$= R\left[(1 + i)^{-1} + (1 + i)^{-2} + (1 + i)^{-3} + \ldots\ldots + (1 + i)^{-(n-1)} + (1 + i)^{-n}\right]$$

$$= R\,(1 + i)^{-1}\left[1 + (1 + i)^{-1} + (1 + i)^{-2} + \ldots + (1 + i)^{-(n-2)} + (1 + i)^{-(n-1)}\right]$$

$$= R(1 + i)^{-1}\left[\begin{array}{l}\text{the sum of the first } n \text{ terms of a geometric progression}\\ \text{with first term 1 and common ratio } (1 + i)^{-1}\end{array}\right]$$

$$= R(1 + i)^{-1}\left[\frac{1 - [1 + i)^{-1}]^n}{1 - (1 + i)^{-1}}\right] \longleftarrow \text{substituting in Formula 6.9, } r < 1$$

$$= R\left(\frac{1}{1 + i}\right)\left[\frac{1 - (1 + i)^{-n}}{1 - \frac{1}{1+i}}\right] \longleftarrow \text{convert } (1 + i)^{-1} \text{ to } \frac{1}{1 + i}$$

$$= R\left(\frac{1}{1 + i}\right)\left[\frac{1 - (1 + i)^{-n}}{\frac{(1 + i) - 1}{1 + i}}\right] \longleftarrow \text{convert } 1 - \frac{1}{1 + i} \text{ to } \frac{(1 + i) - 1}{(1 + i)}$$

$$= R\left(\frac{1}{1 + i}\right)\left[\frac{(1 + i)[1 - (1 + i)^{-n}]}{1 + i - 1}\right]$$

$$= R\left(\frac{1 - (1 + i)^{-n}}{i}\right) \longleftarrow \text{reduced by } (1 + i)$$

$$\boxed{A_n = R\left(\frac{1 - (1 + i)^{-n}}{i}\right)} \longleftarrow \textbf{\textit{Formula 15.2}}\text{ \textit{present value of}} \\ \text{\textit{an ordinary annuity}}$$

The factor $\dfrac{1 - (1 + i)^{-n}}{i}$ is referred to as the **Present Value Factor** or **Discount Factor for Annuities** or the **Discounted Value of one Dollar Per Period** and is customarily represented by the symbol $a_{\overline{n}|i}$ (read "a angle n at i").

$$\boxed{\frac{1 - (1 + i)^{-n}}{i} = a_{\overline{n}|i}}$$

$$\boxed{A_n = R a_{\overline{n}|i}} \longleftarrow \textbf{\textit{Formula 15.2A}}$$

Example 15.3d   Find the present value of payments of $50.00 made at the end of each quarter for ten years, at the beginning of the first payment period if interest is 16% compounded quarterly.

Solution

Since the payments are of equal size made at the end of each quarter, the problem is an ordinary annuity and since the focal date is the beginning of the term of the annuity, the formula for finding the present value of an ordinary annuity is applicable.

$$R = 50.00; \qquad i = \frac{16\%}{4} = 0.04; \qquad n = 10(4) = 40$$

$$A_n = 50.00\left(\frac{1 - (1 + 0.04)^{-40}}{0.04}\right) \quad \longleftarrow \text{substituting in Formula 15.2}$$

$$= 50.00\left(\frac{1 - 0.2082890}{0.04}\right)$$

$$= 50.00\left(\frac{0.7917110}{0.04}\right)$$

$$= 50.00(19.792774)$$

$$= \$989.64$$

Example 15.3e If you want to withdraw $100.00 at the end of each month for five years from an account paying 12% compounded monthly

(i) how much must you have on deposit at the beginning of the month in which the first withdrawal is made?

(ii) how much will you receive in total?

(iii) how much of what you will receive is interest?

Solution

(i) $\qquad R = 100.00; \qquad i = 1\% = 0.01; \qquad n = 60,$

$$A_n = 100.00 \; a_{\overline{60}|1\%}$$

$$= 100.00\left[\frac{(1 - 1.01^{-60})}{0.01}\right]$$

$$= 100.00\left[\frac{(1 - 0.5504496)}{0.01}\right]$$

$$= 100.00\left(\frac{0.4495504}{0.01}\right)$$

$$= 100.00(44.95504)$$

$$= \$4495.50$$

(ii) Total receipts will be $100.00 per month for 60 months or $6000.00.

(iii) Since the initial balance must be $4495.50, the interest received will be 6000.00 − 4495.50 = $1504.50.

C. Present value using preprogrammed financial calculators

To find the present value of the ordinary annuity in Example 15.3e in which $R = 100.00$, $i = 1\%$ and $n = 60$, proceed as follows.

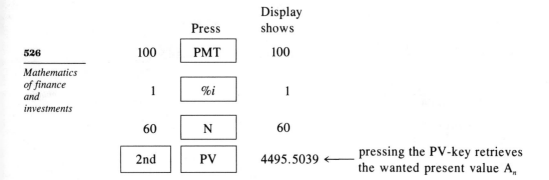

	Press	Display shows	
100	PMT	100	
1	%i	1	
60	N	60	
2nd	PV	4495.5039	← pressing the PV-key retrieves the wanted present value A_n

You must have $4495.50 on deposit.

D. Applications

Example 15.3f A vacation property was bought for $3000.00 down and $1000.00 every half-year for twelve years. If interest is 13% compounded semi-annually, what was the cash value of the property?

Solution

The cash value is the price of the property at the date of purchase and represents the dated value of all payments at that date.

$$\text{CASH VALUE} = \text{DOWN PAYMENT} + \begin{array}{c} \text{PRESENT VALUE OF} \\ \text{THE PERIODIC PAYMENTS} \end{array}$$

Since the first half-yearly payment would be due at the end of the first six-months period, the present value of the periodic payments is the present value of an ordinary annuity.

$$R = 1000.00; \qquad i = \frac{13\%}{2} = 6.5\% = 0.065; \qquad n = 12(2) = 24$$

$$A_n = 1000.00\left[\frac{(1 - 1.065^{-24})}{0.065}\right]$$

$$= 1000.00\left[\frac{(1 - 0.2206020)}{0.065}\right]$$

$$= 1000.00\left(\frac{0.7793980}{0.065}\right)$$

$$= 1000.00(11.990739)$$

$$= \$11990.74$$

The cash value of the property was $3000.00 + 11990.74 = \$14990.74$.

Example 15.3g Mr. Rice expects to retire in seven years and would like to receive $500.00 per month for ten years starting at the end of the first month after his retirement. To achieve this goal he deposited part of the proceeds of $50 000.00 from the sale of a property into a fund earning 10.5% compounded monthly.

(i) How much must be in the fund at the date of his retirement?

(ii) How much of the proceeds did he deposit in the fund?

(iii) How much does he expect to receive from the fund?

(iv) How much of what he will receive is interest?

Solution

As indicated in Figure 15.9, problems of this type may be solved in stages. The first stage involves finding the present value of an annuity. This sum of money becomes the future amount for the second stage which involves finding the present value of that future amount at the date of deposit.

FIGURE 15.9 *Graphical representation of method and data*

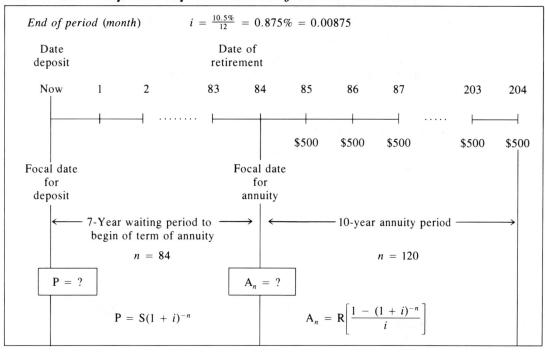

(i) $$R = 500.00; \qquad i = 0.00875; \qquad n = 120$$

$$A_n = 500.00\left[\frac{(1 - 1.00875^{-120})}{0.00875}\right]$$

$$= 500.00\left[\frac{(1 - 0.3515396)}{0.00875}\right]$$

$$= 500.00(74.109758)$$

$$= \$37054.88$$

(ii) $$S = R = 37054.88; \qquad i = 0.00875; \qquad n = 84$$

$$P = 37054.88(1.00875)^{-84}$$

$$= 37054.88(0.4810409)$$

$$= \$17824.91$$

(iii) He expects to receive $500.00(120) = \$60000.00$

(iv) Interest received will be $60000.00 - 17824.91 = \$42175.09$

✓ **Example 15.3h** Sheila Davidson borrowed money from her Credit Union and agreed to repay the loan in blended monthly payments of $180.90 over a four-year period. Interest on the loan was 15% compounded monthly.

(i) How much did she borrow?

(ii) If she missed the first eleven payments, how much would she have to pay at the end of the first year to bring her payments up to date?

(iii) If the Credit Union demanded payment in full after one year, how much money would Mrs. Davidson need?

(iv) If paid off after one year, what would have been the total cost of the loan?

(v) How much of the total loan cost is additional interest paid on the missed payments?

Solution

(i) The amount borrowed is the present value (or discounted value) of the 48 payments as indicated in the time diagram.

$$R = 180.90; \qquad i = \frac{15\%}{12} = 1.25\% = 0.125; \qquad n = 4(12) = 48$$

$$A_n = 180.90\left[\frac{(1 - 1.0125^{-48})}{0.0125}\right] \longleftarrow \text{using Formula 15.2}$$

$$= 180.90\left[\frac{(1 - 0.5508565)}{0.0125}\right]$$

$$= 180.90(35.93148)$$

$$= \$6500.00$$

(ii) As indicated in the diagram below, Mrs. Davidson must pay the accumulated value of the first twelve payments to bring her payments up to date after one year.

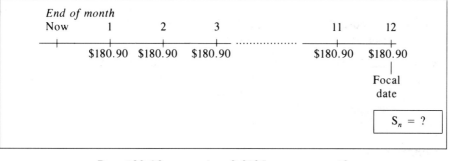

$$R = 180.90; \qquad i = 0.0125; \qquad n = 12$$

$$S_n = 180.90\left[\frac{(1.0125^{12} - 1)}{0.0125}\right] \longleftarrow \text{using Formula 15.1}$$

$$= 180.90\left[\frac{(1.1607545 - 1)}{0.0125}\right]$$

$$= 180.90(12.860361)$$

$$= \$2326.44$$

(iii) The sum of money required to pay off the loan in full is the sum of the accumulated values of the first twelve payments and the discounted values of the remaining 36 payments.

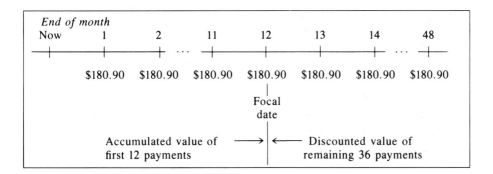

The accumulated value of the first 12 payments, as computed in (ii) above, is $2326.44. The discounted value of the remaining payments is found using formula 15.2.

$$R = 180.90; \qquad i = 0.0125; \qquad n = 36$$

$$A_n = 180.90\left[\frac{(1 - 1.0125^{-36})}{0.0125}\right]$$

$$= 180.90\left[\frac{(1 - 0.6394092)}{0.0125}\right]$$

$$= 180.90(28.847267)$$

$$= \$5218.47$$

The amount of money needed is $5218.47 + 2326.44 = \$7544.91$.

(iv) The total cost of the loan if paid off after one year is
$$7544.91 - 6500.00 = \$1044.91.$$

(v) Since $2326.44 is needed to bring the payments up to date and since the normal amount paid during the first year would have been $180.90(12) = \$2170.80$, the additional interest paid is
$$2326.44 - 2170.80 = \$155.64.$$

Exercise 15.3

A. Use the geometric progression approach to find the present value of each of the following ordinary annuities.

Problem number	Periodic payment	Payment interval	Term	Interest rate	Conversion period
1.	$3000.00	1 year	5 years	16.5%	annually
2.	$920.00	6 months	3 years	21.5%	semi-annually
3.	$75.00	1 month	4 months	13.5%	monthly
4.	$400.00	3 months	15 months	16%	quarterly

B. Determine the present value of the ordinary annuity for each of the following.

Problem number	Periodic payment	Payment interval	Term	Interest rate	Compounding period
1.	$1600.00	6 months	$3\frac{1}{2}$ years	18.5%	semi-annually
2.	$700.00	1 quarter	4 years 9 months	15%	quarterly
3.	$4000.00	1 year	12 years	22.5%	annually
4.	$45.00	1 month	18 years	16.5%	monthly
5.	$250.00	3 months	14 years 3 months	14.4%	quarterly
6.	$80.00	1 month	9.25 years	15.6%	monthly

C. Answer each of the following questions.

1. Find the present value of payments of $375.00 made at the end of every six months for fifteen years if money is worth 17% compounded semi-annually.

2. What is the discounted value of deposits of $60.00 made at the end of each month for nine years if interest is 18% compounded monthly?

3. You want to receive $600.00 at the end of every three months for five years. Interest is 17.6% compounded quarterly.

   (a) How much would you have to deposit at the beginning of the five-year period?

   (b) How much of what you receive is interest?

4. An instalment contract for the purchase of a car requires payments of $270.60 at the end of each month for the next three years. If interest is 13.8% p.a. compounded monthly

   (a) what is the amount financed?

   (b) how much is the interest cost?

5. Ted bought home entertainment equipment paying $400.00 down and signed an instalment contract requiring payments of $69.33 at the end of each month for three years. If interest is 15% compounded monthly

   (a) what was the cash price of the equipment?

   (b) how much was the cost of financing?

6. Herb bought a vacation property for $2500.00 down and quarterly mortgage payments of $633.25 at the end of each quarter for five years. If interest is 14% compounded quarterly

   (a) what was the purchase price of the property?

   (b) how much interest will Herb pay?

7. Ed intends to retire in eight years. To supplement his pension he would like to receive $450.00 every three months for fifteen years. If he is to receive the first payment three months after his retirement and interest is 13% p.a. compounded quarterly, how much must he invest today to achieve his goal?

8. Planning for his son's college education, Mr. Marsh opened an account paying 16.2% compounded monthly. If ordinary annuity payments of $200.00 per month are to be made out of the account for three years starting seven years from now, how much did Mr. Marsh deposit?

9. Bruce signed a chattel mortgage requiring payments of $253.74 at the end of every month for six years at 15% compounded monthly.

   (a) How much was the original mortgage balance?

   (b) If Bruce missed the first five payments, how much would he have to pay after six months to bring the mortgage payments up to date?

   (c) How much would Bruce have to pay after six months to pay out the mortgage?

(d) If the mortgage were paid out, what would the total interest cost be?

(e) How much of the total interest cost is additional interest because of the missed payments?

10. Field Construction agreed to lease payments of $642.79 on construction equipment to be made at the end of each month for three years. Financing is at 18% compounded monthly.

(a) What is the value of the original lease contract?

(b) If, due to delays, the first eight payments were deferred, how much money would be needed after nine months to bring the lease payments up to date?

(c) How much would be required to pay out the lease after nine months?

(d) If the lease were paid off, what would the total interest included in the payout figure be?

(e) How much of the total interest would be due to deferment of the first eight payments?

15.4   Finding the periodic rent

A.   Finding the periodic payment when the amount of the annuity is known

If S_n, i and n are known, R can be determined by substituting the given values in the formula for finding the amount of an ordinary annuity and solving for R.

Example 15.4a   What quarterly deposit will accumulate to $10 000.00 in four years at 14% compounded quarterly?

Solution

$$S_n = 10000.00; \qquad i = \frac{14\%}{4} = 3.5\% = 0.035; \qquad n = 16$$

$$10000.00 = R\left(\frac{1.035^{16} - 1}{0.035}\right) \longleftarrow \text{substituting in Formula 15.1}$$

$$10000.00 = R\left[\frac{(1.733986 - 1)}{0.035}\right]$$

$$10000.00 = R(20.97103)$$

$$R = \frac{10000.00}{20.97103}$$

$$R = \$476.85$$

B.   Finding the periodic payment when the present value of the annuity is known

If A_n, i and n are known, R can be determined by substituting the given values in the formula for finding the present value of the annuity and solving for R.

Example 15.4b What semi-annual payment is required to pay off a loan of $8000.00 in ten years if interest is 16% compounded semi-annually?

Solution

$$A_n = 8000.00; \qquad i = \frac{16\%}{2} = 8\% = 0.08; \qquad n = 10(2) = 20$$

$$8000.00 = R\left(\frac{1 - 1.08^{-20}}{0.08}\right) \quad \longleftarrow \quad \text{substituting in Formula 15.2}$$

$$8000.00 = R\left[\frac{(1 - 0.2145482)}{0.08}\right]$$

$$8000.00 = R(9.8181474)$$

$$R = \frac{8000.00}{9.8181474}$$

$$R = \$814.82$$

C. Finding R using preprogrammed calculators

The periodic payment R may be found by entering the three known values (S_n, n, i or A_n, n, i) and then retrieving the answer by pressing $\boxed{\text{2nd}}$ $\boxed{\text{PMT}}$.

Example 15.4c If you want to have $5000.00 on deposit in your bank account in three years, how much must you deposit at the end of each month if interest is 16.5% compounded monthly?

Solution

$$S_n = 5000.00; \qquad i = 1.375\%; \qquad n = 36$$

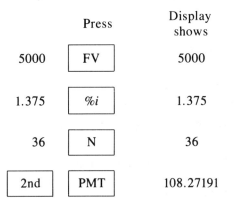

	Press	Display shows
5000	FV	5000
1.375	%i	1.375
36	N	36
2nd	PMT	108.27191

The monthly deposit required is $108.27.

Example 15.4d Derek bought a new car valued $9500. He paid $2000 down and financed the remainder over five years at 15% compounded monthly. How much must Derek pay each month?

Solution

$$A_n = 9500 - 2000 = 7500; \qquad i = \frac{15\%}{12} = 1.25\%; \qquad n = 60$$

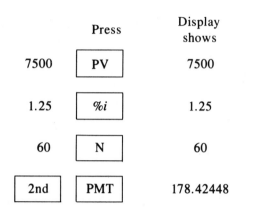

	Press	Display shows
7500	PV	7500
1.25	%i	1.25
60	N	60
2nd	PMT	178.42448

Derek's monthly payment is $178.42.

D. Applications

Example 15.4e Cecile, age 37, expects to retire at age 62. To plan for her retirement she intends to deposit $1500.00 at the end of each of the next 25 years in a Registered Retirement Savings Plan. After her last contribution she intends to convert the then existing balance into a Registered Retirement Income Fund from which she expects to make 20 equal annual withdrawals. If she makes the first withdrawal one year after her last contribution and interest is 10.5% compounded annually, how much is the size of the annual withdrawal?

Solution

As indicated in the time diagram below the problem may be broken into two stages.

Stage 1 Compute the *accumulated* value S_n of the 25 annual deposits of $1500.00 into the RRSP.

$$R = 1500.00; \qquad i = 10.5\% = 0.105; \qquad n = 25$$

$$S_n = 1500.00\left[\frac{(1.105^{25} - 1)}{0.105}\right] \quad \longleftarrow \quad \text{substituting in Formula 15.1}$$

$$= 1500.00\left[\frac{(12.13548 - 1)}{0.105}\right]$$

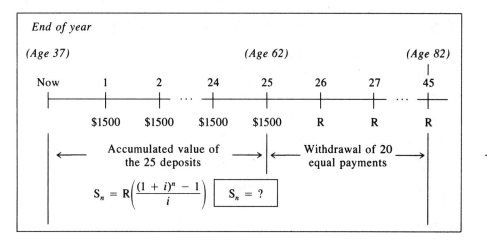

$= 1500.00(106.05219)$

$= \$159078.28$

Step 2 Compute the annual payment that can be withdrawn from the RRIF which has an initial balance of $159 078.28.

$$A_n = 159078.28; \qquad i = 0.105; \qquad n = 20$$

$159078.28 = Ra\overline{_{20|}}\,_{10.5\%} \quad \longleftarrow \quad \text{using Formula 15.2A}$

$159078.28 = R(8.2309089) \quad \longleftarrow a\overline{_{20|}}\,_{10.5\%} = \dfrac{1 - 1.105^{-20}}{0.105}$

$R = 19326.94$

The sum of money which can be withdrawn each year is $19 326.94.

E. Finding R in general terms—supplementary formulae

Depending on whether S_n or A_n is known, the value of R can be obtained in general terms by solving Formulae 15.1 or 15.2.

To find R when S_n is given solve Formula 15.1.

$S = R\left(\dfrac{(1 + i)^n - 1}{i}\right) \quad \longleftarrow \quad \text{Formula 15.1}$

$iS_n = R[(1 + i)^n - 1] \quad \longleftarrow \quad \text{multiply both sides by } i$

$R = \dfrac{iS_n}{(1 + i)^n - 1}$

$$\boxed{R = S_n\left(\dfrac{i}{(1 + i)^n - 1}\right)} \quad \longleftarrow \quad \textbf{\textit{Formula 15.3}}$$

The factor $\dfrac{i}{(1 + i)^n - 1}$ is referred to as the **Sinking Fund Factor** or the

Periodic Deposit which will grow to one dollar at a Future Date. Since this factor is the reciprocal of the accumulation factor $s_{\overline{n}|\,i}$, it may be represented by the symbol $\dfrac{1}{s_{\overline{n}|\,i}}$ and Formula 15.3 may be restated.

$$R = S_n \frac{1}{s_{\overline{n}|\,i}} \qquad \longleftarrow \qquad \textbf{\textit{Formula 15.3A}}$$

To find R when A_n is given solve Formula 15.2.

$$A_n = R\left(\frac{1 - (1 + i)^{-n}}{i}\right) \qquad \longleftarrow \qquad \textbf{\textit{Formula 15.2}}$$

$$iA_n = R\left[1 - (1 + i)^{-n}\right] \qquad \longleftarrow \qquad \text{multiply both sides by } i$$

$$R = \frac{iA_n}{1 - (1 + i)^{-n}}$$

$$R = A_n\left(\frac{i}{1 - (1 + i)^{-n}}\right) \qquad \longleftarrow \qquad \textbf{\textit{Formula 15.4}}$$

The factor $\dfrac{i}{1 - (1 + i)^{-n}}$ is referred to as the **Amortization Factor** or the

Periodic Payment whose Present Value is one dollar. Since this factor is the reciprocal of the discount factor for annuities $a_{\overline{n}|\,i}$, it may be represented by the symbol $\dfrac{1}{a_{\overline{n}|\,i}}$ and Formula 15.4 may be restated.

$$R = A_n \frac{1}{a_{\overline{n}|\,i}} \qquad \longleftarrow \qquad \textbf{\textit{Formula 15.4A}}$$

These special formulae may of course be used when computing with calculators. However, their value is mainly associated with the use of tables and, because of the expanding use of preprogrammed calculators, their usefulness is rapidly diminishing.

Exercise 15.4

A. For each of the following ordinary annuities determine the size of the periodic rent.

No	Amount S_n	Present value A_n	Payment period	Term of annuity	Int. rate	Conversion period
1.	$15 000.00		6 months	7 years 6 months	15.5%	semi-annually
2.	$ 6 000.00		1 quarter	9 years 9 months	13%	quarterly
3.		$12 000.00	12 months	15 years	14.5%	annually
4.		$ 7 000.00	6 months	12.5 years	17.5%	semi-annually
5.	$ 8 000.00		3 months	6 years	16.8%	quarterly
6.		$20 000.00	1 month	20 years	21%	monthly

B. Answer each of the following questions.

1. What deposit made at the end of each quarter for 15 years will accumulate to $20 000.00 at 16% compounded quarterly?

2. What payment is required at the end of each month for five years to repay a loan of $8000.00 at 16.5% compounded monthly?

3. A contract can be fulfilled by making an immediate payment of $7500.00 or equal payments at the end of every six months for ten years. What is the size of the semi-annual payments at 19.6% compounded semi-annually?

4. What payment made at the end of each month for eighteen years will amount to $16 000.00 at 15% compounded monthly?

5. Danny bought a car priced $10 600.00 for 10% down and the balance in equal monthly payments over four years at 16.2% compounded monthly. How much does Danny have to pay each month?

6. The Watsons' bought a rental property valued at $50 000.00 by paying 20% down and mortgaging the balance over 25 years through equal quarterly payments at 14% compounded quarterly. What was the size of the quarterly payment?

7. George plans to deposit $1200.00 at the end of every six months for fifteen years into an RRSP account. After the last deposit he intends to convert the then existing balance into an RRIF and withdraw equal amounts at the end of every six months for twenty years. If interest is expected to be 14.5% compounded semi-annually, how much will George be able to collect every six months?

8. Starting three months after her granddaughter Robin's birth, Mrs. Devine made deposits of $60.00 into a trust fund every three months until Robin was twenty-one years old. The trust fund provides for equal withdrawals at the end of each quarter beginning three months after the last deposit for four years. If interest is 10% compounded quarterly, how much will Robin receive every three months?

9. On the day of his son's birth Mr. Dodd deposited $2000.00 in a trust fund with his Credit Union at 15% compounded quarterly. Following his 18th birthday, the son is to receive equal payments at the end of each month for four years while he is at college. If interest is to be 16.5% compounded monthly after the son's eighteenth birthday, how much will he receive every month?

10. Equal payments are to be made at the end of each month for fifteen years with interest at 9% compounded monthly. After the last payment the fund is to be invested for seven years at 10% compounded quarterly and have a maturity value of $20 000.00. What is the size of the monthly payment?

15.5   Finding the term of an annuity

A.   Finding the term when the amount of the annuity is known

If S_n, R and i are known, n can be determined by substituting the given values in the formula for finding the amount of an annuity and solving for n.

Example 15.5a   How long will it take for $200.00 deposited at the end of each quarter to amount to $6885.29 at 12% compounded quarterly?

Solution

$$S_n = 6885.29; \qquad i = \frac{12\%}{4} = 3\% = 0.03; \qquad R = 200.00$$

$$6885.29 = 200.00\left(\frac{1.03^n - 1}{0.03}\right) \quad \longleftarrow \quad \text{substituting in Formula 15.1}$$

$$34.42645 = \frac{1.03^n - 1}{0.03} \quad \longleftarrow \quad \text{divide both sides by 200.00}$$

$$1.0327935 = 1.03^n - 1 \longleftarrow \quad \text{multiply both sides by 0.03}$$

$$1.03^n = 2.0327935 \longleftarrow \quad \text{add 1 to both sides}$$

$$n \ln 1.03 = \ln 2.0327935 \longleftarrow \quad \text{solve for } n \text{ using natural logarithm}$$

$$0.0295588n = 0.709411$$

$$n = \frac{0.709411}{0.0295588}$$

$$n = 24 \text{ (quarters)}$$

It will take six years for $200.00 per quarter to grow to $6885.29.

B. Finding the term when the present value of the annuity is known

If A_n, R and i are known, n can be determined by substituting the given values in the formula for finding the present value of an annuity and solving for n.

Example 15.5b How many quarterly payments of $600.00 are required to repay a loan of $5400.00 at 14% compounded quarterly?

Solution

$$A_n = 5400.00; \qquad R = 600.00; \qquad i = \frac{14\%}{4} = 3.5\% = 0.035$$

$$5400.00 = 600.00\left(\frac{1 - 1.035^{-n}}{0.035}\right) \longleftarrow \qquad \text{substituting in Formula 15.2}$$

$$9.00 = \frac{1 - 1.035^{-n}}{0.035} \longleftarrow \qquad \text{divide both sides by 600.00}$$

$$0.315 = 1 - 1.035^{-n} \longleftarrow \qquad \text{multiply both sides by 0.035}$$

$$1.035^{-n} = 0.685$$

$$-n \ln 1.035 = \ln 0.685 \longleftarrow \qquad \begin{array}{l} \text{solve for } n \text{ using natural} \\ \text{logarithms} \end{array}$$

$$-0.0344014n = -0.3783364$$

$$n = \frac{0.3783364}{0.0344014}$$

$$n = 10.997696$$

$$n = 11 \text{ quarters}$$

C. Finding n using preprogrammed calculators

Finding the number of periodic payments n is accomplished by entering the three known values (S_n, R, i or A_n, R, i) and then retrieving the answer by pressing

2nd	N

.

Example 15.5c In how many months will your bank account grow to $3000.00 if you deposit $150.00 at the end of each month and the account earns 9% compounded monthly?

Solution

$$S_n = 3000.00; \qquad R = 150.00; \qquad i = \frac{9}{12} = 0.75\%$$

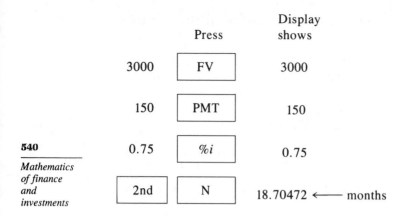

		Press	Display shows
3000		FV	3000
150		PMT	150
0.75		%i	0.75
2nd		N	18.70472 ⟵ months

It will take about 19 months to accumulate $3000.

Interpretation of result

When S_n, R and i are known it is unlikely that n will be a whole number. The fractional time period of 0.7 month indicates that the accumulated value of 18 deposits of $150.00 will be less than $3000.00, while the accumulated value of 19 such deposits will be more than $3000.00. This can be verified by computing S_{18} and S_{19}.

$$S_{18} = 150.00 \left(\frac{1.0075^{18} - 1}{0.0075} \right) = 150.00(19.194717 = \$2879.21$$

$$S_{19} = 150.00 \left(\frac{1.0075^{19} - 1}{0.0075} \right) = 150.00(20.338677) = \$3050.80$$

The concept of an annuity does not provide for making payments at unequal time intervals. Hence the appropriate answer to problems in which n is a fractional value is a whole number. The usual approach is to round upwards so that in this case $n = 19$.

Rounding upwards implies that the deposit made at the end of the 19th month is smaller than the usual deposit of $150.00. The method of computing the size of the final deposit or payment when the term of the annuity is a fractional value rounded upwards is considered in Chapter 18.

Example 15.5d   On his retirement Art received a gratuity of $8000.00 from his employer. Taking advantage of the existing tax legislation, he invested the money in an Income Averaging Annuity which provides for semi-annual payments of $1200.00 at the end of every six months. If interest is 11.5% compounded semi-annually how long will the annuity be in existence?

Solution

$$A_n = 8000.00; \qquad R = 1200.00; \qquad i = \frac{11.5\%}{2} = 5.75\%$$

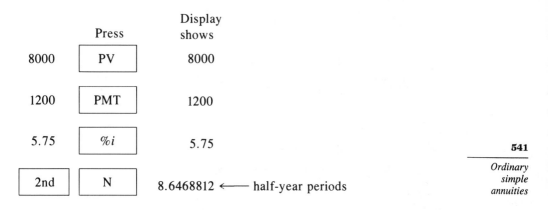

Press	Display shows
8000 [PV]	8000
1200 [PMT]	1200
5.75 [%i]	5.75
[2nd] [N]	8.6468812 ⟵ half-year periods

The annuity will be in existence for four and a half years. Art will receive eight payments of $1200.00 and a final payment which will be less than $1200.00.

Note While special formulae for finding *n* may be developed by solving Formulae 15.1 and 15.2 for *n*, no useful purpose is served any more by such formulae because of the availability of electronic calculators. Accordingly no special formulae for finding *n* are developed or used in this text.

Exercise 15.5

A. Find the term of each of the following ordinary annuities. (State your answer in years and months).

No	Amount S_n	Present value A_n	Periodic rent	Payment interval	Interest rate	Compounding period
1.	$20 000.00		$800.00	1 year	17.5%	annually
2.	$17 000.00		$ 35.00	1 month	12%	monthly
3.		$14 500.00	$190.00	1 month	15%	monthly
4.		$ 5 000.00	$300.00	3 months	20%	quarterly
5.	$ 3 600.00		$175.00	6 months	17.4%	semi-annually
6.		$ 9 500.00	$740.00	1 quarter	15.2%	quarterly

B. Answer each of the following questions.

1. How long would it take you to save $7500.00 by making deposits of $50.00 at the end of every month into a savings account earning 15% compounded monthly?

2. In what period of time could you pay back a loan of $3600.00 by making monthly payments of $96.00 if interest is 19.5% compounded monthly?

3. A deposit of $4000.00 is made today for a five-year period. For how long can $500.00 be withdrawn from the account at the end of every three months starting

three months after the end of the five-year term if interest is 11% compounded quarterly?

4. If $769.14 is deposited into an account earning 11.5% compounded semi-annually at the end of every six months and the balance in the account four years after the last deposit is to be $20 000.00, how many deposits are needed?

15.6 *Finding the rate of interest*

A. *Finding i using preprogrammed calculators*

Finding the rate of interest i per conversion period is accomplished by entering the three known values (S_n, R, n or A_n, R, n) and then retrieving the answer by pressing [2nd] [%i]. The nominal annual rate of interest may then be obtained by multiplying i by the number of compounding periods per year.

Finding i when the amount S_n is known

Example 15.6a Compute the nominal rate of interest at which $50 deposited at the end of each month for ten years will amount to $15 000.

Solution

$$S_n = 15000; \qquad R = 50; \qquad n = 120$$

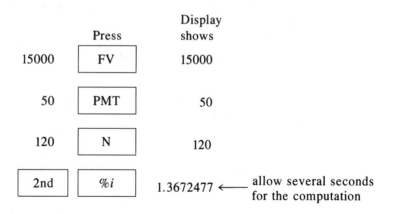

	Press	Display shows
15000	FV	15000
50	PMT	50
120	N	120
2nd	%i	1.3672477 ⟵ allow several seconds for the computation

The monthly conversion rate is 1.3672477%. The nominal rate of interest is (12)(1.3672477%) = 16.41% approximately.

Finding i when the present value A_n is known

Example 15.6b A loan of $6000 is paid off over five years by monthly payments of $157.30. What is the nominal rate of interest on the loan?

Solution

$$A_n = 6000; \qquad R = 157.30; \qquad n = 60$$

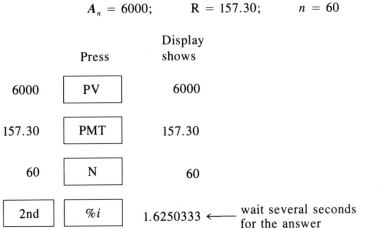

	Press	Display shows	
6000	PV	6000	
157.30	PMT	157.30	
60	N	60	
2nd	%i	1.6250333 ←	wait several seconds for the answer

The monthly compounding rate is 1.6250333%.
The nominal rate of interest is 19.5%.

Note The usefulness of preprogrammed calculators is underlined when finding the conversion rate i. Determination of i requires an iterative process which may take several seconds on a preprogrammed calculator. As illustrated in the following sub-sections B and C, the process is very lengthy when done by hand.

B. Finding the conversion rate i without preprogramming when the amount of an annuity is known

Finding the periodic rate of interest when S_n, R and n are known is a rather awkward problem since substitution of the known values in Formula 15.1 or the general solution of the formula for i result in an exponential equation which is difficult to solve.

For example if $S_n = 25000.00$, $R = 500.00$ and $n = 32$, the substitution in Formula 15.1 gives

$$25000.00 = 500.00\left(\frac{[(1 + i)^{32} - 1]}{i}\right)$$

$$50.00 = \frac{[(1 + i)^{32} - 1]}{i}$$

$$50.00i = (1 + i)^{32} - 1$$

$$(1 + i)^{32} - 50i - 1 = 0$$

Similarly, the general solution of the formula gives

$$\frac{S}{R} = \frac{(1 + i)^n - 1}{i}$$

$$i\left(\frac{S}{R}\right) = (1 + i)^n - 1$$

$$(1 + i)^n - i\left(\frac{S}{R}\right) - 1 = 0$$

The value of i can be found by using an approximation method which is based on trial and error. A value for i is arbitrarily selected and the compounding factor

$$s_{\overline{n}|i} = \frac{\left[(1 + i)^n - 1\right]}{i}$$ is computed. The numerical value of the factor indicates

whether the rate to be found is more or less than the selected rate. The process of selecting a rate, computing the compounding factor and comparing this factor with the actual compounding factor is repeated until an approximation sufficiently close to the actual rate is obtained.

Example 15.6c Finding the nominal rate of interest at which $200.00 deposited at the end of each quarter for 15 years will amount to $20 000.00.

Solution

$$S_n = 20000.00; \qquad R = 200.00; \qquad n = 15(4) = 60$$

$$s_{\overline{n}|i} = \frac{\left[(1 + i)^{60} - 1\right]}{i} = 100.0000$$

We want to find the quarterly rate i for which the accumulation factor $s_{\overline{60}|i} = 100.0000$. The first selection of i should allow for a reasonable range within which the nominal rate may be expected to fall. For most practical purposes this range is 6% to 20%. Thus an initial selection of 12% as the nominal rate is suggested.

Try $i = \frac{12\%}{4} = 3\% = 0.03$.

$$s_{\overline{60}|3\%} = \frac{\left[(1.03)^{60} - 1\right]}{0.03} = 163.05344$$

Since $s_{\overline{60}|3\%} = 163.05343$ is greater than $s_{\overline{60}|i} = 100.0000$,

the selected rate of 3% is greater than the actual rate i and the actual nominal rate must be less than 12%.

A second selection for i must now be made. This selection should allow for the relationship between the value of the actual compounding factor and the factor computed for the selected value of i and should preferably result in a compounding factor which is smaller than 100.00. A considerable drop in rate is indicated since $s_{\overline{60}|3\%}$ is considerably greater than $s_{\overline{60}|i}$.

Try a nominal rate of 6% where $i = 1.5\% = 0.015$.

$s_{\overline{60}|\,1.5\%} = 96.214651$

This means $s_{\overline{60}|\,1.5\%} < s_{\overline{60}|\,i}$, that is, $i > 1.5\%$.

By now we know that $1.5\% < i < 3\%$ and hence that the nominal rate lies between 6% and 12%. Furthermore, because of the closeness of $s_{\overline{60}|\,1.5\%}$ to $s_{\overline{60}|\,i}$, the actual nominal rate must be much closer to 6% than to 12%.

Try a nominal rate of 7% where $i = 1.75\% = 0.0175$.

$s_{\overline{60}|\,1.75\%} = 104.67522$

$1.5\% < i < 1.75\%$ and $6\% <$ nominal rate $< 7\%$.

For closer approximation further rates may be used. In doing so attention should be paid to the size of the computed accumulation factors relative to the actual accumulation factor.

for $i = 1.6\%$ $s_{\overline{60}|\,1.6\%} = 99.495336 \longrightarrow i > 1.6\%$

for $i = 1.62\%$ $s_{\overline{60}|\,1.62\%} = 100.16772 \longrightarrow i < 1.62\%$

for $i = 1.61\%$ $s_{\overline{60}|\,1.61\%} = 99.830835 \longrightarrow i > 1.61\%$

     $1.61\% < i < 1.62\%$

     $i = 1.615\%$ approximately

     $6.44\% <$ nominal rate of interest $< 6.48\%$

The nominal rate of interest is 6.46% approximately. The accuracy of the approximation becomes apparent when comparing the answer with the precise computed value which is 1.6150267% or a nominal rate of 6.4601068%.

Example 15.6d   A debt of $4000.00 is due in two years. An agreement was made whereby the debt could be paid off by making monthly payments of $145.00 at the end of each month for the next two years. What is the nominal rate of interest allowed on the payments?

Solution

$$S_n = 4000.00; \qquad R = 145.00; \qquad n = 24$$

$$s_{\overline{24}|\,i} = \frac{4000.00}{145.00} = 27.586207$$

Try a nominal rate of 12%. $i = 1\% = 0.01$

$$s_{\overline{24}|\,1\%} = 26.973465 \longrightarrow i > 1\%$$

Try a nominal rate of 18%. $i = 1.5\% = 0.015$

$$s_{\overline{24}|\,1.5\%} = 28.633520 \longrightarrow 1\% < i < 1.5\%$$

Try a nominal rate of 15%: $i = 1.25\% = 0.0125$

$$s_{\overline{24}|1.25\%} = 27.788083 \longrightarrow 1\% < i < 1.25\%$$

For $i = 1.15\%$ $s_{\overline{24}|1.15\%} = 27.458606 \longrightarrow 1.15\% < i < 1.25\%$

For $i = 1.19\%$ $s_{\overline{24}|1.19\%} = 27.589811 \longrightarrow i = 1.19\%$ approximately

The nominal rate of interest is approximately 14.28%.
(A more precisely computed value for $i = 1.1889046$ or a nominal rate of 14.266855%).

C. Finding the conversion rate i without preprogramming when the present value of an annuity is known

When A_n, R and n are known, the periodic rate of interest may be found by a method similar to the one used for finding the rate of interest when S_n is known.

The only difference is that the present value factor $a_{\overline{n}|i} = \dfrac{1 - (1 + i)^{-n}}{i}$ is to be approximated. However, care must be taken to allow for the fact that the value of $a_{\overline{n}|i}$ is inversely related to i; that is, the greater i the smaller will be $a_{\overline{n}|i}$.

Example 15.6e What is the nominal rate of interest on a loan of $5000.00 repaid by payments of $425.00 made at the end of each quarter for four years?

Solution

$$A_n = 5000.00; \qquad R = 425.00; \qquad n = 16$$

$$a_{\overline{n}|i} = \frac{[1 - (1 + i)^{-n}]}{i} = \frac{A_n}{R}$$

$$a_{\overline{16}|i} = \frac{5000.00}{425.00} = 11.764706$$

For a nominal rate of 12%, $i = 3\%$ and $a_{\overline{16}|3} = 12.561102$.

Since $a_{\overline{16}|3\%} > a_{\overline{16}|i}$, $3\% < i$ due to the inverse relationship between $a_{\overline{n}|i}$ and i. Hence the next attempt should involve a rate *greater* than 3%.

for $i = 4\%$ $a_{\overline{16}|4\%} = 11.652296 \longrightarrow 3\% < i < 4\%$

for $i = 3.8\%$ $a_{\overline{16}|3.8\%} = 11.826111 \longrightarrow 3.8\% < i < 4\%$

for $i = 3.9\%$ $a_{\overline{16}|3.9\%} = 11.738726 \longrightarrow 3.8\% < i < 3.9\%$

for $i = 3.87\%$ $a_{\overline{16}|3.87\%} = 11.764841$

Thus $i = 3.87\%$ (approximately) and the nominal rate is 15.48%. (A more precisely computed value for $i = 3.870155\%$ or a nominal rate of 15.48062%).

Example 15.6f A car can be bought for $8240.00 plus sales tax of 7%. A financing plan is available requiring a down payment of $800.00 and monthly instalments of $256.00 for three and a half years. What is the nominal rate of interest?

Solution

$$A_n = 8240.00 + 7\% \text{ of } 8240.00 - 800.00 = 8016.80$$

$$R = 256.00; \qquad n = (3.5)(12) = 42$$

$$a_{\overline{42}|i} = \frac{8016.80}{256.00} = 31.315625$$

for $i = 1\%$ $a_{\overline{42}|1\%}$ $= 34.158108 \longrightarrow i > 1\%$

for $i = 1.5\%$ $a_{\overline{42}|1.5\%}$ $= 30.994049 \longrightarrow 1\% < i < 1.5\%$

for $i = 1.4\%$ $a_{\overline{42}|1.4\%}$ $= 31.592375 \longrightarrow 1.4\% < i < 1.5\%$

for $i = 1.44\%$ $a_{\overline{42}|1.4\%}$ $= 31.351073 \longrightarrow 1.44\% < i < 1.5\%$

for $i = 1.45\%$ $a_{\overline{42}|1.45\%}$ $= 31.291160 \longrightarrow 1.44\% < i < 1.45\%$

for $i = 1.446\%$ $a_{\overline{42}|1.446\%}$ $= 31.315105$

The value of $i = 1.1446\%$ approximately and the nominal rate is approximately 17.352%. (The more exact computed rates are $i = 1.4459134$ and the nominal rate $= 17.35096\%$.)

Exercise 15.6

A. Compute the nominal rate of interest for each of the following ordinary annuities.

Problem number	Amount S_n	Present value A_n	Periodic rent	Payment interval	Term	Compounding period
1.	$9000.00		$143.54	3 months	8 years	quarterly
2.	$4800.00		$ 49.00	1 month	5 years	monthly
3.		$7400.00	$119.06	1 month	7 years	monthly
4.		$5540.00	$800.00	6 months	5 years	semi-annually

B. Answer each of the following questions.

1. Compute the nominal rate of interest at which $350.00 paid at the end of every three months for six years accumulates to $12 239.76.

2. What is the nominal rate of interest if a four-year loan of $6000.00 is repaid by montly payments of $171.58?

3. Rene contributed $250.00 every three months into an RRSP for ten years. What was the nominal rate of interest earned by the RRSP if the balance in Rene's account just after he made his last contribution was $19 955.40?

4. Rita converted a RRSP balance of $119 875.67 into an RRIF which will pay her $1800.00 at the end of every month for nine years. What is the nominal rate of interest?

5. A car valued $11 400.00 can be bought for 10% down and monthly payments of $318.56 for three and a half years. What is the effective cost of financing?

6. A property worth $40 000.00 can be purchased for 20% down and quarterly mortgage payments of $1100.00 for 25 years. What effective rate of interest is charged?

Review exercise

1. Payments of $360.00 are made into a fund at the end of every three months for twelve years. If the fund earns interest at 17% compounded quarterly

   (a) how much will be the balance in the fund after twelve years?

   (b) how much of the balance is deposits?

   (c) how much of the balance is interest?

2. A trust fund is set up to make payments of $950.00 at the end of each month for seven and a half years. If interest on the fund is 13.8% compounded monthly

   (a) how much money must be deposited into the fund?

   (b) how much will be paid out of the fund?

   (c) how much interest is earned by the fund?

3. A loan of $4500.00 is to be repaid in equal quarterly payments over two and a half years. If interest is 16% compounded quarterly how much is the quarterly payment?

4. What semi-annual investment will accumulate to $6600.00 in seven and a half years at 12.5% compounded semi-annually?

5. How much interest is included in the accumulated value of $75.90 paid at the end of each month for four years if interest is 9% compounded monthly?

6. If a loan was repaid by quarterly payments of $320.00 in five years at 15% compounded quarterly, how much money had been borrowed?

7. Mr. Arnold borrowed $15 200.00 which he agreed to repay in semi-annual payments of $2000.00 each. If interest on the loan is 17% compounded semi-annually, how long will it take Mr. Arnold to pay off the loan?

8. What nominal rate of interest is paid on quarterly RRSP contributions of $750.00 made for fifteen years if the balance just after the last contribution is $106 000.00?

9. What nominal rate of interest has been charged on a loan of $5600.00 repaid in monthly instalments of $148.90 in four and a half years?

10. Terry bought a car valued at $9300.00 for 20% down and the balance in equal monthly instalments over three and a half years at 15.9% compounded monthly. What was the size of the monthly payment?

11. How long will it take to build up a fund of $10 000.00 by saving $300.00 every six months at 10.5% compounded semi-annually?

12. What is the term of a mortgage of $35 000.00 repaid by monthly payments of $475.00 if interest is 13.5% compounded monthly?

13. An income averaging annuity of $1250.00 per quarter for six years is paid from an initial retirement gratuity of $21 000.00. What nominal rate of interest is paid by the annuity?

14. Donna's annual RRSP contributions of $5500.00 amounted to $100 000.00 after eleven years. What annual interest rate was earned by the contributions?

15. If you were to contribute $1500.00 into an RRSP every six months for twelve years and interest on the deposits is 13.5% compounded semi-annually, how much would the balance in the RRSP be seven years after the last contribution?

16. Doris purchased a piano with $300.00 down and monthly payments of $124.00 for two and a half years at 15% compounded monthly. What was the purchase price of the piano?

17. A truck valued $9650.00 was bought for 20% down and monthly payments for five years. If interest is 16.2% compounded monthly, what is the size of the monthly payment?

18. $10 000.00 is put into a five-year term deposit paying 11.5% compounded semi-annually. After five years the deposit is converted into an ordinary annuity of equal semi-annual payments of $2000.00 each. If interest remains the same, what is the term of the annuity?

19. A trailer valued at $24 000.00 can be bought for 15% down and monthly payments of $495.00 over five years. What is the effective interest rate paid?

20. Glenn has made contributions of $250.00 every three months into an RRSP for ten years. Interest for the first four years was 10% compounded quarterly. Since then the interest rate has been 11% compounded quarterly. How much will Glenn have in his RRSP three years after the last contribution?

21. Mr. Strupp expects to retire in twelve years. Beginning one month after his retirement he would like to receive $500.00 per month for twenty years. How much must he deposit into a fund today to be able to do so if the rate of interest on the deposit is 12% compounded monthly?

22. Al has deposited $125.00 at the end of each month for 15 years at 10.5% compounded monthly. After his last deposit he converted the balance into an ordinary annuity paying $2100.00 every three months for twelve years. If interest on the annuity is compounded quarterly, what is the effective rate of interest paid by the annuity?

23. May received $45 000.00 from her mother's estate. She wants to set aside part of her inheritance for her retirement nine years from now. At the time she would like to receive a pension supplement of $600.00 at the end of each month for 25 years. If the first payment is due one month after her retirement and interest is 10% compounded monthly, how much must May set aside?

24. Ty received a separation payment of $5000.00 at age 35. He invested that sum of money at 11.5% compounded semi-annually until he was 65. At that time he converted the then existing balance into an ordinary annuity paying $8000.00 every three months with interest at 11% compounded quarterly. For how long will the annuity run?

25. Sally contributed $500.00 every six months for fourteen years into an RRSP earning interest at 13.5% compounded semi-annually. Seven years after the last contribution Sally converted the RRSP into an RRIF which is to pay her equal quarterly amounts for sixteen years. If the first payment is due three months after the conversion into the RRIF and interest on the RRIF is 14% compounded quarterly, how much will Sally receive every three months?

26. Wendy deposited $500.00 into an RRSP every three months for 25 years. Upon her retirement she converted the RRSP balance into an RRIF which is to pay her equal quarterly amounts for twenty years. If the first payment is due three months after her retirement and interest is 14% compounded quarterly, how much will Wendy receive every three months?

27. A contract is signed requiring payments of $750.00 at the end of every three months for eight years.

    (a) How much is the cash value of the contract if money is worth 18% compounded quarterly?

(b) If the first three payments are missed, how much would have to be paid after one year to bring the contract up-to-date?

(c) If, because of the missed payments, the contract has to be paid out at the end of one year, how much money is needed?

(d) How much of the total interest paid is due to the missed payments?

28. Aaron deposited $900.00 every six months for twenty years into a fund paying 15.5% compounded semi-annually. Five years after the last deposit he converted the then existing balance in the fund into an ordinary annuity paying him equal monthly payments for fifteen years. If interest on the annuity is 15% compounded monthly, what is the size of the monthly payment he will receive?

29. $8000.00 is invested at a fixed rate of 12.5% compounded semi-annually for seven years. After seven years the fund is converted into an ordinary annuity paying $750.00 per month. If interest on the annuity is 12% compounded monthly, what is the term of the annuity?

30. A savings plan requiring quarterly deposits of $400.00 for twenty years provides for a lump sum payment of $92 000.00 just after the last deposit has been made.

(a) What is the effective rate of interest on the savings plan?

(b) If, instead of the lump sum, monthly ordinary annuity payments of $1350.00 may be accepted at the same nominal rate of interest (correct to two decimals) but compounded monthly, what is the term of the annuity?

Self-test

1. A sum of money is deposited at the end of every month for ten years at 13.5% compounded monthly. After the last deposit, interest for the account is to be 11% compounded quarterly and the account is to be paid out by quarterly payments of $4800 over six years. What is the size of the monthly deposit?

2. You won $100 000 in a lottery and you want to set some of that sum aside for ten years. After ten years you would like to receive $2400 at the end of every three months for eight years. How much of your winnings must you set aside if interest is 10.5% compounded quarterly?

3. A debt can be repaid by payments of $2000 today, $4000 in five years and $3000 in eight years. What single payment would settle the debt three years from today if money is worth 9% compounded quarterly?

4. Compute the nominal annual rate of interest on a loan of $48 000 repaid in semi-annual instalments of $4000 in ten years.

5. A loan of $14 400 is to be repaid in quarterly payments of $600. How many payments are required to repay the loan at 10.5% compounded quarterly?

6. Mr. T. borrowed $7500 at 21.5% compounded quarterly. He repaid $4500 after two years and $7500 after five years. How much will Mr. T. owe at the end of nine years?

7. Determine the effective annual rate of interest earned by quarterly deposits of $3000 made for eight years if the balance just after the last deposit is $180 000.

8. A loan was repaid by monthly payments of $450 in seven years. If interest was 21% compounded monthly, how much interest was paid?

9. Mrs. Simms made quarterly deposits of $540 into a savings account. For the first five years interest was 12% compounded quarterly. Since then the rate of interest has been 10.8% compounded quarterly. How much is the account balance after thirteen years?

10. How much interest is included in the accumulated value of $3200 paid at the end of every six months for four years if the interest rate is 10.5% compounded semi-annually?

11. $46 200 is invested at 19.5% compounded quarterly for four years. After four years the balance in the fund is converted into an annuity. If interest on the annuity is 16.5% compounded semi-annually and payments are made at the end of every six months for seven years, what is the size of the payments?

12. An obligation of $5000 due in four years is to be settled by four equal payments due today, fifteen months from now, twenty-seven months from now and thirty-six months from now respectively. What is the size of the equal payments at 16.5% compounded quarterly?

13. What is the size of semi-annual deposits which will accumulate to $67 200 after eight years at 13.5% compounded semi-annually?

14. Sue contributed $800 every three months for five years into an RRSP earning 19.5% compounded quarterly. Six years after the last contribution she converted the RRSP into an annuity which is to pay her monthly for thirty years. If the first payment is due one month after the conversion into the annuity and interest on the annuity is 13.5% compounded monthly, how much will Sue receive every month?

Summary of formulae used

Formula 15.1 $S_n = R\left[\dfrac{(1 + i)^n - 1}{i}\right]$ Finding the amount (accumulated value) of an ordinary simple annuity.

Formula 15.1A $\quad S_n = R\, s_{\overline{n}|i}$

Finding the amount of an ordinary annuity using the symbol for the accumulation factor.

Formula 15.2 $\quad A_n = R\left[\dfrac{1 - (1 + i)^{-n}}{i}\right]$

Finding the present value (discounted value) of an ordinary annuity.

Formula 15.2A $\quad A_n = R\, a_{\overline{n}|i}$

Finding the present value of an annuity using the symbol for the discount factor.

Formula 15.3 $\quad R = S_n\left[\dfrac{i}{(1 + i)^n - 1}\right]$

Finding the periodic rent when the amount of the ordinary annuity is known.

Formula 15.3A $\quad R = S_n\, \dfrac{1}{s_{\overline{n}|i}}$

Finding the periodic rent when the amount is known using the symbol for the sinking fund factor.

Formula 15.4 $\quad R_n = A\left[\dfrac{i}{(1 - (1 + i)^{-n}}\right]$

Finding the periodic rent when the present value of the ordinary annuity is known.

Formula 15.4A $\quad R = A_n\, \dfrac{1}{a_{\overline{n}|i}}$

Finding the periodic rent when the present value of the ordinary annuity is known using the symbol for the amortization factor.

Glossary of terms used

Accumulation factor for annuities $\quad$ the factor $\dfrac{(1 + i)^n - 1}{i}$ represented by the symbol $s_{\overline{n}|i}$

Accumulated value of one dollar per period $\quad$ see *Accumulation factor*

Amortization factor   the factor $\dfrac{1}{a_{\,\overline{n}|\,i}}$ used to find the periodic rent when the present value of the annuity is known

Amount of an annuity   the sum of the accumulated values of the periodic payments at the end of the term of the annuity

Annual rent   the sum of the periodic payments in one year

Annuity   a series of payments, usually equal in size, made at equal periodic time intervals

Annuity certain   an annuity for which the term is fixed

Annuity due   an annuity in which the payments are made at the beginning of each payment interval

Complex annuity   an annuity in which the conversion (or compounding) period is different from the payment interval

Compounding factor for annuities   see *Accumulation factor*

Contingent annuity   an annuity in which the term is uncertain; that is either the beginning date of the term or the ending date of the term or both are unknown

Deferred annuity   an annuity in which the first payment is delayed for a number of payment periods

Discount factor for annuities   see *Present value factor*

Discounted value of one dollar per period   see *Present value factor*

General annuity   see *Complex annuity*

Ordinary annuity   an annuity in which the payments are made at the end of each payment interval

Payment interval   the length of time between successive payments

Payment period   see *Payment interval*

Periodic deposit (or payment) which will grow to one dollar at a future date   see *Sinking fund factor*

Periodic payment whose present value is one dollar   see *Amortization factor*

Periodic rent   the size of the regular periodic payment

Perpetuity   an annuity for which the payments continue forever

Present value of an annuity   the sum of the present values (or discounted values) of the periodic payments at the beginning of the term of the annuity

Present value factor for annuities   the factor $\dfrac{1-(1+i)^{-n}}{i}$ represented by the symbol $a_{\,\overline{n}|\,i}$

Simple annuity   an annuity in which the conversion period is the same as the payment interval

Sinking fund factor   the factor $\dfrac{1}{s\,\overline{n}|i}$ used to find the periodic rent when the amount of the annuity is known

Term of an annuity   the length of time from the beginning of the first payment interval to the end of the last payment interval

16 *Other simple annuities*

Introduction

The basic type of annuity—the ordinary annuity in which the payments are made at the end of each payment period—was considered in Chapter 15.

In this chapter we will consider other simple annuities resulting from variations in the payment dates. These include Annuities Due in which payments are made in advance, Deferred Annuities in which the first payment is made at a point in time later than the end of the first payment interval and Perpetuities in which payments continue indefinitely.

Objectives

Upon completion of this chapter you will be able to

1. determine the amount and present value of annuities due;
2. find the periodic rent, the term and the interest rate for annuities due;
3. determine the present value of ordinary deferred annuities and deferred annuities due;
4. find the periodic rent, the term and the interest rate for deferred annuities;
5. determine the present value of simple perpetuties.

16.1 *Annuities due—amount and present value*

A. *Amount of an annuity due*

By definition an **annuity due** is an annuity in which the periodic payments are made at the beginning of each payment period.

Finding the amount of such an annuity is very similar to finding the amount of an ordinary annuity. In fact, the amount of an annuity due is very closely related to the amount of an ordinary annuity. This same close relationship also holds for the present value.

Example 16.1a Find the accumulated value of deposits of $3000.00 each made at the beginning of five consecutive years respectively at 12% compounded annually, at the ending date of the last payment period.

Solution

As for any problem involving a series of payments, the method of solution and the data may be represented on a time diagram.

FIGURE 16.1 *Graphical representation of method and data*

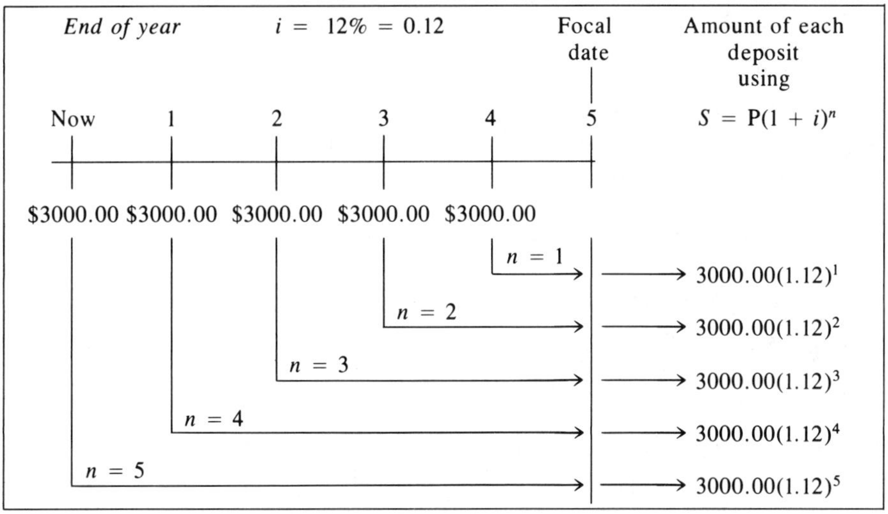

As indicated in the diagram, the first deposit is located at the beginning of Year 1 which is the same as 'now'; the second deposit is located at the beginning of Year 2 which is the same as the end of Year 1; the third at the beginning of Year 3; the fourth at the beginning of Year 4; and the fifth and last deposit at the beginning of Year 5 which is also the beginning of the last payment period. The focal date, however, is located at the *ending* of the last payment period.

The accumulated values of the individual deposits are obtained by using Formula 13.1 $S = P(1 + i)^n$. Finding the combined total of the five accumulated values is facilitated by taking out the common factors 3000.00 and 1.12 as shown below.

Deposit 5	$3000.00(1.12)^1$	(1.12)	$(1. \quad)$	$(1. \qquad)$
Deposit 4	$3000.00(1.12)^2$	$(1.12)^2$	(1.12)	$(1.12 \qquad)$
Deposit 3	$3000.00(1.12)^3 =$	$3000.00(1.12)^3 =$	$3000.00(1.12)(1.12)^2 =$	$3000.00(1.12)(1.2544 \quad)$
Deposit 2	$3000.00(1.12)^4$	$(1.12)^4$	$(1.12)^3$	$(1.404928 \ )$
Deposit 1	$3000.00(1.12)^5$	$(1.12)^5$	$(1.12)^4$	(1.5735194)

$$= 3000.00(1.12)(6.3528474)$$
$$= 19058.54(1.12)$$
$$= \$21345.56$$

Note This example is the same as Example 15.2b, except that the deposits are made at the beginning of each payment period rather than at the end. The answer to Example 15.2b was $19 058.54. This means that we could have obtained the answer to this example by simply multiplying the answer to Example 15.2b by 1.12. This can be verified by writing the problem in equation form and using the geometric series approach.

The amount of the series of deposits

$$= 3000.00(1.12)^1 + 3000.00(1.12)^2 + 3000.00(1.12)^3 + 3000.00(1.12)^4 + 3000.00(1.12)^5$$

$$= 3000.00(1.12 + 1.12^2 + 1.12^3 + 1.12^4 + 1.12^5)$$

$$= 3000.00(1.12)(1 + 1.12 + 1.12^2 + 1.12^3 + 1.12^4)$$

$$= 3000.00(1.12)(\text{the sum of the first five terms of a geometric progression whose first term is 1 with a common ratio 1.12})$$

$$= 3000.00(1.12)\left(\frac{1.12^5 - 1}{1.12 - 1}\right) \longleftarrow \text{using Formula 6.9, } r>1$$

$$= 3000.00(1.12)(6.3528474)$$

$$= 19058.54(1.12)$$

$$= \$21345.56$$

Example 16.1b Use the geometric progression approach to determine the accumulated value of payments of $200.00 made at the beginning of each of six consecutive years if interest is 10% compounded annually.

Solution

Since the payments are equal in size and are made at the beginning of each payment period the problem is an annuity due and the focal date for finding the amount is the end point of the last payment period. The accumulated value of the payments may be written in equation form.

Let the accumulated value of the annuity due be represented by $S_n(\text{due})$.

$$S_n(\text{due}) = 200.00(1.10)^1 + 200.00(1.10)^2 + 200.00(1.10)^3 + 200.00(1.10)^4 + 200.00(1.10)^5 + 200.00(1.10)^6$$

$$= 200.00(1.10 + 1.10^2 + 1.10^3 + 1.10^4 + 1.10^5 + 1.10^6)$$

$$= 200.00(1.10)(1 + 1.10 + 1.10^2 + 1.10^3 + 1.10^4 + 1.10^5)$$

$$= 200.00(1.10)(\text{the sum of the first six terms of a geometric progression with first term 1 and common ratio 1.10})$$

$$= 200.00(1.10)\left(\frac{1.10^6 - 1}{1.10 - 1}\right)$$

$$= 2000.00(1.10)(7.71561)$$

$$= 1543.12(1.10)$$

$$= \$1697.43$$

Note Example 16.1b is the same as Example 15.2c except that the payments have been made at the beginning of each payment period. The answer to Example 15.2c was $1543.12 and again we could have used this answer to find the solution to Example 16.1b by simply multiplying by the factor 1.10. This factor consists of $1 + 0.10$ and, since $0.10 = i$, 1.10 is the factor $(1 + i)$.

Furthermore, as the annuity in Example 15.2c was an ordinary annuity while the answer in Example 16.1b is an annuity due, it appears that the amount of the annuity due can be obtained by multiplying the amount of the ordinary annuity by the factor $(1 + i)$. This implication can be verified by solving the simple annuity due in a general way.

The general notation for annuities due is the same as for ordinary annuities except that the accumulated value of the annuity due is represented by the symbol $S_n(\text{due})$. The simple annuity due is represented in Figure 16.2 and the general solution follows.

FIGURE 16.2 *Graphical representation of the general problem of finding the amount of an annuity due*

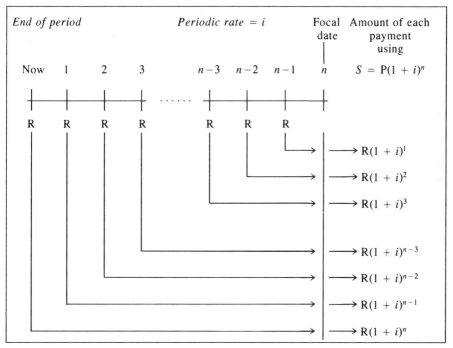

The addition of the accumulated value of the individual payments at the focal gives rise to the following equation.

$$S_n(\text{due}) = R(1 + i)^1 + R(1 + i)^2 + R(1 + i)^3 + \ldots + R(1 + i)^{n-2} + R(1 + i)^{n-1}$$
$$+ R(1 + i)^n$$

$$= R\left[(1 + i)^1 + (1 + i)^2 + (1 + i)^3 + \ldots + (1 + i)^{n-2} + (1 + i)^{n-1} + (1 + i)^n\right]$$

$$= R(1 + i)\left[1 + (1 + i)^1 + (1 + i)^2 + \ldots + (1 + i)^{n-3} + (1 + i)^{n-2} + (1 + i)^{n-1}\right]$$

$= R(1 + i)$(the sum of the first n terms of a geometric progression with first term 1 and common ratio $1 + i$)

$$= R(1 + i)\left(\frac{(1 + i)^n - 1}{(1 + i) - 1}\right) \quad \longleftarrow \text{ substituting in Formula 6.9}$$

$$\boxed{S_n(\text{due}) = R(1 + i)\left(\frac{(1 + i)^n - 1}{i}\right)} \quad \longleftarrow \begin{array}{l} \textbf{\textit{Formula 16.1:}} \\ \textit{Amount of an annuity due} \end{array}$$

Since the factor $\dfrac{(1 + i)^n - 1}{i}$ is represented by the symbol $s_{\overline{n}|i}$

$$\boxed{S_n(\text{due}) = R(1 + i)\, s_{\overline{n}|i} = R\, s_{\overline{n}|i}\,(1 + i)} \quad \longleftarrow \textbf{\textit{Formula 16.1A}}$$

Note Formula 16.1 and 16.1A, The amount of an annuity due, differ from Formula 15.1 and 15.1A, The amount of an ordinary annuity, only by the factor $(1 + i)$.

$$\boxed{\begin{array}{c} \text{THE AMOUNT OF} \\ \text{AN ANNUITY DUE} \end{array} = (1 + i) \times \begin{array}{c} \text{AMOUNT OF THE} \\ \text{ORDINARY ANNUITY} \end{array}}$$

The relationship between an annuity due and the corresponding ordinary annuity is graphically illustrated in the comparison of the line diagrams.

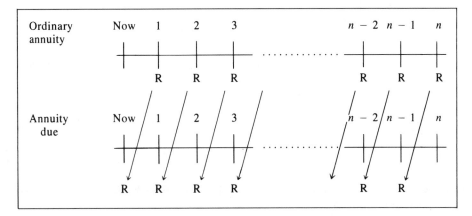

The two line graphs show the shift of the payments by one period. In an annuity due every payment earns interest for one more period than in an ordinary annuity and this explains the factor $(1 + i)$.

Example 16.1c Find the accumulated value of quarterly payments of $50.00 made at the beginning of each quarter for ten years, at the end of the last payment period if interest is 16% compounded quarterly.

Solution

Since the payments are of equal size made at the beginning of each period, the payment series is an annuity due and since the focal date is the end of the last payment period, the amount of the annuity due is to be found.

$$R = 50.00; \qquad i = \frac{16\%}{4} = 4\% = 0.04; \qquad n = 10(4) = 40$$

$$S_n(\text{due}) = 50.00(1.04)\left(\frac{1.04^{40} - 1}{0.04}\right) \quad \longleftarrow \text{substituting in Formula 16.1}$$

$$= 50.00(1.04)(95.025516)$$
$$= 4751.28(1.04)$$
$$= \$4941.33$$

Example 16.1d You deposit $10.00 at the beginning of each month for five years in an account paying 12% compounded monthly.

(i) How much will the balance in your account be at the end of five years?

(ii) How much of the amount will you have contributed?

(iii) How much of the balance will be interest?

Solution

(i) $\qquad R = 10.00; \qquad i = \frac{12\%}{12} = 1\% = 0.01; \qquad n = 5(12) = 60$

$\qquad S_n(\text{due}) = 10.00(1.01) \, s_{\overline{60}|1\%} \quad \longleftarrow \text{using Formula 16.1A}$

$\qquad\qquad = 10.00(1.01)(81.66967)$

$\qquad\qquad = 816.6967(1.01)$

$\qquad\qquad = 824.86$

(ii) Your contribution is $(10.00)(60) = \$600.00$

(iii) The interest earned $= 824.86 - 600.00 = \$224.86$

Example 16.1e Frank deposited monthly rent receipts of $250.00 due at the beginning of each month in a savings account paying 10.5% compounded monthly for four years. Frank made no further deposits after four years but left the money in the account.

(i) How much will the balance be twelve full years after he made the first deposit?

(ii) How much of the total will be due to receipts?

(iii) How much will be interest?

Solution

(i) First determine the balance at the end of four years. This involves finding the amount of an annuity due.

$$R = 250.00; \qquad i = \frac{10.5\%}{12} = 0.875\%; \qquad n = 48$$

$$S_n(\text{due}) = 250.00(1.00875)\, s_{\overline{48}|0.875\%}$$

$$= 250.00(1.00875)(59.335279)$$

$$= 14833.82(1.00875)$$

$$= \$14963.62$$

Now accumulate $14 963.62 for another eight years.

$$P = 14963.62; \qquad i = 0.00875; \qquad n = 8(12) = 96$$

$$S = 14963.62(1.00875)^{96} \longleftarrow \text{substituting in Formula 13.1}$$

$$= 14963.62(2.3079191)$$

$$= \$34534.82$$

The balance in the account after 12 years is $34 534.82.

(ii) The rent receipts in the total are $250.00(48) = \$12000.00$.

(iii) Interest in the balance is $34534.82 - 12000.00 = \$22534.82$.

B.   Present value of an annuity due

Example 16.1f   Find the present value of five payments of $3000.00 each made at the beginning of each of five consecutive years respectively if money is worth 12% compounded annually.

Solution

As indicated in Figure 16.3, the present values of the individual payments are obtained using Formula 13.2 $P = S(1 + i)^{-n}$. The sum of the individual present values is easier to find when the common factor 3000.00 is taken out.

Payment 1	3000.00	(1)	(1.0000000)
Payment 2	$3000.00(1.12)^{-1}$	$(1.12)^{-1}$	(0.8928571)
Payment 3	$3000.00(1.12)^{-2} = 3000.00(1.12)^{-2} =$		$3000.00(0.7971939)$
Payment 4	$3000.00(1.12)^{-3}$	$(1.12)^{-3}$	(0.7117802)

Payment 5 $3000.00(1.12)^{-3}$ $(1.12)^{-4}$ (0.6355181)

$$= 3000.00(4.0373493)$$
$$= \$12112.05$$

FIGURE 16.3   ***Graphical representation of method and data***

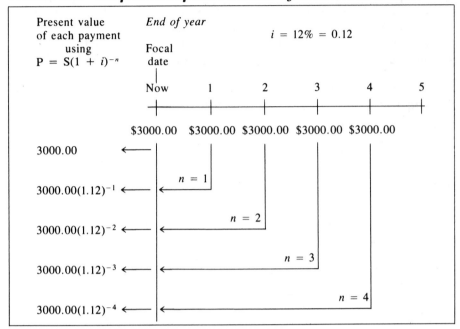

As in previous examples, the problem may be set up in equation form which leads to a solution using the formula for the sum of a geometric progression.

$$A_n(\text{due}) = 3000.00 + 3000.00(1.12)^{-1} + 3000.00(1.12)^{-2} + 3000.00(1.12)^{-3} + 3000.00(1.12)^{-4}$$

$$= 3000.00(1 + 1.12^{-1} + 1.12^{-2} + 1.12^{-3} + 1.12^{-4})$$

$$= 3000.00 \text{ (the sum of the first five terms of a geometric progression with first term 1 and common ratio } 1.12^{-1})$$

$$= 3000.00\left(\frac{1 - (1.12^{-1})^5}{1 - 1.12^{-1}}\right) \longleftarrow \text{substituting in Formula 6.9} \quad r < 1$$

$$= 3000.00\left(\frac{1 - 1.12^{-5}}{1 - 1.12^{-1}}\right)$$

$$= 3000.00\left(\frac{1 - 0.5674269}{1 - 0.8928571}\right)$$

$$= 3000.00\left(\frac{0.4325731}{0.1071429}\right)$$

$$= 3000.00(4.0373473)$$

$$= \$12112.04$$

Note Example 16.1f is the same as Example 15.3b, except that the payments are made at the beginning of each payment period. The answer to Example 15.3b was $10 814.33. If this amount is multiplied by 1.12 the result is $12 112.05 which is the answer to Example 16.1f.

This implies that we could have obtained the present value of the annuity due in Example 16.1f by multiplying the present value of the ordinary annuity in Example 15.3b by the factor 1.12 which is the factor $(1 + i)$.

This implication can be verified by solving the simple annuity due for its present value, represented by the symbol A_n(due), as indicated in Figure 16.4.

FIGURE 16.4 *Graphical representation of the general problem of finding the present value of an annuity due*

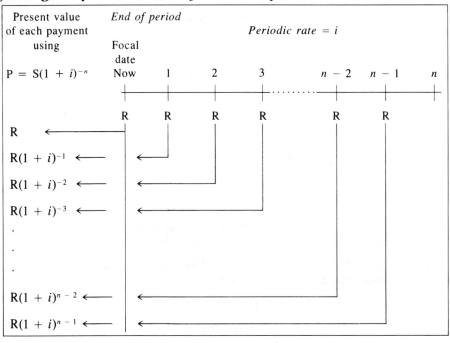

The addition of the present values of the individual payments at the focal date gives rise to the following equation.

$$A_n(\text{due}) = R + R(1 + i)^{-1} + R(1 + i)^{-2} + R(1 + i)^{-3} + \ldots$$
$$+ R(1 + i)^{n-2} + R(1 + i)^{n-1}$$

$$= R\left[1 + (1 + i)^{-1} + (1 + i)^{-2} + (1 + i)^{-3} + \ldots \right.$$
$$\left. + (1 + i)^{n-2} + (1 + i)^{n-1}\right]$$

$$= R \left(\begin{array}{l}\text{the sum of the first terms of a geometric progression} \\ \text{with first term 1 and common ratio } (1 + i)^{-1}\end{array}\right)$$

$$= R\left(\frac{1 - [(1 + i)^{-1}]^n}{1 - (1 + i)}\right) \quad \longleftarrow \text{ substituting in Formula 6.9, } r < 1$$

$$= R\left(\frac{1 - (1 + i)^{-n}}{1 - (1 + i)^{-1}}\right)$$

$$= R\left(\frac{(1 - (1 + i)^{-n}}{1 - \frac{1}{1+i}}\right)$$

$$= R\left(\frac{1 - (1 + i)^{-n}}{\frac{(1+i)-1}{1+i}}\right)$$

$$= R\left(\frac{(1 + i)[1 - (1 + i)^{-n}]}{i}\right)$$

$$\boxed{A_n(\text{due}) = R(1 + i)\left(\frac{1 - (1 + i)^{-n}}{i}\right)} \quad \longleftarrow \quad \textbf{\textit{Formula 16.2}} \\ \textit{Present value of an annuity due}$$

Since the factor $\dfrac{1 - (1 + n)^{-n}}{i}$ is represented by the symbol $a_{\overline{n}|i}$

$$\boxed{A_n(\text{due}) = R(1 + i)\,a_{\overline{n}|i} = R\,a_{\overline{n}|i}\,(1 + i)} \quad \longleftarrow \textbf{\textit{Formula 16.2A}}$$

Note Formulae 16.2 and 16.2A, Present value of an annuity due, differ from Formula 15.2 and 15.2A, Present value of an ordinary annuity, only by the factor $(1 + i)$.

$$\boxed{\begin{array}{l}\text{THE PRESENT VALUE} \\ \text{OF AN ANNUITY DUE}\end{array} = (1 + i) \times \begin{array}{l}\text{PRESENT VALUE OF THE} \\ \text{ORDINARY ANNUITY}\end{array}}$$

Example 16.1g Find the present value of payments of $50.00 made at the beginning of each quarter for ten years if interest is 16% compounded quarterly.

Solution

$$R = 50.00; \qquad i = \frac{16\%}{4} = 4\% = 0.04; \qquad n = 10(4) = 40$$

$$A_n(\text{due}) = 50.00(1.04)\left(\frac{1 - (1.04)^{-40}}{0.04}\right) \quad \longleftarrow \text{ substituting in Formula 16.2}$$

$$= 50.00(1.04)(19.792774)$$

$$= 989.64(1.04)$$

$$= \$1029.22$$

Example 16.1h What is the cash value of a three-year lease of office facilities renting for $536.50 payable at the beginning of each month if money is worth 15% compounded monthly?

Solution

Since the payments are at the beginning of each payment period the problem involves an annuity due and since we want the cash value the present value of the annuity due is required.

$$R = 536.50; \qquad i = \frac{15\%}{12} = 1.25\% = 0.0125; \qquad n = 3(12) = 36$$

$$\begin{aligned}
A_n(\text{due}) &= 536.50(a\,_{\overline{36}|\,1.25\%})(1.0125) \longleftarrow \text{using Formula 16.2A} \\
&= 536.50(28.847267)(1.0125) \\
&= 15476.56(1.0125) \\
&= \$15670.02
\end{aligned}$$

The cash value of the lease is $15 670.02.

Example 16.1i Mr. Willis would like to receive annuity payments of $2000.00 at the beginning of each quarter for seven years. The annuity is to start five years from now and interest is 11.8% compounded quarterly.

(i) How much must Mr. Willis invest today?

(ii) How much will Mr. Willis receive from the annuity?

(iii) How much of what he receives will be interest?

Solution

(i) First, find the present value of the annuity due (focal point five years from now).

$$R = 2000.00; \qquad i = \frac{11.8\%}{4} = 2.95\% = 0.0295; \qquad n = 7(4) = 28$$

$$\begin{aligned}
A_n(\text{due}) &= 2000.00(a\,_{\overline{28}|\,2.95\%})(1.0295) \\
&= 2000.00(18.879335)(1.0295) \\
&= 37758.67(1.0295) \\
&= \$38872.55
\end{aligned}$$

Secondly, determine the present value of $38 872.55 (the focal point is 'now').

$$S = 38872.55; \qquad i = 2.95\%, \qquad n = 5(4) = 20$$

$$\begin{aligned}
P &= 38872.55(1.0295)^{-20} \\
&= 38872.55(0.5590787) \\
&= \$21732.82
\end{aligned}$$

Mr. Willis will have to invest $21 732.82.

(ii) Mr. Willis will receive $28(2000.00) = \$56000.00$.

(iii) Interest will be $56000.00 - 21732.82 = \$34267.18$.

C. Using preprogrammed financial calculators

The amount S_n(due) or the present value A_n(due) can readily be determined using a preprogrammed financial calculator by finding the corresponding value for an ordinary annuity and multiplying by $(1 + i)$ or, if a $\boxed{\text{DUE}}$ key is available, by pressing $\boxed{\text{DUE}}$ instead of $\boxed{\text{2nd}}$ when retrieving the answer.

Example 16.1j Payments of \$425 are to be made at the beginning of each quarter for 10 years. If money is worth 20% compounded quarterly determine
(i) the accumulated value of the payments;
(ii) the present value of the payments.

Solution

(i) $R = 425;$ $i = 5\%;$ $n = 40$

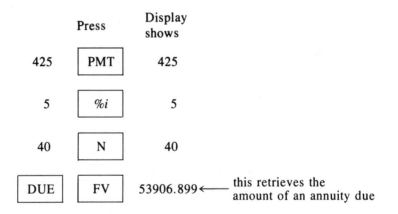

	Press	Display shows	
425	PMT	425	
5	%i	5	
40	N	40	
DUE	FV	53906.899 ←	this retrieves the amount of an annuity due

The accumulated value of the annuity due is \$53 906.90

(ii)

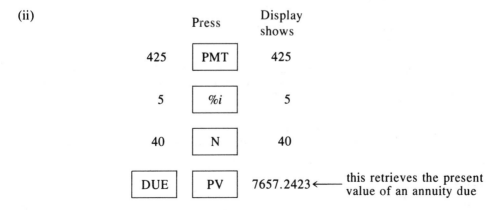

	Press	Display shows	
425	PMT	425	
5	%i	5	
40	N	40	
DUE	PV	7657.2423 ←	this retrieves the present value of an annuity due

The present value of the annuity due is \$7657.24

Exercise 16.1

A. Use the geometric progression approach to find the amount and the present value of each of the following annuities due.

Problem number	Periodic payment	Payment interval	Term	Interest rate	Conversion period
1.	$1200.00	3 months	1 year	14%	quarterly
2.	$250.00	1 month	6 months	12%	monthly
3.	$600.00	6 months	2 years	15%	semi-annually
4.	$800.00	1 year	5 years	17%	annually

B. Find the amount and the present value of each of the following annuities due.

Problem number	Periodic payment	Payment interval	Term	Interest rate	Conversion period
1.	$3000.00	3 months	8 years	18%	quarterly
2.	$750.00	1 month	5 years	12%	monthly
3.	$2000.00	6 months	12 years	15.6%	semi-annually
4.	$450.00	3 months	15 years	14.4%	quarterly
5.	$65.00	1 month	20 years	9%	monthly
6.	$160.00	1 month	15 years	15%	monthly

C. Answer each of the following questions

1. Find the amount of an annuity due of $300.00 payable at the beginning of every month for seven years at 12% compounded monthly.

2. Determine the accumulated value after twelve years of deposits of $360.00 made at the beginning of every three months and earning interest at 14% compounded quarterly.

3. Find the present value of payments of $2500.00 made at the beginning of every six months for ten years if money is worth 19.5% compounded semi-annually.

4. What is the discounted value of deposits of $240.00 made at the beginning of every three months for seven years if money is worth 16.8% compounded quarterly?

5. A washer-dryer combination can be purchased by making monthly payments of $52.50 for two and a half years. The first payment is due on the date of sale and interest is 21% compounded monthly.

   (a) What is the purchase price?

   (b) How much will be paid in instalments?

   (c) How much is the cost of financing?

6. Diane bought a living room suite on time signing an instalment contract which requires monthly payments of $62.25 for three years. The first payment is made on the date of signing and interest is 24% compounded monthly.

   (a) What was the cash price?

   (b) How much will Diane pay in total?

   (c) How much of what she pays will be interest?

7. Until he retires sixteen years from now, Mr. Lait plans to deposit $300.00 at the beginning of every three months in an account paying interest at 10% compounded quarterly.

   (a) What will the balance be in his account when retires?

   (b) How much of the balance will be interest?

8. Mr. Jones contributes $750.00 at the beginning of every six months into an RRSP paying interest at 14% compounded semi-annually.

   (a) How much will his RRSP deposits amount to in twenty years?

   (b) How much of the amount will be interest?

9. The monthly premium on a three-year insurance policy is $64.00 payable in advance. What is the cash value of the policy if money is worth 13.8% compounded monthly?

10. The monthly rent payment on office space is $535.00 payable in advance. What yearly payment in advance would satisfy the lease if interest is 15.6% compounded monthly?

16.2 Annuities due—finding R, n and i

A. Finding the periodic payment when the amount S_n or the present value A_n is known

If S_n(due), n and i are known, R can be found by substituting the given values in Formula 16.1. If A_n(due), n and i are known, R can be found by substituting the given values in Formula 16.2.

Example 16.2a What semi-annual payment must be made into a fund at the beginning of every six months to accumulate to $9600.00 in ten years at 11% compounded semi-annually?

Solution

$$S_n(\text{due}) = 9600.00; \qquad i = \frac{11\%}{2} = 5.5\% = 0.055; \qquad n = 10(2) = 20$$

$$9600.00 = R(1.055)\left[\frac{(1.055^{20} - 1)}{0.055}\right] \longleftarrow \text{substituting in Formula 16.1}$$

$$9600.00 = R(1.055)(34.868318)$$

$$9600.00 = R(36.786075)$$

$$R = \frac{9600.00}{36.786075}$$

$$R = 9600.00(0.0271842)$$

$$R = \$260.97$$

Alternatively, the value of R may be found using a preprogrammed calculator.

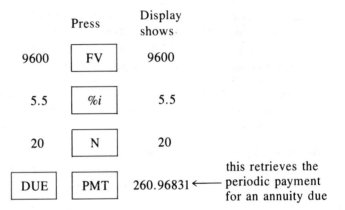

	Press	Display shows
9600	FV	9600
5.5	%i	5.5
20	N	20
DUE	PMT	260.96831 $\longleftarrow$ this retrieves the periodic payment for an annuity due

The semi-annual payment is $260.97

Example 16.2b What monthly rent payment at the beginning of each month for four years is required to fulfill a lease contract worth $7000.00 if money is worth 18% compounded monthly?

Solution

$$A_n(\text{due}) = 7000.00; \qquad i = \frac{18\%}{12} = 1.5\% = 0.015; \qquad n = 4(12) = 48$$

$$7000.00 = R(1.05)\left[\frac{(1 - 1.015^{-48})}{0.015}\right] \longleftarrow \text{substituting in Formula 16.2}$$

$$7000.00 = R(1.05)(34.042554)$$

$$7000.00 = R(34.553192)$$

$$R = \frac{7000.00}{34.553192}$$

$$R = 7000.00(0.0289409)$$

$$R = \$202.59$$

Alternatively, the value of R may be found using a preprogrammed calculator.

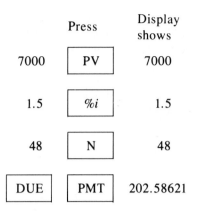

Press		Display shows
7000	PV	7000
1.5	%i	1.5
48	N	48
DUE	PMT	202.58621

The monthly rent payment due at the beginning of each month is $202.59.

Note While special formulae for finding R may be obtained by solving Formulae 16.1 and 16.2 for R, due to the state of the technology no useful purpose is served any more by such formulae. Accordingly, no special formulae for finding R are developed or used in this text.

Example 16.2c How much will you have to deposit into an account at the beginning of every three months for twelve years if you wish to have a balance of $100 000.00 twenty years from now and interest is 12% compounded quarterly?

Solution

First find the balance which you must have in the account at the end of the term of the annuity after 12 years.

$$S = 100000.00; \qquad i = \frac{12\%}{4} = 3\% = 0.03; \qquad n = 8(4) = 32$$

$$P = 100000.00(1.03)^{-32}$$
$$= 100000.00(0.3883370)$$
$$= \$38833.70$$

Next find the quarterly payment needed at the beginning of each quarter to accumulate to $38833.70

$$S_n(due) = 38833.70; \qquad i = 0.03; \qquad n = 12(4) = 48$$

$$38833.70 = R(1.03)(s_{\overline{48}|3\%})$$

$$38833.70 = R(1.03)(104.40839)$$

$$38833.70 = R(107.54065)$$

$$R = \frac{38833.70}{107.54065}$$

$$R = 38833.70(0.0092988)$$

$$R = \$361.11$$

The quarterly deposit at the beginning of each payment period is $361.11

Example 16.2d What payment can be received at the beginning of each month for fifteen years if $10 000.00 is deposited in a fund ten years before the first payment is made and interest is 12% compounded monthly?

Solution

First, find the accumulated value of the initial deposit at the beginning of the term of the annuity due ten years after the deposit.

$$P = 10000.00; \qquad i = \frac{12\%}{12} = 1\% = 0.01; \qquad n = 10(12) = 120$$

$$S = 10000.00(1.01)^{120}$$

$$= 10000.00(3.3003869)$$

$$= \$33003.87$$

Now determine the monthly withdrawal that can be made at the beginning of each month from the initial balance of $33 003.87.

$$A_n(\text{due}) = 33003.87; \qquad i = 1\%; \qquad n = 15(12) = 180$$

$$33003.87 = R(1.01)(a_{\overline{180}|1\%})$$

$$33003.87 = R(1.01)(83.321664)$$

$$R = \frac{33003.87}{84.154881}$$

$$R = 33003.87(0.0118829)$$

$$R = \$392.18$$

A payment of $392.18 can be made at the beginning of each month.

B. Finding the term when the amount S_n or the present value A_n are known

If $S_n(\text{due})$, R and i are known, n can be found by substituting the given values in Formula 16.1 and solving for n. If $A_n(\text{due})$, R and i are known, n can be found by substituting the given values in Formula 16.2 and solving for n.

Finding n when $S_n(\text{due})$ is known

Example 16.2e Over what length of time will $75.00 deposited at the beginning of each month grow to $6500.00 at 12% compounded monthly?

Solution

$$S_n(\text{due}) = 6500.00; \qquad R = 75.00; \qquad i = \frac{12\%}{12} = 1\% = 0.01$$

$$6500.00 = 75.00(1.01)\left[\frac{(1.01^n - 1)}{0.01}\right] \longleftarrow \text{substituting in Formula 16.1}$$

$$6500.00 = 7575.00(1.01^n - 1)$$

$$\frac{6500.00}{7575.00} = 1.01^n - 1$$

$$0.8580858 + 1 = 1.01^n$$

$$n \ln(1.01) = \ln 1.8580858 \longleftarrow \begin{array}{l}\text{use natural logarithm} \\ \text{to solve for } n\end{array}$$

$$n(0.0099503) = 0.6195468$$

$$n = \frac{0.6195468}{0.0099503}$$

$$n = 62.263942$$

As discussed in Chapter 15, n should be rounded upwards.

$$n = 63 \text{ (months)}$$

It will take 5 years and 3 months to accumulate $6500.00.

Example 16.2f Sheridan Credit Union intends to accumulate a building fund of $150 000.00 by depositing $3300.00 at the beginning of every three months at 13% compounded quarterly. How long will it take for the fund to reach the desired amount?

Solution

$$S_n(\text{due}) = 150000.00; \qquad R = 3300.00; \qquad i = \frac{13\%}{4} = 3.25\%$$

Using a preprogrammed calculator

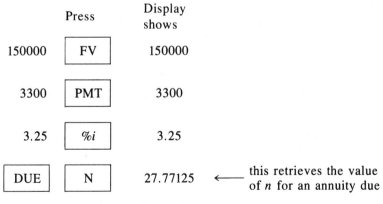

	Press	Display shows	
150000	FV	150000	
3300	PMT	3300	
3.25	%i	3.25	
DUE	N	27.77125	$\longleftarrow$ this retrieves the value of n for an annuity due

$$n = 28 \text{ quarters (approximately)}$$

It will take seven years to build up the fund.

Finding n when A_n (due) is known

Example 16.2g For how long can you withdraw $480.00 at the beginning of every three months from a fund of $9000.00 if interest is 10% compounded quarterly?

Solution

$$A_n(\text{due}) = 9000.00; \quad R = 480.00; \quad i = \frac{10\%}{4} = 2.5\% = 0.025$$

$$9000.00 = 480.00(1.025)\left[\frac{(1 - 1.025^{-n})}{0.025}\right] \longleftarrow \text{substituting in Formula 16.2}$$

$$9000.00 = 19680.00(1 - 1.025^{-n})$$

$$\frac{9000.00}{19680.00} = 1 - 1.025^{-n}$$

$$0.4573171 = 1 - 1.025^{-n}$$

$$1.025^{-n} = 1 - 0.4573171$$

$$1.025^{-n} = 0.5426829$$

$$-n \ln 1.025 = \ln 0.5426829$$

$$-n(0.0246926) = -0.6112301$$

$$n = \frac{0.6112301}{0.0246926}$$

$$n = 24.753561$$

$$n = 25 \text{ (quarters)}$$

Withdrawals of $480.00 can be made for 6 years and 3 months. (The last withdrawal will be less than $480.00.)

Example 16.2h A lease contract valued at $7800.00 is to be fulfilled by rental payments of $180.00 due at the beginning of each month. If money is worth 21% compounded monthly what should the term of the lease be?

Solution

$$A_n(\text{due}) = 7800.00; \quad R = 180.00; \quad i = \frac{21\%}{12} = 1.75\%$$

Using a preprogrammed calculator

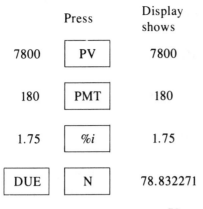

Press		Display shows
7800	PV	7800
180	PMT	180
1.75	%i	1.75
DUE	N	78.832271

$$n = 79 \text{ months (approximately)}$$

The term of the lease should be 6 years and 7 months.

Note While special formulae for finding n may be obtained by solving Formulae 16.1 and 16.2 for n due to the state of the technology no useful purpose is served any more by such formulae. Accordingly no special formulae for finding n are developed or used in this text.

C. Finding the rate of interest i when either $S_n(due)$ or $A_n(due)$ is known using a preprogrammed calculator

Finding the rate of interest per conversion period i is accomplished by entering the three known values $S_n(due)$, R, n or $A_n(due)$, R, n and then retrieving the answer by pressing [DUE] [%i]. The nominal annual rate of interest may then be obtained by multiplying i by the number of compounding periods per year.

Finding i when the amount $S_n(due)$ is known

Example 16.2i Compute the nominal rate of interest at which $50 deposited at the beginning of each month for ten years will amount to $15 000.

Solution

$$S_n \text{ (due)} = 15000; \qquad R = 50; \qquad n = 120$$

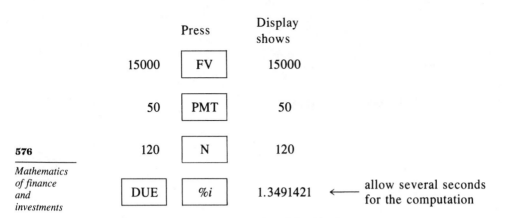

The monthly conversion rate is 1.3491421%.

The nominal rate of interest is $(12)(1.3491421\%) = 16.19\%$ approximately.

Finding i when the present value A_n(due) is known

Example 16.2j A lease agreement valued $7500 requires payment of $620 at the beginning of every quarter for five years. What is the nominal rate of interest charged?

Solution

$$A_n \text{ (due)} = 7500; \qquad R = 620; \qquad n = 20$$

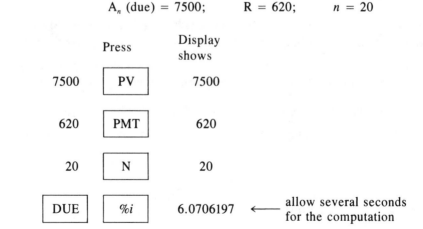

The quarterly compounding rate is 6.0706197%.

The nominal rate of interest is $(4)(6.0706197\%) = 24.28\%$ approximately.

Note For an annuity due the conversion rate i may be computed without using a preprogrammed calculator by the trial and error approach shown in Chapter 15. The needed modifications to Formulae 16.1 and 16.2 and the computation itself are illustrated in the Appendix to this Chapter.

Exercise 16.2

A. Find the unknown value in each of the following annuities due.

No.	Amount	Present value	Periodic payment	Payment period	Term	Int. rate	Conversion period
1.	$20 000.00		?	3 months	15 years	16%	quarterly
2.		$12 000.00	?	1 year	8 years	21%	annually
3.		$18 500.00	?	6 months	12 years	13%	semi-annually
4.	$9 400.00		?	1 month	5 years	12%	monthly
5.	$5 300.00		$35.00	1 month	?	18%	monthly
6.		$8 400.00	$440.00	3 months	?	14%	quarterly
7.		$6 450.00	$1120.00	1 year	?	10%	annually
8.	$15 400.00		$396.00	6 months	?	15%	semi-annually
9.	$70 000.00		$367.00	1 year	25 years	?	annually
10.		$42 000.00	$528.00	1 month	10 years	?	monthly
11.		$28 700.00	$2015.00	6 months	15 years	?	semi-annually
12.	$36 000.00		$235.00	3 months	12 years	?	quarterly

B. Answer each of the following questions.

1. Terry purchased a boat valued at $12 500.00 on the instalment plan requiring equal monthly payments for four years. If the first payment is due on the date of purchase and interest is 16.5% compounded monthly, what is the size of the monthly payment?

2. How much does a depositor have to save at the beginning of every three months for nine years to accumulate $35 000.00 if interest is 12% compounded quarterly?

3. Quarterly payments of $1445.00 are to be made at the beginning of every three months on a lease valued at $25 000.00. What should the term of the lease be if money is worth 16% compounded quarterly?

4. Tom is saving $600.00 at the beginning of each month. How soon can he retire if he wants to have a retirement fund of $120 000.00 and interest is 12% compounded monthly?

5. What nominal rate of interest was paid if contributions of $250.00 made into an RRSP at the beginning of every three months amounted to $18 307.00 after ten years?

6. A vacation property valued at $20 000.00 was bought for fifteen payments of $2750.00 due at the beginning of every six months. What nominal rate of interest was charged?

7. Julia deposited $1500.00 in an RRSP at the beginning of every six months for twenty years earning interest at 11% compounded semi-annually. After twenty years she converted the RRSP into an RRIF from which she wants to withdraw

equal amounts at the beginning of each month for fifteen years. If interest on the RRIF is 12% compounded monthly, how much does she receive each month?

8. Mr. Clark wants to receive payments of $900.00 at the beginning of every three months for twenty years starting on the date of his retirement. If he retires in twenty-five years how much must he deposit in an account at the beginning of every three months if interest on the account is 10% compounded quarterly?

9. If you save $75.00 at the beginning of every month for ten years, for how long can you withdraw $260.00 at the beginning of each month starting ten years from now, assuming that interest is 12% compounded monthly?

10. Ali deposits $450.00 at the beginning of every three months. He wants to build up his acount so that he can withdraw $1000.00 every three months starting three months after the last deposit. If he wants to make the withdrawals for fifteen years and interest is 10% compounded quarterly, for how long must Ali make the quarterly deposits?

11. What is the effective rate of interest on a lease contract valued at $13 500.00 if payments of $1500.00 are made at the beginning of every six months for seven years?

12. An insurance policy provides a benefit of $250 000.00 twenty years from now. Alternatively the policy pays $4220.00 at the beginning of each year for twenty years. What is the effective rate of interest paid?

16.3 Deferred annuities

A. Basic concepts and computation

A **deferred annuity** is an annuity in which the first payment is made at a point in time *later* than the end of the first payment interval. The time period from the point in time referred to as 'now' to the starting point of the term of the annuity is called the **period of deferment** and the number of compounding periods in the period of deferment will be designated by the letter symbol d. The amount of a deferred annuity (designated by the symbol S_n(defer.)) is the accumulated value of the periodic payments at the end of the term of the annuity.

The **present value of a deferred annuity** (designated by the symbol A_n (defer.)) is the discounted value of the periodic payment at the beginning of the period of deferment.

Example 16.3a   Payments of $500.00 are due at the end of each year for ten years. If the annuity is deferred for four years and interest is 12% compounded annually determine

 (i) the amount of the deferred annuity;

 (ii) the present value of the deferred annuity.

Solution

$$R = 500.00; \qquad i = 12\% = 0.12; \qquad n = 10; \qquad d = 4$$

FIGURE 16.5 *Graphical representation of method and data*

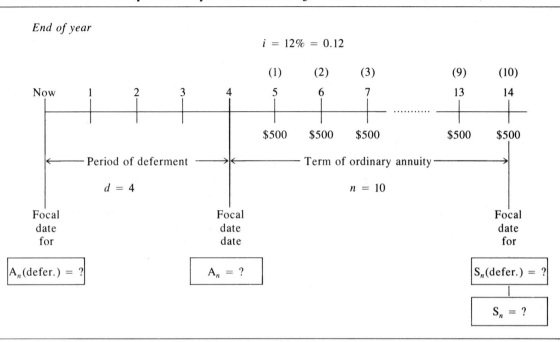

(i) S_n (defer.) $= S_n = 500.00\left(\dfrac{1.12^{10}-1}{0.12}\right) \longleftarrow$ using Formula 15.1

$\qquad\qquad\qquad\quad = 500.00(17.548735)$

$\qquad\qquad\qquad\quad = \$8774.37$

Note The period of deferment does *not* affect the solution to the problem of finding the amount of a deferred annuity: S_n(defer.) $= S_n$. Hence the problem of finding the amount of a deferred annuity is identical to the problem of finding the amount of an annuity. Accordingly no further consideration is given to the problem of finding the amount of a deferred annuity.

(ii) The problem of finding the present value of a deferred annuity may be divided into two smaller problems. This approach has been used in solving example 15.3g in Chapter 15 and in solving Example 16.1i in Chapter 16 and is used again in finding the present value of the deferred annuity in this problem.

First, find the present value of the ordinary annuity (focal date at the beginning of the term of the annuity).

$$A_n = 500.00\left(\frac{(1 - 1.12^{-10})}{0.12}\right) \longleftarrow \text{ using Formula 15.2}$$

$$= 500.00(5.6502230)$$

$$= \$2825.11$$

Secondly, find the present value of A_n at the focal date 'now'.

$$A_n(\text{defer.}) = P = 2825.11(1.12^{-4}) \longleftarrow \text{ using Formula 13.2}$$

$$= 2825.11(0.6355181)$$

$$= \$1795.41$$

Alternatively the present value of the defered annuity may be found by assuming that periodic payments had been made during the period of deferment. This shifts the beginning date of the term of the annuity to the focal date 'now' as indicated in Figure 16.6. The present value of the deferred annuity is obtained by deducting the present value of the annuity representing the assumed payments from the present value of the annuity representing all payment.

FIGURE 16.6 *Graphical representation of method and data*

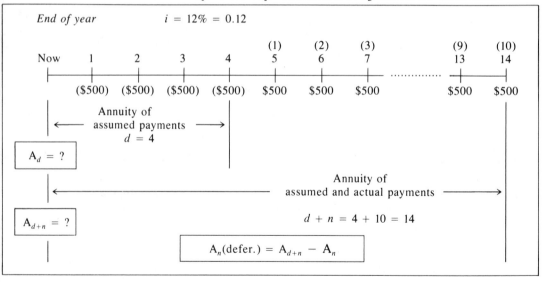

$$A_{d+n} = 500.00\left(\frac{(1 - 1.12^{-14})}{0.12}\right) \longleftarrow \text{ using Formula 15.2}$$

$$= 500.00(6.6281682)$$

$$= \$3314.08$$

$$A_d = 500.00\left(\frac{(1 - 1.12^{-4})}{0.12}\right) \longleftarrow \text{using Formula 15.2}$$

$$= 500.00(3.0373493)$$

$$= \$1518.67$$

$$A_n(\text{defer.}) = 3314.08 - 1518.67 = \$1795.41$$

B. Formula for finding the present value of a deferred ordinary annuity

While the problem of finding the present value of a deferred annuity can always be solved by using the methods described above, general formulae may be obtained for the two methods by solving the general problem graphically represented in Figure 16.7.

FIGURE 16.7 *Graphical representation of the deferred ordinary annuity*

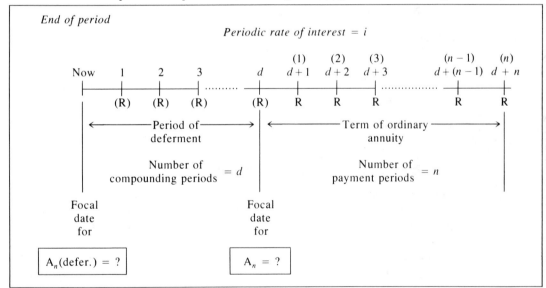

However, since in this text only the original approach to finding the present value of a deferred annuity will be used when finding R, n or i, only the formula for this approach is developed.

Step 1 Find the present value of the ordinary annuity at the end of the period of deferment.

$$A_n = R\left(\frac{1 - (1 + i)^{-n}}{i}\right) = Ra_{\overline{n}|i}$$

Step 2 Find the present value of A_n at the focal point 'now'.

$$P = A_n(1 + i)^{-d}$$

Step 3 Since P represents the present value of the deferred annuity

$$\boxed{A_n(\text{defer.}) = R(1 + i)^{-d}(a_{\overline{n}|i})} \quad \longleftarrow \quad \textbf{\textit{Formula}} \textbf{ 16.3}$$

Example 16.3b   Mr. Peric wishes to receive payments of $800.00 at the end of each month for ten years after his retirement. If he retires in seven years, how much must Mr. Peric invest now if interest on the investment is 12% compounded monthly?

Solution

The monthly payments after retirement form an ordinary annuity.

$$R = 800.00; \qquad i = \frac{12\%}{12} = 1\% = 0.01; \qquad n = 10(12) = 120$$

The period of deferment is 7 years. $d = 7(12) = 84$.
The amount to be invested now is the present value of the deferred annuity.

$$A_n(\text{defer.}) = 800(1.01^{-84})(a_{\overline{120}|1\%}) \quad \longleftarrow \quad \text{using Formula 16.3}$$

$$= 800.00(0.4335155)(69.700522)$$

$$= 800.00(30.216255)$$

$$= \$24173.00$$

Mr. Peric must invest $24 173.00.

C.   *Present value of a deferred annuity due*

Since the present value of an annuity due differs from the present value of an ordinary annuity only by the factor $(1 + i)$, the present value of a deferred annuity due may be found by expanding the right side of Formula 16.3 by $(1 + i)$.

Example 16.3c   Amounts of $2000.00 are to be withdrawn from a fund at the beginning of every three months for twelve years starting ten years from now. If interest is 10% compounded quarterly, what must be the balance in the fund today to permit the withdrawals?

Solution

The withdrawals form an annuity due.

$$R = 2000.00; \qquad i = \frac{10\%}{4} = 2.5\% = 0.025; \qquad n = 12(4) = 48$$

The period of deferment is 10 years. $d = (10)(4) = 40$

$$A_n(\text{defer.}) = 2000.00(1.025^{-40})(a\,\overline{_{48}}|_{2.5\%})(1.025)$$

$$= 2000.00(1.025^{-39})(a\,\overline{_{48}}|_{2.5\%})$$

$$= 2000.00(0.3817414)(27.773154)$$

$$= 2000.00(10.602163)$$

$$= \$21204.33$$

The balance in the fund today must be \$21 204.33.

Exercise 16.3

A. Find the present value of each of the following deferred annuities.

No	Periodic payment	Made at	Payment period	Period of deferment	Term	Int. rate	Conversion period
1.	\$850.00	beginning	1 year	3 years	10 years	20.5%	annually
2.	\$45.00	end	1 month	5 years	7 years	12%	monthly
3.	\$125.00	end	6 months	8 years	15 years	17%	semi-annually
4.	\$720.00	beginning	3 months	6 years	12 years	14%	quarterly
5.	\$85.00	beginning	1 month	20 years	15 years	18%	monthly
6.	\$225.00	end	1 month	12 years	20 years	16.5%	monthly

B. Answer each of the following questions.

1. Jones bought his neighbour's farm for \$10 000 down and payments of \$5000.00 at the end of every three months for ten years. If the payments are deferred for two years and interest is 14% compounded quarterly, what was the purchase price of the farm?

2. Denise intends to retire in twelve years and would like to receive \$2400.00 every six months for fifteen years starting on the date of her retirement. How much must Denise deposit in an account today if interest is 15.5% compounded semi-annually?

3. Dr. C. wants to set up a fund to finance his daughter's university education. He wants to be able to withdraw \$400.00 from the fund at the beginning of each month for four years. His daughter enters university in seven and a half years and interest is 12% compounded monthly.

    (a) How much must Dr. C. deposit in the fund today?

    (b) What will be the amount of the total withdrawals?

    (c) How much of the amount withdrawn will be interest?

4. The Omega Venture Group needs to borrow to finance a project. Repayment of the loan involves payments of \$8500.00 at the end of every three months for eight years. No payments are to be made during the development period of three years. Interest is 20% compounded quarterly.

(a) How much should be borrowed?

(b) What amount will be repaid?

(c) How much of that amount will be interest?

16.4 Deferred annuities—finding R, n and i

When the present value of either a deferred ordinary annuity or a deferred annuity due is known the problem of finding R, n or i can be solved by methods similar to the ones used in Chapters 15 and 16.

A. Finding the periodic payment R

The periodic payment for deferred ordinary annuities may be found by substituting the known values in Formula 16.3. For deferred annuities due, R may be obtained by substituting the known values in Formula 16.3 and multiplying by $(1 + i)$.

Example 16.4a Find the size of the payment required at the end of every three months to repay a five-year loan of $25 000.00 if the payments are deferred for two years and interest is 14% compounded quarterly.

Solution

The payments form a deferred ordinary annuity. $A_n(\text{defer.}) = 25000.00$;

$$i = \frac{14\%}{4} = 3.5\% = 0.035; \qquad n\ 5(4) = 20; \qquad d = 2(4) = 8$$

$25000.00 = R(1.035^{-8})(a_{\overline{20}|\,3.5\%}) \longleftarrow$ substituting in Formula 16.3

$25000.00 = R(0.7594116)(14.212403)$

$25000.00 = R(10.793063)$

$$R = \frac{25000.00}{10.793063}$$

$R = \$2316.30$

The size of the required payment is $2316.30.

Example 16.4b What payment can be made at the beginning of each month for six years if $5000.00 is invested today at 12% compounded monthly and the payments are deferred for ten years?

Solution

The payments form a deferred annuity due. $A_n(\text{defer.}) = 5000.00$;

$$i = \frac{12\%}{12} = 1\% = 0.01; \qquad n = 6(12) = 72; \qquad d = 10(12) = 120$$

$5000.00 = R(1.01^{-120})(a_{\overline{72}|\,1\%})(1.01)$

$$5000.00 = R(1.01^{-119})(a_{\overline{72}|1\%})$$

$$5000.00 = R(0.3060247)(51.150392)$$

$$5000.00 = R(15.653285)$$

$$R = \frac{5000.00}{15.653285}$$

$$R = \$319.42$$

The possible monthly payment is $319.42.

B. Finding the term n of a deferred annuity

The term for deferred ordinary annuities may be found by substituting the known values in Formula 16.3. For deferred annuities due, n may be obtained by substituting the known values in Formula 16.3 and multiplying by $(1 + i)$.

Example 16.4c   For how long can you pay $500.00 at the end of each month out of a fund of $10 000.00, deposited today at 10.5% compounded monthly, if the payments are deferred for nine years?

Solution

The payments form a deferred ordinary annuity. $A_n(\text{defer.}) = 10000.00$;

$$R = 500.00; \qquad i = \frac{10.5\%}{12} = 0.875\% = 0.00875; \qquad d = 9(12) = 108$$

$$10000.00 = 500.00(1.00875^{-108})\left(\frac{1 - 1.00875^{-n}}{0.00875}\right) \quad \longleftarrow \quad \begin{array}{l} \text{substituting in} \\ \text{Formula 16.3} \end{array}$$

$$10000.00 = 500.00(0.3902805)\left(\frac{(1 - 1.00875^{-n})}{0.00875}\right)$$

$$10000.00 = 22301.742(1 - 1.00875^{-n})$$

$$\frac{10000.00}{22301.742} = 1 - 1.00875^{-n}$$

$$0.4483955 = 1 - 1.00875^{-n}$$

$$1.00875^{-n} = 0.5516045$$

$$-n \ln 1.00875 = \ln 0.5516045$$

$$-n(0.0087119) = -0.5949239$$

$$n = \frac{0.5949239}{0.0087119}$$

$$n = 68.288334$$

$$n = 69 \text{ (months)}$$

Payments can be made for 5 years and 9 months.

Example 16.4d A scholarship of $3000.00 per year is to be paid at the beginning of each year from a scholarship fund of $15 000.00 invested at 11% compounded annually. How long will the scholarship be paid if payments are deferred for five years?

Solution

The annual payments form a deferred annuity due. $A_n(\text{defer.}) = 15000.00$;

$$R = 3000.00; \qquad i = 11\% = 0.11; \qquad d = 5$$

$$15000.00 = 3000.00(1.11^{-5})\left(\frac{1 - 1.11^{-n}}{0.11}\right)(1.11)$$

$$15000.00 = 3000.00(1.11^{-4})\left(\frac{(1 - 1.11^{-n})}{0.11}\right)$$

$$15000.00 = 3000.00(0.658731)\left(\frac{(1 - 1.11^{-n})}{0.11}\right)$$

$$15000.00 = 17965.39(1 - 1.11^{-n})$$

$$0.8349387 = 1 - 1.11^{-n}$$

$$1.11^{-n} = 0.1650613$$

$$-n \ln 1.11 = \ln 0.1650613$$

$$-0.10436n = -1.8014385$$

$$n = \frac{1.8014385}{0.10436}$$

$$n = 17.261769$$

$$n = 18 \text{ years (approximately)}$$

The scholarship fund will provide 17 payments of $3000 and a final payment less than $3000.00.

C. Finding the conversion rate i for deferred annuities

The periodic rate of interest for deferred annuities may be determined by trial and error using the method previously explained in Chapter 15. The solution to a problem of finding i for a deferred annuity, more readily found by means of a preprogrammed calculator, is shown in the Appendix to this chapter.

Exercise 16.4

A. For each of the following deferred annuities find the unknown value

No.	Present value	Periodic payment	Made at	Payment interval	Period of deferment	Term	Int. rate	Coumpounding period
1.	$ 7 200.00	?	beginning	3 months	3 years	5 years	21%	quarterly
2.	$14 500.00	?	end	6 months	7 years	10 years	15%	semi-annually
3.	?	$ 220.00	end	1 month	2 years	4 years	18%	monthly
4.	?	$3600.00	beginning	1 year	10 years	15 years	13%	annually
5.	$21 000.00	$3485.00	beginning	3 months	8 years	?	16%	quarterly
6.	$ 8 800.00	$ 325.00	end	1 month	3 years	?	15%	monthly
7.	$45 000.00	$7250.00	end	6 months	7 years	16 years	?	semi-annually
8.	$ 7 500.00	$ 920.00	beginning	3 months	9 years	7 years	?	quarterly

B. Answer each of the following questions.

1. To finance the development of a new product a company borrowed $50 000.00 at 17% compounded quarterly. If the loan is to be repaid in equal quarterly payments over seven years and the first payment is due three years after the date of the loan, what is the size of the quarterly payment?

2. Greg borrowed $6500.00 at 15% compounded monthly to help finance his education. He contracted to repay the loan in monthly payments of $300.00 each. If the payments are due at the end of each month and the payments are deferred for four years, for how long will Greg have to make monthly payments?

3. Edith invested $3500.00 in an annuity deferred for twenty-five years paying her $3000.00 at the end of every six months for twenty years. What rate of interest compounded semi-annually did Edith receive on her investment?

4. Mr. Talbot received a retirement gratuity of $18 000.00 which he deposited in a RRSP. He intends to leave the money for fourteen years. At that time he plans to transfer the balance into a RRIF and make equal withdrawals at the end of every six months for twenty years. If interest is 10.5% compounded semi-annually, what will be the size of each withdrawal?

5. A lease valued at $32 000.00 requires payments of $4000.00 every three months. If the first payment is due three years after the lease was signed and interest is 22% compounded quarterly, what is the term of the lease?

6. A ten-year $15 000.00 promissory note is redeemed by making semi-annual payments of $6200.00 for fifteen years. If the first payment is due at the date of maturity of the promissory note, what is the effective rate if interest is compounded semi-annually?

16.5 Using preprogrammed calculators for problems involving deferred annuities

Deferred annuity problems involving finding the present value A_n(defer.), the periodic payment R and the number of payments n are readily solved by means of preprogrammed calculators using the techniques illustrated for ordinary annuities and annuities due. However, allowance must be made for the period of deferment.

As for finding the conversion rate i, no quick solution is possible because the unknown variable i also appears in the factor which allows for the period of deferment and the preprogramming has not provided for this complication.

A. Finding the present value of deferred annuities

***Example* 16.5a** What sum of money invested now will provide payments of $1200.00 at the end of every three months for six years if the payments are deferred for nine years and interest is 10% compounded quarterly?

Solution

$$R = 1200.00; \qquad i = 2.5\%; \qquad n = 6(4) = 24; \qquad d = 9(4) = 36$$

First, determine the present value of the ordinary annuity at the end of the period of deferment.

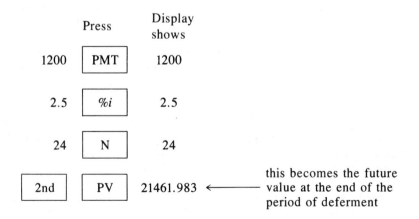

	Press	Display shows	
1200	PMT	1200	
2.5	%i	2.5	
24	N	24	
2nd	PV	21461.983 ←	this becomes the future value at the end of the period of deferment

Secondly, determine the present value of the amount $21 461.98 at the beginning of the period of deferment.

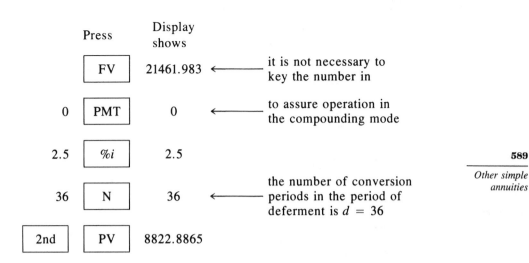

	Press	Display shows	
	FV	21461.983 ←	it is not necessary to key the number in
0	PMT	0 ←	to assure operation in the compounding mode
2.5	%i	2.5	
36	N	36 ←	the number of conversion periods in the period of deferment is $d = 36$
2nd	PV	8822.8865	

The required sum of money is $8822.89.

Example 16.5b   An investment in a lease offers returns of $2500 per month due at the beginning of each month for five years. What investment is justified if the returns are deferred for two years and interest required is 24% compounded monthly?

Solution

$$R = 2500.00; \qquad i = 2\%; \qquad n = 5(12) = 60; \qquad d = 2(12) = 24$$

First, determine the present value of the annuity due at the end of the period of deferment.

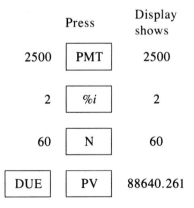

	Press	Display shows
2500	PMT	2500
2	%i	2
60	N	60
DUE	PV	88640.261

Secondly, determine the present value of the amount $88 640.26 at the beginning of the period of deferment.

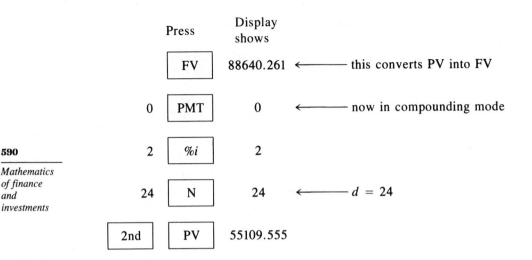

Press		Display shows	
	FV	88640.261	←——— this converts PV into FV
0	PMT	0	←——— now in compounding mode
2	%i	2	
24	N	24	←——— $d = 24$
2nd	PV	55109.555	

The investment justified is $55 109.56.

B. Finding the periodic payment R for deferred annuities

Example 16.5c A deposit of $20 000 is made for a twenty-year term. After the expiration of the term equal withdrawals are to be made for twelve years at the end of every six months. What is the size of the semi-annual withdrawal if interest is 10% compounded semi-annually?

Solution

The problem involves a deferred ordinary annuity.

$$A_n(\text{defer.}) = 20000; \qquad i = 5\%; \qquad n = 24; \qquad d = 40$$

First, determine the accumulated value of the deposit at the end of the deferment period.

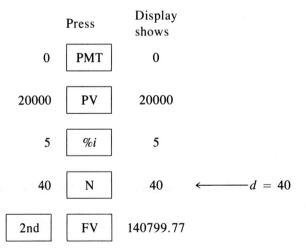

Press		Display shows	
0	PMT	0	
20000	PV	20000	
5	%i	5	
40	N	40	←——— $d = 40$
2nd	FV	140799.77	

Now find the periodic payment for the ordinary annuity whose present value is $140 799.77.

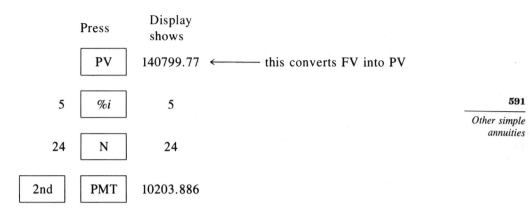

	Press	Display shows	
	PV	140799.77	← this converts FV into PV
5	%i	5	
24	N	24	
2nd	PMT	10203.886	

The size of the semi-annual withdrawal is $10 203.89.

Example 16.5d Payments on a seven-year lease valued at $12 200 are to be made at the beginning of each month during the last five years of the lease. If interest is 18% compounded monthly, what is the size of the monthly payments?

Solution

The problem involves an annuity due deferred for two years.

$$A_n(\text{defer.}) = 12200; \qquad i = 1.5\%; \qquad n = 60; \qquad d = 24$$

First, determine the accumulated value of the lease after two years.

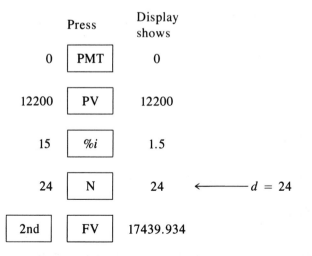

	Press	Display shows	
0	PMT	0	
12200	PV	12200	
15	%i	1.5	
24	N	24	← d = 24
2nd	FV	17439.934	

Now find the periodic payment for the annuity whose present value is $17 439.33.

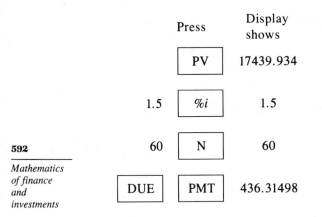

Press		Display shows
	PV	17439.934
1.5	%i	1.5
60	N	60
DUE	PMT	436.31498

The monthly lease payments are $436.31.

C. Finding the term n for deferred annuities

Example 16.5e For how long can $1000 be withdrawn at the end of each month from an account containing $16 000 if the withdrawals are deferred for six years and interest is 12% compounded monthly?

Solution

The problem involves a deferred ordinary annuity.

$$A_n(\text{defer.}) = 16000; \qquad R = 1000; \qquad i = 1\%; \qquad d = 72$$

First, determine the accumulated value of the account balance at the end of six years.

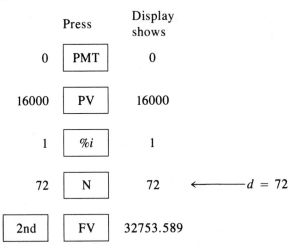

Press		Display shows
0	PMT	0
16000	PV	16000
1	%i	1
72	N	72 ⟵———— $d = 72$
2nd	FV	32753.589

Now find the number of payments for the ordinary annuity whose present value is $32 753.59.

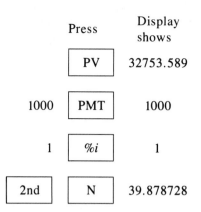

Press		Display shows
	PV	32753.589
1000	PMT	1000
1	%i	1
2nd	N	39.878728

Withdrawals of $1000 can be made for 39 months and a final withdrawal of less than $1000 in Month 40.

Example 16.5f Mr. X paid $24 000 into a retirement fund paying interest at 11% compounded semi-annually. If he retires in seventeen years, how long can Mr. X withdraw $10 000 from the fund every six months under the assumption that the first withdrawal is on the date of retirement?

Solution

Since the first payment is on the date of retirement, the problem involves a deferred annuity due.

$$A_n(\text{defer.}) = 24000; \qquad R = 10000; \qquad i = 5.5\%; \qquad d = 34$$

First, determine the accumulated value of the investment of $24 000 at the date of retirement.

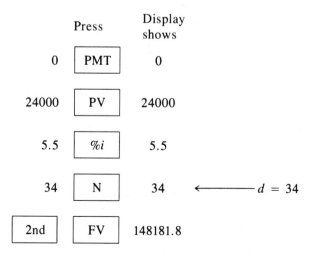

Press		Display shows	
0	PMT	0	
24000	PV	24000	
5.5	%i	5.5	
34	N	34	⟵———— $d = 34$
2nd	FV	148181.8	

Now determine the number of payments for the annuity whose present value is $148 181.80.

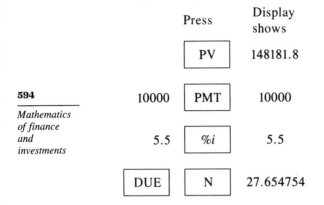

	Press	Display shows
	PV	148181.8
10000	PMT	10000
5.5	%i	5.5
DUE	N	27.654754

Semi-annual withdrawals of $10 000 can be made for 13.5 years plus a final withdrawal of less than $10 000.

D. *Finding the conversion rate i for deferred annuities*

Example 16.5g Payments of $900 are made at the end of every three months for fifteen years from a fund of $8000 earning interest compounded quarterly. If the payments were deferred for ten years, what was the nominal rate of interest?

Solution

While no direct solution is possible with the current (1981) generation of preprogrammed pocket calculators, the preprogramming features can be used in a method of trial and error similar to that used in Chapter 15.

The payments form a deferred ordinary annuity.

$$A_n(\text{defer.}) = 8000; \qquad R = 900; \qquad n = 60; \qquad d = 40$$

First, substitute in Formula 16.3 and determine the numerical value of the factor containing i.

$$8000 = 900(1 + i)^{-40}(a_{\overline{60}|\,i})$$

$$8.8888889 = a_{\overline{60}|\,i} \times \text{PV}(40, i)$$

Secondly, find approximations to the above factor using the following routine repeatedly.

Step 1 Find $a_{\overline{60}|\ i}$

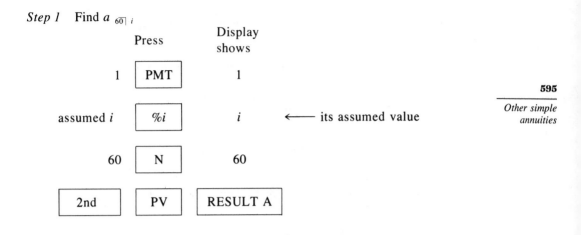

	Press	Display shows	
1	PMT	1	
assumed i	%i	i	⟵ its assumed value
60	N	60	
2nd	PV	RESULT A	

Step 2 Find PV(40, i).

Result A, the value of $a_{\overline{60}|\ i}$ for the assumed value of i, should now be used as the future value for finding PV(40, i). Result A need not be keyed in; just press FV immediately after PV .

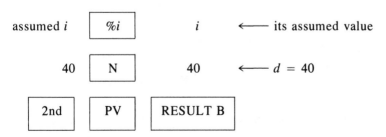

	Press	Display shows	
	FV	RESULT A	
0	PMT	0	
assumed i	%i	i	⟵ its assumed value
40	N	40	⟵ $d = 40$
2nd	PV	RESULT B	

Result B is the factor that is to be compared with 8.8888889.

Try i = 3%

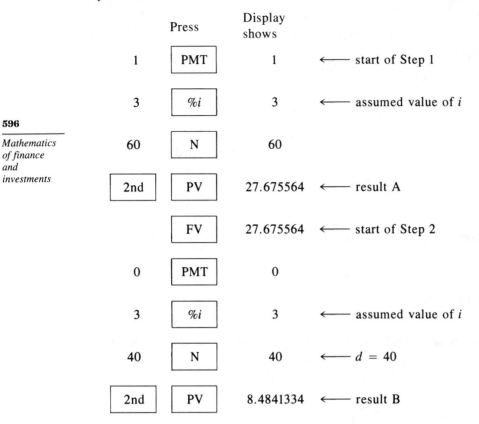

	Press	Display shows	
1	PMT	1	⟵ start of Step 1
3	%i	3	⟵ assumed value of i
60	N	60	
2nd	PV	27.675564	⟵ result A
	FV	27.675564	⟵ start of Step 2
0	PMT	0	
3	%i	3	⟵ assumed value of i
40	N	40	⟵ $d = 40$
2nd	PV	8.4841334	⟵ result B

Since $a_{\overline{60}|3\%} \times PV(40, 3\%) < a_{\overline{60}|i} \times PV(40, i) \longrightarrow 3\% > i$

Try i = 2.9%   Result A = 28.278648
Result B = 9.0124664
$2.9\% < i < 3\%$

Try i = 2.93%   Result B = 8.8503199
$2.9\% < i < 2.93\%$

Try i = 2.92%   Result B = 8.904149
$2.92\% < i < 2.93\%$

Try i = 2.923%   Result B = 8.8878694
$i = 2.923\%$ quarterly (approximately)

The nominal rate of interest $= 4(2.923\%) = 11.69\%$.

Example 16.5h Payments of $500 are to be made at the beginning of each month for four years starting two years after a contract valued at $12 000 was signed. What nominal rate of interest compounded monthly has been charged?

Solution

Since the payments are at the beginning of each month, the problem involves a deferred annuity due.

$$A_n(\text{defer.}) = 12000; \qquad R = 500; \qquad n = 48; \qquad d = 24$$

$$12000 = 500(1 + i)^{-24}(a\,\overline{_{48}}_{|i})(1 + i)$$

$$24 = (1 + i)^{-23}(a\,\overline{_{48}}_{|i})$$

$$24 = a\,\overline{_{48}}_{|i} \times PV(23, i)$$

For $i = 1.5\%$ Result B $= 24.171475 \longrightarrow i > 1.5\%$

For $i = 1.55\%$ Result B $= 23.646096 \longrightarrow 1.5\% < i < 1.55\%$

For $i = 1.52\%$ Result B $= 23.959776 \longrightarrow 1.5 < i < 1.52\%$

For $i = 1.516\%$ Result B $= 24.001949 \longrightarrow i = 1.516\%$

The nominal rate of interest is 18.192% approximately.

Exercise 16.5

Do Exercise 16.4 using a preprogrammed financial calculator.

16.6 *Simple perpetuities*

A. *Basic concepts*

A **perpetuity** is an annuity in which the periodic payments begin on a fixed date and continue indefinitely. Interest payments on permanently invested sums of money are prime examples of perpetuities. Dividends on preferred shares fall into this category based on the assumption that the issuing corporation has an indefinite life. Scholarships paid on a perpetual basis from an endowment fit the definition of perpetuity.

As there is no end to the term, it is *not* possible to determine the amount of a perpetuity. However, the present value of a perpetuity is a definite value and this section deals with the present value of simple perpetuities.

B. Present value of ordinary perpetuities

The following symbols are commonly used when dealing with perpetuities

A = the present value of the perpetuity;

R = the periodic rent (or perpetuity payment);

i = the periodic rate of interest.

FIGURE 16.8 *Graphical representation of ordinary perpetuity*

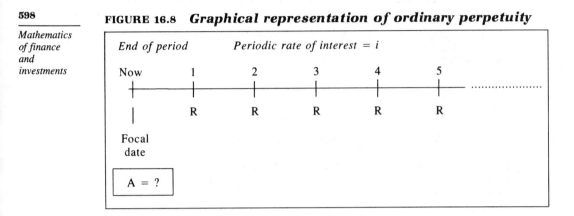

The **perpetuity payment** R is the interest earned by the present value of the perpetuity in one interest period.

$$R = iA$$

$$A = \frac{R}{i}$$ ⟵ *Formula* **16.4** *Present value of an ordinary perpetuity*

Example 16.6a What sum of money invested today at 10% compounded annually will provide a scholarship of $1500.00 at the end of every year?

Solution

$$R = 1500.00; \qquad i = 10\% = 0.10$$

$$A = \frac{1500.00}{0.10} = \$15000.00 \longleftarrow \text{substituting in Formula 16.4}$$

Example 16.6b The maintenance cost for Northern Railroad of a crossing with a provincial highway is $2000.00 at the end of each month. Proposed construction of an overpass would eliminate the monthly maintenance cost. If money is worth 12% compounded monthly, how much should Northern be willing to contribute towards the cost of construction?

Solution

The monthly maintenance expense payments form an ordinary perpetuity.

$$R = 2000.00; \qquad i = \frac{12\%}{12} = 0.01$$

$$A = \frac{2000.00}{0.01} = \$200000.00$$

Northern should be willing to contribute $200 000.00 towards construction.

Example 16.6c   A will provides an endowment of $50 000.00 to a college with the provision that a scholarship be paid at the end of each year. If the money is invested at 11% compounded annually, how much is the annual scholarship?

Solution

$$A = 50000.00; \qquad i = 11\% = 0.11$$

$$R = 50000.00(0.11) = \$5500.00$$

C.   Present value of perpetuities due

A perpetuity due differs from an ordinary perpetuity only in that the first payment is made at the focal date. Hence a perpetuity due may be treated as consisting of an immediate payment R followed by an ordinary perpetuity.

$$\boxed{A = R + \frac{R}{i}} \qquad \longleftarrow \text{ **Formula 16.4A** } \textit{Present value of a perpetuity due}$$

Example 16.5d   A tract of land is leased in perpetuity at $1250.00 due at the beginning of each month. If money is worth 13.5% compounded monthly, what is the value of the lease?

Solution

$$R = 1250.00; \qquad i = \frac{13.5\%}{12} = 1.125\% = 0.01125$$

$$A = 1250.00 + \frac{1250.00}{0.01125} \qquad \longleftarrow \text{ substituting in Formula 16.4A}$$

$$= 1250.00 + 111111.11$$

$$= \$112361.11$$

Example 16.5e   How much money must be invested today in a fund earning 11.5% compounded annually to pay annual scholarships of $2000.00 starting
(i) one year from now?
(ii) immediately?
(iii) four years from now?

Solution

$$R = 2000.00; \qquad i = 11.5\% = 0.115$$

(i) The annual scholarship payments form an ordinary perpetuity.

$$A = \frac{2000.00}{0.115} = \$17391.30$$

(ii) The annual scholarship payments form a perpetuity due.

$$A = 2000.00 + \frac{2000.00}{0.115}$$

$$= 2000.00 + 17391.30$$

$$= \$19391.30$$

(iii) The annual scholarship payments form an ordinary perpetuity deferred for three years.

$$A(\text{defer.}) = A(1.115^{-3})$$

$$= 17391.30(0.7213988)$$

$$= \$12546.06$$

Exercise 16.6

A. Find the present value of each of the following perpetuities

Problem number	Perpetuity payment	Made at	Payment interval	Interest rate	Compounding period
1.	$1250.00	end	3 months	14.8%	quarterly
2.	$985.00	beginning	6 months	11.5%	semi-annually
3.	$125.00	beginning	1 month	12.6%	monthly
4.	$3420.00	end	1 year	15.3%	annually

B. Answer each of the following questions

1. Mr. Rich wants to set up a scholarship fund for his Alma Mater. The annual scholarship payment is to be $2500.00 with the first such payment due four years after his deposit into the fund. If the fund pays 17.25% compounded annually, how much must Mr. Rich deposit?

2. A rental property provides a monthly income of $1150.00 due at the beginning of every month. What is the cash value of the property if money is worth 16.2% compounded monthly?

3. The faculty of Central College collected $1400.00 for the purpose of setting up a memorial fund from which an annual award is to be made to a qualifying student. If the money is invested at 14% compounded annually and the first annual award payment is to be made five years after the money was deposited, what is the size of the payment?

4. Barbara bought an income property for $28 000.00 three years ago. She has held the property for the three years without renting it. If she rents the property out now what should the size of the monthly rent payment due in advance be if money is worth 15% compounded monthly?

16.7 *Appendix—Finding the conversion rate i for annuities due and deferred annuities without preprogrammed calculators*

A. *Finding i with the amount S_n (due) is known*

Since Formula 16.1 is awkward for finding i, the formula may be developed into a more suitable form.

$$S_n(\text{due}) = R(1 + i)\left(\frac{(1 + i)^n - 1}{i}\right) \quad \longleftarrow \quad \textbf{\textit{Formula 16.1}}$$

$$= R\left(\frac{(1 + i)^{n+1} - (1 + i)}{i}\right) \quad \longleftarrow \quad \text{multiplying by } (1 + i)$$

$$= R\left(\frac{(1 + i)^{n+1} - 1 - i}{i}\right)$$

$$= R\left(\frac{(1 + i)^{n+1} - 1}{i} - \frac{i}{i}\right)$$

$$\boxed{S_n(\text{due}) = R\left(\frac{(1 + i)^{n+1} - 1}{i} - 1\right)}$$

Since the factor $\dfrac{(1 + i)^{n+1} - 1}{i}$ may be represented by the symbol $s_{\overline{n+1}|i}$

$$\boxed{S_n(\text{due}) = R(s_{\overline{n+1}|i} - 1)} \quad \longleftarrow \quad \textbf{\textit{Formula 16.5}}$$

Example 16.7a At what nominal rate of interest compounded semi-annually will $320.00 deposited at the beginning of every six months for twelve years accumulate to $15 000.00?

Solution

$$S_n(\text{due}) = 15000.00; \qquad R = 320.00; \qquad n = 12(2) = 24$$

$$15000.00 = 320.00\left(\frac{(1 + i)^{24+1} - 1}{i} - 1\right) \quad \longleftarrow \quad \begin{array}{l}\text{substituting}\\ \text{in Formula 16.5}\end{array}$$

$$\frac{15000.00}{320.00} = \frac{(1 + i)^{25} - 1}{i} - 1$$

$$46.875 + 1 = \frac{(1 + i)^{25} - 1}{i} = s\,\overline{_{25}}_{|\,i}$$

$$s\,\overline{_{25}}_{|\,i} = 47.875$$

Select a reasonable nominal rate, such as 12%; then $i = 6\%$.

for $i = 6\%$ $s\,\overline{_{25}}_{|\,6\%} = 54.864512 \longrightarrow i \quad < 6\%$

for $i = 4\%$ $s\,\overline{_{25}}_{|\,4\%} = 41.645908 \longrightarrow 4\% < i < 6\%$

for $i = 5\%$ $s\,\overline{_{25}}_{|\,5\%} = 47.727098 \longrightarrow 5\% < i < 6\%$

Since 47.727098 is much closer to 47.875 than 54.864512, i is much closer to 5% than to 6%; hence try a value of i very close to 5%, such as 5.1%.

for $i = 5.1\%$ $s\,\overline{_{25}}_{|\,5.1\%} = 48.390405 \longrightarrow 5\% < i < 5.1\%$

for $i = 5.02\%$ $s\,\overline{_{25}}_{|\,5.02\%} = 47.858911 \longrightarrow 5.02\% < i < 5.1\%$

for $i = 5.023\%$ $s\,\overline{_{25}}_{|\,5.023\%} = 47.878720 \longrightarrow i = 5.023\%$ approximately

Since the semi-annual rate of interest is approximately 5.023%, the nominal rate of interest $= 2(5.023\%) = 10.046\%$.

B.   *Finding i when the present value A_n(due) is known*

Formula 16.2 too is awkward to use when finding i and may be developed into a more suitable form.

$$A_n(\text{due}) = R(1 + i)\left(\frac{1 - (1 + i)^{-n}}{i}\right) \quad \longleftarrow \quad \text{Formula 16.2}$$

$$= R\left(\frac{(1 + i) - (1 + i)^{-(n+1)}}{i}\right) \quad \longleftarrow \quad \text{multiplying by } (1 + i)$$

$$= R\left(\frac{1 + i - (1 + i)^{-(n-1)}}{i}\right)$$

$$= R\left(\frac{i}{i} + \frac{1 - (1 + i)^{-(n-1)}}{i}\right)$$

$$\boxed{A_n(\text{due}) = R\left(\frac{1 - (1 + i)^{-(n-1)}}{i} + 1\right)}$$

Since the factor $\dfrac{1 - (1 + i)^{-(n-1)}}{i}$ may be represented by the symbol $a_{\overline{n-1}|i}$

$$\boxed{A_n(\text{due}) = R(a_{\overline{n-1}|i} + 1)} \quad \longleftarrow \quad \textbf{Formula 16.6}$$

Example 16.7b A lease contract valued $16 000.00 is to be fulfilled by making payments of $325.00 at the beginning of each month for ten years. What is the nominal rate of interest paid if interest is compounded monthly?

Solution

$$A_n(\text{due}) = 16000.00; \qquad R = 325.00; \qquad n = 10(12) = 120$$

$$16000.00 = 325.00\left(\frac{1 - (1 + i)^{-(120-1)}}{i} + 1\right) \quad \longleftarrow \quad \begin{array}{l}\text{substituting}\\ \text{in Formula 16.6}\end{array}$$

$$\frac{16000.00}{325.00} = \frac{1 - (1 + i)^{-119}}{i} + 1$$

$$49.2306769 - 1 = \frac{1 - (1 + i)^{-119}}{i} = a_{\overline{119}|i}$$

$$a_{\overline{119}|i} = 48.230769$$

For a nominal rate of 12%, $i = 1\%$.

$$\text{for } i = 1\% \qquad a_{\overline{119}|1\%} = 69.397527$$

$$a_{\overline{119}|1\%} > a_{\overline{119}|i} \text{ and } 1\% < i$$

for $i = 2\%,$ $a_{\overline{119}|2\%}$ $= 45.262496 \longrightarrow 1\% < i < 2\%$

for $i = 1.8\%$ $a_{\overline{119}|1.8\%}$ $= 48.906776 \longrightarrow 1.8\% < i < 2\%$

for $i = 1.83\%$ $a_{\overline{119}|1.83\%}$ $= 48.330360 \longrightarrow 1.83\% < i < 2\%$

for $i = 1.835\%$ $a_{\overline{119}|1.835\%}$ $= 48.235357 \longrightarrow 1.835\% < i < 2\%$

for $i = 1.836\%$ $a_{\overline{119}|1.836\%}$ $= 48.216393 \longrightarrow 1.835\% < i < 1.836\%$

$$i = 1.835\% \text{ approximately}$$

The nominal rate of interest $= 12(1.835\%) = 22.02\%$ (approximately).

C. Finding the rate of interest of a deferred annuity

The rate of interest for a deferred annuity may be determined by trial and error using a method similar to the one previously explained in Chapter 15. For deferred ordinary annuities use Formula 16.3; for deferred annuities due multiply Formula 16.3 by $(1 + i)$.

Example 16.7c Payments of $900.00 are made at the end of every three months for fifteen years from a fund of $8000.00 earning interest compounded quarterly. If the payments were deferred for ten years, what was the nominal rate of interest?

Solution

The payments form a deferred ordinary annuity. $A_n(\text{defer.}) = 8000.00$;

$$R = 900.00; \qquad n = 15(4) = 60; \qquad d = 10(4) = 40$$

$$8000.00 = 900.00(1 + i)^{-40}\left(\frac{1 - (1 + i)^{-60}}{i}\right) \longleftarrow \text{ using Formula 16.3}$$

$$8.8888889 = (1 + i)^{-40}\left(\frac{1 - (1 + i)^{-60}}{i}\right)$$

$$a_{\overline{60}|i} \times \text{PV}(40, i) = 8.8888889$$

For a nominal rate of 12%, the quarterly rate $i = 3\%$.

For $i = 3\%$ $a_{\overline{60}|3\%} \times \text{PV}(40), 3\%)$

      $= (27.675564)(0.3065568) = 8.4841334$

Since $a_{\overline{60}|3\%} \times \text{PV}(40, 3\%) < a_{\overline{60}|i} \times \text{PV}(40, i) \rightarrow 3\% > i$

For $i = 2.9\%$ $a_{\overline{60}|2.9\%} \times \text{PV}(40, 2.9\%)$

      $= (28.278648)(0.3187022) = 9.0124664 \rightarrow 2.9\% < i < 3\%$

For $i = 2.93\%$ $a_{\overline{60}|2.93\%} \times \text{PV}(40, 2.93\%)$

      $= (28.095572)(0.3150076) = 8.8503199 \rightarrow 2.9\% < i < 2.93\%$

For $i = 2.92\%$ $a_{\overline{60}|2.92\%} \times \text{PV}(40, 2.92\%)$

      $= (28.156390)(0.3162342) = 8.9040149 \rightarrow 2.92\% < i < 2.93\%$

For $i = 2.923\%$ $a_{\overline{60}|2.923\%} \times \text{PV}(40, 2.923\%)$

      $= (28.138123)(0.3158658) = 8.8878694 \rightarrow i = 2.923\%$ approximatel

The nominal rate of interest $= 4(2.923\%) = 11.69\%$ approximately.

Review exercise

1. Find the amount and the present value of semi-annual payments of $540.00 for seven and a half years if interest is 13.5% compounded semi-annually and the payments are made

   (a) at the end of every six months;

   (b) at the beginning of every six months.

2. Determine the amount and the present value of monthly payments of $50.00 each for eight years at 15% compounded monthly if

   (a) the payments form an annuity due;

   (b) the payments form an ordinary annuity.

3. A collateral mortgage can be discharged by making payments of $368.00 at the end of each month for fifteen years. If interest is 13.5% compounded monthly, what was the original principal borrowed?

4. Mr. Deed deposited $100.00 in a trust account at the date of his son's birth and every three months thereafter. If interest paid is 14% compounded quarterly, what will the balance in the trust account be before the deposit is made on the son's 21st birthday?

5. If you would like to have $10 000.00 in your savings account and interest is 16% compounded quarterly, how much must you deposit every three months for five years if the deposits are made

   (a) at the end of each quarter;

   (b) at the beginning of each quarter.

6. Equal sums of money are withdrawn monthly from a fund of $20 000.00 for fifteen years. If interest is 9% compounded monthly, what is the size of each withdrawal

   (a) if made at the beginning of each month?

   (b) if made at the end of each month?

7. Annual rent of $6000.00 payable in advance is to be paid in equal monthly amounts at the beginning of each month. If money is worth 16.5% compounded monthly, what is the size of the monthly payment?

8. Joe wishes to save $5000.00 each year. If interest is 13% compounded quarterly, what deposit must Joe make

   (a) at the end of every three months;

   (b) at the beginning of every three months.

9. How long will it take to accumulate $18 000.00 at 12% compounded monthly if $125.00 is deposited in an account at the beginning of every month?

10. A contract valued at $11 500.00 requires payment of $1450.00 at the beginning of every six months. If interest is 15.5% compounded semi-annually, what is the term of the contract?

11. At what nominal rate of interest compounded semi-annually will $1200.00 deposited at the beginning of every six months accumulate to $40 000.00 in nine years?

12. What is the effective rate of interest charged on a lease valued $9600.00 if payments of $300.00 are made at the beginning of each month for the four years?

13. Mr. Maxwell intends to retire in ten years and wishes to receive $4800.00 every three months starting on the date of his retirement for twenty years. How much must he deposit now in order to receive the quarterly payments from an account paying 16% compounded quarterly?

14. Tomac Swim Club bought electronic timing equipment on a contract requiring monthly payments of $725.00 for three years beginning eighteen months after the date of purchase. What was the cash value of the equipment if interest is 15% compounded monthly?

15. Frank invested a retirement gratuity of $15 000.00 in an income averaging annuity paying 12% compounded monthly. He withdraws the money in equal monthly amounts over five years. If the first withdrawal is made nine months after the deposit, what is the size of each withdrawal?

16. Mrs. Gold deposited an inheritance of $25 000.00 in a three-year term deposit. How much will she receive at the end of every three months for fifteen years after the deposit matures if interest is 11% compounded quarterly?

17. An income property is estimated to net $1750.00 per month on a continuing basis. If money is worth 15.6% compounded monthly, what is the cash price of the property?

18. Western Pipelines pay $8000.00 at the beginning of each year for using a tract of land. What should the company offer the property owner as purchase price if interest is 15.5% compounded annually?

19. Home entertainment equipment can be bought on time by making monthly payments of $82.00 for three and a half years. The first payment is due at the time of purchase and the financing cost is 16.5% compounded monthly.
   (a) What is the purchase price?
   (b) How much will be paid in instalments?
   (c) How much is the cost of financing?

20. Jim makes deposits of $225.00 at the beginning of every three months. Interest earned by the deposits is 13% compounded quarterly.
   (a) How much will the balance in Jim's account be after eight years?
   (b) How much of the balance will Jim have contributed?
   (c) How much of the balance is interest?

21. For how long must $1000.00 be deposited at the beginning of every year to accumulate to $180 000.00 twelve years after the end of the year in which the last deposit was made if interest is 11.5% compounded annually?

22. Richard invested a retirement gratuity of $12 500.00 in an RRSP paying 10.5% compounded semi-annually for ten years. At the end of ten years he rolled the RRSP balance over into a RRIF paying him $500.00 at the beginning of each month starting with the date of rollover. If interest on the RRIF is 10.5% compounded monthly, for how long will Richard receive monthly payments?

23. Mr. Smart wants to set up an annual scholarship of $3000.00. If the first payment is to be made in five years and interest is 14.5% compounded annually, how much must Mr. Smart pay into the scholarship fund?

24. Karl plans to invest in a property which after three years will yield $1200.00 at the end of each month indefinitely. How much should Karl be willing to pay if alternative investments yield 18% compounded monthly?

25. Mrs. Bean contibutes $450.00 at the beginning of every three months to a RRSP. Interest on the account is 14% compounded quarterly.

(a) What will the balance in the account be after seven years?

(b) How much of the balance will be interest?

(c) If Mrs. Bean converts the balance after seven years into a RRIF paying 13% compounded quarterly and makes equal quarterly withdrawals for twelve years starting three months after the conversion into the RRIF, what is the size of the quarterly withdrawal?

(d) What will the combined interest earned by the RRSP and the RRIF amount to?

26. Art will receive monthly payments of $850.00 from a trust account starting on the date of his retirement and continuing for twenty years. Interest is 10.5% compounded monthly.

(a) How much is the balance in the trust account at the date of Art's retirement?

(b) How much interest will be included in the payments received by Art?

(c) If Art is able to receive the payments because he made equal monthly deposits at the beginning of each month for fifteen years before his retirement, how much did he deposit each month?

(d) How much interest will Art receive in total?

27. Kelly and Son bought a tractor priced at $10 500.00 on February 1. Kelly agreed to make monthly payments of $475.00 beginning December 1 of the same year. For how long will Kelly and Son have to make these payments if interest is 16.5% compounded monthly?

28. Okinagan Vineyards borrowed $75 000.00 on a five-year promissory note with the undertaking that starting on the date of maturity of the note payments of $6000.00 would be made every three months. If interest is 14% compounded quarterly, for how long will the payments have to be made?

29. Mr. Schmid deposits $550.00 at the beginning of every three months. Starting three months after the last deposit, he intends to withdraw $3500.00 every three months for fourteen years. If interest is 12% compounded quarterly, for how long must Mr. Schmid make deposits?

30. Terry save $50.00 at the beginning of each month for sixteen years. Beginning one month after his last deposit he intends to withdraw $375.00 per month. If interest is 12% compounded monthly, for how long can Terry make withdrawals?

31. Mrs. Ball invested $10 000.00 on her 35th birthday in an annuity which will pay her $5000.00 every six months for twenty years. If the first payment is due six months after her 60th birthday, what is the nominal annual rate of interest compounded semi-annually paid by the annuity?

32. A lease can be bought for $64 000.00. If the lease requires payments of $4700.00 every three months for ten years and the first payment is due two years after the lease is purchased, what is the effective annual rate of interest based on quarterly compounding?

Self-test

1. Payments of $1080.00 are made into a fund at the beginning of every three months for eleven years. If the fund earns interest at 19.5% compounded quarterly, how much will the balance in the fund be after eleven years?

2. What sum of money must be deposited in a trust fund to provide a scholarship of $960.00 payable at the end of each month if interest is 15% compounded monthly?

3. How many months will it take to accumulate $142 400.00 at 14% compounded quarterly, if $700.00 is deposited in an account at the beginning of every three months?

4. Find the present value of payments of $960.00 made at the beginning of every month for seven years if money is worth 18% compounded monthly.

5. Jones bought his neighbour's farm for $30 000.00 down and payments of $6000.00 at the end of every six months for six years. What is the purchase price of the farm if the semi-annual payments are deferred for four years and interest is 15% compounded semi-annually?

6. Western Pipelines pays $400.00 at the beginning of every half-year for using a tract of land. What should the company offer the property owner as purchase price if interest is 21% compounded semi-annually?

7. What is the nominal annual rate of interest charged on a lease valued at $3840.00 if payments of $240.00 are made at the beginning of every three months for six years?

8. $57 426.00 is invested at 21% compounded monthly for six years. After the initial six-year period the balance in the fund is converted into an annuity due paying $5600.00 every three months. If interest on the annuity is 10.5% compounded quarterly, what is the term of the annuity in months?

9. Tim purchased a boat valued at $10 104.00 on the instalment plan requiring equal semi-annual payments for five years. If the first payment is due on the date of purchase and interest is 10.5% compounded semi-annually, what is the size of the semi-annual payments?

10. Deposits of $900.00 made at the beginning of every three months amount to $40 000.00 after six years. What is the effective annual rate of interest earned by the deposits if interest is compounded quarterly?

11. Eden would like to receive $3000.00 at the end of every six months for seven years after her retirement. If she retires ten years from now and interest is 13.5% compounded semi-annually, how much must she deposit into an account every six months starting now?

12. J.J. deposited $1680.00 at the beginning of every six months for eight years into a fund paying 15.5% compounded semi-annually. Fifteen years after the first deposit he converted the then existing balance into an annuity paying him equal monthly payments for twenty years. If the payments are made at the end of each month and interest is 15% compounded monthly, what is the size of the monthly payments?

Summary of formulae used

Formula 16.1 $\quad S_n(\text{due}) = R(1 + i)\left(\dfrac{(1 + i)^n - 1}{i}\right)$
Finding the amount of an annuity due

Formula 16.1A $\quad S_n(\text{due}) = R \times s_{\overline{n}|i} \times (1 + i)$
Finding the amount of an annuity due using the symbol $s_{\overline{n}|i}$ for the accumulation factor

Formula 16.2 $\quad A_n(\text{due}) = R(1 + i)\left(\dfrac{1 - (1 + i)^{-n}}{i}\right)$
Finding the present value of an annuity due

Formula 16.2A $\quad A_n(\text{due}) = R \times a_{\overline{n}|i} \times (1 + i)$
Finding the present value of an annuity due using the symbol $a_{\overline{n}|i}$ for the discount factor

Formula 16.3 $\quad A_n(\text{defer.}) = R(1 + i)^{-d}a_{\overline{n}|i}$
Finding the present value of a deferred ordinary annuity using the symbol $a_{\overline{n}|i}$ for the discount factor

Formula 16.4 $A = \dfrac{R}{i}$

Finding the present value of an ordinary perpetuity

Formula 16.4A $A = R + \dfrac{R}{i}$

Finding the present value of a perpetuity due

Supplementary formulae (Section 16.6)

Formula 16.5 $S_n(\text{due}) = R(s_{\overline{n+1}|i} - 1)$

Alternate form of the formula for finding the amount of an annuity due

Formula 16.6 $A_n(\text{due}) = R(a_{\overline{n-1}|i} + 1)$

Alternate form of the formula for finding the present value of an annuity due

Glossary of terms used

Annuity due   an annuity in which the periodic payments are made at the beginning of each period

Deferred annuity   an annuity in which the first payment is made at a point in time later than the end of the first payment interval

Period of deferment   the time period from the point in time referred to as 'now' to the starting point of the term of the annuity

Perpetuity   an annuity in which the periodic payments begin at a fixed date and continue indefinitely

Perpetuity payment   the perpetual periodic payment which equals the interest earned by the present value of these payments in one interest period

Present value of a deferred annuity   the discounted value of the periodic payments at the beginning of the period of deferment

17 General (or complex) annuities

Introduction

In Chapters 15 and 16 simple annuities were considered in detail. Simple annuities, however, are a special case in which the payment interval and the interest conversion period are of the same length. Yet interest is often compounded more or less frequently than payments are made. In Canada residential mortgages are usually compounded semi-annually while payments are made monthly.

Annuities in which the length of the interest conversion period is different from the length of the payment interval are considered in this chapter. Such annuities are called general (or complex) annuities; they may be ordinary annuities, annuities due, deferred annuities or perpetuities.

Objectives

Upon completion of this chapter you will be able to

1. compute the amount (or accumulated value) of ordinary general annuities;
2. compute the present value (or discounted value) of ordinary general annuities;
3. compute the periodic payment, the term and the interest rate in ordinary general annuities;
4. determine the amount, the present value, the periodic payment, the term and the interest rate in general annuities due;
5. determine the present value, the periodic payment, the term and the rate of interest in deferred general annuities;
6. determine the present value of general perpetuities.

17.1 Amount of an ordinary general annuity

A. Basic concepts and computation

The basic method of solving problems involving interest uses the equivalence of sets of financial obligations at a selected focal date. Thus, when dealing with any kind of annuity the essential tool is an equation of value. The various formulae used in the previous two chapters on simple annuities were introduced because they make the solution of annuity problems easier, not because they are essential to the solution.

This basic approach is equally applicable to **general annuities** and is used to make the basic computations and develop useful formuale.

Example 17.1a   What is the accumulated value of $100.00 deposited at the end of every six months for three years if interest is 12% compounded annually?

Solution

Since the payments are made semi-annually while the compounding is done annually the annuity is classified as general (or complex) annuity. Furthermore, as the payments are at the end of each payment interval the annuity is an ordinary general annuity. While the difference in the length of the payment period as compared to the length of the compounding period introduces a, mathematical complication, the basic approach to finding the amount of the ordinary complex annuity is the same as used in finding the amount of an ordinary simple annuity.

The basic solution and data for the problem are graphically represented in Figure 17.1. Since deposits are made at the end of every six months for three years there are six deposits of $100.00 at the points in time indicated. Since interest is compounded annually, $i = 12\% = 0.12$ and there are three conversion periods.

FIGURE 17.1   *Graphical representation of method and data*

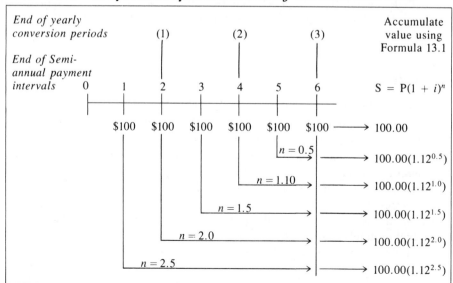

The focal point is at the end of Year 3. The last deposit is made at the focal date and has a value of $100.00 on that date. The fifth deposit is made after 2.5 years and, in terms of conversion periods, has accumulated for a half conversion period ($n = 0.5$); its accumulated value is $100.00(1.12^{0.5}) = \$105.83$ at the focal date. The fourth deposit is made after two years and has accumulated for one conversion period ($n = 1.0$); its accumulated value at the focal date is $100.00(1.12^{1.0}) = \$112.00$. Similarly, the accumulated value of the third deposit is $100.00(1.12^{1.5}) = \$118.53$, while the accumulated value of the second deposit is $100.00(1.12^{2.0}) = \$125.44$. Finally the accumulated value of the first deposit is $100.00(1.12^{2.5}) = \$132.75$ and the total accumulated value after three years is $694.55. This total could have been obtained by setting up the equation of values.

$$S_n = 100.00 + 100.00(1.12^{0.5}) + 100.00(1.12^{1.0}) + 100.00(1.12^{1.5})$$
$$\quad + 100.00(1.12^{2.0}) + 100.00(1.12^{2.5})$$
$$= 100.00(1 + 1.12^{0.5} + 1.12^{1.0} + 1.12^{1.5} + 1.12^{2.0} + 1.12^{2.5})$$

$$= 100.00\left(\begin{array}{l}\text{the sum of the first six terms of a} \\ \text{geometric progression with first term 1} \\ \text{and common ratio } 1.12^{0.5}\end{array}\right)$$

$$= 100.00\left(\frac{(1.12^{0.5})^6 - 1}{1.12^{0.5} - 1}\right) \longleftarrow \text{substituting in Formula 6.8}$$

$$= 100.00\left(\frac{1.4049280 - 1}{1.0583005 - 1}\right)$$

$$= 100.00\left(\frac{0.4049280}{0.0583005}\right)$$

$$= 100.00(6.9455322)$$

$$= \$694.55$$

The accumulated value is $694.55.

Example 17.1b What is the accumulated value of deposits of $100.00 made at the end of each year for four years if interest is 12% compounded quarterly?

Solution

Since the deposits are made at the end of every year for four years, there are four payments of $100.00 at the points in time indicated. Since interest is compounded quarterly, $i = \frac{12\%}{4} = 3\% = 0.03$ and there are $4(4) = 16$ conversion periods. The focal point is the end of Year 4. The last payment is made at the focal point in time and has a value of $100.00 at that date. The third payment is made after three years and, in terms of conversion periods, has accumulated for four conversion periods ($n = 4$); its accumulated value is $100.00(1.03^4) = \$112.55$. The second deposit has accumulated for 8 conversion periods ($n = 8$); its accumulated value is $100.00(1.03^8) = \$126.68$. The first deposit has accumulated for 12 conversion periods ($n = 12$); its accumulated value is $100.00(1.03^{12}) = \$142.58$. The total

FIGURE 17.2 *Graphical representation of method and data*

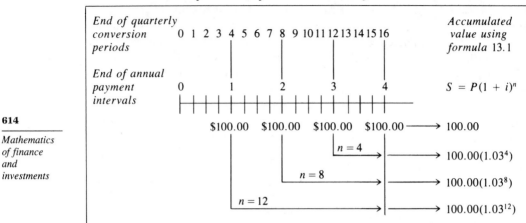

accumulated value of the deposits after four years is \$481.81. An equation of values can be set up to obtain the total.

$$S = 100.00 + 100.00(1.03^4) + 100.00(1.03^8) + 100.00(1.03^{12})$$

$$= 100.00(1 + 1.03^4 + 1.03^8 + 1.03^{12})$$

$$= 100.00 \begin{pmatrix} \text{the sum of the first four terms of a} \\ \text{geometric progression with first term} \\ \text{1 and common ratio } 1.03^4 \end{pmatrix}$$

$$= 100.00 \left(\frac{(1.03^4)^4 - 1}{1.03^4 - 1} \right) \longleftarrow \text{substituting in Formula 6.8}$$

$$= 100.00 \left(\frac{1.03^{16} - 1}{1.03^4 - 1} \right)$$

$$= 100.00 \left(\frac{1.6047064 - 1}{1.1255088 - 1} \right)$$

$$= 100.00 \left(\frac{0.6047064}{0.1255088} \right)$$

$$= 100.00(4.8180399)$$

$$= \$481.80$$

The accumulated value is \$481.80.

B.   *Amount of an ordinary general annuity—basic formula*

Consistent with the symbols previously used for developing formulae for simple annuities, the following notation will be used:

S_{nc} = the amount (or accumulated value) of an **ordinary general annuity**;
R = the size of the periodic payment;
i = the interest rate per interest conversion period;
n = the number of periodic payments;
c = the number of interest conversion periods per payment interval.

Examples 17.1a and 17.1b illustrate the basic solution for the two possible cases of general annuities.

Case 1 The interest conversion period is *longer* than the payment period; each payment interval contains only a fraction of one conversion period; c has a fractional value less than 1. (See Example 17.1a.)

Case 2 The interest conversion period is *shorter* than the payment period; each payment period contains more than one conversion period; c has a value greater than 1. (See Example 17.1b.)

In either case, however, the basic method of solving the problem leads to a geometric progression. In using this approach, it is important that the relationship between the *payment interval* and the number of *interest conversion periods* per payment interval as well as the number of actual payments and the number of total interest conversion periods in the term of the annuity be clearly understood.

$$c = \frac{\text{THE NUMBER OF INTEREST CONVERSION PERIODS PER YEAR}}{\text{THE NUMBER OF PAYMENT PERIODS PER YEAR}}$$

The following table provides a sampling of possible combinations of payment intervals and interest conversion periods that may be encountered when dealing with general annuities. One of the most important combinations is the monthly payment interval associated with semi-annual compounding since this the one usually encountered with residential mortgages in Canada.

TABLE 17.1 *Some possible combinations of payment interval and interest conversion period*

Payment interval	Interest conversion period	Number of interest conversion periods per payment interval	Length of term of annuity	Number of periodic payments n	Number of conversion periods nc
semi-annually	monthly	$c = \dfrac{12}{2} = 6$	5 years	$5(2) = 10$	$10(6) = 60$
quarterly	monthly	$c = \dfrac{12}{4} = 3$	10 years	$10(4) = 40$	$40(3) = 120$
annually	quarterly	$c = \dfrac{4}{1} = 4$	25 years	$25(1) = 25$	$25(4) = 100$
semi-annually	annually	$c = \dfrac{1}{2} = 0.5$	3 years	$3(2) = 6$	$6(0.5) = 3$
quarterly	annually	$c = \dfrac{1}{4} = 0.25$	15 years	$15(4) = 60$	$60(0.25) = 15$
monthly	semi-annually	$c = \dfrac{2}{12} = \dfrac{1}{6}$	20 years	$20(12) = 240$	$240\left(\dfrac{1}{6}\right) = 40$
monthly	quarterly	$c = \dfrac{4}{12} = \dfrac{1}{3}$	2 years	$2(12) = 24$	$24\left(\dfrac{1}{3}\right) = 8$
monthly	annually	$c = \dfrac{1}{12}$	7 years	$7(12) = 84$	$84\left(\dfrac{1}{12}\right) = 7$

The basic formula for finding the amount of an ordinary general annuity can be obtained as follows.

For a general annuity of n payments of size R made at the end of each payment period and compounded c times per payment period at the periodic conversion rate i the accumulated value S_{nc} is given by the equation

$$S_{nc} = R + R(1 + i)^c + R(1 + i)^{2c} + R(1 + i)^{3c} + \ldots + R(1 + i)^{(n-1)c}$$

$$= R\left[1 + (1 + i)^c + (1 + i)^{2c} + (1 + i)^{3c} + \ldots + (1 + i)^{(n-1)c}\right]$$

$$= R\left(\begin{array}{c}\text{the sum of the first } n \text{ terms of a geometric progression}\\ \text{with first term 1 and common ratio } (1 + i)^c\end{array}\right)$$

$$= R\left(\frac{[(1 + i)^c]^n - 1}{(1 + i)^c - 1}\right) \quad \longleftarrow \text{ substituting in Formula 6.8}$$

$$\boxed{S_{nc} = R\left(\frac{(1 + i)^{nc} - 1}{(1 + i)^c - 1}\right)} \quad \longleftarrow \textbf{\textit{Formula 17.1}} \quad \begin{array}{l}\textit{Finding the amount}\\ \textit{of an ordinary}\\ \textit{general annuity}\end{array}$$

Example 17.1c   Jean receives annuity payments of $500.00 at the end of every six months. If she deposits these payments in an account earning interest at 9% compounded monthly, how much will she have in her account after ten years?

Solution

Since the payments are made at the end of every six months while interest is compounded monthly, the problem involves a general annuity.

$$R = 500.00; \qquad i = \frac{9\%}{12} = 0.75\% = 0.0075; \qquad n = 10(2) = 20;$$

$$c = \frac{12}{2} = 6; \qquad nc = 20(6) = 120$$

$$S_{nc} = 500.00\left(\frac{1.0075^{120} - 1}{1.0075^6 - 1}\right) \quad \longleftarrow \text{ substituting in Formula 17.1}$$

$$= 500.00\left(\frac{2.4513569 - 1}{1.0458522 - 1}\right)$$

$$= 500.00\left(\frac{1.4513569}{0.0458522}\right)$$

$$= 500.00(31.652940)$$

$$= \$15826.47$$

The amount after ten years will be $15826.47.

Example 17.1d   Peel Credit Union pays 12% compounded quarterly on its Premium Savings Accounts. What balance will a member depositing $25.00 at the end of every month have in her account after six years?

Solution

Since the payments are made at the end of every month while interest is compounded quarterly, the problem involves a complex annuity.

$$R = 25.00; \qquad i = \frac{12\%}{4} = 3\% = 0.03; \qquad n = 6(12) = 72;$$

$$c = \frac{4}{12} = \frac{1}{3}; \qquad nc = 72\left(\frac{1}{3}\right) = 24$$

$$S_{nc} = 25.00\left(\frac{1.03^{24} - 1}{1.03^{\frac{1}{3}} - 1}\right) \quad \longleftarrow \quad \text{substituting in Formula 17.1}$$

$$= 25.00\left(\frac{2.0327941 - 1}{1.0099016 - 1}\right)$$

$$= 25.00\left(\frac{1.0327941}{0.0099016}\right)$$

$$= 25.00(104.30545)$$

$$= \$2607.64$$

The balance after six years will be $2607.64.

C. Amount of an ordinary general annuity—using the equivalent effective rate of interest per payment period

When using an electronic calculator equipped with a universal power key, the given periodic rate of interest i may be converted into the equivalent effective rate of interest per payment period.

Represent the equivalent effective rate of interest per payment period by f.

$$1 + f = (1 + i)^c$$
$$\underline{f = (1 + i)^c - 1} \quad \longleftarrow \quad \text{this is the same as Formula 14.4 except that } m \text{ is replaced by } c$$

With reference to Example 17.1c, for a semi-annual payment interval with interest at 9% compounded monthly, the equivalent semi-annual rate of interest

$$f = 1.0075^6 - 1 = 1.0458522 - 1 = 0.0458522 = 4.58522\%$$

Similarly, with reference to Example 17.1d, for a monthly payment interval with interest at 12% compounded quarterly, the equivalent monthly rate of interest

$$f = 1.03^{\frac{1}{3}} - 1 = 1.009016 - 1 = 0.0099016 = 0.99016\%$$

In effect, the denominator $(1 + i)^c - 1$ in Formula 17.1 represents the equivalent rate per payment period f and since $(1 + i)^c = 1 + f$, substitution of these values converts the ordinary general annuity problem into an ordinary simple annuity problem.

$$S_{nc} = R\left(\frac{(1+f)^n - 1}{f}\right) = Rs_{\overline{n}|f} \text{ where } f = (1 + i)^c - 1$$

$\longleftarrow$ **Formula**
17.1A

Example 17.1e Determine the accumulated value after ten years of payments of $2000.00 made at the end of each year if interest is 15% compounded monthly.

Solution

This is an ordinary general annuity.

$$R = 2000.00; \quad n = 10; \quad c = 12; \quad i = \frac{15\%}{12} = 1.25\% = 0.0125$$

The equivalent effective annual rate

$$f = 1.0125^{12} - 1 = 1.1607545 - 1 = 0.1607545 = 16.07545\%$$

The given ordinary general annuity can be converted into an ordinary simple annuity.

$$R = 2000.00; \quad n = 10; \quad f = 0.1607545$$

$$S_{nc} = 2000.00\left(\frac{1.1607545^{10} - 1}{0.1607545}\right) \longleftarrow \text{substituting in Formula 17.1A}$$

$$= 2000.00(21.400412)$$

$$= \$42800.82$$

The accumulated value after ten years is $42800.82.

Example 17.1f Creditview Farms set aside $1250.00 at the end of each month for the purchase of a combine. How much money will be available after five years if interest is 14.5% compounded semi-annually?

Solution

This problem involves an ordinary general annuity.

$$R = 1250.00; \quad n = 5(12) = 60; \quad c = \frac{2}{12} = \frac{1}{6}; \quad i = \frac{14.5\%}{2} = 7.25\% = 0.0725$$

The equivalent effective monthly rate of interest

$$f = 1.0725^{\frac{1}{6}} - 1 = 1.0117337 - 1 = 0.0117337 = 1.17337\%$$

$$S_{nc} = 1250.00\left(\frac{1.0117337^{60} - 1}{0.0117337}\right) \longleftarrow \text{substituting in Formula 17.1A}$$

$$= 1250.00(86.383576)$$

$$= \$107979.47$$

After five years the amount available is $107\,949.47.

D. Using preprogrammed calculators to find the amount of an ordinary general annuity

While not the only possible procedure, the most direct procedure parallels the approach taken in developing Formula 17.1A.

Step 1   Convert *i* into the equivalent effective rate of interest.

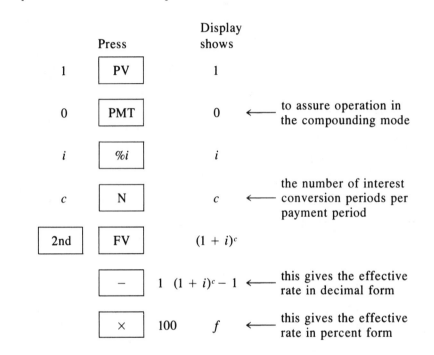

	Press	Display shows	
1	PV	1	
0	PMT	0	← to assure operation in the compounding mode
i	%i	*i*	
c	N	*c*	← the number of interest conversion periods per payment period
2nd	FV	$(1 + i)^c$	
	−	1 $(1 + i)^c - 1$	← this gives the effective rate in decimal form
	×	100 *f*	← this gives the effective rate in percent form

Step 2   Using *f* as the interest rate per payment period, determine the amount of the ordinary annuity.

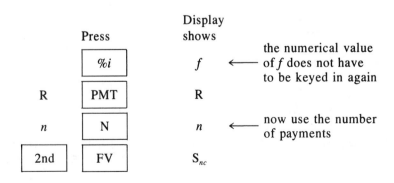

	Press	Display shows	
	%i	*f*	← the numerical value of *f* does not have to be keyed in again
R	PMT	R	
n	N	*n*	← now use the number of payments
2nd	FV	S_{nc}	

***Example* 17.1g** Find the amount of $2500.00 deposited at the end of every six months for ten years if interest is 10% compounded quarterly.

Solution

$$R = 2500.00; \qquad n = 2(10) = 20; \qquad c = \frac{4}{2} = 2;$$

$$i = \frac{10\%}{4} = 2.5\% = 0.025$$

Press	Display shows	
1 PV	1	←——Step 1 of procedure begins
0 PMT	0	
2.5 %i	2.5	
2 N	2	←—— there are 2 conversion periods per payment period
2nd FV	1.050625	←——the value of 1.025^2
− 1	0.050625	
× 100	5.0624999	←——f in percent form
%i	5.0624999	←——Step 2 begins with establishing the rate
2500 PMT	2500	
20 N	20	←——the number of payments
2nd FV	83213.027	

The amount on deposit after ten years will be $83 213.03.

***Example* 17.1h** Determine the accumulated value of payments of $1250.00 made at the end of each quarter for eight years if interest is 12.5% compounded annually.

Solution

$$R = 1250.00; \qquad n = 8(4) = 32; \qquad c = \frac{1}{4} = 0.25;$$

$$i = 12.5\% = 0.125$$

	Press		Display shows	
1	PV		1	
0	PMT		0	
12.5	%i		12.5	

4 $\frac{1}{x}$	N		0.25	← use the reciprocal key to obtain $\frac{1}{4}$

2nd	FV		1.0298836
	−	1	0.0298836
	×	100	2.988357
	%i		2.988357
1250	PMT		1250
32	N		32
2nd	FV		65495.201

The accumulated value of the payments is $65 495.20.

Exercise 17.1

A. Find the amount of each of the following ordinary annuities.

Problem number	Periodic payment	Payment interval	Term	Interest rate	Conversion period
1.	$2500.00	6 months	7 years	20%	quarterly
2.	$900.00	3 months	5 years	12%	monthly
3.	$72.00	1 month	15 years	13%	semi-annually
4.	$225.00	3 months	10 years	15%	annually
5.	$1750.00	6 months	12 years	17%	semi-annually
6.	$680.00	1 month	3 years	18%	monthly
7.	$7500.00	1 year	4 years	16%	quarterly
8.	$143.00	1 month	9 years	14%	quarterly

B. Answer each of the following questions.

1. Find the amount of payments of $425.00 made at the end of every three months for nine years if interest is 9% compounded monthly.

2. What is the accumulated value of deposits of $1500.00 made at the end of every six months for six years if interest is 12% compounded quarterly?

3. To how much will deposits of $15.00 made at the end of each month amount to after ten years if interest is 13% compounded quarterly?

4. What is the amount of payments of $250.00 made at the end of every three months in fifteen years if interest is 17.5% compounded annually?

5. Mr. T. has contributed $1000.00 at the end of each year into an RRSP paying 14% compounded quarterly.

(a) How much will Mr. T. have in the RRSP after ten years?

(b) How much of the amount is interest?

6. Al saves $5.00 at the end of each month and deposits the money in an account paying 16% compounded quarterly.

(a) How much will Al accumulate in 25 years?

(b) How much of the amount is interest?

7. Jones has made deposits of $500.00 into his savings account at the end of every three months for ten years. If interest is 13.5% compounded semi-annually and if he leaves the accumulated balance for another five years, what will be the balance in his account be then?

8. Mrs. Cook has made deposits of $950.00 at the end of every six months for fifteen years. If interest is 12% compounded monthly, how much will Mrs. Cook have accumulated ten years after the last deposit?

17.2 Present value of an ordinary general annuity

A. Present value of an ordinary general annuity—basic computation

Example 17.2a Find the present value of payments of $500.00 made at the end of every year for five years if interest is 12% compounded quarterly.

Solution

FIGURE 17.3 *Graphical representation of method and data*

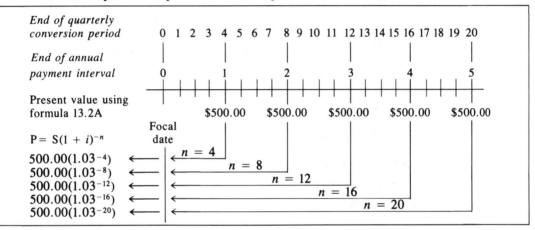

The present values of the five payments are

First payment	$500.00(1.03^{-4})$ = $500.00(0.8884870)$ =	$444.24
Second payment	$500.00(1.03^{-8})$ = $500.00(0.7894092)$ =	394.70
Third payment	$500.00(1.03^{-12})$ = $500.00(0.7013799)$ =	350.69
Fourth payment	$500.00(1.03^{-16})$ = $500.00(0.6231669)$ =	311.58
Fifth payment	$500.00(1.03^{-20})$ = $500.00(0.5536758)$ =	276.84

Total $1778.05

This total present value of the five payments can be obtained by setting up and solving the equation of value.

$$A_n = 500.00(1.03^{-4}) + 500.00(1.03^{-8}) + 500.00(1.03^{-12}) + 500.00(1.03^{-16}) + 500.00(1.03^{-20})$$

$$= 500.00(1.03^{-4} + 1.03^{-8} + 1.03^{-12} + 1.03^{-16} + 1.03^{-20})$$

$$= 500.00(1.03^{-4})(1 + 1.03^{-4} + 1.03^{-8} + 1.03^{-12} + 1.03^{-20})$$

$$= 500.00(1.03^{-4})\left(\begin{array}{l}\text{the sum of the first 5 terms of a geometric progression} \\ \text{with first term 1 and common ratio } 1.03^{-4}\end{array}\right)$$

$$= 500.00(1.03^{-4})\left(\frac{1 - (1.03^{-4})^5}{1 - 1.03^{-4}}\right) \quad \longleftarrow \quad \text{substituting in Formula 6.8, } r < 1$$

$$= 500.00\left(\frac{1}{1.03^4}\right)\left(\frac{1 - 1.03^{-20}}{1 - \frac{1}{1.03^4}}\right) \quad \longleftarrow \quad \text{replace } 1.03^{-4} \text{ by } (\frac{1}{1.03^4})$$

$$= 500.00\left(\frac{1}{1.03^4}\right)\left(\frac{1 - 1.03^{-20}}{\frac{1.03^4 - 1}{1.03^4}}\right)$$

$$= 500.00\left(\frac{1.03^4}{1.03^4}\right)\left(\frac{1 - 1.03^{-20}}{1.03^4 - 1}\right)$$

$$= 500.00\left(\frac{1 - 1.03^{-20}}{1.03^4 - 1}\right) \quad \longleftarrow \quad \begin{array}{l}\text{The steps in the solution to this point reflect}\\ \text{the steps in developing Formula 17.2}\end{array}$$

$$= 500.00\left(\frac{1 - 0.5536758}{1.1255088 - 1}\right)$$

$$= 500.00\left(\frac{0.4463242}{0.1255088}\right)$$

$$= 500.00(3.5561188)$$

$$= \$1778.06$$

The present value of the payments is \$1778.06.

B. Present value of an ordinary annuity—basic formula

For a general (or complex) annuity of n payments of size R made at the end of each payment interval and compounded c times per payment interval at the periodic conversion rate i, the present value A_{nc} is given by the equation

$$A_{nc} = R(1 + i)^{-c} + R(1 + i)^{-2c} + R(1 + i)^{-3c} + \ldots + R(1 + i)^{-(n-1)c} + R(1 + i)^{-nc}$$

$$= R\left[(1 + i)^{-c} + (1 + i)^{-2c} + (1 + i)^{-3c} + \ldots + (1 + i)^{-(n-1)c} + (1 + i)^{-nc}\right]$$

$$= R\left[(1 + i)^{-c}\right]\left[1 + (1 + i)^{-c} + (1 + i)^{-2c} + \ldots + (1 + i)^{-(n-2)c} + (1 + i)^{-(n-1)c}\right]$$

$$= R(1 + i)^{-c}\left(\begin{array}{l}\text{The sum of the first n terms of a geometric progression with}\\ \text{first term 1 and common ratio } (1 + i)^{-c}\end{array}\right)$$

$$= R\left[(1 + i)^{-c}\right]\left(\frac{1 - [(1 + i)^{-c}]^n}{1 - (1 + i)^{-c}}\right) \quad \longleftarrow \quad \text{substituting in Formula 6.8, } r < 1$$

$$= R\left(\frac{1}{(1 + i)^c}\right)\left(\frac{1 - (1 + i)^{-nc}}{1 - \frac{1}{(1 + i)^c}}\right)$$

$$= R\left(\frac{1}{(1 + i)^c}\right)\left(\frac{1 - (1 + i)^{-nc}}{1 - \frac{(1 + i)^c - 1}{(1 + i)^c}}\right)$$

$$= R\left(\frac{(1+i)^c}{(1+i)^c}\right)\left(\frac{1-(1+i)^{-nc}}{(1+i)^c - 1}\right)$$

$$\boxed{A_{nc} = R\left(\frac{1-(1+i)^{-nc}}{(1+i)^c - 1}\right)}$$ ⟵ **Formula 17.2** *Finding the present of an ordinary general annuity*

Example 17.2b A debt agreement requires payment of $1000.00 at the end of every six months for seven years. If interest is 18% compounded monthly, what single payment would settle the debt now?

Solution

$$R = 1000.00; \qquad n = 7(2) = 14; \qquad c = \frac{12}{2} = 6; \qquad nc = 14(6) = 84;$$

$$i = \frac{18\%}{12} = 1.5\% = 0.015$$

$$A_{nc} = 1000.00\left(\frac{1 - 1.015^{-84}}{1.015^6 - 1}\right) \quad \longleftarrow \text{ substituting in Formula 17.2}$$

$$= 1000.00\left(\frac{0.7136795}{0.0934433}\right)$$

$$= 1000.00(7.6375705)$$

$$= \$7637.57$$

The single payment is $7637.57.

Example 17.2c What sum of money would you have to have in an account paying 10% compounded quarterly so that you can withdraw $750.00 at the end of each month for fifteen years?

Solution

$$R = 750.00; \qquad n = 15(12) = 180; \qquad c = \frac{4}{12} = \frac{1}{3};$$

$$nc = 180\left(\frac{1}{3}\right) = 60; \qquad i = \frac{10\%}{4} = 2.5\% = 0.025$$

$$A_{nc} = 750.00\left(\frac{1 - 1.025^{-60}}{1.025^{\frac{1}{3}} - 1}\right) \quad \longleftarrow \text{ substituting in Formula 17.2}$$

$$= 750.00\left(\frac{0.7727164}{0.0082648}\right)$$

$$= 750.00(93.494870)$$

$$= \$70120.83$$

The sum of money is $70120.83.

C. Present value of an ordinary general annuity—using the equivalent effective rate of interest per payment period

As in the case of the amount of an ordinary general annuity, the given periodic rate of interest i may be converted into the equivalent effective rate of interest per payment period.

$$f = (1 + i)^c - 1$$

As in Formula 17.1, the denominator $(1 + i)^c - 1$ in Formula 17.2 represents the equivalent effective rate per payment period f and since $(1 + i)^c = 1 + f$, substitution of these values converts the ordinary general annuity problem into an ordinary simple annuity problem.

$$A_{nc} = R\left(\frac{1 - (1 + f)^{-n}}{f}\right) = Ra_{\overline{n}|f} \qquad \longleftarrow \quad \textbf{Formula 17.2A}$$

Example 17.2d A loan is repaid by making payments of $2000.00 at the end of every six months for twelve years. If interest on the loan is 14% compounded quarterly, what was the principal of the loan?

Solution

$$R = 2000.00; \quad n = 12(2) = 24; \quad c = \frac{4}{2} = 2; \quad i = \frac{14\%}{4} = 3.5\% = 0.035$$

The equivalent effective semi-annual rate of interest

$$f = 1.035^2 - 1 = 1.071225 - 1 = 0.071225 = 7.1225\%$$

$$A_{nc} = 2000.00\left(\frac{1 - 1.071225^{-24}}{0.071225}\right) \qquad \longleftarrow \quad \text{substituting in Formula 17.2A}$$

$$= 2000.00(11.347049)$$

$$= \$22694.10$$

The loan principal was $22694.10.

Example 17.2e A second mortgage requires payment of $370.00 at the end of each month for 15 years. If interest is 15% compounded semi-annually, what was the amount borrowed?

Solution

$$R = 370.00; \quad n = 15(12) = 180; \quad c = \frac{2}{12} = \frac{1}{6}; \quad i = \frac{15\%}{2} = 7.5\% = 0.075$$

The equivalent effective monthly rate of interest

$$f = 1.075^{\frac{1}{6}} - 1 = 1.0121264 - 1 = 0.0121264 = 1.21264\%$$

$$A_{nc} = 370.00\left(\frac{1 - 1.0121264^{-180}}{0.0121264}\right) \longleftarrow \text{ substituting in Formula 17.2A}$$

$$= 370.00(73.045337)$$

$$= \$27026.85$$

The amount borrowed was $27 026.85.

D. Using preprogrammed calculators to find the present value of an ordinary general annuity

While not the only possible procedure, the most direct approach parallels the approach taken in developing Formula 17.2A.

STEP 1 Convert i into the equivalent effective rate of interest as shown in Section 17.1.

STEP 2 Using f as the interest rate per payment period, determine the present value of the ordinary annuity.

Example 17.2f A contract is fulfilled by making payments of $8500.00 at the end of every year for fifteen years. If interest is 13% compounded quarterly, what is the cash price of the contract?

Solution

$$R = 8500.00; \quad n = 15; \quad c = 4; \quad i = \frac{13\%}{4} = 3.25\%$$

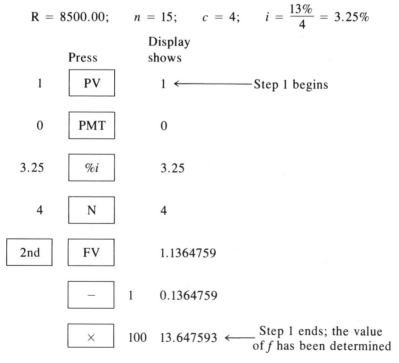

	Press	Display shows	
1	PV	1 ⟵————— Step 1 begins	
0	PMT	0	
3.25	%i	3.25	
4	N	4	
2nd	FV	1.1364759	
	−	1 0.1364759	
	×	100 13.647593 ⟵ Step 1 ends; the value of f has been determined	

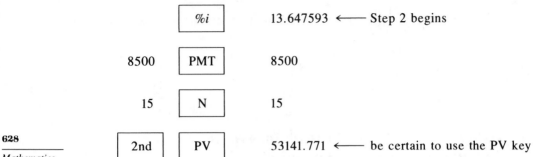

	%i	13.647593 ←—— Step 2 begins
8500	PMT	8500
15	N	15

*Mathematics
of finance
and
investments*

| 2nd | PV | 53141.771 ←—— be certain to use the PV key |

The cash price of the contract is \$53 141.77.

Example 17.2g A 25-year mortgage on a house requires payment of \$625.92 at the end of each month. If interest is 13.5% compounded semi-annually, what was the mortgage principal?

Solution

$$R = 625.92; \qquad n = 25(12) = 300; \qquad c = \frac{2}{12} = \frac{1}{6};$$

$$i = \frac{13.5\%}{2} = 6.75\%$$

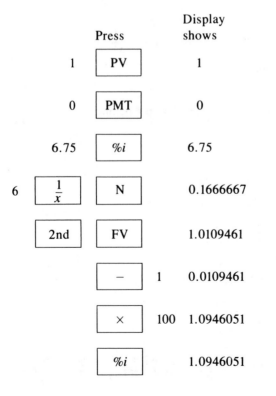

	Press	Display shows
1	PV	1
0	PMT	0
6.75	%i	6.75
6 $\frac{1}{x}$	N	0.1666667
2nd	FV	1.0109461
	− 1	0.0109461
	× 100	1.0946051
	%i	1.0946051

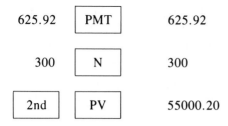

625.92	PMT	625.92
300	N	300
2nd	PV	55000.20

The mortgage principal was $55 000.20.

Exercise 17.2

A. Find the present value of the following ordinary annuities.

Problem number	Periodic payment	Payment interval	Term	Interest rate	Conversion period
1.	$1400.00	3 months	12 years	24%	monthly
2.	$6000.00	1 year	9 years	21%	quarterly
3.	$3000.00	3 months	4 years	16%	annually
4.	$200.00	1 month	2 years	12%	semi-annually
5.	$95.00	1 month	5 years	15%	monthly
6.	$975.00	6 months	8 years	18%	semi-annually
7.	$1890.00	6 months	15 years	17%	quarterly
8.	$155.00	1 month	10 years	18%	quarterly

B. Answer each of the following questions.

1. Find the present value of payments of $250.00 made at the end of every three months for twelve years if money is worth 12% compounded monthly.

2. What is the discounted value of $1560.00 paid at the end of each year for nine years if interest is 16% compounded quarterly?

3. What cash payment is equivalent to making payments of $825.00 at the end of every three months for 16 years if interest is 17% compounded semi-annually?

4. What is the principal from which $175.00 can be withdrawn at the end of each month for twenty years if interest is 13% compounded quarterly?

5. A property was purchased for $5000.00 down and payments of $2500.00 at the end of every six months for six years. Interest is 12% compounded monthly.

    (a) What was the purchase price of the property?

    (b) How much is the cost of financing?

6. A car was bought for $1500.00 down and payments of $265.00 at the end of each month for four years. Interest is 15% compounded monthly.

   (a) What was the purchase price of the car?

   (b) How much will be the amount of interest paid?

7. Payments of $845.19 are made at the end of each month to repay a 25-year mortgage. If interest is 14% compounded semi-annually, what is the original mortgage principal?

8. A 15-year mortgage is amortized by making payments of $1031.61 at the end of every three months. If interest is 13.25% compounded annually, what was the original mortgage balance?

9. Mr. Dale expects to retire in seven years. He purchased a retirement annuity paying $1200.00 every three months for twenty years. If the first payment is due three months after his retirement and interest is 12% compounded monthly, how much did Mr. Dale invest?

10. Georgina has invested an inheritance for her daughter's university education in a fund paying 11% compounded quarterly. If ordinary annuity payments of $450.00 per month are to be made out of the fund for four years and the annuity begins twelve years from now, how much was the inheritance?

17.3   Ordinary general annuities—Finding R, n or i

A.   Finding the periodic rent R

To determine the size of the periodic payment substitute in one of the formulae for finding the amount or the present value. For the electronic calculator use Formula 17.1A when S_{nc} is known and Formula 17.2A when A_{nc} is known. The equivalent effective rate of interest f may be determined by the procedure previously explained in this chapter and R may then be obtained by the procedure shown in Chapter 15, Section 15.4.

***Example* 17.3a**   What sum of money must be deposited at the end of every three months into an account paying 10% compounded monthly to accumulate to $25 000.00 in ten years?

Solution

$$S_{nc} = 25000.00; \qquad n = 10(4) = 40; \qquad c = \frac{12}{4} = 3;$$

$$i = \frac{10\%}{12} = \frac{5}{6}\% = 0.0083333$$

The equivalent effective quarterly rate of interest

$$f = 1.0083333^3 - 1 = 1.0252088 - 1 = 0.0252088 = 2.52088\%$$

$25000.00 = R\ s_{\overline{40}|\ 2.52088\%}$ ⟵ substituting in Formula 17.1A

$25000.00 = R(67.715625)$

$$R = \frac{25000.00}{67.715625}$$

$R = \$369.19$

With a preprogrammed calculator, the procedure, after finding f, is

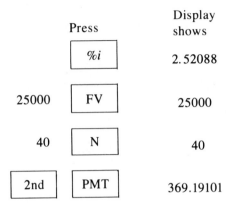

Press	Display shows
%i	2.52088
25000 FV	25000
40 N	40
2nd PMT	369.19101

The required quarterly deposit is $369.19.

Example 17.3b Mr. and Mrs. White applied to their Credit Union for a first mortgage of $60 000.00 for the purchase of a house. The mortgage is to be amortized over 25 years and interest on the mortgage is 13.25% compounded semi-annually. What is the size of the monthly payment if payments are made at the end of each month?

Solution

$$A_{nc} = 60000.00; \qquad n = 25(12) = 300; \qquad c = \frac{2}{12} = \frac{1}{6};$$

$$i = \frac{13.25\%}{2} = 6.625\% = 0.06625$$

The equivalent effective monthly rate of interest

$$f = 1.06625^{\frac{1}{6}} - 1 = 1.0107487 - 1 = 0.0107487 = 1.07487\%$$

$60000.00 = R\ a_{\overline{300}|\ 1.07487\%}$ ⟵ substituting in Formula 17.2A

$60000.00 = R(89.270194)$

$$R = \frac{60000.00}{89.27014}$$

$R = \$672.12$

The monthly payment is $672.12.

B. Finding the term n

The term of an ordinary general annuity may be found by substituting the given values in Formula 17.1A when S_{nc} is known or Formula 17.2A when A_{nc} is known. Since either of these formulae converts the ordinary general annuity into an ordinary simple annuity, the method of solution is exactly the same as used in Chapter 15, Section 15.5.

Example 17.3c What period of time is required for $125.00 deposited at the end of each month at 11% compounded quarterly to grow to $15 000.00?

Solution

$$S_{nc} = 15000.00; \qquad R = 125.00; \qquad c = \frac{4}{12} = \frac{1}{3};$$

$$i = \frac{11\%}{4} = 2.75\% = 0.0275$$

The equivalent effective monthly rate of interest

$$f = 1.0275^{\frac{1}{3}} - 1 = 1.0090839 - 1 = 0.0090839 = 0.90839\%$$

$$15000.00 = 125.00 \; s_{\overline{n}|0.90839\%} \quad \longleftarrow \quad \text{using Formula 17.1A}$$

$$15000.00 = 125.00\left(\frac{1.0090839^n - 1}{0.0090839}\right)$$

$$120.00 = \frac{(1.0090839^n - 1)}{0.0090839}$$

$$1.0900678 = 1.0090839^n - 1$$

$$1.0090839^n = 2.0900678$$

$$n \ln 1.0090839 = \ln 2.0900678$$

$$n(0.0090429) = 0.7371965$$

$$n = \frac{0.7371965}{0.0090429}$$

$$n = 81.522227$$

$$n = 82 \text{ months approximately}$$

It will take 6 years and 10 months to accumulate $15 000.00.

Example 17.3d A business valued at $96 000.00 is purchased for a down payment of 25% and payments of $4000.00 at the end of every three months. If interest is 18% compounded monthly, for how long will payments have to be made?

Solution

$$A_{nc} = 96000.00(0.75) = 72000.00; \qquad R = 4000.00;$$

$$c = \frac{12}{4} = 3; \qquad i = \frac{18\%}{12} = 1.5\% = 0.015$$

The equivalent effective quarterly rate of interest

$$f = 1.015^3 - 1 = 1.0456784 - 1 = 0.0456784 = 4.56784\%$$

$$72000.00 = 4000.00 \; a \; \overline{_{n|}}_{\,4.56784\%} \quad \longleftarrow \text{using Formula 17.2A}$$

$$72000.00 = 4000.00 \left[\frac{1 - 1.0456784^{-n}}{0.0456784} \right]$$

$$0.8222112 = 1 - 1.0456784^{-n}$$

$$1.0456784^{-n} = 0.1777888$$

$$-n \ln 1.0456784 = \ln 0.1777888$$

$$-n(0.0446659) = -1.727159$$

$$n = 38.668403 \text{ (quarters)}$$

With a preprogrammed calculator, the procedure, after finding f, is

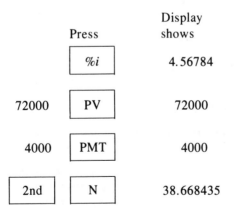

	Press	Display shows
	%i	4.56784
72000	PV	72000
4000	PMT	4000
2nd N		38.668435

Payments will have to be made for 9 years and 9 months.

C. Finding i using preprogrammed calculators

For general ordinary annuities, the interest per conversion period i may be determined by first finding the effective rate per payment period. This is done in the same way used in finding i for simple ordinary annuities explained in Chapter 15, Section 15.6. Enter the three unknown values (S_{nc}, R, n or A_{nc}, R, n) and then retrieve the answer by pressing $\boxed{\text{2nd}}$ $\boxed{\%i}$. The rate per conversion may then be determined using the relationship $1 + f = (1 + i)^c$ and the nominal rate may then be found by multiplying i by the number of compounding periods per year.

Example 17.3e $150 was deposited in a savings account at the end of each month for 52 months. If the accumulated value of the deposits was $10 000 and interest is compounded semi-annually, what was the nominal rate of interest?

Solution

$$S_{nc} = 10000; \qquad R = 150; \qquad n = 52; \qquad c = \frac{2}{12} = \frac{1}{6}$$

First, find the effective monthly rate of interest.

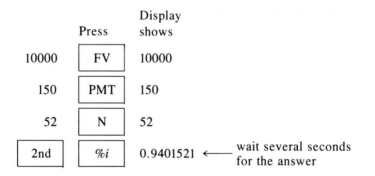

The effective monthly rate is 0.9401521%.

Secondly, convert the effective monthly rate into a semi-annual compounding rate.

$$(1 + i)^{\frac{1}{6}} = 1 + 0.009401521$$
$$1 + i = 1.009401521^6$$
$$1 + i = 1.0577517$$
$$i = 0.0577517$$

The semi-annual compounding rate is 5.77517%;
the nominal rate of interest is 11.55% approximately.

D. Finding i *without a preprogrammed calculator*

Finding the equivalent effective rate per payment period may be done by trial and error according to the same method used in Chapter 15, Section 15.6. When the amount S_{nc} is known Formula 17.1A should be used; if the present value A_{nc} is given Formula 17.2A is applicable.

Example 17.3f An ordinary annuity of $500.00 per quarter accumulates to $12 500.00 in five years. What rate of interest compounded monthly is earned by the deposits?

Solution

$$S_{nc} = 12500.00; \qquad R = 500.00; \qquad n = 5(4) = 20; \qquad c = \frac{12}{4} = 3$$

The equivalent effective quarterly rate of interest

$$f = (1 + i)^3 - 1$$

$$12500.00 = 500.00\, s_{\overline{20}|f} \quad \longleftarrow \quad \text{substituting in Formula 17.1A}$$

$$25.0 = s_{\overline{20}|f}$$

For f = 3%	$s_{\overline{20}|3\%}$	$= 26.870374$	$\longrightarrow f < 3\%$
For f = 2%	$s_{\overline{20}|2\%}$	$= 24.297369$	$\longrightarrow 2\% < f < 3\%$
For f = 2.3%	$s_{\overline{20}|2.3\%}$	$= 25.036609$	$\longrightarrow 2\% < f < 2.3\%$
For f = 2.28%	$s_{\overline{20}|2.28\%}$	$= 24.986482$	$\longrightarrow 2.28\% < f < 2.3\%$
For f = 2.29%	$s_{\overline{20}|2.29\%}$	$= 24.011530$	$\longrightarrow 2.28\% < f < 2.29\%$
For f = 2.285%	$s_{\overline{20}|2.285\%}$	$= 24.999002$	$\longrightarrow 2.285\% < f < 2.29\%$
For f = 2.2854%	$s_{\overline{20}|2.2854\%}$	$= 25.000004$	$\longrightarrow f = 2.2854\%$ approx.

$$(1 + i)^3 = 1.022854$$

$$1 + i = 1.022854^{\frac{1}{3}}$$

$$i = 1.0075607 - 1$$

$$i = 0.0075607 = 0.75607\%$$

The nominal rate of interest is $12(0.75607\%) = 9.07284\%$ compounded monthly.

Example 17.3g A 20-year residential mortgage of $45 000.00 is repaid by making payments of $546.83 at the end of each month. What is the rate of interest compounded semi-annually on the mortgage?

Solution

$$A_{nc} = 45000.00; \qquad R = 546.83; \qquad n = 20(12) = 240;$$

$$c = \frac{2}{12} = \frac{1}{6}.$$

The equivalent effective monthly interest

$$f = (1 + i)^{\frac{1}{6}} - 1$$

$$45000.00 = 546.83 \, a \, \overline{_{240}}_{|f} \longleftarrow \text{substituting in Formula 17.2A}$$

$$a \, \overline{_{240}}_{|f} = 82.292486$$

$For \, f = 1\% \qquad a \, \overline{_{240}}_{|f} = 90.819416 \longrightarrow 1\% < f$

$For \, f = 1.2\% \qquad a \, \overline{_{240}}_{|f} = 78.574552 \longrightarrow 1\% < f < 1.2\%$

$For \, f = 1.14\% \qquad a \, \overline{_{240}}_{|f} = 81.943828 \longrightarrow 1\% < f < 1.14\%$

$For \, f = 1.13\% \qquad a \, \overline{_{240}}_{|f} = 82.529073 \longrightarrow 1.13\% < f < 1.14\%$

$For \, f = 1.134\% \quad a \, \overline{_{240}}_{|f} = 82.294136 \longrightarrow f = 1.134\% \text{ approximately}$

$$(1 + i)^{\frac{1}{6}} = 1.01134$$

$$1 + i = 1.01134^6$$

$$i = 1.0699983 - 1$$

$$i = 0.069983 = 7\% \text{ approximately}$$

The interest rate on the mortgage is 14% compounded semi-annually.

Exercise 17.3

A. For each of the following ordinary general annuities determine the unknown value.

No.	Amount S_{nc}	Present value A_{nc}	Periodic payment R	Payment Interval	Term	Nom. rate of int.	Conversion period
1.	$45 000.00		?	3 months	10 years	12%	monthly
2.		$35 000.00	?	1 year	15 years	20%	quarterly
3.		$21 400.00	$1660.00	6 months	?	15%	monthly
4.	$13 600.00		$140.00	6 months	?	14%	quarterly
5.	$39 200.00		$1100.00	1 year	12 years	?	monthly
6.		$9 600.00	$1220.00	6 months	5 years	?	monthly
7.		$20 000.00	?	1 month	8 years	17%	semi-annually
8.	$16 500.00		?	3 months	15 years	16%	annually
9.	$7 200.00		$90.00	1 month	?	13%	semi-annually
10.		$11 700.00	$315.00	3 months	?	11%	annually
11.		$62 400.00	$5200.00	6 months	25 years	?	annually
12.	$55 500.00		$75.00	1 month	20 years	?	semi-annually

B. Answer each of the following questions.

1. What payment is required at the end of each month for fifteen years to amortize a $32 000.00 mortgage if interest is 13.5% compounded semi-annually?

2. How much must be deposited at the end of each quarter for ten years to accumulate $12 000.00 at 12% compounded monthly?

3. What payment made at the end of every three months for twenty years will accumulate to $20 000.00 at 21% compounded semi-annually?

4. John bought a car priced $9300.00 for 15 percent down and equal monthly payments for four years. If interest is 18% compounded semi-annually, what is the size of the monthly payment?

5. How long will it take to save $15 000.00 by making deposits of $90.00 at the end of every month into an account earning interest at 10% compounded quarterly?

6. For how long will Jack have to make payments of $350.00 at the end of every three months to repay a loan of $6000.00 if interest is 15% compounded monthly?

7. A mortgage of $18 600.00 is to be repaid by making payments of $260.00 at the end of each month. If interest is 14% compounded semi-annually, what is the term of the mortgage?

8. Mr. D. accumulated $100 000.00 in an RRSP. He converted the RRSP into an RRIF and started to withdraw $4500.00 at the end of every three months from the fund. If interest is 12% compounded monthly, for how long can Mr. D. make withdrawals?

9. Compute the rate of interest compounded monthly at which $400.00 paid at the end of very three months for eight years accumulates to $20 000.00.

10. What is the rate of interest compounded quarterly if a loan of $21 500.00 is repaid by payments of $2500.00 made at the end of every six months in seven years?

11. A mortgage of $27 500.00 is repaid by making payments of $382.00 at the end of each month for fifteen years. What is the rate of interest compounded semi-annually?

12. A property worth $35 000.00 is purchased for 10 percent down and semi-annual payments of $2750.00 for twelve years. What is the effective rate of interest if interest is compounded quarterly?

17.4   General (or complex) annuities due

A.   Amount of a general annuity due

As in the case of a simple annuity due, the amount of a **complex annuity due** is greater than the amount of the corresponding ordinary complex annuity by the interest on it for one payment period. Since the interest on a complex annuity for one payment period is $(1 + i)^c$

THE AMOUNT OF A GENERAL (or COMPLEX) ANNUITY DUE	$= (1 + i)^c \times$	AMOUNT OF THE CORRESPONDING ORDINARY GENERAL ANNUITY

Thus, the basic formula for the amount of a general annuity due may be derived directly from Formula 17.1

$$S_{nc}(\text{due}) = R(1 + i)^c \left(\frac{(1 + i)^{nc} - 1}{(1 + i)^c - 1} \right) \qquad \longleftarrow \text{\textbf{\textit{Formula 17.3}}}$$

For computational purposes it is useful to change the problem of solving a **general annuity due** into one of solving the equivalent simple annuity due by means of the equivalent effective rate of interest per payment period.

$$S_{nc}(\text{due}) = R(1 + f)\left(\frac{(1 + f)^n - 1}{f} \right) = R(1 + f)\, s_{\overline{n}|f} \qquad \longleftarrow \text{\textbf{\textit{Formula 17.3A}}}$$
$$\text{where } f = (1 + i)^c - 1$$

Example 17.4a   What is the accumulated value after five years of payments of $20 000 made at the beginning of each year if interest is 15% compounded quarterly?

Solution

$$R = 20000.00; \qquad n = 5; \qquad c = 4; \qquad i = \frac{15\%}{4} = 3.75\% = 0.0375$$

The equivalent effective annual rate of interest

$$f = 1.0375^4 - 1 = 1.1586504 - 1 = 0.1586504 = 15.86504\%$$

$$S_{nc}(due) = 20000.00(1.1586504)\left(\frac{1.1586504^5 - 1}{0.1586504}\right) \quad \longleftarrow \quad \begin{array}{l}\text{substituting in}\\ \text{Formula 17.3A}\end{array}$$

$$= 20000.00(1.1586504)(6.8588039)$$

$$= 20000.00(7.9469559)$$

$$= \$158939.12$$

The accumulated value after five years is \$158 939.12.

B. *Present value of a general annuity due*

For a general annuity due the present value is greater than the present value of the corresponding ordinary general annuity by the interest on it for one payment period.

THE PRESENT VALUE OF A	=	$(1 + i)^c$ × THE PRESENT VALUE OF THE
GENERAL ANNUITY DUE		CORRESPONDING ORDINARY GENERAL ANNUITY

Thus, the basic formula for the present value of a general annuity due may be derived directly from Formula 17.2

$$A_{nc}(due) = R(1 + i)^c\left(\frac{1 - (1 + i)^{-nc}}{(1 + i)^c - 1}\right) \quad \longleftarrow \quad \textbf{\textit{Formula 17.4}}$$

Using the equivalent effective rate of interest per payment period

$$A_{nc}(due) = R(1 + f)\left(\frac{1 - (1 + f)^{-n}}{f}\right) = R(1 + f)\, a_{\overline{n}|f} \quad \longleftarrow \quad \begin{array}{l}\textbf{\textit{Formula}}\\ \textbf{\textit{17.4A}}\end{array}$$

$$\text{where } f = (1 + i)^c - 1$$

Example 17.4b A three-year lease requires payment of \$1600.00 at the beginning of every three months. If money is worth 16.5% compounded monthly, what is the cash value of the lease?

Solution

$$R = 1600.00; \qquad n = 3(4) = 12; \qquad c = \frac{12}{4} = 3;$$

$$i = \frac{16.5\%}{12} = 1.375\% = 0.01375$$

The equivalent effective quarterly rate of interest

$$f = 1.01375^3 - 1 = 1.0418198 - 1 = 0.0418198 = 4.18198\%$$

$$A_{nc}(\text{due}) = 1600.00(1.0418198)\left(\frac{1 - 1.0418198^{-12}}{0.0418198}\right) \longleftarrow \quad \text{substituting in Formula 17.4A}$$

$$= 1600.00(1.0418198)(9.2867522)$$

$$= 1600.00(9.6751223)$$

$$= \$15480.20$$

The cash value of the lease is $15 480.20.

C. General annuity due—finding the periodic payment R

If $S_{nc}(\text{due})$, n and i are known, R can be found by substituting the given values in Formula 17.3 or 17.3A. If $A_{nc}(\text{due})$, n and i are known, R can be found by substituting the given values in Formula 17.4 or 17.4A.

Example 17.4c What deposit made at the beginning of each month will accumulate to $18 000.00 at 13% compounded quarterly at the end of eight years?

Solution

$$S_{nc}(\text{due}) = 18000.00; \qquad n = 8(12) = 96; \qquad c = \frac{4}{12} = \frac{1}{3}$$

$$i = \frac{13\%}{4} = 3.25\% = 0.0325$$

The equivalent effective monthly rate of interest

$$f = 1.0325^{\frac{1}{3}} - 1 = 1.010718 - 1 = 0.010718 = 1.0718\%$$

$$18000.00 = R(1.010718)\, s_{\overline{96}|\,1.0718\%} \longleftarrow \quad \text{substituting in Formula 17.3A}$$

$$18000.00 = R(1.010718)(166.33583)$$

$$18000.00 = R(168.11861)$$

$$R = \frac{18000.00}{168.11861}$$

$$R = \$107.07$$

The monthly deposit is $107.07.

Example 17.4d What monthly payment must be made at the beginning of each month on a five-year lease valued $100 000.00 if interest is 16% compounded semi-annually?

Solution

$$A_{nc}(\text{due}) = 100000.00; \qquad n = 5(12) = 60; \qquad c = \frac{2}{12} = \frac{1}{6};$$

$$i = \frac{16\%}{2} = 8\% = 0.08$$

The equivalent effective monthly rate of interest

$$f = 1.08^{\frac{1}{6}} - 1 = 1.0129095 - 1 = 0.0129095 = 1.29095\%$$

$$100000.00 = R(1.0129095)\, a_{\overline{60}|\,1.29095\%} \qquad \longleftarrow \qquad \begin{array}{l} \text{substituting in} \\ \text{Formula 17.4A} \end{array}$$

$$100000.00 = R(1.0129095)(41.582377)$$

$$100000.00 = R(42.119184)$$

$$R = \frac{100000.00}{42.119184}$$

$$R = \$2374.22$$

The monthly payment is $2374.22.

D. General annuity due—finding the term n

If $S_{nc}(\text{due})$, R and i are known, n can be found by substituting the given values in Formula 17.3A and then solving for n using natural logarithms. If $A_{nc}(\text{due})$, R and i are known, formula 17.4A should be used.

Example 17.4e Ted Davis wants to accumulate $140 000.00 in a RRSP by making annual contributions of $5500.00 at the beginning of each year. If interest on the RRSP is 11% compounded quarterly, for how long will Ted have to make contributions?

Solution

$$S_{nc}(\text{due}) = 140000.00; \qquad R = 5500.00; \qquad c = 4;$$

$$i = \frac{11\%}{4} = 2.75\% = 0.0275$$

The equivalent effective annual rate of interest

$$f = 1.0275^4 - 1 = 1.1146213 - 1 = 0.1146213 = 11.46213\%$$

$$140000.00 = 5500.00(1.1146213)\, s_{\overline{n}|\,11.46213\%} \qquad \longleftarrow \qquad \text{using Formula 17.3A}$$

$$140000.00 = 5500.00(1.1146213)\left(\frac{1.1146213^n - 1}{0.1146213}\right)$$

$$140000.00 = 53484.101(1.1146213^n - 1)$$

$$2.6176003 = 1.1146213^n - 1$$

$$1.1146213^n = 3.6176003$$

$$n \ln 1.1146213 = \ln 3.6176003$$

$$n(0.1085147) = 1.2858109$$

$$n = \frac{1.2858109}{0.1085147}$$

$$n = 11.849186$$

$$n = 12 \text{ years}$$

Ted will have to contribute for 12 years.

Example 17.4f If Ted Davis, having reached his goal of a $140 000.00 balance in his RRSP, immediately converts it into an RRIF and withdraws from it $1650.00 at the beginning of each month and if interest continues at 11% compounded quarterly, for how long can he make withdrawals?

Solution

$$A_{nc}(\text{due}) = 140000.00; \qquad R = 1650.00; \qquad c = \frac{4}{12} = \frac{1}{3};$$

$$i = \frac{11\%}{4} = 2.75\% = 0.0275$$

The equivalent effective monthly rate of interest

$$f = 1.0275^{\frac{1}{3}} - 1 = 1.0090839 - 1 = 0.0090839 = 0.90839\%$$

$$140000.00 = 1650.00(1.0090939) \, a_{\overline{n}|\,0.90839\%} \quad \longleftarrow \text{using Formula 17.4A}$$

$$140000.00 = 1650.00(1.0090839)\left(\frac{1 - 1.0090839^{-n}}{0.0090839}\right)$$

$$140000.00 = 183290.04(1 - 1.0090839^{-n})$$

$$0.7638167 = 1 - 1.0090839^{-n}$$

$$1.0090839^{-n} = 0.2361833$$

$$-n \ln 1.0090839 = \ln 0.2361833$$

$$-n(0.0090429) = -1.4431471$$

$$n = 159.58897$$

$$n = 160 \text{ months (approximately)}$$

Ted will be able to make withdrawals for 13 years and 4 months.

E. Using preprogrammed financial calculators

The variables encountered when dealing with general annuities due—S_{nc}(due), A_{nc}(due), R, n, i—may be determined by the procedures used in Chapter 16, Sections 16.1 and 16.2 for finding values for simple annuities due, except that the equivalent effective rate of interest per payment period must be used.

Example 17.4g If Jones deposits $25.00 at the beginning of each month and interest is 16% compounded quarterly, what is the amount in his account at the end of twelve years?

Solution

$$R = 25.00; \qquad n = 144; \qquad c = \frac{4}{12} = \frac{1}{3}; \qquad i = 4\%$$

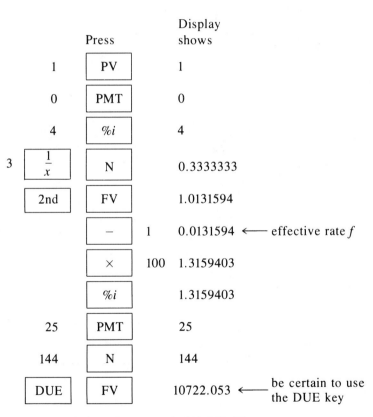

	Press	Display shows	
1	PV	1	
0	PMT	0	
4	%i	4	
3 $\frac{1}{x}$	N	0.3333333	
2nd	FV	1.0131594	
	−	1 0.0131594	⟵ effective rate f
	×	100 1.3159403	
	%i	1.3159403	
25	PMT	25	
144	N	144	
DUE	FV	10722.053	⟵ be certain to use the DUE key

The amount after twelve years is $10 722.05.

Example 17.4h A machine can be purchased by making semi-annual payments of $800 for seven years. If the first payment is made on the date of purchase and money is worth 19% compounded quarterly, what is the cash value of the machine?

Solution

$$R = 800; \qquad n = 14; \qquad c = \frac{4}{2} = 2; \qquad i = 4.75\%$$

$$f = (1.0475^2 - 1 = 1.0972562 - 1 = 9.72562\%$$

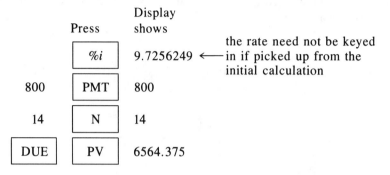

	Press	Display shows	
	%i	9.7256249	← the rate need not be keyed in if picked up from the initial calculation
800	PMT	800	
14	N	14	
DUE	PV	6564.375	

The machine has a cash value of $6564.38.

Example 17.4i What monthly rent payment at the beginning of each month for ten years is required to fulfill a lease contract worth $75 000 if money is worth 20% compounded semi-annually?

Solution

$$A_{nc}(\text{due}) = 75000; \qquad i = 10\%; \qquad n = 120; \qquad c = \frac{2}{12} = \frac{1}{6};$$

$$f = 1.10^{\frac{1}{6}} - 1 = 1.0160119 - 1 = 1.60119\%$$

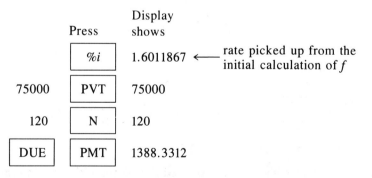

	Press	Display shows	
	%i	1.6011867	← rate picked up from the initial calculation of f
75000	PVT	75000	
120	N	120	
DUE	PMT	1388.3312	

The monthly rent payment is $1388.33.

***Example* 17.4j** Compute the nominal rate of interest compounded monthly at which $300 deposited at the beginning of every three months for ten years will amount to $30 000.

Solution

$$S_{nc}(\text{due}) = 30000; \qquad R = 300; \qquad n = 40; \qquad c = \frac{12}{4} = 3$$

	Press	Display shows	
30000	FV	30000	
300	PMT	300	
40	N	40	
DUE	%i	4.0480574	← the quarterly rate

Converting the quarterly rate into a monthly rate.

$(1 + i)^3 = 1.0404806$

$1 + i = 1.0404806^{\frac{1}{3}}$

$1 + i = 1.0133154$

$\quad i = 0.0133154$

The monthly compounding rate is 1.33154%; the nominal rate is 15.98% approximately.

Note For general annuities due the conversion rate i may be computed without preprogrammed calculators by the trial and error approach shown in the Appendix to Chapter 16. The needed modifications to Formulae 17.1 and 17.2 and the computation itself are illustrated in the Appendix to Chapter 17.

Exercise 17.4

A. For each of the following general annuities due determine the unknown value as indicated.

No.	Amount $S_{nc}(due)$	Present value $A_{nc}(due)$	Periodic payment R	Payment interval	Term	Nom. rate of int.	Conversion period
1.	?		$1500.00	6 months	10 years	13%	quarterly
2.	?		$175.00	1 month	7 years	17%	semi-annually
3.		?	$650.00	3 months	6 years	12%	monthly
4.		?	$93.00	1 month	4 years	20%	quarterly
5.	$16 500.00		?	1 year	10 years	14%	quarterly
6.	$9 200.00		?	3 months	5 years	15%	semi-annually
7.		$10 000.00	?	3 months	3 years	21%	monthly
8.		$24 300.00	?	1 month	20 years	16%	semi-annually
9.	$32 000.00		$450.00	6 months	?	15%	monthly
10.	$7 500.00		$150.00	3 months	?	11%	annually
11.		$12 500.00	$860.00	3 months	?	18%	monthly
12.		$45 000.00	$540.00	1 month	?	14%	semi-annually
13.	$6 400.00		$200.00	6 months	9 years	?	monthly
14.	$25 000.00		$790.00	1 year	15 years	?	quarterly
15.		$7 500.00	$540.00	3 months	5 years	?	monthly
16.		$60 000.00	$725.00	1 month	25 years	?	semi-annually

B. Answer each of the following questions.

1. Bomac Steel sets aside $5000.00 at the beginning of every six months in a fund for replacement of erecting equipment. If interest is 12% compounded quarterly, how much will be in the fund after five years?

2. Mr. Dean contributes $125.00 at the beginning of each month into an RRSP paying interest at 13.5% compounded semi-annually. How much will be the accumulated balance in the RRSP at the end of 25 years?

3. What is the cash value of a lease requiring payments of $750.00 at the beginning of each month for three years if interest is 16% compounded quarterly?

4. A property is bought by making semi-annual payments of $2500.00 for seven years. If the first payment is due on the date of purchase and interest is 14% compounded quarterly, what is the purchase price of the property?

5. How much would you have to pay into an account at the beginning of every six months to accumulate $10 000.00 in eight years if interest is 17% compounded quarterly?

6. Peel Credit Union entered a lease contract valued at $5400.00. The contract provides for payments at the beginning of each month for three years. If interest is 21% compounded quarterly, what is the size of the monthly payment?

7. Mr. T. has saved $85 000.00. If he decides to withdraw $3000.00 at the beginning of every three months and interest is 11.5% compounded annually, for how long can Mr. T. make withdrawals?

8. For what length of time must contributions of $1600.00 be made at the beginning of each year to accumulate to $96 000.00 at 10% compounded quarterly?

9. What is the rate of interest compounded annually on a lease valued at $21 600.00 if payments of $780.00 are made at the beginning of each month for three years?

10. An insurance policy provides for a lumpsum benefit of $50 000.00 fifteen years from now. Alternatively, payments of $1700.00 may be received at the beginning of each of the next fifteen years. What is the effective rate of interest if interest is compounded quarterly?

17.5 *Deferred general (or complex) annuities*

A. *Basic computation*

The amount of a deferred general annuity designated by the symbol S_{nc}(defer.) is the accumulated value of the periodic payments at the end of the term of the annuity. As in the case of a deferred simple annuity, the period of deferment does not affect the amount. Thus the problem of finding the amount of a deferred general annuity is identical to the problem of finding the amount of a general annuity. Accordingly no further consideration is given to the problem of finding the amount of a deferred general annuity.

The present value of a deferred general annuity designated by the symbol A_{nc}(defer.) is the discounted value of the periodic payments at the beginning of the period of deferment. As in the case of a deferred simple annuity, the problem of finding the present value of a deferred general annuity may be divided into two parts and two approaches may be taken as illustrated in Example 17.5a.

Example 17.5a Payments of $1000.00 are due at the end of each year for five years. If the payments are deferred for three years and interest is 10% compounded quarterly, what is the present value of the deferred payments?

Solution

First method

STEP 1 Find the present value of the ordinary general annuity.

$$R = 1000.00; \qquad n = 5; \qquad c = 4; \qquad i = \frac{10\%}{4} = 2.5\% = 0.025$$

The equivalent effective annual rate of interest

$$f = 1.025^4 - 1 = 1.1038129 - 1 = 0.1038129 = 10.38129\%$$

$$A_{nc} = 1000.00 \ a \ \overline{_{5|}} \ _{10.38129\%} \longleftarrow \text{substituting in Formula 17.2A}$$

$$= 1000.00(3.7541489)$$

$$= \$3754.15$$

STEP 1 Find the present value of A_{nc} at the beginning of the period of deferment.

$S = 3754.15$ is the present value of the general annuity A_{nc};

$d = \quad 3 \quad$ is the number of deferred payment intervals;

$f = 10.38129\%$ is the equivalent effective rate of interest per payment interval.

$$A_{nc}(\text{defer.}) = P = 3754.15(1.1038129^{-3}) \longleftarrow \text{substituting in Formula 13.2A}$$

$$= 3754.15(0.7435559)$$

$$= \$2791.42$$

The present value of the deferred payments is $2791.42.

Alternate method

Assume that periodic payments have been made during the period of deferment. Then the number of actual payments is $n = 5$ and the number of assumed payments is $d = 3$.

STEP 1 Find the present value of the annuity in which the number of payments is $d + n = 3 + 5 = 8$.

$$A_{(d+n)c} = 1000.00 \ a \ \overline{_{8|}} \ _{10.38129\%}$$

$$= 1000.00(5.2616725)$$

$$= \$5261.67$$

STEP 2 Find the present value of the annuity consisting of the assumed payments $d = 3$.

$$A_{dc} = 1000.00 \ a \ \overline{_{3|}} \ _{10.38129\%}$$

$$= 1000.00(2.4702531)$$

$$= \$2470.25$$

STEP 3 Find the present value of the deferred general annuity by finding the difference.

$$A_{nc}(\text{defer.}) = A_{(d+n)c} - A_{dc} = 5261.67 - 2470.25 = \$2791.42$$

B. Present value of deferred ordinary general annuities

While the problem of finding the present value of a deferred general annuity can always be solved by using either one of the methods described above, a convenient formula for the first method may be obtained directly from Formula 16.3 by replacing i with f with the understanding that d represents the number of *deferred payment intervals* (rather than the number of periods for compounding i in the period of deferment).

$$A_{nc}(\text{defer.}) = R(1 + f)^{-d}\left(\frac{1 - (1 + f)^{-n}}{f}\right) = R(1 + f)^{-d}\, a_{\overline{n}|f} \qquad \longleftarrow \textbf{\textit{Formula}}$$

17.5

Example 17.5b   Loan payments of $314.08, deferred for eighteen months, are payable at the end of each month for four years. If interest is 14% compounded semi-annually, what is the loan principal?

Solution

$$R = 314.08; \qquad n = 4(12) = 48; \qquad d = 18; \qquad c = \frac{2}{12} = \frac{1}{6};$$

$$i = \frac{14\%}{2} = 7\% = 0.07$$

The equivalent effective monthly rate of interest

$$f = 1.07^{\frac{1}{6}} - 1 = 1.0113403 = 0.0113403 = 1.13403\%$$

$$A_{nc}(\text{defer.}) = 314.08(1.0113403^{-18})\, a_{\overline{48}|1.13403\%} \qquad \longleftarrow \begin{array}{l}\text{substituting}\\ \text{in Formula 17.5}\end{array}$$

$$= 314.08(0.8162973)(36.85899)$$

$$= 314.08(30.087894)$$

$$= \$9450.00$$

The loan principal was $9450.

C. Present value of deferred general annuities due

Since the present value of a general annuity due differs from the present value of an ordinary general annuity only by the factor $(1 + f)$, the present value of a deferred general annuity due may be found by expanding the right side of Formula 17.5 by $(1 + f)$,

Example 17.5c   Tom Casey wants to withdraw $925.00 at the beginning of each quarter for twelve years. If the withdrawals are to begin ten years from now and interest is 12% compounded monthly, how much must Tom deposit today to be able to make the withdrawals?

Solution

$$R = 925.00; \quad n = 12(4) = 48; \quad d = 10(4) = 40; \quad c = \frac{12}{4} = 3;$$

$$i = \frac{12\%}{12} = 1\% = 0.01$$

The equivalent effective quarterly rate of interest

$$f = 1.01^3 - 1 = 1.030301 - 1 = 0.030301 = 3.0301\%$$

For a deferred general annuity due

$$A_{nc}(\text{defer.}) = 925.00(1.030301^{-40})(a_{\overline{48}|\,3.0301\%})(1.030301)$$

$$= 925.00(1.030301^{-39})\left(\frac{1 - 1.030301^{-48}}{0.030301}\right)$$

$$= 925.00(0.3121758)(25.126946)$$

$$= 925.00(7.8440249)$$

$$= \$7255.72$$

Tom must deposit $7255.72 to make the withdrawals.

D. Deferred general annuities— finding the periodic payment R

The periodic payment for a deferred ordinary general annuity may be found by substituting the known values in Formula 17.5. For deferred general annuities due, R can be found by substituting in Formula 17.5 and multiplying by $(1 + f)$.

Example 17.5d A contract having a cash value of $36 000.00 requires payments at the end of every three months for six years. If the payments are deferred for three years and interest is 17% compounded semi-annually, what is the size of the quarterly payments?

Solution

$$A_{nc}(\text{defer.}) = 36000.00; \quad n = 6(4) = 24; \quad d = 3(4) = 12;$$

$$c = \frac{2}{4} = 0.5; \quad i = \frac{17\%}{2} = 8.5\% = 0.085$$

The equivalent effective quarterly rate of interest

$$f = 1.085^{0.5} - 1 = 1.0416333 - 1 = 0.0416333 = 4.16333\%$$

For a deferred ordinary general annuity

$36000.00 = R(1.0416333^{-12}) \, a_{\overline{24}|\,4.16333\%} \longleftarrow$ substituting in Formula 17.5

$36000.00 = R(0.6129451)(14.995161)$

$36000.00 = R(9.1912104)$

$$R = \frac{36000.00}{9.1912104}$$

$R = \$3916.79$

The required quarterly payment is $3916.79.

Example 17.5e A lease contract having a cash value of $64 000.00 requires payments at the beginning of each month for seven years. If the payments are deferred for two years and interest is 20% compounded quarterly, what is the size of the monthly payment?

Solution

$A_{nc}(\text{defer.}) = 64000.00; \qquad n = 7(12) = 84; \qquad n = 2(12) = 24;$

$$c = \frac{4}{12} = \frac{1}{3}; \qquad i = \frac{20\%}{4} = 5\% = 0.05$$

The equivalent effective monthly rate of interest

$$f = 1.05^{\frac{1}{3}} - 1 = 1.0163964 - 1 = 1.63964\%$$

For the deferred general annuity due

$64000.00 = R(1.0163964^{-24})(a_{\overline{84}|\,1.63964\%})(1.0163964)$

$64000.00 = R(1.0163964^{-23})a_{\overline{84}|\,1.63964\%}$

$64000.00 = R(0.6879371)(45.431148)$

$64000.00 = R(31.253771)$

$R = \$2047.75$

The monthly payment is $2047.75.

E. Deferred general annuities—finding the term of the annuity n

To find n, use Formula 17.5 in the same way as when finding R.

Example 17.5f Mr. Kovacs deposited a retirement gratuity of $21 500.00 in an Income Averaging Annuity paying $375.00 at the end of each month. If payments are deferred for nine months and interest is 12% compounded quarterly, for what period of time will Mr. Kovacs receive annuity payments?

Solution

$$A_{nc}(\text{defer.}) = 21500.00; \qquad R = 375.00; \qquad d = 9; \qquad c = \frac{4}{12} = \frac{1}{3};$$

$$i = \frac{12\%}{4} = 3\% = 0.03$$

The equivalent effective monthly rate of interest

$$f = 1.03^{\frac{1}{3}} - 1 = 1.0099016 - 1 = 0.0099016 = 0.99016\%.$$

For a deferred ordinary annuity

$$21500.00 = 375.00(1.0099016^{-9}) a_{\overline{n}|0.99016\%}$$

$$21500.00 = 375.00(1.0099016^{-9})\left(\frac{1 - 1.0099016^{-n}}{0.0099016}\right)$$

$$21500.00 = 34658.856(1 - 1.0099016^{-n})$$

$$0.6203321 = 1 - 1.0099016^{-n}$$

$$1.0099016^{-n} = 0.3796679$$

$$-n \ln 1.0099016 = \ln 0.3796679$$

$$-n(0.0098529) = -0.9684583$$

$$n = \frac{0.9684583}{0.0098529}$$

$$n = 98.291701$$

$$n = 99 \text{ months}$$

Mr. Kovacs will receive payments for 8 years and 3 months.

Example 17.5g At age 65, Janice has accumulated $120 000.00 in an RRSP by making yearly contributions over a period of years. At age 70, she converted the then existing balance into an RRIF from which she started to withdraw $2000.00 per month. If the first withdrawal was on the date of conversion and interest on the account is 11% compounded quarterly, for how long will Janice receive annuity payment?

Solution

$$A_{nc}(\text{defer.}) = 120000.00; \qquad R = 2000.00; \qquad d = 5(12) = 60;$$

$$c = \frac{4}{12} = \frac{1}{3}; \qquad i = \frac{11\%}{4} = 2.75\% = 0.0275$$

The equivalent effective monthly rate of interest

$$f = 1.0275^{\frac{1}{3}} - 1 = 1.0090839 - 1 = 0.0090839 = 0.90839\%$$

Since payments are at the beginning of each month, the problem involves a deferred general annuity due.

$$120000.00 = 2000.00(1.0090839^{-60})(a_{\,\overline{n}|\,0.90839\%})(1.0090839)$$

$$120000.00 = 2000.00(1.0090839^{-59})\left(\frac{1 - 1.0090839^{-n}}{0.0090839}\right)$$

$$120000.00 = 129136.31(1 - 1.0090839^{-n})$$

$$0.9292407 = 1 - 1.0090839^{-n}$$

$$1.0090839^{-n} = 0.0707493$$

$$-n \ln 1.0090839 = \ln 0.0707493$$

$$-n(0.0090429) = -2.6486123$$

$$n = 292.89447$$

$$n = 293 \text{ months}$$

Janice will receive payments for 24 years and 5 months.

F. Finding the conversion rate i for deferred general annuities

The periodic rate of interest for deferred general annuities may be determined by trial and error using the method previously shown in the Appendix to Chapter 16. The solution to a problem of finding *i* for a deferred general annuity, more readily found by means of a preprogrammed calculator, is shown in the Appendix to Chapter 17.

Exercise 17.5

A. For each of the following deferred general annuities determine the unknown value as indicated.

No.	Present value A_{nc}(defer.)	Payment made at	Periodic payment R	Payment period	Period of deferment	Term	Int. rate	Conversion period
1.	?	end	$720.00	3 months	4 years	10 years	12%	monthly
2.	?	beginning	$145.00	6 months	3 years	5 years	14%	quarterly
3.	?	beginning	$225.00	3 months	6 years	8 years	19%	annually
4.	?	end	$1500.00	1 month	2 years	3 years	15%	semi-annually
5.	$9 000.00	end	?	1 month	3 years	7 years	21%	quarterly
6.	$12 650.00	beginning	?	6 months	2 years	4 years	16%	quarterly
7.	$3 740.00	beginning	$4100.00	1 year	10 years	?	18%	monthly
8.	$22 750.00	end	$385.00	1 month	1 year	?	13%	semi-annually
9.	$10 000.00	end	$1200.00	3 months	5 years	10 years	?	semi-annually
10.	$6 675.00	beginning	$980.00	6 months	10 years	15 years	?	monthly

B. Answer each of the following questions.

1. Mrs. Bell expects to retire in seven years and would like to receive $800.00 at the end of each month for ten years following the date of her retirement. How much must Mrs. Bell deposit in an account paying 14.5% compounded semi-annually today to receive the monthly payments?

2. The sale of a property provides for payments of $2000.00 due at the beginning of every three months for five years. If the payments are deferred for two years and interest is 15% compounded monthly, what is the cash value of the property?

3. Dr. Young bought $18 000 worth of equipment from Medical Supply Company. The purchase agreement requires equal payments every six months for eight years. If the first payment is due two years after the date of purchase and interest is 14% compounded quarterly, what is the size of the payments?

4. Ed Junior borrowed $10 000.00 from his uncle to finance his post-graduate studies. The loan agreement calls for equal payments at the end of each month for ten years. The payments are deferred for four years and interest is 8% compounded semi-annually. What is the size of the monthly payments?

5. A property development agreement valued $45 000.00 requires annual lease payments of $15 000.00. The first payment is due five years after the date of the agreement and interest is 15% compounded semi-annually. For how long will payments to be made?

6. A retirement gratuity of $23 600.00 is invested in an annuity deferred for twelve years. The annuity provides payments of $4000.00 due at the beginning of every six months. If interest is 10% compounded annually, for how long will annuity payments be made?

7. A business venture requiring an initial investment of $5000.00 yields no returns for the first three years and net returns of $950.00 at the end of every three months for the following seven years. What rate of interest compounded semi-annually does the venture yield?

8. An investment of $22 000.00 provides quarterly payments of $2565.00 for six years. If the first payment is received four years after the investment was made, what is the effective rate of interest earned on the investment if interest is compounded monthly?

9. A property valued at $50 000.00 is purchased by making payments of $3500.00 at the end of every three months. If the payments are deferred for three years and interest is 14% compounded semi-annually, for how long will payments have to be made?

10. A $40 000.00 lease requires semi-annual payments of $9750.00 for five years due in advance. If the payments are deferred for two years, what is the nominal annual rate of interest charged?

17.6 Using preprogrammed calculators for problems involving deferred general annuities

Deferred general annuity problems involving finding the present value A_{nc}(defer.), the periodic payment R and the number of payments n are readily solved by means of programmed calculators using the techniques illustrated for deferred ordinary annuities and deferred annuities due in Chapter 16. Allowance must be made, however, for the equivalent effective rate of interest per payment interval.

As for finding the conversion rate i, no quick solution is possible because the unknown effective rate f also appears in the factor which allows for the period of deferment and the programming has not provided for this complication.

A. Finding the present value of deferred general annuities

Example 17.6a What sum of money invested now will provide payments of $1200 at the end of every three months for six years if the payments are deferred for nine years and interest is 15% compounded semi-annually?

Solution

$$R = 1200; \qquad i = 7.5\%; \qquad n = 24; \qquad d = 36; \qquad c = \frac{2}{4} = \frac{1}{2}$$

First, determine the equivalent effective quarterly rate of interest.
$$f = 1.075^{\frac{1}{2}} - 1 = 1.0368221 - 1 = 0.0368221 = 3.68221\%$$
Secondly, determine the present value of the ordinary general annuity at the end of the period of deferment.

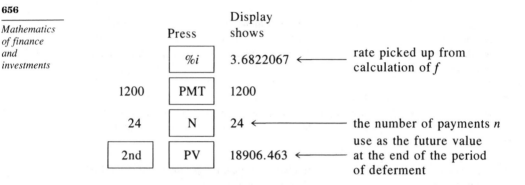

	Press	Display shows	
	%i	3.6822067 ←	rate picked up from calculation of f
1200	PMT	1200	
24	N	24 ←	the number of payments n
2nd	PV	18906.463 ←	use as the future value at the end of the period of deferment

Thirdly, determine the present value of the amount of $18 906.46 at the beginning of the period of deferment.

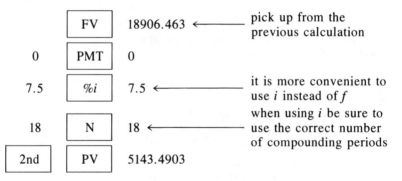

	FV	18906.463 ←	pick up from the previous calculation
0	PMT	0	
7.5	%i	7.5 ←	it is more convenient to use i instead of f
18	N	18 ←	when using i be sure to use the correct number of compounding periods
2nd	PV	5143.4903	

The required sum of money now is $5143.49.

Example 17.6b An investment in a lease offers returns of $2500 per month due at the beginning of each month for five years. What investment is justified if the returns are deferred for two years and interest required is 24% compounded quarterly?

Solution

$$R = 2500; \qquad i = 6\%; \qquad n = 60; \qquad d = 24; \qquad c = \frac{4}{12} = \frac{1}{3}$$

First, determine the effective monthly rate of interest.

$$f = 1.06^{\frac{1}{3}} - 1 = 1.0196128 - 1 = 0.0196128 = 1.96128\%$$

Secondly, determine the present value of the general annuity due at the end of the period of deferment.

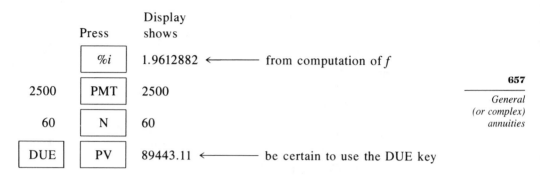

	Press	Display shows	
	%i	1.9612882 ←	from computation of f
2500	PMT	2500	
60	N	60	
DUE	PV	89443.11 ←	be certain to use the DUE key

Thirdly, determine the present value of $89 443.11.

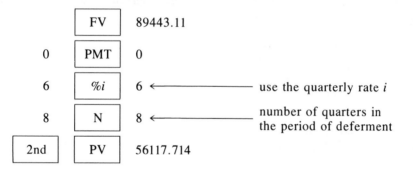

	FV	89443.11	
0	PMT	0	
6	%i	6 ←	use the quarterly rate i
8	N	8 ←	number of quarters in the period of deferment
2nd	PV	56117.714	

The investment justified is $56 117.71.

B. Finding the periodic payment R for deferred general annuities

Example 17.6c   A deposit of $20 000 is made for a twenty-year term. After the expiration of the term, equal withdrawals are to be made for twelve years at the end of every six months. What is the size of the semi-annual withdrawals if interest is 10% compounded quarterly?

Solution

$$A_{nc}(\text{defer.}) = 20000; \qquad i = 2.5\%; \qquad n = 24; \qquad d = 40;$$

$$c = \frac{4}{2} = 2$$

$$f = 1.025^2 - 1 = 1.050625 - 1 = 0.050625 = 5.0625\%$$

First determine the accumulated value of the deposit at the end of the period of deferment.

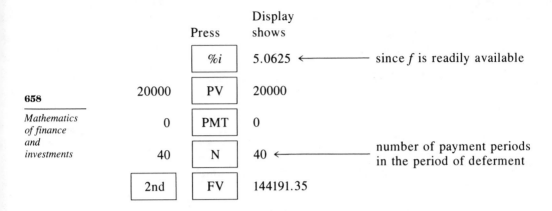

	Press	Display shows	
	%i	5.0625 ←	since f is readily available
20000	PV	20000	
0	PMT	0	
40	N	40 ←	number of payment periods in the period of deferment
2nd	FV	144191.35	

Now determine the periodic payment for the general annuity whose present value is $144 191.35.

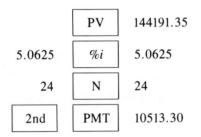

	PV	144191.35
5.0625	%i	5.0625
24	N	24
2nd	PMT	10513.30

The size of the semi-annual withdrawals is $10 513.30.

C. Finding the term n for deferred general annuities

Example 17.6d Mr. X paid $24 000 into a retirement fund paying interest at 11% compounded semi-annually. If he retires in seventeen years, how long can Mr. X withdraw $1630 every month under the assumption that the first withdrawal from the fund is on the date of retirement?

Solution
The problem involves a deferred annuity due.

$$A_{nc}(\text{defer.}) = 24000; \qquad i = 5.5\%; \qquad R = 1630; \qquad d = 204;$$

$$c = \frac{2}{12} = \frac{1}{6}$$

$$f = 1.055^{\frac{1}{6}} - 1 = 1.0089634 - 1 = 0.0089634 = 0.89634\%$$

First find the accumulated value at the end of the period of deferment.

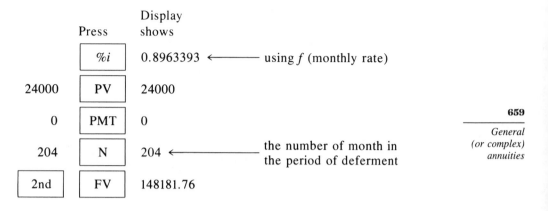

Then find the number of payments for the annuity due whose present value is $148 181.76.

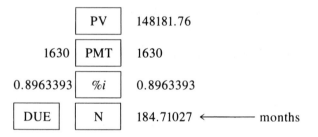

Monthly withdrawals of $1630 can be made for 15 years and four months plus a final withdrawal smaller than $1630.

D.   *Finding the conversion rate i for deferred annuities*

Example 17.6e   Payments of $500 are to be made at the beginning of each month for four years starting two years after a contract valued at $12 000 was signed. What nominal rate of interest compounded quarterly has been charged?

Solution

Since the payments are at the beginning of each month, the problem involves a deferred general annuity.

$$A_{nc}(\text{defer.}) = 12000; \qquad R = 500; \qquad n = 48; \qquad d = 24;$$

$$c = \frac{4}{12} = \frac{1}{3}$$

To find the equivalent monthly rate of interest f, substitute the given values in

Formula 17.5, multiply by $(1 + f)$ and determine the factor for which f is to be computed.

$$12000 = 500(1 + f)^{-24}(a\,\overline{_{48}}_{|f})(1 + f)$$

$$24 = (1 + f)^{-23}(a\,\overline{_{48}}_{|f})$$

$$24 = a\,\overline{_{48}}_{|f} \times PV(23, f)$$

We need to find the monthly rate f for which

$$a\,\overline{_{48}}_{|f} \times PV(23, f) = 24$$

This is exactly the same problem as finding the monthly rate i in Chapter 16, Example 16.41, except that we must now determine the quarterly rate of interest.

$$f = 1.516\%$$
$$(1 + i)^{\frac{1}{3}} = 1.01516$$
$$1 + i = 1.01516^3$$
$$1 + i = 1.046173$$
$$i = 0.046173$$
$$i = 4.6173\%$$

The nominal rate of interest compounded quarterly is 18.469%.

Exercise 17.6

Use a preprogrammed calculator to solve the problems in Exercise 17.5.

17.7 *General (or complex) perpetuities*

A. *Present value of an ordinary general perpetuity*

A **general perpetuity** is an annuity in which the payments begin at a fixed date and continue forever but for which the payment interval is not the same length as the interest conversion period. As in the case of any general annuity, the general perpetuity can be converted into a simple perpetuity by replacing the given periodic rate of interest by the equivalent effective rate of interest per payment interval.

Consistent with other annuities, the following symbols will be used in dealing with general perpetuities:

A = the present value of the perpetuity;
R = the periodic payment or perpetuity payment;
i = the rate of interest per conversion period;
f = the effective rate of interest per payment interval equivalent to i;
c = the number of conversion periods per payment period.

For a general perpetuity, the payment R is the interest earned by the present value of the perpetuity in one payment interval. That is

$$R = fA$$

$$\boxed{A = \frac{R}{f} \text{ where } f = (1 + i)^c - 1}$$ ⟵ *Formula* **17.6**

Example 17.7a What sum of money invested today at 12% compounded quarterly will provide a scholarship of $2500.00 at the end of each year?

Solution

Since the payments are to continue indefinitely the payments form a perpetuity. Furthermore, since the payments are made at the end of each payment interval and the interest conversion period is not the same length as the payment interval, the problem involves an ordinary general perpetuity.

$$R = 2500.00; \qquad c = 4; \qquad i = \frac{12\%}{4} = 3\% = 0.03$$

The equivalent effective annual rate of interest

$$f = 1.03^4 - 1 = 1.1255088 - 1 = 0.1255088 = 12.55082\%$$

$$A = \frac{2500.00}{0.1255088} = \$19918.92 \quad \longleftarrow \text{ substituting in Formula 17.6}$$

The required sum of money is $19918.92.

Example 17.7b The alumni of Peel College collected $32 000.00 to provide a fund for bursaries. If the money is invested at 11% compounded annually, what is the size of the bursary that can be paid every six months?

Solution

$$A = 32000.00; \qquad c = \frac{1}{2}; \qquad i = 11\% = 0.11$$

The equivalent effective semi-annual rate of interest

$$f = 1.11^{0.5} - 1 = 1.0535654 - 1 = 0.0535654 = 5.35654\%$$

$$R = fA = 0.0535654(32000.00) = \$1714.09$$

The size of the bursary is $1714.09.

B. Present value of general perpetuities due

As in the case of the simple perpetuity due, the general perpetuity due may be treated as consisting of an immediate payment R followed by an ordinary general perpetuity. Using the symbol A(due) for the present value

$$A(\text{due}) = R + \frac{R}{f} \text{ where } f = (1 + i)^c - 1 \qquad \longleftarrow \text{\textbf{\textit{Formula 17.7}}}$$

Example 17.7c   What is the present value of perpetuity payments of $750.00 made at the beginning of each month if interest is 14.5% compounded semi-annually?

Solution

$$R = 750.00; \qquad c = \frac{2}{12} = \frac{1}{6}; \qquad i = \frac{14.5\%}{2} = 7.25\% = 0.0725$$

The equivalent effective monthly rate of interest

$$f = 1.0725^{\frac{1}{6}} - 1 = 1.0117337 - 1 = 0.0117337 = 1.17337\%$$

$$A(\text{due}) = 750.00 + \frac{750.00}{0.0117337} = \$64668.46 \longleftarrow \begin{array}{l} \text{substituting in} \\ \text{Formula 17.7} \end{array}$$

The present value of the perpetuity is $64668.46.

Example 17.7d   What sum of money invested today in a fund earning 13% compounded monthly will provide perpetuity payments of $395.00 every three months starting

(i) immediately?

(ii) three months from now?

(iii) one year from now?

Solution

$$R = 395.00; \qquad c = \frac{12}{4} = 3; \qquad i = \frac{12\%}{12} = 1\% = 0.01$$

The equivalent effective quarterly rate of interest

$$f = 1.01^3 - 1 = 1.030301 - 1 = 0.030301 = 3.0301\%$$

(i) The perpetuity payments are at the beginning of each payment interval, hence they form a perpetuity due

$$A(\text{due}) = 395.00 + \frac{395.00}{0.030301} = 395.00 + 13035.87 = \$13430.87$$

The required sum of money is $13430.87.

(ii) Since the first payment is three month from now, the perpetuity payments form an ordinary perpetuity.

$$A = \frac{395.00}{0.030301} = \$13035.87$$

The required sum of money is $13035.87.

(iii) If the payments are considered to be deferred for one year, they form a deferred perpetuity due.

$$A(\text{defer.}) = A(\text{due}) \times (1.01)^{-12}$$
$$= 13430.87(0.8874492)$$
$$= \$11919.22$$

Alternatively the period of deferment could have been considered to be 9 months (3 quarters) in which case the payments would be considered to form a deferred ordinary perpetuity.

$$A(\text{defer.}) = A \times (1.01)^{-9}$$
$$= 13035.87(0.9143398)$$
$$= \$11919.22$$

The required sum of money is $11919.22.

Exercise 17.7

A. Find the present value of each of the following perpetuities

Problem number	Perpetuity payment	Payment made at	Payment interval	Interest rate	Conversion period
1.	$5600.00	end	6 months	12%	monthly
2.	$2150.00	beginning	3 months	15%	monthly
3.	$725.00	beginning	1 month	10%	quarterly
4.	$380.00	end	3 months	18%	semi-annually

B. Answer each of the following questions.

1. The Xorex Company pays a dividend of $4.25 every three months per preferred share. What is the expected market price per share if money is worth 13% compounded semi-annually?

2. Transcontinental Pipelines is considering a technical process which is expected to reduce annual maintenance costs by $85 000.00. What is the maximum amount of money that could be invested in the process to be economically feasible if interest is 14% compounded quarterly?

3. A rental property provides a net income of $4200.00 at the beginning of every three months. What is the cash value of the property if money is worth 18% compounded monthly?

4. Municipal Hydro offers to acquire a right-of-way from a property owner receiving annual lease payments of $2225.00 due in advance. What is a fair offer if money is worth 21.5% compounded quarterly?

5. What is the size of the scholarship which can be paid at the end of every six months from a fund of $25 000.00 if interest is 11% compounded quarterly?

6. What monthly lease payment due in advance should be charged for a tract of land valued at $35 000 if the agreed interest is 14.5% compounded semi-annually?

17.8 *Appendix—finding the conversion rate i for general annuities due and deferred general annuities without preprogrammed calculators*

A   Finding the rate for general annuities due

When finding the rate of interest in a general annuity due, the equivalent effective interest per payment period f should be determined first. This may be done using Formula 17.3A when the amount $S_{nc}(\text{due})$ is known or Formula 17.4A when the present value $A_{nc}(\text{due})$ is known.

The computation, however, can be facilitated by manipulating the two formulae in a manner similar to that used in Chapter 16 to obtain Formulae 16.5 and 16.6. In fact, the latter two formulae are directly applicable in finding f except that i needs to be replaced by f.

$$S_{nc}(\text{due}) = R\left(\frac{(1+f)^{n+1} - 1}{f} - 1\right) \text{ or } S_{nc}(\text{due}) = R(s_{\overline{n+1}|f} - 1) \quad \leftarrow \textit{Formula 17.8}$$

$$A_{nc}(\text{due}) = R\left(\frac{1 - (1+f)^{-(n-1)}}{f} + 1\right) \text{ or } A_{nc}(\text{due}) = R(a_{\overline{n-1}|f} + 1) \quad \leftarrow \textit{Formula 17}$$

Example 17.8a   Deposits of $300.75 made at the beginning of every three months accumulate to $10 000.00 at the end of six years. What rate of interest compounded monthly has been earned by the deposits?

Solution

$$S_{nc}(\text{due}) = 10000.00; \qquad R = 300.75; \qquad n = 6(4) = 24; \qquad c = \frac{12}{4} = 3;$$

$$f = (1 + i)^3 - 1$$

$$10000.00 = 300.75(s_{\overline{24+1}|f} - 1) \longleftarrow \text{ substituting in Formula 17.8}$$

$$33.250208 = s_{\overline{25}|f} - 1$$

$$s_{\overline{25}|f} = 34.250208$$

For $f = 3\%$ $\qquad s_{\overline{25}|3\%} \qquad = 36.459264 \longrightarrow f < 3\%$

$For\ f = 2\%$ $\quad s_{\overline{25}|2\%}$ $\quad = 32.030299 \longrightarrow 2\% < f < 3\%$

$For\ f = 2.5\%$ $\quad s_{\overline{25}|2.5\%}$ $\quad = 34.157763 \longrightarrow 2.5\% < f < 3\%$

$For\ f = 2.52\%$ $\quad s_{\overline{25}|2.52\%}$ $\quad = 34.246386 \longrightarrow 2.52\% < f < 3\%$

$For\ f = 2.521\%$ $\quad s_{\overline{25}|2.521\%}$ $\quad = 34.250824 \longrightarrow 2.52\% < f < 2.521\%$

$For\ f = 2.5208\%$ $\quad s_{\overline{25}|2.5208\%} = 34.249937 \longrightarrow 2.5208\% < f < 2.521\%$

$For\ f = 2.5209\%$ $\quad s_{\overline{25}|2.5209\%} = 34.250381 \longrightarrow 2.5208\% < f < 2.5209\%$

$For\ f = 2.52086\%$ $s_{\overline{25}|2.52086\%} = 34.250203 \longrightarrow f = 2.52086\%$

$$(1 + i)^3 = 1.0252086$$

$$1 + i = 1.02520^{\frac{1}{3}} = 1.0083332$$

$$i = 0.0083332 = 0.83332\%$$

The rate of interest is $12(0.83332\%) = 9.99988\%$ or 10% compounded monthly.

Example 17.8b A property valued at \$74 250.00 can be bought by making payments of \$913.32 at the beginning of each month for fifteen years. What rate of interest compounded semi-annually is being charged?

Solution

$$A_{nc}(\text{due}) = 74250.00; \qquad R = 913.32; \qquad n = 15(12) = 180;$$

$$c = \frac{2}{12} = \frac{1}{6}; \qquad f = (1 + i)^{\frac{1}{6}} - 1$$

$$74250.00 = 913.32(a_{\overline{180-1}|f} + 1) \longleftarrow \text{substituting in Formula 17.9}$$

$$81.296807 = a_{\overline{179}|f} + 1$$

$$a_{\overline{179}|f} = 80.296807$$

$For\ f = 1\%$ $\quad a_{\overline{179}|1\%}$ $\quad = 83.154881 \longrightarrow 1\% < f$

$For\ f = 1.1\%$ $\quad a_{\overline{179}|1.1\%}$ $\quad = 78.081342 \longrightarrow 1\% < f < 1.1\%$

$For\ f = 1.05\%$ $\quad a_{\overline{179}|1.05\%}$ $\quad = 80.555264 \longrightarrow 1.05\% < f < 1.1\%$

$For\ f = 1.06\%$ $\quad a_{\overline{179}|1.06\%}$ $\quad = 80.050665 \longrightarrow 1.05\% < f < 1.06\%$

$For\ f = 1.055\%$ $\quad a_{\overline{179}|1.055\%}$ $\quad = 80.302340 \longrightarrow 1.055\% < f < 1.06\%$

$For\ f = 1.0551\%$ $\quad a_{\overline{179}|1.0551\%}$ $\quad = 80.297295 \longrightarrow 1.0551\% < f < 1.06\%$

$For\ f = 1.05511\%$ $a_{\overline{179}|1.05511\%} = 80.296790 \longrightarrow f = 1.05511\%$

$$(1 + i)^{\frac{1}{6}} = 1.0105511$$

$$1 + i = 1.0105511^6 = 1.0650002$$

$$i = 0.0650002 = 6.5\%$$

The rate of interest is $2(6.5\%) = 13\%$ compounded semi-annually.

B. Finding the rate for deferred general annuities

The rate of interest for a deferred general annuity may be determined by trial and error as previously explained. For deferred ordinary general annuities use Formula 17.5; for deferred general annuities due multiply Formula 17.5 by $(1 + f)$.

Example 17.8c A retirement annuity of $12 000.00 payable at the end of each year for fifteen years is bought for $7560.73. If the payments are deferred for twenty-five years, what is the rate of interest compounded quarterly on the annuity?

Solution

$$A_{nc}(\text{defer} = 7560.73; \quad R = 12000.00; \quad n = 15; \quad d = 25;$$
$$c = 4; \quad f = (1 + i)^4 - 1$$

For a deferred ordinary general annuity use Formula 17.5.

$$7560.73 = 12000.00(1 + f)^{-25}\left(\frac{1 - (1 + f)^{-15}}{f}\right)$$

$$(1 + f)^{-25}\left(\frac{1 - (1 + f)^{-15}}{f}\right) = 0.6300608$$

Hence we need to find the annual rate of interest f for which

$$a_{\overline{15}|f} \times PV(25, f) = 0.6300608$$

For f = 12% $a_{\overline{15}|12\%} \times PV(25, 12\%)$

$= (6.8108645)(0.0588233) = 0.4006376 \longrightarrow f < 12\%$

For f = 10% $a_{\overline{15}|10\%} \times PV(25, 10\%)$

$= (7.6060795)(0.0922960) = 0.7020107 \longrightarrow 10\% < f < 12\%$

For f = 10.4% $a_{\overline{15}|10.4\%} \times PV(25, 10.4\%)$

$= (7.4355148)(0.0842894) = 0.6267354 \longrightarrow 10\% < f < 10.4\%$

For f = 10.38% $a_{\overline{15}|10.38\%} \times PV(25, 10.38\%)$

$= (7.4438978)(0.0846721) = 0.6302904 \longrightarrow 10.38\% < f < 10.4\%$

For f = 10.381% $a_{\overline{15}|10.381\%} \times PV(25, 10.381\%)$

$= (7.4434783)(0.0846529) = 0.6301121 \longrightarrow 10.381\% < f < 10.4\%$

For f = 10.3813% $\quad a_{\overline{15}|\,10.3813\%} \times PV(25, 10.3813\%)$

$$= (7.4433525)(0.0846472) = 0.6300586 \longrightarrow f = 10.3813\%$$

$$\text{Since } (1 + i)^4 = (1 + f) = 1.103813$$
$$1 + i = 1.103813^{\frac{1}{4}}$$
$$1 + i = 1.025$$
$$i = 0.025 = 2.5\%$$

The rate of interest is $4(2.5\%) = 10\%$ compounded quarterly.

Review exercise

1. Payments of \$375.00 made every three months are accumulated at 12% compounded monthly. What is their amount after eight years if the payments are made

   (a) at the end of every three months?

   (b) at the beginning of every three months?

2. What is the accumulated value of monthly deposits of \$145.00 earning interest at 15% compounded semi-annually after twelve years if the deposits are made

   (a) at the end of each month?

   (b) at the beginning of each month?

3. What single cash payment is equivalent to payments of \$3500.00 every six months at 14% compounded quarterly if the payments are made

   (a) at the end of every six months for fifteen years?

   (b) at the beginning of every six months for ten years?

   (c) at the end of every six months for eight years but deferred for four years?

   (d) at the beginning of every six months for nine years but deferred for three years?

   (e) at the end of every six months in perpetuity?

   (f) at the beginning of every six months in perpetuity?

4. What is the principal invested at 12.5% compounded semi-annually from which monthly withdrawals of \$240.00 can be made

   (a) at the end of each month for 25 years?

   (b) at the beginning of each month for 15 years?

   (c) at the end of each month for 20 years but deferred for 10 years?

   (d) at the beginning of each month for 15 years but deferred for 12 years?

   (e) at the end of each month in perpetuity?

   (f) at the beginning of each month in perpetuity?

5. What size payment will accumulate to $12 500.00 at 10% compounded quarterly if made

   (a) at the end of each month for twenty years?

   (b) at the beginning of every six month for eight years?

6. How much must be deposited into an account to accumulate to $32 000.00 at 11% compounded semi-annually

   (a) at the beginning of each month for twenty years?

   (b) at the end of each year for fifteen years?

7. What size payment has a present value of $9600.00 at 18% compounded monthly if made

   (a) at the end of every three months for eight years?

   (b) at the beginning of every six months for ten years?

   (c) at the end of each year for ten years but deferred for three years?

   (d) at the beginning of every six months for seven years but deferred for five years?

   (e) at the end of every three months in perpetuity?

   (f) at the beginning of each year in perpetuity?

8. What sum of money can be withdrawn from a fund of $16 750.00 invested at 16.5% compounded semi-annually

   (a) at the end of every three months for twelve years?

   (b) at the beginning of each year for twenty years?

   (c) at the end of each month for fifteen years but deferred for ten years?

   (d) at the beginning of every three months for 12 years but deferred for 20 years?

   (e) at the end of each month in perpetuity?

   (f) at the beginning of each year in perpetuity?

9. If monthly deposits of $15.00 earn interest at 12% compounded quarterly, how long will it take to save $5000.00 if the deposits are made

   (a) at the end of each month?

   (b) at the beginning of each month?

10. In what period of time will payments of $225.00 accumulate to $20 000.00 at 15% compounded monthly if made

    (a) at the end of every three months?

    (b) at the beginning of every six months?

11. For how long can withdrawals of $2000.00 be made from a fund of $10 000.00 invested at 14.5% compounded annually if withdrawals are made

    (a) at the end of every three months?

    (b) at the beginning of every six months?

    (c) at the end of each month but deferred for fifteen years?

    (d) at the beginning of every three months but deferred for five years?

12. A debt of $20 000.00 is repaid by making payments of $3500.00. If interest is 15% compounded monthly, for how long will payments have to be made

   (a) at the end of every six months?

   (b) at the beginning of each year?

   (c) at the end of every three months with payments deferred for five years?

   (d) at the beginning of every six months with payments deferred for three years?

13. What is the rate of interest compounded quarterly at which payments of $250.00 made at the beginning of every six months accumulate to $8400.00 in eight years?

14. A $42 000.00 mortgage with a 25-year term is repaid by making monthly payments of $480.00. What is the rate of interest compounded semi-annually on the mortgage?

15. An annuity purchased for $32 000.00 provides ordinary annuity payments of $8200.00 every three months for fifteen years. If the payments are deferred for ten years, what rate of interest compounded semi-annually is paid on the investment?

16. A leasing agreement with a cash value of $24 500.00 requires semi-annual payments of $6500.00 for five years. If the first payment is due three years from the date of the agreement, what is the effective rate of interest on the lease if interest is compounded monthly?

17. Contributions of $500.00 are made at the end of every three months into an RRSP. What is the accumulated balance after twenty years if interest is 11% compounded semi-annually?

18. If you save $25.00 at the beginning of each month and interest is 16% compounded quarterly, how much will you accumulate in thirty years?

19. A property was purchased for quarterly payments of $1350.00 for ten years. If the first payment was made on the date of purchase and interest is 15.5% compounded annually, what was the purchase price of the property?

20. A 35-year mortgage is amortized by payments of $761.50 made at the end of each month. If interest is 13.5% compounded semi-annually, what is the mortgage principal?

21. What sum of money invested today in a retirement fund will permit withdrawals of $800.00 at the end of each month for twenty years if interest is 12% compounded semi-annually and the payments are deferred for fifteen years?

22. A lease requires semi-annual payments of $6000.00 for five years. If the first payment is due in four years and interest is 21% compounded monthly, what is the cash value of the lease?

23. The semi-annual dividend per preferred share issued by InterCity Trust is $7.50. If comparable investments yield 14% compounded quarterly, what should be the selling price of such shares?

24. A fund to provide an annual scholarship of $4000.00 is to be set up. If the first payment is due in three years and interest is 11% compounded quarterly, what sum of money must be deposited in the scholarship fund today?

25. How much must be contributed into a RRSP at the end of each year for 25 years to accumulate to $100 000.00 if interest is 13% compounded quarterly?

26. Kelly Associates are the makers of a ten-year $75 000.00 promissory note bearing interest at 16% compounded semi-annually. In order to pay off the note on its due date, Kelly are making payments at the beginning of every three months into a fund paying 13.5% compounded monthly. What is the size of the monthly payments?

27. A debt of $40 000.00 is to be repaid in instalments due at the end of each month for seven years. If the payments are deferred for three years and interest is 17% compounded quarterly, what is the size of the monthly payments?

28. Redden Junior bought his father's farm for $200 000.00. The transfer agreement requires Junior to make quarterly payments for twenty years. If the first payment is due in five years and the rate of interest is 10% compounded annually, what is the size of the quarterly payments?

29. Preferred shares of Western Oil paying a quarterly dividend are to be offered at $55.65 per share. If money is worth 15% compounded semi-annually, what is the minimum quarterly dividend to make investment in such shares economically feasible?

30. A church congregation has raised $37 625.00 for future missionary work. If the money is invested in a fund paying 11% compounded quarterly, what annual payment can be made from the fund to the mission if the first payment is to be made four years from the date of investment in the fund?

31. For how long must $75.00 be deposited at the end of each month to accumulate to $8500.00 at 16% compounded quarterly?

32. Over what period of time will RRSP contributions of $1350.00 made at the beginning of each year amount to $125 000.00 if interest is 17% compounded quarterly?

33. A $60 000.00 mortgage is amortized by making monthly payments of $618.19. If interest is 12.5% compounded semi-annually, what is the term of the mortgage?

34 A lease contract valued at $50 000.00 requires semi-annual payments of $5200.00. If the first payment is due at the date of signing the contract and interest is 18% compounded monthly, what is the term of the lease?

35. An annuity provides payment of $3600.00 at the end of every three months. The annuity is bought for $33 500.00 and payments are deferred for twelve years. If interest is 10% compounded monthly, for how long will payments be received?

36. A retirement gratuity of $25 500.00 is invested in an Income Averaging Annuity paying $1400.00 every three months. If the interest is 11.5% compounded semi-annually and the first payment is due in one year, for how long will payments be received?

Self-test

1. Monthly deposits of $480.00 were made at the end of each month for eight years. If interest is 9.5% compounded semi-annually, what amount can be withdrawn five years after the last deposit?

2. A loan was repaid by quarterly payments of $1200.00 in five years at 19.5% compounded semi-annually. How much interest was paid?

3. A mortgage of $95 000.00 is to be amortized by monthly payments over twenty-five years. If the payments are made at the end of each month and interest is 13.5% compounded semi-annually, what is the size of the monthly payments?

4. Sara wants to withdraw $3000.00 at the beginning of every three months starting at the date of her retirement for thirty years. If she retires in twenty years and interest is 10% compounded quarterly, how much must Sara deposit into an account every month starting now for the next twenty years?

5. A bank pays a quarterly dividend of $0.75 per share. If comparable investments yield 13.5% compounded monthly, what is the sales value of the shares?

6. A lease requires monthly payments of $585.75 due in advance. If interest is 24% compounded quarterly and the cash value of the lease is $20 956.52, what is the term of the lease?

7. A $45 000.00 mortgage is repaid in twenty years by making monthly payments of $486.44. What is the nominal annual rate of interest compounded semi-annually?

8. For how long would you have to deposit $393.00 at the end of every three months to accumulate $20 000.00 at 13.5% compounded monthly?

9. Ken acquired his father's share of their business by agreeing to make payments of $4000.00 at the end of each year for twelve years. If the payments are deferred for three years and money is worth 13% compounded quarterly, what is the cash value of the father's share of the business?

10. A retirement annuity providing equal monthly payments for 25 years is purchased for $20 000.00. If the first payment is due twenty years after the date of purchase and interest is 16% compounded quarterly, what is the size of the monthly payments?

Summary of formulae used

Formula 17.1

$$S_{nc} = R\left(\frac{(1 + i)^{nc} - 1}{(1 + i)^c - 1}\right)$$

Basic formula for finding the amount of an ordinary general annuity

Mathematics of finance and investments

Formula 17.1A

$$S_{nc} = R\left(\frac{(1 + f)^n - 1}{f}\right) = R\,s_{\overline{n}|f}$$

where $f = (1 + i)^c - 1$

In this text the preferred formula for finding the amount using the equivalent effective rate of interest per payment period

Formula 17.2

$$A_{nc} = R\left(\frac{1 - (1 + i)^{-nc}}{(1 + i)^c - 1}\right)$$

Basic formula for finding the present value of an ordinary general annuity

Formula 17.2A

$$A_{nc} = R\left(\frac{1 - (1 + f)^{-n}}{f}\right) = R\,a_{\overline{n}|f}$$

where $f = (1 + i)^c - 1$

Preferred formula for finding the present value using the equivalent effective rate of interest per payment period

Formula 17.3

$$S_{nc}(\text{due}) = R(1 + i)^c\left(\frac{(1 + i)^{nc} - 1}{(1 + i)^c - 1}\right)$$

Basic formula for finding the amount of a general annuity

Formula 17.3A

$$S_{nc}(\text{due}) = R(1 + f)\left(\frac{(1 + f)^n - 1}{f}\right) = R(1 + f)\,s_{\overline{n}|f}$$

where $f = (1 + i)^c - 1$

Preferred formula using the equivalent effective rate of interest per payment period

Formula 17.4

$$A_{nc}(\text{due}) = R(1 + i)^c\left(\frac{1 - (1 + i)^{-nc}}{(1 + i)^c - 1}\right)$$

Basic formula for finding the present value of a general annuity due

Formula 17.4A

$$A_{nc}(\text{due}) = R(1 + f)\left(\frac{1 - (1 + f)^{-n}}{f}\right) = R(1 + f)\ a_{\overline{n}|f}$$

where $f = (1 + i)^c - 1$

Preferred formula using the equivalent effective rate of interest per payment period

Formula 17.5

$$A_{nc}(\text{defer.}) = R(1 + f)^{-d}\left(\frac{1 - (1 + f)^{-n}}{f}\right) = R(1 + f)\ a_{\overline{n}|f}$$

where $f = (1 + i)^c - 1$ and d is the
number of deferred payment intervals

Formula for finding the present value of a deferred ordinary general annuity; for a deferred general annuity due multiply by $(1 + f)$

Formula 17.6

$$A = \frac{R}{f} \quad \text{where } f = (1 + i)^c - 1$$

Formula for finding the present value of an ordinary general perpetuity

Formula 17.7

$$A = R + \frac{R}{f} \quad \text{where } f = (1 + i)^c - 1$$

Formula for finding the present value of a general perpetuity due

Supplementary formulae (Section 17.8)

Formula 17.8

$$S_{nc}(\text{due}) = R(s_{\overline{n+1}|f} - 1)$$

Alternate form of the formula for finding the amount of a general annuity due

Formula 17.9

$$A_{nc}(\text{due}) = R(a_{\overline{n-1}|f} - 1)$$

Alternate form for finding the present value of a general annuity due

Glossary of terms used

Complex annuity   see *General annuity*

General annuity   an annuity in which the interest conversion period is different in length from the payment period

General annuity due   a general annuity in which the payments are made at the beginning of each payment period

General perpetuity   a general annuity in which the payments continue forever

Ordinary general annuity   a general annuity in which the payments are made at the end of each payment period

*Mathematics
of finance
and
investments*

18 Amortization and sinking funds

Introduction

Amortization refers to the repayment of interest-bearing debts by a series of payments, usually equal in size, made at equal intervals of time. The periodic payments, when equal in size, form an annuity whose present value is equivalent to the original loan principal. Mortgages and many consumer loans are repaid by this method. The allocation of each payment to first cover the interest due and then to reduce the principal may be shown in an amortization schedule.

In the sinking fund method of providing for the repayment of a future obligation, periodic payments are accumulated in a fund earmarked for this purpose. The payments, when equal in size, form an annuity whose accumulated value is the maturity value of the debt. A prime example of a sinking fund is a fund associated with the issuance and redemption of corporate or municipal bonds.

Objectives

Upon completion of this chapter you will be able to

1. perform computations associated with amortization of debts involving simple annuities, including the size of the periodic payments, outstanding balance, interest due and principal repaid and construct complete or partial amortization schedules;

2. perform computations as in 1) associated with the amortization of debts when the payments form general annuities and construct complete or partial amortization schedules;

3. find the size of the final payment when all payments, except the final payment, are equal in size;

4. make computations associated with sinking funds when the payments form

simple annuities, including the size of the periodic payments, accumulated balance, interest earned and increase in the fund and construct complete or partial sinking fund schedules.

Note While no specific reference is made in this and the following chapters to preprogrammed calculators, the procedures used in Chapters 13 to 17 are very much applicable.

18.1 *Amortization (simple annuities)*

A. *Finding the periodic payment*

An interest-bearing debt is said to be **amortized** if both principal and interest are repaid by a series of equal payments made at equal intervals of time.

Example 18.1a A debt of $5000.00 with interest at 12% compounded annually is to be repaid by equal payments at the end of each year for six years. What is the size of the annual payments?

Solution

FIGURE 18.1 *Graphical representation of method of solution and data*

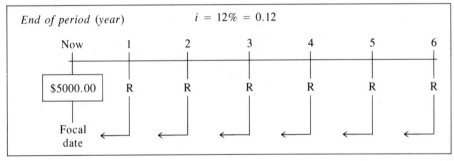

As indicated in the diagram, the equal annual payments (designated by R) form an ordinary annuity in which

$$A_n = 5000.00; \qquad n = 6; \qquad i = 12\% = 0.12.$$

Using as focal date the point designated 'now', the value of the annual payment R may be found using the same method and formulae used in Chapter 15.

$$5000.00 = R\left(\frac{1 - 1.12^{-6}}{0.12}\right) \longleftarrow \text{using Formula 15.2} \quad in \ p.524$$

$$5000.00 = R(4.1114073)$$

$$R = \$1216.13$$

The annual payment is $1216.13.

The basic problem in amortizing a debt is finding the size of the periodic payment. If the payment interval and the interest conversion period are equal in length, the problem involves finding the periodic payment for a simple annuity. Since debts are generally repaid by making payments at the end of the payment interval, the method and formulae used in Chapter 15, Section 15.4 are applicable.

Formulae 15.2 or 15.2A

$$A_n = R\left(\frac{1 - (1 + i)^{-n}}{i}\right) \text{ or } A_n = R \times a_{\overline{n}|i}$$

Example 18.1b A loan of $8000.00 made at 15% compounded monthly is amortized over five years by making equal monthly payments.

(i) What is the size of the monthly payment?

(ii) What is the total amount paid to amortize the loan?

(iii) What is the cost of financing?

Solution

(i) $A_n = 8000.00;$ $n = 5(12) = 60;$ $i = \dfrac{15\%}{12} = 1.25\%$

$8000.00 = R \times a_{\overline{60}|1.25\%}$ ⟵ using Formula 15.2A

$8000.00 = R(42.034591)$

$R = \$190.32$

The monthly payment is $190.32.

(ii) The total amount paid is $60(190.32) = \$11419.20$

(iii) The cost of financing is $11419.20 - 8000.00 = \$3419.20$

B. Amortization schedules

As previously discussed in Chapter 12, Section 12.7, **amortization schedules** show in detail how a debt is repaid. Such schedules normally show the payment number (or payment date), the amount paid, the interest paid, the principal repaid and the outstanding debt balance.

1. *Amortization schedule when all payments are equal (Blended Payments)*
    When all payments are equal, the size of the periodic payment must first be determined as shown in sub-section A.

    Example 18.1c A debt of $5000.00 is amortized by making equal payments at the end of every three months for two years. If interest is 15% compounded quarterly, construct an amortization schedule.

Solution

STEP 1 Determine the size of the quarterly payments.

$$A_n = 5000.00; \qquad n = 4(2) = 8; \qquad i = \frac{15\%}{4} = 3.75\%$$

$$5000.00 = R \times a_{\overline{8}|3.75}$$

$$5000.00 = R(6.8027959)$$

$$R = \$734.99$$

STEP 2 Construct the amortization schedule as shown below.

Payment number	Amount paid	Interest paid $i = 0.0375$	Principal repaid	Outstanding principal balance
0				5000.00
1	734.99	187.50	547.49	4452.51
2	734.99	166.97	568.02	3884.49
3	734.99	145.67	589.32	3295.17
4	734.99	123.57	611.42	2683.75
5	734.99	100.64	634.35	2049.40
6	734.99	76.85	658.14	1391.26
7	734.99	52.17	682.82	708.44
8	735.01	26.57	708.44	0.00
TOTAL	5879.94	879.94	5000.00	

Explanations regarding the construction of the amortization schedule

1. Payment Number 0 is used to introduce the initial balance of the loan.

2. The interest included in the first payment is $0.0375 \times 5000.00 = \$187.50$. Since the amount paid is $734.99, the amount available for repayment of principal is $734.99 - 187.50 = \$547.49$. Hence the outstanding principal balance after the first payment is $5000.00 - 547.49 = \$4452.51$.

3. The interest included in the second payment is $0.0375 \times 4452.51 = \$166.97$. Since the amount paid is $734.99, the amount available for repayment of principal is $734.99 - 166.97 = \$568.02$. Hence the outstanding principal $4452.51 - 568.02 = \$3884.49$.

4. Computation of interest, principal repaid and outstanding balance for payments 3 to 7 are made in a similar manner.

5. The last payment of $735.01 is slightly different from the other payments as a result of rounding in the amount paid or the interest paid. To allow for

such rounding errors the last payment is computed by adding the interest due in the last payment (0.0375 × 708.44 = $26.57) to the then outstanding balance: 708.44 + 26.57 = $735.01.

6. The three totals shown provide useful information and can be used as a check for the accuracy of the schedule.
   (a) The principal repaid must equal the original outstanding balance;
   (b) the amount paid is the periodic payment times the number of such payments plus/minus any adjustment in the last payment
      734.99 × 8 + 0.02 = 5879.92 + 0.02 = $5879.94;
   (c) the interest paid is the difference between the amount paid and the original principal 5879.94 − 5000.00 = $879.94.

2. *Amortization schedule when all payments, except the final payment, are equal*
   When the size of the periodic payment is determined by agreement, usually as a convenient round figure rather than a computed blended payment, the size of the final payment is likely different from the preceding agreed upon payments. This final payment is obtained in the amortization schedule by adding the interest due on the outstanding balance to the outstanding balance.
   This type of loan repayment schedule has been illustrated and explained in Chapter 12, Section 12.7 and the following example is included for review.

Example 18.1d Sheridan Service borrowed $15 000.00 from Peel Community Credit Union at 16% compounded quarterly. The loan agreement requires payment of $2500.00 at the end of every three months. Construct an amortization schedule.

Solution

$$i = \frac{16\%}{4} = 4\% = 0.04$$

Payment number	Amount paid	Interest paid $i = 0.04$	Principal repaid	Outstanding principal balance
0				15 000.00
1	2500.00	600.00	1900.00	13 100.00
2	2500.00	524.00	1976.00	11 124.00
3	2500.00	444.96	2055.04	9 068.96
4	2500.00	362.76	2137.24	6 931.72
5	2500.00	277.27	2222.73	4 708.99
6	2500.00	188.36	2311.64	2 397.35
7	2493.24	95.89	2397.35	0.00
TOTAL	17 493.24	2493.24	15 000.00	

Note   After payment number 6 the outstanding principal is less than the agreed payment. When this happens the following payment will be the final payment, in this case obtained as

$$2397.35 + 2397.35 \times 0.04 = 2397.35 + 95.89 = \$2493.24$$

C.   Finding the oustanding principal balance

For various reasons, such as early partial or full repayment or refinancing, knowledge of the outstanding balance at a certain point in time is frequently required by the borrower or the lender. This can be done by checking the amortization schedule if available, or by direct mathematical computation. This computation is also useful for checking the accuracy of the schedule as it is developed.

1.   *Finding the outstanding principal when all payments are equal*

> **Example 18.1e**   For Example 18.1c compute the outstanding balance just after the third payment has been made.

Solution

The loan history showing the quarterly payments of $734.99 may be represented on a time diagram as shown in Figure 18.2.

FIGURE 18.2   *Graphical representation of loan payments*

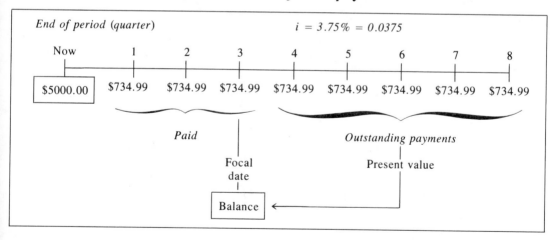

In the same way in which the original loan balance of $5000.00 represents the present value of the number of payments that are necessary to amortize the loan, the outstanding balance at the end of any payment interval just after a payment has been made is the present value of the outstanding payments.

$$\boxed{\begin{array}{ll} \text{OUTSTANDING} \\ \text{BALANCE} \end{array} = \begin{array}{l} \text{PRESENT VALUE OF THE} \\ \text{OUTSTANDING PAYMENTS} \end{array}}$$

Formula 15.2 or 15.2A may be used. Since three of the eight payments have been made, five payments remain outstanding.

$$R = 734.99; \qquad n = 5; \qquad i = 3.75\%$$

$A_3 = 734.99\, a_{\overline{5}|3.75\%} \quad \longleftarrow \quad \text{using Formula 15.2A}$

$\quad = 734.99(4.4832618)$

$\quad = \$3295.15$

The outstanding balance after the third payment is $3295.15.

Note   The amortization schedule shows $3295.17; the difference is due to rounding.

Example 18.1f   You borrow $7500.00 from your Credit Union at 13.5% compounded monthly. If the loan is amortized over five years, what is the loan balance after two years?

Solution

First, determine the size of the monthly payment.

$$A_n = 7500.00; \qquad n = 5(12) = 60; \qquad i = \frac{13.5\%}{12} = 1.125\%$$

$7500.00 = Ra_{\overline{60}|1.125\%}$

$7500.00 = R(43.459657)$

$\qquad R = \$172.57$

Now determine the balance after two years.

After two years 24 of the 60 payments have been made; 36 payments remain outstanding.

$$R = 172.57; \qquad n = 36; \qquad i = 1.125\%$$

$A_{24} = 172.57 a_{\overline{36}|1.125\%}$

$\quad = 172.57(29.467851)$

$\quad = \$5085.27$

The outstanding balance after two years is $5085.27.

The method used in Examples 18.1e and 18.1f is sometimes referred to as the **Prospective Method** of finding the outstanding balance because it considers the future prospects of the debt—the payments that remain outstanding.

Alternatively, the outstanding balance can be found by the **Retrospective**

Method which considers the payments that have been made. When this method is used, the outstanding balance is found by deducting the accumulated value of the payments that have been made from the accumulated value of the original debt.

OUTSTANDING BALANCE	=	ACCUMULATED VALUE OF THE ORIGINAL DEBT— ACCUMULATED VALUE OF THE PAYMENTS MADE

For Example 18.1e

The accumulated value of the original debt at the end of three payment intervals

$S = 5000.00(1.0375^3)$ ⟵——————— using Formula 13.1

$= 5000.00(1.1167715)$

$= \$5583.86$

The accumulated value of the payments made

$S_3 = 734.99\left(\dfrac{1.0375^3 - 1}{0.0375}\right)$ ⟵———— using Formula 15.1

$= 734.99(3.1139063)$

$= \$2288.69$

The outstanding balance is $5583.86 - 2288.69 = \$3295.17$.

For Example 18.1f

The accumulated value of the debt after two years (24 payments)

$S = 7500.00(1.01125^{24})$

$= 7500.00(1.3079912)$

$= \$9809.93$

The accumulated value of the 24 payments made

$S_{24} = 172.57 \times s_{\overline{24}|1.125\%}$ ⟵———— using Formula 15.1A

$= 172.57(27.376998)$

$= \$4724.45$

The outstanding balance is $9809.93 - 4724.45 = \$5085.48$.

Note The difference in the two methods—$5085.48 versus $5085.77—is due to rounding in the payment.

Because the Prospective Method is more direct it is preferred when finding the outstanding balance of loans repaid by instalments which are all equal.

2. *Finding the outstanding balance when all payments, except the final payment are equal*

When the last payment is different from the other payments, the Retrospective Method for finding the outstanding balance is preferable.

Example 18.1g For Example 18.1d, compute the outstanding balance after four payments.

Solution

The accumulated value of the original debt after four payments

$$S = 15000.00(1.04^4)$$
$$= 15000.00(1.1698586)$$
$$= \$17547.88$$

The accumulated value of the four payments

$$S_4 = 2500.00 \, s_{\overline{4}|4\%}$$
$$= 2500.00(4.2464639)$$
$$= \$10616.16$$

The outstanding balance is $17547.88 - 10616.16 = \$6931.72$.

Example 18.1h A debt of $25 000.00 with interest at 14% compounded semi-annually is amortized by making payments of $2000.00 at the end of every six months. Determine the outstanding balance after five years.

Solution

$$A_n = P = 25000.00; \qquad i = \frac{14\%}{2} = 7\%$$

The accumulated value of the original principal after five years

$$S = 25000.00(1.07^{10})$$
$$= 25000.00(1.9671514)$$
$$= \$49178.78$$

The accumulated value of the first ten payments

$$S_{10} = 2000.00 \, s_{\overline{10}|7\%}$$
$$= 2000.00(13.816448)$$
$$= \$27632.90$$

The outstanding balance after five years is $49178.78 - 27532.90 = \$21545.88$.

D. Finding the interest paid and the principal repaid; constructing partial amortization schedules

Apart from computing the outstanding balance at any point in time, all the other information contained in an amortization schedule such as interest paid and principal repaid can be computed.

Example 18.1i For Example 18.1c compute

(i) the interest paid by the fifth payment;

(ii) the principal repaid by the fifth payment.

Solution

(i) The interest due for any given payment period is based on the outstanding balance at the beginning of the period. This balance is the same as the outstanding balance at the end of the previous payment period.

To find the interest paid by the fifth payment, we need to know the outstanding balance after the fourth payment.

$$A_4 = 734.99 \, a_{\overline{4}|\,3.75\%}$$

$$= 734.99(3.6513841)$$

$$= \$2683.73$$

Interest for Payment Period 5 is $2683.73(0.0375) = \$100.64$.

(ii) The Principal Repaid = Amount Paid − Interest Paid

$$= 734.99 - 100.64$$

$$= \$634.35$$

Example 18.1j Jackie borrowed $6000.00 from her trust company at 15% compounded monthly. The loan is amortized over five years.

(i) What is the interest included in the 20th payment?

(ii) What is the principal repaid by the 36th payment?

(iii) Construct a partial amortization schedule showing the details of the first three payments, the 20th payment, the 36th payment and the last three payments and determine the totals of amount paid, interest paid and principal repaid.

Solution

$$A_n = 6000.00; \qquad n = 5(12) = 60; \qquad i = \frac{15\%}{12} = 1.25\%$$

$$6000.00 = R \times a_{\overline{60}|\,1.25\%}$$

$$6000.00 = R(42.034591)$$

$$R = \$142.74$$

(i) The outstanding balance after the 19th payment

$$A_{19} = 142.74 \times a_{\overline{41}|\,1.25\%}$$

$$= 142.74(31.927835)$$

$$= \$4557.38$$

The interest paid by the 20th payment is $4557.38(0.0125) = \$56.97$.

(ii) The outstanding balance after the 35th payment

$$A_{35} = 142.74 \times a_{\overline{25}|1.25\%}$$

$$= 142.74(21.357268)$$

$$= \$3048.54$$

The interest included in Payment 36 is $3048.54 (0.0125) = \$38.11$.
The principal repaid by Payment 36 is $142.74 - 38.11 = \$104.63$.

(iii) The first three payments of the amortization schedule can be developed in
the usual manner. To show the details of the 20th payment we need to know
the outstanding balance after 19 payments (computed in part (i)). For the
36th payment we need to know the outstanding balance after 35 payments
(computed in Part (ii)). Since there are 60 payments, the last three payments
are Payment 58, 59 and 60. To show the details for these payments we must
determine the outstanding balance after Payment 57.

$$A_{57} = 142.74 \times a_{\overline{3}|1.25\%}$$

$$= 142.74(2.9265336)$$

$$= \$417.73$$

Partial amortization schedule

Payment number	Amount paid	Interest paid $i = 0.0125$	Principal repaid	Outstanding principal balance
0				6000.00
1	142.74	75.00	67.74	5932.26
2	142.74	74.15	68.59	5863.67
3	142.74	73.30	69.44	5794.23
.	.	.	.	.
19	.	.	.	4557.38
20	142.74	56.97	85.77	4471.61
.	.	.	.	.
35	.	.	.	3048.54
36	142.74	38.11	104.63	2943.91
.	.	.	.	.
57	.	.	.	417.73
58	142.74	5.22	137.52	280.21
59	142.74	3.50	139.24	140.97
60	142.74	1.77	140.97	0.00
Total	8564.40	2564.40	6000.00	

Note The total principal repaid must be $6000.00; the total amount paid is $142.74(60) = \$8564.40$; the total interest paid is $8564.40 - 6000.00 = \$2564.40$.

Example 18.1k The Erin Construction Company borrowed $75 000.00 at 14% compounded quarterly to purchase construction equipment. Payments of $3500.00 are to be made at the end of every three months.

(i) Determine the principal repaid in the 16th payment.

(ii) Construct a partial amortization schedule showing the details of the first three payments, the 16th payment, the last three payments and the totals.

Solution

(i) Since the quarterly payments are not computed blended payments, the last payment will likely be different from the preceding equal payments. Hence use the Retrospective Method for finding the outstanding balance.

$$P = 75000.00; \qquad R = 3500.00; \qquad i = \frac{14\%}{4} = 3.5\% = 0.035$$

The accumulated value of the original principal after the 15th payment

$$S = 75000.00(1.035^{15})$$

$$= 75000.00(1.6753488)$$

$$= \$125651.16$$

The accumulated value of the first 15 payments

$$S_{15} = 3500.00 \, s_{\overline{15}|3.5\%}$$

$$= 3500.00(19.295681)$$

$$= \$67534.88$$

The outstanding principal after the 15th payment

$$= 125651.16 - 67534.88$$

$$= \$58116.28$$

The interest included in the 16th payment is $58116.28(0.035) = \$2034.07$. The principal repaid by the 16th payment is $3500.00 - 2034.07 = \$1465.93$.

(i) To show details of the last three payments we need to know the number of payments required to amortize the loan principal.

$$\text{For } A_n = 75000.00; \qquad R = 3500.00; \qquad i = 3.5\%$$

$$75000.00 = 3500.00 \, a_{\overline{n}|3.5\%}$$

$$75000.00 = 3500.00\left(\frac{1 - 1.035^{-n}}{0.035}\right)$$

$$0.75 = 1 - 1.035^{-n}$$

$$1.035^{-n} = 0.25$$

$$-n \ln 1.035 = \ln 0.25$$

$$-n(0.344014) = -1.3862944$$

$$n = 40.297584$$

41 payments (40 payments of $3500.00 each plus a final payment) are required. This means details of Payments 39, 40 and 41 are to be shown. To do so we need to know the outstanding balance after 38 payments.

The accumulated value of the original loan principal after 38 payments

$$S = 75000.00(1.035^{38})$$
$$= 75000.00(3.6960113)$$
$$= \$277200.85$$

The accumulated value of the first 38 payments

$$S_{38} = 3500.00 \ s_{\overline{38}|\ 3.5\%}$$
$$= 3500.00(77.028895)$$
$$= \$269601.13$$

The outstanding balance after the 38th payment

$$= 277200.85 - 269601.13$$
$$= \$7599.72$$

Partial amortization schedule

Payment number	Amount paid	Interest paid $i = 0.035$	Principal repaid	Outstanding principal balance
0				75 000.00
1	3 500.00	2 625.00	875.00	74 125.00
2	3 500.00	2 594.38	905.62	73 219.38
3	3 500.00	2 562.68	937.32	72 282.06
.	.	.	.	.
.	.	.	.	.
15	.	.	.	58 116.28
16	3 500.00	2 034.07	1 465.93	56 650.35
.	.	.	.	.
.	.	.	.	.
.	.	.	.	.
38	.	.	.	7 599.72
39	3 500.00	265.99	3 234.01	4 365.71
40	3 500.00	152.80	3 347.20	1 018.51
41	1 054.16	35.65	1 018.51	0.00
TOTAL	141 041.16	66 041.16	75 000.00	

E. Computer application 4—Amortization schedule

A computer solution for the amortization of loans illustrated in Section 18.1 is provided by Program 4 (see Appendix p. 845).

Exercise 18.1

A. For each of the following debts amortized by equal payments made at the end of each payment interval, compute (a) the size of the periodic payments; (b) the outstanding principal at the point in time indicated; (c) the interest paid and the principal repaid by the payment following the point in time indicated for finding the outstanding principal.

No.	Debt principal	Repayment period	Payment interval	Interest rate	Conversion period	Outstanding principal required after
1.	$12 000.00	8 years	3 months	24%	quarterly	20th payment
2.	$ 8 000.00	5 years	1 month	15%	monthly	30th payment
3.	$15 000.00	10 years	6 months	18%	semi-annually	15th payment
4.	$ 9 600.00	7 years	3 months	16%	quarterly	12th payment
5.	$ 5 500.00	4 years	1 month	21%	monthly	14th payment
6.	$24 000.00	12 years	6 months	17%	semi-annually	8th payment

B. For each of the following debts repaid by periodic payments as indicated compute (a) the number of payments required to amortize the debts; (b) the outstanding principal at the point in time indicated.

No.	Debt principal	Debt payment	Payment interval	Interest rate	Conversion period	Outstanding principal required after
1.	$12 000.00	$ 750.00	3 months	18%	quarterly	16th payment
2.	$ 7 800.00	$ 175.00	1 month	12%	monthly	24th payment
3.	$21 000.00	$2000.00	6 months	15%	semi-annually	10th payment
4.	$15 000.00	$ 800.00	3 months	20%	quarterly	12th payment

C. Answer each of the following questions.

1. Mr. and Mrs. Good purchased a ski chalet for $36 000.00. They paid $4 000.00 down and agreed to make equal payments at the end of every three months for fifteen years. Interest is 14% compounded quarterly.

   (a) What size payment are the Goods making every three months?

   (b) How much will they owe after ten years?

   (c) How much will they have paid in total after fifteen years?

   (d) How much interest will they pay in total?

2. A contractor's price for a new building was $96 000.00. Slade Inc., the purchasers of the building, paid $12 000.00 down and financed the balance

making equal payments at the end of every six months for twelve years. Interest is 16% compounded semi-annually.

(a) What is the size of the semi-annual payment?

(b) How much will Slade Inc. owe after eight years?

(c) What is the total cost of the building for Slade Inc.?

(d) How much is the total interest included in the payments?

3. A loan of $10 000.00 with interest at 15% compounded annually is to be amortized by equal payments at the end of each year for seven years. Find the size of the annual payments and construct an amortization schedule showing the total paid and the cost of financing.

4. A loan of $8000.00 is repaid by equal payments made at the end of every three months for two years. If interest is 14% compounded quarterly find the size of the quarterly payments and construct an amortization schedule showing the total paid and the total cost of the loan.

5. Hansco borrowed $9200.00 paying interest at 13% compounded annually. If the loan is repaid by payments of $2000.00 made at the end of each year, construct an amortization schedule showing the total paid and the total interest paid.

6. Pinto Bros. are repaying a loan of $14 500.00 by making payments of $2600.00 at the end of every six months. If interest is 17% compounded semi-annually, construct an amortization schedule showing the total paid and the total cost of the loan.

7. For Question 3, find the interest included in the fourth payment. Verify your answer by checking the amortization schedule.

8. For Question 4, find the principal repaid by the fifth payment. Verify your answer by checking the amortization schedule.

9. For Question 5, find the principal repaid by the fourth payment. Verify your answer by checking the amortization schedule.

10. For Question 6, find the interest included in the fifth payment. Verify your answer by checking the amortization schedule.

11. Amex Corporation borrowed $85 000.00 at 18% compounded quarterly for eight years in order to acquire a warehouse. Equal payments are made at the end of every three months.

(a) Determine the size of the quarterly payments.

(b) Compute the interest included in the 16th payment.

(c) Determine the principal repaid by the 20th payment.

(d) Construct a partial amortization schedule showing details of the first three payments, the last three payments and totals.

12. Mr. Brabham borrowed $7500.00 at 15% compounded monthly. He agreed to repay the loan in equal monthly payments over five years.

(a) What is the size of the monthly payment?

(b) How much of the 25th payment is interest?

(c) What is the principal repaid by the 40th payment?

(d) Prepare a partial amortization schedule showing details of the first three payments, the last three payments and totals.

13. Thornhill Equipment Co. borrowed $24 000.00 at 17% compounded semi-annually. The loan is to be repaid by payments of $2500.00 at the end of every six months.

(a) How many payments are required to repay the loan?

(b) How much of the 6th payment is interest?

(c) How much of the principal will be repaid by the 10th payment?

(d) Construct a partial amortization schedule showing details of the first three payments, the last three payments and totals.

14. Locust Inc. owe $16 000.00 to be repaid by monthly payments of $475.00. Interest is 18% compounded monthly.

(a) How many payments will Locust Inc. have to make?

(b) How much interest is included in the 18th payment?

(c) How much of the principal will be repaid by the 30th payment?

(d) Construct a partial amortization schedule showing details of the first three payments, the last three payments and totals.

18.2 *Amortization involving general annuities*

A. *Finding the periodic payment and constructing amortization schedules*

If the length of the payment interval is different from the length of the interest conversion period the equal debt payments form a general annuity. The amortization of such debts involves the same principles and methods discussed in Section 18.1, except that general annuity formulae are applicable. Provided that the payments are made at the end of the payment intervals, Formula 17.2A may be used.

$$A_{nc} = R\left(\frac{1 - (1 + f)^{-n}}{f}\right) = R \times a_{\overline{n}|f}$$

$$\text{Where } f = (1 + i)^c - 1$$

Example 18.2a A debt of \$30 000.00 with interest at 12% compounded quarterly is to be repaid by equal payments at the end of each year for 7 years.

(i) Compute the size of the yearly payments.

(ii) Construct an amortization schedule.

Solution

(i) $A_{nc} = 30000.00;$ $n = 7;$ $c = 4;$ $i = \dfrac{12\%}{4} = 3\%$

$f = 1.03^4 - 1 = 1.1255088 - 1 = 0.1255088 = 12.55088\%$

$30000.00 = R\, a_{\overline{7}|\,12.55088\%}$ ⟵ using Formula 17.2A

$30000.00 = R(4.4851295)$

$R = \$6688.77$

(ii) **Amortization schedule**

Payment number	Amount paid	Interest paid $i = 0.1255088$	Principal repaid	Outstanding principal balance
0				30 000.00
1	6688.77	3765.26	2923.51	27076.49
2	6688.77	3398.34	3290.43	23786.06
3	6688.77	2985.36	3703.41	20082.65
4	6688.77	2520.55	4168.22	15914.43
5	6688.77	1997.40	4691.37	11223.06
6	6688.77	1408.59	5280.18	5942.88
7	6688.76	745.88	5942.88	0.00
TOTAL	46 821.38	16 821.38	30 000.00	

B.   Finding the outstanding principal

1. *Finding the outstanding principal when all payments are equal*
When all payments are equal the Prospective Method used in Section 18.1 is the most direct method.

Example 18.2b   For Example 18.2a compute the outstanding balance after three payments.

Solution

The outstanding balance after three payments is the present value of the remaining four payments.

$$R = 6688.77; \qquad n = 4; \qquad c = 4; \qquad i = 3\%; \qquad f = 12.55088\%$$

$$A_{nc} = 6688.77 \times a_{\overline{4}|\,12.55088\%}$$

$$= 6688.77(3.0024432)$$

$$= \$20082.65$$

The outstanding balance after three payments is $20082.65.

Example 18.2c A $25 000.00 mortgage amortized by monthly payments over twenty years is renewable after five years.

(i) If interest is 14.5% compounded semi-annually, what is the outstanding balance at the end of the five-year term?

(ii) If the mortgage is renewed for a further three-year term at 13% compounded semi-annually, what is the size of the new monthly payment?

(iii) What is the payout figure at the end of the three-year term?

Solution

(i) $\qquad A_{nc} = 25000.00; \qquad n = 20(12) = 240; \qquad c = \dfrac{2}{12} = \dfrac{1}{6};$

$$i = \frac{14.5\%}{2} = 7.25\% = 0.0725;$$

$$f = 1.0725^{\frac{1}{6}} - 1 = 1.0117337 - 1 = 0.0117337 = 1.17337\%$$

$$25000.00 = R\, a_{\overline{240}|\,1.17337\%}$$

$$25000.00 = R(80.040513)$$

$$R = 312.34$$

The number of outstanding payments after 5 years is 15(12) = 180.

$$A_{nc} = 312.34\, a_{\overline{180}|\,1.17337\%}$$

$$= 312.34(74.785918)$$

$$= \$23358.63$$

The outstanding balance after five years is $23 358.63.

(ii) After the five-year term is up the outstanding balance of $23 358.63 is to be amortized over the remaining 15 years.

$$A_{nc} = 23358.63; \qquad n = 15(12) = 180; \qquad c = \frac{1}{6};$$

$$i = \frac{13\%}{2} = 6.5\% = 0.065;$$

$$f = 1.065^{\frac{1}{6}} - 1 = 1.0105511 - 1 = 0.0105511 = 1.05511\%$$

$$23358.63 = R\, a_{\overline{180}|\,1.05511\%}$$

$$23358.63 = R(80.447976)$$

$$R = \$290.36$$

The monthly payment for the three-year term will be $290.36.

(iii) At the end of the three-year term the number of outstanding payments is 144.

$$A_{nc} = 290.36\, a_{\overline{144}|\,1.05511\%}$$

$$= 290.36(73.868965)$$

$$= \$21448.59$$

The outstanding balance at the end of the three-year term will be $21 448.59.

2. *Finding the outstanding balance when all payments, except the final payment, are equal*

When the final payment is different from the preceding payments, the Retrospective Method for finding the outstanding balance should be used. Since this method requires finding the amount of an ordinary annuity, the applicable formula is 17.1A.

$$S_{nc} = R\left(\frac{(1+f)^n - 1}{f}\right) = R\, s_{\overline{n}|f}$$
$$\text{where } f = (1 + i)^c - 1$$

Example 18.2d A loan of $12 000.00 with interest at 12% compounded monthly and amortized by payments of $700.00 at the end of every three month is repaid in full after three years. What is the payout figure not including the last regular payment?

Solution

Accumulate the value of the original principal after three years.

$$P = 12000.00; \qquad n = 3(12) = 36; \qquad i = \frac{12\%}{12} = 1\% = 0.01$$

$$S = 12000.00(1.01^{36})$$
$$= 12000.00(1.4307688)$$
$$= \$17169.23$$

Accumulate the value of the twelve payments made.

$$R = 700.00; \qquad n = 3(4) = 12; \qquad c = \frac{12}{4} = 3; \qquad i = 1\%$$

$$f = 1.01^3 - 1 = 1.030301 - 1 = 0.030301 = 3.0301\%$$

$$S_{nc} = 700.00 \, s_{\overline{12}|3.0301\%}$$

$$= 700.00(14.216322)$$

$$= \$9951.43$$

The outstanding balance after 3 years is $17169.23 - 9951.43 = \$7217.80$. The payout figure after three years is $7217.80.

C. Finding the interest paid and the principal repaid; constructing partial amortization schedules

***Example* 18.2e**   Mr. and Mrs. Evans took out a $40 000.00, 25-year mortgage renewable after five years. The mortgage bears interest at 12.5% compounded semi-annually and is amortized by equal monthly payments.

(i) What is the interest included in the 13th payment?

(ii) How much of the principal is repaid by the 13th payment?

(iii) What is the total interest cost during the first year?

(iv) What is the total interest cost during the fifth year?

(v) What will be the total interest paid by the Evans' during the initial five-year term?

Solution

(i) First, find the size of the monthly payment.

$$A_{nc} = 40000; \qquad n = 300; \qquad c = \frac{1}{6}; \qquad i = 6.25\%$$

$$f = 1.0625^{\frac{1}{6}} - 1 = 1.0101553 - 1 = 0.0101553 = 1.01553\%$$

$$40000.00 = R\, a_{\overline{300}|1.01553\%}$$

$$40000.00 = R(93.718894)$$

$$R = \$426.81$$

Now find the outstanding balance after one year.

$$R = 426.81; \qquad f = 1.01553\%$$

The number of outstanding payments after one year $n = 288$.

$$A_{nc} = R\,a\,\overline{_{288}|\,1.01553\%}$$
$$= 426.81(93.106352)$$
$$= \$39738.72$$

The interest in the 13th payment is $39738.72(0.0101553) = \$403.56$

(ii) The principal repaid in the 13th payment is $426.81 - 403.56 = \$23.25$.

(iii) The total amount paid during the first year is $426.81(12) = \$5121.72$
The total principal repaid is $40000.00 - 39738.72$ 261.28
$$\underline{\hspace{3cm}}$$
The total cost of interest for the first year $= \underline{\underline{\$4860.44}}$

(iv) After four years $n = 300 - 48 = 252$.

$$A_{nc} = 426.81\,a\,\overline{_{252}|\,1.01553\%}$$
$$= 426.81(90.752936)$$
$$= \$38734.26$$

After five years $n = 300 - 60 = 240$.

$$A_{nc} = 426.81\,a\,\overline{_{240}|\,1.01553\%}$$
$$= 426.81(89.7578064)$$
$$= \$38309.64$$

The total amount paid during the 5th year is $426.81(12)$ $= \quad \$5121.72$
The total principal repaid in Year 5 is $38734.26 - 38309.64 = \quad 424.62$
$$\underline{\hspace{3cm}}$$
The total cost of interest in Year 5 $= \underline{\underline{\$4697.10}}$

(v) The total amount paid during the first 5 years is $426.81(60) = \$25608.60$
The total principal repaid is $40000.00 - 38309.64$ $= \quad 1690.36$
$$\underline{\hspace{3cm}}$$
The total cost of interest for the first five years $= \underline{\underline{\$23918.24}}$

Example 18.2f Confederated Venture Company financed a project by borrowing $120 000.00 at 17% compounded annually and is repaying the loan at the rate of $7000.00 due at the end of every three months.

(i) Compute the interest paid and the principal repaid by the tenth payment.

(ii) Construct a partial amortization schedule showing the first three payments, the tenth payment, the last three payments and the totals.

Solution

(i) Accumulate the value of the original loan after nine payments.

$$P = 120000.00; \qquad n = 9; \qquad c = \frac{1}{4} = 0.25; \qquad i = 17\% = 0.17;$$

$$f = 1.17^{0.25} - 1 = 1.0400314 - 1 = 0.0400314 = 4.00314\%$$

$$S = 120000.00(1.0400314^9)$$
$$= 120000.00(1.4236986)$$
$$= \$170843.85$$

Accumulate the value of the first nine payments.

$$R = 7000.00; \qquad n = 9$$

$$S_{nc} = 7000.00 \; s \; \overline{_{9|}}{}_{\,4.00314\%}$$

$$= 7000.00(10.584157)$$
$$= \$74089.10$$

The outstanding balance after nine payments is $170843.85 - 74089.10 = \$96754.75$.

The interest included in the tenth payment is $96754.75(0.0400314) = \$3873.23$.

The principal repaid by the tenth payment is $7000.00 - 3873.23 = \$3126.77$.

(ii) To show the details of the last three payments we need to know the number of payments required to amortize the loan.

$$A_{nc} = 120000.00; \qquad R = 7000.00; \qquad f = 4.00314\%$$

$$120000.00 = 7000.00 \; a \; \overline{_{n|}}{}_{\,4.00314\%}$$

$$120000.00 = 7000.00\left(\frac{1 - 1.0400314^{-n}}{0.0400314}\right)$$

$$0.6862526 = 1 - 1.0400314^{-n}$$
$$1.0400314^{-n} = 0.3137474$$
$$-n \ln 1.0400314 = \ln 0.3137474$$
$$-n(0.0392509) = -1.159167$$
$$n = 29.532236$$

30 payments (29 payments of $7000.00 plus a final payment) are required. This means details of Payments 28, 29 and 30 are to be shown.

To do so we need to know the outstanding balance after 27 payments. Accumulate the value of the original principal after 27 payments.

$$S = 120000.00(1.0400314^{27})$$
$$= 120000.00(2.8857200)$$
$$= \$346286.40$$

Accumulate the value of the first 27 payments.

$$S_{nc} = 7000.00 \; s_{\overline{27}|\, 4.00314\%}$$

$$= 7000.00(47.106022)$$

$$= \$329742.15$$

The outstanding balance after 27 payments is $346286.40 - 329742.15 = \$16544.25$.

Partial amortization schedule

Payment number	Amount paid	Interest paid $f = 0.0400314$	Principal repaid	Outstanding principal balance
0				120 000.00
1	7000.00	4803.77	2196.23	117 803.77
2	7000.00	4715.85	2284.15	115 519.62
3	7000.00	4624.41	2375.59	113 144.03
.	.	.	.	.
.	.	.	.	.
9	.	.	.	96 754.75
10	7000.00	3873.23	3126.77	93 627.98
.	.	.	.	.
.	.	.	.	.
27	.	.	.	16 544.25
28	7000.00	662.29	6337.71	10 206.54
29	7000.00	408.58	6591.42	3 615.12
30	3759.84	144.72	3615.12	0.00
TOTAL	206 759.84	86 759.84	120 000.00	

D. Computer application 5—Amortization schedule

A computer solution for the amortization of loans involving a general annuity illustrated in Section 18.2 is provided by Program 4 (see Appendix p. 845).

Exercise 18.2

A. For each of the following debts amortized by equal payments made at the end of each payment interval, compute (a) the size of the periodic payments; (b) the outstanding principal at the point in time indicated; (c) the interest paid and the principal repaid by the payment following the point in time indicated for finding the outstanding principal.

No.	Debt principal	Repayment period	Payment interval	Interest rate	Conversion period	Outstanding principal required after
1.	$36 000.00	20 years	6 months	24%	quarterly	25th payment
2.	$15 000.00	10 years	3 months	18%	monthly	15th payment
3.	$ 8 500.00	5 years	1 month	15%	semi-annually	30th payment
4.	$ 9 600.00	7 years	3 months	19%	semi-annually	10th payment
5.	$45 000.00	15 years	6 months	21%	monthly	12th payment
6.	$60 000.00	25 years	1 month	14%	semi-annually	120th payment

B. For each of the following debts repaid by periodic payments as indicated, compute (a) the number of payments required to amortize the debts; (b) the outstanding principal at the point in time indicated.

No.	Debt principal	Debt payment	Payment interval	Interest rate	Conversion period	Outstanding principal required after
1.	$ 6 000.00	$ 400.00	3 months	15%	monthly	10th payment
2.	$ 8 400.00	$1200.00	6 months	16%	quarterly	5th payment
3.	$23 500.00	$1800.00	3 months	21%	annually	15th payment
4.	$18 200.00	$ 430.00	1 month	18%	semi-annually	48th payment

C. Answer each of the following questions.

1. A $36 000.00 mortgage amortized by monthly payments over 25 years is renewable after three years.

   (a) If interest is 13% compounded semi-annually, what is the size of the monthly payments?

   (b) What is the mortgage balance at the end of the three-year term?

   (c) How much interest will have been paid during the first three years?

   (d) If the mortgage is renewed for a further three-year term at 15% compounded semi-annually, what will be the size of the monthly payments for the renewal period?

2. Fink and Associates purchased a property valued $80 000.00 for $15 000.00 down and a mortgage amortized over fifteen years by equal payments due at the end of every three months. Interest on the mortgage is 13.5% compounded annually and the mortgage is renewable after five years.

   (a) What is the size of the quarterly payments?

   (b) What is the outstanding principal at the end of the five-year term?

   (c) What is the cost of the mortgage for the first five years?

   (d) If the mortgage is renewed for a further five years at 18% compounded semi-annually, what will be the size of the quarterly payments?

3. A loan of $10 000.00 with interest at 14% compounded quarterly is repaid by payments of $950.00 made at the end of every six months.

(a) How many payments will be required to amortize the loan?

(b) If the loan is repaid in full after six years, what is the payout figure?

(c) If paid out, what is the total cost of the loan?

4. The owner of the Blue Goose Motel borrowed $12 500.00 at 16% compounded semi-annually and agreed to repay the loan by making payments of $700.00 at the end of every three months.

(a) How many payments will be needed to repay the loan?

(b) How much will be owed at the end of five years?

(c) How much of the payments made at the end of five years will be interest?

5. A loan of $16 000.00 with interest at 19% compounded quarterly is repaid by equal payments made at the end of each year in seven years. Find the size of the annual payments and construct an amortization schedule showing the total paid and the total interest.

6. A debt of $12 500.00 with interest at 17% compounded semi-annually is repaid by payments of $1900.00 made at the end of every three months. Construct an amortization schedule showing the total paid and the total cost of the debt.

7. For Question 5, determine the interest included in the fifth payment. Verify your answer by checking the amortization schedule.

8. For Question 6, find the principal repaid by the sixth payment. Verify your answer by checking the amortization schedule.

9. A $40 000.00 mortgage amortized by monthly payments over 25 years is renewable after five years.

(a) If interest is 16.5% compounded semi-annually, what is the size of the monthly payments?

(b) Find the total interest paid during the first year.

(c) Compute the interest included in the 48th payment.

(d) If the mortgage is renewed after five years at 20.5% compounded semi-annually, what is the size of the monthly payment for the renewal period.

(e) Construct a partial amortization schedule showing details of the first three payments for each of the two five-year terms.

10. A debt of $32 000.00 is repaid by payment of $2950.00 made at the end of every six months. Interest is 16% compounded quarterly.

(a) What is the number of payments needed to retire the debt?

(b) What is the cost of the debt for the first five years?

(c) What is the interest paid by the tenth payment?

(d) Construct a partial amortization schedule showing details of the first three payments, the last three payments, and totals.

18.3 Finding the size of the final payment

A. Three methods for computing the final payment

When all payments except the final payment are equal, three methods are available to compute the size of the final payment.

Method 1 Compute the value of n and determine the present value of the outstanding fractional payment. If the final payment is made at the end of the payment interval add interest for one payment interval to the present value.

Method 2 Use the Retrospective Method to compute the outstanding principal after the last of the equal payments. If the final payment is made at the end of the payment interval add to the outstanding principal the interest for one payment interval.

Method 3 Assume all payments to be equal, compute the overpayment and subtract the overpayment from the size of the equal payments. This method must not be used when the payments are made at the beginning of the payment interval.

Example 18.3a For Example 18.1d compute the size of the final payment using each of the three methods. Compare the results with the size of the payment shown in the amortization schedule.

Solution

METHOD 1 $A_n = 15000.00;$ $R = 2500.00;$ $i = 4\%$

$$15000.00 = 2500.00\, a_{\overline{n}|4\%}$$

$$6.00 = \frac{1 - 1.04^{-n}}{0.04}$$

$$0.24 = 1 - 1.04^{-n}$$

$$1.04^{-n} = 0.76$$

$$-n \ln 1.04 = \ln 0.76$$

$$-n(0.0392207) = -0.2744368$$

$$n = 6.9972427$$

$R = 2500.00;$ $i = 4\%;$ $n = 0.9972427$

$$A_n = 2500.00\, a_{\overline{0.9972427}|4\%}$$

$$= 2500.00(0.9589387)$$

$$= \$2397.35$$

Interest for one interval is $2397.35(0.04) = \$95.89$

Final payment is $2397.35 + 95.89 = \$2493.24$

METHOD 2　Compute the value of n as done in Method 1.
Since $n = 6.9972427$, the number of equal payments is 6.
The accumulated value of the original principal after six payments

$S = 15000.00(1.04^6)$

　$= 15000.00(1.2653190)$

　$= \$18979.79$

The accumulated value of the first six payments

$S_6 = 2500.00\ s\ \overline{_{6}|}\ _{4\%}$

　$= 2500.00(6.6329754)$

　$= \$16582.44$

The outstanding balance after six payments is $18979.79 - 16582.44 = \$2397.35$.

The final payment $=$ outstanding balance $+$ interest for one period

　　　　　$=$ the accumulated value of \$2397.35 for one year

　　　　　$= 2397.35(1.04)$

　　　　　$= \$2493.24$

METHOD 3　Compute the value of n as done in Method 1.
Since $n = 6.9972427$, the number of assumed full payments is 7.
The accumulated value of the original principal after seven payments

$S = 1500(1.04^7)$

　$= 1500(1.3159318)$

　$= \$19738.98$

The accumulated value of seven payments

$S_7 = 2500.00\ s\ \overline{_{7}|}\ _{4\%}$

　$= 2500.00(7.8982944)$

　$= \$19745.74$

Since the accumulated value of seven payments is greater than the accumulated value of the original principal there is an overpayment.

$$19745.74 - 19738.98 = \$6.76$$

The size of the final payment is $2500.00 - 6.76 = \$2493.24$.

Note
1. For all three methods n must be determined. This may be done by the methods shown in Chapter 15, 16 and 17.
2. When using a calculator Method 1 is preferable as the most direct method. It is the method used in Sub-Section B.

B. Applications

Example 18.3b On his retirement Art received a gratuity of $8000.00 from his employer. Taking advantage of the existing tax legislation, he invested his money in an Income Averaging Annuity which provides for semi-annual payments of $1200.00 at the end of every six months. If interest is 11.5% compounded semi-annually, determine the size of the final payment (See Chapter 15, Example 15.5d).

Solution

$$A_n = 8000.00; \qquad R = 1200.00; \qquad i = \frac{11.5\%}{2} = 5.75\%$$

$$8000.00 = 1200.00 \; a \; {}_{\overline{n}|\,5.75\%}$$

$$8000.00 = 1200.00 \left(\frac{1 - 1.0575^{-n}}{0.0575} \right)$$

$$1.0575^n = 1.6216216$$

$$n(0.0559076) = 0.4834266$$

$$n = 8.6468812$$

$$R = 1200.00; \qquad i = 5.75\%; \qquad n = 0.6468812$$

$$A_n = 1200.00 \; a \; {}_{\overline{0.6468812}|\,5.75\%}$$

$$= 1200.00(0.6177293)$$

$$= \$741.28$$

Final payment including the interest for one payment interval is $741.28(1.0575) = \$783.90$

Example 18.3c A lease contract valued at $7800.00 is to be fulfilled by rental payments of $180.00 due at the beginning of each month. If money is worth 21% compounded monthly, determine the size of the final lease payment. (See Chapter 16, Example 16.2h).

Solution

$$A_n(\text{due}) = 7800.00; \qquad R = 180.00; \qquad i = \frac{21\%}{12} = 1.75\%$$

$$n = 78.832271 \text{ (see solution to Example 16.2h)}$$

Present value of the final payment

$$R = 180.00; \qquad i = 1.75\%; \qquad n = 0.832271$$

$$A_n(\text{due}) = 180.00(1.0175) \; a \; {}_{\overline{0.832271}|\,1.75\%}$$

$$= 180.00(1.0175)(0.8191445)$$

$$= 180.00(0.8334795)$$

$$= \$150.03$$

Since the payment is made at the beginning of the last payment interval no interest is added. The final payment is $150.03.

Example 18.3d Payments of $500.00 deferred for nine years are received at the end of each month from a fund of $10 000.00 deposited at 10.5% compounded monthly. Determine the size of the final payment (See Chapter 16, Example 16.4c).

Solution

$$A_n(\text{defer.}) = 10000.00; \qquad R = 500.00; \qquad d = 9(12) = 108;$$

$$i = \frac{10.5\%}{12} = 0.875\%$$

$$n = 68.288334 \text{ (see solution to Example 16.4c)}$$

Present value of the final payment:

$$R = 500.00; \qquad i = 0.875\%; \qquad n = 0.288334$$

$$A_n = 500.00 \, a \, \overline{_{0.288334}} \,_{|\,0.875\%}$$

$$= 500.00(0.2867195)$$

$$= \$143.36$$

The size of the final payment is $143.36(1.00875) = \$144.61$.

Example 18.3e A business valued at $96 000.00 is purchased for a down payment of 25% and payments of $4000.00 at the end of every three months. If interest is 18% compounded monthly, what is the size of the final payment? (See Chapter 17, Example 17.3d).

Solution

$$A_{nc} = 96000.00(0.75) = 72000.00; \qquad R = 4000.00; \qquad c = \frac{12}{4} = 3;$$

$$i = \frac{18\%}{12} = 1.5\% = 0.015; \qquad f = 1.015^3 - 1 = 4.56784\%;$$

$$n = 38.668403 \text{ (see solution to Example 17.3d)}$$

Present value of the final payment:

$$R = 4000.00; \qquad f = 4.56784\%; \qquad n = 0.668403$$

$$A_n = 4000.00 \, a \, \overline{_{0.668403}} \,_{|\,4.56784\%}$$

$$= 4000.00(0.6439267)$$

$$= \$2575.71$$

The final payment is $2575.71(1.0456784) = \$2693.36$

Example 18.3f Ted Davis, having reached his goal of a \$140 000.00 balance in his RRSP, converts it into an RRIF and withdraws from it \$1650.00 at the beginning of each month. If interest is 11% compounded quarterly, what is the size of final withdrawal? (See Chapter 17, Example 17.4f.)

Solution

$$A_{nc}(due) = 140000.00; \qquad R = 1650.00; \qquad c = \frac{4}{12} = \frac{1}{3};$$

$$i = \frac{11\%}{4} = 2.75\% = 0.0275;$$

$$f = 1.0275^{\frac{1}{3}} - 1 = 1.0090839 - 1 = 0.90839\%$$

$$n = 159.58897 \text{ (see solution to Example 17.4f)}$$

Present value of final payment:

$$R = 1650.00; \qquad f = 0.90839\%; \qquad n = 0.58897$$

$$A_n = 1650.00(1.0090839) \, a \, \overline{_{0.58897}|_{0.90839\%}}$$

$$= 1650.00(1.0090839)(0.5847524)$$

$$= 1650.00(0.5900642)$$

$$= \$973.61$$

Since the payment is at the beginning of the last payment interval its size is \$973.61.

Exercise 18.3

A. For each of the following compute the size of the final payment.

No.	Principal	Periodic payment	Payment interval	Payment made at	Interest rate	Conversion period
1.	\$17 500.00	\$1100.00	3 months	end	14%	quarterly
2.	\$35 000.00	\$ 925.00	1 month	end	24%	monthly
3.	\$ 7 800.00	\$ 775.00	6 months	beginning	15%	semi-annually
4.	\$ 9 300.00	\$ 580.00	3 months	beginning	17%	quarterly
5.	\$15 400.00	\$1600.00	6 months	end	16%	quarterly
6.	\$29 500.00	\$1650.00	3 months	end	18%	monthly
7.	\$17 300.00	\$ 425.00	1 month	beginning	20%	quarterly
8.	\$10 500.00	\$ 900.00	3 months	beginning	21%	semi-annually

B. Answer each of the following questions.

1. A loan of $7200.00 is repaid by payments of $360.00 at the end of every three months. Interest is 15% compounded quarterly.

   (a) How many payments are required to repay the debt?

   (b) What is the size of the final payment?

2. Tom O'Brien receives pension payments of $3200.00 at the end of every six months from a retirement fund of $50 000.00. The fund earns 12% compounded semi-annually.

   (a) How many payments will Tom receive?

   (b) What is the size of the final pension payment?

3. Payments of $1200.00 are made out of a fund of $25 000.00 at the end of every three months. If interest is 12% compounded monthly, what is the size of the final payment?

4. A debt of $30 000.00 is repaid in monthly instalments of $550.00. If interest is 16% compounded quarterly, what is the size of the final payment?

5. A lease valued at $20 000.00 requires payments of $1000.00 every three months due in advance. If money is worth 17% compounded quarterly, what is the size of the final lease payment?

6. Smith has saved $125 000.00. If he withdraws $1250.00 at the beginning of every month and interest is 10.5% compounded monthly, what is the size of the last withdrawal?

7. Equipment priced $42 000.00 was purchased on a contract requiring payments of $5000.00 at the beginning of every six months. If interest is 17% compounded quarterly, what is the size of the final payment?

8. Bruce has agreed to purchase his partner's share in the business by making payments of $1100.00 every three months. The agreed transfer value is $16 500.00 and interest is 10% compounded annually. If the first payment is due at the date of the agreement, what is the size of the final payment?

9. Jones has paid $16 000.00 for a retirement annuity from which he will receive $1375.00 at the end of every three months. The payments are deferred for ten years and interest is 10% compounded quarterly.

   (a) How many payments will Jones receive?

   (b) What is the size of the final payment?

   (c) How much will Jones receive in total?

   (d) How much of what he receives will be interest?

10. A contract valued at $27 500.00 requires payments of $6000.00 every six months. The first payment is due in four years and interest is 17% compounded semi-annually.

(a) How many payments are required?

(b) What is the size of the last payment?

(c) How much will be paid in total?

(d) How much of what is paid is interest?

18.4 Sinking funds

A. Finding the size of the periodic payment

Sinking funds are interest bearing funds into which payments are made at periodic time intervals to provide a desired sum of money at a specified future point in time. Such funds usually involve large sums of money used by both the private sector and the public sector to repay loans, redeem bonds, finance future capital acquisitions, provide for the replacement of depreciable plant and equipment and recover investments in depletable natural resources.

The basic problem in dealing with sinking funds is that of determining the *size of the periodic payments* which will accumulate to a known future amount. These payments form an annuity in which the accumulated value is known.

Depending on whether the periodic payments are made at the end or the beginning of each payment period, the annuity formed is an ordinary annuity or an annuity due. Depending on whether or not the payment interval is equal in length to the interest conversion period, the annuity formed is a simple annuity or a complex annuity. However, since sinking funds are normally set up so that the payment interval and the interest conversion period are equal in length, only the simple annuity cases are considered in this text.

(a) For sinking funds with payments at the end of each payment interval

$$S_n = R\left(\frac{(1 + i)^n - 1}{i}\right) \text{ or } S_n = R \times s_{\overline{n}|i}$$

(b) For sinking funds with payments at the beginning of each payment interval

$$S_n(\text{due}) = R(1 + i)\left(\frac{(1 + i)^n - 1}{i}\right) \text{ or } S_n(\text{due}) = R(1 + i) \times s_{\overline{n}|i}$$

Example 18.4a A sinking fund of $20 000.00 is to be created by making equal deposits at the end of every six months for four years. Interest is 12% compounded semi-annually.

(i) What is the size of the semi-annual deposit into the fund?

(ii) What is the total amount deposited into the fund?

(iii) How much of the fund will be interest?

Solution

(i) $\qquad S_n = 20000.00; \qquad n = 4(2) = 8; \qquad i = \dfrac{12\%}{2} = 6\%$

$\qquad 20000.00 = R\, s_{\overline{8}|6\%}$

$\qquad 20000.00 = R(9.8974679)$

$\qquad\qquad R = \$2020.72$

(ii) The total deposited into the sinking fund is $8(2020.72) = \$16165.76$.

(iii) The amount of interest in the fund is $20000.00 - 16165.76 = \$3834.24$.

Example 18.4b Ace Machinery company wants to provide for replacement of equipment estimated to cost $60 000.00 seven years from now. To do so the company set up a sinking fund into which the company will pay equal sums of money at the beginning of each of the next seven years. Interest paid by the fund is 11.5% compounded annually.

(i) What is the size of annual payment into the fund?

(ii) What is the total paid into the fund by Ace Machinery?

(iii) How much of the fund will be interest?

Solution

(i) $\qquad\qquad S_n(\text{due}) = 60000.00; \qquad n = 7; \qquad i = 11.5\%$

$\qquad 60000.00 = R(1.115)(s_{\overline{7}|11.5\%})$

$\qquad 60000.00 = R(1.115)(9.9349216)$

$\qquad 60000.00 = R(11.077438)$

$\qquad\qquad R = \$5416.42$

(ii) The total paid into the fund by Ace Machinery will be $7(5416.42) = \$37914.94$.

(iii) The interest earned by the fund will be $60000.00 - 37914.84 = \$22085.06$.

B. Constructing sinking fund schedules

The details regarding a sinking fund may also be presented in the form of a schedule. Sinking fund schedules normally show the payment number (or payment date), the periodic payment into the fund, the interest earned by the fund, the increase in the fund and the accumulated balance.

Example 18.4c Construct a sinking fund schedule for Example 18.4a.

Solution

$$R = 2020.72; \qquad n = 8; \qquad i = 6\% = 0.06$$

Sinking Fund Schedule

Payment interval number	Periodic payment	Interest for payment interval $i = 0.06$	Increase in fund	Balance in fund at end of payment interval
0				0.00
1	2020.72	0.00	2020.72	2 020.72
2	2020.72	121.24	2141.96	4 162.68
3	2020.72	249.76	2270.48	6 433.16
4	2020.72	385.99	2406.71	8 839.87
5	2020.72	530.39	2551.11	11 390.98
6	2020.72	683.46	2704.18	14 095.16
7	2020.72	845.71	2866.43	16 961.59
8	2020.72	1017.70	3038.42	20 000.01
TOTAL	16 165.76	3834.25	20 000.01	

Explanations regarding the construction of the sinking fund schedule

1. The payment number 0 may be used to introduce the beginning balance.

2. The first deposit is made at the end of the first payment interval. Hence the interest earned by the fund during the first payment interval is $0, the increase in the fund is $2020.72 and the balance is $2020.72.

3. The second deposit is added at the end of the second payment interval. The interest for the interval is $0.06(2020.72) = \$121.24$, hence the increase in the fund is $2020.72 + 121.24 = \$2141.96$ and the new balance in the fund is $2020.72 + 2141.96 = \$4162.68$.

4. The third deposit is made at the end of the third payment interval. The interest for the interval is $0.06(4162.68) = \$249.76$, the increase in the fund is $2020.72 + 249.76 = \$2270.48$ and the new balance in the fund is $2270.48 + 4162.68 = \$6433.16$.

5. Calculations for the remaining payment intervals are made in a similar manner.

6. The final balance in the sinking fund will likely be slightly different than the expected value. This is a result of rounding. The balance may be left as shown ($20 000.01) or the exact balance of $20 000.00 may be obtained by adjusting the last payment to $2020.71.

7. The three totals shown are useful and should be obtained for each schedule. The total increase in the fund must be the same as the final balance. The total periodic payments is 8(2020.72) = 16165.76. The total interest is the difference: 20000.01 − 16165.76 = $3834.25.

Example 18.4d Construct a sinking fund schedule for Example 18.4b (Annuity due type—payments at the beginning of each payment interval).

Solution

R = 5416.42 (made at beginning); $n = 7$; $i = 11.5\% = 0.115$

Sinking fund schedule

Payment interval number	Periodic payment	Interest for payment interval $i = 0.115$	Increase in fund	Balance in fund at end of payment interval
0				0.00
1	5416.42	622.89	6 039.31	6 039.31
2	5416.42	1317.41	6 733.83	12 773.14
3	5416.42	2091.80	7 508.22	20 281.36
4	5416.42	2955.24	8 371.66	28 653.02
5	5416.42	3917.99	9 334.41	37 987.43
6	5416.42	4991.44	10 407.86	48 395.29
7	5416.42	6188.35	11 604.77	60 000.06
TOTAL	37 914.94	22 085.12	60 000.06	

Explanations regarding the constructing of the sinking fund schedule

1. The starting balance is $0.00.

2. The first deposit is made at the beginning of the first payment interval, the interest earned by the fund during the first payment interval is 0.115(5416.42) = $622.89, the increase in the fund is 5416.42 + 622.89 = $6039.31 and the balance is $6039.31.

3. The second deposit is made at the beginning of the second payment interval, the interest earned is 0.115(6039.31 + 5416.42) = $1317.41, the increase is 5416.42 + 1317.41 = $6733.83 and the balance is 6039.31 + 6733.83 = $12773.14.

4. The third deposit is made at the beginning of the third payment interval, the interest earned is 0.115(12773.14 + 5416.42) = $2091.80, the increase is 5416.42 + 2091.80 = $7508.22 and the balance is 12773.14 + 7508.22 = $20281.36.

5. Calculations for the remaining payment intervals are made in a similar manner (be careful to add the deposit to the previous balance when computing the interest earned).

6. The final balance of $60 000.06 is slightly different from the expected balance of $60 000.00 due to rounding. The exact balance may be obtained by adjusting the last payment to $5416.36.

7. The total increase in the fund must equal the final balance of $60 000.06. The total periodic payments are $7(5416.42) = \$37914.94$. The total interest is $60000.06 - 37914.94 = \$22085.12$.

C. Finding the accumulated balance and interest earned or increase in a sinking fund for a payment interval; constructing partial sinking fund schedules

Example 18.4e For Examples 18.4a and 18.4b compute

(i) the accumulated value in the fund at the end of the third payment interval;

(ii) the interest earned by the fund in the fifth payment interval;

(iii) the increase in the fund in the fifth interval.

Solution

(i) The balance in a sinking fund at any point in time is the accumulated value of the payments made into the fund.

For Example 18.4a (when payments are made at the end of each payment interval)

$$R = 2020.72; \qquad n = 3; \qquad i = 6\%$$

$$S_n = 2020.72 \times s_{\overline{3}|6\%}$$

$$= 2020.72(3.1836000)$$

$$= \$6433.16 \longrightarrow \text{See Sinking Fund Schedule, Example 18.4c}$$

For Example 18.4b (when payments are made at the beginning of each payment interval)

$$R = 5416.42; \qquad n = 3; \qquad i = 11.5\%$$

$$S_n(\text{due}) = 5416.42(1.115)(s_{\overline{3}|11.5\%})$$

$$= 5416.42(1.115)(3.3582250)$$

$$= \$20281.36 \longrightarrow \text{See Sinking Fund Schedule, Example 18.4d}$$

(ii) The interest earned during any given payment interval is based on the balance in the fund at the beginning of the interval which is the same as the balance at the end of the previous payment interval.

For Example 18.4a

The balance at the end of the 4th payment interval

$$S_4 = 2020.72 \times s_{\overline{4}|6\%}$$

$$= 2020.72(4.3746160)$$

$$= \$8839.87$$

The interest earned by the fund in the 5th payment interval is $0.06(8839.87) = \$530.39$.

For Example 18.4b

The balance in the fund at the end of the 4th payment interval

$$S_4 = 5416.42(1.115) s_{\overline{4}|11.5\%}$$

$$= 5416.42(1.115)(4.7444209)$$

$$= \$28653.02$$

The interest earned by the fund in the 5th payment interval is $0.115(28653.02 + 5416.42) = 0.115(34069.44) = \$3917.99$.

(iii) The increase in the sinking fund during any given payment interval is the interest earned by the fund during the payment interval plus the periodic payment.

For Example 18.4a

the increase in the fund during the 5th payment interval is $530.39 + 2020.72 = \$2551.11$.

For Example 18.4b

the increase in the fund during the 5th payment period is $3917.99 + 5416.42 = \$9334.41$.

Example 18.4f The Board of Directors of Peel Credit Union decided to establish a building fund of $130 000.00 by making equal deposits at the end of every three months into a sinking fund for seven years. Interest is 12% compounded quarterly

(i) Compute the increase in the fund during the 12th payment interval.

(ii) Construct a partial sinking fund schedule showing details of the first three deposits, the 12th deposit, the last three deposits and totals.

Solution

Size of the quarterly deposit

$$S_n = 130000.00; \qquad n = 7(4) = 28; \qquad i = \frac{12\%}{4} = 3\%$$

$$130000.00 = R\, s_{\overline{28}|\,3\%}$$

$$130000.00 = R(42.930922)$$

$$130000.00 = R(42.930922)$$

$$R = 3028.12$$

(i) Balance in the fund at the end of the 11th payment interval

$$S_{11} = 3028.12\, s_{\overline{11}|\,3\%}$$

$$= 3028.12(12.807796)$$

$$= \$38783.54$$

The interest earned by the fund during the 12th payment interval is $0.03 (38783.54) = \$1163.51$.

The increase in the fund during the 12th payment interval is $1163.51 + 3028.12 = \$4191.63$.

(ii) The last three payments are Payments 26, 27 and 28. To show details we must know the accumulated value after 25 payment intervals.

$$S_{25} = 3028.12\, s_{\overline{25}|\,3\%} = 3028.12(36.459264) = \$110403.03$$

Partial sinking fund schedule

Payment interval number	Periodic payment made at end	Interest for payment interval $i = 0.03$	Increase in fund	Balance in fund at the end of payment interval
0				0.00
1	3028.12	0.00	3028.12	3 028.12
2	3028.12	90.84	3118.96	6 147.08
3	3028.12	184.41	3212.53	9 359.61
.	.	.	.	.
.	.	.	.	.
11	.	.	.	38 783.54
12	3028.12	1163.51	4191.63	42 975.17
.	.	.	.	.
.	.	.	.	.
25	.	.	.	110 403.03
26	3028.12	3312.09	6340.21	116 743.24
27	3028.12	3502.30	6530.42	123 273.66
28	3028.12	3698.21	6726.33	129 999.99
TOTAL	84 787.36	45 212.63	129 999.99	

For Example 18.4g Laurin and Company want to build up a fund of $75 000.00 by making payments of $2000.00 at the beginning of every six months into a sinking fund earning 11% compounded semi-annually. Construct a partial sinking fund schedule showing details of the first three payments, the last three payments and totals.

Solution

To show details of the last three payments we need to know the number of payments.

$$S_n(due) = 75000.00; \qquad R = 2000.00; \qquad i = 11\% = 5.5\%$$

$$75000.00 = 2000.00(1.055)\, s_{\overline{n}|\,5.5\%}$$

$$75000.00 = 2000.00\,(1.055)\left(\frac{1.055^n - 1}{0.055}\right)$$

$$1.055^n = 2.9549763$$

$$n(0.0535408) = 1.0834906$$

$$n = 20.236741$$

21 payments are needed. The last three payments are Payments 19, 20 and 21. The balance in the fund at the end of the 18th payment interval

$$S_{18}(due) = 2000.00(1.055)\, s_{\overline{18}|\,5.5\%}$$

$$= 2000.00\,(1.055)(29.481205)$$

$$= \$62205.34$$

Partial sinking fund schedule

Payment interval number	Periodic payment made at beginning	Interest for payment interval $i = 0.055$	Increase in fund	Balance in fund at the end of payment interval
0				0.00
1	2000.00	110.00	2110.00	2 110.00
2	2000.00	226.05	2226.05	4 336.05
3	2000.00	348.48	2348.48	6 684.53
.	.	.	.	.
18	.	.	.	62 205.34
19	2000.00	3531.29	5531.29	67 736.63
20	2000.00	3835.51	5835.51	73 572.14
21	1427.86	0.00	1427.86	75 000.00
TOTAL	41 427.86	33 572.14	75 000.00	

Note In this particular case the desired balance in the sinking fund will be reached at the beginning of the 21st payment interval by depositing $1427.86.

D. Computer application 6—Sinking fund schedule

A computer solution for the construction of sinking fund schedules is provided by Program 5 (see Appendix p. 845).

E. Debt retirement by the sinking fund method

When a sinking fund is created to retire a debt, the debt principal is repaid in total at the due date from the proceeds of the sinking fund while interest on the principal is paid periodically. The payments into the sinking fund are usually made at the time of the interest payments. The sum of the two payments (debt interest payment plus payment into the sinking fund) is referred to as the *periodic cost of the debt*. The difference between the debt principal and the sinking fund balance at any point in time is referred to as the book value of the debt.

Example 18.4h The City Board of Education borrowed $750 000.00 for twenty years at 13% compounded annually to finance construction of Hillview Elementary School. The Board created a sinking fund to repay the debt at the end of twenty years. Equal payments are made into the sinking fund at the end of each year and interest earned by the fund is 10.5% compounded annually. Rounding all computations to the nearest dollar

(i) determine the annual cost of the debt;

(ii) compute the book value of the debt at the end of ten years;

(iii) construct a partial sinking fund schedule showing details including the book value of the debt, of the three first payments, the three last payments and the totals.

Solution

(i) The annual interest cost on the principal.

$$P = 750000; \qquad i = 13\% = 0.13$$
$$I = 750000(0.13) = \$97500$$

The annual payment into the sinking fund

$$S_n = 750000; \qquad n = 20; \qquad i = 10.5\%$$

$$750000 = R \, s_{\overline{20}|\,10.5\%}$$

$$750000 = R(60.630808)$$

$$R = \$12370$$

The annual cost of the debt is $97500 + 12370 = \$109870$.

(ii) The balance in the sinking fund after the 10th payment

$$S_{10} = 12370 \, s_{\overline{10}|\,10.5\%}$$

$$= 12370(16.324579)$$

$$= \$201935$$

The book value of the debt at the end of the 10th year is $750000 - 201935 = \$548065$.

(iii) The last three payments are Payments 18, 19 and 20. The balance in the sinking fund at the end of Year 17

$$S_{17} = 12370 \, s_{\overline{17}| \, 10.5\%} = 12370(42.47213) = \$525380$$

Partial sinking fund schedule

Payment interval number	Periodic payment made at end	Interest for payment interval $i = 0.105$	Increase in fund	Balance in fund at the end of the payment interval	Book value of debt
0				0	750 000
1	12 370	0	12 370	12 370	737 630
2	12 370	1299	13 669	26 039	723 961
3	12 370	2734	15 104	41 143	708 857
.	.	.	.	.	.
.	.	.	.	.	.
.	.	.	.	.	.
17	.	.	.	525 380	224 620
18	12 370	55165	67 535	592 915	157 085
19	12 370	62256	74 626	667 541	82 459
20	12 367	70092	82 459	750 000	0
TOTAL	247 397	502 603	750 000		

Note The last payment has been adjusted to create a fund of exactly $750 000.

Exercise 18.4

A. For each of the following sinking funds compute (a) the size of the periodic payment (b) the accumulated balance at the point in time indicated.

No.	Amount of sinking fund	Payment interval	Payments made at	Term	Int. rate	Conversion period	Accumulated balance required after
1.	$15 000.00	6 months	end	10 years	13%	semi-ann.	10th payment
2.	$ 9 600.00	1 month	end	8 years	12%	monthly	36th payment
3.	$ 8 400.00	1 month	beginning	15 years	18%	monthly	96th payment
4.	$21 000.00	3 months	beginning	20 years	17%	quarterly	28th payment
5.	$45 000.00	3 months	end	12 years	16%	quarterly	16th payment
6.	$72 000.00	6 months	beginning	15 years	13%	semi-ann.	20th payment

B. Each of the following debts is retired by the sinking fund method. Interest payments are made at the end of each payment interval and the payments into the sinking fund are made at the same time. Determine

(a) the size of the periodic interest expense of the debt;

(b) the size of the periodic payment into the sinking fund;

(c) the periodic cost of the debt;

(d) the book value of the debt at the time indicated.

No.	Debt principal	Term of debt	Payment interval	On debt	On fund	Conversion period	Book value required after
				Interest rate			
1.	$20 000.00	10 years	3 months	14%	12%	quarterly	6 years
2.	$14 500.00	8 years	6 months	15%	12.5%	semi-ann.	5 years
3.	$10 000.00	5 years	1 month	21%	16.5%	monthly	4 years
4.	$40 000.00	15 years	3 months	18%	17%	quarterly	10 years
5.	$95 000.00	20 years	6 months .	24%	19.5%	semi-ann.	15 years
6.	$80 000.00	12 years	1 month	15%	13.5%	monthly	8 years

C. Answer each of the following questions.

1. Hein Engineering expect to expand their plant facilities in six years at an estimated cost of $75 000.00. In order to provide for the expansion a sinking fund has been established into which equal payments are made at the end of every three months. Interest is 15% compounded quarterly.

(a) What is the size of the quarterly payments?

(b) How much of the maturity value will be payments?

(c) How much interest will be fund contain?

2. In order to redeem a $100 000.00 promissory note due in ten years, Cobblestone Enterprises have set up a sinking fund earning 17.5% compounded semi-annually. Equal deposits are made at the beginning of every six months.

(a) What is the size of the semi-annual deposits?

(b) How much of the maturity value of the fund are deposits?

(c) How much is interest?

3. Equal deposits are made into a sinking fund at the end of each year for seven years. Interest is 14.5% compounded annually and the maturity value of the fund is $20 000.00. Find the size of the annual deposits and construct a sinking fund schedule showing totals.

4. A sinking fund amounting to $15 000.00 is to be created by making payments at the beginning of every six months for four years. Interest earned by the fund is 12.5% compounded semi-annually. Determine the size of the semi-annual payments and prepare a sinking fund schedule showing totals.

5. For Question 3, find the increase in the fund for the fourth year. Verify your answer by checking the sinking fund schedule.

6. For Question 4, compute the interest earned during the fifth payment interval. Verify your answer by checking the sinking fund schedule.

7. Kirk, Klein & Co require $100 000.00 fifteen years from now to retire a debt. A sinking fund is established into which equal payments are made at the end of every month. Interest is 16.5% compounded monthly.

   (a) What is the size of the monthly payment?

   (b) What is the balance in the sinking fund after five years?

   (c) How much interest will be earned by the fund in the 100th payment interval?

   (d) By how much will the fund increase during the 150th payment interval?

   (e) Construct a partial sinking fund schedule showing details of the first three payments, the last three payments and totals.

8. The Town of Keewatin issued debentures worth $120 000.00 maturing in ten years to finance construction of water and sewer facilities. To redeem the debentures the town council decided to make equal deposits into a sinking fund at the beginning of every three months. Interest earned by the sinking fund is 16% compounded quarterly.

   (a) What is the size of the quarterly payment into the sinking fund?

   (b) What is the balance in the fund after six years?

   (c) How much interest is earned by the fund in the 28th payment interval?

   (d) By how much will the fund increase in the 33rd payment interval?

   (e) Prepare a partial sinking fund schedule showing details of the first three payments, the last three payments and totals.

9. The Township of Jeffrey Melnick borrowed $300 000 for road improvements. The debt agreement requires that the township pay the interest on the loan at the end of each year and make equal deposits at the time of the interest payments into a sinking fund until the loan is retired in twenty years. Interest on the loan is 18.25% compounded annually and interest earned by the sinking fund is 15.5% compounded annually (round all answers to the nearest dollar).

   (a) What is the annual interest expense?

   (b) What is the size of the annual deposit into the sinking fund?

   (c) What is the total annual cost of the debt?

   (d) How much is the increase in the sinking fund in the 10th year?

   (e) What is the book value of the debt after fifteen years?

   (f) Construct a partial sinking fund schedule showing details, including the book value of the debt, for the first three years, the last three years and totals.

10. Sheridan Credit Union borrowed $225 000 at 13% compounded semi-annually from League Central to construct an office complex. The loan agreement requires payment of interest at the end of every six months. In addition equal payments are to be made by the Credit Union into a sinking fund so that the principal can be retired in total after fifteen years. Interest earned by the fund is 11% compounded semi-annually (round all answers to the nearest dollar).

   (a) What is the semi-annual interest payment on the debt?

   (b) What is the size of the semi-annual deposits into the sinking fund?

(c) What is the total annual cost of the debt?

(d) What is the interest earned by the fund in the 20th payment interval?

(e) What is the book value of the debt after twelve years?

(f) Prepare a partial sinking fund schedule showing details, including the book value of the debt, for the first three years, the last three years and totals.

Review exercise

1. Roger bought a business for $45 000.00. He made a down payment of $10 000.00 and agreed to repay the balance by equal payments at the end of every three months for eight years. Interest is 16% compounded quarterly.

   (a) What is the size of the quarterly payments?

   (b) What will be the total cost of financing?

   (c) How much will Roger owe after five years?

   (d) How much interest will be included in the 20th payment?

   (e) How much of the principal will be repaid by his 24th payment?

   (f) Construct a partial amortization schedule showing details of the first three payments, Payments 10, 11, 12, the last three payments and totals.

2. Mr. Lemay borrowed $8000.00 from his Credit Union. He agreed to repay the loans by making equal monthly payments for five years. Interest is 15% compounded monthly.

   (a) What is the size of the monthly payments?

   (b) How much will the loan cost him?

   (c) How much will Mr. Lemay owe after eighteen months?

   (d) How much interest will he pay in his 36th payment?

   (e) How much of the principal will he repay by his 48th payment?

   (f) Prepare a partial amortization schedule showing details of the first three payments, Payments 24, 25, 26, the last three payments and totals.

3. Comfort Swim Limited borrowed $40 000.00 for replacement of equipment. The debt is repaid in instalments of $2000.00 made at the end of every three months.

   (a) If interest is 15% compounded quarterly, how many payments are needed?

   (b) How much will Comfort Swim owe after two years?

   (c) How much of the 12th payment is interest?

   (d) How much of the principal will be repaid by the 20th payment?

   (e) Construct a partial amortization schedule showing details of the first three payments, the last three payments and totals.

4. A $48 000.00 mortgage amortized by monthly payments over 35 years is renewable after five years. Interest is 14% compounded semi-annually.

   (a) What is the size of the monthly payments?

   (b) How much interest is paid during the first year?

   (c) How much of the principal is repaid during the first five-year term?

   (d) If the mortgage is renewed for a further five-year term at 18% compounded semi-annually, what will be the size of the monthly payments then?

(e) Construct a partial amortization schedule showing details of the first three payments for each of the two five-year terms, the last three payments for the second five-year term and totals at the end of the second five-year term.

5. Pelican Recreational Services owe $27 500.00 secured by a collateral mortgage. The mortgage is amortized over fifteen years by equal payments made at the end of every three months and renewable after three years.

(a) If interest is 15% compounded annually, what is the size of the payments?

(b) How much of the principal is repaid by the fourth payment?

(c) What is the balance at the end of the three-year term?

(d) If the mortgage is renewed for a further four years but amortized over eight years and interest is 17.5% compounded semi-annually, what is the size of the quarterly payments for the renewal period?

(e) Construct a partial amortization schedule showing details of the first three payments for each of the two terms, the last three payments in the four-year term and totals at the end of the four-year term.

6. A debt of $17 500.00 is repaid by payments of $2850.00 made at the end of each year. Interest is 14% compounded semi-annually.

(a) What is the number of payments required to repay the debt?

(b) What is the cost of the debt for the first three years?

(c) What is the principal repaid in the seventh year?

(d) Construct an amortization schedule showing details of the first three payments, the last three payments and totals.

7. A debt of $25 000.00 is repaid by payments of $3500.00 made at the end of every six months. Interest is 21% compounded semi-annually.

(a) How many payments are needed to repay the debt?

(b) What is the size of the final payment?

8. Brian receives payments of $900.00 at the beginning of each month from a pension fund of $72 500.00. Interest earned by the fund is 12% compounded monthly.

(a) What is the number of payments which Brian will receive?

(b) What is the size of the final payment?

9. A lease agreement valued at $33 000.00 requires payment of $4300.00 every three months in advance. The payments are deferred for three years and money is worth 20% compounded quarterly.

(a) How many lease payments are to be made under the contract?

(b) What is the size of the final lease payment?

10. A contract worth $52 000.00 provides benefits of $20 000.00 at the end of each year. The benefits are deferred for ten years and interest is 11% compounded quarterly.

(a) How many payments are to be made under the contract?

(b) What is the size of the last benefit payment?

11. To provide for the purchase of heavy construction equipment estimated to cost $110 000.00, Valmar Construction are paying equal sums of money at the end of every six months for five years into a sinking fund earning 17.5% compounded semi-annually.

(a) What is the size of the semi-annual payment into the sinking fund?

(b) Compute the balance in the fund after the third payment.

(c) Compute the amount of interest earned during the sixth payment interval.

(d) Construct a sinking fund schedule showing totals. Check your answers in (b) and (c) with the values in the schedule.

12. Alpha Corporation are depositing equal sums of money at the beginning of every three months into a sinking fund to redeem a $65 000.00 promissory note due eight years from now. Interest earned by the fund is 12% compounded quarterly.

(a) Determine the size of the quarterly payments into the sinking fund.

(b) Compute the balance in the fund after three years.

(c) Compute the increase in the fund during the 24th payment interval.

(d) Construct a partial sinking fund schedule showing details of the first three deposits, the last three deposits and totals.

13. The municipality of Kirkfield borrowed $100 000.00 for the construction of a recreation centre. The debt principal is to be repaid in eight years and interest at 13.75% compounded annually is to be paid annually. In order to provide for the retirement of the debt, the municipal council set up a sinking fund into which equal payments are made at the time of the annual interest payments. Interest earned by the fund is 11.5% compounded annually.

(a) What is the annual interest payment?

(b) What is the size of the annual payment into the sinking fund?

(c) What is the total annual cost of the debt?

(d) Compute the book value of the debt after three years.

(e) Compute the interest earned by the fund in Year 6.

(f) Construct a sinking fund schedule showing the book value of the debt and totals. Verify your computations in (d) and (e) against the schedule.

14. The Local Board of Education financed the acquisition of a building site through a $300 000 long-term promissory note due in fifteen years. Interest on the promissory note is 19.25% compounded semi-annually and is payable at the end of every six months. To provide for the redemption of the note, the Board agreed to make equal payments at the end of every six months into a sinking fund paying 18% compounded semi-annually. Round all answers to the nearest dollar.

(a) What is the semi-annual interest payment?

(b) What is the size of the semi-annual payment into the sinking fund?

(c) What is the annual cost of the debt?

(d) Compute the book value of the debt after five years.

(e) Compute the increase in the sinking fund in the 20th payment interval.

(f) Construct a partial sinking fund schedule showing details, including the book value of the debt for the first three years, the last three years and totals.

15. A debt of $6500.00 is repaid in equal monthly instalments over four years. Interest is 15% compounded monthly.

(a) What is the size of the monthly payments?

(b) What will be the total cost of borrowing?

(c) What is the outstanding balance after one year?

(d) How much of the 30th payment is interest?

(e) Construct a partial amortization schedule showing details of the first three payments, the last three payments and totals.

16. Milton Investments borrowed $32 000.00 at 21% compounded semi-annually. The loan is repaid by payments of $4500.00 due at the end of every six months.

(a) How many payments are needed?

(b) How much of the principal will be repaid by the fifth payment?

(c) Prepare a partial amortization schedule showing the details of the last three payments and totals.

17. Northern Flying Service are preparing for the purchase of an aircraft estimated to cost $60 000.00 by making equal payments at the end of every three months into a sinking fund for five years. Interest earned by the fund is 16% compounded quarterly.

(a) What is the size of the quarterly payment into the sinking fund?

(b) How much of the maturity value of the fund will be interest?

(c) What is the accumulated value of the fund after two years?

(d) How much interest will be earned by the fund in the 15th payment interval?

18. A sinking fund of $10 000.00 is to be created by equal annual payments at the beginning of each year for seven years. Interest earned by the fund is 17.5% compounded annually.

(a) Compute the annual deposit into the fund.

(b) Construct a sinking fund schedule showing totals.

19. A $28 000.00 mortgage is amortized by quarterly payments over twenty years. The mortgage is renewable after three years and interest is 14% compounded semi-annually.

(a) What is the size of the quarterly payments?

(b) How much interest will be paid during the first year?

(c) What is the balance at the end of the three-year term?

(d) If the mortgage is renewed for another three years at 15% compounded annually, what will be the size of the quarterly payments for the renewal period?

20. The Superior Tool Company is repaying a debt of $16 000.00 by payments of $1000.00 made at the end of every three months. Interest is 16.5% compounded monthly.

(a) How many payments are required to repay the debt?

(b) What is the size of the final payment?

21. Joe purchased a retirement fund for $15 000.00. Commencing twenty-five years from the date of purchase he will receive payments of $17 500.00 at the beginning of every six months. Interest earned by the fund is 12% compounded semi-annually.

(a) How many payments will Joe receive?

(b) What is the size of the last payment?

22. The town of Kildare purchased firefighting equipment for $96 000.00. The financing agreement provides for annual interest payments and equal payments into a sinking fund for ten years. After ten years the proceeds of the sinking fund will be used to retire the principal. Interest on the debt is 14.5% compounded annually and interest earned by the sinking fund is 13% compounded annually.

(a) What is the annual interest payment?

(b) What is the size of the annual payment into the sinking fund?

(c) What is the total annual cost of the debt?

(d) What is the book value of the debt after four years?

(e) Construct a partial sinking fund schedule showing details including the book value of the debt for the last three years and totals.

Self-test

1. A $9000.00 loan is repaid by equal monthly payments over five years. What is the outstanding balance after two years if interest is 12% compounded monthly?

2. A company is making semi-annual payments into a sinking fund for ten years. If the fund is to have a balance of $100 000.00 after ten years and interest is 11% compounded semi-annually, what is the accumulated balance in the fund after seven years?

3. A loan of $15 000.00 is repaid by quarterly payments of $700.00 each at 18% compounded quarterly. What is the principal repaid by the twenty-fifth payment?

4. A fund of $165 000.00 is to be accumulated in six years by making equal payments at the beginning of each month. If interest is 13.5% compounded monthly, how much interest is earned by the fund in the twentieth payment interval?

5. A $50 000.00 mortgage is amortized by monthly payments over twenty years. If interest is 14% compounded semi-annually, how much interest will be paid during the first three years?

6. A debt of $24 000.00 is repaid by quarterly payments of $1100.00. If interest is 16% compounded quarterly, what is the size of the final payment?

7. Ted invested $10 000.00 in an income fund at 13% compounded semi-annually for twenty years. After twenty years he is to receive semi-annual payments of $10 000.00 at the end of every six-month period until the fund is exhausted. What is the size of the final payment?

8. A company financed plant expansion of $750 000.00 at 14% compounded annually. The financing agreement requires annual payment of interest and the funding of the debt through equal annual payments for fifteen years into a sinking fund earning 12% compounded annually. What is the book value of the debt after five years?

9. Annual sinking fund payments made at the beginning of every year for six years earning 11.5% compounded annually amount to $25 000.00 at the end of six years. Construct a sinking fund schedule showing totals.

10. A loan of $12 000.00 is amortized over ten years by equal monthly payments at 15% compounded monthly. Construct an amortization schedule showing details of the first three payments, the fortieth payment, the last three payments and totals.

Summary of formulae used

No new formulae have been introduced in this chapter. However, some of the formulae introduced in Chapters 13 to 17 have been used and are listed below.

Formula 15.1 or 15.1A $\quad S_n = R\left(\dfrac{(1 + i)^n - 1}{i}\right) = R\, s_{\overline{n}|i}$

Formula 15.2 or 15.2A $\quad A_n = R\left(\dfrac{1 - (1 + i)^{-n}}{i}\right) = R\, a_{\overline{n}|i}$

Formula 16.1 or 16.1A $\quad S_n(\text{Due}) = R(1 + i)\left(\dfrac{(1 + i)^n - 1}{i}\right) = R(1 + i)\, s_{\overline{n}|i}$

Formula 17.1A $\quad S_{nc} = R\left(\dfrac{(1 + f)^c - 1}{f}\right) = R\, s_{\overline{n}|f}$ where $f = (1 + i)^c - 1$

Formula 17.2A $\quad A_{nc} = R\left(\dfrac{1 - (1 + f)^{-n}}{f}\right) = R\, a_{\overline{n}|f}$ where $f = (1 + i)^c - 1$

Remember	$s_{\overline{n}|i} = \dfrac{(1 + i)^c - 1}{i}$ and $a_{\overline{n}|i} = \dfrac{1 - (1 + i)^{-n}}{i}$

Glossary of terms used

Amortization   repayment of both interest and principal of interest-bearing debts by a series of equal payments made at equal intervals of time

Amortization schedule   a schedule showing in detail how a debt is repaid

Book value of a debt   the difference at any point in time between the debt principal and the associated sinking fund balance

Periodic cost of a debt   the sum of the interest paid and the payment into the sinking fund when a debt is retired by the sinking fund method

Prospective method   a method for finding the outstanding debt balance which considers the payments that remain outstanding

Retrospective method   a method of finding the outstanding balance of a debt which considers the payments that have been made

Sinking fund   a fund into which payments are made to provide a specific sum of money at a future point in time, usually set up for the purpose of meeting some future obligation

19. *Bond valuation*

Introduction

Bonds are contracts used to borrow sizeable sums of money from a usually large group of investors. The indenture for most bonds provides for the repayment of the principal at a specified future date plus periodic payment of interest at a specified percent of the face value. Bonds are negotiable; that is, they can be freely bought and sold. The mathematical problems arising from the trading of bonds are the topic of this chapter.

Objectives

Upon completion of this chapter you will be able to

1. determine the purchase price of bonds, redeemable at par or otherwise, bought on or between interest dates;
2. determine the premium or discount on the purchase of a bond;
3. construct bond schedules showing the amortization of premium or accumulation of discount;
4. calculate the yield rate for bonds bought on the market by the Method of Averages and more accurately by trial and error;
5. deal with special kinds of bonds such as annuity bonds and serial bonds.

19.1 *Purchase price of bonds*

A. *Basic concepts and terminology*

Bonds are used by corporations and governments to borrow money from a usually large group of lenders (investors). To deal with the expected large number of investors, written contacts, called bonds or **debentures** are printed up in advance by the borrower.

The printed bonds specify the terms of the contract including

(a) the **face value** (or **par value** or **denomination**) which is the amount owed to the holder of the bond, usually a multiple of $100 such as $100, $500, $1000, $5000, $10000, $25000, $100000;

(b) the **bond rate** (or **coupon rate** or **nominal rate**) which is the rate of interest paid, usually semi-annually, based on the face value of the bond;

(c) the **redemption date** (or **maturity date** or **due date**) which is the date on which the principal of the loan is to be repaid;

(d) the **redemption value** which is the money paid by the issuer to the bondholder at the date of surrender of the bonds.

Most bonds are **redeemable at par**; that is, at their *face* value. However, some bonds have a redemption feature to make the bonds more attractive to the investor or because they are callable, that is because they can be redeemed *before* maturity. In either case the bonds will be **redeemed at a premium**; that is, at a value *greater* than their face value. The redemption value in such cases is stated as a percent of the face values. For example, the redemption value of a $5000 bond redeemable at 104 is 104% of $5000 = $5200.

The investors in bonds expect to receive periodic interest payments during the term of the bond from the date of issue to the date of maturity and they expect to receive the principal at the date of maturity.

To facilitate the payment of interest most bonds have dated interest **coupons** attached which can be cashed on or after the stated interest payment date at any bank. For example, a 20-year, $1000.00 bond bearing interest at 10% payable semi-annually will have attached to it 40 coupons of $50 each at the date of issue, each coupon representing the semi-annual interest due on each of the forty interest payment dates.

The issuer may or may not offer security such as real estate, plant or equipment as a guarantee for the repayment of the principal. Bonds for which no security is offered are called debentures.

Bonds are marketable and may be freely bought and sold. When an investor acquires a bond he buys two promises:

1. a promise to be paid the redemption value of the bond at maturity;

2. a promise to be paid the periodic interest payments according to the rate of interest stated on the bond.

With regard to the acquisition of bonds, two basic problems arise for the investor.

1. What should be the purchase price of a bond to provide the investor with a given rate of return?

2. What is the rate of interest which a bond will yield if bought at a given price?

In this section we will deal with the first of these two basic problems.

B. Purchase price of a bond bought on an interest date

***Example* 19.1a**   A $1000 bond bearing interest at 10% payable semi-annually is due in four years. If money is worth 12% compounded semi-annually, what is the value of the bond if bought today?

Solution

The buyer of the bond acquires two promises:

1. a promise of $1000.00 four years from now;
2. a promise of $50.00 interest due at the end of every six months (the annual interest is 10% of 1000.00 = $100.00, half of which is paid after the first six months, the other half at the end of the year).

The two promises may be represented on a time graph as shown in Figure 19.1.

FIGURE 19.1   *Graphical representation of method and data*

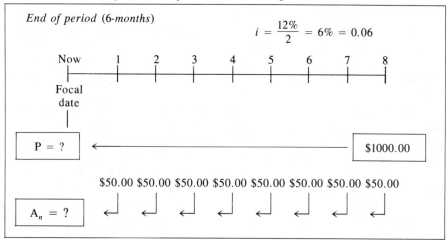

The focal date for evaluating the two promises is 'now' and the rate of interest to be used for the valuation is 12% compounded semi-annually.

The value now of the redemption value of $1000.00 is its present value.

$$S = 1000.00; \qquad n = 4(2) = 8; \qquad i = \frac{12\%}{2} = 6\% = 0.06;$$

$$P = 1000.00(1.06)^{-8} \longleftarrow \text{using Formula 13.2A}$$
$$= 1000.00(0.6274124)$$
$$= \$627.41$$

The value now of the semi-annual interest payments is the present value of an ordinary annuity.

$$R = \frac{10\% \text{ of } 1000.00}{2} = 50.00; \qquad n = 8; \qquad i = 6\%;$$

$$A_n = 50.00 \times a_{\overline{8}|6\%} \quad \longleftarrow \text{ using Formula 15.2A}$$

$$= 50.00(6.2097938)$$

$$= \$310.49$$

The purchase price of the bond is the sum of the present values of the two promises $= P + A_n$

$$= 627.41 + 310.49 = \$937.90$$

> THE PURCHASE PRICE OF A BOND BOUGHT ON AN INTEREST PAYMENT DATE
> = THE PRESENT VALUE OF THE REDEMPTION VALUE
> + THE PRESENT VALUE OF THE INTEREST PAYMENTS

The two steps involved in using the above relationship may be combined.

> PURCHASE PRICE $= P + A_n$
> $= S(1 + i)^{-n} + R\, a_{\overline{n}|i}$ $\quad \longleftarrow$ *Formula 19.1*

where S = the redemption value of the bond;
R = the periodic interest payment (coupon);
n = the number of outstanding interest payments (or compounding periods);
i = the yield rate per payment interval.

Note It is important to recognize that two rates of interest are used in determining the purchase price:
1. the bond rate which determines the size of the periodic interest payments (coupons);
2. the **yield rate** which is used to determine the present values of the two promises.

Example 19.1b A $5000.00 bond bearing interest at 10.5% payable semi-annually is redeemable at par in ten years. If it is bought to yield 9% compounded semi-annually, what is the purchase price of the bond?

Solution

The redemption value S $= 5000.00$;

the coupon R $= \dfrac{5000.00(0.105)}{2} = 262.50$;

$$n = 10(2) = 20; \qquad i = \frac{9\%}{2} = 4.5\% = 0.045.$$

$$\text{Purchase Price} = \begin{array}{c} \text{Present Value of the} \\ \text{Redemption Value} \end{array} + \begin{array}{c} \text{Present Value} \\ \text{of the Coupons} \end{array}$$

$$= \qquad P \qquad + \qquad A_n$$

$$= 5000.00(1.045^{-20}) \quad + 262.50\, a\,_{\overline{20}|\,4.5\%}$$

$$= 5000.00(0.4146429) \ + 262.50(13.007936)$$

$$= 2073.21 + 3414.58$$

$$= \$5487.79$$

Example 19.1c   A bond whose par value is \$10 000.00 is redeemable at 106 in 25 years. The coupon rate is 8% payable semi-annually. What is the purchase price of the bond to yield 10% compounded semi-annually?

Solution

The redemption value S $= 10000.00\,(1.06) = 10600.00$;

$$\text{the coupon R} = \frac{10000.00(0.08)}{2} = 400.00;$$

$$n = 25(2) = 50; \qquad i = \frac{10\%}{2} = 5\% = 0.05.$$

Purchase Price $= P + A_n$

$$= 10600.00(1.05^{-50}) + 400\, a\,_{\overline{50}|\,5\%}$$

$$= 10600.00(0.0872037) + 400.00(18.255925)$$

$$= 924.36 + 7302.37$$

$$= \$8226.73$$

Example 19.1d   A \$25000.00 bond bearing interest at 11% payable quarterly is redeemable at 107 in twelve years. Find the purchase price of the bond to yield 10% compounded quarterly.

Solution

The redemption value S $= 25000.00(1.07) = 26750.00$;

$$\text{the coupon R} = \frac{25000.00(0.11)}{4} = 687.50;$$

$$n = 12(4) = 48; \qquad i = \frac{10\%}{4} = 2.5\% = 0.025.$$

Purchase Price $= 26750.00(1.025^{-48}) + 687.50\, a\,_{\overline{48}|\,2.5\%}$

$$= 26750.00(0.3056712) + 687.50(27.773154)$$

$$= 8176.70 + 19094.04$$

$$= \$27270.74$$

In the preceding problems the bond interest payment period and the yield rate conversion period were equal in length permitting the use of simple annuity formulae. However, when the bond interest payment period and the yield rate conversion period are not equal in length, general annuity formulae must be used.

Example 19.1e A municipality issues 10-year bonds in the amount of $1 000 000. Interest on the bonds is 10% payable annually. What is the issue price of the bonds if the bonds are sold to yield 11% compounded quarterly?

Solution

The redemption value of the bonds S = 1000000;
the annual interest payment R = 1000000(0.10) = $100000.
Since the interest payment period (annual) is not equal in length to the yield rate conversion period (quarterly), the interest payments form an ordinary general annuity.

$$n = 10; \qquad c = \frac{4}{1} = 4; \qquad i = \frac{11\%}{4} = 2.75\% = 0.0275;$$

$$f = 1.0275^4 - 1 = 1.1146213 - 1 = 0.1146213$$

The present value of the redemption value

$$P = 1000000(1.1146213^{-10})$$
$$= 1000000(0.3378521)$$
$$= \$337852.10$$

The present value of the annual interest payments

$$A_{nc} = 100000\left[\frac{(1 - 1.1146213^{-10})}{0.1146213}\right] \quad \longleftarrow \text{ using Formula 17.2A}$$

$$= 100000(5.7768312)$$
$$= \$577683.12$$

The issue price is 337852.10 + 577683.12 = $915535.22.

Formula 19.1 can be modified to allow for the general annuity case by using Formula 17.2A.

$$\boxed{\text{PURCHASE PRICE} = P + A_{nc} = S(1 + f)^{-n} + R\, a_{\overline{n}|f}} \quad \longleftarrow \textbf{\textit{Formula}} \textbf{ 19.1A}$$
$$\text{where } f = (1 + i)^c - 1$$

Example 19.1f A $100 000 bond redeemable at 103 bearing interest at 11.5% payable semi-annually is bought eight years before maturity to yield 10% compounded quarterly. What is the purchase price of the bond?

Solution

$$\text{The redemption value } S = 100000(1.03) = \$103000;$$

$$\text{the size of the semi-annual coupon } R = 100000\left(\frac{0.115}{2}\right) = \$5750.00$$

$$n = 8(2) = 16; \qquad c = \frac{4}{2} = 2; \qquad i = \frac{10\%}{4} = 2.5\% = 0.025;$$

$$f = 1.025^2 - 1 = 1.050625 - 1 = 0.050625 = 5.0625\%.$$

The Purchase Price of the bond using Formula 19.1A

$$= 103000(1.050625^{-16}) + 5750(a\,\overline{_{16}|}\,_{5.0625\%})$$

$$= 103000(0.4537706) + 5750.00(10.789717)$$

$$= 46738.37 + 62040.87$$

$$= \$108779.24$$

C. Purchase price of bonds between interest dates

The trading of bonds is, of course, not restricted to interest dates. In practice, most bonds are bought and sold between interest dates.

In such cases, the price of the bond on the date of purchase may be computed by first finding the purchase price on the interest date immediately preceding the date of the purchase. The resulting value can then be accumulated using the amount formula for simple interest at the nominal yield rate for the number of days elapsed between the interest payment date and the purchase date.

Example 19.1g A bond with a face value of $1000 bearing interest at 10% payable semi-annually matures on August 1, 1987. What is the purchase price of the bond on April 18, 1985 to yield 9% compounded semi-annually?

Solution

STEP 1 Find the purchase price on the preceding interest date.
The redemption value $S = \$1000.00$;

$$\text{the semi-annual coupon } R = 1000.00\left(\frac{0.10}{2}\right) = \$50.00.$$

Since the maturity date is August 1, the semi-annual interest dates are February 1 and August 1. The interest date preceding the date of purchase is February 1, 1985.

The time period from February 1, 1985 to the date of maturity is 2.5 years.

$$n = 2.5(2) = 5; \qquad i = \frac{9\%}{2} = 4.5\% = 0.045$$

The purchase price of the bond on February 1, 1985

$$= 1000.00(1.045^{-5}) + 50.00 \times a_{\overline{5}|4.5\%}$$

$$= 1000.00(0.802451) + 50.00(4.3899767)$$

$$= 802.45 + 219.50$$

$$= \$1021.95$$

STEP 2   Accumulate the purchase price on February 1, 1985 to the purchase date at simple interest.

The number of days from February 1, 1985 to April 18, 1985 is 76; the number of days in the interest interval February 1, 1985 to August 1, 1985 is 181.

$$P = 1021.95; \qquad r = i = 0.045; \qquad t = \frac{76}{181}$$

$$S = 1021.95\left[1 + 0.045\left(\frac{76}{181}\right)\right] = 1021.95(1.018895) = \$1041.26$$

The purchase price of the bond on April 18, 1985 is \$1041.26.

D.   Flat price and quoted price

In Example 19.1g the total purchase price of \$1041.26 is referred to as the **flat price**. This price includes interest that has accrued from February 1, 1985 to April 18, 1985 but will not be paid until August 1, 1985.

The actual accrued interest is $1000.00(0.05)(\frac{76}{181}) = \$20.99$.

As far as the seller of the bond is concerned, the net price of the bond is $1041.26 - 20.99 = \$1020.27$.

The price is referred to as the **quoted price** or market price.

> QUOTED PRICE = FLAT PRICE – ACCRUED INTEREST

> FLAT PRICE = QUOTED PRICE + ACCRUED INTEREST

In a stable market, the flat price of bond will increase as the accrued interest increases and drop suddenly by the amount of the interest paid on the interest date. To avoid this fluctuation in price which is entirely due to the accrued interest, bonds are offered for sale at the quoted price, and the accrued interest is added to obtain the total price or flat price.

Example 19.1h   A \$5000 bond redeemable at par in seven years and four months bearing interest at 10.5% payable semi-annually is purchased to yield 11.5% compounded semi-annually. Determine

(i) the purchase price (flat price);

(ii) the accrued interest;

(iii) the market price (quoted price).

Solution

(i) The redemption value $S = \$5000.00$;

the semi-annual coupon $R = 5000.00 \left(\dfrac{0.105}{2}\right) = \$262.50$.

The interest date preceding the purchase date is 7.5 years before maturity

$$n = 7.5(2) = 15; \qquad i = \dfrac{11.5\%}{2} = 5.75\% = 0.0575$$

The purchase price on the interest date preceding the date of purchase

$$= 5000.00(1.0575^{-15}) + 262.50 \times a_{\overline{15}|\,5.75\%}$$

$$= 5000.00\,(0.4323091) + 262.50\,(9.8728855)$$

$$= 2161.55 + 2591.63$$

$$= \$4753.18$$

The accumulated value two months later

$$P = 4753.18; \qquad r = i = 0.0575; \qquad t = \dfrac{2}{6};$$

$$S = 4753.18\left[1 + 0.0575\left(\dfrac{2}{6}\right)\right]$$

$$= 4753.18\,(1.0191667)$$

$$= \$4844.28$$

The purchase price (flat price) is $\$4844.28$.

(ii) The accrued interest is $5000.00\,(0.0525)\left(\dfrac{2}{6}\right) = \$87.50$

(iii) The quoted price (market price) is $4844.28 - 87.50 = \$4756.78$.

Example 19.1i A $10 000, 11% bond redeemable at 108 matures on May 1, 1995. Interest is payable semi-annually and the bond is purchased on March 21, 1983 to yield 10% compounded semi-annually.

(i) What is the purchase price of the bond?

(ii) What is the accrued interest?

(iii) What is the quoted price?

Solution

(i) The redemption price $S = 10000.00\,(1.08) = \$10800.00$;

the semi-annual coupon $R = 10000.00\left(\dfrac{0.11}{2}\right) = \$550.00$.

The interest dates on the bond are May 1 and November 1.
The interest date preceding the date of purchase is November 1, 1982.

The time period November 1, 1982 to May 1, 1995 is 12.5 years.

$$n = 12.5(2) = 25; \qquad i = \frac{10\%}{2} = 5\% = 0.05$$

The purchase price on November 1, 1982

$$= 10800.00(1.05^{-25}) + 550.00\,(a_{\overline{25}|5\%})$$

$$= 10800.00(0.2953028) + 550.00(14.093945)$$

$$= 3189.27 + 7751.67$$

$$= \$10940.94$$

The time period November 1, 1982 to March 21, 1983 contains 140 days; the number of days in the interest payment interval November 1, 1982 to May 1, 1983 is 181.

$$P = 10940.94; \qquad r = i = 0.05; \qquad t = \frac{140}{181}$$

The accumulated value on March 21, 1983

$$= 10940.94 \left[1 + 0.05 \left(\frac{140}{181} \right) \right] = 10940.94(1.0386740) = \$11364.07$$

(ii) The actual accrued interest is $10000.00(0.055)\left(\dfrac{140}{181} \right) = \$425.41.$

(iii) The quoted price is $11364.07 - 425.41 = \$10938.66.$

Exercise 19.1

A. Determine the purchase price at the indicated time before redemption of each of the following bonds.

No.	Par value	Redeemed at	Bond rate payable semi-annually	Time before redemption	Yield rate	Conversion period
1.	$100 000	par	15.5%	5.5 years	13.5%	semi-annually
2.	$5 000	par	10%	12 years	12%	semi-annually
3.	$25 000	103	16%	7 years	14%	semi-annually
4.	$1 000	110	8.5%	12.5 years	13.5%	semi-annually
5.	$50 000	par	14%	10 years	13%	annually
6.	$20 000	par	10.5%	6.5 years	13%	quarterly
7.	$8 000	104	11.5%	18.5 years	9%	monthly
8.	$3 000	107	10%	20 years	12%	quarterly
9.	$15 000	par	9.5%	6 yrs 4 mo	15%	semi-annually
10.	$5 000	par	11%	12 yrs 9 mo	12%	semi-annually
11.	$10 000	108	12%	9 yrs 5 mo	14%	semi-annually
12.	$2 000	105	17.5%	5 yrs 10 mo	19.5%	semi-annually

B. Answer each of the following questions.

1. A $500 bond is redeemable at par on March 1, 1992. Interest is 11% payable semi-annually. Find the purchase price of the bond on September 1, 1986 to yield 16.5% compounded semi-annually.

2. A $25 000, 13% bond redeemable at par is purchased twelve years before maturity to yield 16% compounded semi-annually. If the bond interest is payable semi-annually, what is the purchase price of the bond?

3. A $1000, 11.5% bond redeemable at 104 is purchased 8.5 years before maturity to yield 13% compounded semi-annually. If the bond interest is payable semi-annually, what is the purchase price of the bond?

4. A $100 000 bond is redeemable at 108 in fifteen years. If interest on the bond is 15.5% payable semi-annually, what is the purchase price to yield 14% compounded semi-annually?

5. A 25-year bond issue of $5 000 000 redeemable at par and bearing interest at 17.25% payable annually is sold to yield 18.5% compounded semi-annually. What is the issue price of the bonds?

6. A $100 000 bond bearing interest at 16% compounded semi-annually is bought eight years before maturity to yield 14.5% compounded annually. If the bond is redeemable at par, what is the purchase price?

7. Bonds with a par value of $40 000 redeemable at 103 in 7.5 years bearing interest at 13% payable quarterly are sold to yield 14% compounded semi-annually. Determine the purchase price of the bonds.

8. Six $1000 bonds with 11.5% coupons payable semi-annually are bought to yield 18% compounded monthly. If the bonds are redeemable at 109 in eight years, what is the purchase price?

9. A $25 000, 10% bond redeemable at par on December 1, 1996 is purchased on September 25, 1985 to yield 14.5% compounded semi-annually. Bond interest is payable semi-annually.

   (a) What is the flat price of the bond?

   (b) What is the accrued interest?

   (c) What is the quoted price?

10. A $100 000 bond redeemable at par on October 1, 2005 is purchased on January 15, 1984. Interest is 13% payable semi-annually and the yield is 11.5% compounded semi-annually.

   (a) What is the purchase price of the bond?

   (b) How much interest has accrued?

   (c) What is the market price?

11. A $5000, 15% bond redeemable at 104 matures on August 1, 1994. If the coupons are payable semi-annually, what is the quoted price on May 10, 1985 to yield 13.5% compounded semi-annually?

12. Bonds in denominations of $1000 redeemable at 107 are offered for sale. If the bonds mature in six years and ten months and the coupon rate is 9.5% payable quarterly, what is the market price of the bonds to yield 12% compounded quarterly?

19.2 Premium and discount

A. Basic concepts—bond rate versus yield (or market) rate

A comparison of the redemption values with the purchase prices obtained in Examples 19.1a to 19.1i (see Table 19.1 below) indicates that the purchase price is sometimes less than the redemption value and sometimes more than the redemption value.

TABLE 19.1 *Comparison of redemption values with purchase prices for Examples 19.1a to i*

Example	Redemption value S	Purchase price PP	Comparison of S and PP	Premium or discount	Amount of premium or discount	Bond rate b	Yield rate i	b versus i
19.1a	$1 000.00	$937.90	S > PP	Discount	$62.10	5%	6%	b < i
19.1b	$5 000.00	$5 487.79	PP > S	Premium	$487.79	5.25%	4.5%	b > i
19.1c	$10 000.00	$8 226.73	S > PP	Discount	$2 373.27	4%	5%	b < i
19.1d	$26 750.00	$27 270.74	PP > S	Premium	$520.74	2.75%	2.5%	b > i
19.1e	$1 000 000.00	$915 535.22	S > PP	Discount	$84 464.78	10%	11.46%	b < i
19.1f	$103 000.00	$108 779.24	PP > S	Premium	$5 779.24	5.75%	5.06%	b > i
19.1g	$1 000.00	$1 041.26	PP > S	Premium	$41.26	5%	4.5%	b > i
19.1h	$5 000.00	$4 844.28	S > PP	Discount	$155.72	5.25%	5.75%	b < i
19.i	$10 800.00	$10 938.66	PP > S	Premium	$138.66	5.5%	5%	b > i

If the purchase price of a bond is greater than the redemption value, the bond is said to be bought at a premium and the difference between the purchase price and the redemption value is called the **premium**.

> PREMIUM = PURCHASE PRICE − REDEMPTION VALUE,
> where purchase price > redemption value

If the purchase price of a bond is less than the redemption value, the bond is said to be bought at a discount and the difference between the redemption value and the purchase price is called the **discount**.

> DISCOUNT = REDEMPTION VALUE − PURCHASE PRICE,
> where redemption value > purchase price

An examination of the size of the bond rate b relative to the size of the market rate i indicates that this relationship determines whether there is a premium or discount.

The bond rate (or coupon rate) stated on the bond is the percent of the *face* value of the bond which will be paid at the end of each interest period to the bondholder. This rate is established at the time of issue of the bonds and remains the same throughout the term of the bond.

On the other hand, the rate at which lenders are willing to provide money fluctuates in response to economic conditions. The combination of factors at work in the capital market at any given point in time in conjunction with the perceived risk associated with a particular bond determines the yield rate (or market rate) for a bond and thus the price at which a bond will be bought or sold.

The bond rate and the market rate are usually *not* equal. However, if the two rates happen to be equal, then bonds which are redeemable at par will sell at their face value. If the bond rate is *less* than the market rate, the bond will sell at a price less than the face value; that is, at a *discount*. If the bond rate is *greater* than the market rate, the bond will sell at a price above its face value; that is, at a *premium*.

Conversely, if a bond is redeemable at par (that is, at 100) the purchaser will realize the bond rate if he pays 100. He will realize less than the bond rate if he buys at a premium and he will realize more than the bond rate if he buys at a discount.

At any point in time one of the three possible situations exists for any given bond

(1) Bond rate = Market rate ($b = i$) $\longrightarrow$ The bond sells at *par*.

(2) Bond rate < Market rate ($b < i$) $\longrightarrow$ The bond sells at a *discount*.

(3) Bond rate > Market rate ($b > i$) $\longrightarrow$ The bond sells at a *premium*.

Example 19.2a   A $10 000 bond is redeemable at par and bears interest at 10% compounded semi-annually.

(i) What is the purchase price ten years before maturity if the market rate compounded semi-annually is

  (a) 10%;   (b) 12%;   (c) 8%.

(ii) What is the purchase price five years before maturity if the market rate compounded semi-annually is

  (a) 10%;   (b) 12%;   (c) 8%.

Solution

(i) $S = 10000.00$; $R = 10000.00(0.05) = 500.00$; $n = 10(2) = 20$

  (a) $i = \frac{10\%}{2} = 5\% = 0.05$;   ($b = i$)

   Purchase price $= 10000.00\,(1.05^{-20}) + 500.00\,(a_{\overline{20}|\,5\%})$

   $= 10000.00\,(0.3768895) + 500.00\,(12.46221)$

   $= 3768.90 + 6231.11$

   $= \$10000.01$

    The bond sells at par.

(b) $i = \frac{12\%}{2} = 6\% = 0.06;$ $(b < i)$

Purchase price $= 10000.00(1.06^{-20}) + 500.00(a_{\overline{20}|6\%})$

$= 10000.00(0.3118047) + 500.00(11.469921)$

$= 3118.05 + 5734.96$

$= \$8853.01$

The bond sells below par.

The discount is $10000.00 - 8853.01 = \$1146.99$

(c) $i = \frac{8\%}{2} = 4\% = 0.04;$ $(b > i)$

Purchase price $= 10000.00(1.04^{-20}) + 500.00(a_{\overline{20}|4\%})$

$= 10000.00(0.4563869) + 500.00(13.590326)$

$= 4563.87 + 6795.16$

$= \$11359.03$

The bond sells above par.

The premium is $11359.03 - 10000.00 = \$1359.03$.

(ii) $S = 10000.00;$ $R = 500.00;$ $n = 5(2) = 10$

(a) $i = 5\%;$ $(b = i)$

Purchase price $= 10000.00(1.05^{-10}) + 500.00\ (a_{\overline{10}|5\%})$

$= 6139.13 + 3860.87$

$= \$10000.00$

The bond sells at par.

(b) $i = 6\%;$ $(b < i)$

Purchase price $= 10000.00(1.06^{-10}) + 500.00\ (a_{\overline{10}|6\%})$

$= 5583.95 + 3680.04$

$= \$9263.99$

The bond sells below par.

The discount is $10000.00 - 9263.99 = \$736.01$ and is smaller than in (i) because the time to maturity is shorter.

(c) $i = 4\%;$ $(b > i)$

$$\text{Purchase price} = 10000.00(1.04^{-10}) + 500.00\,(a_{\overline{10}|4\%})$$

$$= 6755.64 + 4055.45$$

$$= \$10811.09$$

The bond sells above par.

The premium is $10811.09 - 10000.00 = \$811.09$ and is smaller than in (i) because the time to maturity is shorter.

B. Direct method of computing the premium or discount —alternate method for finding the purchase price

Example 19.2b   A $5000.00, 12% bond with semi-annual coupons is purchased six years before maturity to yield 10% compounded semi-annually. Determine the premium.

Solution

$$S = 5000.00; \qquad b = \frac{12\%}{2} = 6\% = 0.06; \qquad R = 5000.00(0.06) = 300.00;$$

$$i = \frac{10\%}{2} = 5\% = 0.05; \qquad n = 6(2) = 12$$

Since $b > i$, the bond will sell at a premium.

$$\text{Purchase Price} = 5000.00(1.05^{-12}) + 300.00(a_{\overline{12}|5\%})$$

$$= 5000.00(0.5568374) + 300.00(8.8632516)$$

$$= 2784.19 + 2658.97$$

$$= \$5443.16$$

The premium is $5443.16 - 5000.00 = \$443.16$.

While the premium may always be obtained by the basic method using Formula 19.1, it is more convenient to determine the premium directly by considering the relationship between the bond rate b and the yield rate i.

As previously indicated a premium results when $b > i$. When this is the case, the premium is paid because the periodic interest payments received exceed the periodic interest required according to the yield rate.

In Example 19.2b

The semi-annual interest payment	5000.00(0.06)	= $300.00
The required semi-annual interest based on the yield rate	5000.00(0.05)	= $250.00
The excess of the actual interest received over the required interest to make the yield rate		= $50.00

This excess is received at the end of every payment interval; thus it forms an ordinary annuity whose present value may be computed at the yield rate i.

$$R \text{ (the excess interest)} = 50.00; \qquad i = 5\%; \qquad n = 12$$

$$A_n = 50.00(a_{\overline{12}|\,5\%})$$

$$= 50.00(8.8632516)$$

$$= \$443.16$$

The purchase price is $5000.00 + 443.16 = \$5443.16$.

The premium is the present value of the ordinary annuity formed by the excess of the actual bond interest over the required interest based on the yield rate and the purchase price may be obtained by adding the premium to the redemption value.

> PREMIUM = (PERIODIC BOND INTEREST − REQUIRED INTEREST) $a_{\overline{n}|i}$
> $= $ (FACE VALUE $\times b$ − REDEMPTION VALUE $\times i$) $a_{\overline{n}|i}$

Example 19.2c   A $5000, 12% bond with semi-annual coupons is purchased six years before maturity to yield 14% compounded semi-annually. Determine the discount.

Solution

$$S = 5000.00; \qquad b = \frac{12\%}{2} = 6\% = 0.06; \qquad R = 5000.00(0.06) = 300.00;$$

$$i = \frac{14\%}{2} = 7\% = 0.07; \qquad n = 6(2) = 12$$

Since $b < i$, the bond will sell at a discount.

$$\text{Purchase Price} = 5000.00(1.07^{-12}) + 300.00(a_{\overline{12}|\,7\%})$$

$$= 5000.00(0.444012) + 300.00(7.9426863)$$

$$= 2220.06 + 2382.81$$

$$= \$4602.87$$

The discount is $5000.00 - 4602.87 = \$397.13$.

As in the case of a premium, the discount may always be determined by the basic method using Formula 19.1 but it is more convenient to determine the discount directly.

When $b < i$ a discount results. The discount on a bond is received because the periodic interest payments are less than the periodic interest required to make the yield rate.

In Example 19.2c

The semi-annual interest payment	5000.00(0.06)	=	$300.00
The required semi-annual interest based on the yield rate	5000.00(0.07)	=	$350.00

The shortage of the actual interest received as compared
to the required interest based on the yield rate $\qquad$ = $\qquad$ $50.00

This shortage occurs at the end of every interest payment interval; it forms an ordinary annuity whose present value may be computed at the yield rate i.

$$R = 50.00; \qquad i = 7\%; \qquad n = 12$$

$$A_n = 50.00(a_{\overline{12}|7\%})$$
$$= 50.00(7.9426863)$$
$$= \$397.13$$

The purchase price is $5000.00 - 397.13 = \$4602.87$.

The discount is the present value of the ordinary annuity formed by the shortage of the actual bond interest received as compared to the required interest based on the yield rate and the purchase price may be obtained by subtracting the discount from the redemption value.

$$
\begin{aligned}
\text{DISCOUNT} &= (\text{REQUIRED INTEREST} - \text{PERIODIC BOND INTEREST})\, a_{\overline{n}|i} \\
&= -(\text{PERIODIC BOND INTEREST} - \text{REQUIRED INTEREST})\, a_{\overline{n}|i} \\
&= -(\text{FACE VALUE} \times b - \text{REDEMPTION VALUE} \times i)\, a_{\overline{n}|i}
\end{aligned}
$$

Since in either case the difference between the periodic bond interest and the required interest is involved, the premium or dicount on the purchase of a bond can be obtained using the same relationship.

$$
\begin{array}{l}
\text{PREMIUM} \\
\quad\text{or} \quad = (b \times \text{FACE VALUE} - i \times \text{REDEMPTION VALUE})\, a_{\overline{n}|i} \\
\text{DISCOUNT}
\end{array}
\qquad \longrightarrow \textbf{\textit{Formula}}\ \textbf{\textit{19.2}}
$$

Example 19.2d A $1000, 11.5% bond with semi-annual coupons redeemable at par in fifteen years is bought to yield 10% compounded semi-annually. Determine

(i) the premium or discount;

(ii) the purchase price.

Solution

$$S = 1000.00; \qquad b = \frac{11.5\%}{2} = 5.75\% = 0.0575;$$

$$R = 1000.00(0.0575) = 57.50;$$

$$i = \frac{10\%}{2} = 5\% = 0.05; \qquad n = 15(2) = 30$$

Since $b > i$, the bond will sell at a premium.

The required interest based on the yield rate is $1000.00(0.05) = 50.00$; the excess interest is $57.50 - 50.00 = 7.50$.

The Premium is $7.50(a_{\overline{30}|5\%}) = 7.50(15.372451) = \$115.29$.

The Purchase Price is $1000.00 + 115.29 = \$1115.29$.

Example 19.2e A \$50 000, 10% bond with quarterly coupons redeemable at par in ten years is purchased to yield 11% compounded quarterly.
 (i) What is the premium or discount?
(ii) What is the purchase price?

Solution

$$S = 50000.00; \qquad b = \frac{10\%}{4} = 2.5\% = 0.025;$$

$$n = 10(4) = 40; \qquad i = \frac{11\%}{4} = 2.75\% = 0.0275$$

Since $b < i$, the bond will sell at a discount.

Discount $= (0.025 \times 50000.00 - 0.0275 \times 50000.00)\, a_{\overline{40}|2.75\%} \longleftarrow$ using Formula 19.2

$= (1250.00 - 1375.00)(24.078101)$

$= -(125.00)(24.078101)$

$= -\$3009.76 \longleftarrow$ the negative sign indicates a discount

The Purchase Price is $50000.00 - 3009.76 = \$46990.24$.

Example 19.2f Bonds with a face value of \$15 000.00 redeemable at 108 with interest at 9% payable semi-annually are bought twelve years before maturity to yield 11% compounded semi-annually.
 (i) What is the premium or discount?
(ii) What is the purchase price?

Solution

$$S = 15000.00(1.08) = 16200.00; \qquad b = \frac{9\%}{2} = 4.5\% = 0.045;$$

$$n = 12(2) = 24; \qquad i = \frac{11\%}{2} = 5.5\% = 0.055$$

Since $b < i$ and the redemption value is greater than par, the bond will sell at a discount.

$$\text{Discount} = (0.045 \times 15000.00 - 0.055 \times 16200.00) \, a_{\overline{24}|\,5.5\%}$$

$$= (675.00 - 891.00)(13.151699)$$

$$= (-216.00)(13.151699)$$

$$= -\$2840.77$$

The Purchase Price is $16200.00 - 2840.77 = \$13359.23$.

Example 19.2g   A \$10 000, 13% bond with quarterly coupons redeemable at 106 in seven years is purchased to yield 11% compounded quarterly.

(i) What is the premium or discount?

(ii) What is the purchase price?

Solution

$$S = 10000.00(1.06) = 10600.00; \qquad b = \frac{13\%}{4} = 3.25\% = 0.0325;$$

$$n = 7(4) = 28; \qquad i = \frac{11\%}{4} = 2.75\% = 0.0275$$

Since $b > i$, the bond is expected to sell at a premium.

$$\text{Premium} = (0.0325 \times 10000.00 - 0.0275 \times 10600.00) \, a_{\overline{28}|\,2.75\%}$$

$$= (325.00 - 291.50)(19.350826)$$

$$= (33.50)(19.350826)$$

$$= \$648.25$$

The Purchase price is $10600.00 + 648.25 = \$11248.25$.

Example 19.2h   A \$1000, 11.5% bond redeemable at 110 with interest payable annually is bought nine years before maturity to yield 11% compounded annually. Determine

(i) the premium or discount;

(ii) the purchase price.

Solution

$$S = 1000(1.10) = 1100.00; \qquad b = 11.5\% = 0.115;$$

$$n = 9; \qquad i = 11\% = 0.11$$

Since $b > i$, the bond is expected to be sold at a premium. While this is always true for bonds redeemable at par it does not necessarily follow for bonds redeemable above par.

In this particular case

the actual bond interest per year $\qquad$ $1000.00(0.115) = \$115.00$

the interest required to make the yield rate $\qquad$ $1100.00(0.11) = \$121.00$

Because of the redemption premium, the required interest exceeds the actual interest: the bond will in fact sell at a discout. This is borne out when using Formula 19.2.

$$Premium/Discount = (0.115 \times 1000.00 - 0.11 \times 1100.00)\, a_{\overline{9}|11\%}$$

$$= (115.00 - 121.00)(5.5370475)$$

$$= (-6.00)(5.5370475)$$

$$= -\$33.22$$

Since the answer is negative, the bond sells at a discount of $33.22. The purchase price is $1100.00 - 33.22 = \$1066.78$.

***Example* 19.2i** A $25 000 bond, redeemable at 104 on July 1, 1996 with 11% coupons payable quarterly is bought on May 20, 1987 to yield 10% compounded quarterly. What is:

(i) the premium or discount?

(ii) the purchase price?

(iii) the quoted price?

Solution

$$S = 25000.00(1.04) = 26000.00; \qquad b = \frac{11\%}{4} = 2.75\% = 0.0275;$$

$$i = \frac{10\%}{4} = 2.5\% = 0.025$$

The interest payment dates are October 1, January 1, April 1 and July 1. The interest payment date preceding the date of purchase is April 1, 1987. The time period April 1, 1987 to July 1, 1996 contains 9 years and 3 months: $n = 9.25(4) = 37$

The premium on April 1, 1987

$$= (25000.00 \times 0.0275 - 26000.00 \times 0.025)\, a_{\overline{37}|2.5\%}$$

$$= (687.50 - 650.00)(23.957318)$$

$$= (37.50)(23.957318)$$

$$= \$898.40$$

The purchase price on April 1, 1987 is $26000.00 + 898.40 = \$26898.40$.

The time period April 1 to May 20 contains 49 days; the number of days in the interest payment interval April 1 to July 1 is 91.

$$P = 26898.40; \qquad r = i = 0.025; \qquad t = \frac{49}{91}$$

The accumulated value on May 20, 1987

$$= 26898.40\left(1 + 0.025\left(\frac{49}{91}\right)\right)$$
$$= 26898.40(1.0134615)$$
$$= \$27260.49$$

The accrued interest to May 20 is $25000.00(0.0275)\left(\dfrac{49}{91}\right) = \$370.19$.

The quoted price is $27260.49 - 370.19 = \$26890.30$.

Thus, on May 20, 1987

  (i) The premium is $26890.30 - 26000.00 = \$890.30$;

 (ii) The purchase price is $27\,260.49$;

(iii) The quoted price is $26\,890.30$.

Example 19.2j A two-million dollar issue of twenty-year municipal bonds redeemable at 104 is offered for sale to yield 11% compounded quarterly. If the bond interest is 12% payable annually, what is the issue price of the bonds?

Solution

$$S = 2000000.00(1.04) = 2080000.00; \qquad n = 20; \qquad c = 4;$$

$$b = 12\% = 0.12; \qquad i = \frac{11\%}{4} = 2.75\% = 0.0275;$$

$$f = 1.0275^4 - 1 = 1.1146213 - 1 = 0.1146213 = 11.46213\%$$

Since $b > f$, the issue is expected to sell at a premium.

$$\text{Premium} = (0.12 \times 2000000.00 - 0.1146213 \times 2080000.00)\, a_{\overline{20}|\,11.46213\%}$$

$$= (240000.00 - 238412.30)(7.72854570)$$

$$= (1587.70)(7.7284570)$$

$$= \$12270.47$$

The issue price is $2080000.00 + 12270.47 = \$2092270.47$.

Exercise 19.2

A. For each of the following bonds use Formula 19.2 to determine

    (a) the premium or discount;   **(b)** the purchase price.

No.	Par value	Redeemed at	Bond rate payable semi-annually	Time before redemption	Yield rate compounded semi-annually
1.	$25 000	par	12%	10 years	15%
2.	$5 000	par	16.5%	8 years	14%
3.	$10 000	104	9%	15 years	11%
4.	$3 000	107	13.5%	9 years	10.5%
5.	$60 000	108	12%	7 years	14.5%
6.	$7 000	110	15%	5 years	14%
7.	$1 000	105	13%	6 years 10 months	17%
8.	$50 000	108	12%	4 years 5 months	11.5%

B. Answer each of the following questions.

1. A $100 000, 11% bond redeemable at par with quarterly coupons is purchased to yield 16.5% compounded quarterly. Find the premium or discount and the purchase price if the bond is purchased

   (a) fifteen years before maturity;   **(b)** five years before maturity.

2. A $25 000, 15% bond redeemable at par with interest payable annually is bought six years before maturity. Determine the premium or discount and the purchase price if the bond is purchased to yield

   (a) 19.5% compounded annually;   **(b)** 12% compounded annually.

3. A $5000, 14.5% bond redeemable at 104 with semi-annual coupons is purchased to yield 13% compounded semi-annually. What is the premium or discount and the purchase price if the bond is bought

   (a) ten years before maturity;   **(b)** six years before maturity.

4. A $1000, 14% bond redeemable at 108 in seven years bears coupons payable annually. Compute the premium or discount and the purchase price if the yield, compounded annually, is

   (a) 12.5%;   **(b)** 13.5%   **(c)** 15.5%.

5. Twelve $1000 bonds redeemable at par bearing interest at 10% payable semi-annually and maturing on September 1, 1990 are bought on June 18, 1985 to yield 17.5% compounded semi-annually. Determine

   (a) the premium or discount on the preceding interest payment date;

   (b) the purchase price;

   (c) the quoted price.

6. Bonds with a face value of $30 000 redeemable at 107 on June 1, 1993 are offered for sale to yield 15.5% compounded quarterly. If interest is 17% payable quarterly and the bonds are bought on January 24, 1984, what is

(a) the premium or discount on the interest payment date preceding the date of sale?

(b) the purchase price?

(c) the quoted price?

7. A $5 000 000 issue of ten-year bonds redeemable at par offers 14% coupons payable semi-annually. What is the issue price of the bonds to yield 15% compounded monthly?

8. Twenty $5000 bonds redeemable at 110 bearing 12% coupons payable quarterly are sold eight years before maturity to yield 11.5% compounded annually. What is the purchase price of the bonds?

19.3 Bond schedules

A. Amortization of premium

If a bond is bought at more than the redemption value, the resulting premium is not recovered when the bond is redeemed at maturity and becomes a capital *loss*. To avoid the capital loss at maturity, the premium is written down gradually over the time period from the date of purchase to the maturity date. The writing down of the premium gradually reduces the book value until it equals the redemption value at the date of maturity.

The process of writing down the premium is referred to as **amortization of the premium**. The most direct method of amortizing a premium assigns the difference between the interest received (coupon) and the interest required according to the yield rate to write down the premium. The details of writing down the premium are often shown in a tabulation referred to as a schedule of amortization of premium.

Example 19.3a A $1000, 12% bond redeemable at par matures in three years. The coupons are payable semi-annually and the bond is bought to yield 10% compounded semi-annually.

(i) Compute the purchase price.

(ii) Construct a schedule of the amortization of premium.

Solution

(i)

$$S = 1000.00; \qquad n = 3(2) = 6;$$

$$b = \frac{12\%}{2} = 6\% = 0.06; \qquad i = \frac{10\%}{2} = 5\% = 0.05$$

Since $b > i$, the bond sells at a premium.

$$\text{Premium} = (0.06 \times 1000.00 - 0.05 \times 1000.00) \, a_{\overline{6}|5\%}$$
$$= (60.00 - 50.00)(5.075692)$$
$$= (10.00)(5.075692)$$
$$= \$50.76$$

The Purchase Price is $1000.00 + 50.76 = \$1050.76$.

(ii) *Schedule of amortization of premium*

End of interest payment interval	Bond interest received (coupon) $b = 6\%$	Interest on book value at yield rate $i = 5\%$	Amount of premium amortized	Book value of bond	Remaining premium
0				1050.76	50.76
1	60.00	52.54	7.46	1043.30	43.30
2	60.00	52.17	7.83	1035.47	35.47
3	60.00	51.77	8.23	1027.24	27.24
4	60.00	51.36	8.64	1018.60	18.60
5	60.00	50.93	9.07	1009.53	9.53
6	60.00	50.47	9.53	1000.00	0.00
TOTAL	360.00	309.24	50.76		

Explanation to schedule

1. The original book value shown is the purchase price of $1050.76.

2. At the end of the first interest payment interval the interest received (coupon) is $1000.00(0.06) = \$60.00$; the interest required according to the yield rate is $1050.76(0.05) = \$52.54$; the difference $60.00 - 52.54 = 7.46$ is used to write down the premium and reduces the book value from $1050.76 to $1043.30.

3. The coupon at the end of the second interest payment interval is again $60.00. The interest required according to the yield rate is $1043.30(0.05) = \$52.17$; the difference $60.00 - 52.17 = 7.83$ reduces the premium to $35.47 and the book value of the bond to $1035.47.

4. Continue in a similar manner until the maturity date when the redemption value is reached. If a rounding error becomes apparent at the end of the final interest payment interval, adjust the final interest on the book value at the yield rate to make the premium zero and to obtain the exact redemption price as the book value.

5. The totals provide useful accounting information showing the total interest received ($360.00) and the net income realized ($309.24).

Example **19.3b**   A $25 000.00, 12.5% bond redeemable at 106 with coupons payable annually matures in seven years. The bond is bought to yield 11% compounded annually.

(i) Compute the premium and the purchase price.

(ii) Construct a schedule of amortization of premium.

Solution

(i)
$$S = 25000.00(1.06) = 26500.00; \qquad n = 7;$$
$$b = 12.5\% = 0.125; \qquad i = 11\% = 0.11$$

Since $b > i$, the bond is expected to sell at a premium.

$$\text{Premium} = (0.125 \times 25000.00 - 0.11 \times 26500.00)\, a\,_{\overline{7}|11\%}$$
$$= (3125.00 - 2915.00)(4.7121963)$$
$$= (210.00)(4.7121963)$$
$$= \$989.56$$

The Purchase Price is $26500.00 + 989.56 = \$27489.56$.

(ii) *Schedule of amortization of premium*

End of interest payment interval	Coupon $b = 12.5\%$	Interest on book value at yield rate $i = 11\%$	Amount of premium amortized	Book value of bond	Remaining premium
0				27 489.56	989.56
1	3125.00	3023.85	101.15	27 388.41	888.41
2	3125.00	3012.73	112.27	27 276.14	776.14
3	3125.00	3000.38	124.62	27 151.52	651.52
4	3125.00	2986.67	138.33	27 013.19	513.19
5	3125.00	2971.45	153.55	26 859.64	359.64
6	3125.00	2954.56	170.44	26 689.20	189.20
7	3125.00	2935.80	189.20	26 500.00	0.00
TOTAL	21 875.00	20 885.44	989.56		

B. Accumulation of discount

If a bond is bought at less than the redemption value, there will be a gain at the time of redemption equal to the amount of discount. It is generally accepted accounting practice that this gain does not accrue in total to the accounting period in which the bond is redeemed, but that some of the gain accrues to each of the accounting periods encompassed by the time period from the date of purchase to the date of redemption.

To adhere to this practice, the discount is decreased gradually so that the book value of the bond increases gradually until at the date of redemption the discount will be reduced to zero while the book value will equal the redemption price. The process of reducing the discount so as to increase the book value is referred to as **accumulation of discount**.

In the case of discount, the interest required according to the yield rate is greater than the actual interest received (the coupon). Similar to amortization of a premium, the most direct method of accumulating a discount assigns the difference between the interest required by the yield rate and the coupon to reduce the discount. The details of decreasing the discount while increasing the book value of a bond are often shown in a tabulation referred to as a schedule of accumulation of discount.

Example 19.3c   A $10 000 bond, redeemable at par in four years with 11.5% coupons payable semi-annually is purchased to yield 13% compounded semi-annually.

(i) Determine the discount and the purchase price.

(ii) Construct a schedule of the accumulation of the discount.

Solution

(i)
$$S = 10000.00; \qquad n = 4(2) = 8;$$

$$b = \frac{11.5\%}{2} = 5.75\% = 0.0575; \qquad i = \frac{13\%}{2} = 6.5\% = 0.065$$

Since $b < i$, the bond sells at a discount.

$$\text{Discount} = (0.0575 \times 10000.00 - 0.065 \times 10000.00)\, a_{\overline{8}|6.5\%}$$

$$= (575.00 - 650.00)(6.088751)$$

$$= (-75.00)(6.088751)$$

$$= -\$456.66$$

The Purchase Price is $10000.00 - 456.66 = \$9543.34$.

(ii) Schedule of accumulation of discount

End of interest payment interval	Coupon b = 5.75%	Interest on book value at yield rate i = 6.5%	Amount of discount accumulated	Book value of bond	Remaining discount
0				9 543.34	456.66
1	575.00	620.32	45.32	9 588.66	411.34
2	575.00	623.26	48.26	9 636.92	363.08
3	575.00	626.40	51.40	9 688.32	311.68
4	575.00	629.74	54.74	9 743.06	256.94
5	575.00	633.30	58.30	9 801.36	198.64
6	575.00	637.09	62.09	8 963.45	136.55
7	575.00	641.12	66.12	9 929.57	70.43
8	575.00	645.43	70.43	10 000.00	0.00
TOTAL	4600.00	5056.66	456.66		

Explanations to schedule

1. The original book value shown is the purchase price of $9543.34.

2. At the end of the first interest payment interval the coupon is 10000.00(0.0575) = $575.00; the interest required according to the yield rate is 9543.34(0.065) = $620.32; the difference used to reduce the discount and to increase the book value is 620.32 − 575.00 = $45.32; the book value is 9543.34 + 45.32 = $9588.66 and the remaining discount is 456.66 − 45.32 = $ 411.34.

3. The coupon at the end of the second interest payment interval is again $575.00; the interest required on the book value is 9588.66(0.065) = $623.26; the difference is 623.26 − 575.00 = $48.26; the book value is 9588.66 + 46.26 = $9636.92 and the remaining discount is 411.34 − 46.26 = $363.08.

4. Continue in a similar manner until the maturity date when the redemption value is reached. If a rounding error becomes apparent at the end of the final interest payment interval, adjust the final interest on the book value at the yield rate to make the remaining discount equal to zero and obtain the exact redemption price as the book value.

5. The totals provide useful accounting information showing the total interest received ($4600.00) and the net income realized ($5056.66).

Example 19.3d   A $5000, 10% bond redeemable at 102 on April 1, 1986 with coupons payable quarterly is bought on October 1, 1984 to yield 13% compounded quarterly.

(i) Compute the discount and the purchase price.

(ii) Construct a schedule showing the accumulation of the discount.

Solution

(i) $$S = 5000.00(1.02) = 5100.00;$$

the time period October 1, 1984 to April 1, 1986 contains 18 months.

$$n = \frac{18}{3} = 6 \text{ (quarters)};$$

$$b = \frac{10\%}{4} = 2.5\% = 0.025; \qquad i = \frac{13\%}{4} = 3.25\% = 0.0325$$

Since $b < i$, the bond sells at a discount.

$$\text{Discount} = (0.025 \times 5000.00 - 0.0325 \times 5100.00) \, a_{\overline{6}|\,3.25\%}$$

$$= (125.00 - 165.75)(5.3725899)$$

$$= (-40.75)(5.3725899)$$

$$= -\$218.93$$

The Purchase Price is 5100.00 − 218.93 = $4881.07.

End of interest payment interval	Coupon $b = 2.5\%$	Interest on book value at yield rate $i = 3.25\%$	Amount of discount accumulated	Book value of bond	Remaining discount
Oct 1, 1984				4881.07	218.93
Jan 1, 1985	125.00	158.63	33.63	4914.70	185.30
Apr 1, 1985	125.00	159.73	34.73	4949.43	150.57
July 1, 1985	125.00	160.86	35.86	4985.29	114.71
Oct 1, 1985	125.00	162.02	37.02	5022.31	77.69
Jan 1, 1986	125.00	163.23	38.23	5060.54	39.46
Apr 1, 1986	125.00	164.46	39.46	5100.00	0.00
TOTAL	750.00	968.93	218.93		

C. Book value of a bond—finding the gain or loss on the sale of a bond

Example 19.3e A $10000, 12% bond redeemable at par with semi-annual coupons was purchased fifteen years before maturity to yield 10% compounded semi-annually. The bond was sold three years later at $101\frac{1}{4}$. Find the gain or loss on the sale of the bond.

Solution

The market quotation of $101\frac{1}{4}$ indicates that the bond was sold at 101.25% of its face value. The proceeds from the sale of the bond are $10000.00(1.0125) = \$10125.00$.

To find the gain or loss on the sale of the bond we need to know the book value of the bond at the date of sale. This we can do by determining the original purchase price, constructing a bond schedule and reading the book value at the time of sale from the schedule.

$$S = 10000.00; \qquad n = 15(2) = 30$$

$$b = \frac{12\%}{2} = 6\% = 0.06; \qquad i = \frac{10\%}{2} = 5\% = 0.05$$

Since $b > i$, the bond was bought at a premium.

Premium $= (0.06 \times 10000.00 - 0.05 \times 10000.00)\, a_{\overline{30}|\,5\%}$

$\qquad = (600.00 - 500.00)(15.372451)$

$\qquad = (100.00)(15.372451)$

$\qquad = \$1537.25$

The Purchase Price is $10000.00 + 1537.25 = \$11537.25$.

Schedule of amortization of premium

End of interest payment interval	Coupon $b = 6\%$	Interest on book value at yield rate $i = 5\%$	Amount of premium amortized	Book value of bond	Remaining premium
0				11 537.25	1537.25
1	600.00	576.86	23.14	11 514.11	1514.11
2	600.00	575.71	24.29	11 489.82	1489.82
3	600.00	574.49	25.51	11 464.31	1464.31
4	600.00	573.22	26.78	11 437.53	1437.53
5	600.00	571.88	28.12	11 409.41	1409.41
6	600.00	570.47	29.53	11 379.88	1379.88
	etc				

The book value after three years (six semi-annual periods) is \$11 379.88. Since the book value is greater than the proceeds, the loss on sale of the bond is $10125.00 - 11379.88 = \$1254.88$.

The problem can be solved more quickly by finding the book value directly by computation. The book value of a bond at a given point in time is the purchase price of the bond on that date. Hence the book value of a bond may be determined without constructing a bond schedule by using Formula 19.1 or 19.2. This approach can also be used to verify book values in a bond schedule.

$$S = 10000.00; \qquad n = (15 - 3)(2) = 24; \qquad b = 6\%; \qquad i = 5\%$$

$$\text{Premium} = (0.06 \times 10000.00 - 0.05 \times 10000.00)\, a_{\overline{24}|\,5\%}$$

$$= (100.00)(13.798642)$$

$$= \$1379.86$$

The Purchase price is $10000.00 + 1379.86 = \$11379.86$.
The Loss on the sale is $11379.86 - 10125.00 = \$1254.86$
(The difference in the loss results is due to rounding)

Example 19.3f A \$5000, 11% bond redeemable at 106 with semi-annual coupons was purchased twelve years before maturity to yield 10.5% compounded semi-annually. The bond is sold five years later at $98\frac{7}{8}$. Find the gain or loss on the sale of the bond.

Solution

Proceeds from the sale of the bond are $5000.00(0.98875) = \$4943.75$.

$$S = 5000.00(1.06) = 5300.00; \qquad n = (12 - 5)(2) = 14;$$

$$b = \frac{11\%}{2} = 5.5\% = 0.055; \qquad i = \frac{10.5\%}{2} = 5.25\% = 0.0525$$

Premium/Discount $= (0.055 \times 5000.00 - 0.0525 \times 5300.00)\, a_{\overline{14}|\,5.25\%}$

$$= (275.00 - 278.25)(9.7423008)$$
$$= (-3.25)(9.7423008)$$
$$= -\$31.66 \longleftarrow \text{Discount}$$

The Purchase Price or Book Value is $5300.00 - 31.66 = \$5268.34$.
The Loss on the Sale is $5268.34 - 4943.75 = \$324.59$.

Example 19.3g   A \$1000, 10% bond with quarterly coupons redeemable at 104 on May 1, 1992 was purchased on August 1, 1982 to yield 12% compounded quarterly. If the bond is sold at $95\frac{1}{2}$ on December 11, 1985, what is the gain or loss on the sale of the bond?

Solution

The interest payment dates are August 1, November 1, February 1 and May 1. The interest date preceding the date of sale is November 1, 1985. The proceeds from the sale of the bond on December 11, 1985

$= 1000.00(0.955) + $ Accrued interest from November 1 to December 11

$$= 955.00 + 1000.00(0.025)\left(\frac{40}{92}\right)$$

$$= 955.00 + 10.87$$
$$= \$965.87$$

$S = 1000.00(1.04) = 1040.00;$

$$b = \frac{10\%}{4} = 2.5\% = 0.025; \qquad i = \frac{12\%}{4} = 3\% = 0.03$$

The time interval November 1,1985 to May 1, 1992 contains six years and 6 months: $n = 6.5(4) = 26$.

Since $b < i$, the bond will sell at a discount.

Discount $= (0.025 \times 1000.00 - 0.03 \times 1040.00)\, a_{\overline{26}|\,3\%}$

$$= (25.00 - 31.20)(17.876842)$$
$$= (-6.20)(17.876842)$$
$$= -\$110.84$$

The Purchase Price on November 1, 1985 is $1040.00 - 110.84 = \$929.16$.
The accumulated value on December 11, 1985

$$= 929.16\left(1 + 0.03\left(\frac{40}{92}\right)\right)$$

$$= 929.16(1.0130435)$$
$$= \$941.28$$

The gain from the sale of the bond is $965.87 - 941.28 = \$24.59$.

Exercise 19.3

A. For each of the following bonds compute the premium or discount and the purchase price and construct the appropriate bond schedule.

1. A \$5000, 9% bond redeemable at par in three-and-a-half years with semi-annual coupons is purchased to yield 16.5% compounded semi-annually.

2. A \$25 000 bond with interest at 12.5% payable quarterly redeemable at par is bought two years before maturity to yield 11% compounded quarterly.

3. A \$1000, 12% bond with semi-annual coupons redeemable at 103 on September 1, 1987 is bought on March 1, 1984 to yield 10% compounded semi-annually.

4. A \$10 000, 14.75% bond with annual coupons redeemable at 110 in seven years is bought to yield 14.25% compounded annually.

B. Find the gain or loss on sale of each of the following bonds without constructing a bond schedule.

1. A \$25 000, 10.5% bond redeemable at par with semi-annual coupons bought ten years before maturity to yield 12% compounded semi-annually is sold four years before maturity at $99\frac{1}{4}$.

2. Four \$5000, 14.5% bonds with interest payable semi-annually redeemable at par were bought twenty years before maturity to yield 13.5% compounded semi-annually. The bonds were sold three years later at $103\frac{5}{8}$.

3. Seven \$1000, 9.25% bonds with annual coupons redeemable at 107 were bought nine years before maturity to yield 13.25% compounded annually. The bonds are sold three years before maturity at $94\frac{1}{2}$.

4. A \$100000, 13% bond with semi-annual coupons redeemable at 102 was purchased eleven-and-a-half years before maturity to yield 12% compounded semi-annually. The bond was sold five years later at $99\frac{1}{8}$.

5. A \$5000 bond with 15% interest payable semi-annually redeemable at par on June 1, 1996 was purchased on December 1, 1982 to yield 16% compounded semi-annually. The bond was sold on September 22, 1986 at $101\frac{3}{8}$.

6. Three \$10 000, 10.5% bonds with quarterly coupons redeemable at 109 on August 1, 1994 were bought on May 1, 1980 to yield 12% compounded quarterly. The bonds were sold on January 16, 1988 at $93\frac{1}{2}$.

19.4 Finding the yield rate

A. Quoted price of a bond—buying bonds on the market

Bonds are usually bought or sold through a bond exchange where the trading of bonds is conducted through agents acting on behalf of their clients. To allow for the different denominations, bonds are offered at a quoted price stated as a percent of their face value.

It is understood that such a quoted price does not include any accrued interest if the bond is purchased between interest dates. As explained in Section 19.1, the seller of a bond is entitled to the interest earned by the bond to the date of sale and the interest is added to the quoted price to obtain the purchase price (flat price).

Example 19.4a A $5000, 12% bond with semi-annual coupons payable April 1 and October 1 is purchased on August 25 at $104\frac{3}{4}$. What is the purchase price of the bond?

Solution

The quoted price is 5000.00(1.0475) = $5237.50.
The time period April 1 to August 25 contains 146 days; the number of days in the interest payment interval April 1 to October 1 is 183.

$$P = 5000.00; \qquad r = i = \frac{12\%}{2} = 6\% = 0.06; \qquad t = \frac{146}{183}$$

The accrued interest is $5000.00(0.06)\left(\dfrac{146}{183}\right) = \$239.34$.

The purchase price (flat price) is 5237.50 + 239.34 = $5476.84.

B. Finding the yield rate—the average investment method

When bonds are bought on the market the yield rate is not directly available and needs to be determined. The most simple method in use is the so called **Method of Averages** which gives a reasonable approximation of the yield rate as the ratio of the average income per interest payment interval to the average book value.

APPROXIMATE VALUE OF i = $\dfrac{\text{AVERAGE INCOME PER INTEREST PAYMENT INTERVAL}}{\text{AVERAGE BOOK VALUE}}$

where

AVERAGE BOOK VALUE = $\dfrac{1}{2}$(QUOTED PRICE + REDEMPTION PRICE)

and

$\left.\begin{array}{l}\text{AVERAGE INCOME}\\ \text{PER INTEREST}\\ \text{PAYMENT INTERVAL}\end{array}\right\}$ = $\dfrac{\text{TOTAL INTEREST PAYMENTS} \begin{array}{l} - \\ + \end{array}\begin{vmatrix}\text{PREMIUM}\\ \text{DISCOUNT}\end{vmatrix}}{\text{NUMBER OF INTEREST PAYMENT INTERVALS}}$

Example 19.4b A $25000, 11.5% bond with semi-annual coupons redeemable at par in ten years is purchased at $103\frac{1}{2}$. What is the approximate yield rate?

The quoted price (initial book value) is $25000(1.035) = \$25875.00$; the redemption price is $25000.00.

The Average book value is $\frac{1}{2}(25875.00 + 25000.00) = \$25437.50$.

The semi-annual interest payment is $25000.00\left(\frac{0.115}{2}\right) = \$1437.50$;

the number of interest payments to maturity is $10(2) = 20$;

the total interest payments are $20(1437.50) = \$28750.00$;

the premium is $25875.00 - 25000.00 = \$875.00$.

$$\text{Average income per interest payment period} = \frac{(28750 - 875.00)}{20}$$

$$= \$1393.75$$

$$\text{Approximate value of } i = \frac{1393.75}{25437.50} = 0.0547912 = 5.48\%$$

The yield rate is $2(5.48) = 10.96\%$.

Example 19.4c Eight $1000, 10% bonds with semi-annual coupons redeemable at 105 in seventeen years are purchased at $97\frac{3}{8}$. What is the approximate yield rate?

Solution

The quoted price is $8000.00(0.97375) = \$7790.00$;
the redemption value is $8000.00(1.05) = \$8400.00$;

$$\text{The Average Book Value is } \frac{(7790.00 + 8400.00)}{2} = \$8095.00.$$

The semi-annual interest payment is $8000.00\left(\frac{0.10}{2}\right) = \$400.00$;

the number of interest payments to maturity is $17(2) = 34$;

the total interest payments are $34(400.00) = \$13600.00$;

the bond discount is $8400.00 - 7790.00 = \$610.00$.

$$\text{Average Income Per Interest Payment Interval} = \frac{(13600.00 + 610.00)}{34}$$

$$= \$417.94$$

$$\text{The approximate value of } i \text{ is } \frac{417.94}{8095.00} = 0.0516295 = 5.16\%.$$

The approximate yield rate is $2(5.16\%) = 10.32\%$.

Example 19.4d A $5000, 10% bond with semi-annual coupons redeemable at par on July 15, 1995 is quoted on December 2, 1983 at $103\frac{3}{4}$. What is the approximate yield rate?

Solution

To find the approximate yield rate for a bond purchased between interest dates assume that the price was quoted on the nearest interest date. Since the interest dates are January 15 and July 15, the nearest interest date is January 15, 1984 which is 11.5 years before maturity.

The quoted price is 5000.00(1.0375) = $5187.50; the redemption value is 5000.00;

the average book value is $\dfrac{(5187.50 + 5000.00)}{2} = \$5093.75$.

The semi-annual interest is $5000.00\left(\dfrac{0.10}{2}\right) = \$250.00$;

the number of interest payments to maturity is 11.5(2) = 23; the total interest payments are 23(250.00) = $5750.00; the premium is 5187.50 − 5000.00 = $187.50.

The average income per interest payment interval = $\dfrac{(5750.00 - 187.50)}{23}$

$$= \$241.85$$

The approximate value of i is $\dfrac{241.85}{5093.75} = 0.047479 = 4.75\%$.

the approximate yield rate is 2(4.75%) = 9.50%.

C. Finding the yield rate by trial and error

A method of trial and error similar to the one used in finding the nominal rate of interest in Chapter 15 may be used to obtain as precise an approximation to the yield rate as desired. When using this method the rate obtained by the Method of Averages should be used for the first attempt by substituting in Formula 19.1
$PP = S(1 + i)^{-n} + R\, a\,_{\overline{n}|\, i}.$

Example 19.4e Compute the yield rate for Example 19.4b.

Solution

The approximate value of i by the Method of Averages is 5.48%; the quoted price is $25 875.00.

Our aim is to find the value of i for which Formula 19.1 gives a purchase price equal to the quoted price of $25 875.00.

$$S = 25000.00; \qquad R = 1437.50; \qquad n = 20;$$

$$PP = 25000.00(1 + i)^{-20} + 1437.50 \, a \, \overline{_{20}}_{|i}$$

For $i = 5.48\%$ $\quad PP = 25000.00(1.0548^{-20}) + 1437.50 \, a \, \overline{_{20}}_{|5.48\%}$

$$= 8600.77 + 17207.22$$

$$= \$25807.99$$

Since the computed purchase price of $25807.99 is less than the quoted price of $25875.00, $i < 5.48\%$.

For $i = 5.46\%$ $\quad PP = 8633.46 + 17235.83 = 25869.29 \longrightarrow i < 5.46\%$

For $i = 5.456\%$ $PP = 8640.01 + 17241.56 = 25881.57 \longrightarrow 5.456\% < i$

$\qquad\qquad\qquad\qquad\qquad\qquad\qquad\qquad\qquad\qquad < 5.46\%$

For $i = 5.458\%$ $PP = 8636.73 + 17238.70 = 25875.43 \longrightarrow i = 5.458\%$

Note The computed purchase price is almost exactly equal to the quoted price; hence $i = 5.458\%$ is a very precise value.

The yield rate is $2(5.458\%) = 10.916\%$.

Example 19.4f Compute the yield rate for Example 19.4d.

Solution

The approximate value of i by the Method of Averages $= 4.75\%$; the quoted price on December 2, 1983 is $5187.50.

We want to find the value of i for which Formula 19.1 gives a purchase price equal to the quoted price of $5187.50.

When the date of purchase is between interest dates, the precise value of i may be approximated by using the theoretically correct number of interest conversion intervals in fractional form.

The number of days from the date of purchase (December 2, 1983) to the next interest payment date (January 15, 1984) is 44;

the number of conversion periods from December 2, 1983 to July 15, 1995 is

$$23 + \frac{44}{184} = 23.23913.$$

$$S = 5000.00; \qquad R = 250.00$$

Substituting in Formula 19.1

$$PP = 5000.00(1 + i)^{-23.23913} + 250.00 \, a \, \overline{_{23.23913}}_{|i}$$

For $i = 4.75\%$ $\quad PP = 5000.00(1.0475^{-23.23913}) + 250.00 \, a \, \overline{_{23.23913}}_{|4.75\%}$

$$= 1700.62 + 3473.03$$

$$= \$5173.65$$

Since the purchase price of $5173.65 is less than the quoted price of $5187.50, $i < 4.75\%$.

For i = 4.73% PP = 1708.19 + 3479.72 = 5187.91 $\longrightarrow$ 4.73 < i < 4.75%

For i = 24.731% PP = 1707.81 + 3479.38 = 5187.19 $\longrightarrow$ 4.73% < i
$< 4.731\%$

For i = 4.7305% PP = 1708.00 + 3479.55 = 5187.55 $\longrightarrow$ i = 4.7305%

The yield rate is 2(4.7305%) = 9.461%.

Example **19.4g** A $10000, 11.5% bond with quarterly coupons redeemable at 106 on September 1, 1993 is bought on April 10, 1984 at $94\frac{1}{2}$. What is the yield rate?

Solution

The quoted price is 10000.00(0.945) = $9450.00;
the redemption value is 10000.00(1.06) = $10600.00;

$$\text{the average book value is } \frac{(9450.00 + 10600.00)}{2} = \$10025.00.$$

The interest payment dates are December 1, March 1, June 1 and September 1; the interest date closest to April 10 is March 1.
Assuming that the price was quoted on March 1, 1984, the time to maturity is 9 years and 6 months; the number of interest payments to maturity is 4(9.5) = 38;

the quarterly interest payment is $10000.00\left(\dfrac{0.115}{4}\right)$ = $287.50;

the total interest payments are 38(287.50) = $10925.00;
the discount is 10600.00 − 9450.00 = $1150.00.

$$\text{The average income per interest payment interval} = \frac{(10925.00 + 1150.00)}{38}$$

$$= \$317.76$$

$$\text{The approximate value of } i = \frac{317.76}{10025.00} = 0.0316968 = 3.17\%$$

The number of days from April 10 to June 1 is 52;
the number of days in the interest payment interval March 1 to June 1 is 92;
the exact number of interest payment intervals from April 10, 1984 to

September 1, 1993 is $37 + \dfrac{52}{92}$ = 37.565217.

$$S = 10600.00; \qquad R = 287.50; \qquad n = 37.565217$$

Substituting in Formula 19.1

$$PP = 10600.00(1 + i)^{-37.565217} + 287.50 \, a \, \overline{_{37.565217}|}\, i$$

$For \ i = 3.17\%$ $PP = 10600.00(0.3096438) + 287.50(21.777797)$

$$= 3282.22 + 6261.12$$

$$= \$9543.34$$

since $9543.34 > 9450.00$ $\longrightarrow i > 3.17\%$

$For \ i = 3.20\%$ $PP = 3246.57 + 6232.64 = 9479.21 \longrightarrow i > 3.20\%$

$For \ i = 3.22\%$ $PP = 3223.03 + 6213.76 = 9436.79 \longrightarrow 3.20\% < i < 3.22\%$

$For \ i = 3.214\%$ $PP = 3230.07 + 6219.41 \ = 9449.48 \longrightarrow i = 3.214\%$

The yield rate is $4(3.214) = 12.856\%$.

Example 19.4h   Ram Snead purchased a \$5000, 10% bond with semi-annual coupons redeemable at par at $93\frac{3}{4}$ twenty years before maturity. He sold the bond nine years later at $100\frac{1}{2}$. What yield rate did Ram realize?

Solution

Ram's purchase price is $5000.00(0.9375) = \$4687.50 \longleftarrow$ Original book value

Ram's selling price is $5000.00(1.005) = \$5025.00 \longleftarrow$ Final book value

The average book value is $4687.50 + 5025.00 = \$4856.25$.

The semi-annual coupon is $5000.00\left(\dfrac{0.10}{2}\right) = \$250.00$;

the number of interest payments received by Ram is $9(2) = 18$;

the total interest payments are $18(250.00) = \$4500.00$;

the gain on the sale is $5025.00 - 4687.50 = \$337.50 \longleftarrow$ discount

The average income per interest interval is $\dfrac{(4500.00 + 337.50)}{18}$

$$= \$268.75$$

The approximate value of i is $\dfrac{268.75}{4856.25}$

$$= 0.0553411$$

$$= 5.53\%.$$

Our aim is to find the value of i for which Formula 19.1 gives a purchase price of \$4687.50 given that

$$S = 5025.00; \qquad R = 250.00; \qquad n = 18$$

$$PP = 5025.00(1 + i)^{-18} + 250.00 \, a \, \overline{_{18}|}\, i$$

$For \ i = 5.53\%$ $PP = 5025.00(1.0553^{-18}) + 250.00 \, a \, \overline{_{18}|}\, 5.53\%$

$$= 5025.00(0.3795186) + 250.00(11.220278)$$

$$= \$4712.15$$

Since $4712.15 > 4687.50, \ i > 5.53\%$.

For $i = 5.55\%$ $PP = 1900.59 + 2800.78 = 4701.37 \longrightarrow i > 5.55\%$

For $i = 5.57\%$ $PP = 1894.12 + 2796.51 = 4690.63 \longrightarrow i > 5.57\%$

For $i = 5.577\%$ $PP = 1891.86 + 2795.01 = 4686.87 \longrightarrow 5.75\% < i < 5.577\%$

For $i = 5.576\%$ $PP = 1892.18 + 2795.22 = 4687.40 \longrightarrow i = 5.576\%$

The yield rate is $2(5.576\%) = 11.152\%$.

Exercise 19.4

A. Use the Method of Averages to find the approximate yield rate for each of the following bonds.

Problem number	Face value	Bond rate payable semi-annually	Time before redemption	Redeemed at	Market quotation
1.	$10 000	12%	15 years	par	$101\frac{3}{8}$
2.	$5 000	10.5%	7 years	par	$94\frac{3}{4}$
3.	$25 000	11.5%	10 years	104	$97\frac{1}{8}$
4.	$1 000	15.5%	8 years	109	101
5.	$50 000	13%	5 years 4 months	par	$98\frac{7}{8}$
6.	$20 000	17%	9 years 8 months	106	$109\frac{1}{4}$

B. Using trial and error find the yield rate for each of the following bonds.

1. Part A, Problems 1, 3, 5.

2. Part A, Problems 2, 4, 6.

3. A $1000, 11.5% bond with semi-annual coupons redeemable at par on November 15, 1996 is bought on April 5, 1983 at $96\frac{3}{4}$.

4. A $5000, 16% bond with interest payable quarterly redeemable at 110 on July 1, 1995 is purchased on October 26, 1982 at $101\frac{7}{8}$.

5. A $10 000, 15% bond with semi-annual coupons was bought seventeen years before maturity at $102\frac{1}{4}$ and sold at $99\frac{1}{2}$ five years later. What was the yield rate realized?

6. Four $1000, 10.5% bond with interest payable semi-annually redeemable at 101 on August 15, 1998 was bought on October 14, 1981 at $87\frac{3}{4}$ and sold on May 25, 1985 at $91\frac{1}{2}$.

(a) What would have been the yield rate if held to maturity?

(b) What was the yield rate realized by selling the bond on May 25, 1985?

19.5 Other types of bonds

A. Annuity bonds

The bonds considered in the previous sections have been bonds redeemed in one payment at maturity. However, some bonds are redeemed in such a way that the repayment of the face value plus interest payments form an ordinary annuity. Such bonds are referred to as **annuity bonds** and may be dealt with by the methods shown in Chapter 18 to amortize debts.

Example 19.5a A 12% annuity bond of $40 000 is to be redeemed by equal semi-annual payments, including principal and interest, over ten years.

(i) What is the purchase price to yield 11% compounded semi-annually?

(ii) If the bond is sold four years later to yield 13% compounded semi-annually, what is the selling price of the bond?

(iii) What is the gain or loss on sale of the bond?

Solution

(i) STEP 1 Determine the size of the semi-annual payment

$$A_n = 40000.00; \qquad i = \frac{12\%}{2} = 6\% = 0.06; \qquad n = 10(2) = 20$$

$$40000.00 = R\, a_{\overline{20}|6\%}$$

$$40000.00 = R(11.469921)$$

$$R = \$3487.38$$

The semi-annual bond redemption payment is $3487.38.

STEP 2 Since the buyer of the bond receives semi-annual payments of $3487.38, the purchase price is the present value of the payments discounted at the yield rate

$$R = 3487.38; \qquad i = \frac{11\%}{2} = 5.5\%; \qquad n = 20$$

$$A_n = 3487.38\, a_{\overline{20}|5.5\%}$$

$$= 3487.38(11.950382)$$

$$= \$41675.52$$

The purchase price of the bond to yield 11% is $41 675.52.

(ii) The selling price four years later is the present value of the outstanding semi-annual payments at the new yield rate.

$$R = 3487.38; \qquad i = \frac{13\%}{2} = 6.5\%; \qquad n = 6(2) = 12$$

$$A_n = 3487.38\, a_{\overline{12}|6.5\%}$$

$$= 3487.38(8.1587253)$$

$$= \$28452.58$$

The selling price four years later to yield 13% is $28 452.58.

(iii) The gain or loss on sale of the bond is the difference between the selling price and the book value.

The book value is the present value of the outstanding semi-annual payments at the time of sale discounted at the original yield rate.

$$R = 3487.38; \qquad i = 5.5\%; \qquad n = 12$$

$$A_n = 3487.38 \, a_{\overline{12}|\,5.5\%}$$

$$= 3487.38(8.6185178)$$

$$= \$30056.05$$

The loss on sale of the bond is $30056.05 - 28452.58 = \$1603.47$.

B. Serial bonds

When a bond issue is redeemed at staggered dates rather than on a common maturity date the bond is called a **serial bond**. For computational purposes such serial bonds may be treated as separate bonds according to their redemption dates.

Example 19.5b A serial bond issue of $20 million with interest at 10% payable semi-annually is to be redeemed by a payment of $12 million in twelve years and $8 million in fifteen years. What is the purchase price of the bond issue to yield 12% compounded semi-annually?

Solution

The purchase price of the serial bond issue is equivalent to the combined purchase price of two separate bond issues:

the purchase price of the $12 million bond issue due in twelve years and the purchase price of the $8 million bond issue due in fifteen years.

Purchase price of the $12 million bond issue

$$S = 12 \text{ million}; \qquad R = 12000000\left(\frac{0.10}{2}\right) = 600000;$$

$$n = 12(2) = 24; \qquad i = \frac{12\%}{2} = 6\% = 0.06$$

$$PP = 12000000(1.06^{-24}) + 600000 \, a_{\overline{24}|\,6\%}$$

$$= 12000000(0.2469785) + 600000(12.550358)$$

$$= 2963742.60 + 7530214.80$$

$$= \$10493957.40$$

Purchase price of the $8 million bond issue

$$S = 8 \text{ million}; \qquad R = 8000000(0.05) = 400000;$$

$$n = 30; \qquad i = 6\%$$

$$PP = 8000000(1.06^{-30}) + 400000 \, a \, _{\overline{30}|6\%}$$

$$= 8000000(0.1741101) + 400000(13.764831)$$

$$= 1392881.00 + 5505932.40$$

$$= \$6898813.40$$

The total purchase price is $10493957.40 + 6898813.40 = \$17392770.80$.

Exercise 19.5

A. Answer each of the following questions.

1. A $75 000, 14.5% annuity bond with interest payable semi-annually is to be repaid by equal semi-annual payments in fifteen years.

   (a) What is the purchase price to yield 12.5% compounded semi-annually?

   (b) What is the book value after five years?

   (c) What is the gain or loss if the bond is sold to yield 12% compounded semi-annually after five years?

2. A 14% annuity bond contracts to repay the principal of $35 000 in equal quarterly payments over eight years. The bond interest is payable quarterly.

   (a) What is the purchase price to yield 16% compounded quarterly?

   (b) For how much will the bond sell in three years to yield 15% compounded quarterly?

   (c) What is the gain or loss on the sale of the bond?

3. A $600 000, 14% serial bond with interest payable semi-annually is to be redeemed in three instalments of $200 000 each in six, eight and ten years respectively. What is the purchase price to yield 12% compounded semi-annually?

4. A $120 000, 13% serial bond issued June 1, 1980 with interest payable annually is to be redeemed by four instalments of $30 000 each due June 1, 1994, 1996, 1998 and 2000 respectively. What is the purchase price to yield 15.75% annually?

Review exercise

1. A $5000, 11.5% bond with interest payable semi-annually is redeemable at par in twelve years. What is the purchase price to yield

   (a) 10.5% compounded semi-annually?   (b) 13% compounded semi-annually?

2. A $10 000, 16% bond with semi-annual coupons is redeemable at 108. What is the purchase price to yield 17.5% compounded semi-annually

   (a) nine years before maturity?   (b) fifteen years before maturity?

3. A $25 000, 13% bond with interest payable quarterly is redeemable at 104 in six years. What is the purchase price to yield 14.25% compounded annually?

4. A $1000, 9.5% bond with semi-annual coupons redeemable at par on March 1, 1992 is purchased on September 19, 1983 to yield 15% compounded semi-annually. What is the purchase price?

5. Four $5000, 13% bonds with semi-annual coupons are purchased seven years before maturity to yield 12% compounded semi-annually. Find the premium or discount and the purchase price, if the bonds are redeemable

(a) at par;   (b) at 107.

6. Nine $1000, 14% bonds with interest payable semi-annually redeemable at par are purchased ten years before maturity. Find the premium or discount and the purchase price if the bonds are bought to yield   (a) 10%;   (b) 14%;   (c) 16%.

7. A $100 000, 15% bond with interest payable semi-annually redeemable at par on July 15, 1994 is bought on April 18, 1983 to yield 17% compounded semi-annually. Determine

(a) the premium or discount;

(b) the purchase price;

(c) the quoted price.

8. Four $10 000 bonds bearing interest at 16% payable quarterly redeemable at 106 on September 1, 1996 are purchased on January 23, 1984 to yield 15% compounded quarterly. Determine

(a) the premium or discount;

(b) the purchase price;

(c) the quoted price.

9. A $5000, 12% bond with semi-annual coupons redeemable at 108 in ten years is purchased to yield 17.5% compounded semi-annually. What is the purchase price?

10. A $1000 bond bearing interest at 16% payable semi-annually redeemable at par on February 1, 1991 is purchased on October 12, 1984 to yield 15% compounded semi-annually. Determine the purchase price.

11. A $25 000, 13% bond with semi-annual coupons redeemable at 107 on June 15, 1994 is purchased on May 9, 1983 to yield 14.5% compounded semi-annually. Determine

(a) the premium or discount;

(b) the purchase price;

(c) the quoted price.

12. A $50 000, 11% with semi-annual coupons redeemable at par on April 15, 1990 is purchased on June 25, 1983 at $92\frac{3}{8}$. What is the approximate yield rate?

13. A $80 000, 13% serial bond with interest payable semi-annually is redeemable by a payment of $30 000 in seven years and a payment of $50 000 in ten years. What is the purchase price to yield 15% compounded semi-annually?

14. A $1000, 14.5% bond with interest payable annually is bought six years before maturity to yield 16.5% compounded annually. Compute the premium or discount and the purchase price and construct the appropriate bond schedule.

15. A \$5000, 12.25% bond with interest payable annually redeemable at par in seven years is purchased to yield 13.5% compounded annually. Find the premium or discount and the purchase price and construct the appropriate bond schedule.

16. A \$20 000, 15.5% bond with semi-annual coupons redeemable at 105 in three years is purchased to yield 14% compounded semi-annually. Find the premium or discount and purchase price and construct the appropriate bond schedule.

17. Three \$25 000, 11% bonds with semi-annual coupons redeemable at par were bought eight years before maturity to yield 12% compounded semi-annually. Determine the gain or loss if the bonds are sold at $89\frac{3}{8}$ five years later.

18. A \$10 000 bond with 13% interest payable quarterly redeemable at 106 on November 15, 1998 was purchased on July 2, 1982 to yield 17% compounded quarterly. If the bond was sold at $92\frac{3}{4}$ on September 10, 1988, what was the gain or loss on sale?

19. A \$25 000, 9.5% bond with semi-annual coupons redeemable at par is bought sixteen years before maturity at $78\frac{1}{4}$. What is the yield rate?

20. A \$10 000, 15% bond with quarterly coupons redeemable at 102 on October 15, 1995 is purchased on May 5, 1983 at $98\frac{3}{4}$. What is the yield rate?

21. If the bond in Question 13 was sold two years before maturity at 97, what yield rate was realized?

22. What is the yield realized if the bond in Question 14 is sold on August 7, 1988 at 92?

23. A 14.5% annuity bond of \$50 000 with interest payable quarterly is to be redeemed by equal quarterly payments over twelve years.

    (a) What is the purchase price to yield 16% compounded quarterly?

    (b) What is the book value after nine years?

    (c) What is the gain or loss if the bond is sold nine years after the date of purchase to yield 17% compounded quarterly?

24. A \$250 000, 15% serial bond with interest payable semi-annually is to be redeemed by two payments, the first for \$100 000 in nine years and the remaining \$150 000 in twelve years. What is the purchase price to yield 14.5% compounded semi-annually?

25. A \$100 000, 10.75% bond with interest payable annually is redeemable at 103 in eight years. What is the purchase price to yield 12% compounded quarterly?

26. A \$5000, 14.5% bond with semi-annual coupons redeemable at par on August 1, 1996 is purchased on March 5, 1985 at $95\frac{1}{2}$. What is the yield rate using the accurate method?

27. A \$25 000, 18% bond with semi-annual coupons, redeemable at 104 in fifteen years, is purchased to yield 16% compounded semi-annually. Determine the gain or loss if the bond is sold three years later at $107\frac{1}{4}$.

28. A \$10 000 12% annuity bond with interest payable quarterly is redeemed by equal quarterly payments over twenty years.

    (a) What is the purchase price to yield 14% compounded quarterly?

    (b) What is the book value after seven years?

    (c) What is the gain or loss if the bond is sold after seven years to yield 15% compounded quarterly?

Self-test

1. A $10 000, 10% bond with quarterly coupons redeemable at par in fifteen years is purchased to yield 11% compounded quarterly. Determine the purchase price of the bond.

2. What is the purchase price of a $1000, 13.5% bond with semi-annual coupons redeemable at 108 in ten years if the bond is bought to yield 12% compounded semi-annually?

3. A $5000, 14% bond with semi-annual coupons redeemable at 104 is purchased six years prior to maturity to yield 12.5% compounded semi-annually. Determine the premium or discount.

4. A $50 000, 15% annuity bond with interest payable monthly is redeemed by equal monthly payments over fifteen years. What is the purchase price of the bond to yield 14.4% compounded monthly?

5. A $20 000, 16% bond with semi-annual coupons redeemable at par March 1, 1995 is purchased on November 15, 1988 to yield 15% compounded semi-annually. What is the purchase price of the bond?

6. A $5000, 13% bond with semi-annual coupons redeemable at 102 on December 15, 1998 is purchased on November 9, 1987 to yield 14.5% compounded semi-annually. Determine the quoted price.

7. A $5000, 11.5% bond with semi-annual coupons redeemable at 105 is bought four years before maturity to yield 13% compounded semi-annually. Construct a bond schedule.

8. A $100 000, 13% bond with semi-annual interest payments redeemable at par on July 15, 1994 is purchased on September 10, 1987 at $102\frac{5}{8}$. What is the approximate yield rate?

9. A $1 000 000, 12% serial bond with interest payable semi-annually is redeemable by payments of $400 000 and $600 000 due six years and ten years from now respectively. What is the purchase price of the bond to yield 10% compounded semi-annually?

10. A $25 000, 14% bond with semi-annual coupons redeemable at 106 in twenty years is purchased to yield 16% compounded semi-annually. Determine the gain or loss if the bond is sold seven years after the date of purchase at $98\frac{1}{4}$.

11. A $75 000, 20-year, 13% annuity bond with interest payable annually is redeemable by equal annual payments. The bond was bought to yield 12% compounded annually. If the bond is sold eight years prior to maturity to yield 14% compounded annually, what is the gain or loss?

12. A $10 000, 12% bond with semi-annual coupons redeemable at par on December 1, 1999 is purchased on July 20, 1988 at $93\frac{7}{8}$. Compute the yield rate using the exact (or accurate) method.

Summary of formulae used

Formula 19.1 $PP = S(1 + i)^{-n} + R\, a_{\overline{n}|i}$ Basic formula for finding the purchase price of a bond when the interest payment interval and the yield rate conversion period are equal

Formula 19.1a $PP = S(1 + f)^{-n} + R\, a_{\overline{n}|f}$ Basic formula for finding the purchase price of a bond when the interest payment interval and the yield rate conversion period are different

where $f = (1 + i)^c - 1$

Formula 19.2   PREMIUM or DISCOUNT   Direct formula for finding the premium or discount of a bond (where a negative answer indicates a discount)

$= (b \times$ FACE VALUE $- i \times$

REDEMPTION VALUE) $a_{\overline{n}|i}$

Glossary of terms used

Accumulation of discount   the process of reducing a bond discount

Amortization of premium   the process of writing down a bond premium

Annuity bond   a bond redeemed by equal periodic payments

Bond rate   the rate of interest paid by a bond, stated as a percent of the face value

Coupon   a voucher attached to a bond to facilitate the collection of interest by the bondholder

Coupon rate   see *Bond rate*

Debentures   bonds for which no security is offered

Denomination   see *Face value*

Discount   the difference between the purchase price of a bond and its redemption value when the purchase price is less than the redemption price

Due date   see *Redemption date*

Face value   amount owed by the issuer of the bond to the bondholder

Flat price   total purchase price of a bond (including any accrued interest)

Maturity date   see *Redemption date*

Method of averages   a method for finding the approximate yield rate

Nominal rate   see *Bond rate*

Par value   see *Face value*

Premium   the difference between the purchase price of a bond and its redemption price when the purchase price is greater than the redemption price

Quoted price   the net price of a bond (without accrued interest) at which a bond is offered for sale

Redeemable at a premium   bonds whose redemption value is greater than the face value

Redeemable at par   bonds that are redeemed at their face value

Redemption date   date at which the bond principal is repaid

Redemption value   the amount which will be paid by the issuer of the bond to the bondholder upon surrender of the bond on or after the date of maturity

Serial bond   a bond whose principal is repaid by more than one payment

Yield rate   the rate of interest which an investor earns on his investment in a bond

20 *Depreciation, depletion, and capitalization*

Introduction

Depreciation is an accounting concept concerned with the allocation of the cost of depreciable assets such as buildings, machinery and equipment to accounting periods to properly measure net income and evaluate assets. As there is no single method of allocation that is suitable for all depreciable assets under all circumstances, various methods of depreciation have been developed.

Depletion refers to the using up of non-renewable natural resources. The sinking fund method for depletion is intended to assure the recovery of the capital invested when the resources have been depleted.

Capitalization is a method used to evaluate assets and liabilities and involves the determination of the present value of an indefinite number of periodic payments.

Objectives

Upon completion of this chapter you will be able to

1. compute the depreciation and the book value for each year in the life of an asset and construct depreciation schedules using averaging methods (Straight-Line, Units of Product, Service Hours), declining balance methods (Simple, Complex, Constant Percentage), Sum-of-the-Years-Digit Method, Annuity Method and Sinking Fund Method;

2. find the value or the yield rate of an investment in wasting assets under the assumption that provision for the recovery of the capital invested is in the form of a sinking fund;

3. determine the capitalized cost of assets and their periodic investment cost and compare the buying cost of assets on the basis of both investment and production cost.

20.1   Depreciation

A.   Basic concepts and methods

The useful life of physical assets such as plant, machinery and equipment that is used in the production of goods and services is limited due to physical deterioration, wear and tear, decay and obsolescence. As a result, such assets lose their value over a period of time. From the accounting point of view, this loss in value, referred to as **depreciation**, is treated as an *expense* of operating a business.

In order to make provision for this expense, various systematic methods of recording the expiration of the usefulness of such assets have been developed. The recording of depreciation is a process of allocating the original cost of assets to the accounting periods that benefit from the use of the assets.

Whatever *method of depreciation* may be used, certain aspects are common to all.

1. The **original cost** of the asset which includes all necessary and reasonable expenditures to ready the assets for its intended purpose.

2. The **residual value (scrap value, salvage value, trade-in value)** at the time when the asset has lost its usefulness.

3. The **wearing value** which is the total amount of depreciation over the useful life of the asset; that is, the difference between original cost and the residual value of the asset.

4. The **useful life** of the asset (usually stated in years).

5. The **accumulated depreciation** which is the total depreciation allocated at any point in the life of the asset to expired accounting periods.

6. The **book value** or net value of the asset at any point in the life of the asset; that is, the difference between the original cost and the accumulated depreciation.

7. **Depreciation schedules** showing the details of allocating the cost of the asset to the various accounting periods.

As there is no single method of allocating the wearing value which is suitable for all depreciable assets, the various assumptions as to how the loss in value should be allocated to accounting periods has led to the development of a variety of methods of depreciation.

Of the methods available, the following are described in this chapter:

(a) *Allocation on the basis of averages*

    1. Straight Line
    2. Service Hours
    3. Units of Product

(b) *Allocation based on a diminishing charge per year*

    1. Sum-of-the-Years-Digits

2. Declining Balance:
   (i) Simple Declining Balance
   (ii) Complex Declining Balance
   (iii) Constant Percentage

(c) *Allocation using compounding principles*

   1. Annuity
   2. Sinking Fund

B.   Methods of allocating depreciation on the basis of an average

Methods of depreciation in this category are based on the assumption that the loss in value (depreciation) is the same for each unit of useful life of the asset, such as time period, service hour, unit of product.

1.   The straight line method of depreciation

This method is the simplest method based on the assumption that the loss in value is the same for equal time periods (usually years). Hence the depreciation per time period is found by dividing the total wearing value by the number of time periods in the life of the asset. Since the wearing value is the difference between the original cost and the residual value, the yearly depreciation is

$$\text{YEARLY DEPRECIATION} = \frac{\text{ORIGINAL COST} - \text{RESIDUAL VALUE}}{n}$$

where n = the numbers of years in the life of the asset

←*Formula* **20.1**

Example 20.1a   A machine costing $20 000.00 has a salvage value of $3200.00 after five years. Use the straight line method to

(i) compute the yearly depreciation expense;

(ii) determine the depreciation in Year 4;

(iii) construct a depreciation schedule.

Solution

(i) The original cost = 20000.00;
   the residual value = 3200.00;
   the wearing value is $20000.00 - 3200.00 = 16800.00$;
   the life of the asset (in years) = 5.
   Yearly depreciation expense is $\dfrac{16800.00}{5} = \$3360.00$.

(ii) The depreciation expense in Year 4 = $3360.00.

(iii) *Depreciation schedule (straight line method)*

End of year	Annual depreciation expense	Accumulated depreciation	Book value
0			20 000.00
1	3360.00	3360.00	16 640.00
2	3360.00	6720.00	13 280.00
3	3360.00	10080.00	9 920.00
4	3360.00	13440.00	6 560.00
5	3360.00	16800.00	3 200.00
TOTAL	16 800.00		

Explanations regarding the schedule

1. The annual depreciation expense is the same for each year and totals the wearing value of $16 800.00.

2. The accumulated depreciation is a running total of the annual depreciation and, after five years, is equal to the wearing value.

3. The book value diminishes each year by the annual depreciation expense and, after five years, must equal the salvage value of $3200.00.

2. The service hours method of depreciation

The underlying assumption for this method is similar to that for the straight line method except that this method is based on the number of useful service hours in the life of the asset.

$$\text{DEPRECIATION PER SERVICE HOUR} = \frac{\text{ORIGINAL COST} - \text{RESIDUAL VALUE}}{n}$$

where n = the number of service hours in the life of the asset

← *Formula* **20.1A**

The depreciation for a time period (such as a year) is found by multiplying the number of service hours in the time period by the depreciation per service hour.

Example 20.1b Assuming that the useful life of the machine in Example 20.1a is 9600 hours, use the service hours method to

(i) determine the depreciation expense per service hour;

(ii) determine the depreciation expense in Year 4 if the number of service hours in Year 4 is 1880;

(iii) construct a depreciation schedule if the service hours per year for the five years are respectively 2000, 1960, 1840, 1880 and 1920.

Solution

(i) The original cost = 20000.00;
the residual value = 3200.00;
the wearing value is 20000.00 − 3200.00 = 16800.00;
the life of the asset (in number of service hours) = 9600.

The depreciation per service hour is $\dfrac{16800.00}{9600} = \$1.75$.

(ii) Depreciation in Year 4 is 1.75(1880) = $3290.00.

(iii) *Depreciation schedule (service hours method)*

End of year	Annual depreciation expense	Accumulated depreciation	Book value
0			20 000.00
1	1.75(2000) = 3500.00	3 500.00	16 500.00
2	1.75(1960) = 3430.00	6 930.00	13 070.00
3	1.75(1840) = 3220.00	10 150.00	9 850.00
4	1.75(1880) = 3290.00	13 440.00	6 560.00
5	1.75(1920) = 3360.00	16 800.00	3 200.00
TOTAL	16 800.00		

3. The units of product method

In this method it is assumed that the loss in value is the same per unit of product.

> DEPRECIATION PER UNIT OF PRODUCT = $\dfrac{\text{ORIGINAL COST} - \text{RESIDUAL VALUE}}{n}$ ← *Formula* **20.1B**
>
> where n = the number of units of product in the life of the asset

The depreciation expense for a time period (such as a year) is found by multiplying the number of units of product in the time period by the depreciation per unit.

Example 20.1c Assuming that the machine in Example 20.1a can make 240 000 units of product during its useful life, use the units of product method to

(i) determine the depreciation expense per unit of product;

(ii) determine the depreciation in Year 4 if the number of units of product in Year 4 is 46400;

(iii) construct a depreciation schedule if the number of units of product during each of the five years is respectively 50800, 49200, 46700, 46400 and 46900.

Solution

(i) The original cost = 20000.00;
   the residual value = 3200.00;
   the wearing value is 20000.00 − 3200.00 = 16800.00;
   the life of the asset (in number of units of product) = 240000.

The depreciation per unit of product is $\dfrac{16800.00}{240000} = \$0.07$.

(ii) The depreciation in Year 4 is 0.07(46400) = $3248.00.

(iii) *Depreciation schedule (units of product method)*

End of year	Annual depreciation expense	Accumulated depreciation	Book value
0			20 000.00
1	0.07(50800) = 3556.00	3 556.00	16 444.00
2	0.07(49200) = 3444.00	7 000.00	13 000.00
3	0.07(46700) = 3269.00	10 269.00	9 731.00
4	0.07(46400) = 3248.00	13 517.00	6 483.00
5	0.07(46900) = 3283.00	16 800.00	3 200.00
TOTAL	16 800.00		

C. Methods of allocating depreciation as a diminishing charge per year

Methods of depreciation in this category are based on the assumption that the loss in value is highest in the first year and then diminishes yearly during the useful life of an asset.

1. The sum-of-the-years-digits method

In this method is is assumed that the loss in value diminishes by a constant amount from year to year. This requires first of all the determination of the number of parts into which the wearing value is to be divided. This number is the sum of the digits corresponding to the years in the life of the asset in sequential order starting with 1. Proportional parts of the total depreciation expense are then assigned to each year in reverse order of the digits.

Example 20.1d Assume that the machine in Example 20.1a is depreciated by the Sum-of-the-Years-Digits Method.

(i) Determine the depreciation for each year.

(ii) Construct a depreciation schedule.

Solution

(i) Original cost = 20000.00;   residual value = 3200.00;
wearing value is 20000.00 − 3200.00 = 16800.00;
the life of the asset (in years) = 5.
The yearly depreciation is now determined by following the steps outlined below.

Year in life of asset	Digit identifying year	Proportional part of wearing value assigned to year	Yearly depreciation expense
One	1	5	5(1120.00) = 5600.00
Two	2	4	4(1120.00) = 4480.00
Three	3	3	3(1120.00) = 3360.00
Four	4	2	2(1120.00) = 2240.00
Five	5	1	1(1120.00) = 1120.00
Sum of the digits		15	

Value of each of the 15 parts is $\dfrac{16800.00}{15} = 1120.00$

STEP 1   Identify each year in the life of the asset by a digit in sequential order starting with 1; e.g. 1, 2, 3, 4, 5.

STEP 2   Assign to each year proportional parts of the total wearing value in *reverse* order of the digits identifying the years; e.g. 5, 4, 3, 2, 1.

STEP 3   Determine the sum of the years-digits: $1 + 2 + 3 + 4 + 5 = 15$. Since the sum of the years-digits is always the sum of an arithmetic progression formed by the first n whole numbers, it may be more conveniently determined by using the formula

$$S_n = \frac{n(n + 1)}{2}$$

$$S_5 = \frac{5(5 + 1)}{2} = 15$$

STEP 4   Compute the value of each of the 15 parts of the wearing value.

$$\frac{16800.00}{15} = \$1120.00$$

STEP 5   Determine the yearly depreciation by multiplying the value of one part ($1120.00) by the number of parts assigned to each of the years.

The arithmetic approach shown above may be replaced by an algebraic approach.

$nk + (n - 1)k + (n - 2)k + \text{.......} + 3k + 2k + k = \text{Wearing Value}$

$n = \text{the digit identifying the last year in the life of the asset}$

$k = \text{the value of one of the } \dfrac{n(n + 1)}{2} \text{ proportional parts}$

$k\big[n + (n - 1) + (n - 2) + \text{.....} + 3 + 2 + 1\big] = \text{Wearing Value}$

$$k\left[\frac{n(n + 1)}{2}\right] = \text{Wearing Value}$$

$$\boxed{k = \frac{\text{WEARING VALUE}}{\frac{n(n + 1)}{2}}} \quad \longleftarrow \quad \textbf{\textit{Formula 20.2}}$$

In our case $5k + 4k + 3k + 2k + k = 16800.00$

or directly by formula $\quad k = \dfrac{16800.00}{\frac{5(5 + 1)}{2}} = \dfrac{16800.00}{15} = \$1120.00$

(ii) *Depreciation schedule (sum-of-the-years-digits method)*

End of year	Parts	Annual depreciation expense	Accumulated depreciation	Book value
0				20 000.00
1	5	5600.00	5 600.00	14 400.00
2	4	4480.00	10 080.00	9 920.00
3	3	3360.00	13 440.00	6 560.00
4	2	2240.00	15 680.00	4 320.00
5	1	1120.00	16 800.00	3 200.00
TOTAL	15	16 800.00		

2. Declining balance methods

In these methods the depreciation for a particular year is based on the book value at the end of the previous year and is calculated over the years at a constant rate. Three variations are in use.

(a) The Simple Declining Balance Method

(b) The Complex Declining Balance Method

(c) The Constant Percentage Method

All three methods work in basically the same manner and differ only in the way in which the rate of depreciation is determined.

(a) *The Simple Declining Balance Method*

When this variation of the declining balance methods is used, the rate of depreciation is determined by

$$\boxed{d = 2 \times \cfrac{1}{\text{Number of Years in the Life of the Asset}}} \quad \longleftarrow \textit{Formula 20.3}$$

No consideration is given to the residual value until the final year in the life of the asset or until the book value would drop below the residual value.

Example 20.1e Assume that the machine in Example 20.1a is depreciated by the Simple Declining Balance Method.

  (i) Determine the rate of depreciation.

 (ii) Compute the depreciation for Year 4.

(iii) Construct a depreciation schedule.

Solution

 (i) The rate of depreciation is $2\left(\dfrac{1}{5}\right) = \dfrac{2}{5} = 40\%$

(ii)

Original book value	20000.00
Depreciation in Year 1: 40% of 20000.00	8000.00
Book Value End of Year 1	12000.00
Depreciation in Year 2: 40% of 12000.00	4800.00
Book Value End of Year 2	7200.00
Depreciation in Year 3: 40% of 7200.00	2880.00
Book Value End of Year 3	4320.00

Ordinarily the depreciation for Year 4 would now be computed as 40% of 4320.00 = 1728.00. However, when $1728.00 is subtracted from $4320.00 the result is smaller than the residual value of $3200.00. When this happens the depreciation is taken to be the difference between the previous book value and the residual value; that is, the depreciation for Year 4 is 4320.00 − 3200.00 = $1120.00.

(iii) **Depreciation schedule (simple declining balance method)**

End of year	Annual depreciation expense	Accumulated depreciation	Book value
0			20 000.00
1	0.40(20000.00) = 8000.00	8 000.00	12 000.00
2	0.40(12000.00) = 4800.00	12 800.00	7 200.00
3	0.40(7200.00) = 2880.00	15 680.00	4 320.00
4	4320.00 − 3200.00 = 1120.00	16 800.00	3 200.00
5	3200.00 − 3200.00 = 0.00	16 800.00	3 200.00
TOTAL	16 800.00		

Alternative Approach to (ii)

Note that taking 40% off each year from the preceding book value is equivalent to taking off a series of discounts all of which are equal. This mathematical feature may be used to obtain the book value at any point in time by multiplying the original book value by the product of the net factors for the series of discounts (see Chapter 9).

The book value at the end of Year 3

$$= 20000.00(1 - 0.40)(1 - 0.40)(1 - 0.40)$$
$$= 20000.00(0.60)^3$$
$$= 20000.00(0.216)$$
$$= \$4320.00$$

Example 20.1f Equipment costing $36 000.00 with a scrap value of $4300.00 is depreciated over twenty years by the Simple Declining Balance Method. Determine the depreciation in Year 8.

Solution

The original cost $= 36000.00$;

the rate of depreciation $= 2\left(\dfrac{1}{20}\right) = \dfrac{1}{10} = 10\%$.

Since the depreciation in Year 8 is 10% of the previous book value we need to determine the book value after seven years. During each of the first seven years depreciation of 10% has been taken off from the successive book values starting with the original book value. This is equivalent to reducing the original book value by the discount series 10%, 10%, 10%, 10%, 10%, 10%, 10%.

Using the net factor approach, the book value after seven years

$$= 36000.00(1 - 0.10)(1 - 0.10)(1 - 0.10)(1 - 0.10)(1 - 0.10)$$
$$(1 - 0.10)(1 - 0.10)$$
$$= 36000.00(1 - 0.10)^7$$
$$= 36000.00(0.90)^7$$
$$= 36000.00(0.4782969)$$
$$= \$17218.69$$

The depreciation in Year 8 is $0.10(17218.69) = \$1721.87$.

(b) The Complex Declining Balance Method

While the Simple Declining Balance Method ignores any residual value in establishing the rate of depreciation, the complex variation takes the residual value into account by using the following formula to determine the rate of depreciation.

$$d = 1 - \sqrt[n]{\dfrac{\text{RESIDUAL VALUE}}{\text{ORIGINAL COST}}} \qquad \longleftarrow \textit{Formula 20.4}$$

Development of Formula 20.4

Let the original cost be represented by C; let the residual value after n years be represented by T_n; let the book value after n years be represented by B_n; let the number of years in the life of the asset be represented by n; and let the rate of depreciation which will reduce the original cost to the residual value in n years be represented by d.

Then the book value after

one year $\quad B_1 = C - Cd = C(1 - d)$

two years $\quad B_2 = B_1 - B_1d = B_1(1 - d) = C(1 - d)(1 - d) = C(1 - d)^2$

three years $\quad B_3 = B_2 - B_2d = B_2(1 - d) = C(1 - d)^2(1 - d) = C(1 - d)^3$

four years $\quad B_4 = C(1 - d)^4$

five years $\quad B_5 = C(1 - d)^5$

n years $\quad B_n = C(1 - d)^n$

However after n years $\quad B_n = T_n$

$$T_n = C(1 - d)^n$$

$$\frac{T_n}{C} = (1 - d)^n \quad\longleftarrow\quad \text{divide both sides by C}$$

$$\sqrt[n]{\frac{T_n}{C}} = 1 - d \quad\longleftarrow\quad \text{take the } n\text{th root}$$

$$d = 1 - \sqrt[n]{\frac{T_n}{C}} = 1 - \sqrt[n]{\frac{\text{Residual Value}}{\text{Original Cost}}}$$

Example 20.1g Assuming that the machine in Example 20.1a is depreciated by the Complex Declining Balance Method
  (i) determine the rate of depreciation;
 (ii) compute the depreciation in Year 4;
(iii) construct a depreciation schedule.

Solution

  (i) The original cost $= 20000.00$; $\qquad$ the residual value $= 3200.00$;
     the life of the asset (in years) $= 5$.

$$d = 1 - \sqrt[5]{\frac{3200.00}{20000.00}} = 1 - \sqrt[5]{0.16} = 1 - 0.6931448 = 0.3068552$$

The rate of depreciation $d = 30.68552\%$.

 (ii) The book value after three years
    $= 20000.00(1 - 0.3068552)^3 = 20000.00(0.6931448)^3$
    $= 20000.00(0.3330213)$
    $= \$6660.43$
    The depreciation in Year 4 is $6660.43(0.3068552) = \$2043.79$.

Depreciation schedule (complex declining balance method)

End of year	Annual depreciation expense	Accumulated depreciation	Book value
0			20 000.00
1	6137.10	6 137.10	13 862.90
2	4253.90	10 391.00	9 609.00
3	2948.57	13 339.57	6 660.43
4	2043.79	15 383.36	4 616.64
5	1416.64	16 800.00	3 200.00
TOTAL	16 800.00		

(c) *The Constant Percentage Method*

This variation of the Declining Balance Method is based on an arbitrarily established yearly rate of depreciation. It is the method commonly used for income tax purposes when computing capital cost allowance.

Under the regulations of the Income Tax Act a capital cost allowance may be claimed for depreciable business assets according to their classification at a maximum rate established for each classification.

The most common classes are

Class 3 Buildings—maximum rate 3%;
Class 8 Machinery and Equipment—maximum rate 20%;
Class 10 Cars, trucks, vans, tractors, contractors equipment—maximum rate 30%.

Example 20.1h Assuming that the machine in Example 20.1a falls into Class 8, develop a capital cost allowance schedule for the five years at the maximum allowable rate.

Capital cost allowance schedule

End of year	Annual capital cost allowance	Accumulated capital cost allowance	Book value
0			20 000.00
1	4000.00	4 000.00	16 000.00
2	3200.00	7 200.00	12 800.00
3	2560.00	9 760.00	10 240.00
4	2048.00	11 808.00	8 192.00
5	1638.40	13 446.40	6 553.60
TOTAL	13 446.40		

Solution

Original cost = 20000.00;   residual value = 3200.00;

life of asset (in years) = 5;   maximum allowable rate = 20%.

Note   The depreciated value of the machine after five years is well above its estimated residual value at that time. The tax implications are beyond the scope of this text and are not considered here.

D.   Methods of depreciation making provision for interest on the capital investment

The methods of depreciation based on averages or diminishing charges make no provision for interest on the original capital investment in depreciable assets or the decreasing amount of the investment. When interest is a consideration (as in the case of depreciable investments of insurance companies and investment firms), the Annuity Method and the Sinking Fund Method are available for use.

1.   The annuity method of depreciation

In addition to counteracting the loss of value of an asset over its useful life, this method also provides for a return of interest on the diminishing book value of the investment in depreciable assets. The method provides for a constant annual charge against operating revenue composed of the yearly depreciation expense and interest on the book value of the asset.

The equal annual depreciation charges are such that their present value at a rate of interest which the capital invested in physical assets could earn elsewhere is equivalent to the difference between the original cost and the present value of the residual value.

> PRESENT VALUE OF THE ANNUAL DEPRECIATION CHARGES
> = ORIGINAL COST − PRESENT VALUE OF THE RESIDUAL VALUE

This means that the annual depreciation charge is found in the same way as the periodic payment required to amortize a debt principal equal in size to the difference between the original cost and the present value of the residual value. Thus the Annuity Method of Depreciation is similar to debt amortization and uses the same mathematical procedures.

Example 20.1i   Assume that money is worth 14% compounded annually and that the machine in Example 20.1a is depreciated by the Annuity Method.

(i) Compute the annual depreciation charge.

(ii) Construct a depreciation schedule.

Solution

(i)   Original cost = 20000.00;   residual value = 3200.00;

the life of the asset (in years), $n = 5$; $i = 14\% = 0.14$.

Present Value of the Depreciation Charges

= Original Cost − Present Value of the Residual Value

= 20000.00 − 3200.00(1.14^{-5})

= 20000.00 − 3200.00(0.5193687)

= 20000.00 − 1661.98

= $18338.02

The five annual depreciation charges form an ordinary annuity whose present value A_n = 18338.02.

$$18338.02 = R\, a_{\overline{5}|\,14\%}$$

$$18338.02 = R(3.433081)$$

$$R = \$5341.56$$

The annual depreciation charge is $5341.56.

(ii) **Depreciation schedule (annuity method)**

End of year	Annual depreciation charge	Provision for		Accumulated depreciation	Book value
		Interest on book value $i = 14\%$	Loss in value		
0					20 000.00
1	5341.56	2800.00	2541.56	2 541.56	17 458.44
2	5341.56	2444.18	2897.38	5 438.94	14 561.06
3	5341.56	2038.55	3303.01	8 741.95	11 258.05
4	5341.56	1576.13	3765.43	12 507.38	7 492.62
5	5341.59	1048.97	4292.62	16 800.00	3 200.00
TOTAL	26 707.83	9907.83	16 800.00		

Note The annual depreciation charge for Year 5 has been adjusted by $0.03 to allow for the accumulated rounding errors.

When using the Annuity Method, the annual depreciation charge may be found by the following formula.

$$\text{ANNUAL DEPRECIATION, R CHARGE} = \frac{\text{ORIGINAL COST} - \text{RESIDUAL VALUE} \times (1 + i)^{-n}}{a_{\overline{n}|\,i}}$$

⟵ **Formula 20.5**

where n = the number of years in the life of the assets

i = the applicable rate of interest

Development of Formula 20.5

Let the original cost be represented by C, the residual value by T, the annual depreciation charge by R, the number of years in the life of the asset by n and the applicable rate of interest per year by i. The present value of the residual value is $T(1 + i)^{-n}$. The present value of the annual depreciation charges is $A_n = C - T(1 + i)^{-n}$. The annual depreciation charges form an ordinary annuity.

$$C - T(1 + i)^{-n} = R\, a_{\overline{n}|i}$$

$$R = \frac{C - T(1 + i)^{-n}}{a_{\overline{n}|i}}$$

The Annual Depreciation Charge

$$= \frac{\text{Original Cost} - \text{Present Value of Residual Value}}{a_{\overline{n}|i}}$$

2. The sinking fund method of depreciation

The Sinking Fund Method, like the Annuity Method, provides for an annual depreciation charge that is composed of a provision for a yearly loss in value plus interest. However, in this case the annual depreciation charge involves an *assumed* payment into a sinking fund which accumulates to the wearing value at the end of the useful life of the asset at a rate of interest which the payments into the sinking fund could earn. The mathematical aspects of the method involve the techniques used in Chapter 18, Section 18.4 for dealing with sinking funds involving ordinary annuities.

Example 20.1j Assume that money is worth 14% compounded annually and that the machine in Example 20.1a is depreciated by the Sinking Fund Method.

(i) Determine the assumed annual sinking fund payment.

(ii) Construct a depreciation schedule.

Solution

(i)   Original cost = 20000.00;   residual value = 3200.00;
            wearing value = 16800.00; $n = 5$; $i = 14\%$.

Since the wearing value is the final amount in the sinking fund
$S_n = 16\,800.00$.

$$16800.00 = R\, s_{\overline{5}|14\%}$$
$$16800.00 = R(6.610104)$$
$$R = \$2541.56$$

(ii) Depreciation schedule (sinking fund method)

End of year	Assumed annual payment into sinking fund	Provision for interest $i = 14\%$	Annual depreciation charge	Accumulated depreciation	Book value
0					20 000.00
1	2541.56	0.00	2541.56	2 541.56	17 458.44
2	2541.56	355.82	2897.38	5 438.94	14 561.06
3	2541.56	761.45	3303.01	8 741.95	11 258.05
4	2541.56	1223.87	3765.43	12 507.38	7 942.62
5	2541.59	1751.03	4292.62	16 800.00	3 200.00
TOTAL	12 707.83	4092.17	16 800.00		

E. Finding the book value and yearly depreciation without depreciation schedule

The book value after a given number of years or the depreciation in any particular year may be determined without constructing a depreciation schedule for any of the methods illustrated.

Example 20.1k Equipment costing $35 720.00 has an estimated trade-in value of $1400.00 after fifteen years. Find (a) the book value after nine years and (b) the depreciation charge in Year 10 for

(i) the Straight Line Method;

(ii) the Sum-of-the-Years-Digits Method;

(iii) the Simple Declining Balance Method;

(iv) the Complex Declining Balance Method;

(v) the Annuity Method if interest is 16% compounded annually;

(vi) the Sinking Fund Method if interest is 12% compounded annually.

Solution

Original cost = 35720.00;   residual value = 1400.00;
wearing value is 35720.00 − 1400.00 = 34320; $n = 15$.

(i) Straight Line Method

The yearly depreciation is $\dfrac{34320.00}{15} = \$2288.00$.

The accumulated depreciation after nine years is 2288.00(9) = $20592.00.

(a) The book value after nine years is 35720.00 − 20592.00 = $15128.00.

(b) The depreciation in Year 10 (as in any year) = $2288.00.

(ii) Sum-of-the-Years-Digits Method

The number of parts into which the wearing value is to be divided is $\frac{(15)(16)}{2} = 120$.

The value of each part is $\frac{34320}{120}$ = \$286.00.

The sum of the number of parts assigned to the first nine years
$= 15 + 14 + 13 + 12 + 11 + 10 + 9 + 8 + 7$
$= 120 -$ sum of the parts in the remaining six years
$= 120 - \frac{6(7)}{2} = 120 - 21 = 99$

The accumulated depreciation for the first nine years $= 99(286.00)$
$$= \$28314$$

(a) The book value after nine years is $35720.00 - 28314 = \$7406.00$

(b) Since Year 10 is the first of the remaining six years, six parts will be assigned; the depreciation in Year 10 is $6(286.00) = \$1716.00$.

(iii) *Simple Declining Balance Method*

The rate of depreciation is $2(\frac{1}{15}) = 0.1333333 = 13.33333\%$.

(a) The book value after nine years
$= 35720.00(1 - 0.1333333)^9 \longleftarrow$ see Example 20.1e
$= 35720.00(0.8666667)^9$
$= 35720.00(0.2758475)$
$= \$9853.27$

(b) The depreciation in Year 10 is $9853.27(0.1333333) = \$1313.77$.

(iv) *Complex Declining Balance Method*

$\text{Rate} = 1 - \sqrt[15]{\frac{1400.00}{35720.00}} = 1 - 0.8057762 = 0.1942238 = 19.42238\%$

(a) The book value after nine years
$= 35720.00(1 - 0.1942238)^9$
$= 35720.00(0.8057762)^9$
$= 35720.00(0.1431957)$
$= \$5114.95$

(b) The depreciation in Year 10 is $5114.95(0.1942238) = \$993.45$.

(v) *Annuity Method*

At 16%, the present value of the depreciation charges
$= 35720.00 - 1400.00(1.16^{-15})$
$= 35720.00 - 1400.00(0.107927)$
$= 35720.00 - 151.10$
$= \$35568.90$

The annual depreciation charge

$R = \dfrac{35568.90}{a_{\,\overline{15}|\,16\%}} = \dfrac{35568.90}{5.5754562} = \$6379.55$

(a) Since the Present Value of the Depreciation Charges =
Original Book Value − The Present Value of the Residual Value,

Original Book Value = Present Value of the Depreciation Charges
+ Present Value of the Residual Value.

Similarly, the Book Value at the End of a Particular Year
= Present Value of the Outstanding Annual Depreciation Charges
+ The Present Value of the Residual Value at that Point in Time.
Hence, after nine years, the depreciation charges for the remaining six years in the life of the asset are outstanding and the Book Value after nine years

$$= 6379.55(a_{\overline{6}|16\%}) + 1400.00(1.16^{-6})$$

$$= 6379.55(3.6847359) + 1400.00(0.4104423)$$

$$= 23506.96 + 574.62$$

$$= \$24081.58$$

(b) The depreciation charge for Year 10 is \$6379.55 and consists of provision for interest at $24081.58(0.16) = \$3853.05$ and provision for loss in value at $6379.55 - 3853.05 = \$2526.50$.

(vi) *Sinking Fund Method*

The assumed annual sinking fund payment at 12%

$$= \frac{34320.00}{s_{\overline{15}|12\%}} = \frac{34320.00}{37.279714} = \$920.61$$

The accumulated value of the sinking fund payments after nine years

$$= 920.61(s_{\overline{9}|12\%}) = 920.61(14.775656) = \$13602.62$$

(a) The book value after nine years is $35720.00 - 13602.62 = \$22117.38$.

(b) The depreciation charge in Year 10
$$= 920.61 + 13602.62(0.12) = 920.61 + 1632.31 = \$2552.92$$

F. Computer application 7—Depreciation schedules

A computer solution for the construction of depreciation schedules by either the Straight-Line Method or the Sum-of-the-Years-Digit Method is provided by Program 6 (see Appendix p. 845).

Exercise 20.1

A. For each of the following construct a depreciation schedule using methods of depreciation as indicated.

1. Equipment with an original book value of \$40 000 is estimated to have a scrap value of \$5000 after ten years. It is also estimated that the number of service hours during each of the first four years will be 2025, for each of the next three years 1900 and for each of the last three years 1775. Furthermore for each of the first four years the number of units of product is expected to be 10 750, for each of the next three years 9800 and for each of the last three years 9200. For income tax

purposes the equipment is grouped into Class 8. Interest is 15%. Construct a depreciation schedule using

(a) the Straight-Line Method;

(b) the Service-Hours Method;

(c) the Units-of-Product Method;

(d) the Sum-of-the-Years-Digit Method;

(e) the Simple Declining Balance Method;

(f) the Complex Declining Balance Method;

(g) the Constant Percentage Method;

(h) the Annuity Method;

(i) the Sinking Fund Method.

2. A combine costing $32 000 has a trade-in value of $5000 after eight years. Construct a depreciation schedule using

(a) the Straight-Line Method;

(b) the Sum-of-the-Years-Digits Method;

(c) the Simple Declining Balance Method;

(d) the Complex Declining Balance Method;

(e) the Annuity Method (assume interest to be 13%);

(f) the Sinking Fund Method (assume interest to be 11.5%).

B. Answer each of the following questions.

1. A building costing $560 000 is estimated to have a life of 40 years and a salvage value of $68 000. Compute the book value after 15 years and the depreciation charge in Year 16 for

(a) the Straight-Line Method;

(b) the Sum-of-the-Years-Digit Method;

(c) the Simple Declining Balance Method;

(d) the Complex Declining Balance Method;

(e) the Annuity Method at 12%;

(f) the Sinking Fund Method at 12%.

2. Heavy machinery costing $150 000 with a scrap value of $13 500 is estimated to have a life of 25 years. Compute the book value after 10 years and the depreciation charge in Year 11 for

(a) the Straight-Line Method;

(b) the Sum-of-the-Years-Digit Method;

(c) the Simple Declining Balance Method;

(d) the Complex Declining Balance Method;

(e) the Annuity Method at 14%;

(f) the Sinking Fund Method at 17%.

20.2 Depletion

A. Basic concepts

Many natural resources such as mines, oil wells, natural gas fields, gravel pits and peat moss bogs are non-replaceable, while other resources such as timber cannot be replaced in the short-term. Such resources are called **wasting assets**.

In contrast to depreciable assets which usually retain their physical characteristics during their useful life, wasting assets are in essence long-term inventories of raw materials that will be removed from the property during the production process.

The value of such wasting assets diminishes as they are used up. The loss in value is referred to as **depletion**. When the resources are exhausted there will be little or no residual value in some cases, while the residual value will be considerable in other cases. As with depreciable assets, the loss in value will be the difference between the original capital investment and the residual value.

Since investors expect the return of their capital, the net annual income from the investment in such wasting assets must provide not only interest on the capital but must also be sufficient to restore the amount of capital invested over the estimated life of the assets.

This restoration of capital is usually accomplished by an annual deposit into a sinking fund. This fund, referred to as **depletion reserve**, must over the life of a wasting asset accumulate to the amount of capital originally invested less any residual value. Interest earned on the depletion reserve is normally lower than the yield required on the capital investment.

ANNUAL NET INCOME FROM OPERATIONS	=	ANNUAL INTEREST ON CAPITAL INVESTMENT	+	ANNUAL DEPOSIT INTO DEPLETION RESERVE

⟵ *Formula* **20.6**

From the computational point of view, two basic problems are encountered when dealing with depletion.

1. What is the value of a property to produce a given yield rate?
2. What is the yield rate for a given investment?

B. Finding the value of the investment

Example **20.2a** A gravel pit is estimated to provide an annual net income of $80 000 for the next fifteen years. If the property is worthless when the gravel pit is exhausted and the depletion reserve earns 8% compounded annually, what is the value of the investment to yield 14% compounded annually?

Solution

Let the value of the property be represented by X;
the annual net income = 80000.00;
the annual interest on the capital investment = 0.14X;
the annual deposit into the depletion reserve

$$= \frac{X}{s_{\overline{15}|8\%}} = \frac{X}{27.152114} = 0.0368295X.$$

$$80000.00 = 0.14X + 0.0368295X \longleftarrow \text{using Formula 20.6}$$
$$80000.00 = 0.1768295X$$
$$X = \$452413.09$$

The value of the property is $452 413.

Example 20.2b   Assuming that the gravel pit in Example 20.2a can be sold for
$100 000 when operations cease, what is the value of the property?

Solution

Let the value of the property be Y;
then the annual deposit into the depletion reserve

$$= \frac{(Y - 100000.00)}{s_{\overline{15}|8\%}}$$

$$= \frac{(Y - 100000.00)}{27.152114}$$

$$= 0.0368295Y - 3682.95$$

$$80000.00 = 0.14Y + 0.0368295Y - 3682.95$$
$$83682.95 = 0.1768295Y$$
$$Y = \$473240.92$$

The value of the property is $473 241.

C.   Finding the yield rate

Example 20.2c   A mining property yields an estimated annual net income of
$200 000 for 25 years. The property can be purchased for $600 000 and an
immediate investment of $800 000 is needed to bring the mine into production.
The depletion reserve can be invested at 10% compounded annually. Find the
yield rate

(i) if there is no residual value after 25 years;

(ii) if the property can be sold after 25 years for $1 000 000 and other mining
assets have a salvage value of $200 000.

Solution

(i) Let the yield rate be represented by i;

the total investment is $600000.00 + 800000.00 = 1400000.00$;

the annual net income is $200\,000.00$;

the annual yield from the investment is $1400000.00i$;

the annual deposit into the depletion reserve

$$= \frac{1400000.00}{s_{\overline{25}|10\%}} = \frac{1400000.00}{98.347059} = \$14235.30$$

$$200000.00 = 1400000.00i + 14235.30$$

$$185764.70 = 1400000.00i$$

$$i = 0.1326891$$

The yield rate is approximately 13.27%.

(ii) The total residual value after 25 years is $\$1\,200\,000.00$;

the annual deposit into the depletion reserve

$$= (1400000.00 - 1200000.00)s_{\overline{25}|10\%}$$

$$= \frac{200000.00}{98.347059}$$

$$= 2033.61$$

$$200000.00 = 1400000.00i + 2033.61$$

$$197966.39 = 1400000.00i$$

$$i = 0.1414046$$

The yield is approximately 14.14%.

D. Finding the depletion for a particular year

The depletion for a particular year is the increase in the depletion reserve for the year. It may be obtained from a sinking fund schedule or computed directly.

Example 20.2d Estimates indicate that an oil well will generate an annual net income of $150\,000 for twenty years after which time the oil well will have no value. If the oil well is purchased to yield 18% p.a. and a sinking fund earning 11% per annum is set up for the recovery of the capital invested, determine the depletion in Year 10.

Solution

STEP 1 Find the purchase price.

Let the purchase price of the oil well be represented by X;

the annual net income is 150 000.00;

the annual yield on the capital invested is 0.18X;

the annual deposit into the sinking fund

$$= \frac{X}{s_{\overline{20}|11\%}} = \frac{X}{64.202832} = 0.0155756X$$

$$150000.00 = 0.18X + 0.0155756X$$

$$150000.00 = 0.1955756X$$

$$X = \$766966.70$$

STEP 2   Find the size of the annual deposit into the sinking fund R.

$$R = 0.0155756(766966.70) = \$11945.97$$

STEP 3   Find the balance in the fund after nine years and determine the increase in the fund.

$$S_9 = 11945.97(s_{\overline{9}|11\%}) = 11945.97(14.163972) = \$169202.38$$

Increase = Interest Earned in Year 10 + Annual Deposit

$$= 0.11(169202.38) + 11945.97$$

$$= 18612.26 + 11945.97$$

$$= \$30558.23$$

The depletion in Year 10 is $30 558.23.

Exercise 20.2

A. For each of the following problems involving depletion of a natural resource find the purchase price or the annual yield rate as indicated.

Problem number	Annual net income before depletion	Number of years	Annual yield rate	Sinking fund rate	Residual value	Purchase price
1	$15 000	15	16%	10%	Nil	?
2	28 500	10	14%	8%	Nil	?
3	36 000	20	15%	11%	$4 000	?
4	54 000	12	18%	12%	9 600	?
5	8 400	8	?	9%	Nil	$32 000
6	13 500	10	?	10%	Nil	62 000
7	86 000	25	?	11%	45 000	440 000
8	54 000	18	?	8%	20 000	335 000

B. Answer each of the following questions.

1. A mine is estimated to yield an annual net income before depletion of $45 000 for the next twelve years. When the mine is exhausted after twelve years, the estimated value of the property is $20 000. If a prospective buyer can set up a sinking fund earning 9%, how much can the buyer offer to realize a yield of 14%?

2. A piece of property containing an oil well is offered for sale. If the total reserve of crude oil is removed over twenty years at a constant rate, annual net income before depletion is estimated to be $75 000 and the value of the property after twenty years is estimated to be $200 000. If a buyer expects a yield of 18% and can make deposits into a sinking fund earning 10.5%, what should the offer be to purchase the property?

3. A paper mill acquired timber rights for ten years at a cost of $500 000. If the estimated annual income before depletion is $100 000 and a depletion reserve earning 11.5% can be set up, what is the yield rate on the investment?

4. A peat bog can be purchased for $44 000. If the annual net income before depletion is estimated to be $12 000 and the property is estimated to have a value of $5000 when all useable peat has been extracted after eight years, determine the yield assuming that a replacement fund earning 10% can be set up.

5. A gravel pit is for sale at $85 000. Estimated annual net income before depletion is $22 000. The gravel pit will be exhausted after seven years and the property will then have a value of $30 000. What is the yield rate if deposits into a depletion reserve earn 12%?

6. A dump truck costing $35 000 has an estimated trade-in value of $7000 after five years. The owner of a fleet of such trucks set up a sinking fund earning 11% to replace the trucks. If the net annual income before depreciation is $10 600, what is the yield rate on the investment?

7. An orchard was purchased to yield 22%. The trees are expected to be productive for fifteen years after which time the property will have an estimated value of $35 000. If annual net income is $20 000 and a replacement fund earning 10% is set up for the recovery of the capital invested, determine the depletion in Year 6.

8. A property containing removeable natural resources is estimated to yield an annual net income of $17 500 before depletion. The property is bought to yield 17.5% and has an expected value of $25 000 after twenty years. If a sinking fund earning 12% is set up for the recovery of the capital invested, what is the depletion in Year 15?

20.3 Capitalization

A. Basic concept—valuation of assets and liabilities

Capitalization is the process of finding the present value of an indefinite number of periodic payments. This process is useful in determining the value of income-producing assets and liabilities.

To capitalize an indefinite number of periodic payments (whether income or outgo) involves finding the present value of a perpetuity. This is done by the methods explained in Chapter 16, Section 16.5 and Chapter 17, Section 17.7 and facilitated by using Formula 16.4 $A = \frac{R}{i}$ and Formula 17.6 $A = \frac{R}{f}$ where $f = (1 + i)^c - 1$.

Example 20.3a A revenue producing property yields a quarterly net income of $3600.00. What is the value of the property to yield

(i) 18% compounded quarterly?

(ii) 18% effective?

Solution

(i) $\qquad\qquad R = 3600.00; \qquad i = \dfrac{18\%}{4} = 4.5\% = 0.045;$

$$A = \frac{3600.00}{0.045} \longleftarrow \text{using Formula 16.4}$$

$$= \$80000.00$$

The value of the property is $80 000.00.

(ii) $\qquad R = 3600.00; \qquad i = 18\% = 0.18; \qquad c = \dfrac{1}{4} = 0.25;$

$$f = 1.18^{0.25} - 1 = 1.0422466 - 1 = 0.0422466 = 4.22466\%$$

$$A = \frac{3600.00}{0.0422466} \longleftarrow \text{using Formula 17.6}$$

$$= \$85213.89$$

The value of the property is $85 213.89.

Example 20.3b A utility is required to make annual right-of-way payments of $1950.00 to a landowner. What is the value of the obligation

(i) at 15% effective?

(ii) at 15% compounded monthly?

Solution

(i)
$$R = 1950.00; \qquad i = 15\% = 0.15$$

$$A = \frac{1950.00}{0.15} = \$13000.00$$

At 15% effective the utility has an obligation of $13 000.00.

(ii) $R = 1950.00; \qquad i = \dfrac{15\%}{12} = 1.25\% = 0.0125; \qquad c = 12;$

$$f = 1.0125^{12} - 1 = 1.1607545 - 1 = 0.1607545$$

$$A = \frac{1950.00}{0.1607545}$$

$$= \$12130.30$$

At 15% compounded monthly, the utility's obligation is $12 130.30.

B.   Capitalized cost of an asset

The concept of **capitalized cost** takes account of the necessity to periodically replace income-producing assets such as plant and equipment. The capitalized cost of an asset is defined to be the original cost plus the present value of an unlimited number of periodic replacements. Since the periodic replacements form a perpetuity, the formulae for finding the present value of perpetuities are useful.

CAPITALIZED COST = ORIGINAL COST $+ \dfrac{\text{PERIODIC REPLACEMENT COST}}{f}$ ⟵ ***Formula 20.7***

where $f = (1 + i)^c - 1$

i = rate of interest per compounding period

$c = \dfrac{\text{number of compounding periods per year}}{\text{number of replacement periods per year}}$

or

c = the number of compounding periods per replacement period

Note   In the special case when the compounding interval coincides with the replacement interval $c = 1$ and $f = i$.

Example 20.3c   A machine costing $40 000 needs to be replaced every six years. If the trade-in value of the machine is $5000, what is the capitalized cost of the machine at 15% effective?

Solution

Original cost = 40000.00;

replacement cost = 40000.00 − 5000.00 = 35000.00;

$i = 15\% = 0.15;$ $c = \dfrac{1}{\frac{1}{6}} = 6;$

$f = 1.15^6 − 1 = 2.3130608 − 1 = 1.3130608.$

Capitalized Cost $= 40000.00 + \dfrac{35000.00}{1.313068}$ ⟵ using Formula 20.7

$= 40000.00 + 26655.28$

$= \$66655.28$

Interpretation

The present value of the investment in the machine and its future replacement is $66 655.28. Deducting the original cost of $40 000.00 leaves $26 655.28 which invested at 15% compounded annually for six years amounts to $26655.28(1.15^6) = 26655.28(2.3130608) = \$61655.28$. After six years $35 000.00 is needed to replace the original machine leaving $26 655.28 to be invested for the next six years and so on in perpetuity.

Example 20.3d Jack Snow purchased a licence to operate a taxi for $25 000 and acquired a taxicab for $10 000. He plans to replace the taxicab every year and expects to pay $3000 for each trade-in. If money is worth 12%, what is the capitalized cost of his business?

Solution

The original cost is 25000.00 + 10000.00 = 35000.00;
the annual replacement cost is $3000.00;
$i = 12\% = 0.12;$ $c = 1;$ $f = i = 12\% = 0.12.$

Capitalized Cost $= 35000.00 + \dfrac{3000.00}{0.12} = 35000.00 + 25000.00 = \$60000.00$

Example 20.3e Lyman Corporation is considering the acquisition of a plant consisting of land valued at $200 000, a building costing $600 000 with an estimated life of 40 years and a salvage value of $100 000 and equipment worth $400 000 with an estimated life of 15 years and a scrap value of $20 000. If money is worth 13% compounded semi-annually, what is the capitalized cost of the plant?

Solution

The original cost of the land is its capitalized cost = 200 000.00.
The original cost of the building is 600 000.00;
the replacement value is 600000.00 − 100000.00 = 500000;

$$i = \frac{13\%}{2} = 6.5\% = 0.065; \qquad c = \frac{2}{\left(\frac{1}{40}\right)} = 80;$$

$$f = 1.065^{80} - 1 = 154.15891 - 1 = 153.15891.$$

Capitalized cost of building $= 600000.00 + \dfrac{500000.00}{153.15891}$

$\qquad\qquad = 600000.00 + 3264.59$ ⟵ rounded upward to prevent shortfall

$\qquad\qquad = \$603264.59$

The original cost of the equipment is 400 000.00;
the replacement value is $400000.00 - 20000.00 = 380000.00$;

$$i = \frac{13\%}{2} = 6.5\% = 0.065; \qquad c = \frac{2}{\left(\frac{1}{15}\right)} = 30;$$

$$f = 1.065^{30} - 1 = 6.6143662 - 1 = 5.6143662.$$

Capitalized cost of Equipment $= 400000.00 + \dfrac{380000.00}{5.6143662}$

$\qquad\qquad = 400000.00 + 67683.51$

$\qquad\qquad = \$467683.51$

Capitalized cost of the plant $= 200000.00 + 603264.59 + 467683.51$

$\qquad\qquad = \$1270948.10$

Alternative Solution

The same result can be obtained by adding the present value of the annual deposit required to finance the replacement of the building and equipment to the original acquisition cost.

$$i = \frac{13\%}{2} = 6.5\% = 0.065; \qquad c = 2;$$

$$f = 1.065^2 - 1 = 1.134225 - 1 = 0.134225 = 13.4225\%;$$

The annual payment into a sinking fund to replace the building

$$R_1 = \frac{500000.00}{s\,\overline{_{40}|\,13.4225\%}} = \frac{500000.00}{1141.0609} = \$438.19$$

The annual payment into a sinking fund to replace the equipment

$$R_2 = \frac{380000.00}{s\,\overline{_{15}|\,13.4225\%}} = \frac{380000.00}{41.828021} = \$9084.82$$

The total annual payment is $438.19 + 9084.82 = \$9523.01$.

The present value of these deposits is $\dfrac{9523.01}{0.134225} = \$70948.10$.

The capitalized cost $= 200000.00 + 600000.00 + 400000.00 + 70948.10$

$\qquad\qquad = \$1270948.10$

Example 20.3f The Beaver Valley Ski Club installed a chairlift at an initial cost of \$225 000. The lift will need to be replaced every ten years at a cost of \$175 000. Seven years after the original installation it became apparent that a major overhaul would extend the useful life of the lift by two years. If money is worth 12% compounded annually, what is the maximum cost that the club could economically afford for the overhaul?

Solution

The original cost is 225 000.00; the replacement cost is 175 000.00;

$$i = 12\% = 0.12; \qquad c = \frac{1}{\left(\frac{1}{10}\right)};$$

$$f = 1.12^{10} - 1 = 3.1058482 - 1 = 2.1058482.$$

$$\text{The capitalized cost} = 225000.00 + \frac{175000.00}{2.1058482}$$

$$= 225000.00 + 83101.91$$

$$= \$308101.91$$

Of the capitalized cost of \$308 101.91 the original cost of \$225 000.00 is required initially leaving \$83 101.91 to accumulate and finance the replacement.
After seven years, the accumulated balance

$$= 83101.91(1.12)^7 = 83101.91(2.2106814) = \$183711.85$$

The required balance to finance the replacement

$$= 175000.00 + 83101.91 = \$258101.91$$

Since the replacement will take place twelve years after the original installation, we need to find the principal which will accumulate to \$258101.91 from the end of Year 7 to the end of Year 12.

$$P = 258101.91(1.12^{-5}) = 258101.91(0.5674269) = \$146453.96$$

The difference between the capitalized cost after seven years and the required principal is $183711.85 - 146453.96 = \$37257.89$.
This difference is the maximum amount that the ski club has economically available for the overhaul. Hence the maximum amount that the ski club should be prepared to pay for the overhaul is \$37 257.89.

C. *Periodic investment cost*

The capitalized cost of an asset represents the investment needed to acquire an asset and replace it indefinitely. The interest that could be earned by that investment is foregone interest revenue and is considered to be the periodic investment cost of the asset. Thus the **periodic investment cost** is defined to be the interest on the capitalized cost of the asset.

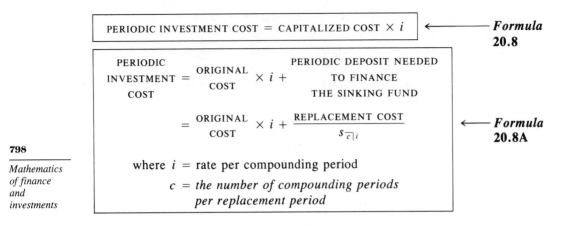

$$\text{PERIODIC INVESTMENT COST} = \text{CAPITALIZED COST} \times i \quad \longleftarrow \quad \textbf{Formula 20.8}$$

$$\begin{array}{l} \text{PERIODIC} \\ \text{INVESTMENT} = \\ \text{COST} \end{array} \begin{array}{l} \text{ORIGINAL} \\ \text{COST} \end{array} \times i + \begin{array}{c} \text{PERIODIC DEPOSIT NEEDED} \\ \text{TO FINANCE} \\ \text{THE SINKING FUND} \end{array}$$

$$= \begin{array}{l} \text{ORIGINAL} \\ \text{COST} \end{array} \times i + \dfrac{\text{REPLACEMENT COST}}{s_{\overline{c}|i}} \quad \longleftarrow \quad \textbf{Formula 20.8A}$$

where i = rate per compounding period

c = *the number of compounding periods per replacement period*

Example 20.3g A machine shop initially spent $3000.00 for machine tools. After that it is estimated that the shop will need to spend $500.00 every three months to replace worn or broken tools. If money is worth 14% effective, determine the annual investment cost.

Solution

Original cost is 3000.00;   replacement cost is 500.00;

$$i = 14\% = 0.14; \qquad c = \frac{1}{4} = 0.25;$$

$$f = 1.14^{0.25} - 1 = 1.0332995 - 1 = 0.0332995 = 3.32995\%.$$

$$\begin{aligned} \text{Capitalized cost} &= 3000.00 + \frac{500.00}{0.0332995} \\ &= 3000.00 + 15015.25 \\ &= \$18015.25 \end{aligned}$$

$$\begin{aligned} \text{Annual investment cost} &= 18015.25(0.14) \quad \longleftarrow \text{ using Formula 20.7} \\ &= \$2522.13 \end{aligned}$$

Alternatively

$$\begin{aligned} \text{Annual investment cost} &= 3000.00(0.14) + \frac{500.00}{s_{\,\overline{0.25}\,|\,14\%}} \quad \longleftarrow \text{ using } \textbf{\textit{Formula 20.8A}} \\ &= 420.00 + \frac{500.00}{0.2378535} \\ &= \$2522.13 \end{aligned}$$

D. Comparison of buying costs—investment cost basis

Decisions concerning investment in plant and equipment usually involve selecting from a number of similar assets all capable of doing the same job but different in price, life span, wear and tear and residual value. After such assets have been acquired decisions regarding whether to repair or replace them periodically confront management of a business. A rational approach to making such decisions involves cost comparisons which can be made on the basis of capitalized cost or periodic investment cost.

Example 20.3h A selection is to be made between two machines. Machine A costs $4000, has a life of 15 years and no salvage value. Machine B costs $3500, has a life of ten years and a scrap value of $400. Which machine is more economical in the long-run if money is worth
(a) 10%? (b) 16%?

Solution

Machine A	**Machine B**
Original cost = 4000.00	Original cost = 3500.00
Replacement cost = 4000.00	Replacement cost = 3100.00

$$c = \frac{1}{\left(\frac{1}{15}\right)} = 15 \qquad\qquad c = \frac{1}{\left(\frac{1}{10}\right)} = 10$$

(a) At 10%

Machine A	Machine B
$f = 1.10^{15} - 1$	$f = 1.10^{10} - 1$
$= 4.1772482 - 1$	$= 2.5937425 - 1$
$= 3.1772482$	$= 1.5937425$

Capitalized Cost   Capitalized Cost

$$= 4000.00 + \frac{4000.00}{3.1772482} \qquad\qquad = 3500.00 + \frac{3100.00}{1.5937425}$$

$$= 4000.00 + 1258.95 \qquad\qquad\quad = 3500.00 + 1945.11$$

$$= \$5258.95 \qquad\qquad\qquad\qquad\quad = \$5445.11$$

Annual Investment Cost   Annual Investment Cost

$$= 5258.95(0.10) = \$525.90 \qquad = 5445.11(0.10) = \$544.51$$

Conclusion Since the capitalized cost of Machine A is smaller than the capitalized cost of Machine B, Machine A is more economical at 10%. The annual investment cost advantage for Machine A is $544.51 - 525.90 = \$18.61$.

(b) At 16%

Machine A	**Machine B**
$f = 1.16^{15} - 1$	$f = 1.16^{10} - 1$
$= 9.2655209 - 1$	$= 4.4114351 - 1$
$= 8.2655209$	$= 3.4114351$

Capitalized Cost	Capitalized Cost
$= 4000.00 + \dfrac{4000.00}{8.2655209}$	$= 3500.00 + \dfrac{3100.00}{3.411351}$
$= 4000.00 + 483.94$	$= 3500.00 + 908.71$
$= \$4483.94$	$= \$4408.71$

Annual Investment Cost	Annual Investment Cost
$= 4483.94(0.16) = \$717.43$	$= \$4408.71(0.16) = \$705.39$

Mathematics of finance and investments

Conclusion Since the capitalized cost of Machine A is greater than the capitalized cost of Machine B, Machine B is more economical at 16%. The annual investment cost advantage for Machine B is 717.43 − 705.39 = $12.04.

Example **20.3i** A machine costing $8000 with a life of eight years and a salvage value of $800 can be replaced by a new model lasting twelve years and a residual value of 10% of the original cost. If money is worth 14%, how much can the buyer afford to pay for the new model?

Solution

Old model	**New model**
Original cost $= 8000.00$	Let the original cost be C
Replacement cost $= 800.00$	Replacement cost $= 0.09C$
$c = \dfrac{1}{\left(\frac{1}{8}\right)} = 8$	$c = \dfrac{1}{\left(\frac{1}{12}\right)} = 12$
$i = 14\% = 0.14$	$i = 14\% = 0.14$
$f = 1.14^8 - 1$	$f = 1.14^{12} - 1$
$= 2.8525864 - 1$	$= 4.8179048 - 1$
$= 1.8525864$	$= 3.8179048$

Capitalized Cost	Capitalized Cost
$= 8000.00 + \dfrac{7200.00}{1.8525864}$	$= C + \dfrac{0.90C}{3.8179048}$
$= 8000.00 + 3886.46$	$= C + 0.2357314C$
$= \$11886.46$	$= \$1.2357314C$

The capitalized costs of the two models are to be equal.
$$1.2357314C = 11886.46$$
$$C = 9618.97$$

A buyer can afford to pay up to $9618.97 for the new model.

The same result would have been obtained using the periodic investment cost.

Annual investment cost for the old model

$$8000(0.14) + \frac{7200.00}{s_{\overline{8}|14\%}} = 1120.00 + \frac{7200.00}{13.232760} = \$1664.10$$

Annual investment cost for the new model

$$0.14C + \frac{0.90C}{s_{\overline{12}|14\%}} = 0.14C + \frac{0.90C}{27.270749} = 0.1730024C$$

The annual investment costs for the two models are to be equal.

$$0.1730024C = 1664.10$$
$$C = \$9618.94$$

Example 20.3j Protection equipment against salt corrosion needs to be replaced every four years at a cost of $12 000. Additional processing can extend the life of the equipment to seven years. At 13% what is the maximum cost of the additional processing to make it economically feasible?

Solution

Old process	**Including additional processing**
Original cost = 12000.00	Original cost = C
Replacement cost = 12000.00	Replacement cost = C

Old process:

$$c = \frac{1}{\left(\frac{1}{4}\right)} = 4$$

$$i = 13\% = 0.13$$

$$f = 1.13^4 - 1$$
$$= 1.6304736 - 1$$
$$= 0.6304736$$

Including additional processing:

$$c = \frac{1}{\left(\frac{1}{7}\right)} = 7$$

$$i = 13\% = 0.13$$

$$f = 1.13^7 - 1$$
$$= 2.3526055 - 1$$
$$= 1.3526055$$

Capitalized Cost (Old process)

$$= 12000.00 + \frac{12000.00}{0.6304736}$$

$$= 12000.00 + 19033.31$$

$$= \$31033.31$$

Capitalized Cost (Including additional processing)

$$= C + \frac{C}{1.3526055}$$

$$= C + 0.7393139C$$

$$= 1.7393139C$$

$$1.7393139C = 31033.31$$
$$C = \$17842.27$$

The maximum cost including additional processing is $17 842.27.
The maximum cost of additional processing is $17842.27 - 12000.00 = \$5842.27$.

E. Comparison of buying costs—production cost basis

The method of comparing assets on the basis of investment cost makes the underlying assumption that the periodic maintenance cost (operating cost plus repair cost) as well as the productive capacity of the assets compared are the same. Since this is often not the case, it is useful to extend the concept of capitalization to allow for differences in capacity and maintenance cost.

To allow for differences in maintenance cost, it is necessary to capitalize the periodic operating expenses and repair costs. Since the capitalized value of periodic payments is the present value of a perpetuity, the periodic maintenance cost is capitalized by dividing by the periodic rate of interest.

$$\begin{array}{c} \text{CAPITALIZED COST} \\ \text{INCLUDING} \\ \text{MAINTENANCE} \end{array} = \begin{array}{c} \text{ORIGINAL} \\ \text{COST} \end{array} + \frac{\begin{array}{c}\text{REPLACEMENT}\\\text{COST}\end{array}}{f} + \frac{\begin{array}{c}\text{MAINTENANCE}\\\text{COST}\end{array}}{i}$$

Formula
20.9

To allow for differences in capacity it is only necessary to determine the capitalized cost per unit of production by dividing the capitalized cost by the number of units of production.

Example 20.3k Equipment costing $15 000 has a life of ten years with a salvage value of $2000. Its annual production capacity is 2400 units. Modification of the equipment can increase production by 25%. If interest is 15% and if the life and salvage value remain the same, how much can economically be spent to increase production?

Solution

Regular capacity	Increased capacity
Original cost = 15000.00	Original cost = C
Replacement cost = 13000.00	Replacement cost = C − 2000.00
Production = 2400(10) = 24000	Production = 3000(10) = 30000

Regular capacity:

$$c = \frac{1}{\left(\frac{1}{10}\right)} = 10$$

$$i = 15\% = 0.15$$

$$f = 1.15^{10} - 1$$
$$= 4.0455577 - 1$$
$$= 3.0455577$$

Capitalized Cost

$$= 15000.00 + \frac{13000.00}{3.0455577}$$

$$= 15000.00 + 4268.51$$

$$= 19268.51$$

Capitalized Cost Per Unit of Production

$$= \frac{19268.51}{24000}$$

Increased capacity:

$$c = 10$$

$$i = 0.15$$

$$f = 3.0455577$$

Capitalized Cost

$$= C + \frac{C - 2000.00}{3.0455577}$$

$$= C + 0.3283471C - 656.69$$

$$= 1.3283471C - 656.69$$

Capitalized Cost Per Unit of Production

$$= \frac{1.3283471C - 656.69}{30000}$$

$$\frac{1.3283471C - 656.69}{30000} = \frac{19268.51}{24000}$$

$$24(1.3283471C - 656.69) = 30(19268.51)$$
$$4(1.3283471C - 656.69) = 5(19268.51)$$
$$5.3133884C - 2626.76 = 96342.55$$
$$5.3133884C = 98969.31$$
$$C = 18626.40$$

The original cost including modification to increase capacity is $18626.40. Hence the maximum cost of modification is $18626.40 - 15000.00 = 3626.40.

Example 20.31 Marshall Printing is considering the purchase of new lithographing presses. Research of available equipment has narrowed down the selection to two alternatives. *Alternative A* Purchase two presses at a cost of $60 000 each. The trade-in value of the presses after eight years is $10 000 per machine. Total operating expenses for the two presses is $6000 per month and annual repair costs are $5000. *Alternative B* Purchase one machine costing $250 000 having a life of ten years and a trade-in-value of $45 000. Operating expenses are $4000 per month and the annual repair cost is $3000.
If money is worth 12%

(i) find the capitalized cost of the alternatives;

(ii) determine which alternative is preferable;

(iii) determine the annual cost of the two alternatives.

Solution

(i)

Alternative A	**Alternative B**

Alternative A

Original cost = 120000.00
Replacement cost = 100000.00

$$c = \frac{1}{\left(\frac{1}{8}\right)} = 8$$

$$i = 12\% = 0.12$$

$$f = 1.12^8 - 1$$
$$= 2.4759632 - 1$$
$$= 1.4759632$$

Operating expenses per month = 6000.00

$$c = \frac{1}{12}$$

$$f = 1.12^{\frac{1}{12}} - 1$$
$$= 1.0094888 - 1$$
$$= 0.0094888$$

Annual repair cost = 5000.00

Alternative B

Original cost = 250000.00
Replacement cost = 205000.00

$$c = \frac{1}{\left(\frac{1}{10}\right)} = 10$$

$$i = 12\% = 0.12$$

$$f = 1.12^{10} - 1$$
$$= 3.1058482 - 1$$
$$= 2.1058482$$

Operating expenses per month = 4000.00

$$c = \frac{1}{12}$$

$$f = 1.12^{\frac{1}{12}} - 1$$
$$= 1.0094888 - 1$$
$$= 0.0094888$$

Annual repair cost = 3000.00

Capitalized Cost for Alternative A

$$= 120000.00 + \frac{100000.00}{1.4759632} + \frac{6000.00}{0.0094888} + \frac{5000.00}{0.12} \quad \longleftarrow \text{ using Formula 20.9}$$

$$= 120000.00 + 67752.37 + 632324.42 + 41666.67$$

$$= \$861743.46$$

Capitalized Cost for Alternative B

$$= 250000.00 + \frac{205000.00}{2.1058482} + \frac{4000.00}{0.0094888} + \frac{3000.00}{0.12}$$

$$= 250000.00 + 97347.95 + 421549.62 + 25000.00$$

$$= \$793897.57$$

(ii) Since the capitalized cost of Alternative B is smaller than the capitalized cost of Alternative A, Alternative B is preferable.

(iii) The total annual cost for Alternative A
is $861743.46(0.12) = \$103409.22$.
The total annual cost for Alternative B
is $793897.57(0.12) = \$ 95267.71$.

F. Total periodic cost of an asset

The **total periodic cost** of an asset is defined as the interest on the capitalized cost including maintenance.

$$\boxed{\text{TOTAL PERIODIC COST} = \text{CAPITALIZED COST} \times i}$$

The Total Periodic Cost may be found by extending Formula 20.8A.

| TOTAL PERIODIC COST | = | ORIGINAL COST | $\times i +$ | $\dfrac{\text{REPLACEMENT COST}}{s_{\overline{c}|i}}$ | $+$ PERIODIC OPERATING EXPENSE | $+$ PERIODIC REPAIR COST | *Formula 20.9A* |

For *Example 20.3l* the total annual cost (also called **annual charge**) could have been found directly.

Annual Charge for Alternative A

$$= 120000.00(0.12) + \frac{100000.00}{s_{\overline{8}|12\%}} + 6000.00(s_{\overline{12}|0.94888\%}) + 5000.00$$

$$= 120000.00(0.12) + \frac{100000.00}{12.299693} + 6000.00(12.646498) + 5000.00$$

$$= 14400.00 + 8130.28 + 75878.99 + 5000.00$$

$$= \$103409.27$$

Annual Charge for Alternative B

$$= 250000.00(0.12) + \frac{205000.00}{s\,\overline{_{10}}\,_{12\%}} + 4000.00(s\,\overline{_{12}}\,_{0.94888\%}) + 3000.00$$

$$= 250000.00(0.12) + \frac{205000.00}{17.548735} + 4000.00(12.646498) + 3000.00$$

$$= 30000.00 + 11681.75 + 50585.99 + 3000.00$$

$$= \$95267.74$$

Formula 20.9A indicates that the periodic charge of owning an asset consists of
1. the periodic interest lost on the investment (Original Cost $\times$ i)

        plus
2. the periodic depreciation charge (Wearing Value/$s\,\overline{_{c}}\,_{i}$)

        plus
3. the periodic operating expense

        plus
4. the periodic repair cost.

Example 20.3m To keep producing, a machine requires major renovation or it can be sold for $2500. If renovated it will have a life of five years with a scrap value of $500. Monthly operating expenses amount to $1800 and annual repair cost is $600. Annual production is 2000 units. A new machine can be purchased for $30 000. The life of the new machine is ten years with a salvage value of $4000. Monthly operating cost of the new machine is $2100 and annual repair cost is $400. Annual production is 2400 units. Assuming interest at 11% and using the Periodic Cost Method, determine the maximum economically feasible cost of renovation.

Solution

Annual charge for old machine

Let the maximum cost of renovation be X.

Interest on investment $= 0.11(X + 2500.00) = 0.11X + 275.00$

Depreciation charge $= \dfrac{X + 2500.00 - 500.00}{s\,\overline{_{5}}\,_{11\%}}$

              $= \dfrac{X + 2000.00}{6.2278014}$

              $= 0.1605703X + 321.14$

Operating expense $= 1800.00(s\,\overline{_{12}}\,_{f})$

              $(f = 1.11^{\frac{1}{12}} - 1)$

              $= 1800.00(s\,\overline{_{12}}\,_{0.87346\%})$

              $= 1800.00(12.593602)$

              $= 22668.48$

Repair cost $= 600.00$

Total annual charge

$$= 0.11X + 275.00 + 0.1605703X + 321.14 + 22668.48 + 600.00$$

$$= 0.2705703X + 23864.62$$

Annual charge per unit of production $= \dfrac{0.2705703X + 23864.62}{2000}$

Annual charge for new machine

Interest on investment $= 0.11(30000.00)$ $\qquad = 3300.00$

Depreciation charge $= \dfrac{26000.00}{s_{\overline{10}|11\%}} = \dfrac{26000.00}{16.722009} = 1554.84$

Operating expense $= 2100.00(s_{\overline{12}|0.87346\%})$

$$= 2100.00(12.593602) \qquad = 26446.56$$

Repair cost $\qquad\qquad\qquad\qquad\qquad\qquad = \quad 400.00$

$\qquad$ Total annual charge $\qquad\qquad\qquad\qquad \underline{31701.40}$

Annual charge per unit of production $= \dfrac{31701.40}{2400} = 13.208918$

$$\dfrac{0.2705703X + 23864.62}{2000} = 13.208918$$

$$0.2705703X + 23864.62 = 26417.84$$

$$0.2705703X = 2553.22$$

$$X = 9436.42$$

The maximum economically feasible cost of renovation is \$9436.42.

Exercise 20.3

A. Find the capitalized cost for each of the following.

Problem number	Original cost	Residual value	Annual maintenance cost	Replacement period in years	Annual rate of interest
1	\$ 8 000	Nil	—	15	13%
2	12 500	Nil	—	20	15%
3	26 000	\$4000	—	10	14%
4	18 000	3200	—	8	22%
5	9 400	900	\$15 000	12	16%
6	16 500	3000	12 400	7	18%

B. Answer each of the following questions.

    1. Determine the annual investment cost for Part A, Problems 1 to 4.

    2. Determine the annual charge for Part A, Problems 5 and 6.

3. An income property yields a monthly net income of $1600. What is the value of the property to yield

   (a) 16.5% compounded monthly?   (b) 16.5% effective?

4. An obligation is met by making quarterly payments of $2625. What is the value of the obligation at

   (a) 13.5% compounded monthly?   (b) 15% effective?

5. A delivery service bought a van for $8600. The van is to be traded-in every two years at a cost of $4000. If interest is 13%, what is the capitalized cost of the van?

6. A swimming pool installed in an apartment building at a cost of $18 000 is to be renovated every seven years at an estimated cost of $9000. If money is worth 14%, what is the capitalized cost of the pool?

7. A machine costing $12 000 has a trade-in value of $1500 after fifteen years. If the machine is overhauled after ten years its useful life can be extended by three years. If the trade-in value then is $1100 and assuming interest at 11%, what is the maximum cost of the overhaul that can economically be justified?

8. A service building costing $25 000 must be totally renovated every twenty years. Major repairs after fifteen years will extend the service life of the building to 24 years. If interest is 15%, what is the maximum amount of money that should be made available for the repair job?

9. A transformer costing $30 000 must be replaced every four years. If its scrap value is $2800 and interest is 16%, what is the annual investment cost?

10. A farmer buys a tractor for $13 000 and intends to trade the tractor every four years at an estimated cost of $7600. What is the annual investment cost at 12%?

11. A choice is to be made between two machines. Machine A costs $9000, has a life of twelve years and a salvage value of $200. Machine B costs $8000, has a life of nine years and a salvage value of $300. Compute the capitalized cost and the annual investment cost to determine which machine is more economical in the long-run under the assumption that money is worth

    (a) 12%;   (b) 18%.

12. Word processing equipment priced at $1450 has to be replaced every five years at a cost of $1300. A similar model priced at $1250 has to be replaced every four years at a cost of $1100. Compare the annual investment costs to determine which model is the more economical buy at

    (a) 10%;   (b) 16%.

13. Equipment costing $15 000 with a life of twelve years and a residual value of $1000 can be replaced by a different model with a life of nine years and residual value of 15% of the original cost. If money is worth 13%, how much can a user afford to pay if switching to the second model?

14. Equipment costing $150 000 with a life of ten years has a salvage value of $18 000. Protective covering can extend the life of the equipment to fifteen years. If interest is 16% and the salvage value after fifteen years is $6000, what is the maximum cost that can be paid for the protective equipment?

15. Machine A, costing $36 000, has a life of fifteen years with a salvage value of $1500 and a productive capacity of 1600 units per year. Machine B, costing $28 000, has a life of twelve years, a salvage value of $1000 and a productive capacity of 1400 per year. At 17%, what is the difference in the annual investment cost per unit?

16. Equipment costing $55 000 has a life of twelve years with a salvage value of $4000. Annual service hours are 1200. Modification of the equipment would increase the number of service hours to 1600 but the life of the equipment would be reduced to ten years and salvage value would then be $6000. If interest is 16%, how much is the maximum amount that should be spent on the modification?

17. A farmer can buy a MF tractor for $15 000. The tractor has an estimated life of eight years with a trade-in value of $2500. Annual operating expenses are $3000 and annual repair cost is estimated to be $600. An IH tractor which can do the same job costs $13 500, has a life of six years and a trade-in value of $2800. Annual operating expenses are expected to be $2300 and annual repair cost is estimated at $500. At 15%, which tractor is the more economical buy and what is the difference in the annual cost?

18. The floors of a school building can be finished at a cost of $50 000. The finish will last twenty years and must then be redone totally. Annual costs are $9000 for servicing and $500 for repairs. Alternatively the school can be carpeted at a cost of $30 000 every five years. Annual costs are $4000 for servicing and $1000 for repairs. If interest is 13%, which method is more economical and what is the difference in the annual costs?

19. A manufacturer requires a drilling machine. Model A costs $16 000 and has an estimated life of fifteen years. Monthly operating expenses are $2450 and annual repair cost is $800. Model B costs $14 000 and has a life of twelve years. Monthly operating expenses are $2550 and annual repair cost is $750. Both machines have a scrap value of $900. If money is worth 18%, what is the more economical model and what is the difference in annual costs?

20. A credit union uses a posting machine to maintain member accounts. The machine costs $12 000, lasts ten years and has a scrap value of $1000. Monthly operating expenses are $1600 and annual service cost is $500. Alternatively the credit union can buy a suitable micro-computer for $40 000. The computer has a life of eight years and a salvage value of $3000. Monthly operating expenses are $900 and annual servicing is $1000. As a third choice the credit union can purchase the services of the Credit Union League at a cost of $2000 per month. If interest is 14%, which of the three alternatives is the most economical and what is the annual cost of each of the three alternatives?

Review exercise

1. A machine costing $12 000 has a trade-in value of $2460 after eight years. Construct a depreciation schedule using

   (a) the Sum-of-the-Years-Digit Method;

   (b) the Simple Declining Balance Method;

   (c) the Complex Declining Balance Method;

(d) the Annuity Method (using interest to be 16%);

(e) the Sinking Fund Method (using interest to be 16%).

2. Equipment with an original cost of $32 000 has an estimated life of 25 years and a scrap value of $480. Compute the book value after 20 years and the depreciation charge in Year 21 using

(a) the Straight-Line Method;

(b) the Sum-of-the-Years-Digit Method;

(c) the Simple Declining Balance Method;

(d) the Complex Declining Balance Method;

(e) the Annuity Method (using interest to be 20%);

(f) the Sinking Fund Method (using interest to be 20%).

3. A property containing oil wells is estimated to yield a net annual income of $200 000 before depletion for fifteen years. When the oil has been removed the property value is estimated to be $500 000. If an investor can set up a depletion reserve earning 11%, what should the investor be prepared to pay to realize a yield of 20%?

4. A machine with an original cost of $9160 has a trade-in value of $2230 after six years. Construct a depreciation schedule using the Sum-of-the-Years-Digit Method.

5. A building has an original cost of $80 000, a life of 25 years and a salvage value of $8500. Find the book value of the building after fifteen years using

(a) the Simple Declining Balance Method;

(b) the Annuity Method using interest at 18%.

6. A turbine costing $75 000 has a life of twenty years and a scrap value of $3500. Determine the depreciation in Year 12 using

(a) the Complex Declining Balance Method;

(b) the Sinking Fund Method using interest at 21%.

7. Timber rights to a tract of land are purchased by a saw mill. Useable trees are expected to last for twenty years and yield an annual net income of $75 000 before depletion. After twenty years the timber rights have no value and a replacement fund earning 9.5% can be set up by the owners of the sawmill. For how much were the timber rights acquired if purchased to yield 16%?

8. Tires for a crane lasting four years with a salvage value of $75.00 can be bought at a cost of $875.00 each. How much should be the price of a tire lasting seven years with a salvage value of 10% of the original cost if money is worth 13%?

9. Artificial turf for a playing field can be installed for $125 000. If the covering needs to be replaced every six years at a cost of $95 000 and interest is 15%

(a) what is the capitalized cost of the turf?

(b) what is the annual investment cost?

10. A property containing natural resources yields an estimated annual net income of $55 000 before depletion for eight years. After removal of the natural resources the property has an estimated value of $150 000. A prospective buyer has offered $270 000 for the property. If the buyer can earn 10% on a sinking fund set up for the recovery of the capital, what is the yield rate on the investment?

11. A mine is offered for sale for $600 000. A prospective buyer has determined the following: net annual income before depletion is expected to be $90 000 for eighteen years; the value of the property when the ore has been removed is expected to be $75 000; the depletion reserve can be set up to earn 12%.

(a) What is the yield rate on the mine if it is purchased for $600 000?

(b) How much should the buyer offer if the investment is to realize 16%?

12. A delivery service purchased a van for $12 600 and expects to trade every two years at a cost of $5200. Interest is 13% compounded semi-annually.

(a) What is the capitalized cost?

(b) What is the annual investment cost?

13. A pool heating and filtration system costs $2300. If exposed to weather, the system needs to be replaced every five years. If an enclosure is provided the life of the system including the enclosure is seven years. Scrap value in either case is $400. If money is worth 13%, what is the maximum amount that should be spent on the enclosure?

14. A machine costs $25 000 when new and has a scrap value of $1700 after twelve years. A second machine which can do the same job costs $22 000, has a life of nine years and a scrap value of $1800. Compute the capitalized cost and the annual investment cost to determine which machine is more economical under the assumption that interest is

(a) 13%;   (b) 20%.

15. A building can be painted at a cost of $1350 every three years if using Brand A. If longer lasting Brand B is used, the paint job needs to be done every five years. If interest is 12%, what is the maximum cost at which it is economical to switch to Brand B?

16. A machine costing $18 000 has a life of six years, a trade-in value of $2500 after six years and an annual productive capacity of 3600 units. A competitor's model costs $21 000, has a life of eight years, a trade-in value of $2200 after eight years and an annual productive capacity of 4000 units. At 16%

(a) which machine is a better buy?

(b) what is the difference in their annual investment cost per unit?

17. A machine that can be disposed of for $3000 must be renovated if it is to be kept in production. If renovated the machine will have a life of seven years with a scrap value of $500. Annual operating expenses amount to $4000 and annual repair cost is $1500. A new machine will cost $34 000, have a life of ten years and a scrap value of $3500. Annual operating expenses amount to $3600 and annual repair cost is $1200. If money is worth 15%, what is the maximum amount that can economically be spent on renovating the old machine?

18. Bomac Steel uses two fabricating machines costing $60 000 each. The machines have a life of twelve years with a trade-in value of $8000 each after twelve years. Monthly operating expenses are $7000 and annual repair costs amount to $2000. A larger machine capable of doing the job of the two machines costs $270 000, has a life of fifteen years and a trade-in value of $30 000 after fifteen years. Monthly operating

expenses are $4000 and annual repair costs amount to $4000. At 17%

(a) is it economical to replace the two machines by the larger machine?

(b) what is the difference in the annual costs?

Self-test

Depreciation, depletion, and capitalization

1. A machine with an original book value of $60 000 has a scrap value of $3000 after six years. If interest is 12% construct a depreciation schedule using the Sinking Fund Method.

2. An asset costing $85 000 has an expected salvage value of $5000 after sixteen years. Compute the book value of the asset after ten years using the Straight Line Method.

3. Equipment costing $25 000 has an estimated disposal value of $1600 after twelve years. What is the book value of the asset after seven years by the Sum-of-the-Digits Method?

4. A vault has been installed at a cost of $45 000 and is expected to have a residual value of $2500 after twenty years. Determine the depreciation charge in Year 15 using the Complex Declining Balance Method.

5. Mining equipment with an original book value of $150 000 and an estimated scrap value of $15 000 after eight years is depreciated by the Annuity Method. If the rate of interest is 13%, what is the accumulated depreciation after five years?

6. A gold mine is estimated to yield an annual net income of $250 000 before depletion for the next eight years. After eight years the gold mine has no value. If the depletion reserve earns 10%, what is the value of the gold mine to yield 15%?

7. A natural resources property yields an annual net income of $42 000 before depletion for ten years. The residual value of the property after ten years is estimated to be $30 000. If a sinking fund for the recovery of the capital investment can be set up to earn 9% and an offer to purchase of $260 000 is made, what is the yield rate on the investment?

8. Timber rights on a tract of land are expected to yield an annual net income of $100 000 before depletion for ten years. After ten years the timber rights have a value of $50 000 and the depletion reserve fund earns 11%. If the rights were purchased to yield 16%, what is the amount of depletion in Year 5?

9. An asset has an original book value of $40 000. The asset is to be replaced after six years and has a residual value of $3000 at that time. Annual maintenance cost is $4800. What is the capitalized cost of the asset at 15%?

10. Equipment costing $70 000 with an expected life of six years has a salvage value of $10 000. Modification of the equipment can extend the life of the equipment to nine years with a salvage value of $6000 after nine years. If interest is 14%, what is the maximum outlay that can be justified for modification of the equipment?

11. A machine costing $4800 has a life of twelve years and a trade-in value of $500 after twelve years. The maximum annual usage is 1250 hours. A competitive model costing $5200 has a life of fifteen years and a trade-in value of $400 after 15 years. The

maximum annual usage is 1300 hours. If interest is 18%, what is the difference in the annual investment cost per hour?

12. A manufacturer uses a machine costing $150 000 which has a life of ten years and a scrap value of $3000. Monthly operating expenses amount to $6000 and the annual repair cost is $4000. A new smaller model with one-third of the productive capacity of the old model can be purchased for $70 000. The new model has a life of fifteen years with a scrap value of $2000. Monthly operating expenses are $1500 and the annual repair cost is $800. If interest is 16% and the same annual production is maintained, what is the difference in the total annual cost of using the old model as compared to the new?

Summary of formulae used

Formula 20.1

$$\frac{\text{YEARLY}}{\text{DEPRECIATION}} = \frac{\text{ORIGINAL COST} - \text{RESIDUAL VALUE}}{n}$$

where n = the number of years in the life of the asset

Formula for finding the yearly depreciation when using the Straight-Line Method

Formula 20.1A

$$\frac{\text{DEPRECIATION}}{\text{PER SERVICE HOUR}} = \frac{\text{ORIGINAL COST} - \text{RESIDUAL VALUE}}{n}$$

where n = the number of service hours in the life of the asset

Formula for finding the depreciation per service hour when using the Service Hours Method

Formula 20.1B

$$\frac{\text{DEPRECIATION PER}}{\text{UNIT OF PRODUCT}} = \frac{\text{ORIGINAL COST} - \text{RESIDUAL VALUE}}{n}$$

where n = the number of product units in the life of the asset

Formula for finding the depreciation per unit of product when using the Unit of Product Method

Formula 20.2

$$k = \frac{\text{ORIGINAL COST} - \text{RESIDUAL VALUE}}{\frac{n(n+1)}{2}}$$

Formula for finding the value of one part (constant of proportion) when using the Sum-of-the-Years-Digit Method

Formula 20.3

$$d = 2 \times \frac{1}{\text{Number of years in the life of the asset}}$$

Formula for finding the rate of depreciation when using the Simple Declining Balance Method

Formula 20.4

$$d = 1 - \sqrt[n]{\frac{\text{RESIDUAL VALUE}}{\text{ORIGINAL COST}}}$$

Formula for finding the rate of depreciation when using the Complex Declining Balance Method

Formula 20.5

$$\begin{array}{c} \text{ANNUAL} \\ \text{DEPRECIATION, R} \\ \text{CHARGE} \end{array} = \frac{\begin{array}{cc} \text{ORIGINAL} & \text{RESIDUAL} \\ \text{COST} & - \text{VALUE} \end{array} \times (1 + i)^{-n}}{a\,\overline{n}|i}$$

where n = the number of years in the life of the asset

i = the applicable rate of interest

Formula for finding the annual depreciation charge when using the Annuity Method

Formula 20.6

$$\begin{array}{c} \text{ANNUAL NET} \\ \text{INCOME FROM} \\ \text{OPERATIONS} \end{array} = \begin{array}{c} \text{ANNUAL INTEREST} \\ \text{ON CAPITAL} \\ \text{INVESTMENT} \end{array} + \begin{array}{c} \text{ANNUAL DEPOSIT} \\ \text{INTO DEPLETION} \\ \text{RESERVE} \end{array}$$

Basic relationship between net income before depletion and the investment in wasting assets

Formula 20.7

$$\begin{array}{c} \text{CAPITALIZED} \\ \text{COST} \end{array} = \begin{array}{c} \text{ORIGINAL} \\ \text{COST} \end{array} + \frac{\begin{array}{c} \text{PERIODIC} \\ \text{REPLACEMENT} \\ \text{COST} \end{array}}{f}$$

where $f = (1 + i)^c - 1$

i = the rate of interest per compounding period

$$c = \frac{\text{the number of compounding periods per year}}{\text{the number of replacement periods per year}}$$

Formula for finding the capitalized cost of an asset

Formula 20.8

$$\begin{array}{c} \text{PERIODIC} \\ \text{INVESTMENT COST} \end{array} = \begin{array}{c} \text{CAPITALIZED} \\ \text{COST} \end{array} \times i$$

Formula for finding the periodic investment cost

Formula 20.8A

$$\begin{array}{c} \text{PERIODIC} \\ \text{INVESTMENT COST} \end{array} = \begin{array}{c} \text{ORIGINAL} \\ \text{COST} \end{array} \times i + \frac{\begin{array}{c} \text{REPLACEMENT} \\ \text{COST} \end{array}}{s\,\overline{c}|i}$$

where i = the rate per compounding period

c = the number of compounding periods per replacement period

Alternative formula for finding the periodic investment cost

Formula 20.9

$$\begin{matrix} \text{CAPITALIZED} \\ \text{COST} \\ \text{INCLUDING} \\ \text{MAINTENANCE} \end{matrix} = \begin{matrix} \text{ORIGINAL} \\ \text{COST} \end{matrix} + \cfrac{\begin{matrix}\text{REPLACEMENT}\\\text{COST}\end{matrix}}{f} + \cfrac{\begin{matrix}\text{MAINTENANCE}\\\text{COST}\end{matrix}}{i}$$

Formula for finding the capitalized cost including operating expenses and repair costs

Formula 20.9A

$$\begin{matrix} \text{TOTAL} \\ \text{PERIODIC} \\ \text{COST} \end{matrix} = \begin{matrix} \text{ORIGINAL} \\ \text{COST} \end{matrix} \times i + \cfrac{\begin{matrix}\text{REPLACEMENT}\\\text{COST}\end{matrix}}{s_{\overline{c}|i}} + \begin{matrix} \text{MAINTENANCE} \\ \text{COST} \end{matrix}$$

Alternative formula for finding the capitalized cost including operating expenses and repair costs

Glossary of terms used

Accumulated depreciation   the total depreciation allocated to accounting periods at any point in the life of an asset

Annual charge   the annual interest on the capitalized cost of an asset including operating expenses and repair costs

Book value   the net value of an asset at any point in its life; the difference between the original cost and the accumulated depreciation

Capitalization   the process of finding the present value of an infinite number of periodic payments

Capitalized cost   the original cost of an asset plus the present value of an unlimited number of periodic replacements of the asset

Depletion   loss in value of wasting assets due to their removal in the process of operation

Depreciation   loss in value of an asset due to physical deterioration, wear and tear or decay and obsolescence

Depreciation schedules   charts showing the details of allocating the loss in value to the various accounting periods

Methods of depreciation   systematic ways of allocating depreciation to accounting periods

Original cost   the necessary and reasonable costs incurred in readying an asset for its intended purpose

Periodic investment cost   the interest on the capitalized cost of an asset including operating expenses and repair costs

Residual value   the value of an asset at the time when it has lost its usefulness or is disposed

Salvage value   see *Residual value*

Scrap value   see *Residual value*

Total periodic cost   the periodic interest on the capitalized cost of an asset including operating expenses and repair costs

Trade-in value   see *Residual value*

Wasting assets   assets that are not renewable in the short-term

Wearing value   the total depreciation over the life of an asset; the difference between original cost and residual value

21 *Investment decision applications*

Introduction

When making investment decisions the comparative effects of alternative courses of action on the cash flows of the business must be considered. Since cash flow analysis needs to take into account the time value of money (interest), present value concepts are useful.

When cash inflows only are considered, the value of the discounted cash flows are helpful in guiding management towards a rational decision. If outlays as well as inflows are involved, the net present value concept is applicable in evaluating projects.

While the net present value technique indicates whether or not a project will yield a specified rate of return, knowing the actual rate of return provides useful information to the decision maker. The rate of return may be computed using the net present value concept.

Objectives

Upon completion of this chapter, you will be able to

1. determine the discounted value of cash flows and choose between alternative investments on the basis of the discounted cash flow criterion;
2. determine the net present value of a capital investment project and infer from the net present value whether a project is feasible or not;
3. compute the rate of return on investment.

21.1 Discounted cash flow

A. Evaluation of capital expenditures—basic concepts

Capital investment projects are defined as projects involving cash outlays expected to generate a continuous flow of future benefits. While benefits may be non-monetary, the methods of analysis considered in this chapter will only deal with investment projects generating an inflow of monetary benefits.

While capital expenditures normally result in the acquisition of assets, the primary purpose of capital expenditures is the acquisition of a future stream of benefits in the form of an inflow of cash. In considering investments involving the acquisition of assets and in making decisions as to the replacement of assets or whether to buy or lease, the decision maker needs to analyze the effects of alternative courses of action on the future cash flow.

While factors other than financial concerns often enter into the decision making process, the techniques of analysis considered here are concerned with the amount and the timing of cash receipts and cash payments under the assumption that the amount and timing of the cash flow is certain.

From the mathematical point of view the major problem in dealing with the evaluation of capital expenditure projects is the time value of money which prevents direct comparison of cash received and cash payments made at different points in time. The concept of present value, as introduced in Chapter 13 and used in the following chapters, provides the vehicle for making sums of money received or paid at different points in time comparable at a selected point in time.

B. Discounted cash flow

When using the discounting technique to evaluate alternatives, two fundamental principles are available to serve as decision criteria.

1. The Bird-in-the-Hand Principle—Given that all other factors are equal, earlier benefits are preferable to later benefits.
2. The Bigger-the-Better Principle—Given that all other factors are equal, bigger benefits are preferable to smaller benefits.

Example 21.1a Suppose you are offered a choice of receiving $1000.00 today or receiving $1000.00 three years from now. What is the preferred choice?

Solution

In adherence to the Bird-in-the-hand Principle you should prefer to receive $1000.00 today rather than three years from now.

The rationale is that $1000.00 can be invested to earn interest and thus will accumulate in three years to a sum of money greater than $1000.00.

Stated in another way, the present value of $1000.00 to be received in three years is less than $1000.00 today.

Example 21.1b Consider a choice of $2000.00 today or $3221.00 five years from now. Which alternative is preferable?

Solution

No definite answer is possible without consideration of interest. A rational choice must consider the time value of money; that is, we need to know the rate of interest. Once a rate of interest is established, the proper choice can be made by considering the present value of the two sums of money and applying the Bigger-the-Better Principle.

If 'now' is chosen as the focal date, three outcomes are possible.

1. The present value of $3221.00 is greater than $2000.00. In this case the preferred choice is $3221.00 five years from now.

2. The present value of $3221.00 is less than $2000.00. In this case the preferred choice is $2000.00 now.

3. The present value of $3221.00 equals $2000.00. In this case either choice is equally acceptable.

   (a) *Suppose the rate of interest is 8%*
     $S = 3221.00;$ $i = 8\% = 0.08;$ $n = 5$
     $P = 3221.00(1.08^{-5}) = 3221.00(0.6805832) = \$2192.16$
     Since at 8% the discounted value of $3221.00 is greater than $2000.00, the preferred choice at 8% is $3221.00 five years from now.

   (b) *Suppose the rate of interest is 12%*
     $S = 3221.00;$ $i = 12\% = 0.12;$ $n = 5$
     $P = 3221.00(1.12^{-5}) = 3221.00(0.5674269) = \$1827.68$
     Since at 12% the discounted value is less than $2000.00, the preferred choice is $2000.00 now.

   (c) *Suppose the rate of interest is 10%*
     $S = 3221.00;$ $i = 10\% = 0.10;$ $n = 5$
     $P = 3221.00(1.10^{-5}) = 3221.00(0.6209213) = \$1999.99$
     Since at 10% the discounted value is equal to $2000.00, the two choices are equally acceptable.

Example 21.1c Two alternative investments are available. Alternative A yields a return of $6000 in two years and $10 000 in five years. Alternative B yields a return of $7000 now and $7000 in seven years. Which alternative is preferable if money is worth

          (i) 11%?   (ii) 15%?

Solution

To determine which alternative is preferable we need to compute the present value of each alternative and choose the alternative with the highest present value.

Let the focal point be 'now'.

(i) For $i = 11\%$

Alternative A

The present value of Alternative A is the sum of the present values of $6000 in two years and $10 000 in five years.

Present Value of $6000 in two years
$= 6000(1.11^{-2}) = 6000(0.8116224)$ $=$ $4870

Present Value of $10 000 in five years
$= 10000(1.11^{-5}) = 10000(0.5934513)$ $=$ 5935

The present value of Alternative A $=$ $10805

Alternative B

The present value of Alternative B is the sum of the present values of $7000 now and $7000 in seven years.

Present value of $7000 now $=$ $7000

Present value of $7000 in seven years
$= 7000(1.11^{-7}) = 7000(0.4816584)$ $=$ 3372

The present value of Alternative B $=$ $10372

Since at 11% the present value of Alternative A is greater than the present value of Alternative B, Alternative A is preferable at 11%.

(ii) For $i = 15\%$

Alternative A

Present value of $6000 in two years
$= 6000(1.15^{-2}) = 6000(0.7561437)$ $=$ $4537

Present value of $10 000 in five years
$= 10000(1.15^{-5}) = 10000(0.4971767)$ $=$ 4972

The present value of Alternative A $=$ $9509

Alternative B

Present value of $7000 now $=$ $7000

Present value of $7000 in seven years
$= 7000(1.15^{-7}) = 7000(0.3759370)$ $=$ 2632

The present value of Alternative B $=$ $9632

Since at 15% the present value of Alternative B is greater than the present value of Alternative A, Alternative B is preferable at 15%.

Note The application of present value techniques to capital investment problems usually involves estimates. For this reason dollar amounts in the preceding example and all following examples are rounded to the nearest dollar. It is suggested that students do the same when working on problems of this nature.

Example 21.1d   An insurance company offers settlement of a claim by either making a payment of $50 000 immediately or by making payments of $8000 at the end of each year for ten years. What offer is preferable if interest is 12% compounded annually?

Solution

Present value of $8000 at the end of each year for ten years is the present value of an ordinary annuity in which $R = 8000$, $n = 10$ and $i = 12\%$.

$$A_n = 8000(a_{\overline{10}|12\%}) = 8000(5.650223) \qquad\qquad = \qquad \$45202$$

Since the immediate payment is larger than the present value of the annual payments of $8000, the immediate payment of $50 000 is preferable.

Example 21.1e   Sheridan Credit Union needs to make a decision whether to purchase a duplicating machine for $6000 and enter a service contract requiring the payment of $45 at the end of every three months for five years, or to enter a five year lease requiring the payment of $435 at the beginning of every three months. If leased the machine can be purchased after five years for $600. At 13% compounded quarterly, should the Credit Union buy or lease?

Solution

To make a rational decision the Credit Union should compare the present value of the cash outlays if buying the machine with the present value of the cash outlays if leasing the machine.

Present value of the decision to buy

Present value of cash payment for the machine	=	$6000
Present value of the service contract involves an ordinary annuity in which $R = 45$, $n = 20$, $i = 3.25\%$		
$= 45(a_{\overline{20}|3.25\%}) = 45(14.539346)$	=	654
Present value of decision to buy	=	$6654

Present value of the decision to lease

Present value of the quarterly lease payments involves an annuity due: $R = 395$, $n = 20$, $i = 3.25\%$		
$= 435(1.0325)(a_{\overline{20}|3.25\%}) = 435(1.0325)(14.539346)$	=	$6530
Present value of purchase price after five years		
$= 600(1.0325^{-20}) = 600(0.5274712)$	=	316
Present value of the decision to lease	=	$6846

In the case of costs the selection criterion follows the Smaller-the-better principle and since the present value of the decision to buy is smaller than the present value of the decision to lease, the Credit Union should buy the duplicating machine.

Example 21.1f Sheridan Service needs a brake machine. The machine can be bought for $4600 and after five years will have a salvage value of $490 or the machine can be leased for five years by making monthly payments of $111 at the beginning of each month. If money is worth 14%, should Sheridan Service buy or lease?

Solution

Alternative 1   Buy machine

Present value of cash price	= $4600
less Present value of salvage value	
$= 490(1.14^{-5}) = 490(0.5193687)$	= 255
Present value of decision to buy	= $4345

Alternative 2   Lease machine

The monthly lease payments form a complex annuity due in which

$$R = 111; \qquad c = \frac{1}{12}; \qquad n = 60; \qquad i = 14\%;$$

$$f = 1.14^{\frac{1}{12}} - 1 = 1.0109789 - 1$$
$$= 0.0109789 = 1.09789\%$$

Present value of the monthly lease payments

$$= 111(1.0109789)(a_{\overline{60}|\,1.09789\%})$$

$$= 111(1.0109789)(43.777866)$$
$$= \$4913$$

The present value of the decision to lease is $4913.

Since the present value of the decision to buy is smaller than the present value of the decision to lease, Sheridan Service should buy the machine.

Exercise 21.1

A. For each of the following compute the present value of each alternative and determine the alternative preferred according to the discounted cash flow criterion.

1. The A company must make a choice between two investment alternatives. Alternative 1 will return the company $20 000 at the end of three years and $60 000 at the end of six years. Alternative 2 will return the company $13 000 at the end of each of the next six years. The A company normally expects to earn a rate of return of 12% on funds invested.

2. An obligation can be settled by making a payment of $10 000 now and a final payment of $20 000 in five years. Alternatively the obligation can be settled by payments of $1500 at the end of every three months for five years. Interest is 18% compounded quarterly.

3. The B Company has a policy of requiring a rate of return on investment of 16%. Two investment alternatives are available but only one may be chosen. Alternative 1 offers a return of $50 000 after four years, $40 000 after seven years and $30 000 after ten years. Alternative 2 will return the company $750 at the end of each month for ten years.

4. An unavoidable cost may be met by outlays of $10 000 now and $2000 at the end of every six months for seven years or by making monthly payments of $500 in advance for seven years. Interest is 17% compounded annually.

B. Answer each of the following questions.

1. A contract offers $25 000 immediately and $50 000 in five years or $10 000 at the end of each year for ten years. If money is worth 13%, which offer is preferable?

2. Bruce wants to sell his business. He has received two offers. If he accepts Offer A he will receive $15 000 immediately and $20 000 in three years. If he accepts Offer B he will receive $3000 now and $3000 at the end of every six months for six years. If interest is 20%, which offer is preferable?

3. A warehouse can be purchased for $90 000. After twenty years the property will have a residual value of $30 000. Alternatively the warehouse can be leased for twenty years at an annual rent of $12 000 payable in advance. If money is worth 15%, should the warehouse be purchased or leased?

4. A car can be purchased for $9500. Alternatively the car can be leased for three years by making payments of $240 at the beginning of each month and can be bought at the end of the lease for $4750. If interest is 15% compounded semi-annually, which alternative is preferable?

21.2 Net present value method

A. Introductory examples

Example 21.2a Net cash inflows from two ventures are as follows.

End of Year	1	2	3	4	5	Total
Venture A	12000	14400	17280	20736	24883	89299
Venture B	17000	17000	17000	17000	17000	85000

Which venture is preferable if the required yield is 20%?

Solution

Present value of Venture A

$= 12000(1.20^{-1}) + 14400(1.20^{-2}) + 17280(1.20^{-3})$
$\quad + 20736(1.20^{-4}) + 24883(1.20^{-5})$

$= 12000(0.8333333) + 14400(0.6944444) + 17280(0.5787037)$
$\quad + 20736(0.4822531) + 24883(0.4018776)$

$= 10000 + 10000 + 10000 + 10000 + 10000$

$= \$50\,000$

Present value of Venture B

$= 17000(a_{\overline{5}|20\%}) = 17000(2.9906121) = \$50840$

Since at 20% the present value of Venture B is greater than the present value of Venture A, Venture B is preferable to Venture A at 20%.

Example 21.2b Assume for Example 21.2a that Venture A requires a non-recoverable outlay of $9000 while Venture B requires a non-recoverable outlay of $11 000. At 20% which venture is preferable?

Solution

	Venture A	*Venture B*
Present value of cash inflows	$50000	$50840
Present value of immediate outlay	$ 9000	$11000
Net present value	$41000	$39840

Since the net present value of Venture A is greater than the net present value of Venture B, Venture A is preferable.

B. The net present value concept

In Example 21.2a when cash inflows only were considered, Venture B was shown to be preferable. However, when as in Example 21.2b outlays are different, the present value of the outlays as well as the present value of the cash inflows must be considered. The resulting difference is called the **Net Present Value**.

NET PRESENT VALUE (NPV)	=	PRESENT VALUE OF INFLOWS	−	PRESENT VALUE OF OUTLAYS

←*Formula* **21.1**

Since the net present value involves the difference between the present value of the inflows and the present value of the outlays, three outcomes are possible.
1. If the present value of the inflows is greater than the present value of the outlays, then the net present value is greater than zero.

2. If the present value of the inflows is smaller than the present value of the outlays, then the net present value is smaller than zero.

3. If the present value of the inflows equals the present value of the outlays, then the net present value is zero.

$$PV_{IN} > PV_{OUT} \longrightarrow NPV > O \text{ (positive)}$$

$$PV_{IN} = PV_{OUT} \longrightarrow NPV = O$$

$$PV_{IN} < PV_{OUT} \longrightarrow NPV < O \text{ (negative)}$$

Criterion rule

At the organization's required rate of return, accept those capital investment projects having a positive or zero net present value, and reject those projects having a negative net present value.

For a given rate of return:

ACCEPT if NPV > O or NPV = O;

REJECT if NPV < O.

To assure the distinction between a negative and a positive net present value $\longrightarrow NPV = PV_{IN} - PV_{OUT}$.

If more than one project is considered but only one can be selected, the project with the greatest positive net present value is preferable.

Assumptions about the timing of inflows and outlays

The net present value method of evaluating capital investment projects is particularly useful in complex situations in which cash outlays are made and cash inflows received at various points in time. Since the *timing* of the cash flows is of prime importance, the following assumptions regarding the timing of cash inflows and cash outlays must be followed.

Unless otherwise stated

1. all cash inflows (benefits) are assumed to be received at the end of a period;

2. all cash outlays (costs) are assumed to be made at the beginning of a period.

C. Applications

Example 21.2c   A company is offered a contract promising annual net returns of $36 000 for seven years. If the contract is accepted the company must spend $150 000 immediately for plant expansion. After seven years no further benefits are available from the contract and the plant expansion undertaken will have no residual value. Should the company accept the contract if the required rate of return is (i) 12%?   (ii) 18%?   (iii) 15%?

Solution

The net inflows and outlays may be represented on a time graph.

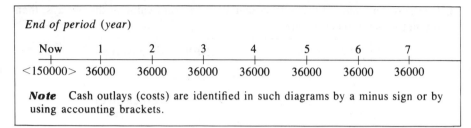

End of period (*year*)

Now	1	2	3	4	5	6	7
<150000>	36000	36000	36000	36000	36000	36000	36000

Note Cash outlays (costs) are identified in such diagrams by a minus sign or by using accounting brackets.

(i) For $i = 12\%$

Since the annual net returns (benefits) are assumed to be received at the end of a period unless otherwise stated, they form an ordinary annuity in which $R = 36000$, $n = 7$, $i = 12\%$.

$PV_{IN} = 36000(a_{\overline{7}|12\%}) = 36000(4.5637565)$ $= \$164295$

PV_{OUT} = Present value of 150000 now $= \underline{\$150000}$

The NET PRESENT VALUE (NPV)
$= 164295 - 150000$ $= \underline{\$14295}$

Since at 12%, the net present value is greater than zero, the contract should be accepted. The fact that the net present value at 12% is positive means that the contract offers a return on investment of more than 12%.

(ii) For $i = 18\%$

$PV_{IN} = 36000(a_{\overline{7}|18\%}) = 36000(3.8115276)$ $= \$137215$

PV_{OUT} $= \underline{150000}$

$NPV = 137215 - 150000$ $= \underline{-\$12785}$

Since at 18%, the net present value is less than zero, the contract should not be accepted since the contract does not offer the required rate of return on investment of 18%.

(iii) For $i = 15\%$

$PV_{IN} = 36000(a_{\overline{7}|15\%}) = 36000(4.1604197)$ $= \$149775$

PV_{OUT} $= \underline{150000}$

$NPV = 149775 - 150000$ $= \underline{-\$225}$

Since the net present value is slightly negative, the net present value method does not provide a clear signal as to whether to accept or reject the contract. The rate of return offered by the contract is almost 15%.

Example 21.2d A project requiring an initial investment of $80 000 with a residual value of $15 000 after six years is estimated to yield annual net returns of $21 000 for six years. Should the project be undertaken at 16%?

Solution

The cash flows are represented in the diagram below.

End of (year)				$i = 16\%$			
	Now	1	2	3	4	5	6
Out	<80>						15
In		21	21	21	21	21	21

Note The residual value of $15 000 is considered to be a reduction in outlays and its present value should be subtracted from the present value of other outlays.

$$PV_{IN} = 21000(a_{\overline{6}|16\%}) = 21000(3.6847359) \qquad\qquad = \$77379$$

$$PV_{OUT} = 80000 - 15000(1.16^{-6})$$

$$= 80000 - 15000(0.4104423) = 80000 - 6157 \qquad\qquad = \quad 73843$$

$$\text{NET PRESENT VALUE (NPV)} \qquad\qquad = \underline{\underline{\$ \ 3536}}$$

Since the net present value is positive (the present value of the benefits is greater than the present value of the costs), the rate of return on the investment is greater than 16%. The project should be undertaken.

Example 21.2e The IRA Corporation is considering the development of a new product. If undertaken the project requires the outlay of $100 000 per year for three years. Net returns commencing in Year 4 are estimated at $65 000 per year for twelve years. The residual value of the outlays after fifteen years is $30 000. If the corporation requires a return on investment of 14%, should the new product be developed?

Solution

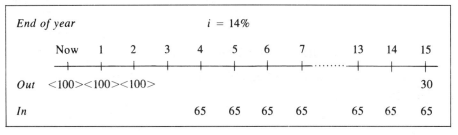

End of year					$i = 14\%$							
	Now	1	2	3	4	5	6	7		13	14	15
Out	<100><100><100>											30
In					65	65	65	65		65	65	65

The net returns, due at the end of Year 4 to Year 15 respectively, form an ordinary annuity deferred for *three* years in which
$R = 65000$, $n = 12$, $d = 3$, $i = 14\%$.

$$PV_{IN} = 65000(a\overline{_{12|}}_{14\%})(1.14^{-3})$$

$$= 65000(5.6602921)(0.6749715)$$

$$= \$248335$$

The outlays, assumed to be made at the beginning of each year, form an annuity due in which $R = 100000$, $n = 3$, $i = 14\%$.

$$PV_{OUT} = 100000(1.14)(a\overline{_{3|}}_{14\%}) - 30000(1.14^{-15})$$

$$= 100000(1.14)(2.3216320) - 30000(0.1400965)$$

$$= 264666 - 4203$$

$$= \$260463$$

$$NPV = 248335 - 260463 = <\$12128>$$

Since the net present value is negative, the investment does not offer a 14% return. Hence the product should not be developed.

Example 21.2f   A feasibility study concerning a comtemplated venture yielded the following estimates:
   initial cost outlay: \$1 300 000;
   further outlays in Years 2 to 5: \$225 000 per year;
   residual value after 20 years: \$625 000;
   net returns: Year 5 to 10: \$600 000 per year;
             Year 11 to 20: \$500 000 per year.
Should the venture be undertaken if the required return on investment is 15%?

Solution

End of year						$i = 15\%$								
Now	1	2	3	4	5	6	9	10	11	12	19	20	
Out <1300>	<225>	<225>	<225>	<225>									625
In						600	600 600	600	500	500 .. 500	500		

$$Pv_{IN} = 600000(a\overline{_{6|}}_{15\%})(1.15^{-4}) + 500000(a\overline{_{10|}}_{15\%})(1.15^{-10})$$

$$= 600000(3.7844827)(0.5717532) + 500000(5.0187686)(0.2471847)$$

$$= 1298274 + 620281$$

$$= \$1918555$$

$PV_{OUT} = 1300000 + 225000(a \, _{\overline{4}|15\%}) - 625000(1.15^{-20})$

$= 1300000 + 225000(2.8549784) - 625000(0.0611003)$

$= 1300000 + 642370 - 38188$

$= \$1904182$

$NPV = 1918555 - 1904182 = \$14373$

Since the net present value is positive, the rate of return on investment is greater than 15%. The venture should be undertaken.

Exercise 21.2

A. For each of the following investment situations compute the net present value and determine which investment should be accepted or rejected according to the net present value criterion.

1. A contract is estimated to yield net returns of $3500 quarterly for seven years. To secure the contract an immediate outlay of $50 000 and a further outlay of $30 000 three years from now are required. Interest is 12% compounded quarterly.

2. Replacement of old equipment at an immediate cost of $50 000 and an additional outlay of $30 000 six years from now will result in savings of $3000 per quarter for twelve years. The required rate of return is 16% compounded annually.

3. A business has two investment alternatives. Alternative 1 requires an immediate outlay of $2000 and offers a return of $7000 after seven years. Alternative 2 requires an immediate outlay of $1800 in return for which $250 will be received at the end of every six months for the next seven years. The required rate of return on investment is 17% compounded semi-annually.

4. Suppose you are offered two investment alternatives. If you choose Alternative 1 you will have to make an immediate outlay of $9000. In return you will receive $500 at the end of every three months for the next ten years. If you choose Alternative 2 you will have to make an outlay of $4000 now and $5000 in two years. In return you will receive $30 000 ten years from now. Interest is 12% compounded semi-annually.

B. Answer each of the following questions.

1. Teck Engineering normally expects a rate of return of 12% on investments. Two projects are available only one of which can be chosen. Project A requires an immediate investment of $4000. In return, revenue payments of $4000 will be received in four years and of $9000 in nine years. Project B requires an investment of $4000 now and another $2000 in three years. In return, revenue payments will be received in the amount of $1500 per year for nine years. Which project should be preferred?

2. The owner of a business is presented with two alternative projects. The first project involves the investment of $5000 now. In return the business will receive a payment of $8000 in four years and a payment of $8000 in ten years. The second project involves an investment of $5000 now and another $5000 three years from now. The returns will be semi-annual payments of $950 for ten years. Which project should be preferred if the required rate of return is 14% compounded annually?

3. Northern Teck is developing a special purpose vehicle for arctic exploration. The development of the vehicle requires an investment of $60 000, $50 000 and $40 000 for the next three years respectively. Net returns commencing in Year 4 are expected to be $33 000 per year for twelve years. If the company requires a rate of return of 14% compute the net present value of the project and determine whether the project should be undertaken or not.

4. The Kellog Company has to make a decision whether or not to expand its production facilities. Research indicates that the desired expansion would require an immediate outlay of $60 000 and an outlay of a further $60 000 in five years. Net returns are estimated to be $15 000 per year for the first five years and $10 000 per year for the following ten years. Find the net present value of the project and indicate whether the expansion project should be undertaken if the required rate of return is 12%.

5. Agate Marketing Inc. intends to distribute a new product which is expected to produce net returns of $15 000 per year for the first four years and $10 000 per year for the following three years. The facilities required to distribute the product will cost $36 000 with a disposal value of $9000 after seven years. The facilities will require a major face lifting job of $10 000 each after three and after five years respectively. If Agate requires a return on investment of 20%, should the company distribute the new product?

6. A company is considering a project which will require a cost outlay of $15 000 per year for four years. At the end of the project the salvage value will be $10 000. The project will yield returns of $60 000 in Year 4 and $20 000 in Year 5. There are no returns after Year 5. Alternative investments are available which will yield a return of 16%. Should the company undertake the project?

7. Demand for a product manufactured by the Eagle Company is expected to be 15 000 units per year during the next ten years. The net return per unit is $2. The manufacturing process requires the purchase of a machine costing $140 000. The machine has an economic life of ten years and a salvage value of $20 000 after ten years. Major overhauls of the machine require outlays of $20 000 after four years and $40 000 after seven years. Should Eagle invest in the machine if it requires a return of 12% on its investments?

8. Magna Electronics Company expects a demand of 20 000 units per year for a special purpose component during the next six years. Net return per unit is $4.00. To produce the component, Magna must purchase a machine costing $250 000 with a life of six years and a salvage value of $40 000 after six years. The company estimates that repair costs will be $20 000 per year during Years 2 to 6. If Magna requires a return on investment of 18%, should it market the component?

21.3 Finding the rate of return on investment

A. Net present value, profitability index, rate of return

The **rate of return** on investment (R.O.I.) is widely used to measure the value of an investment. Since it takes the interest factor into account, knowing the rate of return which results from a capital investment project provides useful information when evaluating a project.

The method of finding the rate of return explained and illustrated in this Section uses the net present value concept introduced in Section 21.2. However, instead of being primarily concerned with a specific discount rate and with comparing the present value of the cash inflows and the present value of the cash outlays, the method is designed to determine the rate of return on the investment.

As explained in Section 21.2, three outcomes are possible when using Formula 21.1. These three outcomes indicate whether the rate of return is greater than, less than or equal to the discount rate used in finding the net present value.

1. If the net present value is greater than zero (positive), then the rate of return (R.O.I.) is greater than the discount rate used to determine the net present value.
2. If the net present value is less than zero (negative), then the rate of return is less than the discount rate used.
3. If net present value is equal to zero, then the rate of return is equal to the rate of discount used.

$$
\begin{array}{l}
\text{If NPV} > 0 \text{ (POSITIVE)} \longrightarrow \text{R.O.I.} > i \\
\text{If NPV} < 0 \text{ (NEGATIVE)} \longrightarrow \text{R.O.I.} < i \\
\text{If NPV} = 0 \longrightarrow \text{R.O.I.} = i
\end{array}
$$

It follows then, that the rate of return on investment (R.O.I.) is that rate of discount for which the NPV $= 0$; that is, for which the $\mathbf{PV_{IN}} = \mathbf{PV_{OUT}}$.

The above definition of the rate of return and the relationship between the net present value, the rate of discount used to compute the net present value and the rate of return are useful in developing a method of finding the rate of return.

However, before computing the rate of return, it is useful to consider a ratio known as the **profitability index** or **discounted benefit-cost ratio** and defined as the ratio which results when comparing the present value of the cash inflows with the present value of the cash outlays.

$$
\text{PROFITABILITY INDEX (or DISCOUNTED BENEFIT} - \text{COST RATIO)} = \frac{PV_{IN}}{PV_{OUT}} \qquad \longleftarrow \textbf{\textit{Formula 21.2}}
$$

Since a division is involved, three outcomes are possible when computing the ratio.

1. If the numerator (PV_{IN}) is greater than the denominator (PV_{OUT}) then the profitability index is greater than one.

2. If the numerator (PV_{IN}) is less than the denominator (PV_{OUT}) then the profitability index is less than one.

3. If the numerator (PV_{IN}) is equal to the denominator (PV_{OUT}) then the profitability index is equal to one.

The three outcomes give an indication of the rate of return.

1. If the profitability index is greater than 1, then the rate of return is greater than the discount rate used.

2. If the profitability index is less than 1, then the rate of return is less than the discount rate used.

3. If the profitability index is equal to 1, then the rate of return equals the discount rate used.

The relationship between the present value of the inflows, the present value of the outlays, the net present value, the profitability index and the rate of return at a given rate of discount i is summarized below.

PV_{IN} versus PV_{OUT}	Net present value (NPV)	Profitability index	Rate of return (R.O.I.)
$PV_{IN} > PV_{OUT}$	$NPV > 0$	> 1	$> i$
$PV_{IN} = PV_{OUT}$	$NPV = 0$	$= 1$	$= i$
$PV_{IN} < PV_{OUT}$	$NPV < 0$	< 1	$< i$

B. Procedure for finding the rate of return by trial and error

From the relationships noted above, the rate of return on investment may be defined to be the rate of discount for which the present value of the inflows (benefits) equals the present value of the outlays (costs). This implies that the rate of return is the rate of discount for which the net present value equals zero or for which the profitability index (benefit-cost ratio) is equal to 1. This permits the determination of the rate of return by trial and error.

STEP 1   Arbitrarily select a discount rate and compute the net present value at that rate.

STEP 2   From the outcome of Step 1 draw one of the three conclusions.

(a) If $NPV = 0$, infer that the R.O.I. $= i$.

(b) If $NPV > 0$, infer that the R.O.I. $> i$.

(c) If $NPV < 0$, infer that the R.O.I. $< i$.

STEP 3

(a)   If in Step 1, NPV = 0, then R.O.I. = i and the problem is solved.

(b)   If in Step 1, NPV > 0 (positive), then we know that R.O.I. > i. A second attempt is needed. This second try requires the selection of a discount rate greater than the rate used in Step 1 and the computation of the net present value using the higher rate.

If the resulting net present value is still positive, a still higher rate of discount must be selected and the net present value for that rate must be computed. This procedure must be repeated until the selected rate of discount yields a negative net present value.

(c)   If in Step 1, NPV < 0 (negative), then we know that R.O.I. < i. The second try requires a selection of a discount rate less than the rate used in Step 1 and the computation of the net present value using the lower rate.

If the resulting net present value is still negative, a still lower rate of discount must be selected and the net present value for that rate must be computed. This procedure must be repeated until the selected rate of discount yields a positive net present value.

STEP 4   The basic aim of Step 3 is to find one rate of discount for which the net present value is positive and a second rate for which the net present value is negative. Once this has been accomplished, the rate of return is known to be a rate between the two rates used to generate a positive and a negative net present value.

A reasonably accurate value of the rate of return can now be obtained by using linear interpolation.

To assure sufficient accuracy in the answer, it is recommended that the two rates of discount used when interpolating be no more than two percentage points apart. In line with this recommendation, the worked examples in this Section have been solved using successive even rates of discounts when interpolating. While it is quite possible to use odd rates, the even rates of discount have been used to allow for the possible use of tables giving values for even rates.

STEP 5   (Optional) The accuracy of the method of interpolation can be checked when using an electronic calculator by computing the net present value using as discount rate the rate of return determined in Step 4. The rate in Step 4 can be expected to be slightly too high. A still more precise answer may be obtained by further trials.

C.   *Selecting the rate of discount—
using the profitability index*

While the selection of a discount rate in Step 1 of the procedure is arbitrary, a sensible choice is one which is neither too high nor too low. Since a negative net present value immediately establishes a range between zero and the rate used, it is preferable to be on the high side. Selection of a rate of discount from the range 12% to 24% usually leads to quick solutions.

While the initial choice of rate is a shot in the dark, the resulting knowledge about the size of the rate of return and the use of the profitability index should assure the selection of a second rate that is fairly close to the actual rate of return.

In making the second choice, the profitability index should be used.

1. Compute the index for the first rate selected and convert the index into a percent.

2. Deduct 100% from the index and divide the difference by 4.

3. If the index is greater than 1, add the result of the division to the rate of discount initially used to obtain the rate that should be used for the second attempt. If, however, the index is smaller than 1, deduct the result of the division from the rate of discount initially used.

Assume that the rate of discount initially selected is 16% with a resulting $PV_{IN} = 150$ and a $PV_{OUT} = 120$.

1. The profitability index is $\dfrac{150}{120} = 1.25 = 125\%$.

2. The difference $(125\% - 100\%)$ divided by 4 $= 6.25\%$.

3. Since the index is greater than 1, add 6.25% to the initially selected rate of 16%; the recommended choice is 22%.

Assume that the rate of discount initially selected is 20% with a resulting $PV_{IN} = 200$ and $PV_{OUT} = 250$.

1. The profitability index is $\dfrac{200}{250} = 0.80 = 80\%$.

2. The difference $(80\% - 100\%)$ divided by 4 $= -5\%$.

3. Since the index is less than 1, subtract 5% from the initially selected rate of 20%; the recommended choice is 15%. (If, as in this text, only even rates are used, either 14% or 16% should be tried.)

D. Using linear interpolation

The method of linear interpolation to be used in Step 4 of the suggested procedure is illustrated in Example 21.3a below.

Example 21.3a   Assume that the net present value of a project is $420 at 14% and $-\$280$ at 16%. Use linear interpolation to compute the rate of return correct to the nearest tenth of a percent.

Solution

The data may be represented on a line diagram.

NPV	$420	$0	$-280

$$A \qquad\qquad\qquad X \qquad\qquad\qquad B$$

$$\longleftarrow\!\!\!- d -\!\!\!\longrightarrow$$

i	14%		16%

The line segment AB is used to represent the distance between the two rates of discount which are associated with a positive and a negative net present value respectively.

At Point A, where i = 14%, the NPV = 420;
at Point B, where i = 16%, the NPV = -280;
at Point X, where i is unknown, the NPV = O.

By definition the rate of return is that rate of discount for which the net present value is zero. Since O is a number between 420 and -280, the NPV = O is located at a point on AB. This point is marked X.

Two useful ratios can now be obtained by considering the line segment from the two points of view indicated in the diagram.

(i) <u>In terms of the discount rate i</u>

AB = 2% $\longleftarrow$ 16% - 14%

AX = d% $\longleftarrow$ the unknown percent which must be added to 14% to obtain the rate of discount at which the NPV = 0

$$\frac{AX}{AB} = \frac{d\%}{2\%}$$

(ii) <u>In terms of the net present value figures</u>

AB = 700 $\longleftarrow$ 420 + 280

AX = 420

$$\frac{AX}{AB} = \frac{420}{700}$$

Since the ratio AX:AB is written, a proportion statement can be obtained.

$$\frac{d\%}{2\%} = \frac{420}{700}$$

$$d\% = \frac{420}{700} \times 2\%$$

$$d\% = 1.2\%$$

Hence the rate at which the net present value is equal to zero is 14% + 1.2% = 15.2%. The rate of return on investment is 15.2%.

E. Computing the rate of return

Example 21.3b   A project requires an initial outlay of $25 000. The estimated returns are $7000 per year for seven years. Compute the rate of return (correct to the nearest tenth of a percent).

Solution

The cash flows are represented in the diagram below.

End of year								
	Now	1	2	3	4	5	6	7
Out	<25>							
In		7	7	7	7	7	7	7

The inflows form an ordinary annuity since inflows are assumed to be received at the end of each year.

$$PV_{IN} = 7000(a_{\overline{7}|i})$$

The outlays consist of an immediate payment.

$$PV_{OUT} = 25000$$

In order to determine the rate of return we will select a rate of discount, compute the net present value and try further rates until we find two successive even rates for one of which the NPV > 0 (positive) and NPV < 0 (negative) for the other.

STEP 1   Try $i = 12\%$

$PV_{IN} = 7000(a_{\overline{7}|12\%}) = 7000(4.5637565)$	$=$	$31946
$PV_{OUT} =$	$=$	25000
NPV at 12%	$=$	$ 6946

Since the NPV > 0, R.O.I > 12%.

STEP 2   Compute the profitability index to estimate what rate should be used next.

$$INDEX = \frac{PV_{IN}}{PV_{OUT}} = \frac{31946}{25000} = 1.278 = 127.8\%$$

Since at $i = 12\%$ the profitability index is 27.8% more than 100%, the rate of discount should be increased by $\frac{27.8\%}{4} = 7\%$ approximately. To obtain another even rate, the increase should be either 6% or 8%. In line with the suggestion that it is better to go too high, increase the previous rate by 8% and try $i = 20\%$.

STEP 3   Try $i = 20\%$

$$PV_{IN} = 7000(a_{\overline{7}|20\%}) = 7000(3.6045918) \qquad\qquad = \qquad \$25232$$

$$PV_{OUT} = \qquad\qquad\qquad\qquad\qquad\qquad\qquad\qquad\qquad = \qquad 25000$$

$$\text{NPV at 20\%} \qquad\qquad\qquad\qquad\qquad\qquad = \qquad \$\ \ \ 232$$

Since the NPV > 0, R.O.I. $> 20\%$.

STEP 4   Since the net present value is still positive a higher rate than 20% is needed. The profitability index at 20% is $\dfrac{25232}{25000} = 1.009 = 100.9\%$. The index exceeds 100% by 0.9%; division by 4 suggests an increase of 0.2%. For interpolation the recommended minimum increase or decrease is 2%. Hence the next try should use $i = 22\%$.

STEP 5   Try $i = 22\%$

$$PV_{IN} = 7000(a_{\overline{7}|22\%}) = 7000(3.4155064) \qquad\qquad = \qquad \$23908$$

$$PV_{OUT} = \qquad\qquad\qquad\qquad\qquad\qquad\qquad\qquad\qquad = \qquad 25000$$

$$\text{NPV at 22\%} \qquad\qquad\qquad\qquad\qquad\qquad\qquad \$-1092$$

Since the NPV < 0, R.O.I. $< 22\%$.

Hence $20\% < \text{NPV} < 22\%$.

STEP 6   Now that the rate of return has been located between two sufficiently close rates of discount, linear interpolation may be used as illustrated in Example 21.3a.

NPV	$232		$0		<$1092>
	A		X		B
i	20%				22%

$$\frac{d}{2} = \frac{232}{232 + 1092}$$

$$d = \frac{232(2)}{1324} = 0.35$$

The rate of discount for which the NPV $= 0$ is approximately $20\% + 0.35\% = 20.35\%$. Hence the rate of return is approximately 20.3%. (A more precisely computed value is 20.3382%.)

Note Three attempts were needed to locate the R.O.I. between 20% and 22%. This is the usual number of attempts necessary. The minimum number is two attempts. Occasionally four attempts may be needed. To produce a more concise solution, the computations should be organized as shown below.

Present value of amounts in general form	Attempts					
	$i = 12\%$		$i = 20\%$		$i = 22\%$	
PV_{IN}	Factor	$	Factor	$	Factor	$
$7000(a_{\overline{7}|i})$	4.5637565	31 946	3.6045918	25 232	3.4155064	23 908
PV_{OUT}						
25000 now		25 000		25 000		25 000
NPV		6946		232		<1092>

Since estimates are involved it is quite sufficient to use present value factors with only three decimal positions. Hence in the following examples all factors are rounded to three decimals.

Example 21.3c A venture requiring an immediate outlay of $320 000 and an outlay of $96 000 after five years has a residual value of $70 000 after ten years. Net returns are estimated to be $64 000 per year for ten years. Compute the rate of return.

Solution

The cash flow is represented in the diagram below.

The computations are organized in a chart and explanations regarding the computations follow.

Explanations for computations

1. Try $i = 20\%$

   Since NPV < 0, R.O.I. < 20%

   Index at 20% $= \dfrac{268288}{347252} = 0.773 = 77.3\%$

   Reduction in rate $= \dfrac{22.7\%}{4} = 5.7\% \Rightarrow 6\%$

Present value of amounts in general form	Attempts					
	$i = 20\%$		$i = 14\%$		$i = 12\%$	
	Factor	$	Factor	$	Factor	$
PV of benefits						
$64000(a_{\overline{10}|i})$	4.192	268288	5.216	333824	5.650	361600
PV of costs						
320000 now		320000		320000		320000
$96000(1 + i)^{-5}$	0.402	38592	0.519	49824	0.567	54432
$<70000(1 + i)^{-10}>$	0.162	$<11340>$	0.270	$<18900>$	0.322	$<22540>$
TOTAL		347252		350924		351892
NPV		$<78964>$		$<17100>$		9708

2. Try $i = 14\%$

NPV < 0; R.O.I. $< 14\%$

$$\text{Index} = \frac{333824}{350924} = 0.951 = 95.1\%$$

$$\text{Reduction in rate} = \frac{4.9\%}{4} = 1.2\% \Rightarrow 2\%$$

3. Try $i = 12\%$

NPV > 0; R.O.I. $> 12\%$

$12\% <$ R.O.I. $< 14\%$

4. $\dfrac{d}{2} = \dfrac{9708}{9708 + 17100} = \dfrac{9708}{26808} = 0.362131$

$d = 2(0.362131) = 0.724$

The rate of discount at which the net present value is zero is $12\% + 0.72\% = 12.72\%$. The rate of return is 12.7%.

Example 21.3d   A project requires an immediate investment of $33 000 which is expected to have a residual value of $7000 at the end of the project. The project is expected to yield a net return of $7000 in Year 1, $8000 in Year 2, $11 000 per year for the following six years and $9000 per year for the remaining four years. Find the rate of return.

Solution

The cash flows for the project are represented in the diagram below.

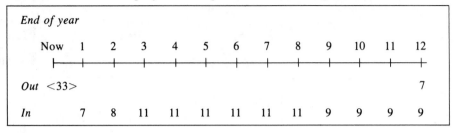

The computations are organized in the chart that follows.

Present value of amounts in general form	Attempts					
	$i = 20\%$		$i = 28\%$		$i = 26\%$	
PV of returns	Factor	$	Factor	$	Factor	$
$7000(1 + i)^{-1}$	0.833	5831	0.781	5467	0.794	5558
$8000(1 + i)^{-2}$	0.694	5552	0.610	4880	0.630	5040
$11000(a_{\overline{6}|i})$	3.326		2.759		2.885	
	×	25391	×	18513	×	19993
$\times (1 + i)^{-2}$	0.694		0.610		0.630	
$9000(a_{\overline{4}|i})$	2.589		2.241		2.320	
	×	5429	×	2803	×	3278
$\times (1 + i)^{-8}$	0.233		0.139		0.157	
TOTAL PV$_{IN}$		42203		31663		33869
PV of costs						
33000 now		33000		33000		33000
$<7000(1 + i)^{-12}>$	0.112	<784>	0.052	<364>	0.062	<434>
TOTAL PV$_{OUT}$		32216		32636		32566
NPV		9987		<973>		1303

Explanations for computations

1. The present value of the returns consists of $7000 discounted for one year, $8000 discounted for two years, the present value of an ordinary annuity of six payments of $11000 each deferred for two years and the present value of an ordinary annuity of four payments of $9000 deferred for eight years. The present value of the costs consists of the lump sum of $33 000 less the salvage value of $7000 discounted for twelve years.

2. The rate of discounted chosen for the first attempt is 20%.

   For $i = 20\%$ NPV > 0; R.O.I $> 20\%$

   $$\text{Index} = \frac{42203}{32216} = 1.310 = 131.0\%$$

   $$\text{Increase in rate} = \frac{31.0\%}{4} = 7.75\% \text{ or } 8\%$$

3. For $i = 28\%$ NPV < 0; R.O.I $< 28\%$

   $$\text{Index} = \frac{31663}{32636} = 0.970 = 97.0\%$$

   $$\text{Decrease in rate} = \frac{3\%}{4} = 0.75\% \text{ or } 2\%$$

4. For $i = 26\%$ NPV > 0; R.O.I $> 26\%$

   $$26\% < \text{R.O.I} < 28\%$$

5. $d = \dfrac{1303}{1303 + 973} \times 2 = \dfrac{2606}{2276} = 1.14499$

The rate of discount for which the net present value is zero is approximately $26\% + 1.14\% = 27.14\%$. The rate of return, correct to the nearest tenth of a percent, is 27.1%.

Exercise 21.3

A. Use linear interpolation to determine the approximate value of the rate of return for each of the following. State your answer correct to the nearest tenth of a percent.

Problem number	Positive NPV at i	Negative NPV at i
1.	$2350 at 24%	−$1270 at 26%
2.	$850 at 8%	−$370 at 10%
3.	$135 at 20%	−$240 at 22%
4.	$56 at 16%	−$70 at 18%

B. Find the rate of return for each of the following (correct to the nearest tenth of a percent).

   1. The proposed expansion of plant facilities of a business requires the immediate outlay of $100 000. Expected net returns are

   Year 1: Nil   Year 2: $30 000   Year 3: $40 000
   Year 4: $60 000   Year 5: $50 000   Year 6: $20 000

2. The introduction of a new product requires an initial outlay of $60 000. The anticipated net returns from the marketing of the product are expected to be $12 000 per year for ten years.

3. Your firm is considering the introduction of a new product for which net returns are expected to be

Year 1 to Year 3 inclusive: $2000 per year;

Year 4 to Year 8 inclusive: $5000 per year;

Year 9 to Year 12 inclusive: $3000 per year.

The introduction of the product requires an immediate outlay of $15 000 for equipment which is estimated to have a salvage value of $2000 after twelve years.

4. A project requiring an immediate investment of $150 000, and a further outlay of $40 000 after four years has a residual value of $30 000 after nine years. The project yields a negative net return of $10 000 in Year 1, a zero net return in Year 2, $50 000 per year for the following four years and $70 000 per year for the last three years.

5. You are thinking of starting a hotdog business requiring an initial investment of $16 000 and a major replacement of equipment after ten years amounting to $8000. From competitive experience you may expect to have a net loss of $2000 the first year, a net profit of $2000 the second year and for the remaining years of the first fifteen years of operation net returns can be expected to be $6000 per year. After fifteen years the net returns will gradually decline and will be zero at the end of 25 years (assume returns of $3000 per year for that period). After 25 years your lease will expire. The salvage value of equipment at that time is expected to be just sufficient to cover the cost of closing the business.

6. The Blue Sky Ski Resort plans to install a new chair lift to serve a new ski area. Construction of the lift is estimated to require an immediate outlay of $220 000. The life of the lift is estimated to be fifteen years with a salvage value of $80 000. Cost of clearing and grooming the new area is expected to be $30 000 for each of the first three years of operation. Net cash inflows from the lift are expected to be $40 000 for each of the first five years and $70 000 for each of the following ten years.

Review exercise

1. Wells Inc. has to make a choice between two investment alternatives. Alternative A will return the company $20 000 after three years, $60 000 after six years and $40 000 after ten years. Alternative B will bring returns of $10 000 per year for ten years. If the company expects a return of 14% on investments, which alternative should it prefer?

2. A piece of property may be acquired by making an immediate payment of $25 000 and payments of $37 500 and $50 000 three and five years from now respectively.

Alternatively the property may be purchased by making quarterly payments of $5150 in advance for five years. Which alternative is preferable if money is worth 15% compounded semi-annually?

3. An investor has two investment alternatives. If he chooses Alternative 1, he will have to make an immediate outlay of $7000 and will receive $500 every three months for the next nine years. If he chooses Alternative 2, he will have to make an immediate outlay of $6500 and will receive $26 000 after eight years. If interest is 12% compounded quarterly, which alternative should the investor prefer on the basis of the net present value criterion?

4. Replacement of old equipment at an immediate cost of $65 000 and $40 000 five years hence will result in a savings of $8000 semi-annually for ten years. At 14% compounded annually, should the old equipment be replaced?

5. A real estate development project requires annual outlays of $75 000 for eight years. Net cash inflows commencing in Year 9 are expected to be $250 000 per year for fifteen years. If the developer requires a rate of return of 18%, compute the net present value of the project.

6. A company is considering a project which will require a cost outlay of $30 000 per year for four years. At the end of the project the company expects to salvage the physical assets for $30 000. The project is estimated to yield net returns of $60 000 in Year 4, $40 000 in Year 5 and $20 000 for each of the following five years. Alternative investments are available yielding a rate of return of 14%. Compute the net present value of the project.

7. An investment requires an initial outlay of $45 000. Net returns are estimated to be $14 000 per year for eight years. Determine the rate of return.

8. A project requires an initial outlay of $10 000 and promises net returns of $2000 per year over a twelve year period. If the project has a residual value of $4000 after twelve years, what is the rate of return?

9. Compute the rate of return for Question 5.

10. Compute the rate of return for Question 6.

11. The Superior Jig Company has developed a new jig for which it expects net returns as follows.

Year 1:	$8000
Year 2 to 6 inclusive:	$12 000 per year
Year 7 to 10 inclusive:	$6000 per year

The initial investment of $36 000 has a residual value of $9000 after ten years. Compute the rate of return.

12. The owner of a sporting goods store is considering remodelling the store so that a larger inventory can be carried. The cost of remodelling and additional inventory is

$60 000. The expected increase in net profit is $8000 per year for the next four years and $10 000 each year for the following six years. After ten years the owner plans to retire and sell the business. He expects to recover the additional $40 000 invested in inventory but not the $20 000 invested in remodelling. Compute the rate of return.

13. Outway Ventures evaluates potential investment projects at 20%. Two alternative projects are available. Project A will return the company $5800 per year for eight years. Alternative B will return the company $13 600 after one year, $17 000 after five years and $20 400 after eight years. Which alternative should the company prefer according to the discounted cash flow criterion?

14. Project A requires an immediate investment of $8000 and another $6000 in three years. Net returns are $4000 after two years, $12 000 after four years and $8000 after six years. Project B requires an immediate investment of $4000, another $6000 after two years and $4000 after four years. Net returns are $3400 per year for seven years. Determine the net present value at 10% and indicate which project should be preferred according to the net present value criterion?

15. Net returns from an investment are estimated to be $13 000 per year for twelve years. The investment involves an immediate outlay of $50 000 and a further outlay of $30 000 after six years. The investments are estimated to have a residual value of $10 000 after twelve years. Find the net present value at 20%.

16. The introduction of a new product requires an immediate outlay of $45 000. Anticipated net returns from the marketing of the product are expected to be $12 500 per year for ten years. What is the rate of return on the investment (correct to the nearest tenth of a percent)?

17. Games Inc. has developed a new electronic game and compiled the following product information.

	Production cost	Promotion cost	Sales revenue
Year 1	$32 000	—	—
Year 2	32 000	$64 000	$64 000
Year 3	32 000	96 000	256 000
Year 4	32 000	32 000	128 000
Year 5	32 000	—	32 000

Should the product be marketed if the company requires a return of 16%?

18. Farmer Jones wants to convert his farm into a golf course. He asked you to determine his rate of return based on the following estimates.

Development cost for each of the first three years, $80 000.

Construction of a club house in Year 4, $240 000.

Upon his retirement in fifteen years improvements in the property will yield him $200 000.

Net returns from the operation of the golf course will be nil for the first three years and $100 000 per year afterwards until his retirement.

Self-test

1. Opportunities Inc. requires a minimum rate of return of 15% on investment proposals. Two proposals are under consideration but only one may be chosen. Alternative A offers a net return of $2500 per year for twelve years. Alternative B offers a net return of $10 000 each year after four, eight and twelve years respectively. Determine the preferred alternative according to the discounted cash flow criterion.

2. A natural resources development project requires an immediate outlay of $10 000 and $50 000 at the end of each year for four years. Net returns are nil for the first two years and $60 000 per year thereafter for fourteen years. What is the net present value of the project at 16%?

3. An investment of $100 000 yields annual net returns of $20 000 for ten years. If the residual value of the investment after ten years is $30 000, what is the rate of return on the investment (correct to the nearest tenth of a percent)?

4. A telephone system with a disposable value of $1200 after five years can be purchased for $6600. Alternatively a leasing agreement is available requiring an immediate payment of $1500 plus payments of $100.00 at the beginning of each month for five years. If money is worth 12% compounded monthly, should the telephone system be leased or purchased?

5. A choice is to be made between two investment proposals. Proposal A requires an immediate outlay of $60 000 and a further outlay of $40 000 after three years. Net returns on Proposal A are $20 000 per year for ten years. The investment has no residual value after ten years. Proposal B requires outlays of $29 000 in each of the first four years. Net returns starting in Year 4 are $ 40 000 per year. The residual value of the investment after ten years is $50 000. Which proposal is preferred at 20%?

6. Introduction of a new product requires an immediate investment in plant facilities of $180 000 with a disposal value of $45 000 after seven years. The facilities will require additional capital outlays of $50 000 each after three and five years respectively. Net returns on the investment are estimated to be $75 000 per year for each of the first four years and $50 000 per year for the remaining three years. Determine the rate of return on investment (correct to the nearest tenth of a percent).

Summary of formulae used

Formula 21.1

$$\text{NET PRESENT VALUE} = \text{PRESENT VALUE OF INFLOWS} - \text{PRESENT VALUE OF OUTLAYS}$$

Formula 21.2

$$\text{PROFITABILITY INDEX} = \frac{\text{PRESENT VALUE OF INFLOWS}}{\text{PRESENT VALUE OF OUTLAYS}}$$

In addition the present value formulae introduced in Chapters 13, 15, 16, and 17 are needed.

Formula 13.2 or 13.2A
Formula 15.2 or 15.2A
Formula 16.2 or 16.2A
Formula 16.3 or 16.3A
Formula 17.2A
Formula 17.4A
Formula 17.5

Glossary of terms used

Discounted benefit-cost ratio   see *Profitability index*

Discounted cash flow   the present value of cash payments

Net present value   the difference between the present value of the inflows (benefits) and the present value of the outlays (costs) of a capital investment project

Profitability index   the ratio of the present value of the inflows (benefits) to the present value of the outlays (costs) of a capital investment project

Rate of return   the rate of discount for which the net present value of a capital investment project is equal to zero

Appendix

A.   Computer applications

Computers, especially micro-computers, play an increasingly important role in business applications. A sampling of business mathematics and mathematics of finance problems that are particularly suitable for solution by computer is presented in this appendix.

Program 1   Computer Application 1—Break-even analysis
Program 2   Computer Application 2—Loan repayment schedule
Program 3   Computer Application 3—Accumulation of principal
Program 4   Computer Application 4—Amortization schedule (Simple)
                Computer Application 5—Amortization schedule (General)
Program 5   Computer Application 6—Sinking fund schedule
Program 6   Computer Application 7—Depreciation schedules

The six programs are written in BASIC for use on IBM PC's or IBM compatibles and are contained on one diskette. The program listings are provided in this appendix and are intended for instructional use in conjunction with this textbook. The program listings may be copied by the original purchaser of the text without express permission from the publisher.

A copy of the diskette is available upon request from the publisher. The diskette directory is reproduced below.

Diskette directory

```
dir

 Volume in drive A has no label
 Directory of  A:\

 BASICA   COM     25984    3-08-83   12:00p
 BREAK EV BAS      3404    1-01-80    2:23a
 AMORTIZA BAS      4072    1-01-80   12:32a
 FORMAT   COM      6016    3-08-83   12:00p
 BASIC    COM     16256    3-08-83   12:00p
 DISKCOPY COM      2444    3-08-83   12:00p
 DEPRECIA BAS      4426    1-01-80   12:16a
 SINKING  BAS      4270    8-02-85   10:06a
 LOAN REP BAS      3992    1-01-80   12:35a
 ACCUMULA BAS      2995    1-01-80   12:10a
         10 File(s)      284672 bytes free

A>basic
```

B. Program 1—Break-even Analysis

The program ''BREAK EV'' provides a numerical solution for Case 1 illustrated in this text (Chapter 7, Section 7.1). When the program is run, the necessary input information is requested through statements 410 to 460.

```
RUN
\\\\\\\\\\\\\\\\\\\\\\\\\\\\\\
                    [                         [
                    [ LOAN REPAYMENT SCHEDULE [
[\\\\\\\\\\\\\\\\\\\\\\\\\\\\\[

What is the AMOUNT of the loan ? 16000

What is the NOMINAL ANNUAL RATE of INTEREST in percent ? 13.95

Monthly, Quarterly, Semi-annually, Annually

Enter the COMPOUNDING PERIOD (M,Q,S or A) M

What is the AMOUNT of the interval PAYMENT ? 700

Monthly, Quarterly, Semi-annually, Annually
```

Enter the PAYMENT INTERVAL (M,Q,S or A) M
**** press any key to continue ****

             P = Printout   A = Another schedule   S = Stop

                     (Enter your selection please)
make sure the printer is turned on

C = Continue   S =Stop

(Enter your selection please)

The output is displayed under five headings as shown in the sample output reproduced below. The program listing follows.

```
    ******************************************
    *                                        *
    *  B R E A K E V E N   A N A L Y S I S  *
    ******************************************
```

QTY	TOTAL COST	TOTAL SALES	GAIN/LOSS	UNIT COST
10	$27,500.00	$11,500.00	-$16,000.00	$2,750.00
20	$35,000.00	$23,000.00	-$12,000.00	$1,750.00
30	$42,500.00	$34,500.00	-$8,000.00	$1,416.67
40	$50,000.00	$46,000.00	-$4,000.00	$1,250.00
50	$57,500.00	$57,500.00	$0.00	$1,150.00
60	$65,000.00	$69,000.00	$4,000.00	$1,083.33
70	$72,500.00	$80,500.00	$8,000.00	$1,035.71
80	$80,000.00	$92,000.00	$12,000.00	$1,000.00
90	$87,500.00	$103,500.00	$16,000.00	$972.22
100	$95,000.00	$115,000.00	$20,000.00	$950.00

----

   50        $57,500.00 $57,500.00 = BREAKEVEN POINT

Total FIXED COSTS   : $20,000.00
VARIABLE COST per UNIT : $750.00
SELLING PRICE per UNIT : $1,150.00

          A = Another analysis   S = Stop

              (Enter your selection please)

```
        LIST
200 KEY OFF : CLS : LOCATE 2,22 : COLOR 15
210 FOR L = 1 TO 42 : PRINT CHR$(220); : NEXT L
220 LOCATE 3,22 : PRINT CHR$(219)
230 LOCATE 3,63 : PRINT CHR$(219)
250 LOCATE 4,22
260 PRINT CHR$(219);" B R E A K E V E N   A N A L Y S I S "; CHR$(219)
270 LOCATE 5,22
280 PRINT CHR$(219);;FOR L = 1 TO 40:PRINT CHR$(220);:NEXT L:PRINT CHR$(219)
290 COLOR 7 : LOCATE 8,1
400 PRINT : PRINT "   What are the total FIXED COSTS", : INPUT FC
410 PRINT : PRINT "   What are the VARIABLE COSTS per UNIT", : INPUT VC
420 PRINT : PRINT "   What is the SELLING PRICE per UNIT", : INPUT SP
430 COLOR 15 : PRINT : PRINT "REPLY TO THE FOLLOWING FOR COMPUTING PURPOSES."
440 COLOR 7 : PRINT : PRINT "   Starting quantity :            ", : INPUT SQ
450 PRINT : PRINT "   Ending quantity :            ", : INPUT EQ
460 PRINT : PRINT "   Increments of quantity : ", : INPUT IN
470 LOCATE 23,22 : COLOR 15
480 PRINT " **** press any key to continue ****"
490 A$ = INKEY$ : IF A$ = "" THEN 490
530 GOSUB 2500
610 QX = FC / (SP - VC)
620 RX = SP * QX
630 CX = FC + (VC * QX)
640 PU$ = "$$########,.##"
680 FOR Q = SQ TO EQ STEP IN
690 VX = VC * Q
700 RV = SP * Q
710 TC = FC + (VC * Q)
720 UC = TC / Q
730 PL = RV - TC
740 IF ZZ < 10 THEN GOTO 780
750 LOCATE 23,22 : COLOR 15 : PRINT "** hit space bar to continue **"
760 A$ = INKEY$ : IF A$ <> " "THEN 760
770 GOSUB 2500
780 PRINT TAB(7)Q;
790 PRINT TAB(15)"";:PRINT USING PU$;TC;
800 PRINT TAB(30)"";:PRINT USING PU$;RV;
810 PRINT TAB(45)"";:PRINT USING PU$;PL;
820 PRINT TAB(59)"";:PRINT USING PU$;UC;
830 ZZ = ZZ + 1 : NEXT Q
840 PRINT : FOR L = 1 TO 79 : PRINT CHR$(196); : NEXT
850 PRINT TAB(5)"";:PRINT USING "####";QX;
860 PRINT TAB(15)"";:PRINT USING PU$;CX;
870 PRINT TAB(30)"";:PRINT USING PU$;RX;
```

```
890 PRINT TAB(45)"= BREAKEVEN POINT"
910 FOR L = 1 TO 79 : PRINT CHR$(196); : NEXT
920 PRINT
930 PRINT "Total FIXED COSTS      : "; :PRINT USING PU$;FC
940 PRINT "VARIABLE COST per UNIT : "; :PRINT USING PU$;VC
950 PRINT "SELLING PRICE per UNIT : "; :PRINT USING PU$;SP
960 FOR L = 1 TO 79 : PRINT CHR$(196); : NEXT
970 PRINT : PRINT TAB(12)"P = Printout    A = Another analysis    S = Stop"
980 PRINT : PRINT TAB(19);"(Enter your selection please)"
990 A$ = INKEY$ : IF A$ <> "P" AND A$ <> "A" AND A$ <> "S" THEN 990
1000 IF A$ = "A" THEN GOTO 200
1010 IF A$ = "S" THEN STOP
1100 CLS : LOCATE 6, 1
1110 PRINT "MAKE SURE THE PRINTER IS TURNED ON"
1120 PRINT : PRINT "C = Continue     S = Stop"
1130 PRINT : PRINT "(Enter your selection please)
1140 A$ = INKEY$ : IF A$ <> "C" AND A$ <> "S" THEN 1140
1150 IF A$ = "S" THEN STOP
1160 LPRINT TAB(18); : FOR L = 1 TO 42 : LPRINT "*"; : NEXT L
1170 LPRINT TAB(18)"*";TAB(59)"*"
1180 LPRINT TAB(18);"* B R E A K E V E N    A N A L Y S I S *"
1190 LPRINT TAB(18); : FOR L = 1 TO 42 : LPRINT "*"; : NEXT L
1200 LPRINT : FOR L = 1 TO 79 : LPRINT "_";:NEXT L : PRINT
1210 LPRINT TAB(8)"QTY";TAB(18)"TOTAL COST";TAB(32)"TOTAL SALES";
1220 LPRINT TAB(49)"GAIN/LOSS";TAB(63)"UNIT COST"
1230 FOR L = 1 TO 79 : LPRINT "_";:NEXT L : PRINT
1240 QX = FC / (SP - VC)
1250 RX = SP * QX
1260 CX = FC + (VC * QX)
1270 PU$ = "$$#######,.##"
1280 FOR Q = SQ TO EQ STEP IN
1290 VX = VC * Q
1300 RV = SP * Q
1310 TC = FC + (VC * Q)
1320 UC = TC / Q
1330 PL = RV - TC
1340 LPRINT TAB(7)Q;
1350 LPRINT TAB(15)"";:LPRINT USING PU$;TC;
1360 LPRINT TAB(30)"";:LPRINT USING PU$;RV;
1370 LPRINT TAB(45)"";:LPRINT USING PU$;PL;
1380 LPRINT TAB(59)"";:LPRINT USING PU$;UC;
1390 NEXT Q
1400 LPRINT : FOR L = 1 TO 79 : LPRINT "_"; : NEXT
1410 LPRINT TAB(5)"";:LPRINT USING "####";QX;
1420 LPRINT TAB(15)"";:LPRINT USING PU$;CX;
```

```
1430 LPRINT TAB(30)"";:LPRINT USING PU$;RX;
1440 LPRINT TAB(45)"= BREAKEVEN POINT"
1450 FOR L = 1 TO 79 : LPRINT "_"; : NEXT
1460 LPRINT
1470 LPRINT "Total FIXED COSTS      : "; :LPRINT USING PU$;FC
1480 LPRINT "VARIABLE COST per UNIT : "; :LPRINT USING PU$;VC
1490 LPRINT "SELLING PRICE per UNIT : "; :LPRINT USING PU$;SP
1500 FOR L = 1 TO 79 : LPRINT "_"; : NEXT
1510 PRINT : PRINT TAB(12)"A = Another analysis    S = Stop"
1520 PRINT : PRINT TAB(13)"(Enter your selection please)"
1530 A$ = INKEY$ : IF A$ <> "A" AND A$ <> "S" THEN 1530
1540 IF A$ = "A" THEN GOTO 200
1550 STOP
1560 ZZ = 0
1599 RETURN
2500 REM      HEADER FOR DATA TABLE
2510 COLOR 7 : CLS
2520 FOR L = 1 TO 79 : PRINT CHR$(196);:NEXT L : PRINT
2530 PRINT TAB(8)"QTY";TAB(18)"TOTAL COST";TAB(32)"TOTAL SALES";
2540 PRINT TAB(49)"GAIN/LOSS";TAB(63)"UNIT COST"
2550 FOR L = 1 TO 79 : PRINT CHR$(196);:NEXT L : PRINT
2560 ZZ = 0
2599 RETURN
Ok
```

C. *Program 2—Loan Repayment Schedule*

The program ''LOAN REP'' creates a loan repayment schedule given the original loan balance, the annual rate of interest, the compounding interval, and the AMOUNT of the periodic payment.

```
RUN
\\\\\\\\\\\\\\\\\\\\\\\\\\\\\\\\
                        [                         [
                        [ LOAN REPAYMENT SCHEDULE [
[\\\\\\\\\\\\\\\\\\\\\\\\\\\\\\[

What is the AMOUNT of the loan ? 16000

What is the NOMINAL ANNUAL RATE of INTEREST in percent ? 13.95

Monthly, Quarterly, Semi-annually, Annually

Enter the COMPOUNDING PERIOD (M,Q,S or A) M
```

What is the AMOUNT of the interval PAYMENT ? 700

Monthly, Quarterly, Semi-annually, Annually

Enter the PAYMENT INTERVAL (M,Q,S or A) M
**** press any key to continue ****

        P = Printout   A = Another schedule   S = Stop

        (Enter your selection please)
make sure the printer is turned on

C = Continue   S =Stop

(Enter your selection please)

The output is a schedule similar to the one shown in Figure 12.4 of the text. A sample output is reproduced below followed by the program listing.

```
*******************************
*                             *
*   LOAN REPAYMENT SCHEDULE   *
*******************************
```

Amount of loan   : 16000
Nominal rate of interest : 13.95 % compounded monthly
Amount of interval payment : 700
Payment interval   : monthly

Payment no.	Payment	Interest	Principal repaid	Balance owing
0				$16,000.00
1	$700.00	$186.00	$514.00	$15,486.00
2	$700.00	$180.03	$519.97	$14,966.03
3	$700.00	$173.98	$526.02	$14,440.01
4	$700.00	$167.87	$532.13	$13,907.88
5	$700.00	$161.68	$538.32	$13,369.56
6	$700.00	$155.42	$544.58	$12,824.98
7	$700.00	$149.09	$550.91	$12,274.07
8	$700.00	$142.69	$557.31	$11,716.76
9	$700.00	$136.21	$563.79	$11,152.97
10	$700.00	$129.65	$570.35	$10,582.62
11	$700.00	$123.02	$576.98	$10,005.64
12	$700.00	$116.32	$583.68	$9,421.96
13	$700.00	$109.53	$590.47	$8,831.49
14	$700.00	$102.67	$597.33	$8,234.16
15	$700.00	$95.72	$604.28	$7,629.88

16	$700.00	$88.70	$611.30	$7,018.58
17	$700.00	$81.59	$618.41	$6,400.17
18	$700.00	$74.40	$625.60	$5,774.57
19	$700.00	$67.13	$632.87	$5,141.70
20	$700.00	$59.77	$640.23	$4,501.47
21	$700.00	$52.33	$647.67	$3,853.80
22	$700.00	$44.80	$655.20	$3,198.60
23	$700.00	$37.18	$662.82	$2,535.78
24	$700.00	$29.48	$670.52	$1,865.26
25	$700.00	$21.68	$678.32	$1,186.94
26	$700.00	$13.80	$686.20	$500.74
27	$506.56	$5.82	$500.74	$0.00

```
---------------------------------------------------------------------

 TOTAL     $18,706.56   $2,706.56    $16,000.00

---------------------------------------------------------------------


A = Another schedule     S = Stop
(Enter your selection please)


Break in 1600
Ok
LOAD"loan rep
Ok
LIST
200 KEY OFF : CLS : LOCATE 3,26 : COLOR 15
210 FOR L = 1 TO 29 : PRINT CHR$(220); : NEXT L
220 PRINT TAB(26)CHR$(219);TAB(54);CHR$(219)
230 PRINT TAB(26)CHR$(219);"  LOAN REPAYMENT SCHEDULE  ";CHR$(219)
240 LOCATE 6,26
250 PRINT CHR$(219);;:FOR L = 1 TO 27:PRINT CHR$(220);:NEXT L:PRINT CHR$(219)
300 COLOR 7
310 PRINT : PRINT "What is the AMOUNT of the loan "; : INPUT PM
320 PRINT : PRINT "What is the NOMINAL ANNUAL RATE of INTEREST in percent "; : INPUT NI
330 COLOR 15 : PRINT
340 PRINT "Monthly, Quarterly, Semi-annually, Annually"
350 COLOR 7  : PRINT
360 PRINT "Enter the COMPOUNDING PERIOD (M,Q,S or A) ";
370 A$ = INKEY$ : IF A$<>"M" AND A$<>"Q" AND A$<>"S" AND A$<> "A" THEN 370
380 IF A$ = "M" THEN CP = 12 : CP$ = "monthly"
390 IF A$ = "Q" THEN CP =  4 : CP$ = "quarterly"
400 IF A$ = "S" THEN CP =  2 : CP$ = "semi-annually"
410 IF A$ = "A" THEN CP =  1 : CP$ = "annually"
420 PRINT A$ : PRINT
430 PRINT "What is the AMOUNT of the interval PAYMENT "; : INPUT R
440 COLOR 15 : PRINT
```

```
450 PRINT "Monthly, Quarterly, Semi-annually, Annually"
460 COLOR 7  : PRINT
470 PRINT "Enter the PAYMENT INTERVAL (M,Q,S or A) ";
480 A$ = INKEY$ : IF A$<>"M" AND A$<>"Q" AND A$<>"S" AND A$<> "A" THEN 480
490 IF A$ = "M" THEN PI = 12 : PI$ = "monthly"
500 IF A$ = "Q" THEN PI =  4 : PI$ = "quarterly"
510 IF A$ = "S" THEN PI =  2 : PI$ = "semi-annually"
520 IF A$ = "A" THEN PI =  1 : PI$ = "annually"
530 PRINT A$
540 COLOR 15 : LOCATE 23,22
550 PRINT "**** press any key to continue ****"
560 A$ = INKEY$ : IF A$ = "" THEN 560
800 GOSUB 2500
810 PU1$ = "##.##"
820 PU$ = "$$########,.##"
821 PA = PM : RA = R : Q = 0
822 TI = 0 : TR = 0 : TP = 0
830 TOT = 0 : IN = NI / (CP*100)
831 C = CP/PI
832 IN = (1 + IN)^C - 1
850 MP = (MP * 100 + .5) / 100
851 PRINT TAB(6)0;TAB(60); : PRINT USING PU$;PA;
860 WHILE PA > 0
861 Q = Q + 1
870 IP = PA * IN
880 IP = INT(IP * 100 + .5)/100
881 IF PA < R THEN R = PA + IP
890 PR = R - IP
900 PA = INT((PA - PR) * 100 + .5)/100
910 TI = TI + INT(IP * 100 + .5)/100
911 TR = TR + INT(R * 100 + .5)/100
912 TP = TP + INT(PR * 100 + .5)/100
913 IF ZZ < 10 THEN GOTO 920
914 LOCATE 22,22 : COLOR 15 : PRINT "** hit space bar to continue **"
915 A$ = INKEY$ : IF A$ <> " " THEN 915
916 GOSUB 2500
920 PRINT TAB(6)Q;TAB(12); : PRINT USING PU$;R;
930 PRINT TAB(25); : PRINT USING PU$;IP;
940 PRINT TAB(42); : PRINT USING PU$;PR;
950 PRINT TAB(60); : PRINT USING PU$;PA
960 ZZ = ZZ + 1 : WEND
970 FOR L = 1 TO 79 : PRINT CHR$(196); : NEXT L : PRINT
980 PRINT "  TOTAL";TAB(12); : PRINT USING PU$;TR;
990 PRINT TAB(25); : PRINT USING PU$;TI;
1000 PRINT TAB(42); : PRINT USING PU$;TP
```

```
1010 FOR L = 1 TO 79 : PRINT CHR$(196); : NEXT L : PRINT
1100 PRINT : PRINT TAB(11)"P = Printout    A = Another schedule    S = Stop"
1110 PRINT : PRINT TAB(19)"(Enter your selection please)"
1120 A$ = INKEY$ : IF A$<>"P" AND A$<>"A" AND A$<>"S" THEN 1120
1130 IF A$ = "A" THEN GOTO 200
1140 IF A$ = "S" THEN STOP
1150 CLS : LOCATE 6,1
1160 PRINT "make sure the printer is turned on"
1170 PRINT : PRINT "C = Continue    S =Stop"
1180 PRINT : PRINT "(Enter your selection please)"
1190 A$ = INKEY$ : IF A$<>"C" AND A$<>"S" THEN 1190
1200 IF A$ = "S" THEN STOP
1210 LPRINT TAB(26); : FOR L = 1 TO 29 : LPRINT "*"; : NEXT L : LPRINT
1220 LPRINT TAB(26)"*";TAB(54);"*"
1230 LPRINT TAB(26)"*";" LOAN REPAYMENT SCHEDULE  *"
1240 LPRINT TAB(26); : FOR L = 1 TO 29 : LPRINT "*"; : NEXT L : LPRINT
1241 LPRINT"Amount of loan            : ";PM
1242 LPRINT"Nominal rate of interest  : ";NI;"%  compounded ";CP$
1243 LPRINT"Amount of interval payment : ";RA
1244 LPRINT"Payment interval          : ";PI$
1250 FOR L = 1 TO 79 : LPRINT "_"; : NEXT L : LPRINT
1260 LPRINT " Payment no.";TAB(18)"Payment";TAB(30)"Interest";
1270 LPRINT TAB(41)"Principal repaid";TAB(64)"Balance owing"
1280 FOR L = 1 TO 79 : LPRINT "_"; : NEXT L : LPRINT
1300 PA = PM : Q = 0
1310 R = RA
1320 LPRINT TAB(6)0;TAB(60); : LPRINT USING PU$;PA;
1330 WHILE PA > 0
1331 Q = Q + 1
1340 IP = PA * IN
1350 IP = INT(IP * 100 + .5)/100
1360 IF PA < R THEN R = PA + IP
1370 PR = R - IP
1380 PA = INT((PA - PR) * 100 + .5)/100
1420 LPRINT TAB(6)Q;TAB(12); : LPRINT USING PU$;R;
1430 LPRINT TAB(25); : LPRINT USING PU$;IP;
1440 LPRINT TAB(42); : LPRINT USING PU$;PR;
1450 LPRINT TAB(60); : LPRINT USING PU$;PA
1451 WEND
1460 FOR L = 1 TO 79 : LPRINT "_"; : NEXT L : LPRINT
1470 LPRINT "  TOTAL";TAB(12); : LPRINT USING PU$;TR;
1480 LPRINT TAB(25); : LPRINT USING PU$;TI;
1490 LPRINT TAB(42); : LPRINT USING PU$;TP
1500 FOR L = 1 TO 79 : LPRINT "_"; : NEXT L : LPRINT
1510 PRINT : PRINT "A = Another schedule    S = Stop"
```

```
1520 PRINT : PRINT "(Enter your selection please)"
1530 A$ = INKEY$ : IF A$<>"A" AND A$ <>"S" THEN 1530
1540 IF A$ = "A" THEN GOTO 200
1600 STOP
2500 REM HEADINGS FOR DATA TABLE
2510 COLOR 7 : CLS
2520 FOR L = 1 TO 79 : PRINT CHR$(196); : NEXT L : PRINT
2530 PRINT " Payment no.";TAB(18)"Payment";TAB(30)"Interest";
2540 PRINT TAB(41)"Principal repaid";TAB(64)"Balance owing"
2550 FOR L = 1 TO 79 : PRINT CHR$(196); : NEXT L : PRINT
2560 ZZ = 0
2599 RETURN
Ok
```

D.   *Program 3—Accumulation of Principal*

The program ''ACCUMULA'' shows how a sum of money grows at compound interest. The required input consists of the original principal, the nominal annual rate of interest, the compounding period, and the compounding term in years.

```
RUN
\\\\\\\\\\\\\\\\\\\\\\\\\\\\\\\\
                        [                           [
                 [  ACCUMULATION OF PRINCIPAL  [
[\\\\\\\\\\\\\\\\\\\\\\\\\\\\\\\\[

What is the ORIGINAL PRINCIPAL ? 10000

What is the NOMINAL ANNUAL RATE of INTEREST in percent ? 9.75

Monthly, Quarterly, Semi-annually, Annually

Enter the COMPOUNDING PERIOD (M,Q,S or A) A

What is the TERM in YEARS ? 15
#### press any key to continue ####


         P = Printout    A = Another schedule    S = Stop

                (Enter your selection please)
make sure the printer is turned on

C = Continue    S =Stop

(Enter your selection please)
```

The output is similar to the solution shown in the text for Example 13.1a. A sample output is reproduced below followed by the program listing.

```
*******************************
*                             *
*  ACCUMULATION OF PRINCIPAL  *
*******************************
Original principal        :  10000
Nominal rate of interest  :  9.75 %  compounded annually
Term in years             :  15
-----------------------------------------------------------------------
 Payment no.                   Interest period no.
                               earned                        value
-----------------------------------------------------------------------
      0                                                   $10,000.00
      1                         $975.00                   $10,975.00
      2                       $1,070.06                   $12,045.06
      3                       $1,174.39                   $13,219.46
      4                       $1,288.90                   $14,508.35
      5                       $1,414.56                   $15,922.92
      6                       $1,552.48                   $17,475.40
      7                       $1,703.85                   $19,179.25
      8                       $1,869.98                   $21,049.23
      9                       $2,052.30                   $23,101.53
     10                       $2,252.40                   $25,353.93
     11                       $2,472.01                   $27,825.94
     12                       $2,713.03                   $30,538.97
     13                       $2,977.55                   $33,516.52
     14                       $3,267.86                   $36,784.38
     15                       $3,586.48                   $40,370.85
-----------------------------------------------------------------------
    TOTAL                    $30,370.85
-----------------------------------------------------------------------

A = Another schedule     S = Stop
(Enter your selection please)


LOAD"accumula
Ok
LIST
200 KEY OFF : CLS : LOCATE 3,26 : COLOR 15
210 FOR L = 1 TO 31 : PRINT CHR$(220); : NEXT L
220 PRINT TAB(26)CHR$(219);TAB(56);CHR$(219)
230 PRINT TAB(26)CHR$(219);" ACCUMULATION OF PRINCIPAL  ";CHR$(219)
240 LOCATE 6,26
```

```
250 PRINT CHR$(219);:FOR L = 1 TO 29:PRINT CHR$(220);:NEXT L:PRINT CHR$(219)
300 COLOR 7
310 PRINT : PRINT "What is the ORIGINAL PRINCIPAL "; : INPUT PM
320 PRINT : PRINT "What is the NOMINAL ANNUAL RATE of INTEREST in percent "; : INPUT NI
330 COLOR 15 : PRINT
340 PRINT "Monthly, Quarterly, Semi-annually, Annually"
350 COLOR 7  : PRINT
360 PRINT "Enter the COMPOUNDING PERIOD (M,Q,S or A) ";
370 A$ = INKEY$ : IF A$<>"M" AND A$<>"Q" AND A$<>"S" AND A$<> "A" THEN 370
380 IF A$ = "M" THEN CP = 12 : CP$ = "monthly" : PI$ = CP$
390 IF A$ = "Q" THEN CP =  4 : CP$ = "quarterly" : PI$ = CP$
400 IF A$ = "S" THEN CP =  2 : CP$ = "semi-annually" : PI$ = "semi-annual"
410 IF A$ = "A" THEN CP =  1 : CP$ = "annually" : PI$ = "yearly"
420 PRINT A$ : PRINT
430 PRINT "What is the TERM in YEARS "; : INPUT TE
540 COLOR 15 : LOCATE 23,22
550 PRINT "**** press any key to continue ****"
560 A$ = INKEY$ : IF A$ = "" THEN 560
800 GOSUB 2500
810 PU1$ = "##.##"
820 PU$ = "$$#######,.##"
821 PA = PM
822 TI = 0
830 TOT = 0 : IN = NI / (CP*100) : TE = TE * CP
850 PRINT TAB(6)0;TAB(60); : PRINT USING PU$;PA;
860 FOR Q = 1 TO TE
870 IP = PA * IN
900 PA = PA + IP
910 TI = TI + IP
913 IF ZZ < 10 THEN GOTO 920
914 LOCATE 22,22 : COLOR 15 : PRINT "** hit space bar to continue **"
915 A$ = INKEY$ : IF A$ <> " " THEN 915
916 GOSUB 2500
920 PRINT TAB(6)Q;
930 PRINT TAB(25); : PRINT USING PU$;IP;
950 PRINT TAB(60); : PRINT USING PU$;PA
960 ZZ = ZZ + 1 : NEXT Q
970 FOR L = 1 TO 79 : PRINT CHR$(196); : NEXT L : PRINT
980 PRINT "  TOTAL";
990 PRINT TAB(25); : PRINT USING PU$;TI
1010 FOR L = 1 TO 79 : PRINT CHR$(196); : NEXT L : PRINT
1100 PRINT : PRINT TAB(11)"P = Printout    A = Another schedule    S = Stop"
1110 PRINT : PRINT TAB(19)"(Enter your selection please)"
1120 A$ = INKEY$ : IF A$<>"P" AND A$<>"A" AND A$<>"S" THEN 1120
1130 IF A$ = "A" THEN GOTO 200
```

```
1140 IF A$ = "S" THEN STOP
1150 CLS : LOCATE 6,1
1160 PRINT "make sure the printer is turned on"
1170 PRINT : PRINT "C = Continue      S =Stop"
1180 PRINT : PRINT "(Enter your selection please)"
1190 A$ = INKEY$ : IF A$<>"C" AND A$<>"S" THEN 1190
1200 IF A$ = "S" THEN STOP
1210 LPRINT TAB(26); : FOR L = 1 TO 31 : LPRINT "*"; : NEXT L : LPRINT
1220 LPRINT TAB(26)"*";TAB(56);"*"
1230 LPRINT TAB(26)"*";" ACCUMULATION OF PRINCIPAL  *"
1240 LPRINT TAB(26); : FOR L = 1 TO 29 : LPRINT "*"; : NEXT L : LPRINT
1241 LPRINT"Original principal      : ";PM
1242 LPRINT"Nominal rate of interest : ";NI;"%  compounded ";CP$
1243 LPRINT"Term in years          : ";TE/CP
1250 FOR L = 1 TO 79 : LPRINT "_"; : NEXT L : LPRINT
1260 LPRINT " Payment no.";TAB(30)"Interest";
1270 LPRINT " period no.";TAB(30)"earned";TAB(63)"value"
1280 FOR L = 1 TO 79 : LPRINT "_"; : NEXT L : LPRINT
1300 PA = PM
1320 LPRINT TAB(6)0;TAB(60); : LPRINT USING PU$;PA;
1330 FOR Q = 1 TO TE
1340 IP = PA * IN
1360 PA = PA + IP
1420 LPRINT TAB(6)Q;
1430 LPRINT TAB(25); : LPRINT USING PU$;IP;
1450 LPRINT TAB(60); : LPRINT USING PU$;PA
1451 NEXT Q
1460 FOR L = 1 TO 79 : LPRINT "_"; : NEXT L : LPRINT
1470 LPRINT " TOTAL";
1480 LPRINT TAB(25); : LPRINT USING PU$;TI
1500 FOR L = 1 TO 79 : LPRINT "_"; : NEXT L : LPRINT
1510 PRINT : PRINT "A = Another schedule    S = Stop"
1520 PRINT : PRINT "(Enter your selection please)"
1530 A$ = INKEY$ : IF A$<>"A" AND A$ <>"S" THEN 1530
1540 IF A$ = "A" THEN GOTO 200
1600 STOP
2500 REM HEADINGS FOR DATA TABLE
2510 COLOR 7 : CLS
2520 FOR L = 1 TO 79 : PRINT CHR$(196); : NEXT L : PRINT
2530 PRINT " ";PI$;TAB(30)"Interest";TAB(60)"Accumulated"
2540 PRINT " period no.";TAB(30)"earned";TAB(63)"value"
2550 FOR L = 1 TO 79 : PRINT CHR$(196); : NEXT L : PRINT
2560 ZZ = 0
2599 RETURN
Ok
```

E. Program 4—Amortization Schedules

The program "AMORTIZA" produces amortization schedules involving either simple annuities (Computer Application 4) or general annuities (Computer Application 5). The required input consists of the original loan principal, the nominal annual rate of interest, the compounding period, the term of the loan in years, and the payment interval.

```
RUN
\\\\\\\\\\\\\\\\\\\\\\\\\\\\\
                 [                         [
                 [  AMORTIZATION SCHEDULE  [
[\\\\\\\\\\\\\\\\\\\\\\\\\\\\\[

What is the PRINCIPAL AMOUNT of the mortgage ? 20000

What is the NOMINAL ANNUAL RATE of INTEREST in percent ? 13.5

Monthly, Quarterly, Semi-annually, Annually

Enter the COMPOUNDING PERIOD (M,Q,S or A) Q

What is the TERM of the mortgage in YEARS ? 5

Monthly, Quarterly, Semi-annually, Annually

Enter the PAYMENT INTERVAL (M,Q,S or A) Q
**** press any key to continue ****

          P = Printout    A = Another schedule    S = Stop

                    (Enter your selection please)
make sure the printer is turned on

C = Continue     S =Stop

(Enter your selection please)
```

The output is similar to the schedules shown as solutions to Example 18.1c (simple annuity) and Example 18.2a (general annuity). Sample outputs for both cases are shown below. The program listing follows.

Example for simple annuity case:

```
*****************************
*                           *
*   AMORTIZATION SCHEDULE   *
*****************************
```

Principal amount of mortgage : 20000
Nominal rate of interest   : 13.5 % compounded quarterly
Term of mortgage in years   : 5
Payment interval   : quarterly

Payment no.	Amount paid	Interest	Principal repaid	Outstanding balance
0				$20,000.00
1	$1,391.35	$675.00	$716.35	$19,283.65
2	$1,391.35	$650.82	$740.53	$18,543.12
3	$1,391.35	$625.83	$765.52	$17,777.60
4	$1,391.35	$600.00	$791.35	$16,986.25
5	$1,391.35	$573.29	$818.06	$16,168.19
6	$1,391.35	$545.68	$845.67	$15,322.52
7	$1,391.35	$517.14	$874.21	$14,448.31
8	$1,391.35	$487.63	$903.72	$13,544.59
9	$1,391.35	$457.13	$934.22	$12,610.37
10	$1,391.35	$425.60	$965.75	$11,644.62
11	$1,391.35	$393.01	$998.34	$10,646.28
12	$1,391.35	$359.31	$1,032.04	$9,614.24
13	$1,391.35	$324.48	$1,066.87	$8,547.37
14	$1,391.35	$288.47	$1,102.88	$7,444.49
15	$1,391.35	$251.25	$1,140.10	$6,304.39
16	$1,391.35	$212.77	$1,178.58	$5,125.81
17	$1,391.35	$173.00	$1,218.35	$3,907.46
18	$1,391.35	$131.88	$1,259.47	$2,647.99
19	$1,391.35	$89.37	$1,301.98	$1,346.01
20	$1,391.44	$45.43	$1,346.01	$0.00
TOTAL	$27,827.09	$7,827.09	$20,000.00	

A = Another schedule   S = Stop

(Enter your selection please)

Example for general annuity case:

```
*****************************
*                           *
*   AMORTIZATION SCHEDULE   *
*****************************
```

Principal amount of mortgage :   60000
Nominal rate of interest   :   11.25 % compounded semi-annually
Term of mortgage in years   :   3
Payment interval   :   monthly

Payment no.	Amount paid	Interest	Principal repaid	Outstanding balance
0				$60,000.00
1	$1,964.18	$549.75	$1,414.43	$58,585.57
2	$1,964.18	$536.79	$1,427.39	$57,158.18
3	$1,964.18	$523.71	$1,440.47	$55,717.71
4	$1,964.18	$510.52	$1,453.66	$54,264.05
5	$1,964.18	$497.20	$1,466.98	$52,797.07
6	$1,964.18	$483.76	$1,480.42	$51,316.65
7	$1,964.18	$470.19	$1,493.99	$49,822.66
8	$1,964.18	$456.50	$1,507.68	$48,314.98
9	$1,964.18	$442.69	$1,521.49	$46,793.49
10	$1,964.18	$428.75	$1,535.43	$45,258.06
11	$1,964.18	$414.68	$1,549.50	$43,708.56
12	$1,964.18	$400.48	$1,563.70	$42,144.86
13	$1,964.18	$386.15	$1,578.03	$40,566.83
14	$1,964.18	$371.70	$1,592.48	$38,974.35
15	$1,964.18	$357.10	$1,607.08	$37,367.27
16	$1,964.18	$342.38	$1,621.80	$35,745.47
17	$1,964.18	$327.52	$1,636.66	$34,108.81
18	$1,964.18	$312.52	$1,651.66	$32,457.15
19	$1,964.18	$297.39	$1,666.79	$30,790.36
20	$1,964.18	$282.12	$1,682.06	$29,108.30
21	$1,964.18	$266.71	$1,697.47	$27,410.83
22	$1,964.18	$251.15	$1,713.03	$25,697.80
23	$1,964.18	$235.46	$1,728.72	$23,969.08
24	$1,964.18	$219.62	$1,744.56	$22,224.52
25	$1,964.18	$203.63	$1,760.55	$20,463.97
26	$1,964.18	$187.50	$1,776.68	$18,687.29
27	$1,964.18	$171.22	$1,792.96	$16,894.33

28	$1,964.18	$154.80	$1,809.38	$15,084.95
29	$1,964.18	$138.22	$1,825.96	$13,258.99
30	$1,964.18	$121.49	$1,842.69	$11,416.30
31	$1,964.18	$104.60	$1,859.58	$9,556.72
32	$1,964.18	$87.56	$1,876.62	$7,680.10
33	$1,964.18	$70.37	$1,893.81	$5,786.29
34	$1,964.18	$53.02	$1,911.16	$3,875.13
35	$1,964.18	$35.51	$1,928.67	$1,946.46
36	$1,964.29	$17.83	$1,946.46	$0.00

TOTAL $70,710.58 $10,710.59 $60,000.01

A = Another schedule   S = Stop
(Enter your selection please)

Break in 1010
Ok

LOAD"amortiza
Ok
LIST
```
200 KEY OFF : CLS : LOCATE 3,26 : COLOR 15
210 FOR L = 1 TO 27 : PRINT CHR$(220); : NEXT L
220 PRINT TAB(26)CHR$(219);TAB(52);CHR$(219)
230 PRINT TAB(26)CHR$(219);" AMORTIZATION SCHEDULE ";CHR$(219)
240 LOCATE 6,26
250 PRINT CHR$(219);:FOR L = 1 TO 25:PRINT CHR$(220);:NEXT L:PRINT CHR$(219)
300 COLOR 7
310 PRINT : PRINT "What is the PRINCIPAL AMOUNT of the mortgage "; : INPUT PM
320 PRINT : PRINT "What is the NOMINAL ANNUAL RATE of INTEREST in percent "; : INPUT N
330 COLOR 15 : PRINT
340 PRINT "Monthly, Quarterly, Semi-annually, Annually"
350 COLOR 7  : PRINT
360 PRINT "Enter the COMPOUNDING PERIOD (M,Q,S or A) ";
370 A$ = INKEY$ : IF A$<>"M" AND A$<>"Q" AND A$<>"S" AND A$<> "A" THEN 370
380 IF A$ = "M" THEN CP = 12 : CP$ = "monthly"
390 IF A$ = "Q" THEN CP =  4 : CP$ = "quarterly"
400 IF A$ = "S" THEN CP =  2 : CP$ = "semi-annually"
410 IF A$ = "A" THEN CP =  1 : CP$ = "annually"
420 PRINT A$ : PRINT
430 PRINT "What is the TERM of the mortgage in YEARS "; : INPUT TE
440 COLOR 15 : PRINT
450 PRINT "Monthly, Quarterly, Semi-annually, Annually"
460 COLOR 7  : PRINT
```

```
470 PRINT "Enter the PAYMENT INTERVAL (M,Q,S or A) ";
480 A$ = INKEY$ : IF A$<>"M" AND A$<>"Q" AND A$<>"S" AND A$<> "A" THEN 480
490 IF A$ = "M" THEN PI = 12 : PI$ = "monthly"
500 IF A$ = "Q" THEN PI =  4 : PI$ = "quarterly"
510 IF A$ = "S" THEN PI =  2 : PI$ = "semi-annually"
520 IF A$ = "A" THEN PI =  1 : PI$ = "annually"
530 PRINT A$
540 COLOR 15 : LOCATE 23,22
550 PRINT "**** press any key to continue ****"
560 A$ = INKEY$ : IF A$ = "" THEN 560
800 GOSUB 2500
810 PU1$ = "##.##"
820 PU$ = "$$#######,.##"
821 PA = PM
822 TI = 0 : TR = 0 : TP = 0
830 TOT = 0 : IN = NI / (CP*100) : TE = TE * PI
831 C = CP/PI
832 IN = (1 + IN)^C - 1
840 R = PA / (( 1 - ( 1 + IN )^-TE) / IN )
850 MP = (MP * 100 + .5) / 100
851 PRINT TAB(6)0;TAB(60); : PRINT USING PU$;PA;
860 FOR Q = 1 TO TE
870 IP = PA * IN
880 IP = INT(IP * 100 + .5)/100
881 IF Q = TE THEN R = PA + IP
890 PR = R - IP
900 PA = INT((PA - PR) * 100 + .5)/100
910 TI = TI + INT(IP * 100 + .5)/100
911 TR = TR + INT(R * 100 + .5)/100
912 TP = TP + INT(PR * 100 + .5)/100
913 IF ZZ < 10 THEN GOTO 920
914 LOCATE 22,22 : COLOR 15 : PRINT "** hit space bar to continue **"
915 A$ = INKEY$ : IF A$ <> " " THEN 915
916 GOSUB 2500
920 PRINT TAB(6)Q;TAB(12); : PRINT USING PU$;R;
930 PRINT TAB(25); : PRINT USING PU$;IP;
940 PRINT TAB(42); : PRINT USING PU$;PR;
950 PRINT TAB(60); : PRINT USING PU$;PA
960 ZZ = ZZ + 1 : NEXT Q
970 FOR L = 1 TO 79 : PRINT CHR$(196); : NEXT L : PRINT
980 PRINT " TOTAL";TAB(12); : PRINT USING PU$;TR;
990 PRINT TAB(25); : PRINT USING PU$;TI;
1000 PRINT TAB(42); : PRINT USING PU$;TP
1010 FOR L = 1 TO 79 : PRINT CHR$(196); : NEXT L : PRINT
1100 PRINT : PRINT TAB(11)"P = Printout     A = Another schedule     S = Stop"
```

```
1110 PRINT : PRINT TAB(19)"(Enter your selection please)"
1120 A$ = INKEY$ : IF A$<>"P" AND A$<>"A" AND A$<>"S" THEN 1120
1130 IF A$ = "A" THEN GOTO 200
1140 IF A$ = "S" THEN STOP
1150 CLS : LOCATE 6,1
1160 PRINT "make sure the printer is turned on"
1170 PRINT : PRINT "C = Continue      S =Stop"
1180 PRINT : PRINT "(Enter your selection please)"
1190 A$ = INKEY$ : IF A$<>"C" AND A$<>"S" THEN 1190
1200 IF A$ = "S" THEN STOP
1210 LPRINT TAB(26); : FOR L = 1 TO 27 : LPRINT "*"; : NEXT L : LPRINT
1220 LPRINT TAB(26)"*";TAB(52);"*"
1230 LPRINT TAB(26)"*";"  AMORTIZATION SCHEDULE  *"
1240 LPRINT TAB(26); : FOR L = 1 TO 27 : LPRINT "*"; : NEXT L : LPRINT
1241 LPRINT"Principal amount of mortgage : ";PM
1242 LPRINT"Nominal rate of interest     : ";NI;"% compounded ";CP$
1243 LPRINT"Term of mortgage in years    : ";TE/PI
1244 LPRINT"Payment interval             : ";PI$
1250 FOR L = 1 TO 79 : LPRINT "_"; : NEXT L : LPRINT
1260 LPRINT " Payment no.";TAB(16)"Amount paid";TAB(30)"Interest";
1270 LPRINT TAB(41)"Principal repaid";TAB(60)"Outstanding balance"
1280 FOR L = 1 TO 79 : LPRINT "_"; : NEXT L : LPRINT
1300 PA = PM
1310 R = PA / (( 1 - ( 1 + IN )^-TE) / IN )
1320 LPRINT TAB(6)0;TAB(60); : LPRINT USING PU$;PA;
1330 FOR Q = 1 TO TE
1340 IP = PA * IN
1350 IP = INT(IP * 100 + .5)/100
1360 IF Q = TE THEN R = PA + IP
1370 PR = R - IP
1380 PA = INT((PA - PR) * 100 + .5)/100
1420 LPRINT TAB(6)Q;TAB(12); : LPRINT USING PU$;R;
1430 LPRINT TAB(25); : LPRINT USING PU$;IP;
1440 LPRINT TAB(42); : LPRINT USING PU$;PR;
1450 LPRINT TAB(60); : LPRINT USING PU$;PA
1451 NEXT Q
1460 FOR L = 1 TO 79 : LPRINT "_"; : NEXT L : LPRINT
1470 LPRINT " TOTAL";TAB(12); : LPRINT USING PU$;TR;
1480 LPRINT TAB(25); : LPRINT USING PU$;TI;
1490 LPRINT TAB(42); : LPRINT USING PU$;TP
1500 FOR L = 1 TO 79 : LPRINT "_"; : NEXT L : LPRINT
1510 PRINT : PRINT "A = Another schedule     S = Stop"
1520 PRINT : PRINT "(Enter your selection please)"
1530 A$ = INKEY$ : IF A$<>"A" AND A$ <>"S" THEN 1530
1540 IF A$ = "A" THEN GOTO 200
```

```
1600 STOP
2500 REM HEADINGS FOR DATA TABLE
2510 COLOR 7 : CLS
2520 FOR L = 1 TO 79 : PRINT CHR$(196); : NEXT L : PRINT
2530 PRINT " Payment no.";TAB(16)"Amount paid";TAB(30)"Interest";
2540 PRINT TAB(41)"Principal repaid";TAB(60)"Outstanding balance"
2550 FOR L = 1 TO 79 : PRINT CHR$(196); : NEXT L : PRINT
2560 ZZ = 0
2599 RETURN
Ok
```

F. Program 5—Sinking Fund Schedules

The program "SINKING" produces sinking fund schedules. The periodic payments may be made either at the end or the beginning of each payment interval. The required input consists of the final balance in the sinking fund, the nominal annual rate of interest, the compounding period, the number of years for which payments are made, and a statement of whether the payments are made at the end or the beginning of the payment intervals.

```
RUN
\\\\\\\\\\\\\\\\\\\\\\\\\\\\\
                      [                         [
                      [  SINKING FUND SCHEDULE  [
[\\\\\\\\\\\\\\\\\\\\\\\\\\\\[

What is the SINKING FUND VALUE              ? 45000

What is the ANNUAL INTEREST RATE IN PERCENT ? 9.8

Monthly, Quarterly, Semi-annually, Annually

Enter the COMPOUNDING PERIOD (M,Q,S or A)   ?S

For how many YEARS are payments to be made  ? 8

Payments made at the (B)eginning or (E)nd   ? E
**** press any key to continue ****

          P = Printout    A = Another schedule    S = Stop

                    (Enter your selection please)
make sure the printer is turned on
```

C = Continue   S = Stop

(Enter your selection please)

The output is similar to the schedules shown as solutions for Examples 18.4c and 18.4d. Sample outputs for the two situations are reproduced below. The program listing follows.

Example for the case in which payments are made at the end of each payment period:

```
*****************************
*                           *
*  SINKING FUND SCHEDULE  *
*****************************
```

Value of fund   :   45000
Interest rate   :   9.8 % compounded semi-annually
No. of payments :   16
Payments made at the END

Payment interval number	Periodic payment	Interest for payment interval i = 0.049000	increase in fund	Balance in fund at end of payment interval
0				$0.00
1	$1,917.64	$0.00	$1,917.64	$1,917.64
2	$1,917.64	$93.96	$2,011.60	$3,929.24
3	$1,917.64	$192.53	$2,110.17	$6,039.41
4	$1,917.64	$295.93	$2,213.57	$8,252.98
5	$1,917.64	$404.40	$2,322.04	$10,575.02
6	$1,917.64	$518.18	$2,435.82	$13,010.84
7	$1,917.64	$637.53	$2,555.17	$15,566.01
8	$1,917.64	$762.73	$2,680.37	$18,246.38
9	$1,917.64	$894.07	$2,811.71	$21,058.09
10	$1,917.64	$1,031.85	$2,949.49	$24,007.58
11	$1,917.64	$1,176.37	$3,094.01	$27,101.59
12	$1,917.64	$1,327.98	$3,245.62	$30,347.21
13	$1,917.64	$1,487.01	$3,404.65	$33,751.86
14	$1,917.64	$1,653.84	$3,571.48	$37,323.34
15	$1,917.64	$1,828.84	$3,746.48	$41,069.82
16	$1,917.64	$2,012.42	$3,930.06	$44,999.88
TOTAL	$30,682.25	$14,317.64	$44,999.88	

A = Another schedule   S = Stop

(Enter your selection please)

Example for the case in which payments are made at the beginning of each payment period:

```
********************************
*                              *
*    SINKING FUND SCHEDULE     *
********************************
```

Value of fund   : 75000
Interest rate   : 10.75 % compounded quarterly
No. of payments : 20
Payments made at the BEGINNING

Payment interval number	Periodic payment	Interest for payment interval i = 0.026875	increase in fund	Balance in fund at end of payment interval
0				$0.00
1	$2,805.63	$75.40	$2,881.03	$2,881.03
2	$2,805.63	$152.83	$2,958.46	$5,839.49
3	$2,805.63	$232.34	$3,037.97	$8,877.46
4	$2,805.63	$313.98	$3,119.61	$11,997.07
5	$2,805.63	$397.82	$3,203.45	$15,200.52
6	$2,805.63	$483.92	$3,289.55	$18,490.07
7	$2,805.63	$572.32	$3,377.95	$21,868.02
8	$2,805.63	$663.10	$3,468.73	$25,336.75
9	$2,805.63	$756.33	$3,561.96	$28,898.71
10	$2,805.63	$852.05	$3,657.68	$32,556.39
11	$2,805.63	$950.35	$3,755.98	$36,312.37
12	$2,805.63	$1,051.30	$3,856.93	$40,169.30
13	$2,805.63	$1,154.95	$3,960.58	$44,129.88
14	$2,805.63	$1,261.39	$4,067.02	$48,196.90
15	$2,805.63	$1,370.69	$4,176.32	$52,373.22
16	$2,805.63	$1,482.93	$4,288.56	$56,661.78
17	$2,805.63	$1,598.19	$4,403.82	$61,065.60
18	$2,805.63	$1,716.54	$4,522.17	$65,587.77
19	$2,805.63	$1,838.07	$4,643.70	$70,231.47
20	$2,805.63	$1,962.87	$4,768.50	$74,999.97
TOTAL	$56,112.59	$18,887.37	$74,999.97	

A = Another schedule   S = Stop

(Enter your selection please)

```
LOAD"sinking
Ok
LIST
200 KEY OFF : CLS : LOCATE 3,26 : COLOR 15
210 FOR L = 1 TO 27 : PRINT CHR$(220); : NEXT L
220 PRINT TAB(26)CHR$(219);TAB(52);CHR$(219)
230 PRINT TAB(26)CHR$(219);" SINKING FUND SCHEDULE ";CHR$(219)
240 LOCATE 6,26
250 PRINT CHR$(219);:FOR L = 1 TO 25:PRINT CHR$(220);:NEXT L:PRINT CHR$(219)
260 COLOR 7
270 PRINT : PRINT "What is the SINKING FUND VALUE          "; : INPUT SV
280 PRINT : PRINT "What is the ANNUAL INTEREST RATE IN PERCENT "; : INPUT AI
290 COLOR 15 : PRINT
292 PRINT "Monthly, Quarterly, Semi-annually, Annually"
294 COLOR 7  : PRINT
296 PRINT "Enter the COMPOUNDING PERIOD (M,Q,S or A)  ?";
298 A$ = INKEY$ : IF A$<>"M" AND A$<>"Q" AND A$<>"S" AND A$<> "A" THEN 298
300 IF A$ = "M" THEN CP = 12 : CP$ = "monthly"
302 IF A$ = "Q" THEN CP =  4 : CP$ = "quarterly"
304 IF A$ = "S" THEN CP =  2 : CP$ = "semi-annually"
306 IF A$ = "A" THEN CP =  1 : CP$ = "annually"
308 PRINT A$
310 PRINT : PRINT "For how many YEARS are payments to be made  "; : INPUT NP
315 PRINT : PRINT "Payments made at the (B)eginning or (E)nd   ? ";
320 A$ = INKEY$ : IF A$ <> "B" AND A$ <> "E" THEN 320
325 PRINT A$ : BE$ = A$
340 COLOR 15 : LOCATE 23,22
350 PRINT "**** press any key to continue ****"
360 A$ = INKEY$ : IF A$ = "" THEN 360
390 PU1$ = "##.######"
400 TP = 0 : TI = 0 : TB = 0 : BA = 0 : IP = 0
410 PU$ = "$$#######,.##"
420 IN = AI/(CP*100) : NP = NP * CP
430 GOSUB 2500
450 IF BE$ = "B" THEN R = SV / ( ( ( (1+IN)^NP - 1) /IN) * (1+IN)) : IP = R*IN
460 IF BE$ = "E" THEN R = SV / ( ( (   (1+IN)^NP - 1) /IN)
465 R = INT(R * 100 + .5)/100
466 IF BE$ = "B" THEN IP = INT((R*IN) * 100 + .5) / 100
470 PRINT TAB(3)0;TAB(60); : PRINT USING PU$;0;
480 FOR Q = 1 TO NP
490 IIF = R + IP
500 BA = BA + IIF
510 TP = TP + R : TI = TI + IP : TB = TB + IIF
520 IF ZZ < 10 THEN GOTO 560
530 LOCATE 22,22 : COLOR 15 : PRINT "** hit space bar to continue **"
```

```
540 A$ = INKEY$ : IF A$ <> " " THEN 540
550 GOSUB 2500
560 PRINT TAB(3)Q;TAB(13); : PRINT USING PU$;R;
570 PRINT TAB(28); : PRINT USING PU$;IP;
580 PRINT TAB(43); : PRINT USING PU$;IIF;
585 PRINT TAB(60); : PRINT USING PU$;BA
586 IF BE$ = "B" THEN IP = INT(((BA + R) * IN) * 100 +.5) / 100
587 IF BE$ = "E" THEN IP = INT((BA * IN) * 100 + .5) / 100
590 ZZ = ZZ + 1 : NEXT Q
600 FOR L = 1 TO 79 : PRINT CHR$(196); : NEXT L : PRINT
610 PRINT "TOTAL";TAB(13); : PRINT USING PU$;TP;
611 PRINT TAB(28); : PRINT USING PU$;TI;
612 PRINT TAB(43); : PRINT USING PU$;TB
620 FOR L = 1 TO 79 : PRINT CHR$(196); : NEXT L : PRINT
930 PRINT : PRINT TAB(11)"P = Printout    A = Another schedule    S = Stop"
940 PRINT : PRINT TAB(19)"(Enter your selection please)"
950 A$ = INKEY$ : IF A$<>"P" AND A$<>"A" AND A$<>"S" THEN 950
960 IF A$ = "A" THEN GOTO 200
970 IF A$ = "S" THEN STOP
1000 CLS : LOCATE 6,1
1010 PRINT "make sure the printer is turned on"
1020 PRINT : PRINT "C = Continue    S =Stop"
1030 PRINT : PRINT "(Enter your selection please)"
1040 A$ = INKEY$ : IF A$<>"C" AND A$<>"S" THEN 1040
1050 IF A$ = "S" THEN STOP
1060 LPRINT TAB(26); : FOR L = 1 TO 27 : LPRINT "*"; : NEXT L : LPRINT
1070 LPRINT TAB(26)"*";TAB(52);"*"
1080 LPRINT TAB(26)"*";"  SINKING FUND SCHEDULE  *"
1090 LPRINT TAB(26); : FOR L = 1 TO 27 : LPRINT "*"; : NEXT L : LPRINT
1100 LPRINT"Value of fund    : ";SV
1110 LPRINT"Interest rate    : ";AI;"% compounded ";CP$
1120 LPRINT"No. of payments : ";NP
1130 IF BE$ = "B" THEN LPRINT"Payments made at the BEGINNING"
1135 IF BE$ = "E" THEN LPRINT"Payments made at the END"
1140 FOR L = 1 TO 74 : LPRINT "_"; : NEXT L : LPRINT
1150 LPRINT TAB(30)"Interest for";TAB(60)"Balance in fund"
1160 LPRINT "Payment";TAB(32)"payment";TAB(63)"at end of"
1161 LPRINT "interval      Periodic      interval";TAB(47)"increase";TAB(64)"payment"
1162 LPRINT " number       payment       i = "; : LPRINT USING PU1$;IN;
1163 LPRINT TAB(47)"in fund";TAB(63)"interval"
1170 FOR L = 1 TO 74 : LPRINT "_"; : NEXT L : LPRINT
1180 IP = 0
1190 IF BE$ = "B" THEN IP = INT((R*IN) * 100 + .5) / 100
1200 BA = 0
1210 LPRINT TAB(3)0;TAB(60); : LPRINT USING PU$;0;
```

```
1220 FOR Q = 1 TO NP
1230 IIF = R + IP
1240 BA = BA + IIF
1260 LPRINT TAB(3)Q;TAB(13); : LPRINT USING PU$;R;
1270 LPRINT TAB(28); : LPRINT USING PU$;IP;
1280 LPRINT TAB(43); : LPRINT USING PU$;IIF;
1290 LPRINT TAB(60); : LPRINT USING PU$;BA
1292 IF BE$ = "B" THEN IP = INT(((BA + R) * IN) * 100 +.5) / 100
1293 IF BE$ = "E" THEN IP = INT((BA * IN) * 100 + .5) / 100
1310 NEXT Q
1320 FOR L = 1 TO 74 : LPRINT "_"; : NEXT L : LPRINT
1330 LPRINT " TOTAL";TAB(13); : LPRINT USING PU$;TP;
1331 LPRINT TAB(28); : LPRINT USING PU$;TI;
1332 LPRINT TAB(43); : LPRINT USING PU$;TB
1360 FOR L = 1 TO 74 : LPRINT "_"; : NEXT L : LPRINT
1380 LPRINT : LPRINT : LPRINT
1800 PRINT : PRINT "A = Another schedule     S = Stop"
1810 PRINT : PRINT "(Enter your selection please)"
1820 A$ = INKEY$ : IF A$<>"A" AND A$ <>"S" THEN 1820
1830 IF A$ = "A" THEN GOTO 200
1840 STOP
2500 REM HEADINGS FOR DATA TABLE
2510 COLOR 15 : CLS
2520 PRINT TAB(30)"SINKING FUND SCHEDULE"
2530 COLOR 7
2540 FOR L = 1 TO 79 : PRINT CHR$(196); : NEXT L : PRINT
2550 PRINT TAB(30)"Interest for";TAB(60)"Balance in fund"
2560 PRINT "Payment";TAB(32)"payment";TAB(63)"at end of"
2570 PRINT "interval     Periodic      interval";TAB(47)"increase";TAB(64)"payment"
2580 PRINT " number       payment        i = "; : PRINT USING PU1$;IN;
2590 PRINT TAB(47)"in fund";TAB(63)"interval"
2600 FOR L = 1 TO 79 : PRINT CHR$(196); : NEXT L : PRINT
2605 ZZ = 0
2610 RETURN
Ok
```

G. Program 6—Depreciation Schedules

The program "DEPRECIA" produces depreciation schedules by the Straight-Line Method and the Sum-of-the-Years-Digit Method. The required input consists of the original cost of the asset, the residual value, and the life of the asset in years.

```
RUN
\\\\\\\\\\\\\\\\\\\\\\\\\\\\\\
                      [                        [
                      [ DEPRECIATION SCHEDULE [
[\\\\\\\\\\\\\\\\\\\\\\\\\\\\[

What is the ORIGINAL COST  ? 36000

What is the RESIDUAL VALUE ? 3000

What is the LIFE of the asset in YEARS ? 10
**** press any key to continue ****


        P = Printout    A = Another schedule   S = Stop

              (Enter your selection please)
make sure the printer is turned on

C = Continue     S =Stop

(Enter your selection please)
```

The output is similar to the schedules shown as solutions to Examples 20.1a and 20.1d. A sample output is reproduced below. The program listing follows.

```
        *****************************
        *                           *
        *  DEPRECIATION SCHEDULE  *
        *****************************
Original cost   :  36000
residual value  :  3000
Life of asset   :  10  years


              STRAIGHT-LINE METHOD
------------------------------------------------------------
End of          Annual depreciation   Accumulated      Book
year                expense           depreciation     value
------------------------------------------------------------
  0                                                  $36,000.00
  1                 $3,300.00           $3,300.00    $32,700.00
  2                 $3,300.00           $6,600.00    $29,400.00
```

3	$3,300.00	$9,900.00	$26,100.00
4	$3,300.00	$13,200.00	$22,800.00
5	$3,300.00	$16,500.00	$19,500.00
6	$3,300.00	$19,800.00	$16,200.00
7	$3,300.00	$23,100.00	$12,900.00
8	$3,300.00	$26,400.00	$9,600.00
9	$3,300.00	$29,700.00	$6,300.00
10	$3,300.00	$33,000.00	$3,000.00

| TOTAL | $33,000.00 | | |

SUM-OF-THE-YEARS-DIGITS METHOD

End of year	Parts	Annual depreciation expense	Accumulated depreciation	Book value
0				$36,000.00
1	10	$6,000.00	$6,000.00	$30,000.00
2	9	$5,400.00	$11,400.00	$24,600.00
3	8	$4,800.00	$16,200.00	$19,800.00
4	7	$4,200.00	$20,400.00	$15,600.00
5	6	$3,600.00	$24,000.00	$12,000.00
6	5	$3,000.00	$27,000.00	$9,000.00
7	4	$2,400.00	$29,400.00	$6,600.00
8	3	$1,800.00	$31,200.00	$4,800.00
9	2	$1,200.00	$32,400.00	$3,600.00
10	1	$600.00	$33,000.00	$3,000.00

| TOTAL | $33,000.00 | | |

A = Another schedule   S = Stop
(Enter your selection please)

Break in 1600
Ok
LOAD"deprecia
Ok
LIST
```
200 KEY OFF : CLS : LOCATE 3,26 : COLOR 15
210 FOR L = 1 TO 27 : PRINT CHR$(220); : NEXT L
```

```
220 PRINT TAB(26)CHR$(219);TAB(52);CHR$(219)
230 PRINT TAB(26)CHR$(219);" DEPRECIATION SCHEDULE ";CHR$(219)
240 LOCATE 6,26
250 PRINT CHR$(219);:FOR L = 1 TO 25:PRINT CHR$(220);:NEXT L:PRINT CHR$(219)
260 COLOR 7
270 PRINT : PRINT "What is the ORIGINAL COST  "; : INPUT OC
280 PRINT : PRINT "What is the RESIDUAL VALUE "; : INPUT RV
290 PRINT : PRINT "What is the LIFE of the asset in YEARS "; : INPUT LA
300 COLOR 15 : LOCATE 23,22
310 PRINT "**** press any key to continue ****"
320 A$ = INKEY$ : IF A$ = "" THEN 320
400 GOSUB 2500
410 TDE = 0
420 PU1$ = "##.##"
430 PU$ = "$$########,.##"
440 WV = OC - RV
450 DE = WV / LA
460 BV = OC
470 PRINT TAB(6)0;TAB(65); : PRINT USING PU$;BV;
480 FOR Q = 1 TO LA
490 BV = BV - DE
500 AD = OC - BV
510 TDE = TDE + DE
520 IF ZZ < 10 THEN GOTO 560
530 LOCATE 22,22 : COLOR 15 : PRINT "** hit space bar to continue **"
540 A$ = INKEY$ : IF A$ <> " " THEN 540
550 GOSUB 2500
560 PRINT TAB(6)Q;TAB(25); : PRINT USING PU$;DE;
570 PRINT TAB(45); : PRINT USING PU$;AD;
580 PRINT TAB(65); : PRINT USING PU$;BV
590 ZZ = ZZ + 1 : NEXT Q
600 FOR L = 1 TO 79 : PRINT CHR$(196); : NEXT L : PRINT
610 PRINT "   TOTAL";TAB(25); : PRINT USING PU$;TDE
620 FOR L = 1 TO 79 : PRINT CHR$(196); : NEXT L : PRINT
630 LOCATE 22,22 : COLOR 15 : PRINT "** hit  N  for Next schedule **"
640 A$ = INKEY$ : IF A$<>"N" THEN 640
650 COLOR 7
700 GOSUB 3500
710 TDE = 0
740 SD = (LA*(LA+1)/2)
750 DE = WV / SD
760 BV = OC
770 PRINT TAB(6)0;TAB(65); : PRINT USING PU$;BV;
780 FOR Q = 1 TO LA : PA = LA + 1 - Q
790 BV = BV - DE * PA
```

```
800 AD = OC - BV
810 TDE = TDE + DE * PA
820 IF ZZ < 10 THEN GOTO 860
830 LOCATE 22,22 : COLOR 15 : PRINT "** hit space bar to continue **"
840 A$ = INKEY$ : IF A$ <> " " THEN 840
850 GOSUB 3500
860 PRINT TAB(6)Q;TAB(15)PA;TAB(25); : PRINT USING PU$;DE*PA;
870 PRINT TAB(45); : PRINT USING PU$;AD;
880 PRINT TAB(65); : PRINT USING PU$;BV
890 ZZ = ZZ + 1 : NEXT Q
900 FOR L = 1 TO 79 : PRINT CHR$(196); : NEXT L : PRINT
910 PRINT "    TOTAL";TAB(25); : PRINT USING PU$;TDE
920 FOR L = 1 TO 79 : PRINT CHR$(196); : NEXT L : PRINT
930 PRINT : PRINT TAB(11)"P = Printout    A = Another schedule    S = Stop"
940 PRINT : PRINT TAB(19)"(Enter your selection please)"
950 A$ = INKEY$ : IF A$<>"P" AND A$<>"A" AND A$<>"S" THEN 950
960 IF A$ = "A" THEN GOTO 200
970 IF A$ = "S" THEN STOP
1000 CLS : LOCATE 6,1
1010 PRINT "make sure the printer is turned on"
1020 PRINT : PRINT "C = Continue    S =Stop"
1030 PRINT : PRINT "(Enter your selection please)"
1040 A$ = INKEY$ : IF A$<>"C" AND A$<>"S" THEN 1040
1050 IF A$ = "S" THEN STOP
1060 LPRINT TAB(26); : FOR L = 1 TO 27 : LPRINT "*"; : NEXT L : LPRINT
1070 LPRINT TAB(26)"*";TAB(52);"*"
1080 LPRINT TAB(26)"*";" DEPRECIATION SCHEDULE  *"
1090 LPRINT TAB(26); : FOR L = 1 TO 27 : LPRINT "*"; : NEXT L : LPRINT
1100 LPRINT"Original cost  : ";OC
1110 LPRINT"residual value : ";RV
1120 LPRINT"Life of asset  : ";LA;" years"
1130 LPRINT : LPRINT TAB(27)"STRAIGHT-LINE METHOD"
1140 FOR L = 1 TO 76 : LPRINT "_"; : NEXT L : LPRINT
1150 LPRINT " End of";TAB(20)"Annual depreciation";
1160 LPRINT TAB(44)"Accumulated";TAB(65)"Book"
1161 LPRINT "  year";TAB(25)"expense";
1162 LPRINT TAB(44)"depreciation";TAB(65)"value"
1170 FOR L = 1 TO 73 : LPRINT "_"; : NEXT L : LPRINT
1180 TDE = 0
1190 DE = WV /LA
1200 BV = OC
1210 LPRINT TAB(3)0;TAB(60); : LPRINT USING PU$;BV;
1220 FOR Q = 1 TO LA
1230 BV = BV - DE
1240 AD = OC - BV
```

```
1250 TDE = TDE + DE
1260 LPRINT TAB(3)Q;TAB(22); : LPRINT USING PU$;DE;
1270 LPRINT TAB(42); : LPRINT USING PU$;AD;
1280 LPRINT TAB(60); : LPRINT USING PU$;BV
1310 NEXT Q
1320 FOR L = 1 TO 73 : LPRINT "_"; : NEXT L : LPRINT
1330 LPRINT " TOTAL";TAB(22); : LPRINT USING PU$;TDE
1360 FOR L = 1 TO 73 : LPRINT "_"; : NEXT L : LPRINT
1380 LPRINT : LPRINT : LPRINT
1400 LPRINT : LPRINT TAB(22)"SUM-OF-THE-YEARS-DIGITS METHOD"
1410 FOR L = 1 TO 73 : LPRINT "_"; : NEXT L : LPRINT
1420 LPRINT " End of   Parts";TAB(20)"Annual depreciation";
1430 LPRINT TAB(44)"Accumulated";TAB(65)"Book"
1440 LPRINT "  year";TAB(25)"expense";
1450 LPRINT TAB(44)"depreciation";TAB(65)"value"
1470 FOR L = 1 TO 73 : LPRINT "_"; : NEXT L : LPRINT
1480 TDE = 0
1490 SD = (LA*(LA+1)/2)
1500 DE = WV / SD
1510 BV = OC
1520 LPRINT TAB(3)0;TAB(60); : LPRINT USING PU$;BV;
1530 FOR Q = 1 TO LA : PA = LA + 1 - Q
1540 BV = BV - DE * PA
1550 AD = OC - BV
1560 TDE = TDE + DE * PA
1570 LPRINT TAB(3)Q;TAB(12)PA;TAB(22); : LPRINT USING PU$;DE*PA;
1580 LPRINT TAB(42); : LPRINT USING PU$;AD;
1590 LPRINT TAB(60); : LPRINT USING PU$;BV
1600 NEXT Q
1610 FOR L = 1 TO 73 : LPRINT "_"; : NEXT L : LPRINT
1620 LPRINT " TOTAL";TAB(22); : LPRINT USING PU$;TDE
1630 FOR L = 1 TO 73 : LPRINT "_"; : NEXT L : LPRINT
1800 PRINT : PRINT "A = Another schedule     S = Stop"
1810 PRINT : PRINT "(Enter your selection please)"
1820 A$ = INKEY$ : IF A$<>"A" AND A$ <>"S" THEN 1820
1830 IF A$ = "A" THEN GOTO 200
1840 STOP
2500 REM HEADINGS FOR DATA TABLE
2510 COLOR 15 : CLS
2520 PRINT TAB(30)"STRAIGHT-LINE METHOD"
2530 COLOR 7
2540 FOR L = 1 TO 79 : PRINT CHR$(196); : NEXT L : PRINT
2550 PRINT "    End of";TAB(23)"Annual depreciation";
2560 PRINT TAB(47)"Accumulated";TAB(71)"Book"
2570 PRINT "     year";TAB(28)"expense";
```

```
2580 PRINT TAB(47)"depreciation";TAB(71)"value"
2590 FOR L = 1 TO 79 : PRINT CHR$(196); : NEXT L : PRINT
2600 ZZ = 0
2610 RETURN
3500 REM HEADINGS FOR DATA TABLE
3510 COLOR 15 : CLS
3520 PRINT TAB(25)"SUM-OF-THE-YEARS-DIGITS METHOD"
3530 COLOR 7
3540 FOR L = 1 TO 79 : PRINT CHR$(196); : NEXT L : PRINT
3550 PRINT "    End of    Parts";TAB(23)"Annual depreciation";
3560 PRINT TAB(47)"Accumulated";TAB(71)"Book"
3570 PRINT "      year";TAB(28)"expense";
3580 PRINT TAB(47)"depreciation";TAB(71)"value"
3590 FOR L = 1 TO 79 : PRINT CHR$(196); : NEXT L : PRINT
3600 ZZ = 0
3610 RETURN
Ok
```

Answers to Odd-numbered problems, Review exercises and Self-tests

Chapter 1:
Exercise 1-1

A. **1.** (a) 2012   (b) 19 245   (c) 332.20   (d) 741.32   **B.** **1.** (a) 4161
(b) 20 501   (c) 58.65   (d) 294.06   (e) 46.9775   (f) 149.281   (g) 0.3268
(h) 0.149175   **B.** **3.** (a) (i) $3\frac{1}{6}$ (ii) 3.17   (iii) $3.16\frac{2}{3}$ (b) (i) $10\frac{2}{3}$
(ii) 10.67   (iii) $10.66\frac{2}{3}$ (c) (i) $5\frac{5}{12}$ (ii) 5.42   (iii) $5.41\frac{2}{3}$ (d) (i) $7\frac{1}{15}$
(ii) 7.07   (iii) $7.06\frac{2}{3}$ (e) (i) $\frac{5}{6}$ (ii) 0.83   (iii) $0.83\frac{1}{3}$ (f) (i) $\frac{7}{9}$ (ii) 0.78
(iii) $0.77\frac{7}{9}$ **C.** **1.** (a) 3740   (b) 12300   (c) 115.4   (d) 1000.35   (e) 7500
(f) 3165   (g) 301.56   (h) 5.85   (i) $33\frac{1}{3}$ (j) $116\frac{2}{3}$ (k) 34165.36   (l) 1040.4
(m) 23156.7   (n) 831.56   **3.** (a) 20   (b) 5.67   (c) 4.50   (d) 0.228
(e) 0.035   (f) 0.004   (g) 0.625   (h) 0.050   (i) 0.0075   (j) 0.000225
D. **1.** 5.63   **3.** 18.00   **5.** 57.70   **7.** 13.00

Exercise 1.2

A. **1.** 2   **3.** $\frac{7}{12}$ **5.** $\frac{5}{8}$ **7.** $\frac{2}{5}$ **9.** $\frac{5}{73}$ **11.** $\frac{1}{5}$ **B.** **1.** $\frac{16}{15}$ **3.** $\frac{3}{50}$
5. $\frac{8}{15}$ **7.** $\frac{4}{15}$ **9.** $\frac{5}{4}$ **C.** **1.** $\frac{29}{8}$ **3.** $\frac{47}{24}$ **5.** $\frac{23}{30}$ **7.** $\frac{47}{24}$ **9.** $\frac{79}{84}$

Exercise 1.3

A. **1.** $\frac{27}{8}$ **3.** $\frac{25}{3}$ **5.** $\frac{100}{3}$ **7.** $\frac{70}{9}$ **B.** **1.** $16\frac{1}{2}$ **3.** $3\frac{3}{4}$ **5.** $1\frac{2}{3}$
C. **1.** $7\frac{13}{15}$ **3.** $11\frac{1}{12}$ **5.** $58\frac{17}{56}$

Exercise 1.4

A. **1.** 1.375   **3.** $1.66\frac{2}{3}$ **5.** $1.83\frac{1}{3}$ **7.** $1.08\frac{1}{3}$ **B.** **1.** $\frac{3}{8}$ **3.** $\frac{1}{200}$ **5.** $\frac{2}{3}$
7. $\frac{1}{12}$ **9.** $\frac{4}{3}$ **11.** $\frac{5}{9}$ **C.** **1.** 2   **3.** 72   **5.** 14   **7.** 77   **9.** 147   **11.** 25

Exercise 1.5

A. 1. 14 **3.** 53 **5.** 23 **7.** 24 **9.** $\frac{4}{3}$ **11.** 36 **B. 1.** $1\frac{11}{16}$ **3.** $\frac{5}{39}$
5. 720 **7.** 630.85 **9.** 1911 **11.** 220000 **13.** 4000

Exercise 1.6

A. 1. $409062.50 **3.** $1147.50 **5.** $176.00 **B. 1.** $0.41 **3.** 2.9

878

Solutions

Review Exercise

1. (a) 153.15 **(b)** 78.92 **(c)** 4872.00 **(d)** 0.09375 **(e)** 840.00 **(f)** 360.00
2. (a) $4.66\frac{2}{3}$ **(b)** $0.16\frac{2}{3}$ **(c)** $0.58\frac{1}{3}$ **(d)** $0.44\frac{4}{9}$ **3. (a)** 6.3 **(b)** 10176.25
(c) 0.625 **(d)** 0.0075 **(e)** 1.645 **(f)** 0.0110 **(g)** 4875 **(h)** 87.5 **4. (a)** $\frac{4}{3}$ **(b)** $\frac{3}{7}$
(c) $\frac{1}{2}$ **(d)** $\frac{4}{5}$ **(e)** 0.07 **(f)** 0.06 **(g)** $\frac{3}{5}$ **(h)** $\frac{7}{12}$ **5. (a)** $\frac{59}{24}$ **(b)** $\frac{6}{5}$
6. (a) $52\frac{1}{2}$ **(b)** $2\frac{2}{15}$ **(c)** $16\frac{19}{60}$ **(d)** $40\frac{47}{84}$ **7. (a)** $\frac{7}{8}$ **(b)** $\frac{3}{400}$ **(c)** $\frac{5}{6}$ **(d)** $\frac{1}{15}$
(e) $\frac{5}{3}$ **(f)** $\frac{7}{6}$ **8. (a)** 24 **(b)** 30 **(c)** 44 **(d)** 64 **9. (a)** 29 **(b)** -8
(c) 11 **(d)** 8 **(e)** 2 **(f)** 75 **(g)** $\frac{5}{6}$ **(h)** $\frac{2}{23}$ **(i)** 1000 **(j)** $\frac{3}{20}$ **(k)** 340
(l) 950 **(m)** 625 **(n)** 1250 **10. (a)** $20\frac{5}{24}$ kg **(b)** $24.25 **(c)** $5\frac{5}{96}$ kg
(d) $6.0625 **11.** $35, $150, $147, $252; Total $584 **12. (a)** $11.1875
(b) $9.60 **13.** $13875 **14.** $13680

Self-test

1. (a) 4417.2 **(b)** 94.5 **(c)** 2606.4 **(d)** 4560 **(e)** 4800 **2.** 7080
3. $203 **4.** $7.35 **5.** $299250 **6.** $650

Chapter 2
Exercise 2.1

A. 1. (a) $-3xy$ **(b)** $4a$; $-5c$; $-2d$ **(c)** x^2; $-\frac{1}{2}x$; -2 **(d)** $1.2x$; $-0.5xy$;
$0.9y$; -0.3 **3. (a)** x **(b)** ab **(c)** y **(d)** xy **(e)** x^2y^2 **(f)** abx **(g)** x^3
(h) by

Exercise 2.2

A. 1. 10 **3.** -14 **5.** 9 **7.** -15 **9.** 17 **11.** -15 **13.** -5 **15.** -4
17. 0.4 **19.** 1 **21.** 0 **B. 1.** 1 **3.** 12 **5.** -1 **7.** -10 **9.** 9
11. 1.03 **13.** -2 **C. 1.** 20 **3.** 24 **5.** -7 **7.** -36 **9.** 0 **11.** 144
D. 1. 6 **3.** -5 **5.** -4 **7.** 16 **9.** 0 **11.** undefined **E. 1.** 9 **3.** 4
5 15 **7.** 9 **9.** 4

Exercise 2.3

A. 1. $19a$ **3.** $-a-10$ **5.** $0.8x$ **7.** $1.4x$ **9.** $-x^2-x-8$ **11.** $x-7y$
13. $-2a^2-6ab+5b^2$ **15.** $14-9x+y$ **B. 1.** $-12x$ **3.** $-10ax$ **5.** $-2x^2$

7. $60xy$ **9.** $-2x + 4y$ **11.** $2ax^2 - 3ax - a$ **13.** $35x - 30$ **15.** $-20ax + 5a$
17. $3x^2 + 5x - 2$ **19.** $x^3 + y^3$ **21.** $7x^2 + 3x + 39$ **C. 1.** $4ab$ **3.** $4x$
5. $10\,m - 4$ **7.** $-2x^2 + 3x + 6$ **D. 1.** -5 **3.** $\frac{-59}{2}$ **5.** 378 **7.** 3000
9. 902 **11.** 1400

Exercise 2.4

A. 1. $4(2x - 3)$ **3.** $4n(n - 2)$ **5.** $5a(x - 2y - 4)$ **B. 1.** $m(x + y)$
3. $(a - b)(m + n)$ **5.** $P(1 + i)$ **7.** $r(1 - r - r^2)$

Exercise 2.5

A. 1. 81 **3.** 16 **5.** $\frac{16}{81}$ **7.** 0.25 **9.** 1 **11.** $\frac{1}{9}$ **13.** 125 **15.** $\frac{1}{1.01}$
B. 1. 2^8 **3.** 4^3 **5.** 2^{15} **7.** a^{14} **9.** 3^{11} **11.** 6 **13.** $\frac{3^{11}}{5^{11}}$ **15.** $\frac{(-3)^{11}}{2^{11}}$
17. 1.025^{150} **19.** 1.04^{80} **21.** $(1 + i)^{200}$ **23.** $(1 + i)^{160}$ **25.** $a^5 b^5$ **27.** $m^{24} n^8$
29. 16 **31.** $\frac{b^8}{a^8}$

Review Exercise

1. (a) -3 **(b)** -10 **(c)** 3 **(d)** -9 **(e)** 7 **(f)** -10 **(g)** 3 **(h)** 2
(i) -5 **(j)** -14 **2. (a)** -40 **(b)** 36 **(c)** -6 **(d)** 0 **(e)** -4 **(f)** 3
(g) 0 **(h)** undefined **(i)** 60 **(j)** 0 **3. (a)** 4 **(b)** 6 **(c)** 12 **(d)** 7
4. (a) $-2x - 7y$ **(b)** $1.97x$ **(c)** $6a - 7$ **(d)** $x + 3y$ **(e)** $9a^2 - 4b - 4c$
(f) $-x^2 + 3x + 1$ **5. (a)** $-15a$ **(b)** $28mx$ **(c)** -7 **(d)** $-3ab$ **(e)** $36xy$
(f) $24abc$ **(g)** $-12x + 20y + 4$ **(h)** $x - 2x^2 - x^3$ **(i)** $-6x + 4$
(j) $7a - 4$ **(k)** $26a - 29$ **(l)** $14ax - 2a^2 + 10a$ **(m)** $2m^2 - 7m + 5$
(n) $3a^3 - 8a^2 - 5a + 6$ **(o)** $-14x^2 + 34x + 36$ **(p)** $-26am^2 + 26am + 37a$
6. (a) -47 **(b)** $6\frac{1}{3}$ **(c)** 0.16 **(d)** 200 **(e)** 644.40 **(f)** 2500 **7. (a)** -243
(b) $\frac{16}{81}$ **(c)** 1 **(d)** $\frac{-1}{3}$ **(e)** $\frac{625}{16}$ **(f)** 1 **(g)** -19683 **(h)** 1024 **(i)** 59049
(j) m^{12} **(k)** $\frac{16}{81}$ **(l)** $\frac{25}{16}$ **(m)** 1.03^{150} **(n)** $(1 + i)^{80}$ **(o)** 1.05^{150} **(p)** $16x^4 y^4$
(q) $\frac{81}{a^8 b^4}$ **(r)** $\frac{1}{(1 + i)^n}$ **8. (a)** $9(3x - 2)$ **(b)** $3a(6a - 7)$ **(c)** $P(1 + rt)$
(d) $i(1 + i)$

Self-test

1. (a) 11 **(b)** -40 **(c)** 4 **(d)** 0 **2. (a)** $-2 - 8x$ **(b)** $-2x - 9$
(c) $-14a - 7$ **(d)** $-6x^2 + 6x + 12$ **3. (a)** 8 **(b)** $\frac{4}{9}$ **(c)** 1 **(d)** 2187
(e) $\frac{9}{16}$ **(f)** $-x^{15}$ **4. (a)** -7 **(b)** $18\frac{2}{3}$ **(c)** 0.192 **(d)** 0.40
(e) 1474.00 **(f)** 1450.00

Chapter 3

Exercise 3.1

A. 1. 3 **3.** 80 **5.** 18 **7.** -35 **9.** -4 **11.** -8 **13.** 5 **15.** 20
17. 200 **B. 1.** $x = 4$; L.S. $= 17 = $ R.S. **3.** $x = 0$; L.S. $= -7 = $ R.S.

Exercise 3.2

A. **1.** $x = -10$; L.S. $= 320 =$ R.S. **3.** $x = -3$; L.S. $= -15 =$ R.S.
B. **1.** 20 **3.** -1 **5.** $\frac{1}{2}$ **C.** **1.** -1 **3.** $\frac{5}{6}$

Exercise 3.3

A. **1.** \$28.28 **3.** \$9.20 **5.** \$670.00 **7.** \$23 500.00 **9.** 18 **11.** 20 dimes;
56 nickels; 16 quarters

Review Exercise

1. (a) -7 **(b)** 880 **(c)** -21 **(d)** -18 **(e)** 3 **(f)** -11 **(g)** 250
(h) 40 **(i)** -5 **(j)** 7 **(k)** 39 **(l)** 56 **2. (a)** $x = -7$; L.S. $= -203 =$ R.S.
(b) $x = 5$; L.S. $= -32 =$ R.S. **(c)** $x = -3$; L.S. $= \frac{-23}{14} =$ R.S. **(d)** $x = -\frac{7}{12}$;
L.S. $= \frac{11}{9} =$ R.S. **(e)** $x = 7$; L.S. $= 25 =$ R.S. **(f)** $x = -\frac{1}{3}$; L.S. $= -1 =$ R.S.
(g) $x = -\frac{1}{2}$; L.S. $= -\frac{31}{6} =$ R.S.
3. (a) 138 **(b)** \$63350 **(c)** \$117 **(d)** \$44500
(e) heat \$814; power \$1056; water \$341 **(f)** \$37500
(g) Machine A, 17; Machine B, 25; Machine C, 35
(h) superlight, 27; ordinary, 45 **(i)** 164 **(j)** \$1400; \$1680; \$3200

Self-test

1. (a) -36 **(b)** 9.00 **(c)** 20 **(d)** -3 **(e)** 3 **(f)** 35 **(g)** 25 **(h)** 2
2. (a) \$240 **(b)** 4600 **(c)** 40 **(d)** \$4500

Chapter 4
Exercise 4.1

A. **1. (a)** 3:8 **(b)** 3:2 **(c)** 5:8:13 **(d)** 3:6:13 **3. (a)** 5:16 **(b)** 2:7
(c) 2:7:11 **(d)** 23:14:5 **(e)** 5:4 **(f)** 25:21 **(g)** 9:16:18 **(h)** 28:40:25
(i) 8:15 **(j)** 9:10 **B.** **1.** 8:7 **3.** 2:3:12 **C.** **1.** \$2295; \$510; \$255
3. \$5250; \$2800; \$1400

Exercise 4.2

A. **1.** 4 **3.** 56 **5.** 7.4 **7.** 2.4 **9.** $\frac{7}{10}$ **11.** 1 **B.** **1.** 21 months
3. 600 km **5. (a)** \$3600 **(b)** \$9000 **7.** \$100 800

Exercise 4.3

A. **1.** 0.64 **3.** 0.025 **5.** 0.005 **7.** 2.5 **9.** 4.5 **11.** 0.009

13. 0.0625   **15.** 0.99   **17.** 0.0005   **19.** 0.005   **21.** 0.09375   **23.** 1.625

25. 0.0025   **27.** 0.0175   **29.** 1.375   **31.** 0.00875   **33.** $0.33\frac{1}{3}$ **35.** $0.16\frac{2}{3}$

37. $1.83\frac{1}{3}$ **39.** $1.33\frac{1}{3}$ **B.** **1.** $\frac{1}{4}$ **3.** $\frac{7}{4}$ **5.** $\frac{3}{8}$ **7.** $\frac{1}{25}$ **9.** $\frac{2}{25}$ **11.** $\frac{2}{5}$

13. $\frac{5}{2}$ **15.** $\frac{1}{8}$ **17.** $\frac{9}{400}$ **19.** $\frac{1}{800}$ **21.** $\frac{3}{400}$ **23.** $\frac{1}{16}$ **25.** $\frac{1}{6}$ **27.** $\frac{3}{400}$

29. $\frac{1}{1000}$ **31.** $\frac{5}{6}$ **33.** $\frac{4}{3}$ **35.** $\frac{5}{3}$ **C.** **1.** 350%   **3.** 0.5%   **5.** 2.5%

7. 12.5%   **9.** 22.5%   **11.** 145%   **13.** 0.25%   **15.** 9%   **17.** 75%

19. $166\frac{2}{3}\%$ **21.** 4.5%   **23.** 0.75%   **25.** 1.125%   **27.** 37.5%   **29.** $133\frac{1}{3}\%$

31. 65%

Exercise 4.4

A. **1.** 36   **3.** 300   **5.** 18   **7.** 6   **9.** 0.50   **11.** 2   **13.** 7.50   **15.** 17.50
B. **1.** $16   **3.** $1950   **5.** $9   **7.** $200   **9.** $600   **11.** $49   **13.** $135
15. $60   **C.** **1.** $15.60   **3.** $1.62   **5.** $48.40   **7.** $22.42   **D.** **1.** 20
3. 440   **5.** 36   **7.** 30   **E.** **1.** 60%   **3.** 115%   **5.** 5%   **7.** 600%
9. $166\frac{2}{3}$ **F.** **1.** $200   **3.** $3.60   **5.** $3.06   **7.** $200   **9.** $1.10   **11.** $240
13. 500%   **15.** $300   **G.** **1.** $28   **3.** $1500   **5.** $45000   **7.** 45000

Exercise 4.5

A. **1.** 168   **3.** $1140   **5.** $88   **B.** **1.** 50%   **3.** 200%   **5.** 2%
C. **1.** 32   **3.** $130   **5.** $4.40

Exercise 4.6

A. **1.** 27   **3.** 12.5%   **5.** $4320   **7.** (a) $180\,000   (b) $225\,000
B. **1.** $14.52   **3.** 33.6¢   **5.** $79.18   **7.** $5000   **9.** 7.5%   **11.** 325%
13. $96.69   **15.** $680   **17.** $44800   **19.** $7660

Review Exercise

1. (a) 5:6   (b) 6:1   (c) 9:40   (d) 6:1   (e) 240:20:1   (f) 15:4:3
2. (a) 3   (b) 18   (c) 1.61   (d) 2.70   (e) $\frac{9}{5}$ (f) 2   **3.** (a) 1.85
(b) 0.075   (c) 0.004   (d) 0.00025   (e) 0.0125   (f) 0.0075   (g) 1.625
(h) 0.1175   (i) $0.08\frac{1}{3}$ (j) $0.83\frac{1}{3}$ (k) $2.66\frac{2}{3}$ (l) 0.10375   **4.** (a) $\frac{1}{2}$ (b) $\frac{3}{8}$
(c) $\frac{1}{6}$ (d) $\frac{5}{3}$ (e) $\frac{1}{200}$ (f) $\frac{3}{40}$ (g) $\frac{3}{400}$ (h) $\frac{1}{160}$
5. (a) 225%   (b) 2%   (c) 0.9%   (d) 12.75%   (e) 125%   (f) 137.5%
(g) 2.5%   (h) 28%   **6.** (a) 210   (b) 7.20   (c) 195   (d) 3.60
7. (a) $112   (b) $930   (c) $1155   (d) $1320   **8.** (a) $6.66   (b) $8.30
(c) $90.00   (d) $27.72   **9.** (a) 62.5%   (b) 175%   (c) $0.48   (d) $22.50
(e) $280   (f) $440   (g) 2%   (h) 500%   (i) $132   (j) $405   **10.** (a) $18
(b) $1955   (c) $16\frac{2}{3}\%$ (d) 550%   (e) $56   (f) $340   (g) $140   **11.** $1200;
$1800; $1500   **12.** $2400; $4200; $4800   **13.** $63000; $47250; $70875; $7875

14. $75000; $50000; $60000   **15.** 16 minutes   **16.** $182000   **17. (a)** $14700
(b) $36750   **18.** 540   **19. (a)** 59250   **(b)** 19750   **20.** $56250; $84375; $9375
21. (a) $42600   **(b)** $8520   **22. (a)** $400000   **(b)** $280000   **23. (a)** 50.00%;
22.22%; 27.78%   **(b)** 125%   **24. (a)** 7.5%   **(b)** $16\frac{2}{3}$%   **25. (a)** 8%   **(b)** 92%
26. (a) $166\frac{2}{3}$%   **(b)** $266\frac{2}{3}$%   **27.** $350000   **28.** $165   **29.** $84000   **30.** $15000
31. (a) $300000   **(b)** $23400   **(c)** $17550   **(d)** 37.5%
32. (a) $80000   **(b)** $250000   **(c)** 312.5%

Self-test

1. (a) $350.00   **(b)** $76.05   **(c)** $145.00   **(d)** $13.20   **2. (a)** 20   **(b)** 3
3. (a) 1.75   **(b)** 0.00375   **4. (a)** $\frac{1}{40}$ **(b)** $\frac{7}{6}$ **5. (a)** 112.5%   **(b)** 2.25%
6. 45%   **7.** $4800   **8.** $10 000   **9.** $72   **10.** $16875; $11250; $6750; $5625
11. 14%   **12.** $15.00   **13.** 5%   **14.** 180   **15.** $72000

Chapter 5

Exercise 5.1

A.   1. A($-4, -3$) B(0, -4) C(3, -4) D(2, 0) E(4, 3) F(0, 3) G(-4, 4) H(-5, 0)

3. (a)

x	-5	-4	-3	-2	-1	0	1	2	3
y	-3	-2	-1	0	1	2	3	4	5

(b)

x	3	2	1	0	-1	-2
y	5	3	1	-1	-3	-5

(c)

x	3	2	1	0	-1	-2	-3
y	6	4	2	0	-2	-4	-6

(d)

x	-5	-4	-3	-2	-1	0	1	2	3	4	5
y	5	4	3	2	1	0	-1	-2	-3	-4	-5

B 1.

x	0	3	2
y	-3	0	-1

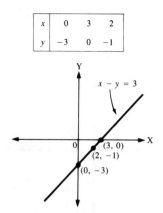

3.

x	0	-2	2
y	0	2	-2

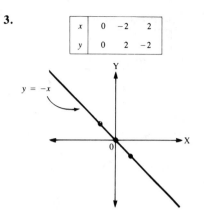

5.

x	0	4	-4
y	-3	0	-6

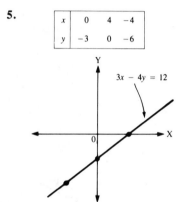

7.

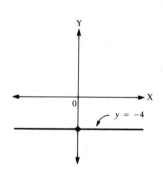

Exercise 5.2

A 1.

For $x + y = 4$

x	0	4	2
y	4	0	2

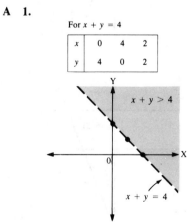

3.

For $x - 2y = 4$

x	0	4	-4
y	-2	0	-4

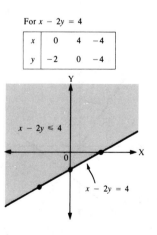

5. Graph $2x = -3y$

x	0	-3	3
y	0	2	-2

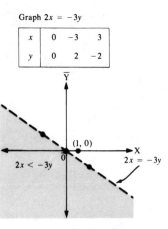

$2x < -3y$

(1, 0)

$2x = -3y$

7.

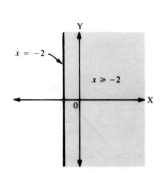

$x = -2$

$x \geq -2$

Exercise 5.3

A. 1.

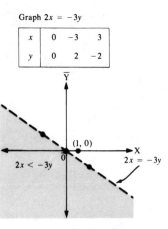

$x + y = 4$
$x - y = -4$

(0, 4)

$x - y = -4$ $x + y = 4$

3.

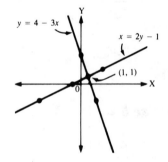

$y = 4 - 3x$

$x = 2y - 1$

(1, 1)

5.

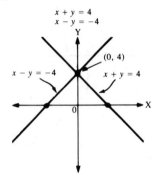

$2y = -3x$

(2, −3)

$3x - 4y = 18$

7.

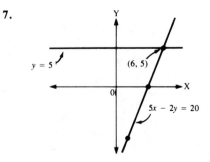

$y = 5$

(6, 5)

$5x - 2y = 20$

B. 1.

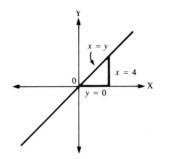

3.

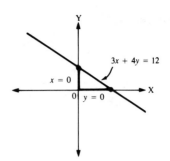

C. 1.

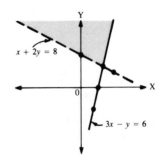

3.

5.

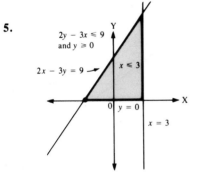

7.

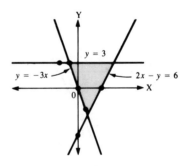

Exercise 5.4

A. **1.** $x = -8, y = -1$ **3.** $x = 10, y = 12$ **5.** $x = -3, y = 3$
B. **1.** $x = -4, y = 3$ **3.** $x = -1, y = 3$ **5.** $x = 4, y = 3$ **C.** **1.** $x = 12$,
$y = 8$ **3.** $x = 1.5, y = 2.5$ **5.** $x = 6, y = 10$ **7.** $x = \frac{1}{2}, y = \frac{3}{4}$

Exercise 5.5

A. **1.** $x = -5$, $y = 4$, $z = 3$ **3.** $a = 10$, $b = 12$, $c = 15$ **5.** $m = 0.8$, $n = 0.6$, $k = 1.2$

Exercise 5.6

A. **1.**   **3.**

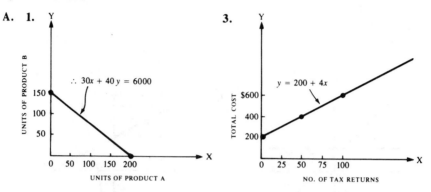

B. **1.** 15; 9   **3.** Brand X, 90; No-name, 50   **5.** Ken, $31500; Fred, $23500
7. Type A, 42; Type B, 18   **9.** 20 dimes; 56 nickels; 16 quarters

Review exercise

1. **(a)**   **(b)**

(c)   **(d)**

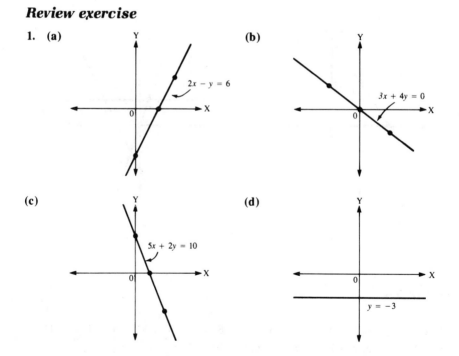

(e)

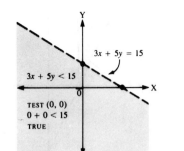

$3x + 5y = 15$

$3x + 5y < 15$

TEST $(0, 0)$
$0 + 0 < 15$
TRUE

(f)

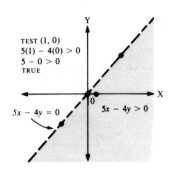

TEST $(1, 0)$
$5(1) - 4(0) > 0$
$5 - 0 > 0$
TRUE

$5x - 4y = 0$

$5x - 4y > 0$

(g)

$x = -2$

$x > -2$

(h)

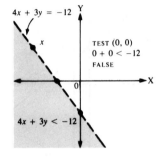

$4x + 3y = -12$

x

TEST $(0, 0)$
$0 + 0 < -12$
FALSE

$4x + 3y < -12$

2. **(a)**

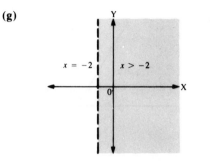

$3x + y = 6$

$x - y = 2$

$(2, 0)$

(b)

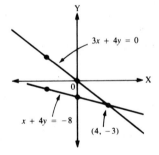

$3x + 4y = 0$

$x + 4y = -8$

$(4, -3)$

(c)

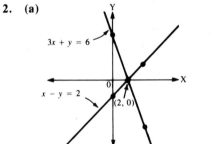

$5x = 3y$

$(-3, -5)$

$y = -5$

(d)

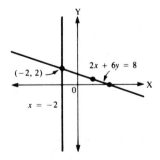

$(-2, 2)$

$2x + 6y = 8$

$x = -2$

3. **(a)**

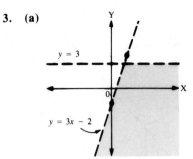

(b)

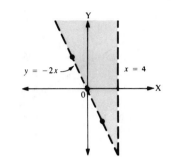

(c)

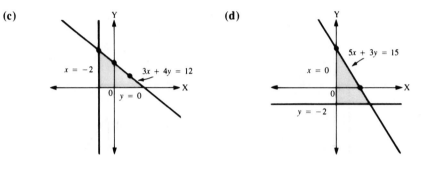

(d)

4. **(a)** $x = -1, y = 1$ **(b)** $x = 5, y = -1$ **(c)** $x = -1, y = 10$
(d) $x = -3, y = 4$ **(e)** $x = 2, y = -3$ **(f)** $x = -4, y = 1$ **(g)** $a = 4,$
$b = -2, c = 2$ **(h)** $a = 10, b = 6, c = -20$ **(i)** $a = 1, b = 2, c = -3$
(j) $a = -2, b = 1, c = 3$ **(k)** $m = 6, n = 8, k = 10$ **(l)** $m = \frac{2}{3}, n = \frac{2}{5},$
$k = \frac{3}{5}$

5. **(a)**

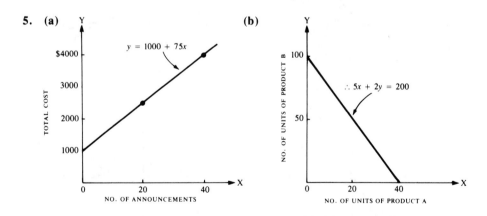

(b)

6. **(a)** first number 8; second number 9   **(b)** 275 at \$2.50; 175 at \$3.50
(c) \$105   **(d)** white \$36; red \$66   **(e)** 17, 25, 35   **(f)** heat \$814; power \$1056;
water \$341   **(g)** direct selling \$37500; TV advertising \$37750; newspaper advertising
\$12250   **(h)** 164 quarters; 16 50¢ coins; 25 \$1 bills

Self-test

1. (a)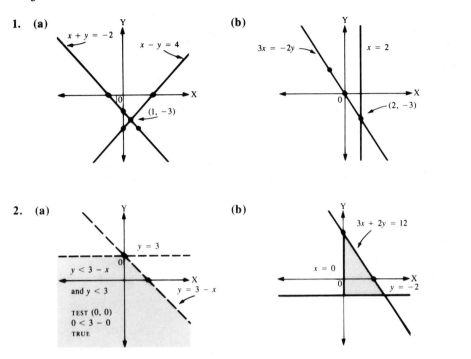

   (b)

2. (a)

   (b)

3. (a) $x = 4, y = -3$ (b) $x = 0, y = 3$ (c) $a = 3, b = 2, c = -2$
(d) $a = 2, b = -2, c = 5$ 4. \$8000; \$4000   5. \$7500   6. \$1400; \$1680;
\$3200

Chapter 6

Exercise 6.1

A. 1. 72   3. 3   5. 1.0758857   7. 1.0132999   B. 1. 55   3. 12.25
5. 1.0711221   7. 0.6299605   9. 163.05343

Exercise 6.2

A. 1. 32   3. 12   5. 7.75   B. 1. 9; 15; 21; 27; 33   3. $1\frac{1}{4}$; $1\frac{1}{2}$; $1\frac{3}{4}$; 2; $2\frac{1}{4}$; $2\frac{1}{2}$;
$2\frac{3}{4}$ C. 1. 120   3. -18 5. n^2 D. 1. 13   3. -1 5. $-3\frac{3}{4}$ 7. 4
9. 306   11. 0

Exercise 6.3

A. **1.** 3072   **3.** $\frac{3}{16}$ **B.** **1.** 12 or -12 **C.** **1.** 4095   **3.** 170.625
5. 21.578563   **D.** **1.** -5 **3.** 5   **5.** -54 **7.** 4   **9.** -81

Exercise 6.4

A. **1.** $9 = \log_2 512$ **3.** $-3 = \log_5 \frac{1}{125}$ **5.** $\ln 18 = 2j$ **B.** **1.** $2^5 = 32$
3. $10^1 = 10$ **C.** **1.** 0.6931472   **3.** -2.2537949 **5.** 10.66

Review Exercise

1. **(a)** 0.96   **(b)** 1.0121264   **(c)** 1.07   **(d)** 0.9684416   **(e)** 1.0986123
(f) -2.9957323 **(g)** 11.849186   **(h)** 98.291653   **2.** **(a)** -45 **(b)** $\frac{6}{5}$
(c) 3, -2, -7 **(d)** 99   **(e)** 528   **(f)** 1320   **3.** **(a)** 1458   **(b)** $\frac{3}{64}$
(c) 8;4   **(d)** -171 **(e)** 26.97346   **(f)** 14.877473   **(g)** 5   **(h)** 2;4

Self-test

1. **(a)** 1.0253241   **(b)** 23.114772   **(c)** 0.024926   **(d)** -2.995723
2. **(a)** $n = 6$ **(b)** $n = 5$ **3.** 160   **4.** 250; -9 **5.** $\frac{-8}{81}$ **6.** $-20\frac{21}{25}$
7. 12   **8.** $+3$, -3

Chapter 7

Exercise 7.1

A. **1.** **(a)** **(i)** Revenue $= 120x$ **(ii)** Cost $= 2800 + 50x$

(b)

(c) **(i)** 40   **(ii)** 40%   **(iii)** $4800

3. **(a)** **(i)** Revenue $= x$ **(ii)** Cost $= 220000 + 0.45x$

(b)

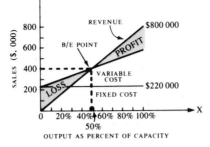

OUTPUT AS PERCENT OF CAPACITY

(c) (i) not applicable   **(ii)** 50%   **(iii)** $400000   **B. 1. (a)** $2100   **(b)** −$700
(c) $3150   **(d)** 72%   **(e)** 55   **(f)** $4200   **(g)** 45   **(h)** 40%   **(i)** $5600
3. (a) (i) 44   **(ii)** 66   **(b) (i)** $9000   **(ii)** $10500

Exercise 7.2

A. 1. (a) Objective function: $P = 7x_1 + 5x_2$
Operational constraints:
1. $8x_1 + 5x_2 \le 4200$
2. $2x_1 + 5x_2 \le 2000$
3. $4x_1 + 6x_2 \le 2800$
Non-negative constraints: $x_1 \ge 0, x_2 \ge 0$

(b)

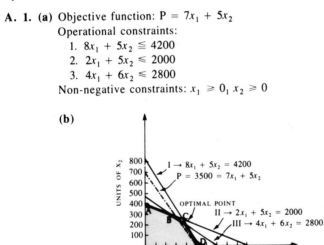

(c) Co-ordinates of the optimal point are C(400, 200)
The optimal profit $= 7(400) + 5(200) = \$3800$
Resource utilization for optimal production:
Machine I: $8x_1 + 5x_2 = 8(400) + 5(200) = 4200$
Machine II: $2x_1 + 5x_2 = 2(400) + 5(200) = 1800$
Machine III: $4x_1 + 6x_2 = 4(400) + 6(200) = 2800$
Machines I and III are used to capacity; 200 hours are unused on Machine II, that is
Machine II is used to 90% of capacity.

Review Exercise

1. (a)

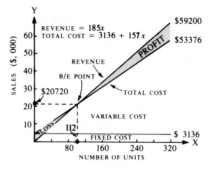

(b) (i) 112 **(ii)** 35% **(iii)** $20720   **(c) (i)** −$896 **(ii)** $644
(d) (i) 60% **(ii)** 110%   **(e) (i)** 30% **(ii)** 38.75% **(iii)** 70%

2. (a) Revenue $= x$; cost $= 4800 + 0.70x$

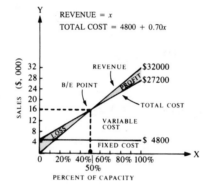

(b) (i) $16 000   **(ii)** 50%   **(c) (i)** $2400   **(ii)** −$1920   **(d)** 84%
(e) (i) 43.75% or $14000   **(ii)** 39.375% or $12600

3. (a)

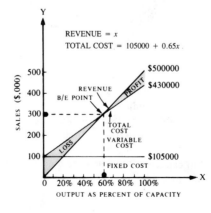

(b) (i) 60%   **(ii)** $300 000   **(c)** −$35 000   **(d)** 95%   **(e)** $335 000
4. (a) (i) 96   **(ii)** 64%   **(iii)** $61440   **(b) (i)** $7280   **(ii)** −$6720
(c) 74%   **(d)** $73600   **(e)** 62%

5.(a) OBECTIVE FUNCTION: $P = 4x_1 + 6x_2$
OPERATIONAL CONSTRAINTS:

① $4x_1 + 10x_2 \leqslant 4800$
② $4x_1 \qquad\ \leqslant 2400$
③ $\qquad 6x_2 \leqslant 2400$
④ $\quad x_1 + x_2 \leqslant\ 750$

NON-NEGATIVE CONSTRAINTS: $x_1 \geqslant 0; x_2 \geqslant 0$

(b)

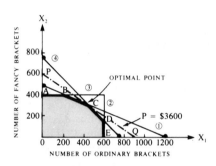

(c) The optimal mix is 450 ordinary brackets and 300 fancy brackets for a maximum profit of $4(450) + 6(300) =$ **$3600**
Utilization of facilities:

① Dept. A; $4(450) + 10(300) = 1800 + 3000 = 4800$
   unused time $= 0$; utilization 100%
② Dept. B: $4(450) = 1800$
   unused time $= 600$; utilization 75%
③ Dept. C: $6(300) = 1800$
   unused time $= 600$; utilization 75%
④ Material: $450 + 300 = 750$
   unused $= 0$; utilization 100%

6. Objective function: $P = 30x_1 + 20x_2$
   Operational constraints:
   1. $20x_1 + 30x_2 \leqslant 12000$
   2. $20x_1 + 10x_2 \leqslant\ \ 8000$
   3. $100x_1 + 100x_2 \leqslant 45000$
   4. $\qquad\qquad x_2 \leqslant\ \ 350$
   Non-negative constraints: $x_1 \geqslant 0_1; x_2 \geqslant 0$

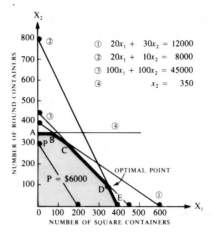

$$
\begin{array}{ll}
① & 20x_1 + 30x_2 = 12000 \\
② & 20x_1 + 10x_2 = 8000 \\
③ & 100x_1 + 100x_2 = 45000 \\
④ & x_2 = 350
\end{array}
$$

NUMBER OF ROUND CONTAINERS

P = $6000

OPTIMAL POINT

NUMBER OF SQUARE CONTAINERS

OPTIMAL PRODUCTION is 350 square containers and 100 round containers;
Contribution to profit = 30(350) + 20(100)
$$
\begin{aligned}
&= 10500 + 2000 \\
&= \$12500
\end{aligned}
$$
Resource utilization:
① Money: 20(350) + 30(100) = 7000 + 3000 = \$10000
            unused amount = \$2000
            utilization is $83\frac{1}{3}\%$
② Space: 20(350) + 10(100) = 8000 square unit
            unused space = 0; 100% utilization
③ Weight: 100(350) + 100(100) = 45000 kg
            unused = 0; 100% utilization
④ Demand: unused 250; utilization 28.6%

Self-test

1. (a)

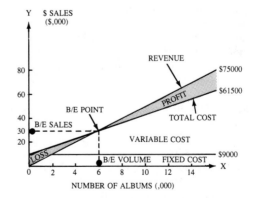

REVENUE

\$75000

\$61500

B/E POINT

PROFIT

B/E SALES

TOTAL COST

VARIABLE COST

LOSS

B/E VOLUME   FIXED COST   \$9000

NUMBER OF ALBUMS (,000)

(b) **(i)** 6000 **(ii)** 30000 **(iii)** 40% **(c)** $3375 **(d)** $53000 **(e)** 5600
(f) 5500 **2. (a) (i)** $500000 **(ii)** 62.5% **(b)** $-$55000 **(c)** $650000
(d) $525000
3. (a) OBJECTIVE FUNCTION: $P = 30x_1 + 40x_2$
OPERATIONAL CONSTRAINTS:
① $3x_1 + x_2 \leqslant 24$
② $x_1 + 3x_2 \leqslant 30$
③ $x_1 + x_2 \leqslant 12$

NON-NEGATIVE CONSTRAINTS: $x_1 \geqslant 0; x_2 \geqslant 0$

(b)

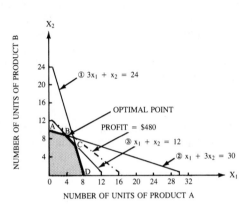

(c) The optimal mix is 3 units of Product A and 9 units of Product B for a maximum profit of $3(30) + 9(40) = \$450$
Utilization of facilities:
① Material: $3(3) + 9(1) = 18$
        unused $= 6$; utilization 75%
② Fabricating: $3(1) + 9(3) = 30$
        unused $= 0$; utilization 100%
③ Finishing: $3(1) + 9(1) = 12$
        unused $= 0$; utilization 100%.

Chapter 8
Exercise 8.1

A. 1. (a) $691.08 **(b)** $8.86 **(c)** $837.27 **3. (a)** $7.26 **(b)** $1185.50
5. (a) $16.47 **(b)** $875.94 **7.** $1568.06 **9. (a)** $225.00 **(b)** $332.25
11. 9.25% **13.** $19680 **15.** $425.21 **17.** $5.95

Exercise 8.2

A. 1. (a) $3.79 **(b)** $5.98 **(c)** $12.85 **(d)** $231.93 **3. (a)** $4.33
(b) $6.70 **(c)** $30.20 **(d)** $226.67 **5. (a)** $6.26 **(b)** $9.21 **(c)** $53.20

(d) $307.33   **B. 1.** $260.58   **3.** $398.61   **5. (a)** $6.59   **(b)** $13.51
(c) $110.24

Exercise 8.3

A. 1. Total gross commission $1226.65   **B. 1.** Total gross earnings $2204.76; total net pay $1599.37; total uninsured wages $30.20.

Review Exercise

1. (a) $9.24   **(b)** $918.61   **2. (a)** $1456.00   **(b)** $9.60   **(c)** 16.5 hours
3. (a) $845.52   **(b)** $10.84   **(c)** $1048.77   **4. (a)** $367.50   **(b)** $8.55
(c) $283.99   **5. (a)** $387.45   **(b)** $26.65   **(c)** $255.64   **(d)** $89.62
6. $1924.25   **7. (a)** $398.65   **(b)** $11.39   **(c)** $309.80   **8.** 4.25%
9. $21 750   **10.** $8.44   **11. (a)** $8.40   **(b)** 13   **12.** $5945.00
13. (a) $453.60   **(b)** $308.56   **(c)** $36.00   **(d)** $7.35   **(e)** $14.92
14. $10.56   **15.** 41.5 hours   **16. (a)** $43.52   **(b)** $33.45   **(c)** $492.32

Self-Test

1. 15.5%   **2.** $2382.41   **3.** $788.50   **4.** $8.90   **5.** $687.00   **6.** $9.00
7. $298.07   **8.** Total gross earnings $2125.80; total net pay $1600.78; total uninsured wages $35.20.

Chapter 9

Exercise 9.1

A. 1. $13.53   **3.** $134.96   **5.** $33\frac{1}{3}$%   **7.** $30.24; 32.5%   **9.** $137.89; 48.55%
11. $1583.33; 61%   **B. 1. (a)** $127.68   **(b)** $112.32   **(c)** 46.8%   **3.** 15.9%
5. (a) 38.75%   **(b)** $48.26\frac{2}{3}$%   **7.** $74.10   **9.** 15%   **11.** $426.00   **13.** $180.00

Exercise 9.2

A. 1. $640.00   **3.** $776.11   **5.** $1136.80   **7.** $4581.50
B. 1. $582.00; $850.00   **3.** $564.50; $536.28   **5.** $810.00; $810.00
C. 1. (a) Sept. 10   **(b)** $5276.85   **(c)** $103.20   **3.** $2507.19   **5.** $2184.00
7. (a) $1164.00   **(b)** $733.54   **(c)** $600.00   **9. (a)** $1925.00   **(b)** $3400.00

Exercise 9.3

A. 1. (a) $6.00   **(b)** $3.84   **(c)** $2.16   **(d)** 25%   **(e)** 20%   **3. (a)** $35.00
(b) $31.50   **(c)** $3.50   **(d)** $66\frac{2}{3}$%   **(e)** 40%   **5. (a)** $10.50   **(b)** $12.75
(c) −$2.25   **(d)** $38\frac{8}{9}$%   **(e)** 28%   **B. 1.** $6.25; 25%; 20%
3. $102.40; 60%; 37.5%   **5.** $75.95; $21.70; 28.6%   **7.** $44.24; $22.12; $33\frac{1}{3}$%
9. $78.10; $46.86; 150%   **11.** $111.30; $133.56; 20%   **C. 1.** $5.12
3. (a) $75.00   **(b)** $63.00   **(c)** $8160   **(d)** 147.14%   **5. (a)** 120%
(b) 54.55%   **7. (a)** $22.80   **(b)** $26.22   **(c)** 13.04%   **9. (a)** $53.25
(b) 28.57%   **11. (a)** $32.00   **(b)** 150%

Exercise 9.4

A. 1. $68.00; $85.00; $62.90   **3.** 200%; $120.00; 37.5%   **5.** $45.50; 24.36%; $96.25   **B. 1.** $51.00; $59.00; − $8.00   **3.** $96.40; $30.65; $7.91
5. $160.00; 12%; $124.20   **C. 1. (a)** $228.69   **(b)** 54%   **3.** $70.00
5. (a) 40%   **(b)** − $8.00   **(c)** 10.294%   **(d)** $9\frac{1}{3}\%$ **7.** − $6.50
9. (a) $19.00   **(b)** $4.00   **(c)** 21.05%   **11.** − $97.50   **13.** − $82.50

Review exercise

1. (a) $31.92   **(b)** $24.08   **(c)** 43%   **2.** 37.5%   **3.** 45.66%   **4.** $2.16
5. 15%   **6.** $465.00   **7.** $30.00   **8. (a)** June 10   **(b)** $2584.00
9. $2520.67   **10. (a)** $1940.00   **(b)** $2813.00   **11. (a)** $2000.00
(d) $9310.00   **12. (a)** $1645.00   **(c)** $1500.00   **13. (a)** $7.92   **(b)** $3.12
(c) 39.4%   **(d)** 65%   **(e)** $6.96   **(f)** − $0.96   **14. (a)** $90.00   **(b)** $58.50
(c) 53.85%   **(d)** $74.88   **(e)** − $6.48   **15. (a)** $6.60   **(b)** 25.9%
16. (a) $77.50   **(b)** 42.86%   **17. (a)** $1217.70   **(b)** 32%   **18.** $240.00
19. (a) 25%   **(b)** $3.06   **(c)** 25%   **20. (a)** − $0.60   **(b)** 21.25%
21. (a) $253.00   **(b)** $189.75   **(c)** 25%   **22. (a)** − $13.20   **(b)** 25%
23. 12.5%   **24. (a)** $189.00   **(b)** 21.25%   **(c)** $133\frac{1}{3}\%$ **25. (a)** $154.00
(b) 27.27%   **(c)** $138.95   **(d)** 21%

Self-Test

1. $295.77   **2.** 37.5%   **3.** 50.5%   **4.** 6.5%   **5.** $1630.10   **6.** $1940.00
7. $1450.00   **8.** $1587.50   **9.** $240.00   **10.** $1010.00   **11.** $348.36
12. $1360.00   **13.** 180%   **14.** $110.00   **15.** 23.4%   **16.** $1130.00
17. − $660.45   **18.** − $94.77

Chapter 10
Exercise 10.1

A. 1. 0.125; 1.25   **3.** 0.1025; $\frac{165}{365}$

Exercise 10.2

A. 1. 112 days   **3.** 166 days   **B. 1.** 244 days   **3.** 341 days

Exercise 10.3

A. 1. $945.00   **3.** $215.80   **5.** $75.34   **B. 1.** $10.87   **3.** $31.71

Exercise 10.4

A. 1. $1224.00   **3.** $10.75%   **5.** 14 months   **7.** 144 days
B. 1. $1648.00   **3.** 9.5%   **5.** 11 months   **7.** $876.00

Exercise 10.5

A. **1.** $516.16 **3.** $892.26

Exercise 10.6

A. **1.** $266.00; $39.90 **3.** $345.00; $374.67 **5.** $2025.00; 292 days
B. **1.** $1222.00 **3.** $1704.60

Exercise 10.7

A. **1.** $829.33 **3.** $632.50 **5.** $1108.24 **7.** $885.05 **9.** $622.41
B. **1.** $1156.80 **3.** $538.66 **5.** $1438.68

Review Exercise

1. (a) 172 days (b) 186 days **2.** (a) $168.69 (b) $67.15
3. (a) $1160.00 (b) $601.77 **4.** (a) 7.5% (b) 265 days (c) 11%
(d) 8 months **5.** (a) $640.00 (b) $5709.97 **6.** $1225.03 **7.** $1175.06
8. 13.75% **9.** 16.25% **10.** 7 months **11.** 244 days **12.** $4642.75
13. $1661.77 **14.** $1320.00 **15.** $3200.00 **16.** $3467.89 **17.** $1690.52
18. $3127.53 **19.** $2682.09 **20.** $1044.38 **21.** $3474.83 **22.** $2351.17
23. $1559.86 **24.** $3544.91 **25.** $1002.50 **26.** $1056.12

Self-test

1. $64.20 **2.** 7 months **3.** 12.5% **4.** $9797.92 **5.** $5901.04
6. $1552.49 **7.** $4484.94 **8.** 14% **9.** 359 days **10.** $1372.91
11. $7293.39 **12.** $154.42 **13.** $1163.85 **14.** $2942.86 **15.** $1959.52
16. $1335.77

Chapter 11
Exercise 11.1

A. **1.** October 30, 1988 **3.** $530.00 **5.** 154 days **7.** $560.19
B. **1.** (a) March 3, 1988 (b) 155 days (c) $42.81 (d) $882.81
3. (a) April 3, 1988 (b) 63 days (c) $22.65 (d) $1272.65

Exercise 11.2

A. **1.** $644.61 **B.** $871.56

Exercise 11.3

A. **1.** $455.00 **B.** **1.** $1166.60 **3.** $1622.66

Exercise 11.4

A. **1.** $978.68; $21.32 **3.** $857.48; $12.43

Exercise 11.5

A. **1.** $922.80; $27.20   **3.** $2502.98; $44.49   **B.** **1.** $1657.21; $57.21

Exercise 11.6

A. **1.** 9.41935%; 9.125%   **B.** **1.** 13.21%   **3.** 13.30%   **5.** (a)13.67%
(b) 13.37%   **(c)** 13.08%   **(d)** 12.67%

Review Exercise

1. (a) November 2   **(b)** $79.45   **(c)** $1679.45   **2.** $1316.34   **3.** $735.60
4. $3029.62   **5.** $5251.51   **6.** $940.00   **7.** $824.64   **8.** (a) $29.84;
$1899.36   **(b)** $30.31; $1898.89   **9.** (a) $641.89   **(b)** 640.81
10. $3500.00   **11.** $1218.62   **12.** $712.18; $19.23   **13.** $2424.09
14. $1713.51   **15.** (a) 17.00%   **(b)** 15.92%   **16.** 17.45%   **17.** (a) 15.39%
(b) 14.83%   **18.** (a) 15.44%   **(b)** 16.26%   **19.** 12.91%   **20.** 13.43%

Self-test

1. $53.38   **2.** $1208.19   **3.** $1160.00   **4.** $2240.56   **5.** $1747.34
6. $1717.06   **7.** $17.398%   **8.** 13.38%   **9.** 13.50%   **10.** $3120.75

Chapter 12
Exercise 12.1

A. **1.** (a) $160.00   **(b)** $640.00   **(c)** $96.00   **(d)** $736.00   **(e)** $46.00
B. **1.** $92.61   **3.** $1062.50

Exercise 12.2

A. **1.** (a) 10.84%   **(b)** 20.69%   **3.** (a) 10.37%   **(b)** 20.18%
B. **1.** (a) $98.56   **3.** (a) $57.60   **(b)** 12.50%   **(c)** 18.75%

Exercise 12.3

A. **1.** (a) $\frac{28}{78}$ **(b)** $\frac{3}{78}$ **3.** (a) $\frac{66}{378}$ **(b)** $\frac{105}{378}$ **B.** **1.** $333.75
3. $965.45   **5.** $1408.72

Exercise 12.4

A. **1.** (a) $154.00   **(b)** 16%   **(c)** 30%   **(d)** 15%   **B.** **1.** (a) $691.20
(b) 12%   **(c)** 23.35%   **(d)** 15.57%   **(e)** $1818.29   **(f)** $2218.90

Exercise 12.5

A. **1.** (a) $2.73   **(b)** $185.98   **(c)** $3.25   **B.** **1.** (a) $9.91   **(b)** $143.58
(c) $63.71   **(d)** $646.09   **(e)** $11.31

Exercise 12.6

A. **1.** $61.89   **3.** $602.47   **B.** **1.** $1980.49   **3.** $442.53

Exercise 12.7

A. **1.** Totals are $1267.29; $67.29; $1200.00

Review Exercise

1. (a) $168.00   (b) $1512.00   (c) $529.20   (d) $2041.20   (e) $68.04
(f) 27.10%   **2.** (a) $1332.90   (b) 10.00%   (c) 19.29%   **3.** $65.45
4. (a) 12.90%   (b) 24.62%   **5.** (a) 113.40   (b) $132.30   (c) 18%
(d) 32%   **6.** (a) $\frac{10}{78}$ (b) $\frac{36}{465}$ **7.** $1172.62   **8.** $2035.60   **9.** $2875.39
10. (a) $322.50   (b) 12%   (c) 23.23%   (d) 16.51%   (e) $1672.30
(f) $1005.37   **11.** (a) $749.16   (b) 29.2%; 18.4%   (c) $2560.34; $1494.43
12. $929.97   **13.** $183.64   **14.** Totals are $3168.05; $168.05; $3000.00

Self-test

1. $38.40   **2.** $192.00   **3.** 5.1%   **4.** 11.7%   **5.** $328.77   **6.** $798.20
7. (a) 14.74   (b) $892.44   (c) $15.62   **8.** $353.44   **9.** $691.57
10. Totals are $4149.24; $149.24; $4000.00

Chapter 13

Exercise 13.1

A. **1.** 0.12; 5   **3.** 0.03375; 36   **5.** 0.0775; 27   **7.** 0.0125; 150
9. 0.06125; 9   **B.** **1.** 1.7623417   **3.** 3.3033821   **5.** 7.5035457
7. 6.4454727   **9.** 1.7074946   **C.** **1.** (a) 48   (b) 3.5%   (c) 1.035^{48}
(d) 5.2135890

Exercise 13.2

A. **1.** $1101.61   **3.** $5356.62   **5.** $22819.71   **7.** $17519.84   **9.** $815.99
B. **1.** $9167.68; $4167.68   **3.** $2075.07   **5.** (a) $305.90   (b) $318.08
(c) $324.80   (d) $329.55   **7.** (a) $198.98; $98.98   (b) $395.93; $295.93
(c) $1567.57; $1467.57   **9.** 519   **11.** (a) Bank $9721.46; Credit Union $9783.23
(preferred)   (b) $61.77   **C.** **1.** $4513.28   **3.** $1714.21   **5.** $3942.41
7. $1102.13   **9.** $2830.30

Exercise 13.3

A. **1.** $381.65   **3.** $245.31   **5.** $189.04   **7.** $203.50   **B.** **1.** $721.65;
$878.35   **3.** $572.64   **5.** $1178.02

Exercise 13.4

A. **1.** $1494.52; $505.48   **3.** $2603.25; $1527.78   **5.** $1830.33; $493.70
B **1.** $3681.95   **3.** $1084.96   **5.** $4222.77   **7.** $1532.09

Exercise 13.5

A. **1.** $7153.84   **3.** $2537.13   **5.** $1742.51   **7.** $641.36   **9.** $2589.22
B. **1.** $4226.45   **3.** $1536.03   **5.** $1003.80   **C.** **1.** **(a)** $2269.71
(b) $2847.12   **(c)** $4000.00   **(d)** $7049.37   **3.** $6805.32   **5.** $749.64
7. $2653.87   **9.** **(a)** $3113.90   **(b)** $1847.95   **11.** **(a)** $646.41   **(b)** $946.41

Review Exercise

1. **(a)** $3341.24   **(b)** $3663.54   **(c)** $3745.47   **2.** **(a)** $19261.12
(b) $40266.93   **(c)** $265099.04   **3.** **(a)** $4122.06   **(b)** $2122.06·
4. **(a)** $7654.08   **(b)** $7665.57   **5.** **(a)** 15190.57; $13390.57   **(b)** $9363.67;
$8113.67   **6.** **(a)** $979.38; $2620.62   **(b)** $3952.65; $5047.35   **7.** $9791.31
8. $5537.42   **9.** $643.23   **10.** $4612.63   **11.** $8855.18   **12.** $22826.47
13. $5051.70   **14.** $1344.92; $2655.08   **15.** $641.28   **16.** 43059.20
17. $3680.65   **18.** $14417.83   **19.** $58484.82   **20.** **(a)** $2294.73
(b) $2743.63   **(c)** $3922.02   **21.** 3950.07   **22.** $5000.01   **23.** $3036.21
24. $1857.55   **25.** $3271.60   **26.** $3574.57

Self-test

1. $898.83   **2.** $2027.06   **3.** 6.2106725   **4.** $11078.60   **5.** $7941.94
6. $19466.71   **7.** $775.07   **8.** $6225.43   **9.** $833.11   **10.** $18715.77
11. $3251.23   **12.** $2971.97

Chapter 14

Exercise 14.1

A. **1.** **(a)** $9812.94   **(c)** $3820.34   **2.** **(a)** $429.44   **(c)** $3493.26
B. **1.** $6625.24   **3.** $1102.89   **5.** $34961.66

Exercise 14.2

A. **1.** **(a)** $155.03   **(c)** $2526.28   **2.** **(a)** $3050.92   **(c)** $428.11
B. **1.** $856.46   **3.** $7561.57   **5.** $1296.77

Exercise 14.3

A. **1.** $2604.43   **(b)** 1996.73   **3.** $1056.70   **7.** $2201.49
B. **1.** $3150.53   **3.** $1997.42   **5.** $2174.95   **7.** $6480.63

Exercise 14.4

A. **1.** **(a)** 20.451%   **(c)** 16.075%   **(e)** 15.419%   **2.** **(a)** 12.5%   **(c)** 16.2%
(e) 9.778%   **3.** **(a)** 5.775 years   **(c)** 59.1 months   **(e)** 20.149 quarters
B. **1.** 9.237%   **3.** **(a)** 10.402%   **(b)** 7.585%   **5.** 6.991%   **7.** 17.998%
9. 3.934 years   **11.** 8.327 years   **13.** 2.818 years   **15.** November 1, 1987
17. 21 months

Exercise 14.5

A. **1.** (a) $n = 10$ quarters (2.5 years)   (c) $n = 1.2068263$ (37 days)
2. (a) 12.891%   (c) 14.974%   **3.** (a) $1410.17   (c) $3747.62
4. (a) $245.80   (c) $3038.52   **5.** (a) 25.232%   **B.** **1.** $n = 32.282417$ months
(2 years 252 days)   **3.** $n = 7.37049$ half-years (3 years 208 days)   **5.** 16.894%
7. $34.42   **9.** $2470.63   **11.** 20.508%   **13.** (a) 3.2164602 years (3 years
79 days)   (b) 4.5 years   **15.** 13.76%

Review Exercise

1. $9548.77   **2.** $7041.80   **3.** $27024.72   **4.** $4815.20   **5.** $18574.92
6. $30851.84   **7.** $996.10   **8.** $3394.71   **9.** $1040.76   **10.** 14.072%
11. 15.109%   **12.** 10.665 months (325 days)   **13.** $2555.70   **14.** $346.65
15. 12.105 half-years (6 years 20 days)   **16.** 18.235%   **17.** (a) $14772.44
(b) $23450.65   **18.** (a) $1353.35   (b) $3576.00   **19.** (a) 13.08%
(b) 14.35%   (c) 22.20%   (d) 16.99%   (e) 17.35%   **20.** (a) 17.81%
(b) 19.10%   (c) 20.92%   **21.** (a) 18.22%   (b) 18.65%   **22.** (a) $n = 16$
half-years (8 years)   (b) $n = 24.958883$ quarters (6 years 88 days)
(c) $n = 39.576737$ months (3 years 109 days)   (d) $n = 5.3319014$ (5 years
122 days)   **23.** $n = 3.1637199$ months (97 days)   **24.** $n = 3.5228126$ half-years
(1 year 278 days)   **25.** $n = 15.289101$ quarters (3 years 301 days—September 28,
1990)   **26.** $2013.35   **27.** $6324.34   **28.** 42.6 months   **29.** 7.742 years (7 years
271 days)   **30.** 16.316%

Self-test

1. 63 months   **2.** $3681.12   **3.** 16.07545%   **4.** 22.4576%   **5.** 19 months
6. 13.456508%   **7.** 5.3373 years   **8.** 19.31712%   **9.** $24253.31
10. $37104.58   **11.** $555.58   **12.** $1494.03

Chapter 15
Exercise 15.1

A. **1.** (a) annuity certain   (b) annuity due   (c) complex annuity
3. (a) perpetuity   (b) deferred annuity   (c) complex annuity   **5.** (a) annuity
certain   (b) deferred annuity due   (c) simple annuity

Exercise 15.2

A. **1.** $10430.86   **3.** $804.37   **B.** **1.** $74324.70   **3.** $206977.78
5. $29508.34   **C.** **1.** $22413.48   **3.** $73587.28   **5.** (a) $41220.21
(b) $4500.00   (c) $36720.21   **7.** $104924.73

Exercise 15.3

A. **1.** $9709.39   **3.** $291.75   **B.** **1.** $7985.62   **3.** $16220.94
5. $6019.47   **C.** **1.** $4030.07   **3.** (a) $7872.83   (b) $4127.17   **5.** (a) $2399.98
(b) $495.90   **7.** $4245.42   **9.** (a) $12000.00   (b) $1570.82   (c) $12928.59
(d) $928.59   (e) $48.38

Exercise 15.4

A. **1.** \$563.28 **3.** \$2002.75 **5.** \$199.49 **B.** **1.** \$84.04 **3.** \$868.95 **5.** \$271.34 **7.** \$9153.99 **9.** \$810.02

Exercise 15.5

A. **1.** n = 10.428337 years (10 years 5 months) **3.** n = 247.77343 months (20 years 8 months) **5.** n = 12.298243 half-years (6 years 2 months)
B. **1.** n = 85.011148 months (7 years 1 month) **3.** n = 17.531631 quarters (4 years 5 months)

Exercise 15.6

A. **1.** 16% **3.** 9% **B.** **1.** 12.5% **3.** 13% **5.** 16.765%

Review Exercise

1. **(a)** \$53984.04 **(b)** \$17280.00 **(c)** \$36704.04 **2.** **(a)** \$53090.08 **(b)** \$85500.00 **(c)** \$32409.92 **3.** \$554.81 **4.** \$278.20 **5.** \$722.62 **6.** \$4446.79 **7.** 12.73 half-years (8 years 2 months) **8.** 10.43% **9.** 16.94% **10.** \$232.12 **11.** n = 19.770076 half-years (9 years 11 months) **12.** n = 157.83982 months (13 years 2 months) **13.** 12.28% **14.** 9.65% **15.** \$210475.21 **16.** \$3386.22 **17.** \$188.56 **18.** n = 12.5 half-years (6 years 3 months) **19.** 17.11% **20.** \$24418.00 **21.** \$10836.05 **22.** 12.027% **23.** \$26945.42 **24.** 24.97 quarters (6 years 3 months) **25.** \$3802.54 **26.** \$16124.32 **27.** **(a)** \$12591.67 **(b)** \$3208.64 **(c)** \$15015.80 **(d)** \$208.64 **28.** \$6446.13 **29.** n = 28.811254 months (2 years 5 months) **30.** **(a)** 9.726% **(b)** n = 97.758303 months (8 years 2 months)

Self-test

1. \$332.21 **2.** \$18277.44 **3.** \$7882.30 **4.** 10.90% **5.** n = 38.37 **6.** \$12562.27 **7.** 15.887% **8.** \$18073.74 **9.** \$60946.71 **10.** \$5231.73 **11.** \$12176.55 **12.** \$837.27 **13.** \$2460.25 **14.** \$937.19

Chapter 16

Exercise 16.1

A. **1.** \$5234.96; \$4561.96 **3.** \$2885.03; \$2160.32 **B.** **1.** \$215268.68; \$52633.17 **3.** \$140009.31; \$23083.77 **5.** \$43738.24; \$7278.61
C. **1.** \$39593.70 **3.** \$23763.29 **5.** **(a)** \$1238.56 **(b)** \$1575.00 **(c)** \$336.44 **7.** **(a)** \$47435.50 **(b)** \$28235.50 **9.** \$1899.50

Exercise 16.2

A. **1.** \$80.80 **3.** \$1448.69 **5.** n = 78.91352 months (6 years 7 months) **7.** n = 7.7784905 years (7 years 10 months) **9.** 13.495% **11.** 12.5%

B. **1.** $352.61   **3.** $n = 27.916189$ quarters (7 years)   **5.** 11.0%   **7.** $2568.82
9. $n = 109.48123$ months (9 years 2 months)   **11.** 16.165%

Exercise 16.3

A. **1.** $2413.15   **3.** $364.18   **5.** $150.35   **B.** **1.** $91086.44
3. (a) $6265.33   (b) $19200.00   (c) $12934.67

Exercise 16.4

A. **1.** $1035.95   **3.** $5239.14   **5.** $n = 42.75398$ quarters (10 years 9 months)
7. 12.03%   **B.** **1.** $4880.66   **3.** 10.815%   **5.** $n = 29.410361$ quarters (7 years
5 months)

Exercise 16.5

See answers to Exercise 16.4

Exercise 16.6

A. **1.** $33783.78   **3.** $12029.76   **B.** **1.** $8991.09   **3.** $331.04

Review Exercise

1. (a) $13311.22; $4996.89   (b) $14209.72; $5334.18   **2.** (a) $9296.83;
$2821.06   (b) $9182.05; $2786.23   **3.** $28344.35   **4.** $50236.74
5. (a) $335.82   (b) $322.90   **6.** (a) $201.34   (b) $202.85   **7.** $538.40
8. (a) $1190.69   (b) 1153.21   **9.** $n = 89.05638$ months (7 years 6 months)
10. $n = 11.32563$ half-years (5 years 8 months)   **11.** 12.34%   **12.** 25.10%
13. $24866.72   **14.** $16932.74   **15.** $361.31   **16.** $1184.68   **17.** $134615.38
18. $59612.90   **19.** (a) $2638.84   (b) $3444.00   (c) $805.16
20. (a) $12743.59   (b) $7200.00   (c) $5543.59   **21.** $n = 16.502949$ years
(16 years 7 months)   **22.** $n = 106.15677$ months (8 years 11 months)
23. $12037.36   **24.** $46807.18   **25.** (a) $21559.86   (b) $8959.86
(c) $864.97   (d) $28918.56   **26.** (a) $85882.89   (b) $118117.11
(c) $196.16   (d) $168691.20   **27.** $n = 31.367147$ months (2 years 8 months)
28. $n = 53.47007$ quarters (13 years 5 months)   **29.** $n = 60.605569$ quarters
(15 years 2 months)   **30.** $n = 146.61299$ months (12 years 3 months)
31. 9.05%   **32.** 19.1%

Self-test

1. $165429.69   **2.** $76800   **3.** 180 months   **4.** $43360.62   **5.** $56023.13
6. $5051.43   **7.** 15.6%   **8.** 285 months   **9.** $1258.38   **10.** 19.91%
11. $625.42   **12.** $2012.54

Chapter 17

Exercise 17.1

A. **1.** $71222.66   **3.** $38312.15   **5.** $125270.63   **7.** $38545.95

B. **1.** $23268.48   **3.** $3630.61   **5.** **(a)** $20059.65   **(b)** $10059.65
7. $77934.83

Exercise 17.2

A. **1.** $21551.85   **3.** $35530.59   **5.** $3993.29   **7.** $19980.59
B. **1.** $6281.74   **3.** $18359.52   **5.** **(a)** $25786.03   **(b)** $9213.97
7. $71999.91   **9.** $15592.21

Exercise 17.3

A. **1.** $592.75   **3.** $n = 80.878233$ (half-years)   **5.** 16.94%   **7.** $375.62
9. $n = 58.307344$ (months)   **11.** 17.0%   **B.** **1.** $407.73   **3.** $19.22
5. $n = 105.21875$ (months)   **7.** $n = 147.86752$ *(months)*   **9.** 10.75%
11. 15.313%

Exercise 17.4

A. **1.** $62800.18   **3.** $11304.61   **5.** $716.80   **7.** $1091.82   **9.** $n = 24.27752$
(half-years)   **11.** $n = 22.559972$ (quarters)   **13.** 11.28%   **15.** 16.66%
B. **1.** $70213.74   **3.** $21677.07   **5.** $286.47   **7.** $n = 52.541832$ (quarters)
9. 20.81%

Exercise 17.5

A. **1.** $10272.72   **3.** $1398.84   **5.** $375.77   **7.** $n = 12.400424$ (years)
9. 17.31%   **B.** **1.** $19279.62   **3.** $2361.32   **5.** $n = 12.359779$ (years)
7. 29.45%   **9.** $n = 39.56$

Exercise 17.6

See answer to Exercise 17.5

Exercise 17.7

A. **1.** $91027.09   **3.** $88446.04   **B.** **1.** $132.86   **3.** $96147.23
5. $1393.91

Review Exercise

1. **(a)** $19792.33   **(b)** $20392.06   **2.** **(a)** $55875.44   **(b)** $57063.57
3. **(a)** $42902.49   **(b)** $39344.62   **(c)** $18913.98   **(d)** $24739.60
(e) $49140.05   **(f)** $52640.05   **4.** **(a)** $22492.54   **(b)** $20000.05
(c) $6407.77   **(d)** $4668.08   **(e)** $23632.98   **(f)** $23872.98   **5.** **(a)** $16.44
(b) $500.37   **6.** **(a)** $37.84   **(b)** $907.84   **7.** **(a)** $576.59   **(b)** $985.49
(c) $3855.55   **(d)** $2750.04   **(e)** $438.51   **(f)** $1570.68   **8.** **(a)** $796.00
(b) $2563.40   **(c)** $1198.61   **(d)** $18231.17   **(e)** $222.27   **(f)** $2455.83
9. **(a)** $n = 148.05199$ (months)   **(b)** $n = 147.28515$ (months)
10. **(a)** $n = 39.604049$ (years)   **(b)** $n = 26.824629$ (half years)
11. **(a)** $n = 5.5811165$ (quarters)   **(b)** $n = 5.8560171$ (half-years)
(c) $n = 50.201818$ (months)   **(d)** $n = 11.721502$ (quarters)   **12.** **(a)** $n = 7.8316936$
(half-years)   **(b)** $n = 10.513419$ (years)   **(c)** $n = 16.395667$ (quarters)
(d) $n = 13.77754$ (half-years)   **13.** 16.219%   **14.** 13.567%   **15.** 17.699%
16. 21.302%   **17.** $138458.79   **18.** $211076.50   **19.** $29122.52

20. $68849.58   21. $12885.42   22. $17072.87   23. $105.30   24. $28089.24
25. $580.97   26. $4079.07   27. $1338.04   28. $8908.36   29. $2.05
30. $5972.06   31. $n = 69.823657$ (months)   32. $n = 16.345641$ (years)
33. $n = 420.01797$ (months)   34. $n = 19.302708$ (half-years)
35. $n = 59.909808$ (quarters)   36. $n = 28.605079$ (quarters)

Self-test

1. $108276.76   2. $8738.42   3. $1081.13   4. $153.98   5. $21.97
6. 60 months (5 years)   7. 12%   8. 30 quarters (7.5 years)   9. $15666.17
10. $6108.59

Chapter 18

Exercise 18.1

A. 1. (a) $852.03   **(b)** $7143.29   **(c)** $428.60; $423.43   **3. (a)** $1643.20
(b) $6391.48   **(c)** $575.23; $1067.97   **5. (a)** $170.31   **(b)** $4336.50
(c) $75.89; $94.42   **B. 1. (a)** $n = 28.91994$ **(b)** $7228.94
3. (a) $n = 21.415917$ **(b)** $14987.48   **C. 1. (a)** $1282.84   **(b)** $18232.24
(c) $80970.40   **(d)** $44970.40   **3.** Payment $2403.60; total paid $16825.25; cost
$6825.25   **5.** Total paid $14943.16; interest paid $5743.16   **7.** $1029.33
9. $1160.09   **11. (a)** $5062.87   **(b)** $2667.24   **(c)** $2856.83   **(d)** totals
$162011.89; $77011.89; $85000.00   **13. (a)** $n = 20.750427$ **(b)** $1808.32
(c) $958.57   **(d)** totals $51895.03; $27895.03; $24000.00

Exercise 18.2

A. 1. (a) $4492.06   **(b)** $30015.75   **(c)** $3709.95; $782.11   **3. (a)** $200.22
(b) $5010.15   **(c)** $60.76; $139.46   **5. (a)** $5164.01   **(b)** $39844.31
(c) $4371.02; $792.99   **B. 1. (a)** $n = 22.61883$ **(b)** $3952.19
3. (a) $n = 21.277415$ **(b)** $9535.04   **C. 1. (a)** $396.87   **(b)** $35259.23
(c) $13546.55   **(d)** $446.08   **3. (a)** $n = 20.1335$ **(b)** $5716.23
(c) $7116.23   **5.** Payments $4487.21; total paid $31410.44; interest paid $15410.44
7. $1916.06   **9. (a)** $542.30   **(b)** $6374.84   **(c)** $523.13   **(d)** $653.69
(e) Balances $39968.68; $39023.44

Exercise 18.3

A. (using Method 1)   **1.** $725.07   **3.** $585.20   **5.** $1005.90   **7.** $312.17
B. 1. (a) $n = 37.656744$ **(b)** $237.92   **3.** $511.30   **5.** $591.61
7. $1809.15   **9. (a)** $n = 61.523813$ **(b)** $724.48   **(c)** $84599.48   **(d)** $68599.48

Exercise 18.4

A. 1. (a) $386.35   **(b)** $5213.57   **3. (a)** $9.14   **(b)** $1964.15
5. (a) $323.13   **(b)** $7052.16   **B. 1. (a)** $700.00   **(b)** $265.25
(c) $965.25   **(d)** $10868.38   **3. (a)** $175.00   **(b)** $108.35   **(c)** $283.35
(d) $2702.23   **5. (a)** $11400.00   **(b)** $229.71   **(c)** $11629.71
(d) $58957.77   **C. 1. (a)** $1981.42   **(b)** $47554.08   **(c)** $27445.92
3. Deposits $1835.31; totals $12847.17; $7152.80; $19999.97   **5.** $2755.03

7. (a) $128.71   **(b)** $11879.62   **(c)** $368.76   **(d)** $984.72   **(e)** Totals
$23167.80; $76833.29; $100001.09   **9. (a)** $54750   **(b)** $2760   **(c)** $57510
(d) $10096   **(e)** $163172   **(f)** totals $55161; $244839; $300000

Review Exercise

1. (a) $1958.20   **(b)** $27662.40   **(c)** $18377.85   **(d)** $782.16   **(e)** $1375.81
(f) totals $62662.40; $27662.40; $35000.00   **2. (a)** $190.32   **(b)** $3419.20
(c) $6189.46   **(d)** $50.81   **(e)** $161.94   **(f)** totals $11419.20; $3419.20;
$8000.00   **3. (a)** $n = 37.656744$ **(b)** $35433.72   **(c)** $1250.38
(d) $1006.34   **(e)** totals $75321.78; $35321.78; $40000.00   **4. (a)** $549.15
(b) $6528.08   **(c)** $411.02   **(d)** $692.38   **(e)** totals $74491.80; $73708.73;
$783.07   **5. (a)** $1114.86   **(b)** $152.15   **(c)** $25493.06   **(d)** $1478.18
(e) final balance $16869.77; totals $37029.20; $26398.97; $10630.23
6. (a) $n = 16.294188$ **(b)** $7464.05   **(c)** $707.75   **(d)** totals $46478.84;
$28978.84 $17500.00   **7. (a)** $n = 13.884418$ **(b)** $3113.09
8. (a) $n = 160.53831$ **(b)** $485.59   **9. (a)** $n = 21.888956$ **(b)** $3832.80
10. (a) $n = 19.700707$ **(b)** $14240.01   **11. (a)** $7327.06   **(b)** $23960.63
(c) $3817.84   **(d)** totals $73270.60; $36729.37; $109999.97   **12. (a)** $1201.97
(b) $17570.15   **(c)** $2443.36   **(d)** totals $38463.04; $26536.90; $64999.94
13. (a) $13750.00   **(b)** $8279.90   **(c)** $22029.90   **(d)** $72194.23
(e) $5989.29   **(f)** totals $66239.23; $33760.07; $100000.00   **14. (a)** $28875
(b) $2201   **(c)** $50152   **(d)** $266560   **(e)** $11317   **(f)** totals $66017;
$233983; $300000   **15. (a)** $180.90   **(b)** $2183.20   **(c)** $5218.47
(d) $38.03   **(e)** totals $8683.20;$2183.20; $6500.00   **16. (a)** $n = 13.75176$
(b) $1699.63   **(c)** totals $61924.49; $29924.49; $32000.00   **17. (a)** $2014.91
(b) $19701.80   **(c)** $18565.84   **(d)** $1474.26   **18. (a)** $711.87   **(b)** totals
$4983.09; $5016.91; $100000.00   **19. (a)** $1032.37   **(b)** $3839.26
(c) $26996.81   **(d)** $1058.30   **20. (a)** $n = 26.995779$ **(b)** $995.86
21. (a) $n = 38.468063$ **(b)** $8318.12   **22. (a)** $13920.00   **(b)** $5211.80
(c) $19131.80   **(d)** $70723.83   **(e)** totals $52117.95; $43882.05; $96000.00

Self-test

1. $6027.52   **2.** $58197.77   **3.** $71.90   **4.** $371.86   **5.** $20081.81
6. $620.82   **7.** $1297.87   **8.** $622192.28   **9.** Totals: $16788.06; $8211.95;
$25 000.01   **10.** Balance after 3rd: $11867.56; Balance after 40th: $9754.86; Totals:
$23232.00; $11232.00; $12000.00

Chapter 19

Exercise 19.1

A. 1. $107592.94   **3.** $27477.23   **5.** $53909.88   **7.** $9706.28
9. $11939.29   **11.** $9294.84.   **B. 1.** $403.02   **3.** $937.89   **5.** $4462591
7. $39020.77   **9. (a)** $19656.14   **(b)** $792.35   **(c)** $18863.79   **11.** $5449.01

Exercise 19.2

A. 1. (a) $3822.93 (discount)   **(b)** $21177.07   **3. (a)** $1773.12 (discount)
(b) $8628.88   **5. (a)** $9460.20 (discount)   **(b)** $55339.80   **7. (a)** $194.24

(discount)   **(b)** $880.01   **B.** **1.** **(a)** $30384.99 (discount); $69615.01
(b) $18481.56 (discount); $81518.44   **3.** **(a)** $269.95 (premium); $5469.95
(b) $199.89 (premium); $5399.89   **5.** **(a)** $3098.85 (discount)   **(b)** $9362.53
(c) $9007.10   **7.** $4630385

Exercise 19.3

A. **1.** **(a)** $967.90 (discount); $4032.10; totals $1575.00; $2542.90; $967.90
3. $49.18 (premium); $1079.18; totals $420.00; $370.82; $49.18   **B.** **1.** $976.84
(gain)   **3.** $64.02 (loss)   **5.** $313.43 (gain)

Exercise 19.4

A. **1.** 11.83%   **3.** 12.12%   **5.** 13.28%   **B.** **1.** 11.802%; 12.2207%;
13.301%   **3.** 11.990%   **5.** 14.676%

Exercise 19.5

A. **1.** **(a)** $83059.44   **(b)** $69652.79   **(c)** $1420.23   **3.** $659919.33

Review exercise

1. **(a)** $5336.73   **(b)** $4550.35   **2.** **(a)** $9508.99   **(b)** $9276.67
3. $24894.85   **4.** $746.05   **5.** **(a)** $929.50 (premium); $20929.50   **(b)** $148.72
(premium); $21548.72   **6.** **(a)** $2243.20 (premium); $11243.20   **(b)** Nil;
$9000.00   **(c)** $883.64 (discount); $8116.36   **7.** **(a)** $9962.95 (discount)
(b) $93969.33   **(c)** $90115.74   **8.** **(a)** $225.87 (premium)   **(b)** $43556.85
(c) $42624.98   **9.** $3796.87   **10.** $1071.17   **11.** **(a)** − $3469.30 (discount)
(b) $24625.42   **(c)** $23330.78   **12.** 12.56%   **13.** $72356.00   **14.** − $72.73
(discount); $927.27; totals $870.00; $942.73; $72.73   **15.** $272.16 (discount);
$4727.84; totals $4287.50; $4559.66; $272.16   **16.** $381.32 (premium); $21381.32;
totals $9300.00; $8918.68; $381.32   **17.** $6124.75 (loss)   **18.** $993.69 (gain)
19. 12.712%   **20.** 14.990%   **21.** 12.796%   **22.** 14.296%
23. **(a)** $46906.73   **(b)** $20770.01   **(c)** $298.05 (loss)   **24.** $256678.26
25. $92388.48   **26.** 15.347%   **27.** $977.39 (loss)   **28.** **(a)** $8857.03
(b) $7879.25   **(c)** $351.27 (loss)

Self-test

1. $9269.44   **2.** $1110.97   **3.** $206.75 (premium)   **4.** $51503.53
5. $21459.38   **6.** $4613.34   **7.** − $327.27 (discount); totals $2300.00; $2627.27;
$327.27   **8.** 12.46%   **9.** $1110226.27   **10.** $2062.19   **11.** $1707.25 (loss)
12. 13.048%

Chapter 20

Exercise 20.1

A. **1.** **(a)** annual depreciation $3500   **(b)** depreciation year 1 to 4, $3705.75; year 5
to 7, $3477.00; year 8 to 10, $3248.25   **(c)** depreciation per unit $0.35; year 1 to 4,
$3762.50; year 5 to 7, $3430.00; year 8 to 10, $3220.00   **(d)** constant part 636.3636;
year 1, $6363.64; year 10, $636.35   **(e)** rate 20%; year 1, $8000.00; year 10,

$368.71   **(f)** rate 18.77476%; year 1, $7509.90; year 10, $1155.72   **(g)** rate 20%; year 1, $8000; year 10, $1073.74   **(h)** annual charge $7723.82; depreciation year 1, $1723.82; year 10, $6064.24   **(i)** assumed payment $1723.82; depreciation year 1, $1723.82; year 10, $6064.25   **B.** **1. (a)** $375500; $12300   **(b)** $263000; $15000   **(c)** $259443.09; $12972.15   **(d)** $253985.20; $13041.02   **(e)** $536089.36; $3510.66   **(f)** $536089.54; $3510.64

Exercise 20.2

A. **1.** $78339.71   **3.** $217799.60   **5.** 17.18%   **7.** 18.76%
B. **1.** $242514   **3.** 14.16%   **5.** 19.47%   **7.** $2479.28

Exercise 20.3

A. **1.** $9522.57   **3.** $34126.41   **5.** $104872.03   **B.** **1.** $1237.93; $1997.02; $4777.70; $4973.38   **3. (a)** $116363.64   **(b)** $124921.08   **5.** $23045.65
7. $1944.03   **9.** $10168.60   **11. (a)** Machine A $12038.70, $1444.64; Machine B $12342.73, $1481.13   **(b)** Machine A $10399.58. $1871.92; Machine B $10241.33, $1843.44   **13.** $13480.74   **15.** $4.21; $3.99; difference $0.22.   **17.** IH Tractor; $713.30   **19.** Model A; $1013.38

Review Exercise

1. (a) constant value $265; depreciation year 1, $2120; year 8, $265   **(b)** rate 25%; depreciation year 1, $3000; year 8, nil   **(c)** rate 17.97066%; depreciation year 1, $2156.48; year 8, $538.93   **(d)** annual charge $2589.94; depreciation year 1, $669.94; year 8, $1893.39   **(e)** assumed payment $669.94; depreciation year 1, $669.94; year 8, $1893.39   **2. (a)** $6784.00; $1260.80   **(b)** $1934.77; $484.92   **(c)** $6038.19; $483.06   **(d)** $1111.79; $171.92   **(e)** $21320.39; $2193.13   **(f)** $21319.58; $2193.29   **3.** $936556.85   **4.** constant part is 330; depreciation year 1, $1980; year 6, $330   **5. (a)** $22903.79   **(b)** $67276.81   **6. (a)** $1974.82   **(b)** $2761.59   **7.** $420222.93   **8.** $1287.32   **9. (a)** $197350.04   **(b)** $29602.51   **10.** 16.48%   **11. (a)** 13.43%   **(b)** $513356.67   **12. (a)** $30752.22   **(b)** $4127.72   **13.** $489.09   **14. (a)** Machine 1 $31987.50, $4158.38; Machine 2 $32079.63, $4170.35   **(b)** Machine 1 $27943.37, $5588.67; Machine 2 $26856.03; $5371.05   **15.** $2026.14   **16. (a)** Machine B   **(b)** $0.11   **17.** $21743.55   **18. (a)** Yes   **(b)** $10116.63

Self-test

1. Assumed payment $7023.87; totals $42143.22; $14856.78; $57000.00   **2.** $35000
3. $6100   **4.** $800.65   **5.** $68575.56   **6.** $1052879.80   **7.** 10.33%
8. $37997.99   **9.** $100178.44   **10.** $15089.77   **11.** $0.01   **12.** $14230.15

Chapter 21
Exercise 21.1

A. **1.** Alternative 2; present values are $44634; $53448   **3.** Alternative 1; present values are $48569; $46604   **B.** **1.** Offer 2; present values are $52138; $54262
3. Lease; present values are $88167; $86379

Exercise 21.2

A. **1.** Reject; NPV is $-$5367$ **3.** Alternative 1; NPV's are $234; $203
B. **1.** Project B; NPV's are $1787; $2568 **3.** No; NPV is $-$8561$ **5.** Yes; NPV is $5696 **7.** Yes; NPV is $5142

Exercise 21.3

A. **1.** 25.3% **3.** 20.7% **B.** **1.** at 18%, NPV = $6101; at 20%, NPV = $-$292$; R.O.I. = 19.9% **3.** at 18%, NPV = $1286; at 20%, NPV = $-$104$; R.O.I. = 19.9% **5.** at 22%, NPV = $148; at 24%, NPV = $-$1538$; R.O.I. = 22.2%

Review exercise

1. Alternative B; present values are $51624; $52161 **2.** Alternative 1; present values are $73559; $74653 **3.** Alternative 1; NPV's are $3916; $3597 **4.** Yes; NPV = $508 **5.** $-$22227$ **6.** $404 **7.** at 26%, NPV = $370; at 28%, NPV = $-$1939$; R.O.I. = 26.3% **8.** at 18%, NPV = $135; at 20%, NPV = $-$673$; R.O.I. = 18.3% **9.** at 16%, NPV = $47272; at 18%, NPV = $-$22227$; R.O.I. = 17.4% **10.** at 14%, NPV = $404; at 16%, NPV = $-$4383$; R.O.I. = 14.2% **11.** at 24%, NPV = 2035; at 26%, NPV = $-$184$; R.O.I. = 25.8% **12.** at 12%, NPV = $3307; at 14%, NPV = $-$2876$; R.O.I. = 13.1% **13.** Project B; present values are $22256; $22909 **14.** Project B; NPV's are $3510; $4862 **15.** $-$1215 **16.** at 24%, NPV = $1023; at 26%, NPV = $-$1690$; R.O.I. = 24.8% **17.** Yes; NPV = $28940 **18.** at 14%, NPV = $36347; at 16%, NPV = $-$7635$; R.O.I. = 15.7%

Self-test

1. Alternative A; present values are $13552; $10856 **2.** $3887 **3.** at 16%, NPV = $3466; at 18%, NPV = $-$4368$; R.O.I. = 16.9% **4.** Present values are $5939; $6040; purchase **5.** Proposal B, net present values are $701; $1427 **6.** at 26%, NPV = $356; at 28%, NPV = $-$7526$; R.O.I. = 26.1%

Index